Course	GENERAL BIOLOGY
Course Number	**BSC 1005**
	BROWARD COLLEGE CENTRAL

http://create.mheducation.com

ISBN-10: 1308188951   ISBN-13: 9781308188959

Contents

Online Supplements 539

Credits

The Diversity of Life 343

Online Supplements 539

Preface

Vision and Change in Undergraduate Biology Education: A Call to Action encourages instructors to improve student engagement and learning in introductory biology courses. The central idea of the *Vision and Change* report is that we need to turn away from teaching methods that reward students who memorize and regurgitate superficial knowledge. Instead, we need to emphasize deeper learning that requires students to understand and apply course content. This idea is precisely what I have tried to achieve since I started teaching at the University of Oklahoma in 1997, and it has been a guiding principle in the creation of my books and digital material as well.

As you examine this new edition and its supplements, I hope you will see an emphasis on connections and the "big picture." In addition to new features like chapter summary figures, integrated media icons, SmartBook™, and tutorial animations, we've updated and improved many features present in the last edition, including chapter opening essays, Investigating Life sections, boxed readings, and multiple choice and open-ended questions. Every chapter also has a study tip, so students learn to master the skills they need to be successful in biology and every other class.

I agree with the *Vision and Change* report's call for instructors to embrace active learning techniques, but I also believe that one set of tools and techniques does not work in every classroom. For that reason, my team and I are proud to create a package that gives you the flexibility to teach introductory biology in a way that works best for you. Pages viii–xiii illustrate the features and resources for this edition that can help you meet your teaching goals.

I hope that you and your students enjoy this text and that it helps cultivate an understanding of, and deep appreciation for, biology.

Mariëlle Hoefnagels
The University of Oklahoma

Author's Guide *To Using this Textbook*

This guide lists the main features of each chapter and describes some of the ways that I use them in my own classes.

The Learning Outline introduces the chapter's main headings and helps students keep the big picture in mind.

Each heading is a complete sentence that summarizes the most important idea of the section.

The gradual change in leaf colors as a chapter unfolds indicates where the student is in the chapter's big picture.

Students can also flip to the end of the chapter before starting to read; the chapter summary and Pull It Together concept map can serve as a review or provide a preview of what's to come.

Learn How to Learn study tips help students develop their study skills.

Each chapter has one Learn How to Learn study tip, and you can find a complete list in the inside back cover of the book.

I present a *Study Minute* in class each week, with examples of how to use these study tips.

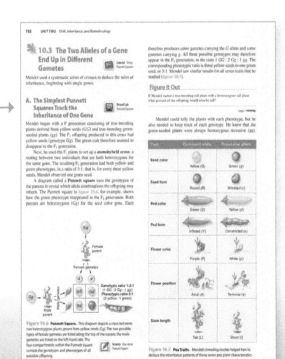

New media icons direct students to resources that can help them understand difficult topics.

Animation		Video	
3-D Animation		Virtual Lab	
Tutorial		Activity	

Investigating Life describes a real experiment focusing on an evolutionary topic related to each chapter's content.

Each case concludes with critical thinking questions that can be used as an in-class group activity. The studies touch on concepts found in other units; you can encourage students to draw a concept map illustrating the relationships between ideas. You might also use the case as a basis for discussion of the nature of science.

This edition offers Connect interactive and test bank questions focused on the Investigating Life cases. Questions assess students' understanding of the science behind the Investigating Life case and their ability to integrate those concepts with information from other units.

New summary figures emphasize the relationships among topics in the chapter.

These figures consist of "big-picture" combinations of art from the chapter.

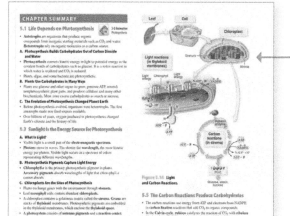

The Chapter Summary highlights key points and terminology from the chapter.

Write It Out and Mastering Concepts questions are useful for student review or as short in-class writing assignments.

I compile them into a list of *Guided Reading Questions* that help students focus on material I cover in class. I also use them as discussion questions in Action Centers, where students can come for additional help with course material.

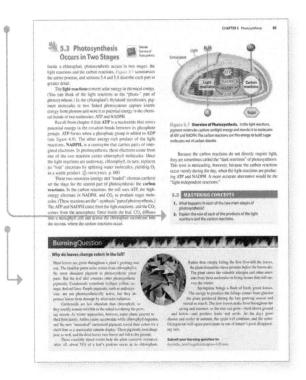

Burning Questions cover topics that students wonder about.

I ask my students to write down a Burning Question on the first day of class. I answer all of them during the semester, whenever a relevant topic comes up in class.

Figure It Out questions reinforce chapter concepts and typically have numeric answers (supporting student math skills).

Students can work on these in small groups, in class, or in Action Center. Most could easily be used as clicker questions as well.

Figure It Out

If you could expose plants to just one wavelength of light at a time, would a wavelength of 300 nm, 450 nm, or 600 nm produce the highest photosynthetic rate?

Answer: 450 nm.

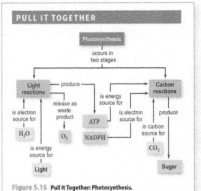

Figure 5.15 **Pull It Together: Photosynthesis.**

Refer to figure 5.15 and the chapter content to answer the following questions.

1. Where do electron transport chains fit into this concept map?
2. How would you incorporate the Calvin cycle, rubisco, C₃ plants, C₄ plants, and CAM plants into this concept map?
3. Where do humans and other heterotrophs fit into this concept map?
4. Build another small concept map showing the relationships among the terms *chloroplast, stroma, grana, thylakoid, photosystem,* and *chlorophyll.*
5. Add a connecting phrase to the concept map to show what happens to sugar after it is produced.

Pull It Together concept maps help students see the big picture.

After spending class time discussing the key points in constructing concept maps, I have my students draw concept maps of their own.

Author's Guide *To Using Digital Tools*

McGraw-Hill LearnSmart® is a popular tool that helps students learn material ahead of class and practice with it afterward.

I assign LearnSmart before each week's lectures and let my students practice with it all they want throughout the semester. You can assign any sections you want and adjust the amount of detail depending on how much time you expect students to spend on the assignment.

Reports show which topics students struggled with, so your in-class time can be spent more productively.

New SmartBook™ measures what students know and then highlights the content they most need to study.

SmartBook predicts when students are likely to forget specific information and revisits that content to promote long-term memory.

McGraw-Hill Connect® question banks contain integrative activities that can be sorted by Bloom's Level, Topic, Section, or Learning Outcome.

I assign Connect homework assignments using interactive questions before each exam.

This edition features new question banks that integrate content from each chapter in the unit and between units.

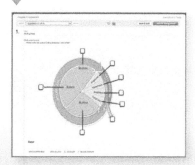

Connect reports reveal which topics need additional review prior to the exam.

Reports can help assess overall class performance or data for a specific student, using several different criteria.

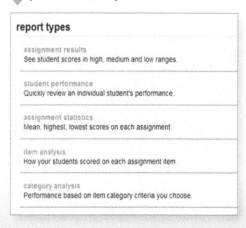

report types

assignment results
See student scores in high, medium and low ranges.

student performance
Quickly review an individual student's performance.

assignment statistics
Mean, highest, lowest scores on each assignment.

item analysis
How your students scored on each assignment item.

category analysis
Performance based on item category criteria you choose.

You can use McGraw-Hill Tegrity® to record your lectures and make them available to students in Connect as a first step to learning your content or as review.

Whether your course is traditional, fully online, or a hybrid, your students can access your content when it works for them.

Students can search your lecture by key term and go right to that point in your lecture to review.

New customizable PowerPoint® Lecture Outlines are focused on concepts and are useful for online, hybrid, or traditional courses.

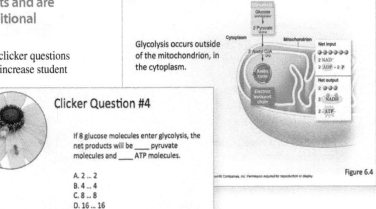

I use clickers in my course, and I find the clicker questions in the PowerPoints® to be a handy way to increase student engagement and assess where I need to spend more time.

Use McGraw-Hill Create™ to develop course material that matches what you do in the classroom.

Create lets you select the chapters you want to use, arrange them to follow your syllabus, combine material from other sources, and upload your own notes.

You can choose the delivery method that best suits you and the students you teach.

http://create.mcgraw-hill.com

Animated tutorials guide students through complicated topics, using illustrations and examples from the book.

I created these to walk students through the most difficult material, step by step. You can assign the tutorials with accompanying critical thinking questions from the interactive question banks, or use the embedded PowerPoint® files in your presentations.

Your students can review the tutorials through the eBook or by using the media tab in Connect. Topics include

Organization of Life
Scientific Method and Interpreting a Graph
Chemical Bonding
Dehydration Synthesis and Hydrolysis
Anatomy of a Cell Membrane
ATP
Enzymes
Reaction Energetics
Osmosis
Cell Structure
Overview of Photosynthesis
Light Reactions
The Calvin Cycle
Overview of Respiration
Mitochondrial Electron Transport Chain
Fermentation
Protein Structure
Protein Synthesis
Overview of DNA Replication
Stages of Mitosis
Stages of Meiosis
Comparison of Mitosis and Meiosis
Crossing Over
Nondisjunction
Homologous Chromosomes
Constructing and Interpreting a Punnett Square
DNA Profiling
Mechanisms of Evolution
Genetic Variation: The Basis of Natural Selection
Understanding the Hardy–Weinberg Equation
Evidence for Evolution
Evidence for Human Evolution
Radiometric Dating
Reading an Evolutionary Tree
Origin of Life
Endosymbiont Theory
Viral Replication
Lytic and Lysogenic Cycles
Replication of HIV
Prokaryote Diversity
Protist Diversity
Plant Diversity

Moss Reproductive Cycle
Fern Reproductive Cycle
Conifer Reproductive Cycle
Sexual Reproduction in Angiosperms
Basidiomycete Reproductive Cycle
Diversity of Fungi
Animal Diversity
Overview of Plant Tissues
Phloem Sap Transport
Water Movement Through the Xylem
Alternation of Generations
Fruit Development
Overview of Animal Tissues
Organ System Interactions
Example of Negative Feedback
Action Potential
The Synapse
Overview of the Senses
Sense of Vision
Sense of Hearing
Cell Responses to Hormones
Role of ATP in Muscle Contraction
The Heartbeat
Respiratory Surfaces
Digestion and Food Molecules
Nephron Function
Adaptive Immunity
Allergies
Oogenesis
Human Male and Female Reproductive Systems
Ovarian and Menstrual Cycles
Proximate and Ultimate Behaviors
Population Growth Models
Biomagnification
Water Cycle
Nitrogen Cycle
Phosphorus Cycle
Carbon Cycle
Earth's Climate and Biomes
CO_2 and Earth's Average Temperature
Threats to Biodiversity

Science. Chemistry, and Cells

CHAPTER

1

The Scientific Study of Life

Stingray Squadron. Golden cownose rays cruise coastal waters near Santa Cruz Island, one of the Galápagos Islands off the coast of Ecuador.

Enhance your study |BIOLOGY
of this chapter with practice quizzes,
animations and videos, answer keys,
and downloadable study tools.
www.mhhe.com/hoefnagels

UNIT 1

Life Is Everywhere

WELCOME TO BIOLOGY, THE SCIENTIFIC STUDY OF LIFE. Living organisms surround us. You are alive, and so are your friends, your pets, and the plants in your home and yard. Bacteria thrive on and in your body. Any food you ate today was (until recently, anyway) alive. And the news is full of biology-related discoveries about fossils, new cancer treatments, genetics, global climate change, and the environment.

Stories such as these enjoy frequent media coverage because this is an exciting time to study biology. Not only is the field changing rapidly, but its new discoveries and applications might change your life. DNA technology has brought us genetically engineered bacteria that can manufacture life-saving drugs—and genetically engineered plants that produce their own pesticides. This same technology may one day enable physicians to routinely cure hemophilia, cystic fibrosis, and other genetic diseases by replacing faulty DNA with a functional "patch."

Biology also includes the study of nonhuman life. We exist only because of our interactions with other species, which provide food, oxygen, clean water, clothing, shelter, and other necessities. Even species that do not directly "serve" us are essential to the ecosystems that sustain all life. Human activities, however, are pushing many ecosystems dangerously out of balance.

Consider the stingrays pictured on the facing page. These oddly shaped fish consume shellfish in shallow coastal waters. In waters near Ecuador's Galápagos Islands, overfishing and habitat destruction are causing stingray populations to decline. But the opposite problem affects the east coast of the United States. There, other stingray species are exploding as sharks—their natural predators—disappear. Schools of hungry rays devastate oyster beds and crab fisheries, with far-reaching consequences not only to coastal ecosystems but also to the economy.

The list of biology-related topics goes on and on: global climate change, stem cell therapies, infectious disease, improved crop plants, synthetic life, infertility treatment, endangered species, DNA fingerprinting, biofuels, pollution, the history of life, and more. This book will bring you a taste of what we know about life and help you make sense of the science-related news you see every day. Chapter 1 begins your journey by introducing the scope of biology and explaining how science teaches us what we know about life.

LEARNING OUTLINE

 1.1 What Is Life?
- A. Life Is Organized
- B. Life Requires Energy
- C. Life Maintains Internal Constancy
- D. Life Reproduces Itself, Grows, and Develops
- E. Life Evolves

 1.2 The Tree of Life Includes Three Main Branches

 1.3 Scientists Study the Natural World
- A. The Scientific Method Has Multiple Interrelated Parts
- B. An Experimental Design Is a Careful Plan
- C. Theories Are Comprehensive Explanations
- D. Scientific Inquiry Has Limitations
- E. Biology Continues to Advance

 1.4 Investigating Life: The Orchid and the Moth

LEARN HOW TO LEARN
Real Learning Takes Time

You got good at basketball, running, dancing, art, music, or video games by putting in lots of practice. Likewise, you will need to commit time to your biology course if you hope to do well. To get started, look for the "Learn How to Learn" tip in each chapter of this textbook. Each hint is designed to help you use your study time productively.

1.1 What Is Life?

Biology is the scientific study of life. The second half of this chapter explores the meaning of the term *scientific,* but first we will consider the question, "What is life?" We all have an intuitive sense of what life is. If we see a rabbit on a rock, we know that the rabbit is alive and the rock is not. But it is difficult to state just what makes the rabbit alive. Likewise, in the instant after an individual dies, we may wonder what invisible essence has transformed the living into the dead.

One way to define life is to list its basic components. The **cell** is the basic unit of life; every **organism,** or living individual, consists of one or more cells. Every cell has an outer membrane that separates it from its surroundings. This membrane encloses the water and other chemicals that carry out the cell's functions. One of those biochemicals, deoxyribonucleic acid (DNA), is the informational molecule of life (figure 1.1). Cells use genetic instructions—as encoded in DNA—to produce proteins, which enable cells to carry out specialized functions in tissues, organs, and organ systems.

A list of life's biochemicals, however, provides an unsatisfying definition of life. After all, placing DNA, water, proteins, and a membrane in a test tube does not create artificial life. And a crushed insect still contains all of the biochemicals that it had immediately before it died.

In the absence of a concise definition, scientists have settled on five qualities that, in combination, constitute life (table 1.1). An organism is a collection of structures that function together and exhibit all of these qualities. Note, however, that each of the traits listed in table 1.1 may also occur in nonliving objects. A rock crystal is highly organized, but it is not alive. A fork placed in a pot of boiling water absorbs heat energy and passes it to the hand that grabs it, but this does not make the fork alive. A fire can "reproduce" and grow very rapidly, but it lacks most of the other characteristics of life. It is the *combination* of these five characteristics that makes life unique.

A. Life Is Organized

Tutorial
Organization of Life

Just as the city where you live belongs to a county, state, and nation, living matter also consists of parts organized in a hierarchical pattern (figure 1.2). At the smallest scale, all living structures are composed of particles called **atoms,** which bond

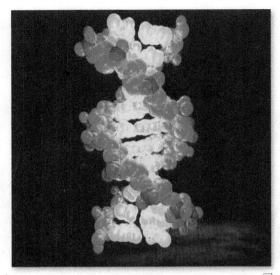

Figure 1.1 Informational Molecule of Life. All cells contain DNA, a series of "recipes" for proteins that each cell can make.

together to form **molecules.** These molecules are often grouped into **organelles,** which are compartments that carry out specialized functions in cells (note that not all cells contain organelles). Many organisms consist of single cells. In multicellular organisms (such as the tree illustrated in figure 1.2), however, the cells are organized into specialized **tissues** that make up **organs.** Multiple organs are linked into an individual's **organ systems.**

We have now reached the level of the organism, which may consist of just one cell or of many cells organized into tissues, organs, and organ systems. Organization in the living world extends beyond the level of the individual organism as well. A **population** includes members of the same species occupying the same place at the same time. A **community** includes the populations of different species in a region, and an **ecosystem** includes both the living and nonliving components of an area. Finally, the **biosphere** refers to all parts of the planet that can support life.

Biological organization is apparent in all life. Humans, eels, and evergreens, although outwardly very different, are all organized into specialized cells, tissues, organs, and organ systems.

TABLE **1.1** **Characteristics of Life: A Summary**

Characteristic	Example
Organization	Atoms make up molecules, which make up cells, which make up tissues, and so on.
Energy use	A kitten uses the energy from its mother's milk to fuel its own growth.
Maintenance of internal constancy	Your kidneys regulate your body's water balance by adjusting the concentration of your urine.
Reproduction, growth, and development	An acorn germinates, develops into an oak seedling, and, at maturity, reproduces sexually to produce its own acorns.
Evolution	Increasing numbers of bacteria survive treatment with antibiotic drugs.

ORGANELLE
A membrane-bounded structure that has a specific function within a cell.
Example: Chloroplast

CELL
The fundamental unit of life. Multicellular organisms consist of many cells; unicellular organisms consist of one cell.
Example: Leaf cell

TISSUE
A collection of specialized cells that function in a coordinated fashion. (Multicellular life only.)
Example: Epidermis of leaf

MOLECULE
A group of joined atoms.
Example: DNA

ORGAN
A structure consisting of tissues organized to interact and carry out specific functions. (Multicellular life only.)
Example: Leaf

ATOM
The smallest chemical unit of a type of pure substance (element).
Example: Carbon atom

ORGANISM
A single living individual.
Example: One acacia tree

ORGAN SYSTEM
Organs connected physically or chemically that function together. (Multicellular life only.)
Example: Aboveground part of a plant

POPULATION
A group of the same species of organism living in the same place and time.
Example: Multiple acacia trees

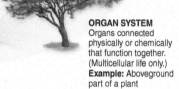

COMMUNITY
All populations that occupy the same region.
Example: All populations in a savanna

ECOSYSTEM
The living and nonliving components of an area.
Example: The savanna

BIOSPHERE
The global ecosystem; the parts of the planet and its atmosphere where life is possible.

Figure 1.2 Life's Organizational Hierarchy. This diagram applies life's organizational hierarchy to a multicellular organism (an acacia tree). At the smallest level, atoms are arranged into molecules, which form organelles in the plant's cells. Multiple cells are organized into tissues, which make up organs and, in turn, organ systems. A population consists of individuals of the same species, and communities are multiple populations sharing the same space. Communities interact with the nonliving environment to form ecosystems, and the biosphere consists of all places on Earth where life occurs.

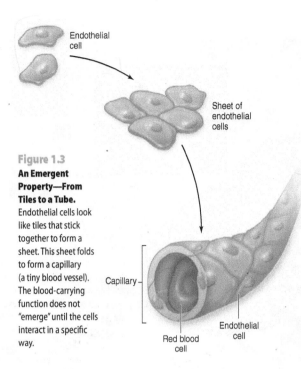

Figure 1.3

An Emergent Property—From Tiles to a Tube. Endothelial cells look like tiles that stick together to form a sheet. This sheet folds to form a capillary (a tiny blood vessel). The blood-carrying function does not "emerge" until the cells interact in a specific way.

and nutrients from nonliving sources. The most familiar producers are the plants and microbes that capture light energy from the sun, but some bacteria can derive chemical energy from rocks. **Consumers,** in contrast, obtain energy and nutrients by eating other organisms, living or dead; consumers are also called heterotrophs. You are a consumer, relying on energy and atoms from food to stay alive. **Decomposers** are heterotrophs that obtain energy and nutrients from wastes or dead organisms. These organisms, which include fungi and some bacteria, recycle nutrients to the nonliving environment.

Within an ecosystem, organisms are linked into elaborate food webs, beginning with producers and continuing through several levels of consumers (including decomposers). Although atoms are continuously recycled, energy is not; instead, energy is lost as heat at every step (see figure 1.4). Because no organism can use heat as an energy source, it represents a permanent loss from the cycle of life. All ecosystems therefore depend on a continuous stream of energy from an outside source, usually the sun.

C. Life Maintains Internal Constancy

An important characteristic of life is the ability to sense and react to stimuli. The conditions inside cells must remain within a constant range, even if the surrounding environment changes. For

Single-celled bacteria, although less complex than animals or plants, still contain DNA, proteins, and other molecules that interact in highly organized ways.

An organism, however, is more than a collection of successively smaller parts. When those components interact, they create new, complex functions called **emergent properties** (figure 1.3). These characteristics arise from physical and chemical interactions among a system's components, much as flour, sugar, butter, and chocolate can become brownies—something not evident from the parts themselves. For an emergent property, the whole is greater than the sum of the parts.

Emergent properties explain why structural organization is closely tied to function. Disrupt a structure, and its function ceases. Shaking a fertilized hen's egg, for instance, disturbs critical interactions and stops the embryo from developing. Likewise, if a function is interrupted, the corresponding structure eventually breaks down, much as unused muscles begin to waste away. Biological function and form are interdependent.

B. Life Requires Energy

Inside each living cell, countless chemical reactions sustain life. These reactions, collectively called metabolism, allow organisms to acquire and use energy and nutrients to build new structures, repair old ones, and reproduce.

Biologists divide organisms into broad categories, based on their source of energy and raw materials (figure 1.4). **Producers,** also called autotrophs, make their own food by extracting energy

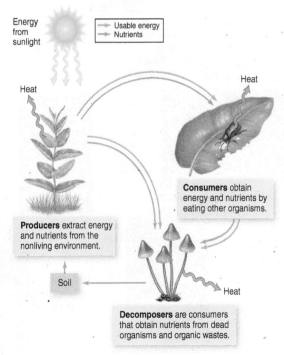

Producers extract energy and nutrients from the nonliving environment.

Consumers obtain energy and nutrients by eating other organisms.

Decomposers are consumers that obtain nutrients from dead organisms and organic wastes.

Figure 1.4 **Life Is Connected.** All organisms extract energy and nutrients from the nonliving environment or from other organisms. Decomposers recycle nutrients back to the nonliving environment. At every stage along the way, heat is lost to the system.

a.   b.

Figure 1.5 **Temperature Homeostasis.** (a) Shivering and (b) sweating are responses that maintain body temperature within an optimal range.

a.   b.

Figure 1.6 **Asexual and Sexual Reproduction.** (a) Identical plantlets develop along the runners of a wild strawberry plant. (b) Two swans protect their offspring, the products of sexual reproduction.

example, a living cell must maintain a certain temperature—not too high and not too low. The cell must also take in nutrients, excrete wastes, and regulate its many chemical reactions to prevent a shortage or surplus of essential substances. **Homeostasis** is the process by which a cell or organism maintains this state of internal constancy, or equilibrium.

Your body, for example, has several mechanisms that maintain your internal temperature at about 37°C (figure 1.5). When you go outside on a cold day, you may begin to shiver; heat from these muscle movements warms the body. In severe cold, your lips and fingertips may turn blue as your circulatory system diverts blood away from your body's surface. Conversely, on a hot day, sweat evaporating from your skin helps cool your body.

D. Life Reproduces Itself, Grows, and Develops

Organisms reproduce, making other individuals that are similar to themselves (figure 1.6). Reproduction transmits DNA from generation to generation; this genetic information defines the inherited characteristics of the offspring.

Reproduction occurs in two basic ways: asexually and sexually. In **asexual reproduction,** genetic information comes from only one parent, and all offspring are virtually identical. One-celled organisms such as bacteria reproduce asexually by doubling and then dividing the contents of the cell. Many multicellular organisms also reproduce asexually. For example, a strawberry plant's "runners" sprout roots and leaves, forming new plantlets identical to the parent (figure 1.6a). The green, white, or black powder on moldy bread or cheese is made of the countless asexual spores of fungi. Some animals, including sponges, reproduce asexually when a fragment of the parent animal detaches and develops into a new individual.

In **sexual reproduction,** genetic material from two parent individuals unites to form an offspring, which has a new combination of inherited traits. By mixing genes at each generation, sexual reproduction results in tremendous diversity in a

population. Genetic diversity, in turn, enhances the chance that some individuals will survive even if conditions change. Sexual reproduction is therefore a very successful strategy, especially in an environment where conditions change frequently; it is extremely common among plants and animals (figure 1.6b).

If each offspring is to reproduce, it must grow and develop to adulthood. Each young swan in figure 1.6b, for example, started as a single fertilized egg cell. That cell divided over and over, developing into an embryo. Continued cell division and specialization yielded the newly hatched swans, which will eventually mature into adults that can also reproduce—just like their parents.

E. Life Evolves

Video
Natural Selection

One of the most intriguing questions in biology is how organisms become so well-suited to their environments. A beaver's enormous front teeth, which never stop growing, are ideal for gnawing wood. Tubular flowers have exactly the right shapes for the beaks of their hummingbird pollinators. Some organisms have color patterns that enable them to fade into the background (figure 1.7).

Figure 1.7 **Hiding in Plain Sight.** This pygmy seahorse is barely visible in its coral habitat, thanks to its unique body shape, skin color, and texture.

These examples, and countless others, illustrate adaptations. An **adaptation** is an inherited characteristic or behavior that enables an organism to survive and reproduce successfully in its environment.

Where do these adaptive traits come from? The answer lies in natural selection. The simplest way to think of natural selection is to consider two facts. First, resources such as food and habitat are limited, so populations produce many more offspring than will survive to reproduce. A single mature oak tree may release thousands of acorns in one season, but only a few are likely to germinate, develop, and reproduce. The rest die. Second, no organism is exactly the same as any other. Genetic mutations—changes in an organism's DNA sequence—generate variability in all organisms, even those that reproduce asexually.

Of all the offspring in a population, which will survive long enough to reproduce? The answer is those with the best adaptations to the current environment; poorly adapted organisms are most likely to die before reproducing. **Natural selection,** then, is a process in which individuals with certain inherited characteristics contribute more offspring to the next generation than do individuals lacking those characteristics (figure 1.8). That is, individuals with the best gene combinations survive and reproduce, while those with less suitable characteristics fail to do so. Over many generations, individuals with adaptive traits make up most or all of the population.

Tutorial
Variation and
Natural Selection

But the environment is constantly changing. Continents shift, sea levels rise and fall, climates warm and cool. What happens to a population when the selective forces that drive natural selection change? Only some organisms survive: those with the "best" traits in the *new* environment. Features that may once have been rare become more common as the reproductive success of individuals with those traits improves. Notice, however, that this outcome depends on variability within the population. If no individual can reproduce in the new environment, the species may go extinct.

Natural selection is one mechanism of **evolution,** which is a change in the genetic makeup of a population over multiple generations. Although evolution can also occur in other ways, natural selection is the mechanism that selects for adaptations. Charles Darwin became famous in the 1860s after the publication of his book *On the Origin of Species by Means of Natural Selection,* which introduced the theory of evolution by natural selection; another naturalist, Alfred Russel Wallace, independently developed the same idea at around the same time.

Evolution is the single most powerful idea in biology. As unit 3 describes in detail, evolution has been operating since life began, and it explains the current diversity of life. In fact, the similarities among existing organisms strongly suggest that all species descend from a common ancestor. Evolution has molded the life that has populated the planet since the first cells formed almost 4 billion years ago, and it continues to act today.

1.1 MASTERING CONCEPTS

1. Does any nonliving object possess all of the characteristics of life? Explain your answer.

2. List the levels of life's organizational hierarchy from smallest to largest, starting with atoms and ending with the biosphere.

3. If evolution requires genetic variation, can populations of asexually reproducing organisms evolve? Explain.

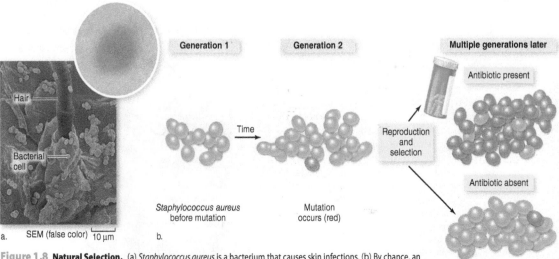

Figure 1.8 Natural Selection. (a) *Staphylococcus aureus* is a bacterium that causes skin infections. (b) By chance, an *S. aureus* cell undergoes a random genetic mutation. If the population is subsequently exposed to an antibiotic, the drug kills most of the unmutated cells. The mutated cell, however, is unaffected and can reproduce. After many generations of exposure to the antibiotic, the mutation is common.

1.2 The Tree of Life Includes Three Main Branches

Biologists have been studying life for centuries, documenting the existence of everything from bacteria to blue whales. An enduring problem has been how to organize the ever-growing list of known organisms into meaningful categories. **Taxonomy** is the biological science of naming and classifying organisms.

The basic unit of classification is the **species**, which designates a distinctive "type" of organism. Closely related species are grouped into the same **genus**. Together, the genus and a specific descriptor denote the unique, two-word scientific name of each species. A human, for example, is *Homo sapiens*. (Note that scientific names are always italicized and that the genus is capitalized, but the specific descriptor is not). Scientific names help taxonomists and other biologists communicate with one another.

Taxonomists also strive to classify organisms according to what we know about evolutionary relationships; that is, how recently one type of organism shared an ancestor with another type of organism. The more recently they diverged from a shared ancestor, the more closely related the two types of organisms are. Researchers infer these relationships by comparing anatomical, behavioral, cellular, genetic, and biochemical characteristics.

Section 14.6 describes the taxonomic hierarchy in more detail. For now, it is enough to know that genetic evidence suggests that all species fall into one of three **domains**, the broadest (most inclusive) taxonomic category. Figure 1.9 depicts the three domains: Bacteria, Archaea, and Eukarya. Species in domains Bacteria and Archaea are superficially similar to one another; all are prokaryotes, meaning that their DNA is free in the cell and not confined to an organelle called a nucleus. Major differences in DNA sequences separate these two domains from each other. Domain Eukarya, on the other hand, contains all species of eukaryotes, which are unicellular or multicellular organisms whose cells contain a nucleus.

The species in each domain are further subdivided into **kingdoms**; figure 1.9 shows the kingdoms within domain Eukarya. Three of these kingdoms—Animalia, Fungi, and Plantae—are familiar to most people. Within each one, organisms share the same general strategy for acquiring energy. For example, plants are autotrophs. Fungi and animals are consumers, although they differ in the details of how they obtain food. But the fourth group of eukaryotes, the Protista, contains a huge collection of unrelated species. Protista is a convenient but artificial "none of the above" category for the many species of eukaryotes that are not plants, fungi, or animals.

1.2 MASTERING CONCEPTS

1. What are the goals of taxonomy?
2. How are domains related to kingdoms?
3. List and describe the four main groups of eukaryotes.

Figure 1.9 Life's Diversity. The three domains of life (Bacteria, Archaea, and Eukarya) arose from a hypothetical common ancestor, shown at the base of the evolutionary tree. Just as a tree trunk produces numerous branches and twigs, the first cells eventually diversified into many unique types of organisms.

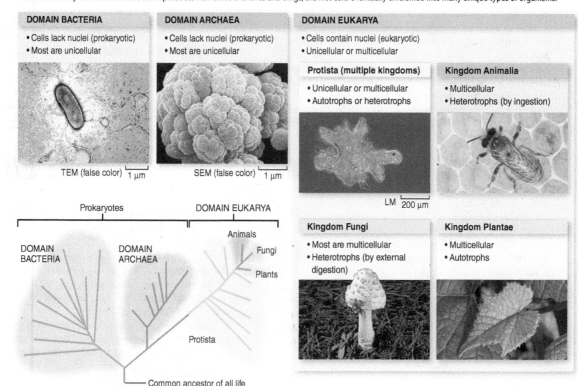

1.3 Scientists Study the Natural World

Tutorial
Experiments
and Graphs

The idea of biology as a "rapidly changing field" may seem strange if you think of science as a collection of facts. After all, the parts of a frog are the same now as they were 50 or 100 years ago. But memorizing frog anatomy is not the same as thinking scientifically. Scientists use evidence to answer questions about the natural world. For example, if you compare a frog to a snake, can you determine how the frog can live in water and on land, whereas the snake survives in the desert? Understanding anatomy simply gives you the vocabulary you need to ask these and other interesting questions about life.

A. The Scientific Method Has Multiple Interrelated Parts

Scientific knowledge arises from application of the **scientific method,** which is a general way of using evidence to answer questions and test ideas (figure 1.10). Although this diagram may give the impression that science is a dry, step-by-step process, that is not at all true. Instead, science combines thinking, detective work, communicating with other scientists, learning from mistakes, and noticing connections between seemingly unrelated events. The resulting insights have taught us everything we know about the natural world.

Observations and Questions The scientific method begins with observations and questions. The observations may rely on what we can see, hear, touch, taste, or smell, or they may be based on existing knowledge and experimental results. Often, a great leap forward happens when one person makes connections between previously unrelated observations. Charles Darwin, for example, developed the idea of natural selection by combining his understanding of Earth's long history with his detailed observations of organisms. Another great advance occurred decades later, when biologists realized that mutations in DNA generate the variation that Darwin saw but could not explain.

Hypothesis and Prediction A **hypothesis** is a tentative explanation for one or more observations. The hypothesis is the essential "unit" of scientific inquiry. To be useful, the hypothesis must be testable—that is, there must be a way to collect data that can support or reject it. Interestingly, a hypothesis cannot be *proven* true, because future discoveries may contradict today's results. Nevertheless, a hypothesis becomes widely accepted when multiple lines of evidence support it, no credible data refute it, and plausible alternative hypotheses have been rejected.

A hypothesis is a general statement that should lead to specific **predictions.** Often, the prediction is written as an if–then statement. As a simple example, suppose you hypothesize that your lawn mower stopped working because it ran out of gas. A reasonable prediction would be, "If I put fuel into the tank, then my lawn mower should start."

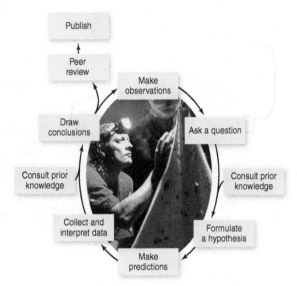

Figure 1.10 Scientific Inquiry. This researcher is collecting insects; the resulting observations could lead to questions and testable hypotheses. Additional data, combined with prior findings, can help support or reject each hypothesis. Peer review determines whether the results are publishable.

Data Collection Investigators draw conclusions based on data (figure 1.11). The data may come from careful observations of the natural world, an approach called discovery science. For example, thousands of volunteers participate in the National Audubon Society's annual Christmas Bird Count. For more than a century, these "citizen scientists" have documented the ups and downs of hundreds of bird species nationwide. Another way to gather data is to carry out an **experiment** to test a hypothesis under controlled conditions (section 1.3B explores experimental design in more detail).

Discovery and experimentation work hand in hand. As just one example, consider the well-known connection between cigarettes and lung cancer. In the late 1940s, scientists showed that smokers are far more likely than nonsmokers to develop cancer. Since that time, countless laboratory experiments have revealed how the chemicals in tobacco damage living cells.

Analysis and Peer Review After collecting and interpreting data, investigators decide whether the evidence supports or falsifies the hypotheses. Often, the most interesting results are those that are unexpected, because they provide new observations that force scientists to rethink their hypotheses; figure 1.10 shows this feedback loop. Science advances as new information arises and explanations continue to improve.

Once a scientist has enough evidence to support or reject a hypothesis, he or she may write a paper and submit it for publication in a scientific journal. The journal's editors send the paper to

a.

b.

Figure 1.11 Different Types of Science. (a) Scientists track the number of migratory birds that visit a wildlife refuge each year—an example of discovery science. (b) Controlled experiments can help food scientists objectively compare different techniques for roasting or brewing coffee.

anonymous reviewers knowledgeable about the research topic. In a process called **peer review,** these scientists independently evaluate the validity of the methods, data, and conclusions. Overall, peer review ensures that journal articles—the tangible products of the global scientific conversation—are of high quality.

B. An Experimental Design Is a Careful Plan

Virtual Lab
Experimental Design

Scientists test many hypotheses with the help of experiments. An **experiment** is an investigation carried out in controlled conditions. This section considers a real study that tested the hypothesis that a new vaccine protects against a deadly virus. The virus, called rotavirus, causes severe diarrhea and takes the lives of hundreds of thousands of young children each year. An effective, inexpensive vaccine would prevent many childhood deaths.

Sample Size One of the most important decisions that an investigator makes in designing an experiment is the **sample size,** which is the number of individuals that he or she will study. For example, about 100 infants were assigned to each treatment in the rotavirus study. In general, the larger the sample size, the more credible the results of a study.

Variables A systematic consideration of variables is also important in experimental design (table 1.2). A **variable** is a changeable element of an experiment, and there are several types. The investigator directly manipulates the levels of the **independent variable.** For example, in the rotavirus study, the independent variable was the dose of the vaccine. The **dependent variable** is any response that might *depend on* the value of the independent variable, such as the number of children with rotavirus-related illness during the study period.

A **standardized variable** is anything that the investigator holds constant for all subjects in the experiment, ensuring the best chance of detecting the effect of the independent variable. For example, rotavirus infection is most common among very young children. The test of the new vaccine therefore included only infants younger than 12 weeks. Furthermore, vaccines work best in people with healthy immune systems, so the study excluded infants who were ill or had weak immunity. Age and health were therefore among this study's standardized variables.

TABLE **1.2** **Types of Variables in an Experiment: A Summary**

Type of Variable	Definition	Example
Independent variable	What the investigator manipulates to determine whether it influences the phenomenon of interest	Dose of experimental vaccine
Dependent variable	What the investigator measures to determine whether the independent variable influenced the phenomenon of interest	Number of children with illness caused by rotavirus
Standardized variable	Any variable intentionally held constant for all subjects in an experiment, including the control group	Age of children in study

Controls   Well-designed experiments compare a group of "normal" individuals to a group undergoing treatment. The untreated group is called an experimental **control** and provides a basis for comparison. Ideally, the only difference between the control and the experimental group is the one factor being tested.

Experimental controls may take several forms. Sometimes, the control group simply receives a "zero" value for the independent variable. If a gardener wants to test a new fertilizer in her garden, she may give some plants a lot of fertilizer, others only a little, and still others—the control plants—none. In medical research, a control group might receive a **placebo,** an inert substance that resembles the treatment given to the experimental group. The control infants in the rotavirus study received a placebo that contained all components of the vaccine except the active ingredient.

The investigators in the rotavirus study used a double-blind design, in which neither the researchers nor the participants knew who received the vaccine and who received the placebo. Double-blind studies help avoid bias in medical research. The investigators break the "code" of who received which treatment only after the experiment is complete and the data are tabulated.

Statistical Analysis   Once an experiment is complete, the investigator compiles the data and decides whether the results support the hypothesis. Look at the results in figure 1.12. Did the vaccine prevent illness, or do the data simply reflect random chance? The researchers concluded that the vaccine was effective, but only after applying a statistical analysis.

Researchers may use many different statistical tests, depending on the type of data. All such tests consider both variation and sample size to yield a measure of **statistical significance:** the probability that the results arose purely by chance. Appendix B shows how scientists illustrate statistical significance in graphs.

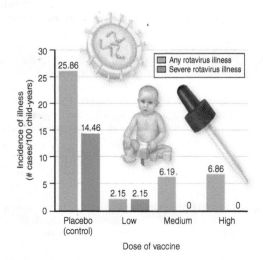

Figure 1.12 Vaccine Test. In this test of a new vaccine against rotavirus, the independent variable was the dose of the vaccine; control infants received a placebo. The statistical analysis (not shown) suggests that all vaccine doses prevented illness when compared with the placebo.

C. Theories Are Comprehensive Explanations

Outside of science, the word *theory* is often used to describe an opinion or a hunch. For instance, immediately after a plane crash, experts offer their "theories" about the cause of the disaster. These tentative explanations are really untested hypotheses.

In science, the word *theory* has a distinct meaning. Like a hypothesis, a **theory** is an explanation for a natural phenomenon, but a theory is typically broader in scope than a hypothesis. For example, the germ theory—the idea that some microorganisms cause human disease—is the foundation for medical microbiology. Individual hypotheses relating to the germ theory, such as the suggestion that rotavirus causes illness, are narrower. Not all theories are as "large" as the germ theory, but they generally encompass multiple hypotheses. Note also that the germ theory does not imply that *all* microbes make us sick or that all diseases have microbial causes. But it does explain many illnesses.

A second difference between a hypothesis and a theory is their degree of acceptance, based on evidence. A hypothesis is tentative, whereas theories reflect broader agreement. This is not to imply that theories are not testable; in fact, the opposite is true. Every scientific theory is *potentially* falsifiable, meaning that a particular set of observations could prove the theory wrong. The germ theory remains widely accepted because many observations support it and no reliable tests have disproved it. The same is true for the theory of evolution and other scientific theories.

Another quality of a scientific theory is its predictive power. A good theory not only ties together many existing observations, but also suggests predictions about phenomena that have yet to be observed. Both Charles Darwin and naturalist Alfred Russel Wallace, for example, used the theory of evolution by natural selection to predict the existence of a moth that could pollinate orchid flowers with unusually long nectar tubes (figure 1.13). Decades later, scientists discovered the long-tongued insect (see section 1.4). This finding was consistent with evolutionary theory, but the theory would have been weakened if subsequent research had not supported its predictions.

What is the relationship between facts and a theory? One definition of the word *fact* is "a repeatable observation that everyone can agree on." It is a fact, for example, that a dropped pencil falls toward the ground; no reasonable person disagrees with that statement. Gravity is a *fact*; gravitational *theory* explains the forces that cause pencils and other objects fall.

Biologists also consider biological evolution to be a fact. Yet the phrase "theory of evolution" persists, because evolution is both a fact *and* a theory. Like gravity, evolution is a *fact*. No one can dispute that antibiotics drive evolutionary change in bacteria (see figure 1.8). On a broader scale, the combined evidence for genetic change over time is so persuasive and comes from so many different fields of study that to deny its existence is unrealistic. Evolutionary *theory* explains how life has diversified since its origin. Note that biologists do not understand everything about life's evolutionary history; many questions remain. But the scientific debates swirl around *how*, not *whether*, evolution occurred.

Figure 1.13 **Prediction Confirmed.** When Charles Darwin saw this orchid, he predicted that its pollinator would have long, thin mouthparts that could reach the bottom of the elongated nectar tube. He was right; the unknown pollinator turned out to be a moth with an extraordinarily long tongue.

D. Scientific Inquiry Has Limitations

Scientific inquiry is neither foolproof nor always easy to implement. One problem is that experimental evidence may lead to multiple interpretations, and even the most carefully designed experiment can fail to provide a definitive answer (see the Apply It Now box on page 14). Consider the observation that animals fed large doses of vitamin E live longer than similar animals that do not ingest the vitamin. So, does vitamin E slow aging? Possibly, but excess vitamin E also causes weight loss, and other research has connected weight loss with longevity. Does vitamin E extend life, or does weight loss? The experiment alone does not distinguish between these possibilities.

Another limitation is that researchers may misinterpret observations or experimental results. For example, centuries ago, scientists sterilized a bottle of broth, corked the bottle shut, and observed bacteria in the broth a few days later. They concluded that life arose directly from the broth. The correct explanation, however, was that the cork did not keep airborne bacteria out. Although scientists may make mistakes in the short term, science is also self-correcting because it remains open to new data and new interpretations.

A related problem is that the scientific community may be slow to accept new evidence that suggests unexpected conclusions. Every investigator should try to keep an open mind about observations, not allowing biases or expectations to cloud interpretation of the results. But it is human nature to be cautious in accepting an observation that does not fit what we think we know. The careful demonstration that life does not arise from broth surprised many people who believed that mice sprang from moldy grain and that flies came from rotted beef. More recently, it took many years to set aside the common belief that stress causes ulcers. Today, we know that a bacterium causes most ulcers.

Although science is a powerful tool for answering questions about the natural world, it cannot answer questions of beauty, morality, ethics, religion, or the meaning of life (see this chapter's Burning Question). Nor can we directly study some phenomena that occurred long ago and left little physical evidence. For example, many experiments have attempted to re-create the chemical reactions that might have produced life on early Earth. Although the experiments produce interesting results and reveal ways that these early events may have occurred, we cannot know if they accurately re-create conditions at the beginning of life.

BurningQuestion

Why am I here?

The Burning Questions featured in each chapter of this book came from students. On the first day of class, I always ask students to turn in a "burning question"—anything they have always wondered about biology. I answer most of the questions as the relevant topics come up during the semester.

Why not answer all of the questions? It is because at least one student often asks something like "Why am I here?" or "What is the meaning of life?" Such puzzles have fascinated humans throughout the ages, but they are among the many questions that we cannot approach scientifically. Biology can explain how you developed after a sperm from your father fertilized an egg cell from your mother. But no one can develop a testable hypothesis about life's meaning or the purpose of human existence. Science must remain silent on such questions.

Instead, other ways of knowing must satisfy our curiosity about "why." Philosophers, for example, can help us see how others have considered these questions. Religion may also provide the meaning that many people seek. Part of the value of higher education is to help you acquire the tools you need to find your own life's purpose.

In the meantime, this book's Burning Questions can help you discover the answers to many questions—asked by students just like you—about human health, environmental quality, life's diversity, and the rest of the biological world.

Submit your burning question to
Marielle.Hoefnagels@mheducation.com

Apply It **Now**

It's Hard to Know What's Bad for You

You have probably heard reports that a food previously considered healthy is actually bad for you, or vice versa. These conflicting reports may tempt you to mistakenly conclude that scientific studies are not valid.

Instead, the problem lies in the fact that some questions are extremely hard to answer. Take, for example, the controversy surrounding the artificial sweetener called saccharin. In 1977, the U.S. Food and Drug Administration (FDA) proposed a ban on saccharin, based on a handful of studies suggesting that the sugar substitute caused bladder cancer in rats. Congress opted to require warning labels on products containing saccharin. In 1991, the FDA withdrew its proposed ban, and in 1998, saccharin was rated as "not classifiable as to its carcinogenicity to humans." Two years later, legislation removed the warning label requirement.

This tangled history raises an important issue. Why can't science reply "yes" or "no" to the seemingly simple question of whether saccharin is bad for you? To understand the answer, consider one of the studies that prompted the FDA to propose the ban on saccharin in the first place. Researchers divided 200 rats into two groups. The control animals ate standard rodent chow, whereas the experimental group got the same food supplemented with saccharin. At reproductive maturity the animals were bred, and the researchers fed the offspring the same dose of saccharin throughout their lives as well. To measure the incidence of cancer, they counted the tumors in both generations of rats for 24 months or until the rats died, whichever came first. Figure 1.A summarizes the results.

At first glance, the conclusion seems obvious: Saccharin causes cancer in male lab rats. But closer study reveals several hidden complexities that make the data hard to interpret. First, the dose of saccharin was huge: 5% of the rats' diets, for life. The equivalent dose in humans would require drinking hundreds of cans of saccharin-sweetened soda every day. In addition, the experimental rats weighed much less than the control rats by the end of the study, suggesting that high doses of the sweetener are toxic. Rather than causing cancer, the saccharin may have simply made the animals more susceptible to disease. Moreover, follow-up studies using other animals were inconclusive.

Perhaps the scientists should have studied the saccharin–cancer connection in humans instead. Unfortunately, however, documenting a link between any food and cancer in people is extremely difficult. One strategy might be to measure the incidence of cancer in saccharin users versus nonusers. But with so many other possible causes of cancer—smoking, poor diet, exposure to job-related chemicals, genetic predisposition—it would be difficult to separate out just the effects of saccharin.

So what are we to make of the mixed news reports? It is hard to say, but one thing is certain: No matter what the headlines say, one study, especially a small one, cannot reveal the whole story.

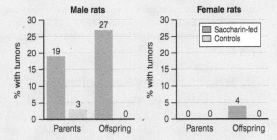

Figure 1.A   The Saccharin Scare. These graphs summarize the results of one study examining the link between saccharin and bladder cancer in rats. Sample sizes ranged from 36 to 49 rats per treatment. (Data adapted from Office of Technology Assessment Report, October 1977, *Cancer Testing Technology and Saccharin*, page 52.)

E. Biology Continues to Advance

Science is just one of many ways to investigate the world, but its strength is its openness to new information. Theories change to accommodate new knowledge. The history of science is full of long-established ideas changing as we learned more about nature, often thanks to new technology. For example, people thought that Earth was flat and at the center of the universe before inventions and data analysis revealed otherwise. Similarly, biologists thought all organisms were plants or animals until the first microscopes unveiled a world of life invisible to our eyes.

Technology is the practical application of scientific knowledge. Science and technology are therefore intimately related. For example, centuries of scientific inquiry have uncovered many of the differences between humans and bacteria. We can exploit these differences to invent new antibiotic drugs that kill germs without harming our own bodies. These antibiotics, in turn, can be useful tools that help biologists learn even more about bacterial cells. The new scientific discoveries spawn new technologies, and so on.

Biology is changing rapidly, in part because technology has expanded our ability to spy on living cells, compare DNA sequences, track wildlife, and make many other types of observations. Scientists can now learn about the natural world in ways that previous generations could never have imagined.

1.3   MASTERING CONCEPTS

1. Identify the elements of the experiment summarized in the Apply It Now box.
2. Why is statistical analysis important?
3. What is the difference between a hypothesis and a theory? What is the relationship between theories and facts?
4. What are some limitations of scientific inquiry?
5. Compare and contrast *science* and *technology*.

INVESTIGATING LIFE

1.4 The Orchid and the Moth

Each chapter of this book ends with a section that examines how biologists use systematic, scientific observations to solve a different evolutionary puzzle from life's long history. This first installment of Investigating Life revisits the story of the orchid plant pictured in figure 1.13.

Charles Darwin

In a book on orchids published in 1862, Charles Darwin speculated about which type of insect might pollinate the unusual flowers of the *Angraecum sesquipedale* orchid, a species that lives on Madagascar (an island off the coast of Africa). As described in section 1.3C, the flowers have unusually long nectar tubes (also called nectaries). Darwin observed nectaries "eleven and a half inches long, with only the lower inch and a half filled with very sweet nectar." Darwin found it "surprising that any insect should be able to reach the nectar; our English sphinxes [moths] have probosces as long as their bodies; but in Madagascar there must be moths with probosces capable of extension to a length of between ten and eleven inches!"

Alfred Russel Wallace

Alfred Russel Wallace picked up the story in a book published in 1895. According to Wallace, "There is a Madagascar orchid—the *Angraecum sesquipedale*—with an immensely long and deep nectary. How did such an extraordinary organ come to be developed?" He went on to summarize how natural selection could explain this unusual flower. He wrote: "The pollen of this flower can only be removed by the base of the proboscis of some very large moths, when trying to get at the nectar at the bottom of the vessel. The moths with the longest probosces would do this most effectually; they would be rewarded for their long tongues by getting the most nectar; whilst on the other hand, the flowers with the deepest nectaries would be the best fertilized by the largest moths preferring them. Consequently, the deepest nectaried orchids and the longest tongued moths would each confer on the other an advantage in the battle of life."

At that time, the pollinator had not yet been discovered. However, as Wallace wrote, moths with very long tongues were known to exist: "I have carefully measured the proboscis of a specimen . . . from South America . . . and find it to be nine inches and a quarter long! One from tropical Africa . . . is seven inches and a half. A species having a proboscis two or three inches longer could reach the nectar in the largest flowers of *Angraecum sesquipedale* . . . That such a moth exists in Madagascar may be safely predicted; and naturalists who visit that island should search for it with as much confidence as astronomers searched

Figure 1.14 Found at Last. More than 40 years after Darwin predicted its existence, scientists finally discovered the sphinx moth that pollinates the Madagascar orchid.

for the planet Neptune—and I venture to predict they will be equally successful!"

A taxonomic publication from 1903 finally validated Darwin's and Wallace's predictions. The authors described a moth species, *Xanthopan morgani*, with a 225-millimeter (8-inch) tongue (figure 1.14). Given the correspondence between lengths of the orchid's nectary and the moth's tongue, the authors concluded that "*Xanthopan morgani* can do for *Angraecum* what is necessary [for pollination]; we do not believe that there exists in Madagascar a moth with a longer tongue. . . ."

This story not only illustrates how theories lead to testable predictions but also reflects the collaborative nature of science. Darwin and Wallace asked a simple question: Why are these nectar tubes so long? Other biologists cataloging the world's insect species finally solved the puzzle, decades after Darwin first raised the question of the mysterious Madagascan orchid.

Darwin, C. R. 1862. *On the Various Contrivances by Which British and Foreign Orchids Are Fertilised by Insects, and on the Good Effects of Intercrossing.* London: John Murray, pages 197–198.

Rothschild, W., and K. Jordan. 1903. A revision of the lepidopterous family Sphingidae. *Novitates Zoologicae,* vol. 9, supplement part 1, page 32.

Wallace, Alfred Russel. 1895. *Natural Selection and Tropical Nature: Essays on Descriptive and Theoretical Biology.* London: MacMillan and Co., pages 146–148.

1.4 MASTERING CONCEPTS

1. What observations led Darwin and Wallace to predict the existence of a long-tongued moth in Madagascar?
2. How does this story illustrate discovery science?

CHAPTER SUMMARY

1.1 What Is Life?

- A combination of characteristics distinguishes life: organization, energy use, internal constancy, reproduction and development, and evolution.

A. Life Is Organized (figure 1.15)

- **Atoms** form **molecules.** These molecules form **organelles** inside many **cells.** An **organism** consists of one or more cells. In most multicellular organisms, cells form **tissues** and then **organs** and **organ systems.**
- Whether unicellular or multicellular, multiple individuals of the same species make up **populations;** multiple populations form **communities. Ecosystems** include living communities plus their nonliving environment. The **biosphere** incorporates all of the world's ecosystems.
- **Emergent properties** arise from interactions among the parts of an organism.

B. Life Requires Energy

- Life requires energy to maintain its organization and functions. **Producers** make their own food, using energy and nutrients extracted from the nonliving environment. **Consumers** eat other organisms, living or dead. **Decomposers** recycle nutrients to the nonliving environment.
- Because of heat losses, all ecosystems require constant energy input from an outside source, usually the sun.

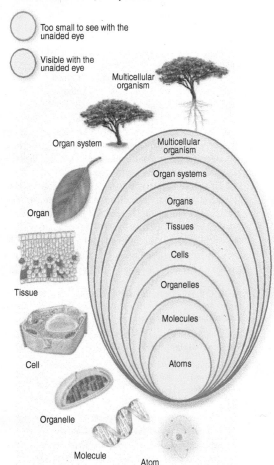

Figure 1.15 Life Is Organized: A Summary.

C. Life Maintains Internal Constancy

- Organisms must maintain **homeostasis,** an internal state of constancy in changing environmental conditions.

D. Life Reproduces Itself, Grows, and Develops

- Organisms reproduce asexually, sexually, or both. **Asexual reproduction** yields virtually identical copies of one parent, whereas **sexual reproduction** generates tremendous genetic diversity by combining and scrambling DNA from two parents.

E. Life Evolves

- In **natural selection,** environmental conditions select for organisms with inherited traits that increase the chance of survival and reproduction. The result of natural selection is **adaptations,** features that enhance reproductive success.
- **Evolution** through natural selection explains how common ancestry unites all species, producing diverse organisms with many similarities.

1.2 The Tree of Life Includes Three Main Branches

- **Taxonomy** is the science of classification. Biologists classify types of organisms, or **species,** according to probable evolutionary relationships. A **genus,** for example, consists of closely related species.
- The two broadest taxonomic levels are **domain** and **kingdom.**
- The three domains of life are Archaea, Bacteria, and Eukarya. Within each domain, mode of nutrition and other features distinguish the kingdoms.

1.3 Scientists Study the Natural World

A. The Scientific Method Has Multiple Interrelated Parts

- Scientific inquiry, which uses the **scientific method,** is a way of using evidence to evaluate ideas.
- A scientist makes observations, raises questions, and uses reason to construct a testable explanation, or **hypothesis.** Specific **predictions** follow from a scientific hypothesis.
- After collecting data and making conclusions based on the evidence, the investigator may seek to publish scientific results. **Peer review** ensures that published studies meet high standards for quality.

B. An Experimental Design Is a Careful Plan

- An **experiment** is a test of a hypothesis carried out in controlled conditions.
- The larger the **sample size,** the more credible the results of an experiment.
- Experimental **controls** are the basis for comparison. The **independent variable** in an experiment is the factor that the investigator manipulates. The **dependent variable** is a measurement that the investigator makes to determine the outcome of an experiment. **Standardized variables** are held constant for all subjects in an experiment.
- **Placebo**-controlled, double-blind experiments minimize bias.
- **Statistically significant** results are unlikely to be due to chance.

C. Theories Are Comprehensive Explanations

- A **theory** is more widely accepted and broader in scope than a hypothesis.
- The acceptance of scientific ideas may change as new evidence accumulates.

D. Scientific Inquiry Has Limitations

- The scientific method does not always yield a complete explanation, or it may produce ambiguous results. Science cannot answer all possible questions—only those for which it is possible to develop testable hypotheses.

E. Biology Continues to Advance

- **Technology** is the practical application of scientific knowledge. Advances in science lead to new technologies, and vice versa.

1.4 Investigating Life: The Orchid and the Moth

- Charles Darwin and Alfred Russel Wallace knew of an orchid in Madagascar with an extremely long nectar tube. They predicted that the orchid's pollinator would be a moth with an equally long tongue.
- Years later, other scientists discovered the moth, illustrating the predictive power of evolutionary theory.

MULTIPLE CHOICE QUESTIONS

1. Which of the following is the basic unit of life?
   a. Atom   c. Organelle
   b. Molecule   d. Cell

2. All of the following are characteristics of life EXCEPT
   a. evolution.   c. homeostasis.
   b. reproduction.   d. multicellularity.

3. Which two levels are farthest apart on the hierarchy of biological organization?
   a. Organism and population   c. Atom and cell
   b. Ecosystem and biosphere   d. Tissue and organ

4. Because plants extract nutrients from soil and use sunlight as an energy source, they are considered to be
   a. autotrophs.   c. heterotrophs.
   b. consumers.   d. decomposers.

5. Evolution through natural selection will occur most rapidly for populations of plants that
   a. are already well adapted to the environment.
   b. live in an unchanging environment.
   c. are in the same genus.
   d. reproduce sexually and live in an unstable environment.

6. What is the correct way to write the scientific name for humans?
   a. Homo sapiens   c. *Homo Sapiens*
   b. *Homo sapiens*   d. homo sapiens

7. In an experiment to test the effect of temperature on the rate of bacterial reproduction, temperature would be the
   a. standardized variable.   c. dependent variable.
   b. independent variable.   d. control variable.

8. A scientist has just observed a new phenomenon and wonders how it happens. What is the next step in his or her discovery of the answer?
   a. Observe   c. Experiment
   b. Hypothesize   d. Peer review

9. Can a theory be proven wrong?
   a. No, theories are exactly the same as facts.
   b. No, because there is no good way to test a theory.
   c. Yes, a new observation could disprove a theory.
   d. Yes, theories are exactly the same as hypotheses.

10. Which of the following statements is false?
    a. Emergent properties are functions that arise from the interactions between an organism's parts.
    b. Two of the three domains contain prokaryotic organisms.
    c. In a double-blind experiment, neither the researcher nor the subjects know which subject is assigned to which treatment.
    d. For a scientific study to be considered valid, the researchers must conduct experiments.

Answers to these questions are in appendix A.

WRITE IT OUT

1. Describe each of the five characteristics of life, and list several nonliving things that possess at least two of these characteristics.

2. Explain how an atom relates to the biosphere by describing the levels of life's organization.

3. Why is a cell, and not an atom or a molecule, considered the basic unit of life?

4. Think of an analogy that will help you remember the differences between populations, communities, and ecosystems.

5. Other than the brownie example given in the text, name an example of emergent properties from everyday life.

6. Draw and explain the relationship between producers and consumers (including decomposers).

7. How does a home's air conditioning system illustrate homeostasis?

8. Describe the main differences between asexual and sexual reproduction. Why are both types of reproduction common?

9. How are the members of the three domains similar? How are they different?

10. List each step of the scientific method and explain why it is important.

11. Give two examples of questions that you cannot answer using the scientific method. Explain your reason for choosing each example.

12. Design an experiment to test the following hypothesis: "Eating chocolate causes zits." Include sample size, independent variable, dependent variable, the most important variables to standardize, and an experimental control.

PULL IT TOGETHER

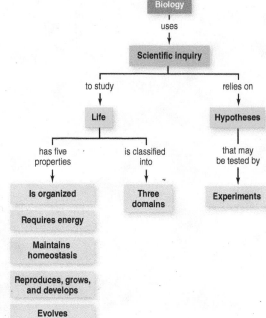

Figure 1.16 Pull It Together: The Scientific Study of Life.

Refer to figure 1.16 and the chapter content to answer the following questions.

1. What are the elements of a controlled experiment?

2. What is the relationship between natural selection and evolution?

3. Give an example of each of the five properties of life.

CHAPTER

2 The Chemistry of Life

Eat Me and You're Dead. The skin of the Sierra newt contains a potent toxin that protects the animal from predators.

Chemical Warfare

THE THOUGHT OF CHEMISTRY OFTEN BRINGS TO MIND LABORATORY BENCHES, WHITE LAB COATS, AND FLASKS FILLED WITH BUBBLING SOLUTIONS. It may be hard for you to connect that image with living organisms. Yet chemistry and biology are intimately connected.

What does the complexity of life have to do with chemistry? A living body is a mixture of thousands of different types of interacting chemicals. Some of these chemicals are familiar to anyone who has read a nutrition label: sugars, proteins, and fats. Others, like DNA and water, are frequently in the news. But the vast majority are substances you may never have thought of as chemicals, like the hair on your head, the hormones in your bloodstream, or the red pigment in your blood cells.

Chemistry is not just limited to animals; all organisms, plants included, are made of chemicals. Some of these substances are the same as those in your own body, but others are unique to the plant kingdom. Some of the most interesting chemicals are those that plants deploy in their never-ending fight against herbivores and competitors. Whereas humans and other animals defend ourselves by using our wits and our ability to escape, many plants use chemical warfare.

Black walnut trees, for example, release a chemical that inhibits the growth of many other plants. Landscapers therefore often find it hard to establish new plants around black walnut trees. How does it benefit the trees to be such bad neighbors? By putting up a chemical "Keep Out" sign, they are reducing competition for vital resources like light, water, and soil nutrients.

Plants also produce chemicals that limit damage from animals that might otherwise dine on their foliage, flowers, fruits, or seeds. Consider the hot, spicy taste of a chili pepper; most mammals can't tolerate it, so they leave the peppers alone (see section 24.8).

Of course, plants don't have an exclusive hold on the chemical warfare market. Chemists who study nature's chemical weapons have spent decades identifying antibiotics produced by bacteria and fungi. Manufactured as drugs, these antibiotics have saved millions of lives. Other toxins occur in organisms ranging from mushrooms to sponges to snails to frogs and salamanders. Some of these chemicals protect their owners against competitors, predators, and disease. The race is on to determine whether they may also find new uses in medicine or other applications.

Defensive chemicals make up a relatively small proportion of any organism's body. The majority of a cell consists of water and four classes of organic compounds. This chapter describes these basic chemical constituents of life.

 LEARN HOW TO LEARN
Organize Your Time, and Don't Try to Cram

Get a calendar, and study the syllabus for every class you are taking. Write each due date in your calendar. Include homework assignments, quizzes, and exams, and add new dates as you learn them. Then, block out time before each due date to work on each task. Success comes much more easily if you take a steady pace instead of waiting until the last minute.

2.1 Atoms Make Up All Matter

If you have ever touched a plant in a restaurant to see if it's fake, you know that we all have an intuitive sense of what life is made of. Most living leaves feel moist and pliable; a fake one is dry and stiff. But what does chemistry tell us about the composition of life?

Your desk, your book, your body, your sandwich, a plastic plant—indeed, all objects in the universe, including life on Earth—are composed of matter and energy. **Matter** is any material that takes up space, such as organisms, rocks, the oceans, and gases in the atmosphere. This chapter and the next concentrate on the building blocks that make up living matter. Physicists define energy, on the other hand, as the ability to do work. In this context, *work* means moving matter. Heat, light, and chemical bonds are all forms of energy; chapter 4 discusses the energy of life in detail.

A. Elements Are Fundamental Types of Matter

The matter that makes up every object in the universe consists of one or more elements. A chemical **element** is a pure substance that cannot be broken down by chemical means into other substances. Examples of elements include oxygen (O), carbon (C), nitrogen (N), sodium (Na), and hydrogen (H).

Scientists had already noticed patterns in the chemical behavior of the elements by the mid-1800s, and several had proposed schemes for organizing the elements into categories. Nineteenth-century Russian chemist Dmitry Mendeleyev invented the **periodic table,** the chart that we still use today. The chart is "periodic" because the chemical properties of the elements repeat in each column of the table. Figure 2.1 illustrates an abbreviated periodic table, emphasizing the elements that make up organisms. (Appendix D contains a complete periodic table.)

About 25 elements are essential to life. Of these, the **bulk elements** are required in the largest amounts because they make up the vast majority of every living cell. The four most abundant bulk elements in life are carbon, hydrogen, oxygen, and nitrogen. Other bulk elements include phosphorus (P), sodium (Na), magnesium (Mg), potassium (K), and calcium (Ca). **Trace elements,** such as iron (Fe) and zinc (Zn), are required in small amounts.

A person whose diet is deficient in any essential element can become ill or die. The thyroid gland, for example, requires the trace element iodine (I). If the diet does not supply enough iodine, the thyroid may become enlarged, forming a growth called a *goiter* in the neck. Similarly, red blood cells require iron (Fe) to carry oxygen to the body's tissues. An iron-poor diet can cause anemia, which is a decline in the number of red blood cells.

B. Atoms Are Particles of Elements

An **atom** is the smallest possible "piece" of an element that retains the characteristics of the element. An atom is composed of three types of subatomic particles (figure 2.2 and table 2.1). **Protons,** which carry a positive charge, and **neutrons,** which are uncharged, together form a central **nucleus.** Negatively charged **electrons** surround the nucleus. An electron is vanishingly small compared with a proton or a neutron.

For simplicity, most illustrations of atoms show the electrons closely hugging the nucleus. In reality, however, if the nucleus of a hydrogen atom were the size of a meatball, the electron belonging to that atom could be about 1 kilometer away from it! Thus, most of an atom's mass is concentrated in the nucleus, while the electron cloud occupies virtually all of its volume.

How can this electron cloud, which is mostly empty space, account for the solid "feel" of the objects in our world? The fact that the electrons are in constant motion helps explain this paradox. A good analogy is a ceiling fan. When the fan is not

1 Hydrogen **H** 1.0079																	2 Helium **He** 4.0026
3 Lithium **Li** 6.941	4 Beryllium **Be** 9.0122																
11 Sodium **Na** 22.989	12 Magnesium **Mg** 24.305										13 Aluminum **Al** 26.9815	14 Silicon **Si** 28.086	15 Phosphorus **P** 30.9738	16 Sulfur **S** 32.064	17 Chlorine **Cl** 35.453	18 Argon **Ar** 39.948
19 Potassium **K** 39.098	20 Calcium **Ca** 40.08	21 Scandium **Sc** 44.956	22 Titanium **Ti** 47.90	23 Vanadium **V** 50.942	24 Chromium **Cr** 51.996	25 Manganese **Mn** 54.938	26 Iron **Fe** 55.847	27 Cobalt **Co** 58.933	28 Nickel **Ni** 58.71	29 Copper **Cu** 63.546	30 Zinc **Zn** 65.38	31 Gallium **Ga** 69.723	32 Germanium **Ge** 72.59	33 Arsenic **As** 74.922	34 Selenium **Se** 78.96	35 Bromine **Br** 79.904	36 Krypton **Kr** 83.80
37 Rubidium **Rb** 85.468	38 Strontium **Sr** 87.62	39 Yttrium **Y** 88.905	40 Zirconium **Zr** 91.22	41 Niobium **Nb** 92.906	42 Molybdenum **Mo** 95.94	43 Technetium **Tc** (99)	44 Ruthenium **Ru** 101.07	45 Rhodium **Rh** 102.905	46 Palladium **Pd** 106.4	47 Silver **Ag** 107.868	48 Cadmium **Cd** 112.40	49 Indium **In** 114.82	50 Tin **Sn** 118.69	51 Antimony **Sb** 121.75	52 Tellurium **Te** 127.60	53 Iodine **I** 126.904	54 Xenon **Xe** 131.30

Legend: ▨ Bulk elements (most abundant) ▨ Bulk elements (less abundant) ▢ Trace elements

6 Carbon **C** 12.012 — Atomic number / Element / Symbol / Atomic weight

Figure 2.1 The Periodic Table of Elements. This abbreviated periodic table shows the first 54 elements, each with a unique atomic number and a symbol. A complete periodic table appears in appendix D.

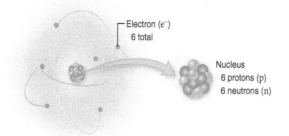

Figure 2.2 **Atom Anatomy.** The nucleus of an atom is made of protons and neutrons. A cloud of electrons surrounds the nucleus. This example has six protons, so it is a carbon atom.

Animation
Atom
Structure

TABLE **2.1** **Types of Subatomic Particles**

Particle	Charge	Mass	Location
Electron	–	0	Surrounding nucleus
Neutron	None	1	Nucleus
Proton	+	1	Nucleus

spinning, it is easy to move your hand between two blades. But when the fan is on, the rotating blades essentially form a solid disk.

Each element has a unique **atomic number,** the number of protons in the nucleus. Hydrogen, the simplest type of atom, has an atomic number of 1. In contrast, an atom of uranium has 92 protons. Elements are arranged sequentially in the periodic table by atomic number, which appears above each element's symbol (see figure 2.1).

When the number of protons equals the number of electrons, the atom is electrically neutral; that is, it has no net charge. An **ion** is an atom (or group of atoms) that has gained or lost electrons and therefore has a net negative or positive charge. Common positively charged ions, also called cations, include hydrogen (H^+), sodium (Na^+), and potassium (K^+). Negatively charged ions (anions) include hydroxide (OH^-) and chloride (Cl^-). Ions participate in many biological processes, including the transmission of messages in the nervous system. They also form ionic bonds, discussed in section 2.2. ⓘ *action potential*, p. 540

TABLE **2.2** **A Miniglossary of Matter**

Term	Definition
Element	A fundamental type of substance
Atom	The smallest unit of an element that retains the characteristics of that element
Atomic number	The number of protons in an atom's nucleus
Mass number	The number of protons plus the number of neutrons in an atom's nucleus
Isotope	Any of the different forms of the same element, distinguished from one another by the number of neutrons in the nucleus
Atomic weight	The average mass of all isotopes of an element

C. Isotopes Have Different Numbers of Neutrons

An atom's **mass number** is the total number of protons and neutrons in its nucleus. Because neutrons and protons have the same mass (see table 2.1), subtracting the atomic number from the mass number therefore yields the number of neutrons in an atom.

All atoms of an element have the same number of protons but not necessarily the same number of neutrons. An **isotope** is any of these different forms of a single element (figure 2.3). For example, carbon has three isotopes, designated ^{12}C (six neutrons), ^{13}C (seven neutrons), and ^{14}C (eight neutrons). The superscript denotes the mass number of each isotope.

Figure It Out

The most abundant isotope of iron (Fe) has a mass number of 56. Using the information in figure 2.1, how many neutrons are in each atom of ^{56}Fe?

Answer: 30.

Often one isotope of an element is very abundant, and others are rare. For example, about 99% of carbon isotopes are ^{12}C, and only 1% are ^{13}C or ^{14}C. An element's **atomic weight** is the average mass of all isotopes. The atomic weight is typically close to the mass number of the most abundant isotope.

Many of the known isotopes are unstable and **radioactive,** which means they emit energy as rays or particles when they break down into more stable forms. Every radioactive isotope has a characteristic half-life, which is the time it takes for half of the atoms in a sample to emit radiation, or "decay," to a different, more stable form. Scientists have determined the half-life of each radioactive isotope experimentally. Depending on the isotope, the half-life might range from a fraction of a second to millions or even billions of years. Physicists use large samples of isotopes and precise measurements to calculate the longest half-lives.

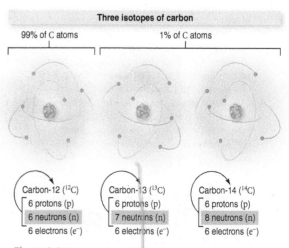

Figure 2.3 **Three Isotopes of Carbon.** Carbon's atomic number is 6, so its nucleus always contains six protons. These three carbon isotopes, however, have different numbers of neutrons.

Radioactive isotopes have many uses in medicine and science, ranging from detecting broken bones to determining the ages of fossils. But the same properties that make radioactive isotopes useful can also make them dangerous. Exposure to excessive radiation can lead to radiation sickness, and radiation-induced mutations of a cell's DNA can cause cancer (see chapter 8). The lead-containing "bib" that a dentist places on your chest during mouth X-rays protects you from radiation. ⓘ *radiometric dating*, p. 266

Table 2.2 on page 21 reviews the terminology of matter.

2.1 MASTERING CONCEPTS

1. Which four chemical elements do organisms require in the largest amounts?
2. Where in an atom are protons, neutrons, and electrons located?
3. What does an element's atomic number indicate?
4. What is the relationship between an atom's mass number and an element's atomic weight?
5. How are different isotopes of the same element different from one another?

2.2 Chemical Bonds Link Atoms

Tutorial
Chemical Bonding

Like all organisms, you are composed mostly of carbon, hydrogen, oxygen, and nitrogen atoms. But the arrangement of these atoms is not random. Instead, your atoms are organized into molecules (see figure 1.2). A **molecule** is two or more chemically joined atoms.

Some molecules, such as the gases hydrogen (H_2), oxygen (O_2), or nitrogen (N_2), are "diatomic," meaning that they consist of two atoms of the same element. More often, however, the elements in a molecule are different. A **compound** is a molecule composed of two or more different elements. Carbon monoxide, for example, is a compound consisting of one carbon and one oxygen atom. Likewise, water (H_2O) is made of two atoms of hydrogen and one of oxygen. Many large biological compounds, including DNA and proteins, consist of tens of thousands of atoms.

A compound's characteristics can differ strikingly from those of its constituent elements. Consider table salt, sodium chloride. Sodium (Na) is a silvery, highly reactive solid metal, whereas chlorine (Cl) is a yellow, corrosive gas. But when equal numbers of these two atoms combine, the resulting compound forms the familiar white salt crystals that we sprinkle on food—an excellent example of an emergent property. Another example is methane, the main component of natural gas. Its components are carbon (a black, sooty solid) and hydrogen (a light, combustible gas). ⓘ *emergent properties*, p. 6

Scientists describe molecules by writing the symbols of their constituent elements and indicating the numbers of atoms of each element as subscripts. For example, methane is written CH_4, which denotes a molecule with one carbon atom and four hydrogen atoms. This representation of the atoms in a compound is termed a *molecular formula*. Table salt's formula is NaCl, that of water is H_2O, and that of the gas carbon dioxide is CO_2.

What forces hold together the atoms that make up each of these molecules? To understand the answer, we must first learn more about how electrons are arranged around the nucleus.

A. Electrons Determine Bonding

Electrons occupy distinct energetic regions around the nucleus. They are constantly in motion, so it is impossible to determine the exact location of any electron at any given moment. Instead, chemists use the term **orbitals** to describe the most likely location for an electron relative to its nucleus. Each orbital can hold up to two electrons. Consequently, the more electrons in an atom, the more orbitals they occupy.

Electron orbitals exist in several energy levels; an **energy shell** is a group of orbitals that share the same level. The number of orbitals in each shell determines the number of electrons the shell can hold. The lowest energy shell, for example, contains just one orbital and thus holds up to two electrons. The next two shells each contain four orbitals and therefore hold as many as eight electrons each.

Electrons occupy the lowest energy level available to them, starting with the innermost one. As each energy shell fills, any additional electrons must reside in higher energy shells. For example, hydrogen has only one electron in the lowest energy orbital, and helium has two. Carbon has six electrons; two occupy the lowest energy orbital, and four are in the next energy shell. Oxygen, with eight electrons total, has two electrons in the lowest energy orbital and six at the next higher energy level.

We can thus envision any atom's electrons as occupying a series of concentric energy shells, each having a higher energy level than the one inside it. In accordance with this view, electrons often are illustrated as dots moving in two-dimensional circles around a nucleus (figure 2.4). These depictions, called Bohr models, are useful for visualizing the interactions between atoms to form bonds. However, most orbitals are not spherical. Bohr models therefore do not accurately portray the three-dimensional structure of atoms.

An atom's **valence shell** is its outermost occupied energy shell. Atoms are most stable when their valence shells are full. The gases helium (He) and neon (Ne), for example, are inert—that is,

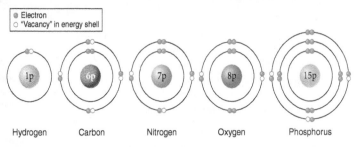

Figure 2.4 Energy Shells. Shown here are Bohr models of the most common atoms in organisms. Each pair of electrons represents one orbital.

they are chemically unreactive. Because their outermost shells are full, they exist in nature without combining with other atoms.

For most atoms, however, the valence shell is only partially filled. Look again at the first few rows of the periodic table in figure 2.1. Lithium (Li), which occupies the first column, has one valence electron, as do all other elements directly below it. Beryllium (Be) has two, as does magnesium (Mg). Working across the table, Bohr models reveal that boron (B) has three valence electrons, carbon has four, nitrogen has five, oxygen has six, and fluorine (F) has seven.

An atom of each of these elements will become most stable if its valence-shell "vacancies" fill. As you will soon see, atoms may donate, steal, or share electrons to arrive at exactly the right number. The exact "strategy" that an atom uses depends in part on its **electronegativity,** which measures the atom's ability to attract electrons on a scale of 0 to 4 (figure 2.5). Fluorine and oxygen, for example, have high electronegativity compared to sodium and potassium. Elements with high electronegativity tend to strip electrons away from those with lower values. Elements with moderate electronegativity often share electrons.

Whether electrons are stolen or shared, the transfer of electrons from one atom to another creates a **chemical bond,** an attractive force that holds atoms together. The remainder of this section describes three types of chemical bonds that are important in biology. Table 2.3 on page 25 provides a summary.

B. In an Ionic Bond, One Atom Transfers Electrons to Another Atom

Sometimes, two atoms have such different electronegativities that one actually takes one or more of its partner's electrons. Recall that an atom is most stable if its valence shell is full. The most electronegative atoms, such as chlorine (Cl), are usually those whose valence shells have only one "vacancy." Likewise, sodium (Na) and other weakly electronegative atoms have only one electron in the outermost shell. Neither chlorine nor sodium would benefit from sharing. Instead, sodium is most stable if it

Figure 2.5 **Unequal Attraction.** Atoms vary widely in their electronegativity, the ability to attract electrons. Note that the most electronegative atoms tend to have the smallest radius; these atoms pull electrons close to the nucleus, decreasing the overall radius.

Animation
Electronegativity

simply releases its extra electron to chlorine, which needs this "scrap" electron to complete its own valence shell (figure 2.6).

An ion is an atom that has lost or gained electrons. The atom that has lost electrons—such as the sodium atom in figure 2.6— is an ion carrying a positive charge. Conversely, the one that has gained electrons—chlorine in this case—acquires a negative charge. An **ionic bond** results from the electrical attraction between two ions with opposite charges. In general, such bonds form between an atom whose outermost shell is almost empty and one whose valence shell is nearly full.

The ions in figure 2.6 have bonded ionically to form NaCl. In NaCl, the most stable configuration of Na^+ and Cl^- is a three-dimensional crystal. Ionic bonds in crystals are strong, as demonstrated by the stability of the salt in your shaker. Those same crystals, however, dissolve when you stir them into water. As described in section 2.3, water molecules pull ionic bonds apart.

Figure 2.6 **Table Salt, an Ionically Bonded Molecule.** (a) A sodium atom (Na) can donate the one electron in its valence shell to a chlorine atom (Cl), which has seven electrons in its outermost shell. Notice that the valence shells of both atoms are now full. The resulting ions (Na^+ and Cl^-) form the compound sodium chloride (NaCl). (b) The ions that constitute NaCl occur in a repeating pattern that produces salt crystals.

Animation
Ionic Bonds

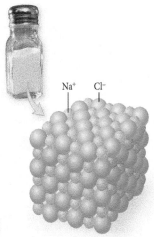

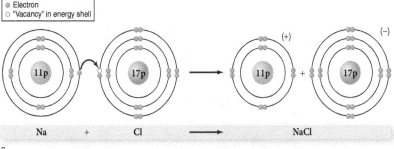

a.

b.

C. In a Covalent Bond, Atoms Share Electrons

So far, we have seen ionic bonds in which one highly electronegative atom fills its outermost shell by taking one or more electrons from another atom. However, it is also possible for two atoms to fill their outermost shells by pooling their resources. In a **covalent bond,** two atoms share electrons. The shared electrons travel around both nuclei, strongly connecting the atoms together. Most of the bonds in biological molecules are covalent.

Methane provides an excellent example of how atoms share electrons to fill their valence shells. A carbon atom has six electrons, two of which occupy its innermost shell. That leaves four electrons in its valence shell, which has a capacity of eight. Carbon therefore requires four more electrons to fill its outermost shell. A carbon atom can attain the stable eight-electron configuration by sharing electrons with four hydrogen atoms, each of which has one electron in its only shell. The resulting molecule is methane, CH_4 (figure 2.7a). Figure 2.7b shows how oxygen and hydrogen form covalent bonds as they combine to produce water.

Figure It Out

Use the information in figure 2.1 to predict the number of covalent bonds that nitrogen (N) forms.

Answer: 3.

Covalent bonds are usually depicted as lines between the interacting atoms, with each line representing one bond. Each

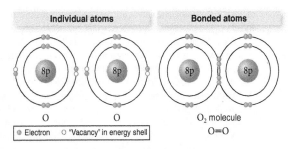

Electron   "Vacancy" in energy shell

O   O O_2 molecule
                      O=O

Figure 2.8 Double Bond. A pair of atoms can share two pairs of electrons, forming a double covalent bond.

single bond contains two electrons, one from each atom. Atoms can also share two pairs of electrons, forming a double covalent bond. The O_2 molecule, for example, has one double bond (figure 2.8). The greater the number of shared electrons, the stronger the bond. A triple covalent bond (three shared pairs of electrons) is therefore extremely strong. The atoms in nitrogen gas, N_2, are joined by a triple bond.

Covalent bonding means "sharing," but the partnership is not necessarily equal. A **polar covalent bond** is a lopsided union in which one nucleus exerts a much stronger pull on the shared electrons than does the other nucleus. Polar bonds form whenever a highly electronegative atom such as oxygen shares electrons—unequally—with a less electronegative partner such as carbon or hydrogen. Like a battery, a polar covalent bond has a positive end and a negative end.

Polar covalent bonds are critical to biology. As described in section 2.2D, they are responsible for hydrogen bonds, which in turn help define not only the unique properties of water (see section 2.3) but also the shapes of DNA and proteins (section 2.5).

In contrast, a **nonpolar covalent bond** is a "bipartisan" union in which both atoms exert approximately equal pull on their shared electrons. A bond between two atoms of the same element is nonpolar; after all, a bond between two identical atoms must be electrically balanced. H_2, N_2, and O_2 are all nonpolar molecules. Carbon and hydrogen atoms have similar electronegativity. A carbon–hydrogen bond is therefore also nonpolar.

Ionic bonds, polar covalent bonds, and nonpolar covalent bonds represent points along a continuum. If one atom is so electronegative that it rips electrons from another atom's valence shell, an ionic bond forms. If one atom tugs at shared electrons much more than the other, a covalent bond is polar. And two atoms of similar electronegativity share electrons equally in nonpolar covalent bonds. Notice that the bond type depends on the *difference* in electronegativity, so the same element can participate in different types of bonds. Oxygen, for example, forms nonpolar bonds with itself (as in O_2) and polar bonds with hydrogen (as in H_2O).

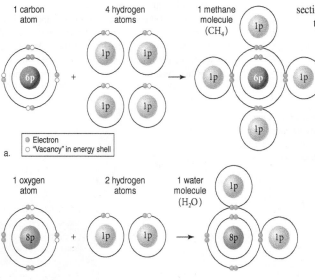

Figure 2.7 Covalent Bonds. (a) In methane (CH_4), one carbon atom and four hydrogen atoms complete their outermost shells by sharing electrons. (b) A water molecule (H_2O) has covalent bonds between one oxygen atom and two hydrogen atoms.

TABLE **2.3**   **Chemical Bonds: A Summary**

Type	Chemical Basis	Strength	Example
Ionic bond	One atom donates one or more electrons to another atom; electronegativity difference between atoms is very large (>1.7). The resulting oppositely charged ions attract each other.	Strong but breaks easily in water	Sodium chloride (NaCl)
Covalent bond	Two atoms share pairs of electrons.	Strong	
Nonpolar	Electronegativity difference between atoms is small (<0.4)		H—H bond in H_2 molecule
Polar	Electronegativity difference between atoms is moderate or large (0.4 to 1.7)		O—H bond within water molecule
Hydrogen bond	An atom with a partial negative charge attracts a hydrogen atom with a partial positive charge in an adjacent molecule or in a different part of a large molecule.	Weak	Attraction between adjacent water molecules

D. Partial Charges on Polar Molecules Create Hydrogen Bonds

When a covalent bond is polar, the negatively charged electrons spend more time around the nucleus of the more electronegative atom than around its partner. The "electron-hogging" atom therefore has a partial negative charge (written as "δ⁻"), and the less electronegative partner has an electron "deficit" and a partial positive charge (δ⁺).

In a **hydrogen bond,** opposite partial charges on *adjacent molecules*—or within a single large molecule—attract each other. The name comes from the fact that the atom with the partial positive charge is always hydrogen. The atom with the partial negative charge, on the other hand, is a highly electronegative atom such as oxygen or nitrogen.

Water provides the simplest illustration of hydrogen bonds (figure 2.9). Each water molecule has a "boomerang" shape, owing to the oxygen atom's two pairs of unshared valence electrons. Moreover, the two O—H bonds in water are polar, with the nucleus of each oxygen atom attracting the shared electrons more strongly than do the hydrogen nuclei.

Each hydrogen atom in a water molecule therefore has a partial positive charge, which attracts the partial negative charge of the oxygen atom on an adjacent molecule. This attraction is the hydrogen bond. The partial charges on O and H, plus the bent shape, cause water molecules to stick to one another and to some other substances. (This slight stickiness is another example of an emergent property, because it arises from interactions between O and H.)

Hydrogen bonds are relatively weak compared with ionic and covalent bonds. In 1 second, the hydrogen bonds between one water molecule and its nearest neighbors form and re-form some 500 billion times. Even though hydrogen bonds are weak, they account for many of water's unusual characteristics—the subject of section 2.3. In addition, multiple hydrogen bonds help stabilize some large molecules, including proteins and DNA (see section 2.5).

2.2 MASTERING CONCEPTS

1. How are atoms, molecules, and compounds related?
2. How does the number of valence electrons determine an atom's tendency to form bonds?
3. Explain how electronegativity differences between atoms result in each type of chemical bond.

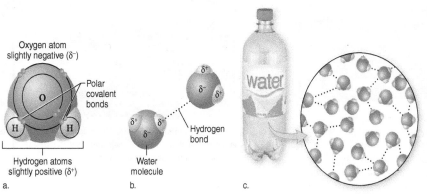

Figure 2.9 Hydrogen Bonds in Water. (a) An oxygen atom attracts electrons more strongly than do the hydrogen atoms in water. The O atom therefore bears a partial negative charge (δ⁻), and the H atoms carry partial positive charges (δ⁺). (b) The hydrogen bond is the attraction between partial charges on adjacent molecules. (c) In liquid water, many molecules stick to one another with hydrogen bonds.

Oxygen atom slightly negative (δ⁻)

Polar covalent bonds

O

H   H

Hydrogen atoms slightly positive (δ⁺)

a.

δ⁺

δ⁻   δ⁺

δ⁺   δ⁻   δ⁺

Hydrogen bond

Water molecule

b.

water

c.

2.3 Water Is Essential to Life

Video Properties of Water

Although water may seem to be a rather ordinary fluid, it is anything but. The tiny, three-atom water molecule has extraordinary properties that make it essential to all organisms, which explains why the search for life on other planets begins with the search for water. Indeed, life on Earth began in water, and for at least the first 3 billion years of life's history on Earth, all life was aquatic (see chapter 15). It was not until some 475 million years ago, when plants and fungi colonized land, that life could survive without being surrounded by water. Even now, terrestrial organisms cannot live without it. This section explains some of the properties that make water central to biology.

A. Water Is Cohesive and Adhesive

Hydrogen bonds contribute to a property of water called **cohesion**—the tendency of water molecules to stick together. Without cohesion, water would evaporate instantly in most locations on Earth's surface. Cohesion also contributes to the observation that you can sometimes fill a glass so full that water is above the rim, yet it doesn't flow over the side unless disturbed.

This tendency of a liquid to hold together at its surface is called surface tension, and not all liquids exhibit it. Water has high surface tension because it is cohesive. At the boundary between water and air, the water molecules form hydrogen bonds with neighbors to their sides and below them in the liquid. These bonds tend to hold the surface molecules together, creating a thin "skin" that is strong enough to support small animals without breaking through (figure 2.10).

A related property of water is **adhesion,** the tendency to form hydrogen bonds with other substances. For example, when water soaks into a paper towel, it is adhering to the molecules that make up the paper.

Both adhesion and cohesion are at work when water seemingly defies gravity as it moves from a plant's roots to its highest leaves (figure 2.11). This movement depends upon cohesion of water within the plant's conducting tubes. Water entering roots is drawn up through these tubes as water evaporates from leaf cells. Adhesion to the walls of the conducting tubes also helps lift water to the topmost leaves of trees. ① *transpiration*, p. 487

B. Many Substances Dissolve in Water

Another reason that water is vital to life is that it can dissolve a wide variety of chemicals. To illustrate this process, picture the slow disappearance of table salt as it dissolves in water. Although the salt crystals appear to vanish, the sodium and chloride ions remain. Water molecules surround each ion individually, separating them from one another (figure 2.12).

In this example, water is a **solvent:** a chemical in which other substances, called **solutes,** dissolve. A **solution** consists of one or more solutes dissolved in a liquid solvent. In a so-called aqueous solution, water is the solvent. But not all solutions are aqueous. According to the rule "Like dissolves like," polar solvents such as water dissolve polar molecules; similarly, nonpolar solvents dissolve nonpolar substances.

Scientists divide chemicals into two categories, based on their affinity for water. **Hydrophilic** substances are either polar or charged, so they readily dissolve in water (the term literally

1 Water evaporates through pores in leaves.

2 Evaporating molecules pull water up stem.

3 Water molecules are pulled into roots.

Figure 2.11 Defying Gravity. Thanks to hydrogen bonds, water evaporating from the leaves of a palm tree is replaced by water pulled up from the soil and through the tree's trunk.

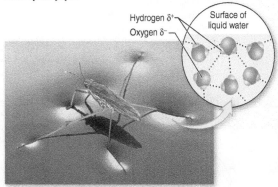

Hydrogen δ⁺

Oxygen δ⁻

Surface of liquid water

Figure 2.10 Running on Water. A lightweight body and water-repellent legs allow this water strider to "skate" across a pond without breaking the water's surface tension.

Video Lizard Runs on Water

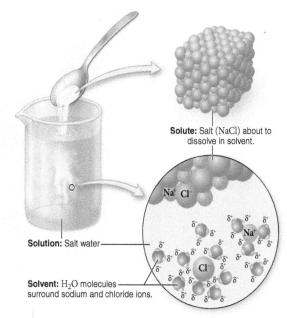

Solute: Salt (NaCl) about to dissolve in solvent.

Na⁺ Cl⁻

Na⁺

Cl⁻

Solution: Salt water

Solvent: H_2O molecules surround sodium and chloride ions.

Figure 2.12 Dissolving Salt. As salt crystals dissolve, polar water molecules surround each sodium and chloride ion.

means "water-loving"). Examples include sugar, salt, and ions. Electrolytes are ions in the body's fluids, and the salty taste of sweat illustrates water's ability to dissolve them. Sports drinks replace not only water but also sodium, potassium, magnesium, and calcium ions that are lost in perspiration during vigorous exercise. Electrolytes are essential to many processes, including heart and nerve function.

Not every substance, however, is water-soluble. Nonpolar molecules made mostly of carbon and hydrogen, such as fats and oils, are called **hydrophobic** ("water-fearing") because they do not dissolve in, or form hydrogen bonds with, water. This is why water alone will not remove grease from hands, dishes, or clothes. Dry cleaning companies use nonpolar solvents to remove oily spots from fabric. Detergents contain molecules that attract both water and fats, so they can dislodge greasy substances and carry the mess down the drain with the wastewater.

C. Water Regulates Temperature

Another unusual property of water is its ability to resist temperature changes. When molecules absorb energy, they move faster. Water's hydrogen bonds tend to counter this molecular movement; as a result, more heat is needed to raise water's temperature than is required for most other liquids, including alcohols. Because an organism's fluids are aqueous solutions, the same effect holds: an organism may encounter considerable heat before its body temperature becomes dangerously high. Likewise, the body cools slowly in cold temperatures.

At a global scale, water's resistance to temperature change explains why coastal climates tend to be mild. People living along the California coast have good weather year-round because

the Pacific Ocean's steady temperature helps keep winters warm and summers cool. Far away from the ocean, in the central United States, winters are much colder and summers are much hotter. These differences in local climate contribute to the unique ecosystems that occur in each region. (Chapter 39 describes climate in more detail.)

Hydrogen bonds also mean that a lot of heat is required to evaporate water. **Evaporation** is the conversion of a liquid into a vapor. When sweat evaporates from skin, individual water molecules break away from the liquid droplet and float into the atmosphere. Surface molecules must absorb energy to escape, and when they do, heat energy is removed from those that remain, drawing heat out of the body—an important part of the mechanism that regulates body temperature.

D. Water Expands As It Freezes

Water's unusual tendency to expand upon freezing also affects life. In liquid water, hydrogen bonds are constantly forming and breaking, and the water molecules are relatively close together. But in an ice crystal, the hydrogen bonds are stable, and the molecules are "locked" into roughly hexagonal shapes. Therefore, the less-dense ice floats on the surface of the denser liquid water below (figure 2.13). This characteristic benefits aquatic organisms. When

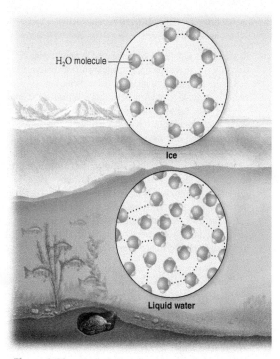

H_2O molecule

Ice

Liquid water

Figure 2.13 Ice Floats. The water molecules in ice form hexagons stabilized by hydrogen bonds. Ice is therefore less dense than—and floats on top of—the liquid water in this lake.

the air temperature drops, a small amount of water freezes at the pond's surface. This solid cap of ice retains heat in the water below. If ice were to become denser upon freezing, it would sink to the bottom. The lake would then gradually turn to ice from the bottom up, entrapping the organisms that live there.

The formation of ice crystals inside cells, however, can be deadly. The expansion of ice inside a frozen cell can rupture the delicate outer membrane, killing the cell. How, then, do organisms survive in extremely cold weather? Mammals have thick layers of insulating fur and fat that help their bodies stay warm. Ice fishes that live in the subfreezing waters of the Antarctic have a different adaptation: they produce antifreeze chemicals that prevent their cells from freezing solid.

E. Water Participates in Life's Chemical Reactions

Life exists because of thousands of simultaneous chemical reactions. In a **chemical reaction,** two or more molecules "swap" their atoms to yield different molecules; that is, some chemical bonds break and new ones form. Chemists depict reactions as equations with the **reactants,** or starting materials, to the left of an arrow; the **products,** or results of the reaction, are listed to the right.

Consider what happens when the methane in natural gas burns inside a heater or gas oven:

$$CH_4 + 2O_2 \longrightarrow CO_2 + 2H_2O$$
$$\text{methane} + \text{oxygen} \longrightarrow \text{carbon dioxide} + \text{water}$$

In words, this says that one methane molecule combines with two oxygen molecules to produce a carbon dioxide molecule and two molecules of water. The bonds of the methane and oxygen molecules have broken, and new bonds have formed in the products.

Note that the total number of atoms of each element is the same on either side of the equation: that is, one carbon, four hydrogens, and four oxygens. In chemical reactions, atoms are neither created nor destroyed.

Nearly all of life's chemical reactions occur in the watery solution that fills and bathes cells. Moreover, water is either a reactant in or a product of many of these reactions. In photosynthesis, for example, plants use the sun's energy to assemble food out of just two reactants: carbon dioxide and water (see chapter 5). Section 2.5 describes two other water-related reactions, hydrolysis and dehydration synthesis, that are vital to life.

2.3   MASTERING CONCEPTS

1. How are cohesion and adhesion important to life?
2. Distinguish between a solute and a solvent and between a hydrophilic and a hydrophobic molecule.
3. How does water help an organism regulate its body temperature?
4. How does the density difference between ice and water affect life?
5. What happens in a chemical reaction?
6. How does water participate in the chemistry of life?

2.4 Organisms Balance Acids and Bases

One of the most important substances dissolved in water is one of the simplest: H^+ ions. Each H^+ is a hydrogen atom stripped of its electron; in other words, it is simply a proton. But its simplicity belies its enormous effects on living systems. Too much or too little H^+ can ruin the shapes of critical molecules inside cells, rendering them nonfunctional.

One source of H^+ is pure water. At any time, about one in a million water molecules spontaneously breaks into two pieces, with one of the hydrogen atoms separating from the rest of the molecule. The highly electronegative oxygen atom keeps the electron from the breakaway hydrogen atom. The result is one hydrogen ion (H^+) and one hydroxide ion (OH^-):

$$H_2O \longrightarrow H^+ + OH^-$$

In pure water, the number of hydrogen ions must exactly equal the number of hydroxide ions. A **neutral** solution likewise contains as much H^+ as it does OH^-.

Some substances, however, alter this balance. An **acid** is a chemical that adds H^+ to a solution, making the concentration of H^+ ions exceed the concentration of OH^- ions. Examples include hydrochloric acid (HCl), sulfuric acid (H_2SO_4), and sour foods such as vinegar and lemon juice. Adding hydrochloric acid to pure water releases H^+ ions into the solution:

$$HCl \longrightarrow H^+ + Cl^-$$

Because no OH^- ions were added at the same time, the balance of H^+ to OH^- skews toward extra H^+.

A **base** is the opposite of an acid: it makes the concentration of OH^- ions exceed the concentration of H^+ ions. Bases work in one of two ways. They come apart to directly add OH^- ions to the solution, or they absorb H^+ ions. Either way, the result is the same: the balance between H^+ and OH^- shifts toward OH^-. Two common household bases are baking soda and sodium hydroxide (NaOH), an ingredient in oven and drain cleaners. When NaOH dissolves in water, it releases OH^- into solution:

$$NaOH \longrightarrow Na^+ + OH^-$$

What happens if a person mixes an acid with a base? The acid releases protons, while the base either absorbs the H^+ or releases OH^-. Acids and bases therefore neutralize each other.

Both acids and bases are important in everyday life. The tart flavors of yogurt and sour cream come from acid-producing bacteria. Many household cleaners are strong bases, which break down grease without corroding metal. At the opposite end of the spectrum, your stomach produces strong acids that kill microbes and activate enzymes that begin the digestion of food. Antacids contain bases that neutralize excess acid, relieving an upset stomach. In the environment, some air pollutants return to Earth as acid precipitation. The acidic rainfall kills plants and aquatic life, and it damages buildings and outdoor sculptures. ⓘ *stomach acid,* p. 651; *acid deposition,* p. 814

A. The pH Scale Expresses Acidity or Alkalinity

Scientists use the **pH scale** to measure how acidic or basic a solution is. The pH scale ranges from 0 to 14, with 7 representing a neutral solution such as pure water (figure 2.14). An acidic solution has a pH lower than 7, whereas an **alkaline,** or basic, solution has a pH greater than 7. Note that the higher the H^+ concentration of a solution, the lower its pH. Thus, 0 represents a strongly acidic solution and 14 represents an extremely basic one (low H^+ concentration).

Each unit on the pH scale represents a 10-fold change in H^+ concentration. A solution with a pH of 4 is therefore 10 times more acidic than one with a pH of 5, and it is 100 times more acidic than one with a pH of 6.

All species have optimal pH requirements. Some organisms, such as the bacteria that cause ulcers in human stomachs, are adapted to low-pH environments. In contrast, the normal pH of human blood is 7.35 to 7.45. Extremely shallow breathing or kidney failure can cause the blood's pH to drop below 7. Vomiting, hyperventilating, or taking some types of alkaloid drugs, on the other hand, can raise the blood's pH above 7.8. Straying too far from the normal pH in either direction can cause death by destroying the shapes of critical proteins (see section 2.5B).

B. Buffers Regulate pH in Organisms

Maintaining the correct pH of body fluids is critical, yet organisms frequently encounter conditions that could alter their internal pH. How do they maintain homeostasis? The answer lies in **buffers,** pairs of weak acids and bases that resist pH changes.

Hydrochloric acid is a strong acid because it releases all of its H^+ when dissolved in water. As you can see in figure 2.14, the pH of pure HCl is 0. A weak acid, in contrast, does not release all of its H^+ into solution. An example is carbonic acid, H_2CO_3, which forms one part of the human body's pH buffer:

$$H_2CO_3 \rightleftharpoons H^+ + HCO_3^-$$

carbonic acid   bicarbonate

The dual arrow indicates that the reaction can proceed in either direction, depending on the pH of the fluid. If a base removes H^+ from the solution, the reaction moves to the right to produce more H^+, restoring acidity. Alternatively, if an acid contributes H^+ to the solution, the reaction proceeds to the left and consumes the excess H^+. This action keeps the pH of the solution relatively constant. Carbonic acid is just one of several buffers that maintain the pH of blood at about 7.4.

2.4   MASTERING CONCEPTS

1. How do acids and bases affect a solution's H^+ concentration?
2. How do the values of 0, 7, and 14 relate to the pH scale?
3. How do buffers regulate the pH of a fluid?

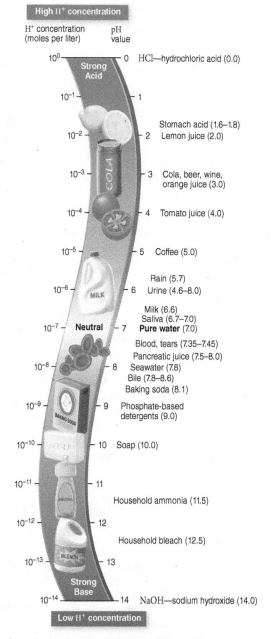

Figure 2.14   The pH Scale. A neutral solution has a pH of 7. The higher the H^+ concentration, the more acidic the solution (pH < 7). The lower the H^+ concentration, the more basic the solution (pH > 7).

Figure It Out

Flask A contains 100 ml of a solution with pH 5. After you add 100 ml of solution from Flask B, the pH rises to 7. What was the pH in Flask B?

Answer: 9.

2.5 Organic Molecules Generate Life's Form and Function

Organisms are composed mostly of water and **organic molecules,** chemical compounds that contain both carbon and hydrogen. (See the Burning Question on page 35 to learn about the use of the term *organic* in describing food.) As you will see later in this unit, plants and other autotrophs can produce all the organic molecules they require, whereas heterotrophs—including humans—must obtain their organic building blocks from food.

Life uses a tremendous variety of organic compounds. Organic molecules consisting almost entirely of carbon and hydrogen are called *hydrocarbons;* methane (CH_4) is the simplest example. Because a carbon atom forms four covalent bonds, however, this element can assemble into much more complex molecules, including long chains, intricate branches, and rings. Many organic compounds also include other essential elements, such as oxygen, nitrogen, phosphorus, or sulfur. A peek ahead at the molecules illustrated in this section reveals the diversity of shapes and sizes of organic molecules. Without carbon's versatility, organic chemistry—and life—would be impossible.

All organisms, from bacteria to plants to people, consist largely of the same four types of organic molecules: carbohydrates, proteins, nucleic acids, and lipids. This unity in life's chemistry is powerful evidence that all species inherited the same basic chemical structures and processes from a common ancestor.

A. Large Organic Molecules Are Composed of Smaller Subunits

Proteins, nucleic acids, and some carbohydrates all share a property in common with one another: they are **polymers,** which are chains of small molecular subunits called **monomers.** A polymer is made of monomers that are linked together, just as a train is made of individual railcars.

Railcars include two connectors, which enable one to hook to another in a long train. Similarly, organic molecules have small groups of atoms, called functional groups, that serve the same function. Figure 2.15 shows four of the most common functional groups: hydroxyl, carboxyl, amino, and phosphate groups. As you study this section, you will see that these functional groups can act as molecular "connectors" that hook one subunit of an organic molecule to another.

Cells use a chemical reaction called dehydration synthesis, also called a condensation reaction, to link monomers together into polymers (figure 2.16a). In a **dehydration synthesis** reaction, a protein called an enzyme removes an ——OH (hydroxyl group) from one molecule and a hydrogen atom from another, forming

Name	Structure	Formula
Hydroxyl group	—O—H	—OH
Carboxyl group	(structure with C double bonded to O and single bonded to O—H)	—COOH
Amino group	(structure with N bonded to two H)	$-NH_2$
Phosphate group	(structure with P double bonded to O, bonded to O—, O—, and O)	$-PO_4^{-2}$

Figure 2.15 Functional Groups. Each of these groups of atoms occurs in one or more types of organic molecules. Look through the illustrations in the rest of section 2.5 to find examples of each type.

H_2O and a new covalent bond between the two smaller components. (The term *dehydration* means that water is lost). By repeating this reaction many times, cells can build extremely large polymers consisting of thousands of monomers.

The reverse reaction also occurs, breaking the covalent bonds that link monomers (figure 2.16b). In **hydrolysis,** enzymes use atoms from water to add a hydroxyl group to one molecule and a hydrogen atom to another (*hydrolysis* means "breaking with water.") Hydrolysis happens in your body when digestive enzymes in your stomach and intestines break down the proteins and other polymers in food.

The rest of this section takes a closer look at the four major types of organic molecules in life. Table 2.4 on page 38 reviews their characteristics.

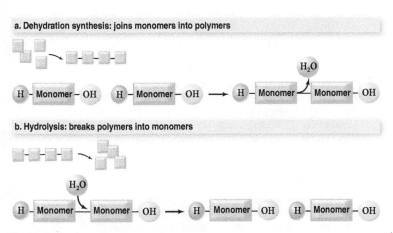

Figure 2.16 Opposite Reactions. (a) In dehydration synthesis, water is removed and a new covalent bond forms between two monomers. (b) In hydrolysis, water is added when the bond between monomers is broken.

B. Carbohydrates Include Simple Sugars and Polysaccharides

Anyone following a "low-carb" diet can recite a list of the foods to avoid: potatoes, pasta, bread, cereal, sugary fruits, and sweets. All are rich in **carbohydrates,** organic molecules that consist of carbon, hydrogen, and oxygen, often in the proportion 1:2:1.

Carbohydrates are the simplest of the four main types of organic compounds, mostly because just a few monomers account for the most common types in cells. The two main groups of carbohydrates are simple sugars and complex carbohydrates.

Sugars (Simple Carbohydrates)
The smallest carbohydrates, the **monosaccharides,** usually contain five or six carbon atoms (figure 2.17a). Monosaccharides with the same number of carbon atoms can differ from one another by how their atoms are bonded. For example, glucose (blood sugar) and fructose (fruit sugar) are both six-carbon monosaccharides with the molecular formula $C_6H_{12}O_6$, but their chemical structures differ.

A **disaccharide** ("two sugars") is two monosaccharides joined by dehydration synthesis. Figure 2.17b shows how sucrose (table sugar) forms when a molecule of glucose bonds to a molecule of fructose. Lactose, or milk sugar, is also a disaccharide.

Together, the sweet-tasting monosaccharides and disaccharides are called sugars, or simple carbohydrates. Their function in cells is to provide a ready source of energy, which is released when their bonds are broken (see chapter 6). Sugarcane sap and sugar beet roots contain abundant sucrose, which the plants use to fuel growth. The disaccharide maltose provides energy in sprouting seeds; beer brewers also use it to promote fermentation.

Complex Carbohydrates
Chains of monosaccharides are collectively called complex carbohydrates. **Oligosaccharides** consist of three to 100 monomers. Such a carbohydrate chain sometimes attaches to a protein, forming a glycoprotein ("sugar protein"). Among other functions, glycoproteins on cell surfaces are important in immunity. For example, a person's blood type—A, B, AB, or O—refers to the combination of glycoproteins in the membranes of his or her red blood cells. A transfusion of the "wrong" blood type can trigger a harmful immune reaction. ⓘ *blood type,* p. 613

Polysaccharides ("many sugars") are huge molecules consisting of hundreds or thousands of monosaccharide monomers (figure 2.17c). The most common polysaccharides are cellulose, chitin, starch, and glycogen. All are long chains of glucose, but they differ from one another by the orientation of the bonds that link the monomers.

Cellulose forms part of plant cell walls. Multiple cellulose molecules, held together along their length by hydrogen bonds, align

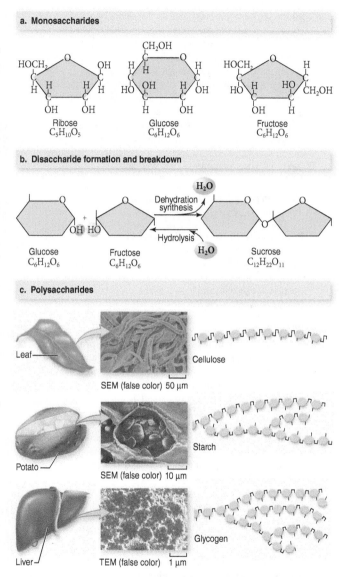

a. Monosaccharides

Ribose
$C_5H_{10}O_5$

Glucose
$C_6H_{12}O_6$

Fructose
$C_6H_{12}O_6$

b. Disaccharide formation and breakdown

H_2O

Dehydration synthesis

Hydrolysis

H_2O

Glucose
$C_6H_{12}O_6$

Fructose
$C_6H_{12}O_6$

Sucrose
$C_{12}H_{22}O_{11}$

c. Polysaccharides

Leaf

Cellulose

SEM (false color) 50 μm

Potato

Starch

SEM (false color) 10 μm

Liver

Glycogen

TEM (false color) 1 μm

Figure 2.17 Carbohydrates—Simple and Complex. (a) Monosaccharides are composed of single sugar molecules, such as glucose or fructose. (b) Disaccharides form by dehydration synthesis. In this example, glucose and fructose bond to form sucrose. (c) Polysaccharides are long chains of monosaccharides such as glucose. Different orientations of covalent bonds produce different characteristics in the polymers.

side by side to form strong fibrils. Although it is the most common organic compound in nature, humans cannot digest it. Yet cellulose is an important component of the human diet, making up much of what nutrition labels refer to as "fiber." Cotton fibers, wood, and paper consist largely of cellulose. ⓘ *plant cell wall,* p. 64

Like cellulose, chitin also supports cells. The cell walls of fungi contain chitin, as do the flexible exoskeletons of insects, spiders, and crustaceans. Chitin is the second most common polysaccharide in nature. It resembles a glucose polymer, but a nitrogen-containing group replaces one hydroxyl group in each monomer. Because it is tough, flexible, and biodegradable, chitin is used in the manufacture of surgical thread.

Starch and glycogen have similar structures and functions. Both act as storage molecules that readily break down into their glucose monomers when cells need a burst of energy. Most plants store starch. Potatoes, rice, and wheat are all starchy, high-energy staples in the human diet. On the other hand, glycogen occurs in animal and fungal cells. In humans, for example, skeletal muscles and the liver store energy as glycogen.

C. Proteins Are Complex and Highly Versatile

Proteins do more jobs in the cell than any other type of biological molecule. Cells produce thousands of kinds of proteins; they literally control all the activities of life, so much so that illness or death can result if even one is missing or faulty. To name one example, the protein insulin controls the amount of sugar in the blood. The failure to produce insulin leads to one form of diabetes, an illness that can be deadly.

Amino Acid Structure and Bonding A **protein** is a chain of monomers called **amino acids.** Each amino acid has a central carbon atom bonded to four other atoms or groups of atoms (figure 2.18a). One is a hydrogen atom; another is a carboxyl group; a third is an amino group (—NH_2); and the fourth is a side chain, or **R group,** which can be any of 20 chemical groups.

Organisms use 20 types of amino acids; figure 2.18 shows three of them. (Appendix E includes a complete set of amino acid structures.) The R groups distinguish the amino acids from one another, and they have diverse chemical structures. An R group may be as simple as the lone hydrogen atom in glycine or as complex as the two rings of tryptophan. Some R groups are acidic or basic; some are strongly hydrophilic or hydrophobic.

Just as the 26 letters in our alphabet combine to form a nearly infinite number of words in many languages, mixing and matching the 20 amino acids gives rise to an endless diversity of unique proteins. This variety means that proteins have a seemingly limitless array of structures and functions.

The **peptide bond,** which forms by dehydration synthesis, is the covalent bond that links each amino acid to its neighbor (figure 2.18b). Two linked amino acids form a dipeptide; three form a tripeptide. Chains with fewer than 100 amino acids are peptides; examples

include the nine-amino-acid-long hormone oxytocin, which plays a role in pair bonding and is sometimes called the "love hormone." Finally, chains with 100 or more amino acids are **polypeptides.** A polypeptide is called a *protein* once it folds into its functional shape; a protein may consist of one or more polypeptide chains. ① *peptide hormones*, p. 578

Where do the amino acids in your own proteins come from? Humans can synthesize most of them from scratch. However, eight amino acids are considered "essential" because they must come from protein-rich foods such as meat, fish, dairy products, beans, and tofu. Digestive enzymes catalyze the hydrolysis reaction that releases amino acids from proteins in food. The body then uses these monomers to build its own polypeptides.

Protein Folding Unlike polysaccharides, most proteins do not exist as long chains inside cells. Instead, the peptide chain folds into a unique three-dimensional structure determined by the order and kinds of amino acids. Biologists describe the conformation of a protein at four levels (figure 2.19):

- **Primary (1°) structure:** The amino acid sequence of a polypeptide chain. This sequence determines all subsequent structural levels.
- **Secondary (2°) structure:** A "substructure" with a defined shape, resulting from hydrogen bonds between parts of the polypeptide. These interactions fold the chain of amino acids into coils, sheets, and loops. Figure 2.19 shows two common shapes: an alpha helix and a beta

a. Amino acids

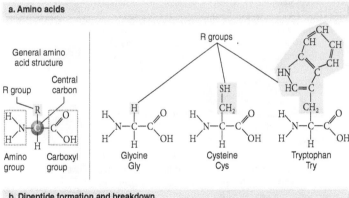

b. Dipeptide formation and breakdown

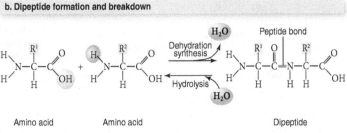

Figure 2.18 Amino Acids. (a) An amino acid is composed of an amino group, a carboxyl group, and one of 20 R groups attached to a central carbon atom. Three examples appear here. (b) A peptide bond forms by dehydration synthesis, joining two amino acids together.

sheet. Each protein can have multiple types of secondary structure.

- **Tertiary (3°) structure:** The overall shape of a polypeptide, arising primarily through interactions between R groups and water. Inside a cell, water molecules surround each polypeptide. The hydrophobic R groups move away from water toward the protein's interior. In addition, hydrogen bonds and ionic bonds form between the peptide backbone and some R groups. Covalent bonds between

sulfur atoms in some R groups further stabilize the structure. These disulfide bridges are abundant in structural proteins such as keratin, which forms hair, scales, beaks, feathers, wool, and hooves.

- **Quaternary (4°) structure:** The shape arising from interactions between multiple polypeptide subunits of the same protein. The protein in figure 2.19 consists of two polypeptides; similarly, the oxygen-toting blood protein hemoglobin is composed of four polypeptide chains.

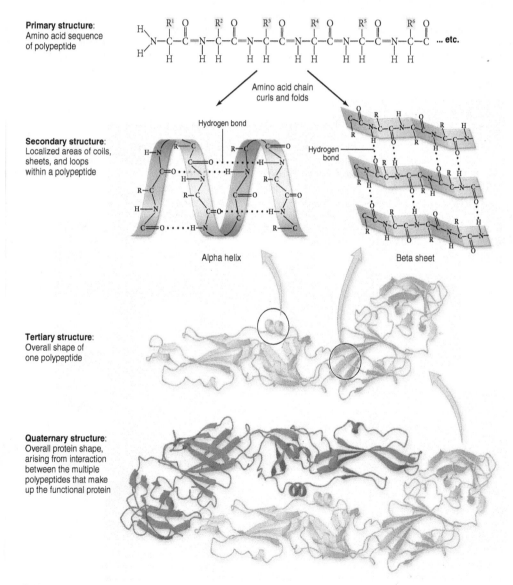

Primary structure: Amino acid sequence of polypeptide

Amino acid chain curls and folds

Secondary structure: Localized areas of coils, sheets, and loops within a polypeptide

Hydrogen bond

Alpha helix

Hydrogen bond

Beta sheet

Tertiary structure: Overall shape of one polypeptide

Quaternary structure: Overall protein shape, arising from interaction between the multiple polypeptides that make up the functional protein

Figure 2.19 Four Levels of Protein Structure. The amino acid sequence of a polypeptide forms the primary structure, while hydrogen bonds create secondary structures such as helices and sheets. The tertiary structure is the overall three-dimensional shape of a protein. The interaction of multiple polypeptides forms the protein's quaternary structure.

Tutorial
Protein Structure

As detailed in chapter 7, an organism's genetic code specifies the amino acid sequence of each protein. A genetic mutation may therefore change a protein's primary structure. The protein's secondary, tertiary, and quaternary structures all depend upon the primary structure. Genetic mutations are often harmful because they result in misfolded, nonfunctional proteins.

Many biologists devote their careers to deducing protein structures, in part because the research has so many practical applications. Misfolded infectious proteins called prions, for instance, cause mad cow disease. Knowledge of protein structure can also aid in the treatment of infectious disease. If scientists can determine the shape of a protein unique to the organism that causes malaria, for example, they may be able to use that information to create effective new drugs with few side effects. Some consumer products also exploit protein shape. "Permanent wave" solutions and hair straighteners break disulfide bridges in keratin. The bonds return once the hair is in the desired conformation. ⓘ prions, p. 340

Denaturation: Loss of Function   It is impossible to overstate the importance of a protein's shape in determining its function. Examine figure 2.20, which illustrates the major categories of protein function: structural, contractile, transport, storage, and enzymes. Notice the great variety of protein shapes, reflecting their different jobs in the cell. A digestive enzyme, for example, has a groove that holds a food molecule in just the right way to break the nutrient apart. Muscle proteins form long, aligned fibers; as the proteins slide past one another, the muscle contracts. A membrane channel includes pores that admit some molecules but not others into a cell.

Proteins are therefore vulnerable to conditions that alter their shapes. Heat, excessive salt, or the wrong pH can **denature** a protein, disrupting the hydrogen bonds that maintain the protein's secondary and tertiary structures. As an example, consider what happens to an egg as it cooks (figure 2.21). Proteins unfold in the heat, then clump and refold randomly as the once-clear egg protein turns solid white. Similarly, fish turns from translucent to opaque as it cooks.

Most denatured proteins will not renature; there is no way to uncook an egg. Gentle denaturation, however, is sometimes reversible. Edible gelatin, for example, is a protein derived from pig and cow collagen. Short chains of amino acids in powdered gelatin wrap around each other, forming minuscule "ropes." When a cook dissolves the powder in hot water, the ropes unwind. As the gelatin cools, some of the ropes re-form. Pockets of liquid trapped within the tangled strands create a jellylike texture in the finished product.

D. Nucleic Acids Store and Transmit Genetic Information

How does a cell "know" which amino acids to string together to form a particular protein? The answer is that each protein's primary structure is encoded in the sequence of a **nucleic acid,** a polymer consisting of monomers called nucleotides. Cells contain two types of nucleic acids, **deoxyribonucleic acid (DNA)** and **ribonucleic acid (RNA)**.

Each **nucleotide** monomer consists of three components (figure 2.22a). At the center is a five-carbon sugar—ribose in RNA and deoxyribose in DNA. Attached to one of the sugar's

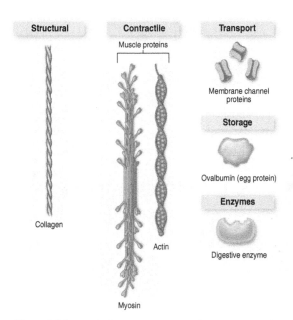

Figure 2.20   Protein Diversity. The function of a protein is a direct consequence of its shape. Shown here are a few of the thousands of types of known proteins.

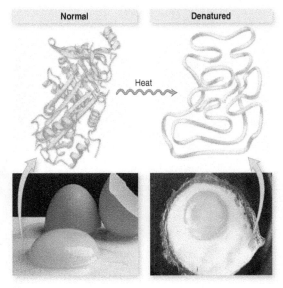

Figure 2.21   Denatured Proteins. Heat from a frying pan causes the proteins in an egg to denature. The protein chains unravel, ruining their overall shape. The new arrangement causes the proteins to clump and refold at random. The clear, fluid, raw egg white becomes a rubbery solid as the proteins denature.

BurningQuestion

What does it mean when food is "organic" or "natural"?

The word *organic* has multiple meanings. To a chemist, an organic compound contains carbon and hydrogen. Chemically, all food is therefore organic. To a farmer or consumer, however, organic foods are produced according to a defined set of standards.

The U.S. Department of Agriculture (USDA) certifies crops as organically grown if the farmer did not apply pesticides (with few exceptions), petroleum-based fertilizers, or sewage sludge. Organically raised cows, pigs, and chickens cannot receive growth hormones or antibiotics, and they must have access to the outdoors and eat organic food. In addition, no food labeled "organic" may be genetically engineered or treated with ionizing radiation.

A natural food may or may not be organic. The term *natural* refers to the way in which foods are processed, not how they are grown. Standards for what constitutes a natural food are fuzzy. The USDA specifies that meat and poultry labeled as natural cannot contain artificial ingredients or added color, but no such standards exist for other foods.

Submit your burning question to
Marielle.Hoefnagels@mheducation.com

a. Nucleotides and nitrogenous bases

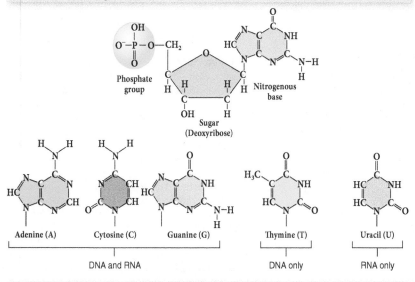

Figure 2.22 Nucleotides. (a) A nucleotide consists of a sugar, one or more phosphate groups, and one of several nitrogenous bases. In DNA, the sugar is deoxyribose, whereas RNA nucleotides contain ribose. In addition, the base thymine appears only in DNA; uracil is only in RNA. (b) Dehydration synthesis joins two nucleotides together.

b. Nucleic acid formation and breakdown

carbon atoms is at least one phosphate group. Attached to the opposite side of the sugar is a **nitrogenous base:** adenine (A), guanine (G), thymine (T), cytosine (C), or uracil (U). DNA contains A, C, G, and T, whereas RNA contains A, C, G, and U.

Dehydration synthesis links nucleotides together (figure 2.22b). In this reaction, a covalent bond forms between the sugar of one nucleotide and the phosphate group of its neighbor.

A DNA polymer is a double helix that resembles a spiral staircase. Alternating sugars and phosphates form the rails of the staircase, and nitrogenous bases form the rungs (figure 2.23). Hydrogen bonds between the bases hold the two strands of nucleotides together: A with T, C with G. The two strands are therefore complementary to, or "opposites" of, each other. Because of complementary base pairing, one strand of DNA contains the information for the other, providing a mechanism for the molecule to replicate. ⓘ *DNA replication,* p. 150

DNA's main function is to store genetic information; its sequence of nucleotides "tells" a cell which amino acids to string together to form each protein. (This process, which is summarized at the top of figure 2.23, is described in detail in chapter 7.) Every organism inherits DNA from its parents (or parent, in the case of asexual reproduction). Slight changes in DNA from generation to generation, coupled with natural selection, account for many of the evolutionary changes that have occurred throughout

life's history. As a result, DNA and protein sequences reveal important information about how species are related to one another. ⓘ *molecular evidence for evolution,* p. 274

Unlike DNA, RNA is typically single-stranded (see figure 2.23). One function of RNA is to enable cells to use the protein-encoding information in DNA (see chapter 7). In addition, a modified RNA nucleotide, adenosine triphosphate (ATP), carries the energy that cells use in many biological functions. ⓘ *ATP,* p. 76

If DNA encodes only protein, where do the rest of the molecules in cells come from? The answer relates to the diverse functions of proteins: some of them synthesize the carbohydrates, nucleic acids, and lipids that are essential to a cell's function.

E. Lipids Are Hydrophobic and Energy-Rich

Lipids are organic compounds with one property in common: they do not dissolve in water. They are hydrophobic because they contain large areas dominated by nonpolar carbon–carbon and carbon–hydrogen bonds. Moreover, lipids are not polymers consisting of long chains of monomers. Instead, they have extremely diverse chemical structures.

This section discusses several groups of lipids: triglycerides, sterols, and waxes. Another important group, phospholipids, forms the majority of cell membranes; chapter 3 describes them. ⓘ *phospholipids,* p. 54

Triglycerides   A **triglyceride** consists of three long hydrocarbon chains called **fatty acids** bonded to **glycerol,** a three-carbon molecule that forms the triglyceride's backbone. Although triglycerides do not consist of long strings of similar monomers, cells nevertheless use dehydration synthesis to produce them (figure 2.24). Enzymes link the carboxyl group from one fatty acid to each of glycerol's three hydroxyl groups, yielding three water molecules per triglyceride.

Many dieters try to avoid triglycerides, commonly known as *fats.* Red meat, butter, margarine, oil, cream, lard, cheese, fried foods, and chocolate are all examples of high-fat foods. (A high fat content characterizes many junk foods, as described in the Burning Question on page 37.) Nutrition labels divide these fats into two groups: saturated and unsaturated. The degree of saturation is a measure of a fatty acid's hydrogen content. A **saturated** fatty acid contains all the hydrogens it possibly can. That is, single bonds connect all the carbons, and each carbon has two hydrogens (see the straight chains in figure 2.24a). Animal fats are saturated and tend to be solid; bacon fat and butter are two examples. Most nutritionists recommend a diet low in saturated fats, citing their tendency to clog arteries.

A fatty acid is **unsaturated** if it has at least one double bond between carbon atoms (figure 2.24b). These fats have an oily (liquid) consistency at room temperature. Olive oil, for example, is an unsaturated fat, as are most plant-derived lipids. These fats are healthier than are their saturated counterparts.

Why are saturated fats like butter solid at room temperature, while unsaturated olive oil is a liquid? The answer relates to the

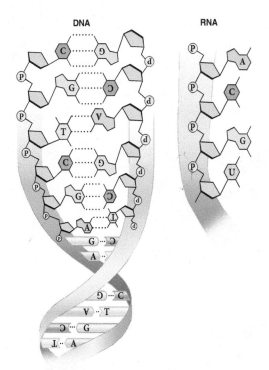

DNA   RNA

Figure 2.23   Nucleic Acids: DNA and RNA. DNA consists of two strands of nucleotides entwined to form a double-helix shape held together by hydrogen bonds (dotted lines). RNA is usually single-stranded.

Animation
DNA
Structure

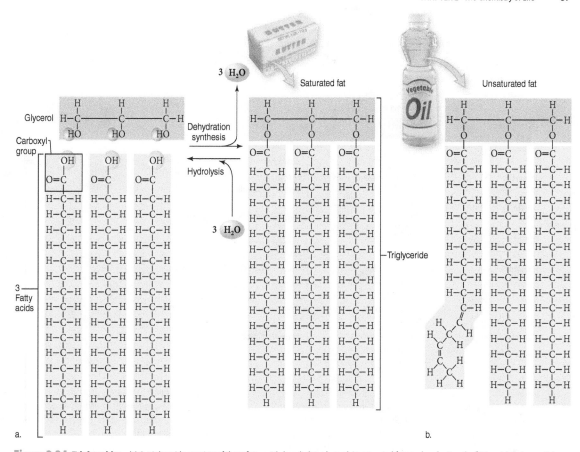

Figure 2.24 Triglycerides. (a) A triglyceride consists of three fatty acids bonded to glycerol. In saturated fats such as butter, the fatty acid chains contain only single carbon–carbon bonds. (b) In unsaturated fats, one or more double bonds bend the fatty acid tails, making the lipid more fluid. Vegetable oil is an unsaturated fat.

BurningQuestion

What is junk food?

Your favorite potato chips contain carbohydrates, protein, and fat—three of the four organic molecules described in section 2.5. If you must obtain these molecules from your diet, why are potato chips considered a junk food?

In general, junk foods like chips and candy are high in fat or sugar (or both) but low in protein and complex carbohydrates. They also typically have few vitamins and minerals. Junk foods therefore are high in calories but deliver little nutritional value.

Many junk foods also contain chemical additives. One common ingredient in packaged cookies, pies, and other baked goods is partially hydrogenated vegetable oil, a type of chemically processed fat. Partial hydrogenation causes fats to remain solid at room temperature; it also produces trans fats, which have been linked to several diseases (see section 2.5E).

Some junk foods also contain artificial colors, flavor enhancers, and artificial flavors that make food look or taste more appealing without adding nutritional value. One example is monosodium glutamate (MSG). This chemical consists of an amino acid and a sodium atom connected by an ionic bond. It enhances the flavor of many packaged snacks and fast foods, imparting a savory taste. Moreover, preservatives such as BHA and BHT increase the shelf life of many junk foods. These chemicals prevent oxygen from interacting with fat, so it takes longer for the food to become stale.

Potato chips, pizza, fries, candy bars, snack cakes, and other junk foods are hard to resist because they tap into our desire to eat sweet, salty, and fatty foods. These snacks are tasty, appealing, easily available, and often cheap. But for a more nutritious diet, reach for whole grains, fresh fruits, and vegetables instead. ⓘ *healthful diet*, p. 656

Submit your burning question to
Marielle.Hoefnagels@mheducation.com

TABLE **2.4**   **The Macromolecules of Life: A Summary**

Type of Molecule	Chemical Structure	Function(s)
Carbohydrates		
Simple sugars	Monosaccharides and disaccharides	Provide quick energy
Complex carbohydrates (cellulose, chitin, starch, glycogen)	Polymers of monosaccharides	Support cells and organisms (cellulose, chitin); store energy (starch, glycogen)
Proteins	Polymers of amino acids	Carry out nearly all the work of the cell
Nucleic acids (DNA, RNA)	Polymers of nucleotides	Store and use genetic information and transmit it to the next generation
Lipids	Diverse; hydrophobic	
Triglycerides (fats, oils)	Glycerol + 3 fatty acids	Store energy
Phospholipids	Glycerol + 2 fatty acids + phosphate group (see chapter 3)	Form major part of biological membranes
Sterols	Four fused rings, mostly of C and H	Stabilize animal membranes; sex hormones
Waxes	Fatty acids + other hydrocarbons or alcohols	Provide waterproofing

Carbohydrates (starch); lipids

Proteins; lipids

Carbohydrates (cellulose)

shapes of the fatty acid "tails." When the tails are straight, as they are in butter, the fat molecules form tight, dense stacks. When double bonds cause kinks in the tails, as in olive oil, the molecules cannot pack tightly together. The fat molecules in butter are like flat pieces of paper, which pack neatly together. In olive oil, the molecules are more like crumpled paper.

Food chemists have discovered how to turn vegetable oils into solid fats such as margarine, shortening, and peanut butter. A technique called partial hydrogenation adds hydrogen to the oil to solidify it—in essence, partially saturating a formerly unsaturated fat. One byproduct of this process is **trans fats,** which are unsaturated fats whose fatty acid tails are straight, not kinked (figure 2.25). Trans fats are common in fast foods, fried foods, and many snack products, and they raise the risk of heart disease even more than saturated fats. Nutritionists therefore recommend a diet as low as possible in trans fats.

Despite their unhealthful reputation, fats and oils are vital to life. Fat is an excellent energy source, providing more than twice as much energy as equal weights of carbohydrate or protein. Animals must have dietary fat for growth; this requirement explains why human milk is rich in lipids, which fuel the brain's rapid growth during the first 2 years of life. Fats also slow digestion, and they are required for the use of some vitamins and minerals.

Fat cells aggregate as adipose tissue in animals. White adipose tissue forms most of the fat in human adults, cushioning organs and helping to retain body heat as insulation. Brown adipose tissue releases heat energy that keeps infants and hibernating mammals warm.

As different as carbohydrates, proteins, and fats are, food chemists have discovered ways to use all three substances to make artificial sweeteners and fat substitutes. The Apply It Now box on page 40 describes how they do it.

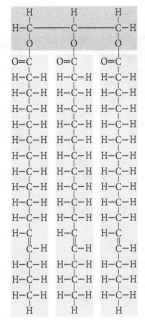

Figure 2.25   Trans Fats. Donuts are among the many foods that are high in trans fats. The fatty acids in a trans fat contain double bonds yet remain straight, so the fat remains a solid.

Cholesterol

Testosterone

Figure 2.26 Steroids. All steroid molecules consist of four interconnected rings. Cholesterol and testosterone are two variations on this theme.

Figure 2.27 A Waxy Nest. Beeswax makes up this honeycomb.

Sterols   Sterols are lipids that have four interconnected carbon rings. Vitamin D and cortisone are examples of sterols, as is cholesterol (figure 2.26). Cholesterol is a key part of animal cell membranes. In addition, animal cells use cholesterol as a starting material to make other lipids, including the sex hormones testosterone and estrogen. ⓘ *steroid hormones*, p. 579

Although cholesterol is essential, an unhealthy diet can easily contribute to cholesterol levels that are too high, increasing the risk of cardiovascular disease (see the Apply It Now box). Because saturated fats stimulate the liver to produce more cholesterol, it is important to limit dietary intake of both saturated fats and cholesterol. ⓘ *cardiovascular disease*, p. 622

Waxes   Waxes are fatty acids combined with alcohols or other hydrocarbons, usually forming a stiff, water-repellent material. The waxy compartments of a honeycomb may hold pollen, honey, or larval bees (figure 2.27). In other species, waxes keep fur, feathers, leaves, fruits, and stems waterproof. Jojoba oil, used in cosmetics and shampoos, is unusual in that it is a liquid wax.

2.5   MASTERING CONCEPTS

1. Distinguish between hydrolysis and dehydration synthesis.
2. Compare and contrast the structures of polysaccharides, proteins, and nucleic acids.
3. List examples of carbohydrates, proteins, nucleic acids, and lipids, and name the function of each.
4. What is the significance of a protein's shape, and how can that shape be destroyed?
5. What are some differences between RNA and DNA?
6. What are the components of a triglyceride?

→ Apply It **Now**

Bad and Good Cholesterol

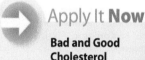

You may know someone who is concerned because a blood test has revealed higher-than-normal cholesterol levels. To understand the problem, you need to know a bit more about this sterol.

Cholesterol is not water-soluble, so it travels in the bloodstream encased in proteins. The resulting packets of cholesterol and protein are called lipoproteins, and they occur in low- and high-density varieties.

Low-density lipoprotein (LDL) particles carry cholesterol to the arteries. Excess LDL cholesterol that does not enter cells may accumulate inside blood vessels, blocking blood flow to the heart. Less blood flow means low oxygen delivery, which can damage the heart's muscle. Too much LDL cholesterol (commonly called "bad cholesterol") therefore increases the risk of heart attack.

In contrast, high-density lipoproteins (HDL) carry cholesterol away from the heart and to the liver, which removes it from the bloodstream. High levels of HDL cholesterol ("good cholesterol") promote heart health. Fortunately, it is possible to raise your HDL level. Exercising, losing weight, avoiding trans fats, and replacing meat and dairy with unsaturated dietary fats are among the most effective strategies.

Cholesterol-lowering statin drugs like Lipitor can reduce the risk of heart attack by lowering LDL levels, although they typically have little effect on HDL. These drugs block a liver enzyme that normally helps produce cholesterol; they also boost the liver's ability to get rid of LDL.

Apply It **Now**

Sugar Substitutes and Fake Fats

Many weight-conscious people turn to artificial sweeteners and fat substitutes to cut calories without sacrificing their favorite foods. Chemically, how do these sugar and fat replacements compare with the real thing?

Artificial Sweeteners

Table sugar delivers about 4 Calories per gram. (As described in chapter 4, a nutritional Calorie—with a capital C—is a measure of energy that represents 1000 calories.) Consuming artificial sweeteners reduces calorie intake, but not always because the additives are truly calorie-free. Instead, most are hundreds of times sweeter-tasting than sugar, so a tiny amount of artificial sweetener achieves the same effect as a teaspoon of sugar. Figure 2.A shows a few popular artificial sweeteners. They include:

- **Sucralose** (sold as Splenda): This sweetener is a close relative of sucrose, except that three chlorine (Cl) atoms replace three of sucrose's hydroxyl groups. Sucralose is about 600 times sweeter than sugar, but the body digests little if any of it, so it is virtually calorie-free.

- **Aspartame** (sold as NutraSweet and Equal): Surprisingly, aspartame's chemical structure does not resemble sugar. Instead, it consists of two amino acids, phenylalanine and aspartic acid. Like sugar, it delivers about 4 Calories per gram, but it is about 200 times sweeter than sugar, so less is needed.

- **Saccharin** (sold as Sweet'n Low and Sugar Twin): This sweetener, which has only 1/32 of a Calorie per gram, was originally derived from coal tar in 1879. It consists of a double-ring structure that includes nitrogen and sulfur. (Saccharin's eventful history as a food additive is the topic of the Apply It Now box in chapter 1.)

Fat Substitutes

Because fat is so calorie-dense (about 9 Calories per gram), cutting fat is a quick way to trim calories from the diet. Excess dietary fat can be harmful, leading to weight gain and increasing the risk of heart disease and cancer. It is important to remember, however, that some dietary fat is essential for good health. Fat aids in the absorption of some vitamins and provides fatty acids that human bodies cannot produce. Fats also lend foods taste and consistency.

Fat substitutes are chemically diverse. The most common ones are based on carbohydrates, proteins, or even fats, and a careful reading of nutrition labels will reveal their presence in many processed foods.

- **Carbohydrate-based fat substitutes:** Modified food starches, dextrins, guar gum, pectin, and cellulose gels are all derived from polysaccharides, and they all mimic fat's "mouth feel" by absorbing water to form a gel. Depending on whether they are indigestible (cellulose) or digestible (starches), these fat substitutes deliver 0 to 4 Calories per gram. They cannot be used to fry foods.

- **Protein-based fat substitutes:** These food additives are derived from egg whites or whey (the watery part of milk). When ground into "microparticles," these proteins mimic fat's texture as they slide by each other in the mouth. Protein-based fat substitutes deliver about 4 Calories per gram, and they cannot be used in frying.

- **Fat-based fat substitute:** Olestra (marketed as Olean) is a hybrid molecule that combines a central sucrose molecule with six to eight fatty acids (figure 2.B). Its chief advantage is that it tastes and behaves like fat—even for frying. Olestra is currently approved only for savory snacks such as chips. It is indigestible and calorie-free, but some people have expressed concern that olestra removes fat-soluble vitamins as it passes through the digestive tract. Others have publicized its reputed laxative properties. Most people, however, do not experience problems after eating small quantities of olestra.

Sugar and fat substitutes can be useful for people who cannot—or do not wish to—eat much of the real thing. But nutritionists warn that these food additives should not take the place of a healthy diet and moderate eating habits.

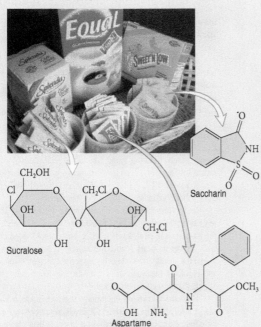

Figure 2.A **Three Artificial Sweeteners.**

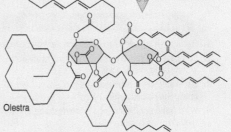

Figure 2.B **Olestra, a Fat Substitute.**

INVESTIGATING LIFE

2.6 Infected Insects Go Green

Hunters often change into green and brown clothing before embarking into the woods; success depends on not being seen. Chameleons and octopuses use similar tactics, changing their color patterns to blend into the background. Most other animals, however, cannot readily change color. Researchers were therefore surprised when they observed reddish pea aphids that turn green as they age. How do these insects change their color?

To understand the answer, it is important to recall the role of chemistry in biology. You have already learned about the four main types of organic molecules—carbohydrates, proteins, nucleic acids, and lipids. But life produces many other molecules containing carbon and hydrogen. Pigments are one example. These colorful organic compounds are abundant in a plant's leaves, a bird's feathers, and your hair and eyes. Pea aphids also produce pigments. Some have red pigments like the ones in carrots and tomatoes, whereas others produce mostly green hues.

An aphid's DNA determines whether it is born red or green. But some aphids trade in a red "birthday suit" for a green one as they develop (figure 2.28). If DNA were the only factor contributing to aphid color, then green aphids should be green from birth. What explains the color change?

A Japanese research group led by Ryuichi Koga and Takema Fukatsu teamed up with six other scientists to answer this question. They hypothesized that bacteria might make red aphids turn green.

Previous studies showed that aphids have up to three types of bacteria living inside their cells. The team soon discovered that some aphids also have a fourth type of bacteria, called *Rickettsiella*. To test whether these bacteria affect aphid color, the researchers used antibiotics to selectively kill some species without affecting *Rickettsiella*. All aphids remained green after treatment, suggesting that *Rickettsiella* alone has a role in maintaining green aphid coloration.

The team then injected *Rickettsiella* bacteria into red aphids and allowed the infected insects to breed. The parents transferred the bacteria to their offspring, which changed from red to green through development. These observations were strong evidence that *Rickettsiella* bacteria cause aphid body color to change.

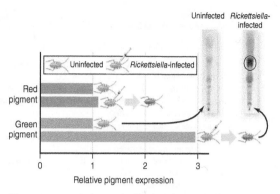

Figure 2.29 **Pigment Production.** Injecting aphids with *Rickettsiella* did not affect red pigment production, but green pigment production tripled. Separating these pigments reveals a much larger and darker green band (circled area) in the infected aphids compared to uninfected aphids.

Next, the scientists wondered how *Rickettsiella* could make red aphids turn green. Did the aphids produce more green pigments? Or did the aphids simply produce fewer red pigments, making the green pigments more apparent?

The team used solvents to extract pigments from two groups of aphids: uninfected red aphids and *Rickettsiella*-infected green aphids that were once red. They applied each extract to special paper that separated the pigment mixture into individual bands, revealing an array of colored chemicals. The scientists analyzed the color bands and determined that *Rickettsiella* bacteria increase green pigment production in aphids three-fold without affecting red pigment production (figure 2.29).

This study represents the first known case of a bacterium causing a color change in a healthy host. The result raises a new question: How might being green increase the survival and reproductive success of both the aphids and their live-in bacteria? Predation may provide part of the answer. Ladybird beetles, which eat aphids, easily spot red prey against a leafy background. The green aphids that avoid detection are most likely to produce offspring—and to pass on the bacterial infection. Therefore, stimulating green pigment production may increase the bacterium's chance to spread to a new host.

This story reveals how one organism might influence the chemicals produced by another. These subtle changes in life's chemistry can mean the difference between life and death. In this case, bacteria induce an aphid wardrobe change that benefits both species.

Tsutomu, T., and seven coauthors, including R. Koga and T. Fukatsu. 2010. Symbiotic bacterium modifies aphid body color. *Science*, vol. 330, pages 1102–1104.

2.6 MASTERING CONCEPTS

1. How did the researchers determine that bacteria increased green pigment production in aphids?
2. How might the color change be adaptive to both aphids and the bacteria that infect them?

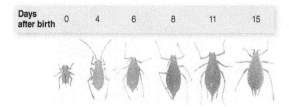

Figure 2.28 **Color change.** Some pea aphids (*Acyrthosiphon pisum*) change from red to green in the first couple of weeks after birth.

CHAPTER SUMMARY

2.1 Atoms Make Up All Matter

- All **matter** can be broken down into pure substances called **elements.**

A. Elements Are Fundamental Types of Matter

- **Bulk elements** are essential to life in large quantities. The most abundant are C, H, O, and N. **Trace elements** are required in smaller amounts.

B. Atoms Are Particles of Elements

- An **atom** is the smallest unit of an element. Positively charged **protons** and neutral **neutrons** form the **nucleus.** The negatively charged, much smaller **electrons** circle the nucleus.
- Elements are organized in the **periodic table** according to **atomic number** (the number of protons).
- An **ion** is an atom that gains or loses electrons.

C. Isotopes Have Different Numbers of Neutrons

- **Isotopes** of an element differ by the number of neutrons. A **radioactive** isotope is unstable.
- An element's **atomic weight** reflects the average **mass number** of all isotopes, weighted by the proportions in which they naturally occur.

2.2 Chemical Bonds Link Atoms

- A **molecule** is two or more atoms joined together; if they are of different elements, the molecule is called a **compound.**

A. Electrons Determine Bonding

- Electrons move constantly; they are most likely to occur in volumes of space called **orbitals.** Orbitals are grouped into **energy shells.**
- An atom's tendency to fill its **valence shell** with electrons drives it to form **chemical bonds** with other atoms.
- The more **electronegative** an atom, the more strongly it attracts electrons.

B. In an Ionic Bond, One Atom Transfers Electrons to Another Atom

- An **ionic bond** is an attraction between two oppositely charged ions, which form when one highly electronegative atom strips one or more electrons from another atom (figure 2.30).

C. In a Covalent Bond, Atoms Share Electrons

- **Covalent bonds** form between atoms that can fill their valence shells by sharing one or more pairs of electrons (see figure 2.30).
- Atoms in a **nonpolar covalent bond** share electrons equally. If one atom is more electronegative than the other, a **polar covalent bond** forms.

D. Partial Charges on Polar Molecules Create Hydrogen Bonds

- **Hydrogen bonds** result from the attraction between opposite partial charges on adjacent molecules or between oppositely charged parts of a large molecule.

2.3 Water Is Essential to Life

A. Water Is Cohesive and Adhesive

- Water is **cohesive** and **adhesive,** sticking to itself and other materials.

B. Many Substances Dissolve in Water

- A **solution** consists of a **solute** dissolved in a **solvent.**
- Water dissolves **hydrophilic** (polar and charged) substances but not **hydrophobic** (nonpolar) substances.

C. Water Regulates Temperature

- Water helps regulate temperature in organisms because it resists both temperature change and **evaporation.**

D. Water Expands As It Freezes

- Ice floats because it is less dense than liquid water.

E. Water Participates in Life's Chemical Reactions

- In a **chemical reaction,** the **products** are different from the **reactants.**
- Most biochemical reactions occur in a watery solution.

2.4 Organisms Balance Acids and Bases

- In pure water, the concentrations of H^+ and OH^- are equal, so the solution is **neutral.** An **acid** adds H^+ to a solution, and a **base** adds OH^- or removes H^+.

A. The pH Scale Expresses Acidity or Alkalinity

- The **pH scale** measures H^+ concentration. Pure water has a pH of 7, acidic solutions have a pH below 7, and an **alkaline** solution has a pH between 7 and 14.

B. Buffers Regulate pH in Organisms

- **Buffers** consist of weak acid–base pairs that maintain the pH ranges of body fluids by releasing or consuming H^+.

2.5 Organic Molecules Generate Life's Form and Function

A. Large Organic Molecules Are Composed of Smaller Subunits

- Many **organic molecules** consist of small subunits called **monomers,** which link together to form **polymers. Dehydration synthesis** is the chemical reaction that joins monomers together, releasing a water molecule (figure 2.31).
- The **hydrolysis** reaction uses water to break polymers into monomers.

B. Carbohydrates Include Simple Sugars and Polysaccharides

- **Carbohydrates** consist of carbon, hydrogen, and oxygen in the proportions 1:2:1.
- **Monosaccharides** are single-molecule sugars such as glucose. Two bonded monosaccharides form a **disaccharide.** These simple sugars provide quick energy.
- Complex carbohydrates include **oligosaccharides** (chains of three to 100 monosaccharides) and **polysaccharides** (chains of hundreds of monosaccharides). Polysaccharides provide support and store energy.

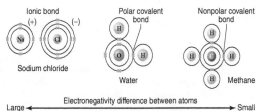

Ionic bond

Polar covalent bond

Nonpolar covalent bond

Sodium chloride

Water

Methane

Electronegativity difference between atoms

Large ◄——————————————————► Small

Figure 2.30 Electronegativity and Bonds.

Animation
Ionic and Covalent Bonds

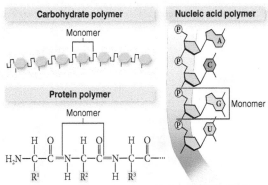

Carbohydrate polymer

Monomer

Protein polymer

Monomer

Nucleic acid polymer

Monomer

Figure 2.31 Monomers and Polymers.

Tutorial
Dehydration and Hydrolysis

C. Proteins Are Complex and Highly Versatile

- **Proteins** consist of **amino acids,** which join into **polypeptides** by forming **peptide bonds** through dehydration synthesis.
- A protein's three-dimensional shape is vital to its function. A **denatured** protein has a ruined shape.

D. Nucleic Acids Store and Transmit Genetic Information

- **Nucleic acids,** including **DNA** and **RNA,** are polymers consisting of **nucleotides.** DNA carries genetic information and transmits it from generation to generation. RNA helps the cell use DNA's information to make proteins.

E. Lipids Are Hydrophobic and Energy-Rich

- **Lipids** are diverse hydrophobic compounds consisting mainly of carbon and hydrogen.
- **Triglycerides** (fats and oils) consist of **glycerol** and three **fatty acids,** which may be **saturated** (no double bonds) or **unsaturated** (at least one double bond). They store energy, slow digestion, cushion organs, and preserve body heat.
- **Sterols** are lipids consisting of four carbon- and hydrogen-rich rings.
- **Waxes** are hard, waterproof coverings made of fatty acids combined with other molecules.

2.6 Investigating Life: Infected Insects Go Green

- An infection by specialized bacteria induces red aphids to produce green pigments as they age, perhaps protecting against predation.

MULTIPLE CHOICE QUESTIONS

1. A carbon-14 atom has ___ neutrons, ___ protons, and a mass number of ___.
   a. 8; 6; 14
   b. 6; 8; 14
   c. 7; 7; 14
   d. 8; 6; 12

2. How many valence electrons does a neutral atom of magnesium have?
   a. 0
   b. 6
   c. 2
   d. 8

3. A *covalent bond* forms when
   a. electrons are present in a valence shell.
   b. a valence electron is removed from one atom and added to another.
   c. a pair of valence electrons is shared between two atoms.
   d. the electronegativity of one atom is much greater than that of another atom.

4. A hydrophilic substance is one that can
   a. form covalent bonds with hydrogen.
   b. dissolve in water.
   c. buffer a solution.
   d. mix with nonpolar solvents.

5. A hydrogen bond is distinct from ionic and covalent bonds in that it
   a. forms between adjacent molecules rather than within molecules.
   b. forms only between two hydrogen atoms.
   c. is considerably stronger than the other two types of bonds.
   d. occurs more commonly in lipids than in other types of molecules.

6. _____ are monomers that form polymers called _____.
   a. Nucleotides; nucleic acids
   b. Amino acids; nucleic acids
   c. Monoglycerides; triglycerides
   d. Carbohydrates; monosaccharides

Answers to these questions are in appendix A.

WRITE IT OUT

1. Describe how the number of protons, neutrons, and electrons in an atom affects its atomic number, mass number, and charge.

2. Distinguish between nonpolar covalent bonds, polar covalent bonds, and ionic bonds.

3. If oxygen is highly electronegative, why is a covalent bond between two oxygen atoms considered nonpolar?

4. Can nonpolar molecules such as CH_4 participate in hydrogen bonds? Why or why not?

5. Define *solute, solvent,* and *solution.*

6. Give an example from everyday life of each of the following properties of water: cohesion, adhesion, ability to dissolve solutes, resistance to temperature change.

7. Draw from memory a diagram showing the interactions among a few water molecules.

8. How do hydrogen ions relate to the pH scale?

9. Sketch a monosaccharide, amino acid, nucleotide, glycerol molecule, and fatty acid. Then show how those smaller molecules form carbohydrates, proteins, nucleic acids, or fats.

10. Refer to figure 2.21 and explain why regulating body temperature is essential to survival.

11. You eat a sandwich made of starchy bread, ham, and cheese. What types of chemicals are in it?

PULL IT TOGETHER

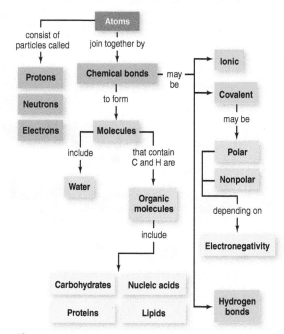

Figure 2.32 Pull It Together: The Chemistry of Life

Refer to figure 2.32 and the chapter content to answer the following questions.

1. How do ions and isotopes fit into this concept map?

2. Besides water, what other molecules are essential to life?

3. Describe how hydrogen bonds form.

4. Add *monomers, polymers, dehydration synthesis,* and *hydrolysis* to this concept map.

CHAPTER

3 Cells

Think Pink. For decades, the Komen Race for the Cure has raised money for the fight against breast cancer. The color pink symbolizes support for women with this disease.

Enhance your study BIOLOGY
of this chapter with practice quizzes,
animations and videos, answer keys,
and downloadable study tools.
www.mhhe.com/hoefnagels

Cancer Cells: A Tale of Two Drugs

"YOU HAVE CANCER." Physicians deliver this frightening diagnosis to millions of patients each year. The term *cancer* refers to a family of diseases with one feature in common: a person's own cells multiply out of control. The abnormal cells form tumors that may invade nearby tissues and spread to other parts of the body. The illness can turn deadly if the cancerous cells destroy normal tissues or interfere with vital body functions. ① *cancer*, p. 156

Not long ago, cancer patients had few options. Surgery became a common treatment in the 1800s, after anaesthesia was invented. In the early 1900s, physicians discovered that radiation could kill cancer cells. The first drugs designed to treat cancer were developed in the mid-1900s. While these strategies saved countless lives, the side effects were often devastating, and medical professionals have continued to search for better tools.

Cancer research and cell biology are intimately related, since the goal of the treatment is to kill cancer cells while leaving normal cells alone. Biologists must therefore scrutinize the structural and chemical differences between cancer cells and normal cells. Their findings have yielded spectacular new treatments that exploit some of these differences. Research into the chemical signals that control cell division has been especially fruitful, producing new drugs that inhibit only abnormal cells.

One example is Herceptin (trastuzumab). This drug, which was created to treat some forms of breast cancer, got its name from its target: HER2, a receptor protein on the surface of breast cells. The HER2 receptor binds to a molecule that stimulates the cell to divide. A normal breast cell has thousands of HER2 receptors, but cells of one form of breast cancer have many millions. Cells with too many HER2 receptors divide and spread rapidly. Herceptin prevents this by binding to HER2 receptors.

Another successful drug is Gleevec (imatinib), which treats some forms of leukemia and gastrointestinal cancers. Leukemia is a disease in which the body produces many abnormal white blood cells. In a type of leukemia called chronic myeloid leukemia, a genetic mutation causes cells to produce an abnormal protein. This protein prompts the body to produce cancerous cells. Gleevec blocks the protein, selectively slowing division of the abnormal cells without harming normal cells.

Both Herceptin and Gleevec took decades to develop. Each interferes with a feature that is unique to the cancer cells, producing fewer side effects than older treatments that destroy healthy cells, too. These drugs owe their success to generations of cell biologists who painstakingly documented the structures in and on cells. These cellular parts are the subject of this chapter.

LEARNING OUTLINE

 3.1 Cells Are the Units of Life
   A. Simple Lenses Revealed the Cellular Basis of Life
   B. The Cell Theory Emerges
   C. Microscopes Magnify Cell Structures
   D. All Cells Have Features in Common

 3.2 Different Cell Types Characterize Life's Three Domains
   A. Domain Bacteria Contains Earth's Most Abundant Organisms
   B. Domain Archaea Includes Prokaryotes with Unique Biochemistry
   C. Domain Eukarya Contains Organisms with Complex Cells

 3.3 A Membrane Separates Each Cell from Its Surroundings

 3.4 Eukaryotic Organelles Divide Labor
   A. The Nucleus, Endoplasmic Reticulum, and Golgi Interact to Secrete Substances
   B. Lysosomes, Vacuoles, and Peroxisomes Are Cellular Digestion Centers
   C. Mitochondria Extract Energy from Nutrients
   D. Photosynthesis Occurs in Chloroplasts

 3.5 The Cytoskeleton Supports Eukaryotic Cells
   A. Proteins Form the Cytoskeleton
   B. Cilia and Flagella Help Cells Move

 3.6 Cells Stick Together and Communicate with One Another
   A. Animal Cell Junctions Occur in Several Forms
   B. Cell Walls Are Strong, Flexible, and Porous

 3.7 Investigating Life: The Tiniest Compass

 LEARN HOW TO LEARN

Interpreting Images from Microscopes

Any photo taken through a microscope should include information that can help you interpret what you see. First, read the caption and labels so you know what you are looking at—usually an organ, a tissue, or an individual cell. Then study the scale bar and estimate the size of the image. Finally, check whether a light microscope (LM), scanning electron microscope (SEM), or transmission electron microscope (TEM) was used to create the image. Note that stains and false colors are often added to emphasize the most important features.

3.1 Cells Are the Units of Life

A human, a plant, a mushroom, and a bacterium appear to have little in common other than being alive. However, on a microscopic level, these organisms share many similarities. For example, all organisms consist of one or more microscopic structures called **cells,** the smallest unit of life that can function independently (see this chapter's Apply It Now box). Within cells, highly coordinated biochemical activities carry out the basic functions of life. This chapter introduces the cell, and the chapters that follow delve into the cellular events that make life possible.

A. Simple Lenses Revealed the Cellular Basis of Life

The study of cells began in 1660, when English physicist Robert Hooke melted strands of spun glass to create lenses. He focused on bee stingers, fish scales, fly legs, feathers, and any type of insect he could hold still. When he looked at cork, which is bark from a type of oak tree, it appeared to be divided into little boxes, left by cells that were once alive. Hooke called these units "cells" because they looked like the cubicles (Latin, *cellae*) where monks studied and prayed. Although Hooke did not realize the significance of his observation, he was the first person to see the outlines of cells. His discovery initiated a new field of science, now called cell biology.

In 1673, Antony van Leeuwenhoek of Holland improved lenses further (figure 3.1). One of his first objects of study was tartar scraped from his own teeth, and his words best describe what he saw there:

> *To my great surprise, I found that it contained many very small animalcules, the motions of which were very pleasing to behold. The motion of these little creatures, one among another, may be likened to that of a great number of gnats or flies disporting in the air.*

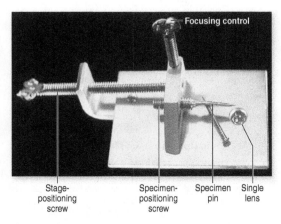

Figure 3.1 Early Microscope. Antony van Leeuwenhoek made many simple microscopes like this one. The object he was studying would have been at the tip of the specimen pin.

Stage-positioning screw   Specimen-positioning screw   Specimen pin   Single lens   Focusing control

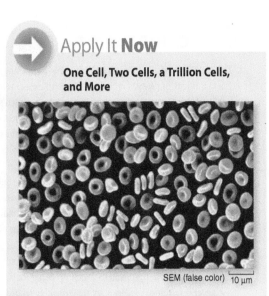
Leeuwenhoek opened a vast new world to the human eye and mind. He viewed bacteria and protists that people hadn't known existed. He also described microscopic parts of larger organisms, including human red blood cells and sperm. However, he failed to see the single-celled "animalcules" reproduce. He therefore perpetuated the idea of spontaneous generation, which suggested that life arises from nonliving matter or from nothing.

B. The Cell Theory Emerges

In the nineteenth century, more powerful microscopes with improved magnification and illumination revealed details of structures inside cells. In the early 1830s, Scottish surgeon Robert Brown noted a roughly circular object in cells from orchid plants. He saw the structure in every cell, then identified it in cells of a variety of organisms. He named it the "nucleus," a term that stuck. Soon microscopists distinguished the translucent, moving material that made up the rest of the cell, calling it the cytoplasm.

In 1839, German biologists Mathias J. Schleiden and Theodor Schwann proposed a new theory, based on many observations made with microscopes. Schleiden first noted that cells were the basic units of plants, and then Schwann compared animal cells to plant cells. After observing similarities in many different plant and animal cells, Schleiden and Schwann formulated the **cell theory,** which originally had two main components: all organisms are made of one or more cells, and the cell is the fundamental unit of all life.

German physiologist Rudolf Virchow added a third component to the cell theory in 1855, when he proposed that all cells come from preexisting cells. This idea contradicted spontaneous generation. When the French chemist and microbiologist Louis Pasteur finally disproved spontaneous generation in 1859, he provided additional evidence in support of the cell theory.

The existence of cells is an undisputed fact, yet the cell theory is still evolving (table 3.1). For 150 years after its formulation, biologists focused on documenting the parts of a cell and the process of cell division. Since the discovery of DNA's structure and function in the 1950s, however, the cell theory has focused on the role of genetic information in dictating what happens inside cells. Modern cell theory therefore adds the ideas that all cells have the same basic chemical composition (chapter 2), use energy (chapters 4, 5, and 6), and contain DNA that is duplicated and passed on as each cell divides (chapters 7, 8, and 9).

Like any scientific theory, the cell theory is *potentially* falsifiable—yet many lines of evidence support each of its components, making it one of the most powerful ideas in biology.

TABLE **3.1** **The Cell Theory: A Summary**

Early cell theory
All organisms are made of one or more cells.
The cell is the fundamental unit of life.
All cells come from preexisting cells.
Additional ideas in modern cell theory
All cells have the same basic chemical composition.
All cells use energy.
All cells contain DNA that is duplicated and passed on as each cell divides.

50 µm
LM

C. Microscopes Magnify Cell Structures

The unaided eye can see objects that are larger than about 0.2 mm. Cells are typically smaller than this lower limit of human vision, so studying life at the cellular and molecular levels requires magnification. Cell biologists use a variety of microscopes to produce different types of images. As you will see, some microscopes show full-color structures and processes inside living cells. Others can greatly magnify cell structures, but with two significant drawbacks: they require that cells be killed, and they produce only black-and-white images. This section describes several types of microscopes; figure 3.2 provides a sense of the size of objects that each can reveal.

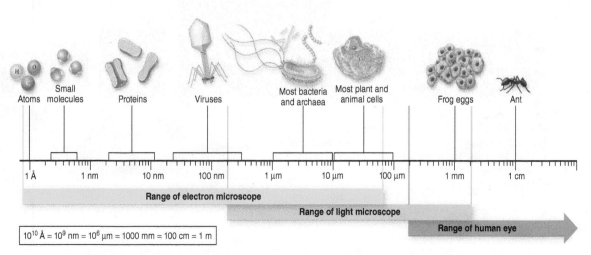

Figure 3.2 **Ranges of Light and Electron Microscopes.** Biologists use light microscopes and electron microscopes to view a world too small to see with the unaided eye. This illustration uses the metric system to measure size (see appendix C). Thanks to the overlapping capabilities of the different microscopes, we can visualize objects ranging in size from large molecules to entire cells.

Light Microscopes   Light microscopes are ideal for generating true-color views of living or preserved cells. Because light must pass through an object to reveal its internal features, however, the specimens must be transparent or thinly sliced to generate a good image.

Two types of light microscopes are the compound microscope and the confocal microscope (figure 3.3a, b). A compound scope, the type you are likely to use in a biology lab course, uses two or more lenses to focus visible light through a specimen. The most powerful ones can magnify up to 1600 times and resolve objects that are 200 nanometers apart. A confocal microscope enhances resolution by focusing white or laser light through a lens to the object. The image then passes through a pinhole. The result is a scan of highly focused light on one tiny part of the specimen at a time. Computers can integrate multiple confocal images of specimens exposed to fluorescent dyes to produce spectacular three-dimensional peeks at living structures.

Transmission and Scanning Electron Microscopes

Light microscopes are useful, but their main disadvantage is that many cell structures are too small to see using light. Electron microscopes provide much greater magnification and resolution. Instead of using light, these microscopes use electrons.

Instead of using light, a transmission electron microscope (TEM) sends a beam of electrons through a very thin slice of a specimen, using a magnetic field to focus the beam. The microscope translates the contrasts in electron transmission into a high-resolution, two-dimensional image that shows the internal features of the object (figure 3.3c). TEMs can magnify up to 50 million times and resolve objects less than 1 angstrom (10^{-10} meters) apart.

A scanning electron microscope (SEM) scans a beam of electrons over the surface of a metal-coated, three-dimensional specimen. Its images have lower resolution than the TEM; in SEM, the maximum magnification is about 250,000 times, and the resolution limit is 1 to 5 nanometers. SEM's chief advantage is its ability to reveal crevices and textures on a specimen's external surface (figure 3.3d).

Both TEM and SEM provide much greater magnification and resolution than light microscopes. Nevertheless, they do have limitations. First, they are extremely expensive to build, operate, and maintain. Second, electron microscopy normally requires that a specimen be killed, chemically fixed, and placed in a vacuum. These treatments can distort natural structures. Light microscopy, in contrast, allows an investigator to view living organisms. Third, unlike light microscopes, all images from electron microscopes are black and white, although artists often add false color to highlight specific objects in electron micrographs. (In this book, each photo taken through a microscope is tagged with the magnification and the type of microscope; the addition of false color is also noted where applicable.)

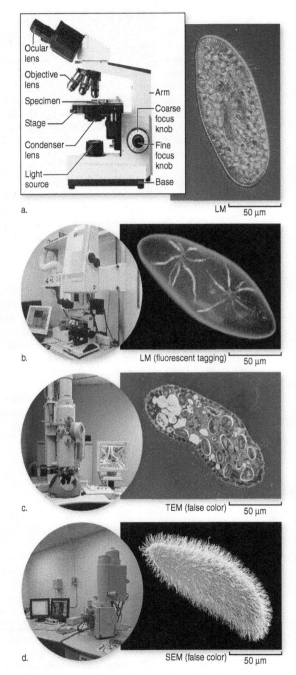

a.   LM   50 μm

b.   LM (fluorescent tagging)   50 μm

c.   TEM (false color)   50 μm

d.   SEM (false color)   50 μm

Figure 3.3   Images from Four Types of Microscopes. These photographs show four types of microscopes, along with sample images of a protist called *Paramecium*. (a) Compound light microscope. (b) Confocal microscope. (c) Transmission electron microscope. (d) Scanning electron microscope.

D. All Cells Have Features in Common

Microscopes and other tools clearly reveal that although cells can appear very different, they all have some of the same features. For example, all cells contain DNA, the cell's genetic information. They also contain RNA, which participates in the production of proteins (see chapter 7). These proteins, in turn, are essential to life because they carry out all of the cell's work, from orchestrating reproduction to processing energy to regulating what enters and leaves the cell.

Since all cells require proteins, they also contain **ribosomes,** which are the structures that manufacture proteins. All cells also contain **cytoplasm,** the fluid that occupies much of the volume of the cell. Each cell is also surrounded by a lipid-rich **cell membrane** (also called the plasma membrane) that forms a boundary between the cell and its environment (see section 3.3).

One other feature common to nearly all cells is small size, typically less than 0.1 millimeter in diameter (see figure 3.2 and the Burning Question on page 50). Why so tiny? The answer is that nutrients, water, oxygen, carbon dioxide, and waste products enter or leave a cell through its surface. Each cell must have abundant surface area to accommodate these exchanges. As an object grows, however, its volume increases much faster than its surface area. Figure 3.4a illustrates this principle for a series of cubes, but the same applies to cells: Small cell size maximizes the ratio of surface area to volume.

Figure It Out

For a cube 5 centimeters on each side, calculate the ratio of surface area to volume.

Answer: 1.2

Cells avoid surface area limitations in several ways. Nerve cells may be long (up to a meter or so), but they are also extremely thin, so the ratio of surface area to volume remains high. The flattened shape of a red blood cell maximizes its ability to carry oxygen, and the many microscopic extensions of an amoeba's membrane provide a large surface area for absorbing oxygen and capturing food (figure 3.4b). A transportation system that quickly circulates materials throughout the cell also helps.

The concept of surface area is everywhere in biology; many structures illustrate the principle that a large surface area maximizes contact with the environment. For example, a pine tree's pollen grains have extensions that enable them to float on air currents; root hairs have tremendous surface area for absorbing water; the broad, flat leaves of plants maximize exposure to light; a fish's feathery gills absorb oxygen from water; a jackrabbit's enormous ears help the animal lose excess body heat in the desert air—the list goes on and on. Conversely, low surface areas minimize the exchange of heat or materials with the environment. A hibernating animal, for example, conserves warmth by tucking its limbs close to its body; a cactus plant produces few if any leaves, reducing water loss in its dry habitat.

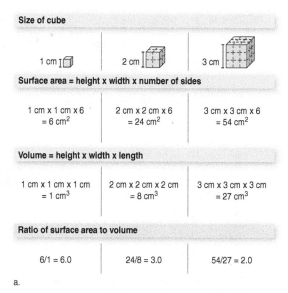

Size of cube

| 1 cm | 2 cm | 3 cm |

Surface area = height x width x number of sides

| 1 cm x 1 cm x 6 = 6 cm^2 | 2 cm x 2 cm x 6 = 24 cm^2 | 3 cm x 3 cm x 6 = 54 cm^2 |

Volume = height x width x length

| 1 cm x 1 cm x 1 cm = 1 cm^3 | 2 cm x 2 cm x 2 cm = 8 cm^3 | 3 cm x 3 cm x 3 cm = 27 cm^3 |

Ratio of surface area to volume

| 6/1 = 6.0 | 24/8 = 3.0 | 54/27 = 2.0 |

a.

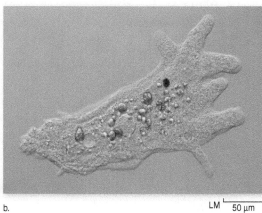

b.   LM ⌐ 50 µm

Figure 3.4 Surface Area and Volume. (a) This simple example shows that smaller objects have more surface area *relative to their volume* than do larger objects with the same overall shape. (b) A highly folded membrane produces a large surface area relative to the amoeba's volume.

3.1 MASTERING CONCEPTS

1. Why are cells, not atoms, the basic units of life?
2. How have microscopes advanced the study of cells?
3. What are the original components of the cell theory, and what parts of the theory came later?
4. Rank the three main types of microscopes from lowest to highest potential magnification.
5. Which molecules and structures occur in all cells?
6. Describe adaptations that increase the ratio of surface area to volume in cells.

3.2 Different Cell Types Characterize Life's Three Domains

Tutorial
Cell
Structure

Until recently, biologists organized life into just two categories: prokaryotic and eukaryotic. **Prokaryotes,** the simplest and most ancient forms of life, are organisms whose cells lack a nucleus (*pro* = before; *karyon* = kernel, referring to the nucleus). **Eukaryotes** have cells that contain a nucleus and other membranous organelles (*eu* = true).

In 1977, however, microbiologist Carl Woese studied key molecules in many cell types. He detected differences suggesting that prokaryotes actually include two forms of life that are distantly related to each other. Biologists subsequently divided life into three domains: Bacteria, Archaea, and Eukarya (figure 3.5). This section describes them briefly; chapters 17 through 21 cover prokaryotic and eukaryotic life in much more detail.

A. Domain Bacteria Contains Earth's Most Abundant Organisms

Bacteria are the most abundant and diverse organisms on Earth, perhaps because they have existed longer than any other group. Some species, such as *Streptococcus* and *Escherichia coli*, can cause illnesses, but most are not harmful. In fact, the bacteria living on your skin and inside your intestinal tract are essential for good health. Bacteria are also very valuable in research, food and beverage processing, and pharmaceutical production. In ecosystems, bacteria play critical roles as decomposers and producers.

Bacterial cells are structurally simple (figure 3.6a). The **nucleoid** is the area where the cell's circular DNA molecule congregates. Unlike a eukaryotic cell's nucleus, the bacterial nucleoid is not bounded by a membrane. Located near the DNA in the cytoplasm are the enzymes, RNA molecules, and ribosomes needed to produce the cell's proteins.

BurningQuestion

What is the smallest living organism?

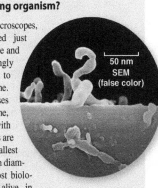

Since the invention of microscopes, investigators have wondered just how small an organism can be and still sustain life. This seemingly simple question is hard to answer; *life* is hard to define. Some people consider viruses alive because they share some, but not all, characteristics with cells (see chapter 16). Viruses are indeed minuscule: The smallest are less than 20 nanometers in diameter (see figure 3.2). Yet most biologists do not consider them alive, in part because viruses do not consist of cells or reproduce on their own.

Figure 3.A   Nanobes. Alive or not?

Some scientists consider "nanobes" to be the world's smallest microorganisms, at about 20 to 150 nanometers long (figure 3.A). Other researchers are skeptical. These minuscule filaments are hard to analyze for hallmarks of life such as DNA, RNA, ribosomes, and protein. Their status remains controversial.

For now, the smallest certifiable living organisms are bacteria called mycoplasmas. Besides their small size (150 nanometers and larger), these microorganisms are unusual among bacteria because they lack cell walls. Biologists have studied mycoplasmas in detail for two reasons. First, some cause human disease such as urinary tract infections and pneumonia. Second, with only 482 genes, mycoplasmas have the smallest amount of genetic material of any known free-living cell. Studies on mycoplasmas are helping to reveal which genes are minimally required to sustain life.

Submit your burning question to
Marielle.Hoefnagels@mheducation.com

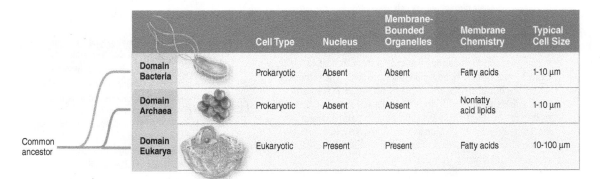

		Cell Type	Nucleus	Membrane-Bounded Organelles	Membrane Chemistry	Typical Cell Size
Domain Bacteria		Prokaryotic	Absent	Absent	Fatty acids	1-10 µm
Domain Archaea		Prokaryotic	Absent	Absent	Nonfatty acid lipids	1-10 µm
Domain Eukarya		Eukaryotic	Present	Present	Fatty acids	10-100 µm

Common ancestor

Figure 3.5   The Three Domains of Life. Biologists distinguish domains Bacteria, Archaea, and Eukarya based on unique features of cell structure and biochemistry. The small evolutionary tree shows that archaea are the closest relatives of the eukaryotes.

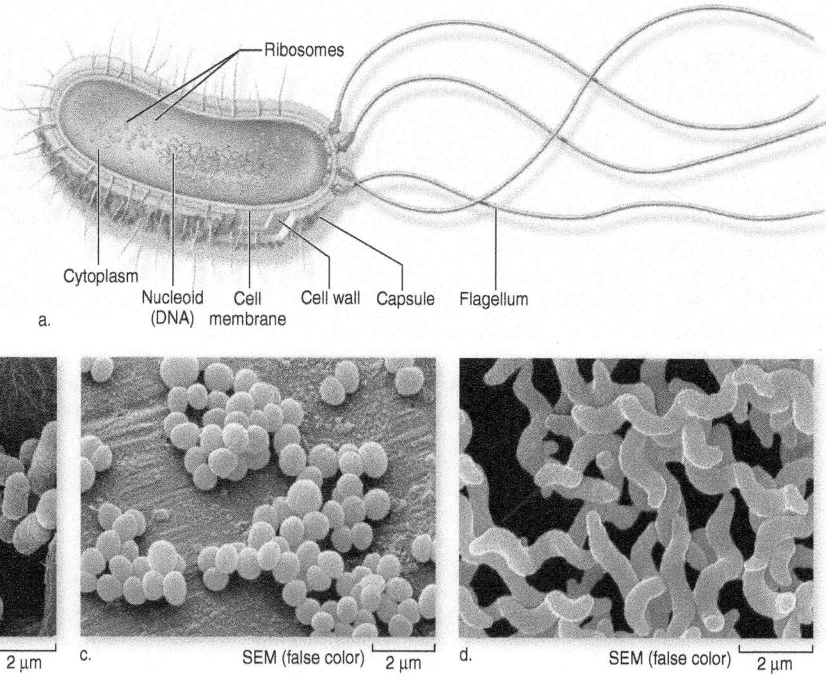

Figure 3.6 Anatomy of a Bacterium. (a) Bacterial cells lack internal compartments. (b) Rod-shaped cells of *E. coli* inhabit human intestines. (c) Spherical *Staphylococcus aureus* cells cause "staph" infections that range from mild to deadly. (d) These corkscrew-shaped bacteria live in the digestive tract of many animals.

Ribosomes

Cytoplasm

Nucleoid (DNA) Cell membrane Cell wall Capsule Flagellum

a.

b.   SEM (false color) 2 μm   c.   SEM (false color) 2 μm   d.   SEM (false color) 2 μm

A rigid **cell wall** surrounds the cell membrane of most bacteria, protecting the cell and preventing it from bursting if it absorbs too much water. This wall also gives the cell its shape: usually rod-shaped, round, or spiral (figure 3.6b, c, d). Many antibiotic drugs, including penicillin, halt bacterial infection by interfering with the microorganism's ability to construct its protective cell wall. In some bacteria, polysaccharides on the cell wall form a capsule that adds protection or enables the cell to attach to surfaces.

Video Dying Bacteria

Many bacteria can swim in fluids. **Flagella** (singular: flagellum) are tail-like appendages that enable these cells to move. One or more flagella are anchored in the cell wall and underlying cell membrane. Bacterial flagella rotate like a propeller, moving the cell forward or backward.

B. Domain Archaea Includes Prokaryotes with Unique Biochemistry

Archaean cells resemble bacterial cells in some ways. Like bacteria, they are smaller than most eukaryotic cells, and they lack a membrane-bounded nucleus and other organelles. Most have cell walls, and flagella are also common. Because of these similarities, Woese first named his newly recognized group Archaebacteria.

The name later changed to Archaea after it became obvious that the resemblance to bacteria was only superficial. Archaea have their own domain because they build their cells out of biochemicals that are different from those in either bacteria or eukaryotes. Their cell membranes, cell walls, and flagella are all chemically unique. Their ribosomes, however, share similarities

with those of both bacteria and eukaryotes, and key genetic sequences suggest that archaea are actually the closest relatives of eukaryotes.

The first members of Archaea to be described were methanogens, microbes that use carbon dioxide and hydrogen from the environment to produce methane. Archaea subsequently became famous as "extremophiles" because scientists discovered many of them in habitats that are extremely hot, acidic, or salty (figure 3.7). This characterization is somewhat misleading, however, because bacteria also occupy the same environments. Moreover, researchers have now discovered archaea in a variety of moderate habitats, including soil, swamps, rice paddies, oceans, and even the human mouth.

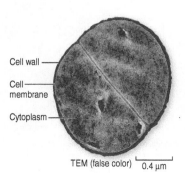

Cell wall

Cell membrane

Cytoplasm

TEM (false color) 0.4 μm

Figure 3.7 An Archaeon. *Natronococcus* is an extremophile archaeon that lives in a salty, high-pH lake in Kenya. This cell is dividing.

C. Domain Eukarya Contains Organisms with Complex Cells

An astonishing diversity of organisms, including humans, belong to domain Eukarya. Our fellow animals are eukaryotes, as are yeasts, mushrooms, and other fungi. Plants are also eukaryotes, and so are one-celled protists such as *Amoeba* and *Paramecium*.

Despite their great differences in external appearance, all eukaryotic organisms share many features on a cellular level. Figures 3.8 and 3.9 depict generalized animal and plant cells. Although both of the illustrated cells have many structures in common, there are some differences. Most notably, plant cells have chloroplasts and a cell wall, which animal cells lack.

One obvious feature that sets eukaryotic cells apart is their large size, typically 10 to 100 times greater than prokaryotic

Figure 3.8 Anatomy of an Animal Cell. The large, generalized view shows the relative sizes and locations of a typical animal cell's components. The electron micrograph at right shows a human white blood cell with a prominent nucleus and many mitochondria.

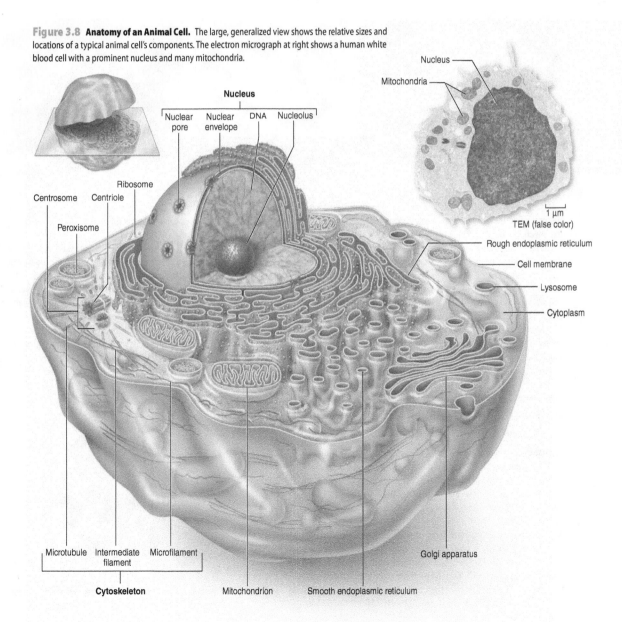

Nucleus

Mitochondria

1 μm

TEM (false color)

Nucleus

Nuclear pore | Nuclear envelope | DNA | Nucleolus

Ribosome

Centrosome | Centriole

Peroxisome

Rough endoplasmic reticulum

Cell membrane

Lysosome

Cytoplasm

Microtubule | Intermediate filament | Microfilament

Cytoskeleton

Mitochondrion

Smooth endoplasmic reticulum

Golgi apparatus

cells. The other main difference is that the cytoplasm of a eukaryotic cell is divided into **organelles** ("little organs"), compartments that carry out specialized functions. An elaborate system of internal membranes creates these compartments.

Sections 3.4, 3.5, and 3.6 describe the structure of the eukaryotic cell in greater detail, and the illustrated table at the end of the chapter summarizes the functions of the eukaryotic organelles (see table 3.3 on page 66).

3.2 MASTERING CONCEPTS

1. How do prokaryotic cells differ from eukaryotic cells?
2. Compare and contrast bacteria and archaea.
3. What is the relationship between cells and organelles?
4. How do organelles contribute to efficiency in eukaryotic cells?

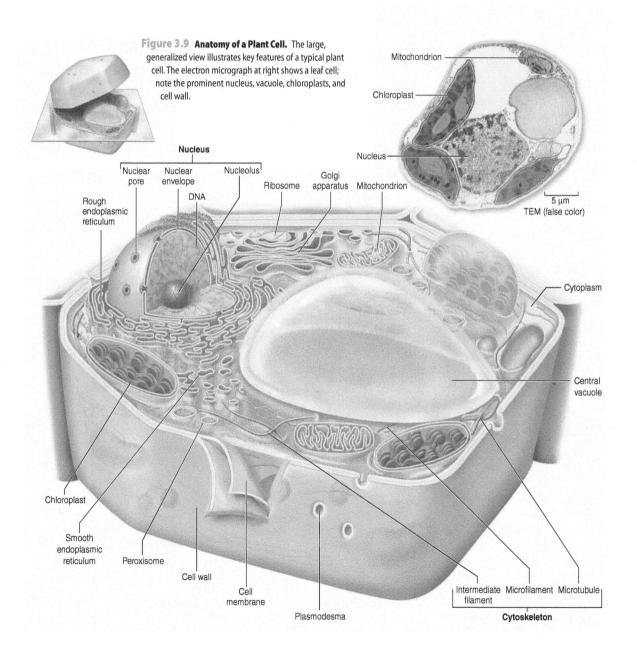

Figure 3.9 Anatomy of a Plant Cell. The large, generalized view illustrates key features of a typical plant cell. The electron micrograph at right shows a leaf cell; note the prominent nucleus, vacuole, chloroplasts, and cell wall.

Mitochondrion

Chloroplast

Nucleus

5 μm
TEM (false color)

Nucleus

Nuclear pore
Nuclear envelope
DNA
Nucleolus
Ribosome
Golgi apparatus
Mitochondrion

Rough endoplasmic reticulum

Cytoplasm

Central vacuole

Chloroplast

Smooth endoplasmic reticulum

Peroxisome

Cell wall

Cell membrane

Plasmodesma

Intermediate filament
Microfilament
Microtubule

Cytoskeleton

3.3 A Membrane Separates Each Cell from Its Surroundings

A cell membrane is one feature common to all cells. The membrane separates the cytoplasm from the cell's surroundings. The cell's surface also transports substances into and out of the cell (see chapter 4), and it receives and responds to external stimuli. Inside a eukaryotic cell, internal membranes enclose the organelles.

The cell membrane is composed of phospholipids, which are organic molecules that resemble triglycerides (figure 3.10). In a triglyceride, three fatty acids attach to a three-carbon glycerol molecule. But in a **phospholipid,** glycerol bonds to only two fatty acids; the third carbon binds to a phosphate group attached to additional atoms. ⓘ *triglycerides,* p. 36

This chemical structure gives phospholipids unusual properties in water. The phosphate "head" end, with its polar covalent

Tutorial Cell Membranes

bonds, is attracted to water; that is, it is hydrophilic. The other end, consisting of two fatty acid "tails," is hydrophobic. In water, phospholipid molecules spontaneously arrange themselves into the most energy-efficient organization: a **phospholipid bilayer** (figure 3.11). In this two-layered, sandwichlike structure, the hydrophilic surfaces (the "bread" of the sandwich) are exposed to the watery medium outside and inside the cell. The hydrophobic tails face each other on the inside of the sandwich, like cheese between the bread slices. Unlike a sandwich, however, the bilayer forms a three-dimensional sphere, not a flat surface.

Thanks to this hydrophobic middle portion, the phospholipid bilayer has selective permeability, meaning that some but not all substances can pass through it. Lipids and small, nonpolar molecules such as O_2 and CO_2 pass freely into and out of a cell. The fatty acid tails at the bilayer's interior, however, block ions and polar molecules like glucose from passing through.

Cell membranes consist not only of phospholipid bilayers but also of sterols, proteins, and other molecules (figure 3.12). The cell membrane is often called a **fluid mosaic** because many of the proteins and phospholipids are free to move laterally within the bilayer. Sterols maintain the membrane's fluidity as the temperature fluctuates. Both animal and plant cell membranes

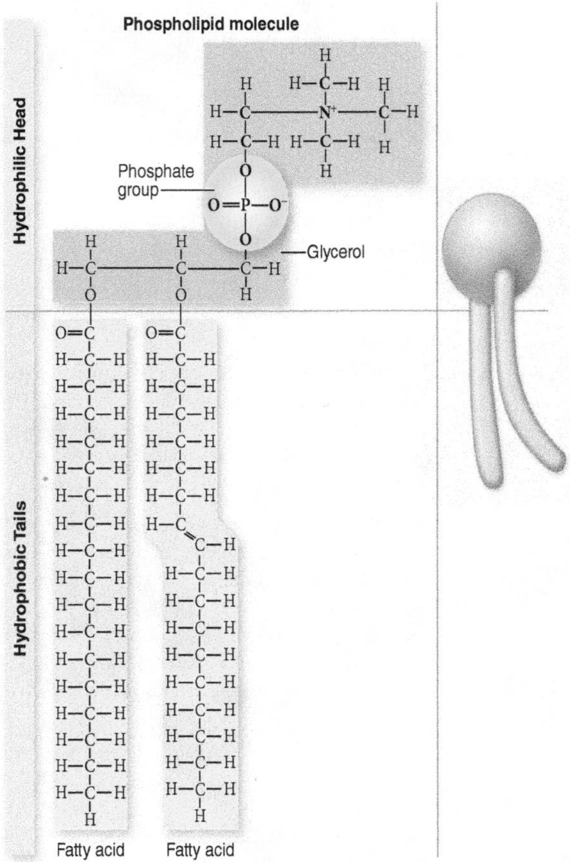

Figure 3.10 Membrane Phospholipid. A phospholipid molecule consists of a glycerol molecule attached to a hydrophilic phosphate "head" group and two hydrophobic fatty acid "tails." The drawing at right shows a simplified phospholipid structure.

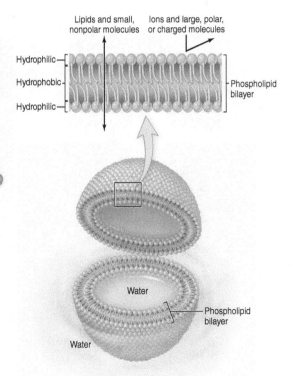

Figure 3.11 Phospholipid Bilayer. In water, phospholipids form a bilayer. The hydrophilic head groups are exposed to the water; the hydrophobic tails face each other, minimizing contact with water. This bilayer has selective permeability, allowing only some substances to freely pass through.

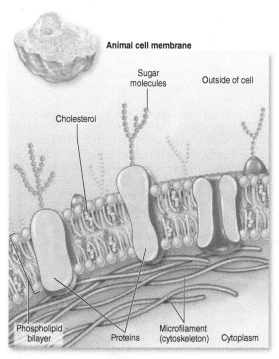

Animal cell membrane

Sugar molecules

Outside of cell

Cholesterol

Phospholipid bilayer

Proteins

Microfilament (cytoskeleton)

Cytoplasm

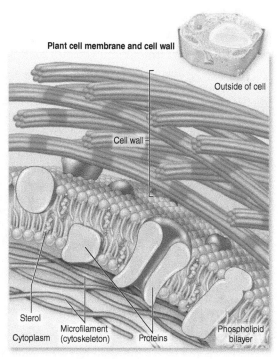

Plant cell membrane and cell wall

Outside of cell

Cell wall

Sterol

Cytoplasm

Microfilament (cytoskeleton)

Proteins

Phospholipid bilayer

Figure 3.12 Anatomy of a Cell Membrane. The cell membrane is a "fluid mosaic" of proteins embedded in a phospholipid bilayer. Sterol molecules, such as the cholesterol in animal membranes, add fluidity. The outer face of the animal cell membrane also features carbohydrate (sugar) molecules linked to proteins. A rigid cell wall of cellulose fibers surrounds plant cells.

3-D Animation
Lipid Bilayer

contain sterols; the cholesterol in animal membranes is the most familiar example. ⓘ *sterols,* p. 39

Whereas phospholipids and sterols provide the membrane's structure, proteins are especially important to its function. As you can see in figure 3.13, some of the proteins extend through the phospholipid bilayer, whereas others face only the inside or the outside of the cell. Cells have multiple types of membrane proteins:

- **Transport proteins:** Transport proteins embedded in the phospholipid bilayer create passageways through which ions, glucose, and other polar substances pass into or out of the cell. Section 4.5 describes membrane transport in more detail.

- **Enzymes:** These proteins facilitate chemical reactions that otherwise would proceed too slowly to sustain life. (Not all enzymes, however, are associated with membranes.) ⓘ *enzymes,* p. 78

- **Recognition proteins:** Carbohydrates attached to cell surface proteins serve as "name tags" that help the body recognize its own cells. The immune system attacks cells with unfamiliar surface molecules, which is why transplant recipients often reject donated organs. Surface proteins also distinctively mark specialized cells within an individual, so a bone cell's surface is different from that of a nerve cell or a muscle cell.

- **Adhesion proteins:** These membrane proteins enable cells to stick to one another.

- **Receptor proteins:** Receptor proteins bind to molecules outside the cell and trigger an internal response, a process called signal transduction. For example, when a hormone binds to a receptor, the resulting chain reaction produces the hormone's effects on the cell (see section 28.2).

Understanding membrane proteins is a vital part of medicine, in part because at least half of all drugs bind to them. One example is omeprazole (Prilosec). This drug relieves heartburn by blocking some of the transport proteins that pump hydrogen ions into the stomach. Another is the antidepressant drug fluoxetine (Prozac), which prevents receptors on brain cell surfaces from absorbing a mood-altering biochemical called serotonin.

3.3   MASTERING CONCEPTS

1. Chemically, how is a phospholipid different from a triglyceride?
2. How does the chemical structure of phospholipids enable them to form a bilayer in water?
3. Where in the cell do phospholipid bilayers occur?
4. What are some functions of membrane proteins?
5. How does a cell membrane differ from a cell wall?

3.4 Eukaryotic Organelles Divide Labor

In eukaryotic cells, organelles have specialized functions that carry out the work of the cell. If you think of a eukaryotic cell as a home, each organelle would be analogous to a room. For example, your kitchen, bathroom, and bedroom each hold unique items that suit the uses of those rooms. Likewise, each organelle has distinct sets of proteins and other molecules that fit the organelle's function. The "walls" of these cellular compartments are membranes, often intricately folded and studded with enzymes and other proteins. These folds provide tremendous surface area where many of the cell's chemical reactions occur.

In general, organelles keep related biochemicals and structures close together. This arrangement saves energy because high concentrations of each chemical occur only in certain organelles, not throughout the cell. The overall boost in efficiency helps eukaryotic cells make up for their large volume and correspondingly small external surface area (see section 3.1D).

Many of the cell's internal membranes form a coordinated **endomembrane system,** which consists of several interacting organelles: the nuclear envelope, endoplasmic reticulum, Golgi apparatus, lysosomes, vacuoles, and cell membrane. As you will see, the organelles of the endomembrane system are connected by small "bubbles" of membrane that can pinch off from one organelle, travel within the cell, and fuse with another. These membranous spheres, which are also part of the endomembrane system, form **vesicles** that transport materials inside the cell.

The organelles of the endomembrane system enable cells to produce, package, and release complex mixtures of biochemicals. This section focuses on each step involved in the production and secretion of one such mixture: milk (figure 3.13).

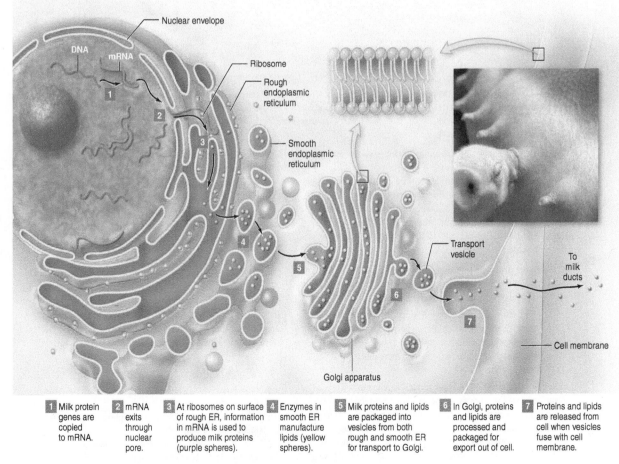

| 1 Milk protein genes are copied to mRNA. | 2 mRNA exits through nuclear pore. | 3 At ribosomes on surface of rough ER, information in mRNA is used to produce milk proteins (purple spheres). | 4 Enzymes in smooth ER manufacture lipids (yellow spheres). | 5 Milk proteins and lipids are packaged into vesicles from both rough and smooth ER for transport to Golgi. | 6 In Golgi, proteins and lipids are processed and packaged for export out of cell. | 7 Proteins and lipids are released from cell when vesicles fuse with cell membrane. |

Figure 3.13 Making Milk. Several types of organelles work together to produce and secrete milk from a cell in a mammary gland; the numbers (1) through (7) indicate each organelle's role. Note that membranes enclose each organelle and the entire cell. (The inset shows a piglet suckling from a sow.)

A. The Nucleus, Endoplasmic Reticulum, and Golgi Interact to Secrete Substances

Special cells in the mammary glands of female mammals produce milk, which contains proteins, fats, carbohydrates, and water in a proportion ideal for the development of a newborn. Human milk is rich in lipids, which the rapidly growing baby's nervous system requires. (Cow's milk contains a higher proportion of protein, better suited to a calf's rapid muscle growth.) Milk also contains calcium, potassium, and antibodies that help jump-start the infant's immunity to disease.

The milk-producing cells of the mammary glands are dormant most of the time, but they undergo a burst of productivity shortly after the female gives birth. How do each cell's organelles work together to manufacture milk?

The Nucleus   The process of milk production and secretion begins in the **nucleus** (see figure 3.13, step 1), the most prominent organelle in most eukaryotic cells. The nucleus contains DNA, an informational molecule that specifies the "recipe" for every protein a cell can make (such as milk protein and enzymes required to synthesize carbohydrates and lipids). The cell copies the genes encoding these proteins into another nucleic acid, messenger RNA (mRNA).

The mRNA molecules exit the nucleus through **nuclear pores,** which are holes in the double-membrane **nuclear envelope** that separates the nucleus from the cytoplasm (figure 3.13, step 2, and figure 3.14). Nuclear pores are highly specialized channels composed of dozens of types of proteins. Traffic through the nuclear pores is busy, with millions of regulatory proteins entering and mRNA molecules leaving each minute.

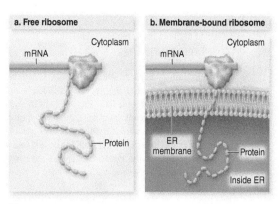

Figure 3.15 **Ribosomes.** (a) Free ribosomes produce proteins used in the cell's cytoplasm. (b) Proteins produced by ribosomes attached to the rough ER's membrane are typically used in specialized organelles or in the cell membrane; they may also be secreted outside the cell.

Also inside the nucleus is the **nucleolus,** a dense spot that assembles the components of ribosomes. These ribosomal subunits leave the nucleus through the nuclear pores, and they come together in the cytoplasm to form complete ribosomes.

The Endoplasmic Reticulum and Golgi Apparatus

The remainder of the cell, between the nucleus and the cell membrane, is the cytoplasm. In all cells, the cytoplasm contains a watery mixture of ions, enzymes, RNA, and other dissolved substances. In eukaryotes, the cytoplasm also includes organelles and arrays of protein rods and tubules called the cytoskeleton (see section 3.5).

Once in the cytoplasm, mRNA coming from the nucleus binds to a ribosome, which manufactures proteins (see figure 3.13, step 3). Ribosomes that produce proteins for use inside the cell are free-floating in the cytoplasm (figure 3.15a). But many proteins are destined for the cell membrane or for secretion (in milk,

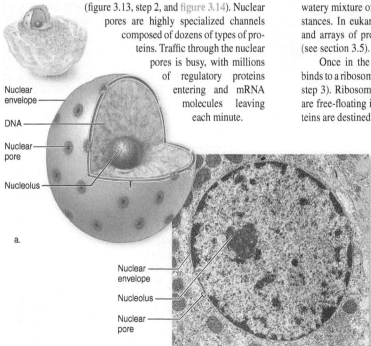

Nuclear envelope

DNA

Nuclear pore

Nucleolus

a.

Nuclear envelope

Nucleolus

Nuclear pore

b.   TEM (false color)   2 μm

Figure 3.14 **The Nucleus.** (a) The nucleus contains DNA and is surrounded by two membrane layers, which make up the nuclear envelope. Large pores in the nuclear envelope allow proteins to enter and mRNA molecules to leave the nucleus. (b) This transmission electron micrograph shows the nuclear envelope and nucleolus.

for example). In that case, the entire complex of ribosome, mRNA, and partially made protein anchors to the membrane of the endoplasmic reticulum (see figure 3.15b).

The **endoplasmic reticulum (ER)** is a network of sacs and tubules composed of membranes (figure 3.16). This complex organelle originates at the nuclear envelope and winds throughout the cell (*endoplasmic* means "within the cytoplasm," and *reticulum* means "network"). Close to the nucleus, the membrane surface is studded with ribosomes making proteins that enter the inner compartment of the ER (see figure 3.15b). This section of the network is called the **rough ER** because the ribosomes give these membranes a roughened appearance.

Adjacent to the rough ER, a section of the network called the **smooth ER** synthesizes lipids—such as those that will end up in the milk—and other membrane components (see figure 3.13, step 4, and figure 3.16). The smooth ER also houses enzymes that detoxify drugs and poisons. In muscle cells, a specialized type of smooth ER stores and delivers the calcium ions required for muscle contraction. ⓘ *muscle function*, p. 600

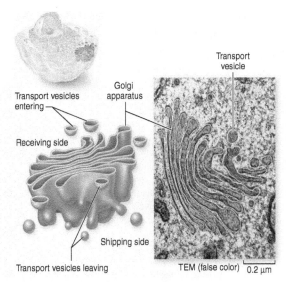

Figure 3.17 **The Golgi Apparatus.** The Golgi apparatus consists of a series of flattened sacs, plus transport vesicles that deliver and remove materials. Proteins are sorted and processed as they move through the Golgi apparatus on their way to the cell surface or to a lysosome.

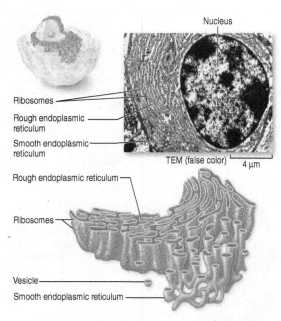

Figure 3.16 **Rough and Smooth Endoplasmic Reticulum.** The endoplasmic reticulum is a network of membranes extending from the nuclear envelope. Ribosomes dot the surface of the rough ER, giving it a "rough" appearance. The smooth ER is a series of interconnecting tubules and is the site for lipid production and other metabolic processes.

The lipids and proteins made by the ER exit the organelle in vesicles. A loaded transport vesicle pinches off from the tubular endings of the ER membrane (see figure 3.13, step 5) and takes its contents to the next stop in the production line, the **Golgi apparatus** (figure 3.17). This organelle is a stack of flat, membrane-enclosed sacs that functions as a processing center. Proteins from the ER pass through the series of Golgi sacs, where they complete their intricate folding and become functional (see figure 3.13, step 6). Enzymes in the Golgi apparatus also manufacture and attach carbohydrates to proteins or lipids, forming glycoproteins or glycolipids.

The Golgi apparatus sorts and packages materials into vesicles, which move toward the cell membrane. Some of the proteins it receives from the ER will become membrane surface proteins; other substances (such as milk protein and fat) are packaged for secretion from the cell. In the production of milk, these vesicles fuse with the cell membrane and release the proteins outside the cell (see figure 3.13, step 7). The fat droplets stay suspended in the watery milk because they retain a layer of surrounding membrane when they leave the cell.

This entire process happens simultaneously in countless specialized cells lining the milk ducts of the breast, beginning shortly after a baby's birth. When the infant suckles, hormones released in the mother's body stimulate muscles surrounding balls of these cells to contract, squeezing milk into the ducts that lead to the nipple.

B. Lysosomes, Vacuoles, and Peroxisomes Are Cellular Digestion Centers

Besides producing molecules for export, eukaryotic cells also break down molecules in specialized compartments. All of these "digestion center" organelles are sacs surrounded by a single membrane.

Lysosomes   **Lysosomes** are organelles containing enzymes that dismantle and recycle food particles, captured bacteria, worn-out organelles, and debris (figure 3.18). They are so named because their enzymes lyse, or cut apart, their substrates.

The rough ER manufactures the enzymes inside lysosomes. The Golgi apparatus detects these enzymes by recognizing a sugar attached to them, then packages them into vesicles that eventually become lysosomes. The lysosomes, in turn, fuse with transport vesicles carrying debris from outside or from within the cell. The enzymes inside the lysosome break down the large organic molecules into smaller subunits by hydrolysis, releasing them into the cytoplasm for the cell to use.

What keeps a lysosome from digesting the entire cell? The lysosome's membrane maintains the pH of the organelle's interior at about 4.8, much more acidic than the neutral pH of the rest of the cytoplasm. If one lysosome were to burst, the liberated enzymes would no longer be at their optimum pH, so they could not digest the rest of the cell. Nevertheless, a cell injured by extreme cold, heat, or another physical stress may initiate its own death by bursting all of its lysosomes at once. ⓘ *pH*, p. 29; *cell death*, p. 162

Some cells have more lysosomes than others. White blood cells, for example, have many lysosomes because these cells engulf and dispose of debris and bacteria. Liver cells also require many lysosomes to process cholesterol.

Malfunctioning lysosomes can cause illness. In Tay-Sachs disease, for example, a defective lysosomal enzyme allows a lipid to accumulate to toxic levels in nerve cells of the brain. The nervous system deteriorates, and an affected person eventually becomes unable to see, hear, or move. In the most severe forms of the illness, death usually occurs by age 5.

Vacuoles   Most plant cells lack lysosomes, but they do have an organelle that serves a similar function. In mature plant cells, the large central **vacuole** contains a watery solution of enzymes that degrade and recycle molecules and organelles (see figure 3.8).

The vacuole also has other roles. Most of the growth of a plant cell comes from an increase in the volume of its vacuole. In some plant cells, the vacuole occupies up to 90% of the cell's volume (figure 3.19). As the vacuole acquires water, it exerts pressure (called turgor pressure) against the cell membrane. Turgor pressure helps plants stay rigid and upright.

Besides water and enzymes, the vacuole also contains a variety of salts, sugars, and weak acids. Therefore, the pH of the vacuole's solution is usually somewhat acidic. In citrus fruits, the solution is very acidic, producing the tart taste of lemons and oranges. Water-soluble pigments also reside in the vacuole, producing blue, purple, and magenta colors in some leaves, flowers, and fruits.

Some protists have vacuoles, although their function is different from that in plants. The contractile vacuole in *Paramecium*, for example, pumps excess water out of the cell. In *Amoeba*, food vacuoles digest nutrients that the cell has engulfed.

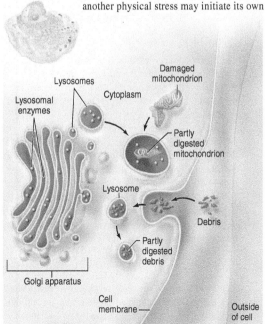

Figure 3.18 Lysosomes. Lysosomes contain enzymes that dismantle damaged organelles and other debris, then release the nutrients for the cell to use.

Animation Lysosomes

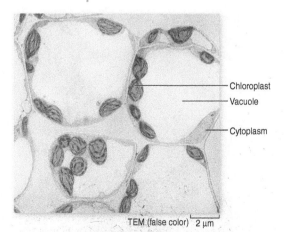

Figure 3.19 Vacuole. Much of the volume of a spinach leaf cell is occupied by the large central vacuole. The cytoplasm (containing numerous chloroplasts) is confined to the edges of the cell.

Peroxisomes All eukaryotic cells contain **peroxisomes,** organelles that contain several types of enzymes that dispose of toxic substances. Although they resemble lysosomes in size and function, peroxisomes originate at the ER (not the Golgi) and contain different enzymes. In some peroxisomes, the concentration of enzymes reaches such high levels that the proteins condense into easily recognized crystals (figure 3.20).

The peroxisome's name comes from one of its roles in protecting the cell. Some chemical reactions in the peroxisome produce hydrogen peroxide, H_2O_2. This highly reactive compound can produce oxygen free radicals that can damage the cell. To counteract the free-radical buildup, peroxisomes contain an enzyme that detoxifies H_2O_2 and produces harmless water molecules in its place.

Peroxisomes in liver and kidney cells help dismantle toxins from the blood. Peroxisomes also break down fatty acids and produce cholesterol and some other lipids. In a disease called adrenoleukodystrophy (ALD), a faulty enzyme causes fatty acids to accumulate to toxic levels in the brain, causing severe brain damage and eventually death.

C. Mitochondria Extract Energy from Nutrients

Growth, cell division, protein production, secretion, and many chemical reactions in the cytoplasm all require a steady supply of energy. **Mitochondria** (singular: mitochondrion) are organelles that use a process called cellular respiration to extract this needed energy from food (see chapter 6). With the exception of a few types of protists, all eukaryotic cells have mitochondria.

A mitochondrion has two membrane layers: an outer membrane and an intricately folded inner membrane that encloses the mitochondrial matrix (figure 3.21). Within the matrix is DNA

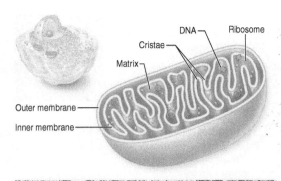

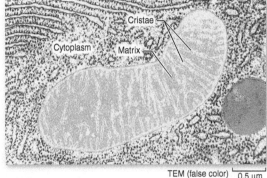

Figure 3.21 **Mitochondria.** Cellular respiration occurs inside mitochondria. Each mitochondrion contains a highly folded inner membrane, where many of the reactions of cellular respiration occur.

that encodes proteins essential for mitochondrial function; ribosomes occupy the matrix as well. **Cristae** are the folds of the inner membrane. The cristae add tremendous surface area to the inner membrane, which houses the enzymes that catalyze the reactions of cellular respiration.

In most mammals, mitochondria are inherited from the female parent only. (This is because the mitochondria in a sperm cell degenerate after fertilization.) Mitochondrial DNA is therefore useful for tracking inheritance through female lines in a family. For the same reason, genetic mutations that cause defective mitochondria also pass only from mother to offspring. Mitochondrial illnesses are most serious when they affect the muscles or brain, because these energy-hungry organs depend on the functioning of many thousands of mitochondria in every cell.

D. Photosynthesis Occurs in Chloroplasts

Plants and many protists carry out photosynthesis, a process that uses energy from sunlight to produce glucose and other food molecules (see chapter 5). These nutrients sustain not only the photosynthetic organisms but also the consumers (including humans) that eat them.

The **chloroplast** (figure 3.22) is the site of photosynthesis in eukaryotes. Each chloroplast contains multiple membrane layers. Two outer membrane layers enclose an enzyme-rich fluid called

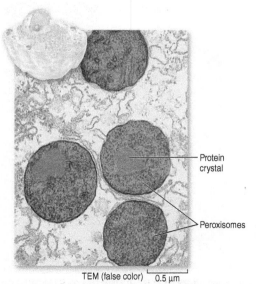

Figure 3.20 **Peroxisomes.** Protein crystals give peroxisomes their characteristic appearance in an animal cell.

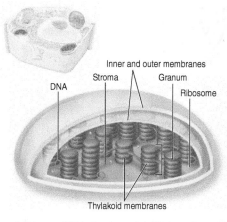

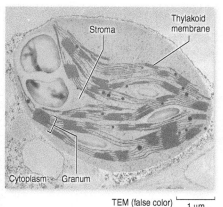

Figure 3.22 Chloroplasts. Photosynthesis occurs inside chloroplasts. Each chloroplast contains stacks of thylakoids that form the grana within the inner compartment, the stroma. Enzymes and light-harvesting pigments embedded in the membranes of the thylakoids convert sunlight to chemical energy.

the stroma. Within the stroma is a third membrane system folded into flattened sacs called thylakoids, which are stacked and interconnected in structures called grana. Photosynthetic pigments such as chlorophyll are embedded in the thylakoids.

A chloroplast is one representative of a larger category of plant organelles called plastids. Some plastids synthesize lipid-soluble red, orange, and yellow carotenoid pigments, such as those found in carrots and ripe tomatoes. Plastids that assemble starch molecules are important in cells specialized for food storage, such as those in potatoes and corn kernels. Interestingly, any plastid can convert into any other type.

Like mitochondria, all plastids (including chloroplasts) contain their own DNA and ribosomes. The genetic material encodes proteins unique to plastid structure and function, including some of the enzymes required for photosynthesis.

The similarities between chloroplasts and mitochondria—both have their own DNA and ribosomes, and both are surrounded by double membranes—provide clues to the origin of eukaryotic cells, an event that apparently occurred about 2.7 billion years ago. According to the endosymbiosis theory, some ancient organism engulfed bacterial cells. Rather than digesting them as food, the host cells kept them on as partners: mitochondria and chloroplasts. The structures and genetic sequences of today's bacteria, mitochondria, and chloroplasts supply powerful evidence for this theory. ⓘ *endosymbiosis*, p. 311

Organelles divide a cell's work, just as departments in a large store group related items together. Some specialty stores, however, sell only shoes or women's clothing. Likewise, cells can also have specialized functions (figure 3.23). For example, a heart muscle cell is roughly cylindrical when compared with a neuron, which produces extensions that touch adjacent nerve cells. A leaf cell is packed with chloroplasts. The protective epidermis of an onion, on the other hand, is dry and tough; because it forms underground, it lacks chloroplasts. Keep these specialized structures and functions in mind as you study cell processes throughout this book.

3.4 MASTERING CONCEPTS

1. How do organelles help eukaryotic cells compensate for a small ratio of surface area to volume?
2. Which parts of a cell interact to produce and secrete a complex substance such as milk?
3. What is the function of the nucleus and its contents?
4. Which organelles are the cell's "recycling centers"?
5. How are the functions of plastids essential to the life of a plant cell?
6. Which organelle houses the reactions that extract chemical energy from nutrient molecules?
7. Which three organelles contain DNA?

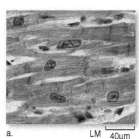

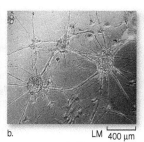

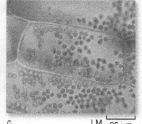

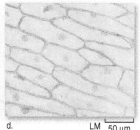

Figure 3.23 Specialized Cells. (a) Muscle cells in the heart are packed with protein-rich fibers that can contract in unison. (b) These highly branched neurons are beginning to form a communication network. (c) The chloroplasts in these leaf cells carry out photosynthesis. (d) The cells of an onion's protective epidermis lack chloroplasts; the onion bulb forms underground, away from light.

3.5 The Cytoskeleton Supports Eukaryotic Cells

The cytoplasm of a eukaryotic cell contains a **cytoskeleton,** an intricate network of protein "tracks" and tubules. The cytoskeleton is a structural framework with many functions. It is a transportation system, and it provides the structural support necessary to maintain the cell's characteristic three-dimensional shape (figure 3.24). It aids in cell division and helps connect cells to one another. The cytoskeleton also enables cells—or parts of a cell—to move.

Given the cytoskeleton's many functions, it is not surprising that defects can cause disease. For example, people with Duchenne muscular dystrophy lack a protein called dystrophin, part of the cytoskeleton in muscle cells. Without dystrophin, muscles—including those in the heart—degenerate. Another faulty cytoskeleton protein, ankyrin, causes a genetic disease of blood. In healthy red blood cells, the cytoskeleton maintains a concave disk shape. When ankyrin is missing, red blood cells are small, fragile, and misshapen, greatly reducing their ability to carry oxygen.

Injuries can also cause serious damage to the cytoskeleton. When a person suffers a strong blow to the head, such as in a fall or an auto accident, the cells that make up the brain can become stretched and distorted. The resulting damage to the cytoskeleton can trigger a chain reaction that ends with the death of the affected brain cells. People with such injuries may recover, but many die, lapse into a coma, or suffer from permanent disabilities (see the opening essay for chapter 26).

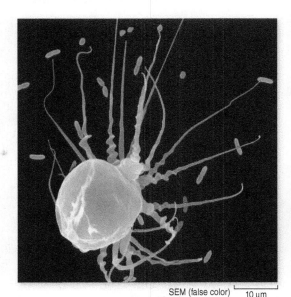

SEM (false color) 10 μm

Figure 3.24 Cellular Architecture. Thanks to its cytoskeleton, this white blood cell can produce long, thin extensions that reach out to and engulf "foreign" substances, including bacteria.

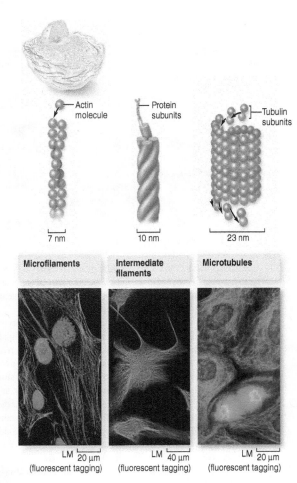

Actin molecule — 7 nm — **Microfilaments**

Protein subunits — 10 nm — **Intermediate filaments**

Tubulin subunits — 23 nm — **Microtubules**

LM 20 μm (fluorescent tagging) LM 40 μm (fluorescent tagging) LM 20 μm (fluorescent tagging)

Figure 3.25 Proteins of the Cytoskeleton. The cytoskeleton includes three types of protein filaments, arranged in this figure from smallest to largest diameter. Arrows indicate protein subunits being added to or removed from microfilaments and microtubules. The photos show actin microfilaments (left, colored red), intermediate filaments (center, colored green), and microtubules (right, colored green).

A. Proteins Form the Cytoskeleton

The cytoskeleton includes three major components: microfilaments, intermediate filaments, and microtubules (figure 3.25). They are distinguished by protein type, diameter, and how they aggregate into larger structures. Other proteins connect these components to one another, creating an intricate meshwork.

The thinnest component of the cytoskeleton is the **microfilament,** a long rod composed of the protein actin. Each microfilament is only about 7 nanometers in diameter. Actin microfilament networks are part of nearly all eukaryotic cells. Muscle contraction, for example, relies on actin filaments and another protein, myosin. Microfilaments also provide strength for cells to survive stretching and compression, and they help to anchor one cell to another (see section 3.6). ⓘ *sliding filaments,* p. 599

Intermediate filaments are so named because their 10-nanometer diameters are intermediate between those of microfilaments and microtubules. Unlike the other components of the cytoskeleton, which consist of a single protein type, intermediate filaments are made of different proteins in each specialized cell type. They maintain a cell's shape by forming an internal scaffold in the cytoplasm and resisting mechanical stress. Intermediate filaments also help bind some cells together (see section 3.6).

A **microtubule** is composed of a protein called tubulin, assembled into a hollow tube 23 nanometers in diameter. The cell can change the length of a microtubule rapidly by adding or removing tubulin molecules. Microtubules have many functions in eukaryotic cells. For example, they form a type of "trackway" along which substances move within a cell. Specialized motor proteins "walk" along the tracks toting their cargo, such as an organelle or vesicle. In addition, chapter 8 describes how microtubules split a cell's duplicated chromosomes apart during cell division.

B. Cilia and Flagella Help Cells Move

In animal cells, structures called **centrosomes** organize the microtubules. (Plants typically lack centrosomes and assemble microtubules at sites scattered throughout the cell.) The centrosome contains two centrioles, which are visible in figure 3.8. The centrioles form the basis of structures called basal bodies, which in turn give rise to the extensions that enable some cells to move: cilia and flagella (figure 3.26).

Cilia are short and numerous, like a fringe. Some protists, such as the *Paramecium* in figure 3.3, have thousands of cilia that enable the cells to "swim" in water. In the human respiratory tract, coordinated movement of cilia sets up a wave that propels particles up and out; other cilia can move an egg cell through the female reproductive tract. ⓘ *ciliates,* p. 371

Unlike cilia, flagella occur singly or in pairs, and a flagellum is much longer than a cilium. Flagella are more like tails, and their whiplike movement propels cells. Sperm cells in many species (including humans) have prominent flagella. A man whose sperm cells have defective flagella is infertile because the sperm are unable to swim to the egg cell.

Figure 3.26 shows the internal microtubules underlying the functions of both cilia and flagella. Inside each appendage's shaft, a protein called dynein links a ring of outer microtubule pairs to a central pair, a little like a wheel. Dynein molecules shift in a way that slides adjacent microtubules against each other. This movement bends the appendage from side to side. (The bacterial flagellum has a different structure.)

3.5   MASTERING CONCEPTS

1. What are some functions of the cytoskeleton?
2. What are the main components of the cytoskeleton?
3. Why are flagella and cilia important?

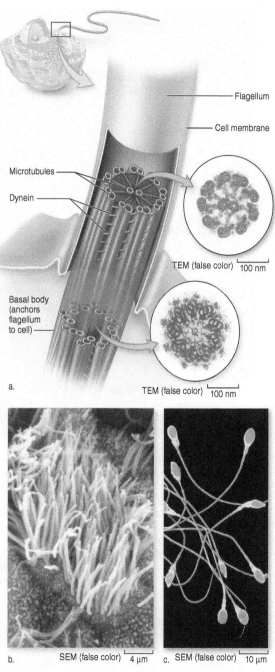

Flagellum

Cell membrane

Microtubules

Dynein

TEM (false color)   100 nm

Basal body (anchors flagellum to cell)

a.

TEM (false color)   100 nm

b.   SEM (false color)   4 μm   c.   SEM (false color)   10 μm

Figure 3.26 Microtubules Move Cells. (a) Cilia and eukaryotic flagella contain microtubules, as does the anchoring basal body. (b) These cilia line the human respiratory tract, where their coordinated movements propel dust particles upward so the person can expel them. (c) Flagella enable mature human sperm cells to swim.

3.6 Cells Stick Together and Communicate with One Another

So far, this chapter has described individual cells. But multicellular organisms, including plants and animals, are made of many cells that work together. How do these cells adhere to one another so that your body—or that of a plant—doesn't disintegrate in a heavy rain? Also, how do cells in direct contact with one another communicate to coordinate development and respond to the environment?

This section describes how the cells of animal and plant tissues stick together and how neighboring cells share signals. Table 3.2 lists the types of cell–cell connections for animals and plants.

A. Animal Cell Junctions Occur in Several Forms

Unlike plants and fungi, animal cells lack cell walls. Instead, many animal cells secrete a complex extracellular matrix that holds them together and coordinates many aspects of cellular life. In such tissues, cells are not in direct contact with one another. ⓘ *extracellular matrix*, p. 522

In other tissues, however, the plasma membranes of adjacent cells directly connect to one another via several types of junctions (figure 3.27): tight junctions, anchoring junctions, and gap junctions.

A **tight junction** fuses cells together, forming an impermeable barrier between them. Proteins anchored in membranes connect to actin in the cytoskeleton and join cells into sheets, such as those lining the inside of the human digestive tract and the tubules of the kidneys. These connections allow the body to control where biochemicals move, since fluids cannot leak between the joined cells. For example, tight junctions prevent stomach acid from seeping into the tissues surrounding the stomach. Likewise, tight junctions create the "blood–brain barrier," densely packed cells that prevent many harmful substances from entering the brain. However, this barrier readily admits lipid-soluble drugs such as heroin and cocaine across its cell membranes, accounting for the rapid action of these drugs.

A second type of animal cell junction, an **anchoring** (or **adhering) junction,** connects a cell to its neighbors or to the extracellular matrix, somewhat like a rivet. Protein complexes at each anchoring junction span the cell membrane and link to each cell's cytoskeleton. These junctions hold skin cells in place by anchoring them to the extracellular matrix.

A **gap junction** is a protein channel that links the cytoplasm of adjacent cells, allowing exchange of ions, nutrients, and other small molecules. Gap junctions link heart muscle cells to one another, allowing groups of cells to contract together. Similarly, the muscle cells that line the digestive tract coordinate their contractions to propel food along its journey, courtesy of countless gap junctions.

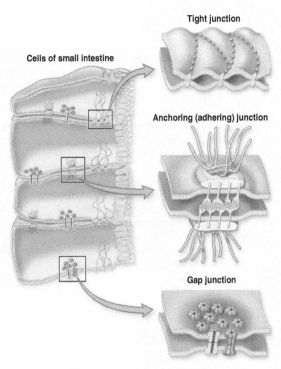

Figure 3.27 Animal Cell Connections. Tight junctions fuse neighboring cell membranes, anchoring junctions connect adjacent cells in one place, and gap junctions allow small molecules to move from cell to cell.

B. Cell Walls Are Strong, Flexible, and Porous

Cell walls surround the cell membranes of nearly all bacteria, archaea, fungi, algae, and plants. But *cell wall* is a misleading term: it is not just a barrier that outlines the cell. Cell walls impart shape, regulate cell volume, prevent bursting when a cell takes in too much water, and interact with other molecules to help determine how a cell in a complex organism specializes. In plants, for example, a given cell may become a root, shoot, or leaf, depending on which cell walls it touches.

Many materials may make up a cell wall. Bacterial cell walls, for example, are composed of peptidoglycan, whereas those of fungi contain chitin. Much of the plant cell wall consists of cellulose molecules aligned into microfibrils, which in turn aggregate and twist to form larger fibrils (figure 3.28). This fibrous organization imparts great strength. Other molecules, including the polysaccharides hemicellulose and pectin, glue adjacent cells together and add strength and flexibility. Plant cell walls also contain glycoproteins, enzymes, and many other proteins. ⓘ *cellulose*, p. 31

A plant cell secretes many of the components of its wall from the inside. The oldest layer of a cell wall is therefore on the exterior of the cell, and the newer layers hug the cell membrane. The region where adjacent cell walls meet is called the middle lamella.

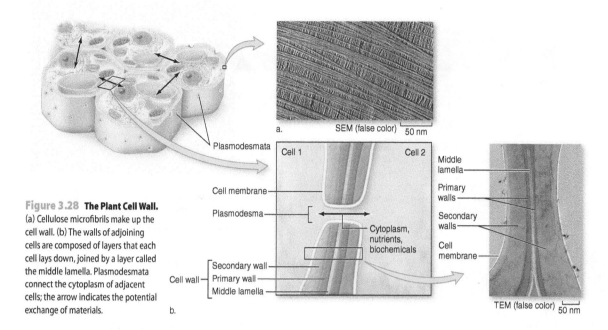

Figure 3.28 The Plant Cell Wall. (a) Cellulose microfibrils make up the cell wall. (b) The walls of adjoining cells are composed of layers that each cell lays down, joined by a layer called the middle lamella. Plasmodesmata connect the cytoplasm of adjacent cells; the arrow indicates the potential exchange of materials.

Some cells have rigid secondary cell walls beneath the initial, more flexible primary one (see figure 3.28b). The secondary cell wall typically supports plant cells that are no longer growing. For example, the tough texture of walnut shells, wood, apple cores, and other durable plant parts comes from their thick secondary cell walls. In addition to cellulose and other polysaccharides, the secondary cell wall includes lignin. This strong, rigid polymer is so complex that only a few types of organisms can break it down.

How do plant cells communicate with their neighbors through the wall? **Plasmodesmata** (singular: plasmodesma) are channels that connect adjacent cells. They are essentially "tunnels" in the cell wall, through which the cytoplasm, hormones, and some of the organelles of one plant cell can interact with those of another (see figure 3.28). Plasmodesmata are especially plentiful in parts of plants that conduct water or nutrients and in cells that secrete oils and nectars.

Like the gap junctions of animal cells, plasmodesmata enable cell-to-cell communication and coordination of function within a plant. Plasmodesmata, however, may also play a role in the spread of disease within a plant; viruses use them as conduits to pass from cell to cell.

We have now completed our tour of the eukaryotic cell. Table 3.3 (on page 66) summarizes the structures and functions of the main organelles and other structures in the cells of both animals and plants.

3.6 MASTERING CONCEPTS

1. What are the three types of junctions that link cells in animals?
2. What are the functions of a cell wall?
3. What is the chemical composition of a plant cell wall?
4. What are plasmodesmata?

TABLE **3.2**   **Intercellular Junctions: A Summary**

Type	Function	Example of Location
Animal cells		
Tight junctions	Close the spaces between animal cells by fusing cell membranes	Cells in inner lining of small intestine
Anchoring (adhering) junctions	Connect adjacent animal cell membranes in one spot	Cells in outer skin layer
Gap junctions	Form channels between animal cells, allowing exchange of substances	Muscle cells in heart and digestive tract
Plant cells		
Plasmodesmata	Allow substances to move between plant cells	Plant cell walls

TABLE **3.3**   **Structures in Eukaryotic Cells: A Summary**

Structure		Description	Function(s)	Plant Cells?	Animal Cells?
Nucleus	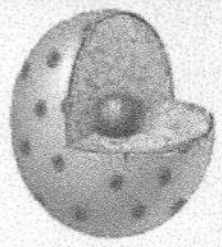	Perforated sac containing DNA, proteins, and RNA; surrounded by double membrane	Separates DNA from rest of cell; site of first step in protein synthesis; nucleolus produces ribosomal subunits	Yes	Yes
Ribosome		Two globular subunits composed of RNA and protein	Location of protein synthesis	Yes	Yes
Rough endoplasmic reticulum	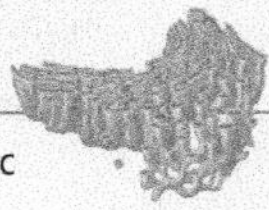	Membrane network studded with ribosomes	Produces proteins destined for secretion from the cell	Yes	Yes
Smooth endoplasmic reticulum		Membrane network lacking ribosomes	Synthesizes lipids; detoxifies drugs and poisons	Yes	Yes
Golgi apparatus	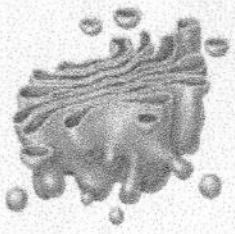	Stacks of flat, membranous sacs	Packages materials to be secreted; produces lysosomes	Yes	Yes
Lysosome		Sac containing digestive enzymes; surrounded by single membrane	Dismantles and recycles components of food, debris, captured bacteria, and worn-out organelles	Rarely	Yes
Central vacuole		Sac containing enzymes, acids, water-soluble pigments, and other solutes; surrounded by single membrane	Produces turgor pressure; recycles cell contents; contains pigments	Yes	No
Peroxisome		Sac containing enzymes, often forming visible protein crystals; surrounded by single membrane	Disposes of toxins; breaks down fatty acids; eliminates hydrogen peroxide	Yes	Yes
Chloroplast	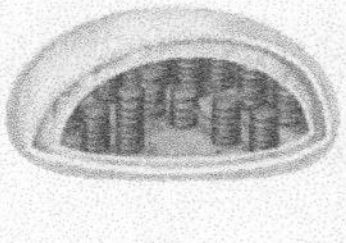	Two membranes enclosing stacks of membrane sacs, which contain photosynthetic pigments and enzymes; contains DNA and ribosomes	Produces food (sugars) by photosynthesis	Yes	No
Mitochondrion	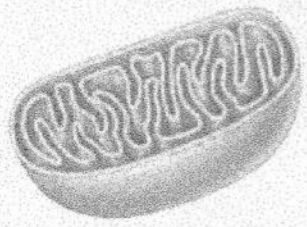	Two membranes; inner membrane is folded into enzyme-studded cristae; contains DNA and ribosomes	Releases energy from food by cellular respiration	Yes	Yes
Cytoskeleton	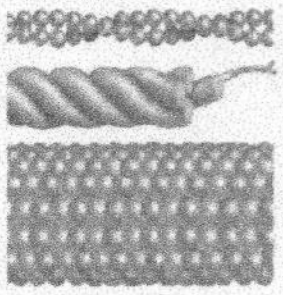	Network of protein filaments and tubules	Transports organelles within cell; maintains cell shape; basis for flagella/cilia; connects adjacent cells	Yes	Yes
Cell wall	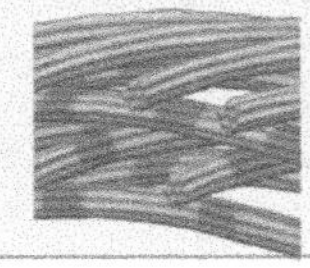	Porous barrier of cellulose and other substances (in plants)	Protects cell; provides shape; connects adjacent cells	Yes	No

INVESTIGATING LIFE

3.7 The Tiniest Compass

Submarine captains steer their vessels through the dark ocean. They could wander in all directions in search of their destination, but that approach wastes time and fuel. Instead, they rely on navigation systems to find their way. Surprisingly, massive ships have something in common with marine bacteria: Compasses guide some of these tiny vessels as well.

Until recently, biologists thought that prokaryotic cells lacked any internal membranes. But microscopes revealed that some bacteria have small lipid bilayer spheres in their cytoplasm. Scientists found high concentrations of magnetic iron crystals within these membrane bubbles and aptly named them "magnetosomes" (figure 3.29). What is the function of these structures?

When scientists found magnetosomes, they already knew that Earth's magnetic field leaves the planet from the southern hemisphere, circles far into space, and returns to Earth in the northern hemisphere. In most parts of the ocean, the magnetic field lines are roughly vertical. Experiments on magnetic bacteria collected from oceans revealed that magnetosomes align with the magnetic field lines and that the bacteria swim either against or with the field.

These studies showed how bacteria respond to magnetism; they did not explain why orienting to magnetic fields is adaptive. A team of four researchers led by Richard Frankel at California Polytechnic State University aimed to answer this question.

The observation that the bacteria do not always swim in the same direction along the magnetic field lines led them to hypothesize that another factor must influence bacterium movement. One clue was that these bacteria cannot survive if oxygen levels are too high or too low. So Frankel and his colleagues devised an experiment to test whether magnetism and oxygen concentration jointly guided bacterial movement.

The scientists put the bacteria in a solution. They then drew the mixture into narrow glass tubes and sealed one end. Within

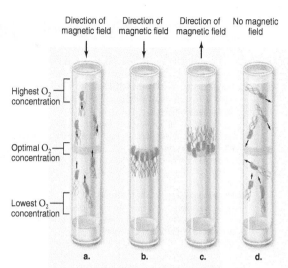

Figure 3.30 Magnetic Orientation. (a) Bacteria with magnetosomes turn toward magnetic fields and (b) move in straight lines toward their optimal oxygen concentration. (c) Switching the direction of the magnetic field rotates the bacteria. (d) Without a magnetic field, bacteria move toward an optimal O_2 concentration but do not take a direct path. Small arrows in (a) and (d) indicate the direction of movement.

each tube, the dissolved oxygen concentration was lowest at the sealed end and increased toward the open end. When the team produced a magnetic field across one of the tubes, all of the bacteria turned toward the field. Some then swam forward, while others moved backward. They aggregated in a distinct band in the center of the tube (figure 3.30). The scientists then switched the direction of the magnetic field. All of the bacteria turned 180°, but none migrated out of the band in the center of the tube.

These results indicate that magnetic fields influence the direction that magnetosome-containing bacteria face, helping the cells follow a straight line through the water. Since the dissolved oxygen concentration decreases with depth, and since Earth's magnetic field runs almost vertically through the water column, bacterial cells use magnetism to find the shortest path toward or away from oxygen. Decreasing the swimming distance saves energy for other cellular tasks, such as reproduction.

Scientists used powerful microscopes and clever experiments to reveal how some bacteria avoid getting lost at sea. Lipid-enclosed magnetosomes guide them like compasses through the deep unknown.

Frankel, Richard B., Dennis A. Bazylinski, Mark S. Johnson, and Barry L. Taylor. 1997. Magneto-aerotaxis in marine coccoid bacteria. *Biophysical Journal*, vol. 73, pages 994–1000.

3.7 MASTERING CONCEPTS

1. How did the researchers determine that both magnetism and oxygen guided bacteria movements?
2. How do magnetosomes help bacteria save energy?

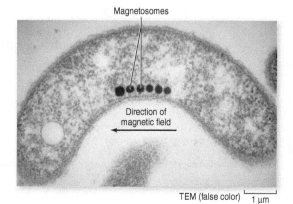

Magnetosomes

Direction of magnetic field

TEM (false color) | 1 μm

Figure 3.29 Magnetosomes. This bacterial cell contains a row of magnetosomes, which are lipid spheres containing iron crystals that align with Earth's magnetic field.

CHAPTER SUMMARY

3.1 Cells Are the Units of Life

- **Cells** are the microscopic components of all organisms.

A. Simple Lenses Revealed the Cellular Basis of Life

- Robert Hooke and Antony van Leeuwenhoek pioneered cell biology.

B. The Cell Theory Emerges

- Schleiden, Schwann, and Virchow's formulation of the **cell theory** states that all life is composed of cells, that cells are the functional units of life, and that all cells come from preexisting cells.
- Contemporary cell biology focuses on the role of genetic information, the cell's chemical components, and the metabolic processes inside cells.

C. Microscopes Magnify Cell Structures

- Light microscopes, transmission electron microscopes, and scanning electron microscopes are essential tools for viewing the parts of a cell.

D. All Cells Have Features in Common

- All cells have DNA, RNA, **ribosomes** that build proteins, **cytoplasm,** and a **cell membrane** that is the interface between the cell and the outside environment (figure 3.31).
- Complex cells also have specialized compartments called **organelles.**
- The surface area of a cell must be large relative to its volume.

3.2 Different Cell Types Characterize Life's Three Domains

- **Prokaryotic** cells lack a nucleus and other organelles; **eukaryotic** cells have a **nucleus** and other organelles. Prokaryotic cells include bacteria and archaea.

A. Domain Bacteria Contains Earth's Most Abundant Organisms

- Bacterial cells are structurally simple, but they are abundant and diverse. Most have a **cell wall** and one or more **flagella.** DNA occurs in an area called the **nucleoid.**

B. Domain Archaea Includes Prokaryotes with Unique Biochemistry

- Archaea share some characteristics with bacteria and eukaryotes but also have unique structures and chemistry.

C. Domain Eukarya Contains Organisms with Complex Cells

- Eukaryotic cells include those of protists, plants, fungi, and animals. Most eukaryotic cells are larger than prokaryotic cells.

	Prokaryote	Eukaryote
Nucleus	No	Yes
Membrane-bounded organelles	No	Yes

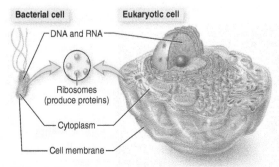

Bacterial cell   **Eukaryotic cell**

DNA and RNA

Ribosomes (produce proteins)

Cytoplasm

Cell membrane

Figure 3.31   Features Present in All Cells.

3.3 A Membrane Separates Each Cell from Its Surroundings

- A biological membrane consists of a **phospholipid bilayer** embedded with movable proteins and sterols, forming a **fluid mosaic.**
- Membrane proteins carry out a variety of functions.

3.4 Eukaryotic Organelles Divide Labor

- The **endomembrane system** includes the nuclear envelope, endoplasmic reticulum, Golgi apparatus, lysosomes, vacuoles, cell membrane, and **vesicles** that transport materials within cells.

A. The Nucleus, Endoplasmic Reticulum, and Golgi Interact to Secrete Substances

- A eukaryotic cell houses DNA in a **nucleus. Nuclear pores** allow the exchange of materials through the two-layered **nuclear envelope;** assembly of the ribosome's subunits occurs in the **nucleolus.**
- The **smooth** and **rough endoplasmic reticulum** and the **Golgi apparatus** work together to synthesize, store, transport, and release molecules.

B. Lysosomes, Vacuoles, and Peroxisomes Are Cellular Digestion Centers

- A eukaryotic cell degrades wastes and digests nutrients in **lysosomes.**
- In plants, a watery **vacuole** degrades wastes, exerts turgor pressure, and stores acids and pigments.
- **Peroxisomes** help digest fatty acids and detoxify many substances.

C. Mitochondria Extract Energy from Nutrients

- **Mitochondria** house the reactions of cellular respiration. The **cristae** (folds) of the inner mitochondrial membrane add surface area.

D. Photosynthesis Occurs in Chloroplasts

- In the cells of plants and algae, **chloroplasts** carry out photosynthesis.

3.5 The Cytoskeleton Supports Eukaryotic Cells

- The **cytoskeleton** is a network of protein rods and tubules that provides cells with form, support, and the ability to move.

A. Proteins Form the Cytoskeleton

- **Microfilaments,** the thinnest components of the cytoskeleton, are composed of the protein actin. **Intermediate filaments** consist of various proteins, and they strengthen the cytoskeleton. **Microtubules** are hollow tubes made of tubulin subunits. They form an internal trackway and include the fibers that move chromosomes during cell division.

B. Cilia and Flagella Help Cells Move

- **Cilia** are short, numerous extensions; flagella are less numerous but much longer. They move when microtubules slide past one another.

3.6 Cells Stick Together and Communicate with One Another

A. Animal Cell Junctions Occur in Several Forms

- **Tight junctions** create a seal between adjacent cells. **Anchoring junctions** secure cells in place. **Gap junctions** allow adjacent cells to exchange signals and cytoplasmic material.

B. Cell Walls Are Strong, Flexible, and Porous

- Cell walls provide protection and shape. Plant cell walls consist of cellulose fibrils connected by hemicellulose, pectin, and various proteins.
- **Plasmodesmata** are pores extending between adjacent plant cell walls.

3.7 Investigating Life: The Tiniest Compass

- Some bacteria contain magnetosomes, specialized structures that help the cells navigate vertically in the water column. This adaptation boosts their efficiency in finding the optimal concentration of oxygen.

MULTIPLE CHOICE QUESTIONS

1. Which of the following is NOT a feature found in all cells?
   a. Proteins
   c. Cell wall
   b. Ribosomes
   d. Cell membrane

2. One property that distinguishes cells in domain Bacteria from those in domain Eukarya is the presence of
   a. a cell wall.
   c. flagella.
   b. DNA.
   d. membranous organelles.

3. What chemical property of phospholipids is key to the formation of the cell membrane?
   a. The positively charged nitrogen atom
   b. The covalent bond between the phosphate and the glycerol
   c. The kink in the fatty acid tail
   d. The hydrophilic head and hydrophobic tails

4. Which of the following organelles are associated with the job of cellular digestion?
   a. Lysosomes and peroxisomes
   b. Golgi apparatus and vesicles
   c. Nucleus and nucleolus
   d. Smooth and rough endoplasmic reticulum

5. Within a single cell, which of the following is physically the smallest?
   a. Nuclear envelope
   c. Cell membrane
   b. Phospholipid molecule
   d. Mitochondrion

6. Which of the following organelles does NOT contain DNA?
   a. Nucleus
   b. Chloroplast
   c. Rough endoplasmic reticulum
   d. Mitochondrion

7. Which of the following statements about plasmodesmata is true?
   a. They prevent cytoplasm from passing between cells.
   b. They are important in the formation of tight junctions.
   c. They may float freely in the cytoplasm or be membrane-bound.
   d. They allow adjacent plant cells to communicate with each other.

Answers to these questions are in appendix A.

WRITE IT OUT

1. How does the formation of the cell theory illustrate the process of science?

2. List the features that all cells share, then name three structures found in eukaryotic cells but not in bacteria or archaea.

3. If a eukaryotic cell is like a house, how is a prokaryotic cell like an efficiency (one-room) apartment?

4. List three structural differences between plant and animal cells. Explain how each structural difference reflects a functional difference between plants and animals.

5. Suppose you find a sample of cells at a crime scene. What criteria might you use to determine if the cells are from prokaryotes, plants, or animals?

6. Rank the following in order from smallest to largest: ant, prokaryotic cell, actin molecule, microtubule, nitrogen atom. What type of microscope (if any) would you need if you wanted to see each?

7. Which cell in figure 3.31 has the highest ratio of surface area to volume? Explain your answer.

8. What advantages does compartmentalization confer on a large cell?

9. List the chemicals that make up cell membranes.

10. Emulsifiers are common food additives. A typical emulsifier molecule has a hydrophilic end and a hydrophobic end. Draw a diagram explaining how an emulsifier can enable oil to mix with water.

11. Choose an organelle in a human cell, and imagine that a disease causes that organelle to be faulty. How would the malfunctioning organelle affect the cell's function?

12. One way to understand cell function is to compare the parts of a cell to the parts of a factory. For example, the Golgi apparatus would be analogous to the factory's shipping department. How would the other cell parts fit into this analogy?

13. Why does a muscle cell contain many mitochondria and a white blood cell (an immune cell that engulfs bacteria) contain many lysosomes?

14. How does the cytoskeleton interact with other structures in eukaryotic cells?

15. How do plant cells form cell walls?

16. Describe how animal cells use junctions in different ways.

PULL IT TOGETHER

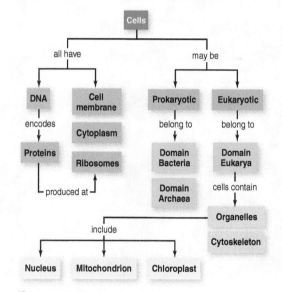

Figure 3.32 Pull It Together: Cells.

Refer to figure 3.32 and the chapter content to answer the following questions.

1. How might you connect the terms *proteins* and *cytoskeleton*?

2. Add the three main components of the cytoskeleton to this map.

3. In what ways are domains Bacteria and Archaea different?

4. Add the eukaryotic kingdoms to this concept map.

5. Add *chloroplast, lysosome,* and *vacuole* to this concept map.

6. Which cell types have a cell wall?

CHAPTER

4 The Energy of Life

Exercise on Wheels. Riding a bicycle up a hill takes energy, which comes from metabolic reactions inside cells.

Enhance your study |BIOLOGY
of this chapter with practice quizzes,
animations and videos, answer keys,
and downloadable study tools.
www.mhhe.com/hoefnagels

Whole-Body Metabolism: Energy on an Organismal Level

"I WISH I HAD YOUR METABOLISM!" Perhaps you have overheard a calorie-counting friend make a similar comment to someone who stays slim on a diet of fattening foods.

In that context, the word *metabolism* means how fast a person burns food. But biochemists define metabolism as all of the chemical reactions that build and break down molecules within any cell. How are these two meanings related?

Interlocking networks of metabolic reactions supply the energy that every cell needs to stay alive. In humans, teams of metabolizing cells perform specialized functions such as digestion, muscle movement, hormone production, and countless other activities. It all takes a reliable energy supply—food, which we "burn" at an ever-changing rate.

Minimally, a body needs energy to maintain heartbeat, temperature, breathing, brain activity, and other basic life requirements. For an adult human male, the average energy use is 1750 Calories in 24 hours; for a female, 1450 Calories. These numbers do not include the energy required for physical activity or digestion, so the number of Calories needed to get through a day generally exceeds the minimum requirement.

Of course, these averages mask the fact that people have different metabolic rates. Age, sex, weight, and activity level all influence metabolic rates, as does body fat composition. All other things being equal, a person with the most lean tissue (muscle, nerve, liver, and kidney) will have the highest metabolic rate, because lean tissue consumes more energy than relatively inactive fat tissue. A thyroid hormone, thyroxine, also influences energy expenditure.

So why *do* some people gain weight? The simple answer is that if you eat more Calories than you spend, you gain weight. A typical food plan for a healthy, active adult includes 2000 Calories per day. By comparison, a single fast-food meal of a burger, large fries, and a chocolate shake may contain nearly 2500 Calories. These foods are inexpensive and easy to find, and it is hard to exercise enough to offset a steady diet of energy-rich foods. It is little wonder that Americans are facing an obesity epidemic.

On the other hand, if you eat fewer Calories than you spend, you slim down. This is why reducing caloric intake and exercising are two basic weight-loss recommendations. Unfortunately, metabolic differences make it difficult to translate this simple energy balance into a one-size-fits-all weight-loss plan.

This chapter describes the fundamentals of metabolism, including how cells organize, regulate, and fuel the chemical reactions that sustain life.

LEARN HOW TO LEARN
Focus on Understanding, Not Memorizing

When you are learning the language of biology, be sure to concentrate on how each new term fits with the others. Are you studying multiple components of a complex system? Different steps in a process? The levels of a hierarchy? As you study, always make sure you can see how each part relates to the whole.

4.1 All Cells Capture and Use Energy

You're running late. You overslept, you have no time for breakfast, and you have a full morning of classes. You rummage through your cupboard and find something called an "energy bar"—just what you need to get through the morning. But what is energy?

A. Energy Allows Cells to Do Life's Work

Physicists define **energy** as the ability to do work—that is, to move matter. This idea, abstract as it sounds, is fundamental to biology. Life depends on rearranging atoms and trafficking substances across membranes in precise ways. These intricate movements represent work, and they require energy.

Although it may seem strange to think of a "working" cell, all organisms do tremendous amounts of work on a microscopic scale. For example, a plant cell assembles glucose molecules into long cellulose fibers, moves ions across its membranes, and performs thousands of other tasks simultaneously. A gazelle grazes on a plant's tissues to acquire energy that will enable it to do its own cellular work. A crocodile eats that gazelle for the same reason.

The total amount of energy in any object is the sum of energy's two forms: potential and kinetic (figure 4.1 and table 4.1). **Potential energy** is stored energy available to do work. A bicyclist at the top of a hill illustrates potential energy. Similarly, unburned gasoline—like that energy bar you grabbed—contains potential energy stored in the chemical bonds of its molecules. A chemical gradient is another form of potential energy (see section 4.5).

Kinetic energy is energy being used to do work; any moving object possesses this form of energy. The bicyclist coasting down the hill in figure 4.1 demonstrates kinetic energy, as do moving pistons, a rolling bus, and contracting muscles. Light and sound are other types of kinetic energy. Inside a cell, each molecule also has kinetic energy; in fact, all of the chemical reactions that sustain life rely on collisions between moving molecules, and many substances enter and leave cells by random motion alone.

TABLE 4.1   Examples of Energy in Biology

Type of Energy	Examples
Potential energy	Chemical energy (stored in bonds)
	Concentration gradient across a membrane
Kinetic energy	Light
	Sound
	Movement of atoms and molecules
	Muscle contraction

Calories are units used to measure energy. One **calorie** (cal) is the amount of energy required to raise the temperature of 1 gram of water from 14.5°C to 15.5°C. The most common unit for measuring the energy content of food, however, is the **kilocalorie** (kcal), which equals 1000 calories. (In nutrition, one food Calorie—with a capital C—is actually a kilocalorie.) A typical energy bar, for example, contains 240 kilocalories of potential energy stored in the chemical bonds of its ingredients: mostly carbohydrates, proteins, and fats.

B. The Laws of Thermodynamics Describe Energy Transfer

Thermodynamics is the study of energy transformations. The first and second laws of thermodynamics describe the energy conversions vital for life, as well as those that occur in the nonliving world. They apply to all energy transformations—gasoline combustion in a car's engine, a burning chunk of wood, or a cell breaking down glucose.

The **first law of thermodynamics** is the law of energy conservation. It states that energy cannot be created or destroyed, although energy can be converted to other forms. This means that the total amount of energy in the universe is constant.

Every aspect of life centers on converting energy from one form to another (figure 4.2). The most important energy transformations are photosynthesis and cellular respiration. In photosynthesis, plants and some microorganisms use carbon dioxide, water, and the kinetic energy in sunlight to produce sugars that are

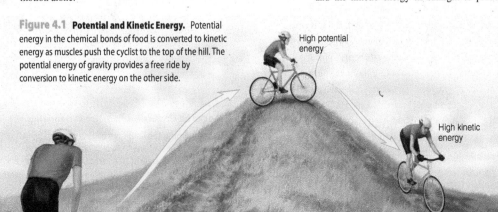

Figure 4.1   Potential and Kinetic Energy. Potential energy in the chemical bonds of food is converted to kinetic energy as muscles push the cyclist to the top of the hill. The potential energy of gravity provides a free ride by conversion to kinetic energy on the other side.

High potential energy

High kinetic energy

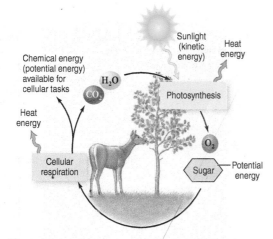

Figure 4.2 Energy Can Take Many Forms. In photosynthesis, plants transform the kinetic energy in sunlight into potential energy stored in the chemical bonds of sugars and other organic molecules. Respiration, in turn, releases this potential energy. Heat energy is lost at every step along the way.

Animation
Energy
Conversions

assembled into glucose and other carbohydrates. These molecules contain potential energy in their chemical bonds. During cellular respiration, the energy-rich glucose molecules change back to carbon dioxide and water, liberating the energy necessary to power life. Cells translate the potential energy in glucose into the kinetic energy of molecular motion and use that burst of kinetic energy to do work.

Most organisms obtain energy from the sun, either directly through photosynthesis or indirectly by consuming other organisms. Even the potential energy in fossil fuels originated as solar energy. However, a few types of microbes can extract potential energy from the chemical bonds of inorganic chemicals; they use the energy to produce organic compounds, which are nutrients for their cells (and for the organisms that consume them).

The **second law of thermodynamics** states that all energy transformations are inefficient because every reaction loses some energy to the surroundings as heat. If you eat your energy bar on the way to your first class, your cells can use the potential energy in its chemical bonds to make proteins, divide, or do other forms of work. According to the second law of thermodynamics, however, you will lose some energy as heat with every chemical reaction. This process is irreversible; the lost heat energy will not return to a useful form.

Heat energy is disordered because it results from random molecular movements. Because heat is disordered, and all energy eventually becomes heat, it follows that all energy transformations must head toward increasing disorder. **Entropy** is a measure of this randomness. In general, the more disordered a system is, the higher its entropy (figure 4.3).

Because organisms are highly organized, they may seem to defy the second law of thermodynamics. But organisms are not closed systems. Instead, a constant stream of incoming energy and matter allows organisms to maintain their organization and stay alive. The second law of thermodynamics implies that organisms can increase in complexity *as long as something else decreases in complexity by a greater amount.* Ultimately, life remains ordered and complex because the sun is constantly supplying energy to Earth. But the entropy of the universe as a whole, including the sun, is always increasing.

The ideas in this chapter and the two that follow describe how organisms acquire and use the energy they need to sustain life.

4.1 MASTERING CONCEPTS

1. What are some examples of the "work" of a cell?
2. Give an example of how your body has both potential and kinetic energy.
3. What are the first and second laws of thermodynamics?
4. Why does the amount of entropy in the universe always increase?

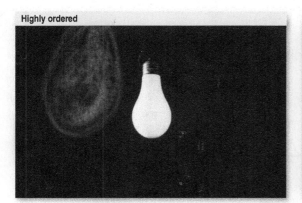

Highly ordered

Highly disordered

Figure 4.3 Entropy. In an instant, a highly organized light bulb is transformed into broken glass and metal fragments. Entropy has irreversibly increased; no matter how many times you drop the glass and metal, the pieces will not arrange themselves back into a light bulb.

4.2 Networks of Chemical Reactions Sustain Life

The number of chemical reactions occurring in even the simplest cell is staggering. Thousands of reactants and products form interlocking pathways that resemble complicated road maps.

The word **metabolism** encompasses all of these chemical reactions in cells, including those that build new molecules and those that break down existing ones. Each reaction rearranges atoms into new compounds, and each reaction either absorbs or releases energy. Digesting your morning energy bar and using its carbohydrates to fuel muscle movement are part of your metabolism. Photosynthesis and respiration are part of the metabolism of the grass under your feet as you hurry to class.

A. Chemical Reactions Absorb or Release Energy

Biologists group metabolic reactions into two categories based on energy requirements: endergonic and exergonic (figure 4.4).

An **endergonic reaction** requires an input of energy to proceed (the prefix *end-* or *endo-* means "put into"). That is, the products contain more energy than the reactants. Typically, endergonic reactions build complex molecules from simpler components.

The top half of figure 4.4 shows one example of an endergonic reaction: photosynthesis. Glucose ($C_6H_{12}O_6$), the product of photosynthesis, contains more potential energy than do carbon dioxide (CO_2) and water (H_2O), the reactants. The energy source that powers this reaction is sunlight. Another familiar example of an endergonic process is muscle contraction, since muscles contract only with an input of energy.

In contrast, an **exergonic reaction** releases energy (*ex-* or *exo-* means "out of"). The products contain less energy than the reactants. Such reactions break large, complex molecules into their smaller, simpler components. Cellular respiration, the breakdown of glucose to carbon dioxide and water, is an example (see the bottom half of figure 4.4). The products, carbon dioxide and water, contain less energy than glucose. Similarly, your digestive system breaks down an energy bar's protein into individual amino acids. This process also releases energy.

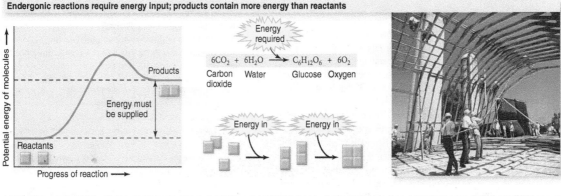

Endergonic reactions require energy input; products contain more energy than reactants

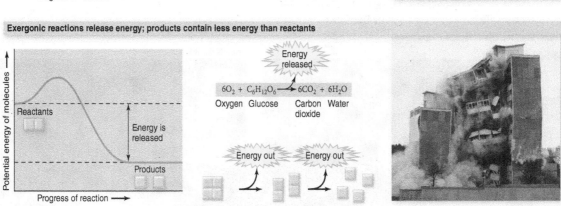

Exergonic reactions release energy; products contain less energy than reactants

Figure 4.4 Endergonic and Exergonic Reactions. Endergonic reactions require an input of energy to build complex molecules from small components, like building a barn from bricks and boards. Exergonic reactions release energy by dismantling complex molecules. Likewise, as an old building collapses into dust and chunks of concrete and steel, it releases energy in the form of sound and heat.

Tutorial Reaction Energetics

Both graphs in figure 4.4 feature a "hump," which represents the amount of potential energy needed to start the reaction in the first place. Note that even exergonic reactions require this initial energy input. Overall, however, exergonic reactions release more energy than the amount they need to get started.

What happens to the energy released in an exergonic reaction? According to the second law of thermodynamics, some is lost as heat; entropy always increases. But some of the energy released can be used to do work. For example, the cell may use the energy to form other bonds or to power other endergonic reactions. As we shall see, life's biochemistry is full of endergonic reactions that proceed at the expense of exergonic ones.

Figure It Out

Complete these sentences by selecting the correct term from each pair of words in parentheses:

In an endergonic reaction, products contain (*less/more*) energy than reactants. Entropy in the universe (*decreases/increases*) through this reaction.

Answers: more; increases.

B. Linked Oxidation and Reduction Reactions Form Electron Transport Chains

Electrons can carry energy. Most energy transformations in organisms occur in **oxidation–reduction ("redox") reactions,** which transfer energized electrons from one molecule to another. (i) *electrons,* p. 20

A redox reaction is similar to a person presenting a gift to a friend (figure 4.5). **Oxidation** means the loss of electrons from a molecule, atom, or ion. In figure 4.5, the electron donor molecule being oxidized is analogous to the gift-giver. Conversely, **reduction** means a gain of electrons; the electron acceptor being reduced is analogous to the woman receiving the package.

Each redox reaction links an exergonic process with an endergonic one. The "oxidation" half is exergonic, since energized electrons are removed from the electron donor. That is, the electron donor has more potential energy before it is oxidized than it does after the reaction is complete. On the other hand, the "reduction" half is endergonic. The acceptor molecule has gained the

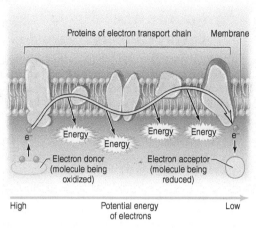

Figure 4.6 Electron Transport Chain. An electron donor molecule transfers an electron to the first protein in an electron transport chain. When the recipient passes the electron to its neighbor, energy is released. The electron continues along the chain, releasing energy at each step, until it reaches a final electron acceptor.

energy-rich electrons, so it ends up with more potential energy than it had before the reaction started.

Oxidations and reductions always occur simultaneously because electrons removed from one molecule during oxidation must join another molecule and reduce it. That is, if one molecule is reduced (gains electrons), then another must be oxidized (lose electrons). Continuing the analogy from figure 4.5, a person can only give a gift if a recipient is willing to accept it.

Of course, the woman receiving the gift is free to either keep the package or pass it on to someone else. Likewise, some molecules act as electron carriers, hanging onto the electrons they receive for a short time before delivering them to another molecule. As you will see in chapters 5 and 6, electron carrier molecules such as NADPH and NADH play key roles in photosynthesis and respiration.

Groups of proteins that are electron-shuttling "specialists" often align in membranes. In an **electron transport chain,** each protein accepts an electron from the molecule before it and passes it to the next, like a bucket brigade (figure 4.6). Since each protein in the chain attracts electrons more strongly than the one before it, each transfer releases a small amount of energy; the cell can use this energy in other reactions. Both photosynthesis and respiration rely on electron transport chains to harvest energy.

4.2 MASTERING CONCEPTS

1. What is metabolism on a cellular level?
2. Distinguish between endergonic and exergonic reactions.
3. What are oxidation and reduction, and why are they always linked?
4. What is an electron transport chain?

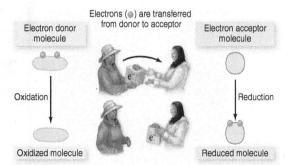

Figure 4.5 Redox Reaction. An electron donor molecule loses electrons and is therefore being oxidized. The molecule that accepts the electrons is being reduced.

4.3 ATP Is Cellular Energy Currency

Tutorial
ATP

All cells contain a maze of interlocking chemical reactions, some releasing energy and others absorbing it. The covalent bonds of **adenosine triphosphate,** a molecule more commonly known as **ATP,** temporarily store much of the released energy. ATP holds energy released in exergonic reactions—such as the digestion of an energy bar—just long enough to power muscle contraction and all other endergonic reactions.

In eukaryotic cells, organelles called mitochondria produce most of a cell's ATP. As you will see in chapter 6, a mitochondrion uses the potential energy in the bonds of one glucose molecule to generate dozens of ATP molecules in cellular respiration. Not surprisingly, the most energy-hungry cells, such as those in the muscles and brain, also contain the most mitochondria.

A. Coupled Reactions Release and Store Energy in ATP

ATP is a type of nucleotide (figure 4.7). Its components are the nitrogen-containing base adenine, the five-carbon sugar ribose, and three phosphate groups (PO_4). Each phosphate group has a negatively charged oxygen atom. The negative charges on neighboring phosphate groups repel one another, making the molecule unstable. It therefore releases energy when the covalent bonds between the phosphates break. ⓘ *nucleotides,* p. 34

All cells depend on the potential energy in ATP to power their activities. When a cell requires energy for an endergonic reaction, it "spends" ATP by removing the endmost phosphate group (figure 4.8). The products of this exergonic hydrolysis reaction are adenosine *di*phosphate (ADP, in which only two phosphate groups remain attached to ribose), the liberated phosphate group, and a burst of energy:

$$ATP + H_2O \longrightarrow ADP + ⓟ + energy$$

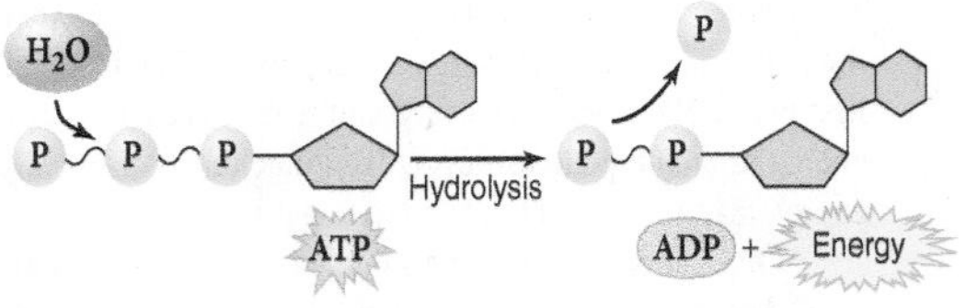

Figure 4.8 ATP Hydrolysis. Removing the endmost phosphate group of ATP yields ADP and a free phosphate group. The cell uses the released energy to do work.

In the reverse situation, energy can be temporarily stored by adding a phosphate to ADP, forming ATP and water:

$$ADP + ⓟ + energy \longrightarrow ATP + H_2O$$

The energy for this endergonic reaction comes from molecules broken down in other reactions, such as those in cellular respiration.

These reactions are fundamental to biology because ATP is the "go-between" that links endergonic to exergonic reactions. **Coupled reactions,** as their name implies, are simultaneous reactions in which one provides the energy that drives the other (figure 4.9). Cells couple the hydrolysis of ATP to endergonic reactions. The ATP hydrolysis reaction drives the endergonic one, which does work or synthesizes new molecules.

How does this coupling work? A cell uses ATP as an energy source by **phosphorylating** (transferring its phosphate group to) another molecule. This transfer may have either of two effects (figure 4.10). In one scenario, the presence of the phosphate may energize the target molecule, making it more likely to bond with other molecules. ATP fuels endergonic reactions in this way. The other possible consequence of phosphorylation is a change in the shape of the target molecule. For example, adding phosphate can force a protein to take a different shape; removing phosphate returns the protein to its original form. Muscle contraction is the large-scale effect of millions of small molecules changing shape, and then changing back again, in a coordinated way. ATP hydrolysis provides the energy.

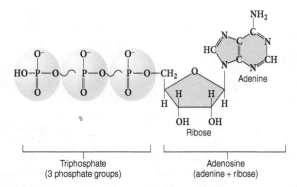

Triphosphate
(3 phosphate groups)

Adenosine
(adenine + ribose)

Figure 4.7 ATP Chemical Structure. ATP is a nucleotide consisting of adenine, ribose, and three phosphate groups.

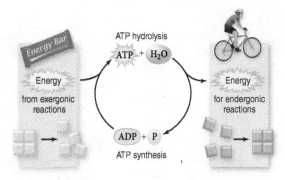

Figure 4.9 Coupled Reactions. Cells use ATP hydrolysis, an exergonic reaction, to fuel endergonic reactions. The cell regenerates ATP in other exergonic reactions, such as cellular respiration.

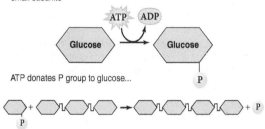

a. ATP energizes target molecule, making it more likely to bond with other molecules.

E.g., ATP provides the energy to build large molecules out of small subunits

ATP donates P group to glucose...

... glucose + P then reacts with short polysaccharide to build longer polysaccharide

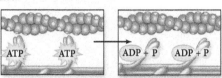

b. ATP donates a phosphate group that changes the shape of the target molecule.

E.g., ATP binding changes shape of proteins involved in muscle contraction

Figure 4.10 ATP Use. When ATP donates a phosphate group to a molecule, the recipient may (a) be more likely to bond or (b) change its shape in a useful way.

ATP is sometimes described as energy "currency." Just as you can use money to purchase a variety of different products, all cells use ATP in many chemical reactions to do different kinds of work. Besides muscle contraction, other examples of jobs that require ATP include transporting substances across cell membranes, moving chromosomes during cell division, and synthesizing the large molecules that make up cells. (The Apply It Now box describes another use of ATP: the flash of a firefly's light.)

ATP is also analogous to a fully charged rechargeable battery. A full battery represents a versatile source of potential energy that can provide power to many types of electronic devices. Although a dead battery is no longer useful as an energy source, you can recharge a spent battery to restore its utility. Likewise, the cell can use respiration to reconstitute its pool of ATP.

B. ATP Represents Short-Term Energy Storage

Organisms require huge amounts of ATP. A typical human cell uses the equivalent of 2 billion ATP molecules a minute just to stay alive. Organisms recycle ATP at a furious pace, adding phosphate groups to ADP to reconstitute ATP, using the ATP to drive reactions, and turning over the entire supply every minute or so. If you ran out of ATP, you would die instantly.

Apply It **Now**

Summer Light Show

Many organisms emit light in a process called bioluminescence. Some fishes, squids, and jellyfishes, for example, harbor pockets of glowing bacteria or protists in special light organs. The live-in microbes convert chemical energy into light energy.

Bioluminescence is much less common on land than in the sea, but one familiar example in many parts of the United States is the summertime glow of fireflies. Members of each of the more than 1900 species of fireflies use a distinctive repertoire of light signals to attract mates. Typically, flying males emit a pattern of flashes. Wingless females, called glowworms, usually are on leaves, where they emit light in response to the male's signals.

A series of chemical reactions generates the glow (figure 4.A). First, a molecule called luciferin reacts with ATP, yielding an intermediate compound and two phosphate groups. The enzyme luciferase then catalyzes a reaction of this intermediate with O_2 to yield oxyluciferin and a flash of light. Oxyluciferin is then reduced to luciferin, and the cycle starts over.

In some firefly species, the males flash in unison. Although we understand the biochemistry of the firefly's glow, no one yet knows what the fireflies are doing—or saying—when they synchronize their signals.

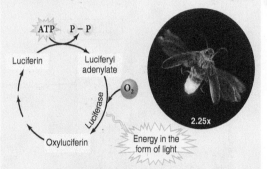

Figure 4.A The Flash of the Firefly. ATP hydrolysis creates flashes of light as energy is transferred to a specialized molecule called luciferin.

Even though ATP is essential to life, cells do not stockpile it in large quantities. ATP's high-energy phosphate bonds make the molecule too unstable for long-term storage. Instead, cells store energy-rich molecules such as fats, starch, and glycogen. When ATP supplies run low, cells divert some of their lipid and carbohydrate reserves to the metabolic pathways of cellular respiration. This process soon produces additional ATP.

4.3   MASTERING CONCEPTS

1. What are the main parts of an ATP molecule?
2. How does ATP hydrolysis supply energy for cellular functions?
3. Describe the relationships among endergonic reactions, ATP hydrolysis, and cellular respiration.

4.4 Enzymes Speed Biochemical Reactions

Tutorial
Enzymes

Enzymes are among the most important of all biological molecules. An **enzyme** is an organic molecule that catalyzes (speeds up) a chemical reaction without being consumed. Most enzymes are proteins, although some are made of RNA.

Many of the cell's organelles, including mitochondria, chloroplasts, lysosomes, and peroxisomes, are specialized sacs of enzymes. Enzymes copy DNA, build proteins, digest food, recycle a cell's worn-out parts, and catalyze oxidation–reduction reactions, just to name a few of their jobs. Without enzymes, all of these reactions would proceed far too slowly to support life.

A. Enzymes Bring Reactants Together

Enzymes speed reactions by lowering the **activation energy,** the amount of energy required to start a reaction (figure 4.11a). Even exergonic reactions, which ultimately release energy, require an initial "kick" to get started (see figure 4.4). The enzyme brings reactants (also called substrates) into contact with one another, so that less energy is required for the reaction to proceed. Just as it is easier to climb a small hill than a tall mountain, reactions occur

more rapidly if the activation energy is low. Enzyme-catalyzed reactions therefore occur much faster—millions to billions of times faster—than they do in the absence of an enzyme.

Most enzymes can catalyze only one or a few chemical reactions. An enzyme that dismantles a fatty acid, for example, cannot break down the starch in your energy bar. The key to this specificity lies in the shape of the enzyme's **active site,** the region to which the substrates bind (figure 4.11b). The substrates fit like puzzle pieces into the active site. Once the reaction occurs, the enzyme releases the products. Note that the reaction does not consume or alter the enzyme. Instead, after the protein releases the products, its active site is empty and ready to pick up more substrate.

Enzymes are very sensitive to conditions in the cell. An enzyme can become denatured and stop working if the pH changes or if the salt concentration becomes too high or too low. Temperature also greatly influences enzymes (figure 4.12). Enzyme action generally speeds up as the temperature climbs because reactants have more kinetic energy at higher temperatures. If it gets too hot, however, the enzyme rapidly denatures and can no longer function. ① *denatured proteins,* p. 34

Virtual Lab
Enzyme Reaction
Rates

Enzymes are so critical to life that just one faulty or missing enzyme can have dramatic effects. Lactose intolerance is one example. People whose intestinal cells do not secrete an enzyme called lactase cannot digest milk sugar (lactose). Fortunately, a product called Lactaid® can supply the missing enzyme. Phenylketonuria (PKU) is a much more serious disease. A PKU sufferer lacks an enzyme required to break down an amino acid called phenylalanine. When this amino acid accumulates in the bloodstream, it causes brain damage. People with PKU must avoid foods containing phenylalanine, including the artificial sweetener aspartame (NutraSweet). ① *artificial sweeteners,* p. 40

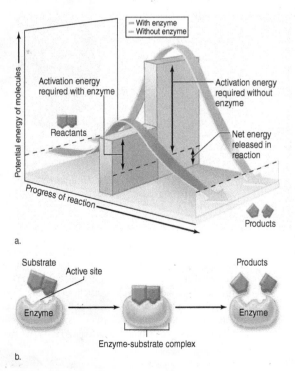

Figure 4.11   How Enzymes Work.   (a) Enzymes lower the amount of energy required to start a reaction. These "walls" represent the activation energy for the same reaction, with and without an enzyme. (b) An enzyme's active site has a specific shape that binds to one or more substrates. After the reaction, the enzyme releases the products.

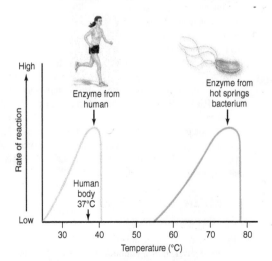

Figure 4.12   Temperature Matters.   These graphs show how temperature affects the activity of enzymes from a human (left) and a bacterium that lives in hot springs (right). The microbes have heat-tolerant enzymes that denature only at very high temperatures.

Enzymes also have household applications. Many detergents contain enzymes that break down food stains on clothing or dirty dishes. Raw pineapple contains an enzyme that breaks down protein. A gelatin dessert containing raw pineapple will fail to solidify because the fruit's enzymes destroy the gelatin protein. Some meat tenderizers contain the same enzyme, which breaks down muscle tissue and makes the meat easier to chew.

B. Enzymes Have Partners

Nonprotein "helpers" called **cofactors** are substances that must be present for an enzyme to catalyze a chemical reaction. Cofactors are often oxidized or reduced during the reaction, but, like enzymes, they are not consumed. Instead, they return to their original state when the reaction is complete.

Some cofactors are metals such as zinc, iron, and copper. Magnesium ions (Mg^{2+}), for example, help to stabilize many important enzymes. Other cofactors are organic molecules; an organic cofactor is called a coenzyme. The cell uses many water-soluble vitamins, including B_1, B_2, B_6, B_{12}, niacin, and folic acid, to produce coenzymes; vitamin C is a coenzyme itself. Diets lacking in vitamins can lead to reduced enzyme function and, eventually, serious illness or even death.

C. Cells Control Reaction Rates

The intricate network of metabolic pathways may seem chaotic, but in reality it is just the opposite. Cells precisely control the rates of their chemical reactions. If they did not, some vital compounds would always be in short supply, and others might accumulate to wasteful (or even toxic) levels.

One way to regulate a metabolic pathway is by **negative feedback** (also called feedback inhibition), in which a reaction's products inhibit the enzyme that catalyzes the reaction

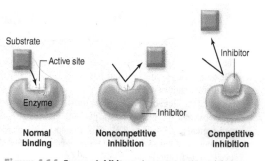

Figure 4.14 Enzyme Inhibitors. In noncompetitive inhibition, a substance binds somewhere other than the active site, changing the enzyme's shape. A competitive inhibitor blocks an enzyme's active site .

(figure 4.13). As reaction products accumulate, the reaction rate slows. For example, amino acid production requires multiple steps. When an amino acid accumulates, it binds to an enzyme that acts early in the synthesis pathway. For a time, the synthesis of that amino acid stops. But when the level falls, the block on the enzyme lifts, and the cell can once again produce the amino acid.

Negative feedback works in two general ways to prevent too much of a substance from accumulating (figure 4.14). In **noncompetitive inhibition,** product molecules bind to the enzyme at a location other than the active site, in a way that alters the enzyme's shape so that it can no longer bind substrate. (Figure 4.14 shows an example.) Alternatively, in **competitive inhibition,** the product of a reaction binds to the enzyme's active site, preventing it from binding substrate. It is "competitive" because the product competes with the substrate to occupy the active site.

Enzyme inhibitors have many practical applications. Aspirin relieves pain by binding to an enzyme that cells use to produce pain-related molecules called prostaglandins. Some antibiotics kill microorganisms—but not people—by inhibiting enzymes not present in our own cells. And the active ingredient in the herbicide Roundup® competitively inhibits an enzyme found in plant cells but not in animals.

The opposite of negative feedback is **positive feedback,** in which a product activates the pathway leading to its own production. Blood clotting, for example, involves a biochemical pathway with multiple steps. Damage to a blood vessel wall initiates these reactions. As a clot begins to form, the reactions accelerate, which further stimulates clotting, speeding up the reactions even more, and so on. Once the clot is large enough to stem the flow of blood, however, the pathway shuts down—an example of negative feedback. Positive feedback is much rarer than negative feedback in organisms.

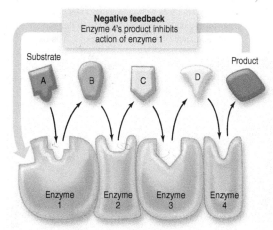

Figure 4.13 Negative Feedback. Some metabolic pathways require several enzyme-catalyzed steps. When the final product accumulates, it inhibits the activity of the first enzyme in the pathway, temporarily halting further production.

 Animation
Negative Feedback

4.4   MASTERING CONCEPTS

1. What do enzymes do in cells?
2. How does an enzyme lower a reaction's activation energy?
3. Distinguish between an enzyme and a coenzyme.
4. What are the roles of negative and positive feedback?
5. List three conditions that influence enzyme activity.

80   **UNIT ONE**   Science, Chemistry, and Cells

🍁 4.5 Membrane Transport May Release Energy or Cost Energy

The membrane surrounding each cell or organelle is a busy place. Like a well-used border crossing between two countries, raw materials enter and wastes exit in a continuous flow of traffic. How do membranes regulate this constant traffic?

A biological membrane is a phospholipid bilayer studded with proteins (see section 3.3). This arrangement means that a membrane is "choosy," or **selectively permeable.** Some substances pass freely through the bilayer, but others—such as the sugar from a digested energy bar—require help from proteins. This section describes the basic forms of traffic across the membrane; table 4.2 on page 82 provides a summary.

Thanks to the regulation of membrane transport, the interior of a cell is chemically different from the outside. Concentrations of some dissolved substances (solutes) are higher inside the cell than outside, and others are lower. Likewise, the inside of each organelle in a eukaryotic cell may be chemically quite different from the solution in the rest of the cell.

The term *gradient* describes any such difference between two neighboring regions. In a **concentration gradient,** a solute is more concentrated in one region than in a neighboring region. For example, the images in table 4.2 all illustrate concentration gradients in which the solution on the right side of the membrane has a higher solute concentration than the solution on the left.

If a substance moves from an area where it is more concentrated to an area where it is less concentrated, it is said to be "moving down" or "following" its concentration gradient. As the solute moves, the gradient dissipates—that is, it disappears. Any concentration gradient will eventually dissipate *unless energy is expended to maintain it.* Why? Random molecular motion always increases the amount of disorder (entropy), and it costs energy to counter this tendency toward disorder. By the same token, however, an existing concentration gradient represents a form of stored potential energy. Cells therefore spend ATP to create some types of concentration differences, which they can later "cash in" to do work (see section 4.5B).

A. Passive Transport Does Not Require Energy Input

In **passive transport,** a substance moves across a membrane without the direct expenditure of energy. All forms of passive transport involve **diffusion,** the spontaneous movement of a substance from a region where it is more concentrated to a region where it is less concentrated. Because diffusion represents the dissipation of a chemical gradient—and the loss of potential energy—it does not require energy input.

For a familiar example of diffusion, picture what happens when you first place a tea bag in a cup of hot water: near the tea bag, there are many more brown tea molecules than elsewhere in the cup (figure 4.15). Over time, however, the brownish color spreads to create a uniform brew.

How do the tea molecules "know" which way to diffuse? The answer is, of course, that atoms and molecules know nothing. Diffusion occurs because all substances have kinetic energy; that is, they are in constant, random motion. To simplify the tea example, suppose each molecule can move randomly along one of 10 possible paths (in reality, the number of possible directions is infinite). Assume further that only one path leads back to the tea bag. Since 9 of the 10 possibilities point away from the tea bag, the tea molecules tend to spread out; that is, they move down their concentration gradient.

If diffusion continues long enough, the gradient disappears. Diffusion *appears* to stop at that point, but the molecules do not stop moving. Instead, they continue to travel randomly back and forth at the same rate, so at equilibrium the concentration remains equal throughout the solution.

Simple Diffusion: No Proteins Required   In a form of passive transport called **simple diffusion,** a substance moves down its concentration gradient without the use of a carrier molecule (see table 4.2). Substances may enter or leave cells by simple diffusion only if they can pass freely through the membrane. Lipids and small, nonpolar molecules such as oxygen (O_2) and carbon dioxide (CO_2), for example, diffuse easily across the hydrophobic portion of a biological membrane (see figure 3.11).

Figure 4.15 Diffusion in a Cup.
The solute particles leaving a tea bag can move in any direction, with only a few paths leading back to the source. Eventually, the solutes are distributed uniformly throughout the cup.   **Animation** Diffusion

Solvent

Solute

If gradients dissipate without energy input, how can a cell use simple diffusion to acquire essential substances or get rid of toxic wastes? The answer is that the cell maintains the gradients, either by continually consuming the substances as they diffuse in or by producing more of the substances that diffuse out. For example, mitochondria consume O_2 as soon as it diffuses into the cell, maintaining the O_2 gradient that drives diffusion. Respiration also produces CO_2, which diffuses out because its concentration always remains higher in the cell than outside.

Osmosis: Diffusion of Water Across a Selectively Permeable Membrane

Tutorial Osmosis

Two solutions of different concentrations may be separated by a selectively permeable membrane through which water, but not solutes, can pass. In that case, water will diffuse down its own gradient toward the side with the high solute concentration. **Osmosis** is this simple diffusion of water across a selectively permeable membrane (see table 4.2 and figure 4.16).

A human red blood cell demonstrates the effects of osmosis (figure 4.17). The cell's interior is normally **isotonic** to the surrounding blood plasma, which means that the plasma's solute concentration is the same as the inside of the cell (*iso-* means "equal," and *tonicity* is the ability of a solution to cause water movement). Water therefore moves into and out of the cell at equal rates. In a **hypotonic** environment, the solute concentration is lower than it is inside the cell (*hypo-* means "under," as in *hypodermic*). Water therefore moves by osmosis into a blood cell placed into hypotonic surroundings; since animal cells lack a cell wall, the membrane may even burst. Conversely, **hypertonic** surroundings have a higher concentration of solutes than the cell's cytoplasm (*hyper-* means "over," as in *hyperactive*). In a hypertonic environment, a cell shrivels and may die for lack of water. (The movement of water out of cells also plays a role in some headaches; see the Burning Question on page 83.)

Hypotonic and *hypertonic* are relative terms that can refer to the surrounding solution or to the solution inside the cell. The same

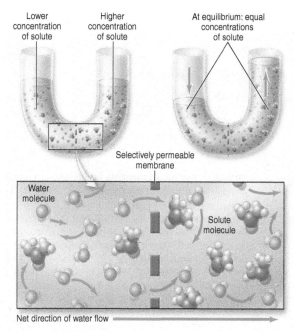

Figure 4.16 Osmosis. The selectively permeable membrane dividing this U-shaped tube permits water but not solutes to pass. Water diffuses from the left side (low solute concentration) toward the right side (high solute concentration). At equilibrium, water flow is equal in both directions, and the solute concentrations will be equal on both sides of the membrane.

Animation Osmosis

solution might be hypertonic to one cell but hypotonic to another, depending on the solute concentrations inside the cells.

A plant's roots are often hypertonic to the soil, particularly after a heavy rain. Water rushes in, and the central vacuoles of the plant cells expand until the cell walls constrain their growth.

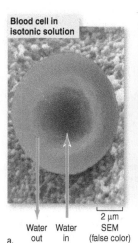

Blood cell in isotonic solution

Water out Water in 2 μm SEM (false color)
a.

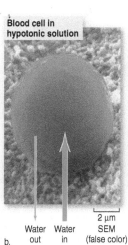

Blood cell in hypotonic solution

Water out Water in 2 μm SEM (false color)
b.

Blood cell in hypertonic solution

Water out Water in 2 μm SEM (false color)
c.

Figure 4.17 Osmosis and Red Blood Cells. (a) A human red blood cell is isotonic to the surrounding fluid. Water enters and leaves the cell at the same rate, and the cell maintains its shape. (b) When the salt concentration of the plasma decreases, water flows into the cell faster than it leaves. The cell swells and may even burst. (c) In salty surroundings, the cell loses water and shrinks.

Animation Osmosis and Red Blood Cells

Turgor pressure is the resulting force of water against the cell wall (figure 4.18). A limp, wilted piece of lettuce demonstrates the effect of lost turgor pressure. But the leaf becomes crisp again if placed in water, as individual cells expand like inflated balloons. Turgor pressure helps keep plants erect.

Figure It Out

A 0.9% salt solution is isotonic to human red blood cells. What will happen if you place a red blood cell in a 2.0% solution of salt water?

Answer: Water will leave the cell.

Facilitated Diffusion: Proteins Required

Animation
Facilitated
Diffusion

Ions and polar molecules cannot freely cross the hydrophobic layer of a membrane; instead, transport proteins form channels that help these solutes cross. **Facilitated diffusion** is a form of passive transport in which a membrane protein assists the movement of a polar solute along its concentration gradient (see table 4.2). Facilitated diffusion does not require energy expenditure because the solute moves from where it is more concentrated to where it is less concentrated.

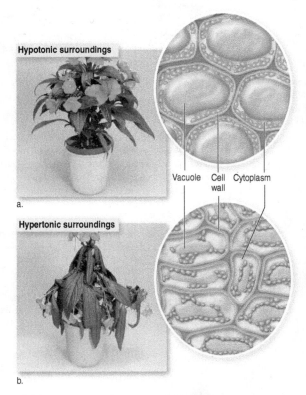

Hypotonic surroundings

Vacuole   Cell wall   Cytoplasm

a.

Hypertonic surroundings

b.

Figure 4.18 Osmosis and Plant Turgor Pressure. (a) The interior of a plant cell usually contains more concentrated solutes than its surroundings. Water enters the cell by osmosis, generating turgor pressure. (b) In a hypertonic environment, water leaves cells, so turgor pressure is low. The plant wilts.

Glucose moves into red blood cells via facilitated diffusion. This sugar is too hydrophilic to pass freely across the membrane, but glucose transporter proteins form channels that allow it in. Respiration inside the red blood cells consumes the glucose and maintains the concentration gradient.

Membrane proteins can enhance osmosis, too. Although membranes are somewhat permeable to water, osmosis can be

TABLE **4.2** **Movement Across Membranes: A Summary**

Mechanism	Characteristics
Passive transport	Net movement is down concentration gradient; does not require energy input.
Simple diffusion	Substance moves across membrane without assistance of transport proteins.
Osmosis	Water diffuses across a selectively permeable membrane.
Facilitated diffusion	Substance moves across membrane with assistance of transport proteins.
Active transport	Net movement is against concentration gradient; requires transport protein and energy input, often from ATP.
Transport in vesicles	Vesicle carries large particles into or out of a cell; requires energy input.
Endocytosis	Membrane engulfs substance and draws it into cell.
Exocytosis	Vesicle fuses with cell membrane, releasing substances outside of cell.

slow. The cells of many organisms, including bacteria, plants, and animals, use membrane proteins called aquaporins to increase the rate of water flow. Kidney cells control the amount of water that enters urine by changing the number of aquaporins in their membranes.

B. Active Transport Requires Energy Input

Both simple diffusion and facilitated diffusion dissipate an existing concentration gradient. Often, however, a cell needs to do the opposite: create and maintain a concentration gradient. A plant's root cell, for example, may need to absorb nutrients from soil water that is much more dilute than the cell's interior. In **active transport,** a cell uses a transport protein to move a substance *against* its concentration gradient—from where it is less concentrated to where it is more concentrated (see table 4.2). Because a gradient represents a form of potential energy, the cell must expend energy to create it. Energy for active transport often comes from ATP.

Cells must contain high concentrations of K^+ and low concentrations of Na^+ to perform many functions. In animals, for example, sodium and potassium ion gradients are essential for nerve and muscle function (see chapters 26 and 29). One active transport system in the membranes of most animal cells is a protein called the **sodium–potassium pump** (figure 4.19), which uses ATP as an energy source to expel three sodium ions (Na^+) for every two potassium ions (K^+) it admits. Maintaining these ion gradients is costly: the million or more sodium–potassium pumps embedded in a cell's membrane use some 25% of the cell's ATP.

Animation
Sodium–Potassium Pump

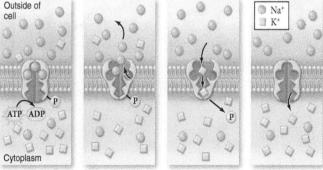

① ATP binds to transport protein along with three Na^+ from cytoplasm. ATP transfers phosphate to protein.

② Phosphate changes the shape of the protein, moving Na^+ across the membrane.

③ Two K^+ from outside of cell bind to protein, causing phosphate release.

④ Release of phosphate changes the shape of the protein, moving K^+ into the cytoplasm.

Figure 4.19 The Sodium–Potassium Pump. This "pump" is a protein embedded in the cell membrane. It uses energy released in ATP hydrolysis to move sodium ions (Na^+) out of the cell and potassium ions (K^+) into the cell. The process costs energy because both types of ions are moving from where they are less concentrated to where they are more concentrated.

Concentration gradients are an important source of potential energy that cells can use to do work. For example, chapters 5 and 6 describe how cells establish concentration gradients of hydrogen ions (H^+) during photosynthesis and respiration. A chloroplast or mitochondrion can control how and when the H^+ gradient dissipates. As it does so, the organelle converts the potential energy stored in the gradient into another form of potential energy—that is, chemical energy in the bonds of ATP.

C. Endocytosis and Exocytosis Use Vesicles to Transport Substances

Most molecules dissolved in water are small, and they can cross cell membranes by simple diffusion, facilitated diffusion, or active transport. Large particles, however, must enter and leave cells with the help of transport vesicles that travel within the cell on the cytoskeleton's "tracks." ① *cytoskeleton*, p. 62

Endocytosis allows a cell to engulf fluids and large molecules and bring them into the cell. The cell membrane indents, forming a "bubble" of membrane

Animation
Endocytosis and Exocytosis

that closes in on itself. The resulting vesicle traps the incoming substance (figure 4.20). The formation and movement of this vesicle require energy.

The two main forms of endocytosis are pinocytosis and phagocytosis. In pinocytosis, the cell engulfs small amounts of fluids and dissolved substances. In **phagocytosis,** the cell captures and engulfs large particles, such as debris or even another cell (*phag-* means "eating"). The vesicle then fuses with a lysosome, where hydrolytic enzymes dismantle the cargo. ⓘ *lysosomes,* p. 59

When biologists first viewed endocytosis in the 1930s, they thought a cell would gulp in anything at its surface. They now recognize a more selective form of the process. In receptor-mediated endocytosis, a receptor protein on a cell's surface binds a biochemical; the cell membrane then indents, drawing the substance into the cell. Liver cells use receptor-mediated endocytosis to absorb cholesterol-toting proteins from the bloodstream.

Exocytosis, the opposite of endocytosis, uses vesicles to transport fluids and large particles out of cells (figure 4.21). Inside a cell, the Golgi apparatus produces vesicles filled with substances to be secreted. The vesicle moves to the cell membrane and joins with it, releasing the substance outside the membrane. For example, the tip of a neuron releases neurotransmitters by exocytosis; these chemicals then stimulate or inhibit neural impulses in a neighboring cell. The secretion of milk into milk ducts, depicted in figure 3.13, is another example. As in endocytosis, moving the transport vesicle requires energy.

4.5 MASTERING CONCEPTS

1. What is diffusion?
2. What types of substances diffuse freely across a biological membrane?
3. How do differing concentrations of solutes in neighboring solutions drive osmosis?
4. Why does it cost energy for a cell to maintain a concentration gradient?
5. What are the characteristics of active transport? Give an example of active transport.
6. How do exocytosis and endocytosis use vesicles to transport materials across cell membranes?

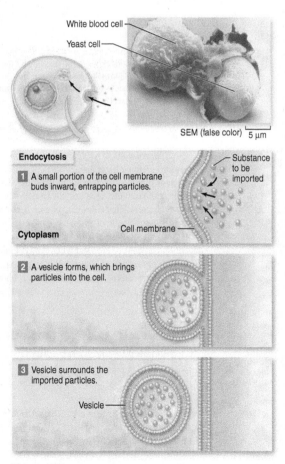

Figure 4.20 Endocytosis. Large particles enter a cell by endocytosis. The inset (top right) shows a white blood cell engulfing a yeast cell by phagocytosis, a form of endocytosis.

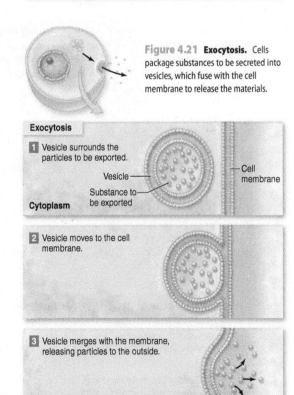

Figure 4.21 Exocytosis. Cells package substances to be secreted into vesicles, which fuse with the cell membrane to release the materials.

INVESTIGATING LIFE

4.6 Does Natural Selection Maintain Some Genetic Illnesses?

An individual enzyme or membrane protein may seem too small to be very important—until you consider that a single faulty one can cause serious illness. Cystic fibrosis, a disease that affects about 30,000 Americans, is one example. One in every 2500 babies born each year in the United States has cystic fibrosis. Each affected person lacks a protein called CFTR in his or her cell membranes.

CFTR, which stands for "cystic fibrosis transmembrane conductance regulator," is a membrane transport protein that moves chloride ions (Cl⁻) out of cells by active transport. As it does so, the solute concentration outside the cell increases, drawing water out by osmosis. Not surprisingly, CFTR occurs in tissues that secrete watery fluids such as mucus and perspiration.

One of the many locations where CFTR does its job is in cells lining the airspaces of the lungs. Water moving out of these cells thins the lung's mucus, which beating cilia clear away. Patients with cystic fibrosis, however, lack a working CFTR protein. The mucus in the lungs remains thick, making breathing difficult and creating an ideal breeding ground for bacteria. The patient eventually succumbs to chronic infections, often before age 30.

Cystic fibrosis renders many patients too sick to have children, or it may even take their lives before they are old enough to reproduce. So why hasn't natural selection eliminated this deadly disease from the population? The answer to this evolutionary puzzle may lie not in the lungs but in another place where CFTR proteins occur: the cells lining the digestive tract.

Some disease-causing bacteria that affect the digestive tract exploit CFTR. For example, the bacteria that cause cholera produce a toxin that overstimulates CFTR. Water and Cl⁻ therefore pour from the lining of the small intestine and leave the body in watery diarrhea; the resulting dehydration can be deadly if left untreated. Researcher Sherif Gabriel and his colleagues at the University of North Carolina hypothesized that the abnormal CFTR protein associated with cystic fibrosis may actually protect against cholera.

The team knew that DNA is divided into genes, each of which encodes one protein (including CFTR). They also knew that everyone has two versions of every gene, one inherited from each parent. To test their hypothesis, the researchers therefore bred three groups of mice. The animals in one group had two normal (functioning) *CFTR* gene copies. A second set of mice had two defective copies, and a third group had one normal and one defective copy.

The team then gave all the mice the cholera toxin (via a feeding tube) and measured the amount of fluid produced in the small intestine (figure 4.22). As predicted, mice with two normal copies of the CFTR-encoding gene produced the most fluid, indicating they were highly vulnerable to cholera. Mice with two faulty genes resisted the toxin's effects, and those with two different

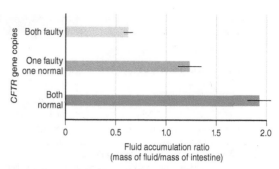

Figure 4.22 **Cholera Toxin and CFTR.** This graph shows the amount of fluid accumulated in the small intestines of mice after exposure to the cholera toxin. Mice with normal CFTR proteins lost the most fluid and were therefore the most susceptible to cholera. (Error bars represent standard errors; see appendix B.)

copies lost intermediate amounts of fluid. The amount of faulty CFTR was therefore correlated with resistance to cholera.

This study helps explain how natural selection might maintain harmful genes in populations. A person develops cystic fibrosis only if he or she receives a defective copy of the CFTR-encoding gene from both parents. On average, cystic fibrosis sufferers leave fewer offspring than healthy people do. But inheriting just one normal *CFTR* gene is enough to keep cystic fibrosis from developing. Evolutionary biologists suggest that, in some areas of the world, cholera resistance gives people with one faulty *CFTR* gene a reproductive edge over people with two copies of the normal gene.

From an evolutionary point of view, improved resistance to infectious disease apparently offsets losing some children to cystic fibrosis. A similar phenomenon occurs in human populations with a high frequency of the sickle cell trait. In that case, inheriting one copy of a faulty hemoglobin gene confers some resistance to another infectious disease, malaria. ⓘ *sickle cell*, p. 251

Membrane proteins are among the most important components of cells. Studying their connection to genetic diseases such as cystic fibrosis may someday lead to a cure. At the same time, it is intriguing to consider that the defective gene that causes this terrible illness also has a flip side.

Gabriel, Sherif E., K. N. Brigman, B. H. Koller, et al. Oct. 7, 1994. Cystic fibrosis heterozygote resistance to cholera toxin in the cystic fibrosis mouse model. *Science*, vol. 266, pages 107–109.

4.6 MASTERING CONCEPTS

1. What is the normal role of CFTR in humans, and how can faulty CFTR proteins cause cystic fibrosis?

2. Summarize the question Gabriel and his colleagues asked, and explain how their experiment helped answer the question.

3. How do you think the results in figure 4.22 would have been different if, before adding cholera toxin, the researcher had added a chemical that blocked the site at which the toxin binds to CFTR?

86   UNIT ONE   Science, Chemistry, and Cells

CHAPTER SUMMARY

4.1 All Cells Capture and Use Energy

A. Energy Allows Cells to Do Life's Work
- **Energy** is the ability to do work. **Potential energy** is stored energy, and **kinetic energy** is action.
- Energy is measured in units called **calories.** One food Calorie is 1000 calories, or 1 **kilocalorie.**

B. The Laws of Thermodynamics Describe Energy Transfer
- The **first law of thermodynamics** states that energy cannot be created or destroyed but only converted to other forms.
- The **second law of thermodynamics** states that all energy transformations are inefficient because every reaction results in increased **entropy** (disorder) and the loss of usable energy as heat.

4.2 Networks of Chemical Reactions Sustain Life

- **Metabolism** is the sum of the chemical reactions in a cell.

A. Chemical Reactions Absorb or Release Energy
- **Endergonic reactions** require energy input because the products have more energy than the reactants.
- Energy is released in **exergonic reactions,** in which the products have less energy than the reactants.

B. Linked Oxidation and Reduction Reactions Form Electron Transport Chains
- Many energy transformations in organisms occur via **oxidation-reduction (redox) reactions. Oxidation** is the loss of electrons; **reduction** is the gain of electrons. Oxidation and reduction reactions occur simultaneously.
- In both photosynthesis and respiration, proteins shuttle electrons along **electron transport chains.**

4.3 ATP Is Cellular Energy Currency

A. Coupled Reactions Release and Store Energy in ATP
- **ATP** stores energy in its high-energy phosphate bonds. Cellular respiration generates ATP.
- Many energy transformations involve **coupled reactions,** in which the cell uses the energy released in ATP hydrolysis to drive another reaction.
- **Phosphorylation** is the transfer of a phosphate group from ATP to another molecule, causing the recipient to become energized or to change shape.

B. ATP Represents Short-Term Energy Storage
- ATP is too unstable for long-term storage. Instead, cells store energy as fats and carbohydrates.

4.4 Enzymes Speed Biochemical Reactions

Animation
How Enzymes
Work

A. Enzymes Bring Reactants Together
- **Enzymes** are organic molecules (usually proteins) that speed biochemical reactions by lowering the **activation energy.**
- Substrate molecules fit into the enzyme's **active site.**
- Enzymes have narrow ranges of conditions in which they function.

B. Enzymes Have Partners
- **Cofactors** are inorganic or organic substances that enzymes require to catalyze reactions. Like enzymes, cofactors are not consumed in the reaction.

C. Cells Control Reaction Rates
- In **negative feedback,** a reaction product temporarily shuts down its own synthesis whenever its levels rise. Negative feedback may occur by **competitive** or **noncompetitive inhibition.**
- In **positive feedback,** a product stimulates its own further production.

4.5 Membrane Transport May Release Energy or Cost Energy

3-D Animation
Membrane Transport

- A **concentration gradient** is a difference in solute concentration between two neighboring regions, such as across a membrane. Gradients dissipate without energy input.

A. Passive Transport Does Not Require Energy Input
- All forms of **passive transport** involve **diffusion,** the dissipation of a chemical gradient by random molecular motion.
- In **simple diffusion,** a substance passes through a membrane along its concentration gradient without the aid of a transport protein.
- **Osmosis** is the simple diffusion of water across a selectively permeable membrane. Terms describing tonicity (**isotonic, hypotonic,** and **hypertonic**) predict whether cells will swell or shrink when the surroundings change. When plant cells lose too much water, the resulting loss of **turgor pressure** causes the plant to wilt.
- In **facilitated diffusion,** a membrane protein admits a substance along its concentration gradient without expending energy.

B. Active Transport Requires Energy Input
- In **active transport,** a carrier protein uses energy (ATP) to move a substance against its concentration gradient. For example, the **sodium-potassium pump** uses active transport to exchange sodium ions for potassium ions across an animal cell membrane.
- Figure 4.23 shows how enzymes and ATP interact in a cell to generate energy for active transport and other activities that require energy input.

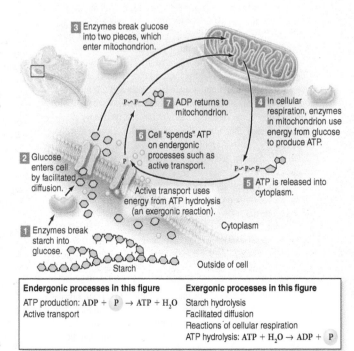

3 Enzymes break glucose into two pieces, which enter mitochondrion.

P~P 7 ADP returns to mitochondrion.

4 In cellular respiration, enzymes in mitochondrion use energy from glucose to produce ATP.

6 Cell "spends" ATP on endergonic processes such as active transport.

2 Glucose enters cell by facilitated diffusion.

P~P~P

5 ATP is released into cytoplasm.

Active transport uses energy from ATP hydrolysis (an exergonic reaction).

Cytoplasm

1 Enzymes break starch into glucose.

Starch

Outside of cell

Endergonic processes in this figure	Exergonic processes in this figure
ATP production: $ADP + P \rightarrow ATP + H_2O$ Active transport	Starch hydrolysis Facilitated diffusion Reactions of cellular respiration ATP hydrolysis: $ATP + H_2O \rightarrow ADP + P$

Figure 4.23 Enzymes, Energy, and ATP.

C. Endocytosis and Exocytosis Use Vesicles to Transport Substances

- In **endocytosis**, a cell engulfs liquids or large particles. Pinocytosis brings in fluids; **phagocytosis** brings in solid particles.
- In **exocytosis**, vesicles inside the cell carry substances to the cell membrane, where they fuse with the membrane and release the cargo to the outside of the cell.

4.6 Investigating Life: Does Natural Selection Maintain Some Genetic Illnesses?

- The faulty membrane protein that causes cystic fibrosis may help protect against cholera.

MULTIPLE CHOICE QUESTIONS

1. Which of the following is the best example of potential energy in a cell?
   a. Cell division
   b. A molecule of glucose
   c. Movement of a flagellum
   d. Assembly of a cellulose fiber

2. In an exergonic reaction,
   a. energy is absorbed.
   b. the products have more energy than the reactants.
   c. entropy increases.
   d. All of the above are true.

3. How does ATP participate in coupled reactions?
   a. Hydrolysis of ATP fuels endergonic reactions.
   b. Synthesis of ATP fuels endergonic reactions.
   c. Hydrolysis of ADP fuels exergonic reactions.
   d. Synthesis of ADP fuels exergonic reactions.

4. How does an enzyme affect the energy of a reaction?
   a. The activation energy is lowered.
   b. The net energy released is lowered.
   c. The energy of the reactants is raised.
   d. The energy of the products is raised.

5. Imagine that you turn on a space heater in a cold room. At first, the air is hottest near the heater, but the warmth eventually spreads throughout the room. This example illustrates
   a. facilitated diffusion.
   b. decreasing entropy.
   c. osmosis.
   d. simple diffusion.

6. A cell is at osmotic equilibrium with its environment. If you added salt to the surrounding solution, what would happen to the cell?
   a. There would be no change.
   b. It would swell and burst.
   c. It would exhibit turgor pressure.
   d. It would shrink.

7. A concentration gradient is an example of
   a. oxidation-reduction.
   b. potential energy.
   c. entropy.
   d. usable heat energy.

Answers to these questions are in appendix A.

WRITE IT OUT

1. Cite everyday illustrations of the first and second laws of thermodynamics. How do the laws of thermodynamics underlie every organism's ability to function?

2. Some people claim that life's high degree of organization defies the second law of thermodynamics. What makes this statement false?

3. List some examples of endergonic and exergonic reactions that have been introduced in previous chapters.

4. Describe where oxidation and reduction occur along an electron transport chain.

5. Classify oxidation reactions and reduction reactions as exergonic or endergonic processes. Explain your answer.

6. Provide an example of an appliance that uses coupled reactions.

7. Name at least four ways that the cell uses ATP.

8. In what ways is an enzyme's function similar to engineers digging a tunnel through a mountain rather than building a road over the peak?

9. Considering that enzymes are essential to all cells, including microbes, why might refrigeration and freezing help preserve food?

10. When a person eats a fatty diet, excess cholesterol accumulates in the bloodstream. Cells then temporarily stop producing cholesterol. What phenomenon described in the chapter does this control illustrate?

11. Explain the differences among diffusion, facilitated diffusion, active transport, and endocytosis.

12. Diffusion is an efficient means of transport only over small distances. How does this relate to a cell's surface-area-to-volume ratio (see chapter 3)?

13. Liver cells are packed with glucose. If the concentration of glucose in a liver cell is higher than in the surrounding fluid, what mechanism could the cell use to import even more glucose? Why would only this mode of transport work?

14. List three ways the content in this chapter relates to an organism's ability to maintain homeostasis.

PULL IT TOGETHER

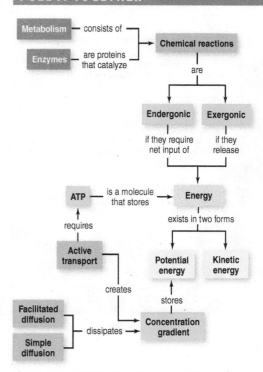

Figure 4.24 Pull It Together: The Energy of Life.

Refer to figure 4.24 and the chapter content to answer the following questions.

1. Add *competitive inhibitor* and *noncompetitive inhibitor* to this concept map.

2. What are some examples of potential energy and kinetic energy?

3. Add the terms *substrate*, *active site*, and *activation energy* to this concept map.

CHAPTER

5 Photosynthesis

Coral Competition. These two brain coral colonies are competing for space off the coast of Roatan, Honduras. Photosynthetic algae, which live inside each coral animal's tissues, provide one source of their food.

Enhance your study |BIOLOGY
of this chapter with practice quizzes,
animations and videos, answer keys,
and downloadable study tools.
www.mhhe.com/hoefnagels

Is It Easier Being Green?

FOOD IS EXPENSIVE. It would be much cheaper and easier if we could feed ourselves using photosynthesis. Imagine the benefit of being photosynthetic: You could make your own food, free of charge, simply by sitting outside in the sun.

Of course, your body would have to have some new adaptations for photosynthesis to work. Your skin would have to be green, for starters. You might even have skin flaps that capture extra sunlight. You wouldn't eat, so you would need another way to acquire essential minerals; perhaps your feet would grow root-like extensions that would absorb water and nutrients from soil.

Maybe photosynthetic cows, pigs, and chickens—or pets such as dogs and cats—would be a better idea. Feed-free animals would be a commercial and environmental triumph, costing less to own and generating less waste than the animals we raise now.

Fortunately or unfortunately, scientists will probably never be able to create photosynthetic people, chickens, or pooches. Mammals and birds move, breathe, pump blood, and maintain high body temperatures. All of this activity would likely require energy beyond what photosynthesis alone could supply.

Some invertebrate animals, however, have adopted the "green" lifestyle by harboring live-in photosynthetic partners (see section 5.7). The closest to a true plant–animal hybrid is probably the sea slug *Elysia chlorotica,* a solar-powered mollusk with chloroplasts (photosynthetic organelles) in the cells lining its digestive tract. The chloroplasts come from algae in the slug's diet. As the animal grazes, it punctures the algal cells and discards everything but the chloroplasts, which migrate into the animal's cells. Light passes through the slug's skin and strikes the food-producing chloroplasts. Once its "solar panels" are in place, the animal may not eat again for months!

Perhaps the most famous animals to "farm" photosynthetic partners are corals. Inside the coral are single-celled protists called dinoflagellates, which use the sun's energy to feed the coral. In exchange, the animals provide a home for the protists. Sometimes, however, the partners break up. Corals under stress sometimes expel their dinoflagellates, or the protists may leave on their own. The reef then turns white. The coral animals eventually die, endangering the entire reef ecosystem. Pollution, disease, shading, excessively warm water, and ultraviolet radiation all trigger coral bleaching. Biologists predict that global climate change will only make this problem worse.

Corals and sea slugs are not the only animals whose lives depend on photosynthesis. Yours does, too, as you will learn in the next two chapters.

 LEARN HOW TO LEARN
See What's Coming

Check out the Learning Outline at the beginning of each chapter. Each heading is a complete sentence that summarizes the most important idea of the section. Read through these statements before you start each chapter. That way, you can keep the "big picture" in mind while you study. You can also flip to the end of the chapter before you start to read; the chapter summary and Pull It Together concept map can provide a preview of what's to come.

5.1 Life Depends on Photosynthesis

Video Plants and Ecosystems

It is spring. A seed germinates, its tender roots and pale yellow stem extending rapidly in a race against time. For now, the seedling's sole energy source is food stored along with the embryonic plant in the seed itself. If its shoot does not reach light before its reserves run out, the seedling will die. But if it makes it, the shoot quickly turns green and unfurls leaves that spread and catch the light. The seedling begins to feed itself, and an independent new life begins.

The plant is an **autotroph** ("self feeder"), meaning it uses inorganic substances such as water and carbon dioxide (CO_2) to produce organic compounds. The opposite of an autotroph is a **heterotroph,** which is an organism that obtains carbon by consuming preexisting organic molecules. You are a heterotroph, and so are all other animals, all fungi, and many other microorganisms.

Organisms that can produce their own food underlie every ecosystem on Earth. It is not surprising, therefore, that if asked to designate the most important metabolic pathway, most biologists would not hesitate to cite **photosynthesis:** the process by which plants, algae, and some microorganisms harness solar energy and convert it into chemical energy. With the exception of deep-ocean hydrothermal vent communities, all life on this planet ultimately depends on photosynthesis.

A. Photosynthesis Builds Carbohydrates Out of Carbon Dioxide and Water

3-D Animation Photosynthesis Summary

Most plants are easy to grow (compared with animals, anyway) because their needs are simple. Give a plant water, essential elements in soil, carbon dioxide, light, and a favorable temperature, and it will produce food and oxygen that sustain its life. How can plants do so much with such simple raw materials?

In photosynthesis, pigment molecules in plant cells capture energy from the sun (figure 5.1). In a series of chemical reactions, that energy is then used to assemble CO_2 molecules into carbohydrates such as glucose ($C_6H_{12}O_6$). The plant uses water in the process and releases oxygen gas (O_2) as a byproduct. The reactions of photosynthesis are summarized as follows:

$$6CO_2 + 6H_2O \xrightarrow{\text{light energy}} C_6H_{12}O_6 + 6O_2$$

Photosynthesis is an oxidation–reduction (redox) process. "Oxidation" means that electrons are removed from an atom or molecule; "reduction" means that electrons are added. As you will soon see, photosynthesis strips electrons from the oxygen atoms in H_2O (i.e., the oxygen atoms are oxidized). These electrons are eventually used to

reduce the carbon in CO_2. Because oxygen atoms attract electrons more strongly than do carbon atoms (as depicted in figure 2.5), moving electrons from oxygen to carbon requires energy input. The energy source for this endergonic reaction is, of course, sunlight. ⓘ *redox reactions,* p. 75

Photosynthesis provides not only food for the plant but also the energy, raw materials, and oxygen that support most heterotrophs. Animals, fungi, and other heterotrophs eat the leaves, stems, roots, flowers, pollen, nectar, fruits, and seeds of the world's producers. Even the waste product of photosynthesis, O_2, is essential to much life on Earth.

Because humans live on land, we are most familiar with the contribution that plants make to Earth's terrestrial ecosystems. In fact, however, more than half of the world's photosynthesis occurs in the vast oceans, courtesy of countless algae and bacteria (figure 5.2). Several groups of bacteria are photosynthetic, some using pigments and metabolic pathways that are completely different from those in plants. For example, some photosynthetic microbes do not use water as an electron source or generate oxygen gas. (This chapter focuses on photosynthesis as it occurs in plants and algae.)

B. Plants Use Carbohydrates in Many Ways

Several fates await the glucose produced in photosynthesis. A plant's cells use about half of the glucose as fuel for their own cellular respiration, the metabolic pathway described in chapter 6. Roots, flowers, fruits, seeds, and other nonphotosynthetic plant parts could not grow without sugar shipments from green leaves and stems. Some sugars also participate indirectly in plant reproduction; sweet, sugary nectar and fruits attract animals that carry pollen and seeds (see chapter 24).

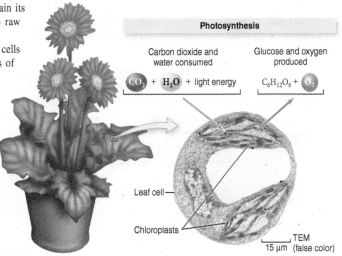

Photosynthesis

Carbon dioxide and water consumed	Glucose and oxygen produced
CO_2 + H_2O + light energy	$C_6H_{12}O_6$ + O_2

Leaf cell

Chloroplasts

TEM
15 μm   (false color)

Figure 5.1   Sugar from the Sun. In photosynthesis, a plant produces carbohydrates and O_2 from simple starting materials: CO_2, water, and sunlight.

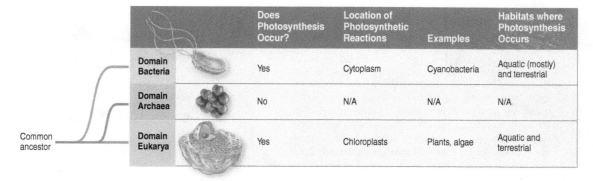

	Does Photosynthesis Occur?	Location of Photosynthetic Reactions	Examples	Habitats where Photosynthesis Occurs
Domain Bacteria	Yes	Cytoplasm	Cyanobacteria	Aquatic (mostly) and terrestrial
Domain Archaea	No	N/A	N/A	N/A
Domain Eukarya	Yes	Chloroplasts	Plants, algae	Aquatic and terrestrial

Common ancestor

Figure 5.2 Autotroph Diversity. Photosynthesis produces carbohydrates in organisms belonging to domains Bacteria and Eukarya. Some archaeans can use light to produce ATP, but not to build carbohydrates.

A plant also uses glucose as a raw material to build a cellulose wall for each of its cells. Wood is the remains of dead cells (see chapter 22), and it is mostly made of cellulose. The timber in the world's forests therefore stores enormous amounts of carbon. So do vast deposits of coal and other fossil fuels, which are the remains of plants and other organisms that lived long ago. Burning wood or fossil fuels releases this stored carbon into the atmosphere as CO_2. As the amount of CO_2 in the atmosphere has increased, Earth's average temperature has risen. Living forests help reduce climate change by locking carbon in wood. ⓘ *global climate change*, p. 816

In addition, plants often combine carbohydrates with other substances to manufacture additional compounds. Examples include amino acids and a host of economically important products such as natural dyes, latex rubber, medicines, and spices.

Figure It Out

Imagine that you plant a seedling weighing 1 kg in a pot containing 10 kg of soil. After the tree grows for 5 years, you uproot the tree, cut it up, and put the pieces in an oven to remove the water. When drying is complete, the tree weighs 50 kg. What is the main source of the atoms that make up the tree's dry weight?

Answer: The dried tree consists mainly of carbon, which was absorbed as CO_2.

Finally, if a plant produces more glucose than it immediately needs, it may store the excess as starch. Carbohydrate-rich tubers and grains, such as potatoes, rice, corn, and wheat, are all energy-storing plant organs that people and animals eat. Some plants, including sugarcane and sugar beets, store energy as sucrose instead. Table sugar comes from these crops, just as maple syrup comes from the sucrose-rich sap of a sugar maple tree. In addition, people use both starch (from corn kernels) and sugar (from sugarcane) to produce biofuels such as ethanol. ⓘ *biofuels*, p. 384

C. The Evolution of Photosynthesis Changed Planet Earth

Most of today's organisms rely directly or indirectly on photosynthesis, so it may seem surprising that early life lacked the ability to capture sunlight. For the first billion or so years of life's history, however, all organisms were heterotrophs. As these early heterotrophs oxidized the carbon compounds from their surroundings, they released CO_2 into the environment. But these organisms could not use the carbon in CO_2, so they faced extinction as soon as they depleted the organic compounds in their habitats. ⓘ *first organic molecules*, p. 306

Some 3.5 billion years ago, however, some microbes developed a new talent: the ability to make their own food by photosynthesis. Little is known about the first photosynthetic pathway, but it is clear that the novel ability to convert light energy into chemical energy soon supported most other forms of life.

The evolution of photosynthesis radically altered Earth in other ways as well. Until about 2.4 billion years ago, the atmosphere contained little O_2. But thanks to photosynthesis by ancient cyanobacteria, O_2 gradually accumulated over the next billion or more years. The organisms that could use O_2 in respiration had an advantage: they could extract the most energy from food. Eventually, organisms using aerobic cellular respiration outcompeted most other life forms. With more energy available, life took on new shapes and sizes.

In addition, atmospheric O_2 reacted with free oxygen atoms to produce ozone (O_3). As ozone accumulated high in the atmosphere, it blocked harmful ultraviolet radiation from reaching the planet's surface, which prevented some genetic damage and allowed new varieties of life to arise. The ozone layer therefore also helps explain the explosion in the diversity of life that followed the evolution of photosynthesis.

5.1 MASTERING CONCEPTS

1. What is photosynthesis? Describe the reactants and products in words and in chemical symbols.
2. How is an autotroph different from a heterotroph?
3. Why is photosynthesis essential to life on Earth?
4. What happens to the sugars that plants produce?
5. How did the origin of photosynthesis alter Earth's atmosphere and the evolution of life?

92   UNIT ONE   Science, Chemistry, and Cells

5.2 Sunlight Is the Energy Source for Photosynthesis

3-D Animation
Properties
of Light

Each minute, the sun converts more than 100,000 kilograms of matter to energy, releasing much of it outward as waves of electromagnetic radiation. After an 8-minute journey through space, about two billionths of this energy reaches Earth's upper atmosphere. Of this, only about 1% is used for photosynthesis, yet this tiny fraction of the sun's power ultimately produces nearly 2 quadrillion kilograms of carbohydrates a year! Light may seem insubstantial, but it is a powerful force on Earth.

A. What Is Light?

Visible light is a small sliver of a much larger **electromagnetic spectrum,** the range of possible frequencies of radiation (figure 5.3). All electromagnetic radiation, including light, consists of **photons,** discrete packets of kinetic energy. A photon's **wavelength** is the distance it moves during a complete vibration. The shorter a photon's wavelength, the more energy it contains.

The sunlight that reaches Earth's surface consists of three main components of the electromagnetic spectrum: ultraviolet radiation, visible light, and infrared radiation. Of the three, ultraviolet radiation has the shortest wavelengths. Its high-energy photons damage DNA, causing sunburn and skin cancer. In the middle range of wavelengths is visible light, which provides the energy that powers photosynthesis; we perceive visible light of different wavelengths as distinct colors. Infrared radiation, with its longer wavelengths, contains too little energy per photon to be useful to organisms. Most of its energy is converted immediately to heat.

TABLE 5.1   Pigments of Photosynthesis

Pigment	Color(s)	Organisms
Major pigment		
Chlorophyll *a*	Blue-green	Plants, algae, cyanobacteria
Accessory pigments		
Chlorophyll *b*	Yellow-green	Plants, green algae
Carotenoids (carotenes and xanthophylls)	Red, orange, yellow	Plants, algae, bacteria

B. Photosynthetic Pigments Capture Light Energy

Plant cells contain several pigment molecules that capture light energy (see this chapter's Burning Question). The most abundant is **chlorophyll *a*,** a green photosynthetic pigment in plants, algae, and cyanobacteria. Photosynthetic organisms usually also have several types of **accessory pigments,** which are energy-capturing pigment molecules other than chlorophyll *a* (table 5.1). Chlorophyll *b* and carotenoids are accessory pigments in plants.

The photosynthetic pigments have distinct colors because they absorb only some wavelengths of visible light, while transmitting or reflecting others (figure 5.4). Chlorophylls *a* and *b* absorb red and blue wavelengths; they appear green because they reflect green light. Carotenoids, on the other hand, reflect longer wavelengths of light, so they appear red, orange, or yellow. These pigments also act as antioxidants that protect the plant from damage caused by free radicals. (Carrots, tomatoes, lobster shells,

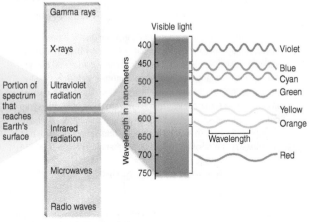

Figure 5.3   The Electromagnetic Spectrum. Sunlight reaching Earth consists of ultraviolet radiation, visible light, and infrared radiation, all of which is just a small part of a continuous spectrum of electromagnetic radiation. Short wavelengths of light carry more energy than do long wavelengths.

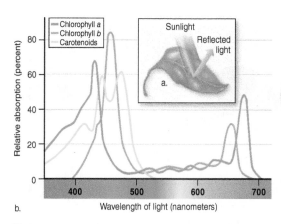

b.

Wavelength of light (nanometers)

Figure 5.4 **Everything but Green.** (a) Overall, a leaf reflects green and yellow wavelengths of light and absorbs the other wavelengths. (b) Each type of pigment absorbs some wavelengths of light and reflects others.

and the flesh of salmon all owe their distinctive colors to carotenoid pigments, which the animals must obtain from their diets.)

Only absorbed light is useful in photosynthesis. Accessory pigments absorb wavelengths that chlorophyll *a* cannot, so they extend the range of light wavelengths that a cell can harness. This is a little like the members of the same team on a quiz show, each contributing answers from a different area of expertise.

Figure It Out

If you could expose plants to just one wavelength of light at a time, would a wavelength of 300 nm, 450 nm, or 600 nm produce the highest photosynthetic rate?

Answer: 450 nm.

C. Chloroplasts Are the Sites of Photosynthesis

 3-D Animation Chloroplast Structure

In plants, leaves are the main organs of photosynthesis. Their broad, flat surfaces expose abundant surface area to sunlight. But light is just one requirement for photosynthesis. Water is also essential; roots absorb this vital ingredient, which moves up stems and into the leaves. And plants also exchange CO_2 and O_2 with the atmosphere. How do these gases get into and out of leaves?

The answer is that CO_2 and O_2 enter and exit a plant through **stomata** (singular: stoma), tiny openings in the epidermis of a leaf or stem (figure 5.5a). Stomata allow for gas exchange, but water evaporates through the same openings. When the plant loses too much water, pairs of specialized "guard cells" surrounding each stoma collapse against one another, closing the pores. Stomata therefore help balance the competing needs of gas exchange and water conservation. ⓘ *leaf epidermis*, p. 468

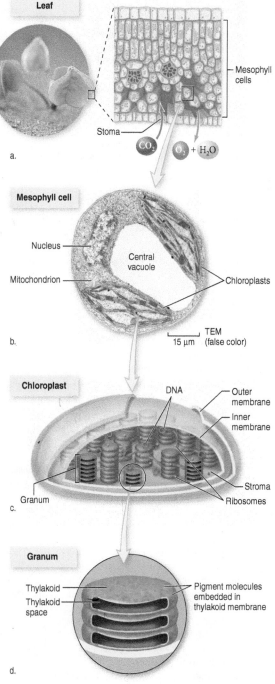

Figure 5.5 **Leaf and Chloroplast Anatomy.** (a) The tissue inside a leaf is called mesophyll. (b) Each mesophyll cell contains many chloroplasts. (c) A chloroplast contains light-harvesting pigments, embedded in (d) the stacks of thylakoid membranes that make up each granum.

Figure 5.6 Photosystem. This diagram shows one of the many photosystems embedded in a typical thylakoid membrane. Each photosystem consists of a complex grouping of proteins (purple) and pigments (green).

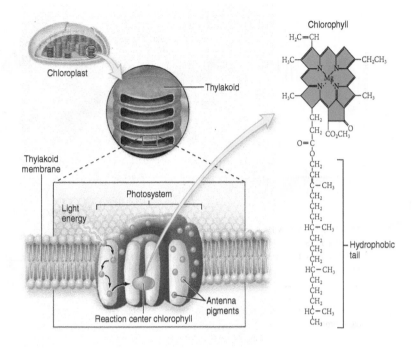

Most photosynthesis occurs in cells filling the leaf's interior (see figure 5.5b). **Mesophyll** is the collective term for these internal cells (*meso-* means "middle," and *-phyll* means "leaf"). In many plants, at least part of the mesophyll has a "spongy" texture, reflecting the air spaces that maximize gas exchange within the leaf.

Leaf mesophyll cells contain abundant **chloroplasts,** the organelles of photosynthesis in plants and algae (see figure 5.5c). Most photosynthetic cells contain 40 to 200 chloroplasts, which add up to about 500,000 per square millimeter of leaf—an impressive array of solar energy collectors. Each chloroplast contains tremendous surface area for the reactions of photosynthesis.

Two membranes surround each chloroplast. The inner membrane encloses the **stroma,** which is a gelatinous fluid containing ribosomes, DNA, and enzymes. (Be careful not to confuse the *stroma* with a *stoma*, or leaf pore.) Suspended in the stroma are between 10 and 100 **grana** (singular: granum), each composed of a stack of 10 to 20 disk-shaped thylakoids (see figure 5.5d). Each **thylakoid,** in turn, consists of a membrane studded with photosynthetic pigments and enclosing a volume called the **thylakoid space.**

Anchored in the thylakoid membranes are many **photosystems,** which are clusters of photosynthetic pigments and proteins that participate in photosynthesis (figure 5.6). Each photosystem includes some 300 chlorophyll *a* molecules and 50 accessory pigments. The photosystem's **reaction center** includes a special pair of chlorophyll *a* molecules that actually use the energy in photosynthetic reactions. The other pigments of the photosystem make up the light-harvesting complex that surrounds the reaction center. These additional pigments are called **antenna pigments** because they capture photon energy and funnel it to the reaction center. If the array of pigments in a photosystem is like a quiz show team, then the reaction center is analogous to the one member who announces the team's answer to the show's moderator.

Each photosystem has a few hundred chlorophyll molecules, so why does only the reaction center chlorophyll actually participate in the photosynthetic reactions? A single chlorophyll *a* molecule can absorb only a small amount of light energy. But because many pigment molecules are arranged close together, each antenna pigment can quickly pass its energy to the reaction center, freeing the antenna to absorb other photons as they strike. Thus, the photosystem's organization greatly enhances the efficiency of photosynthesis.

5.2   MASTERING CONCEPTS

1. What are the three main components of sunlight?
2. Describe the relationships among the chloroplast, stroma, grana, thylakoids, and photosystems.
3. How does it benefit a photosynthetic organism to have more than one type of pigment?
4. How does the reaction center chlorophyll interact with the antenna pigments in a photosystem?

5.3 Photosynthesis Occurs in Two Stages

Tutorial
Overview of
Photosynthesis

Inside a chloroplast, photosynthesis occurs in two stages: the light reactions and the carbon reactions. Figure 5.7 summarizes the entire process, and sections 5.4 and 5.5 describe each part in greater detail.

The **light reactions** convert solar energy to chemical energy. (You can think of the light reactions as the "photo-" part of photosynthesis.) In the chloroplast's thylakoid membranes, pigment molecules in two linked photosystems capture kinetic energy from photons and store it as potential energy in the chemical bonds of two molecules: ATP and NADPH.

Recall from chapter 4 that **ATP** is a nucleotide that stores potential energy in the covalent bonds between its phosphate groups. ATP forms when a phosphate group is added to ADP (see figure 4.9). The other energy-rich product of the light reactions, **NADPH,** is a coenzyme that carries pairs of energized electrons. In photosynthesis, these electrons come from one of the two reaction center chlorophyll molecules. Once the light reactions are underway, chlorophyll, in turn, replaces its "lost" electrons by splitting water molecules, yielding O_2 as a waste product. ⓘ *coenzymes,* p. 79

These two resources (energy and "loaded" electron carriers) set the stage for the second part of photosynthesis: the **carbon reactions.** In the carbon reactions, the cell uses ATP, the high-energy electrons in NADPH, and CO_2 to produce sugar molecules. (These reactions are the "-synthesis" part of photosynthesis.) The ATP and NADPH come from the light reactions, and the CO_2 comes from the atmosphere. Once inside the leaf, CO_2 diffuses into a mesophyll cell and across the chloroplast membrane into the stroma, where the carbon reactions occur.

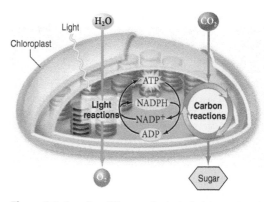

Figure 5.7 Overview of Photosynthesis. In the light reactions, pigment molecules capture sunlight energy and transfer it to molecules of ATP and NADPH. The carbon reactions use this energy to build sugar molecules out of carbon dioxide.

Because the carbon reactions do not directly require light, they are sometimes called the "dark reactions" of photosynthesis. This term is misleading, however, because the carbon reactions occur mostly during the day, when the light reactions are producing ATP and NADPH. A more accurate alternative would be the "light-independent reactions."

5.3 MASTERING CONCEPTS

1. What happens in each of the two main stages of photosynthesis?
2. Explain the role of each of the products of the light reactions and the carbon reactions.

Burning Question

Why do leaves change colors in the fall?

Most leaves are green throughout a plant's growing season. The familiar green color comes from chlorophyll *a,* the most abundant pigment in photosynthetic plant parts. But the leaf also contains other photosynthetic pigments. Carotenoids contribute brilliant yellow, orange, and red hues. Purple pigments, such as anthocyanins, are not photosynthetically active, but they do protect leaves from damage by ultraviolet radiation.

Carotenoids are less abundant than chlorophyll, so they usually remain invisible to the naked eye during the growing season. As winter approaches, however, many plants prepare to shed their leaves. Anthocyanins accumulate while chlorophyll degrades, and the now "unmasked" carotenoid pigments reveal their colors for a short time as a spectacular autumn display. These pigments soon disappear as well, and the dead leaves turn brown and fall to the ground.

These carefully timed events help the plant conserve resources. After all, about 75% of a leaf's proteins occur in its chloroplasts.

Rather than simply letting the first frost kill the leaves, the plant dismantles these proteins *before* the leaves die. The plant stores the valuable nitrogen and other nutrients from these molecules in living tissues that will survive the winter.

Springtime brings a flush of fresh, green leaves. The energy to produce the foliage comes from glucose the plant produced during the last growing season and stored as starch. The new leaves make food throughout the spring and summer, so the tree can grow—both above ground and below—and produce fruits and seeds. As the days grow shorter and cooler in autumn, the cycle will continue, and the colorful pigments will again participate in one of nature's great disappearing acts.

Submit your burning question to
Marielle.Hoefnagels@mheducation.com

5.4 The Light Reactions Begin Photosynthesis

Tutorial
Light Reactions

An animal deprived of food can die of hunger; similarly, a plant placed in a dark closet literally starves. Without light, the plant cannot generate ATP or NADPH. And without these two critical energy and electron carriers, the plant cannot produce sugars to feed itself. Once its stored reserves are gone, the plant dies. The plant's life thus depends on the light reactions of photosynthesis, which occur in the membranes of chloroplasts.

We have already seen that the pigments and proteins of the chloroplast's thylakoid membranes are organized into photosystems (see figure 5.6). More specifically, the thylakoid membranes of algae and higher plants contain two types of photosystems, dubbed I and II. The two photosystems "specialize" in slightly different wavelengths of light. The reaction center chlorophyll of photosystem I, called P700, has a light absorption peak at 700 nm (see figure 5.4). Photosystem II's

reaction center chlorophyll is called P680 because its long-wavelength peak is at 680 nm.

An electron transport chain connects the two photosystems. Recall from chapter 4 that an **electron transport chain** is a group of proteins that shuttle electrons like a bucket brigade, releasing energy with each step. As you will see, the electron transport chain that links photosystems I and II provides energy for ATP synthesis. A second electron transport chain extending from photosystem I ends in the production of NADPH.

Figure 5.8 depicts the arrangement of the photosystems and electron transport chains in the thylakoid membrane. Refer to this illustration as you work through the rest of this section.

A. Light Striking Photosystem II Provides the Energy to Produce ATP

Photosynthesis begins in the cluster of pigment molecules of photosystem II. This may seem illogical, but the two photosystems were named as they were discovered. Photosystem II was discovered after photosystem I, but it functions first in the overall process.

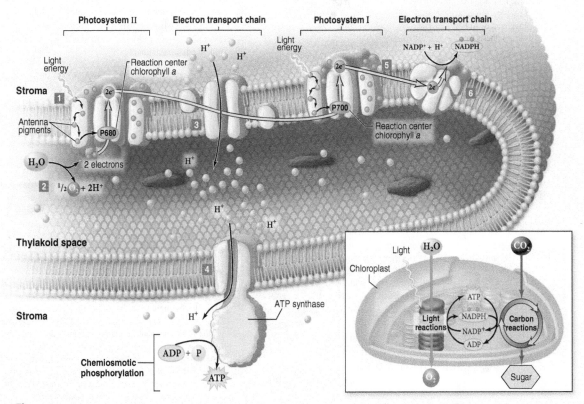

Figure 5.8   The Light Reactions.   The proteins and pigments of the light reactions are embedded in the chloroplast's thylakoid membranes. (*1*) Chlorophyll molecules in photosystem II transfer light energy to electrons. (*2*) Electrons are stripped from water molecules, releasing O_2. (*3*) The energized electrons pass to photosystem I via an electron transport chain. Each transfer releases energy that is used to pump hydrogen ions (H^+) into the thylakoid space. (*4*) The resulting H^+ gradient is used to generate ATP. (*5*) In photosystem I, the electrons absorb more light energy and (*6*) are passed to $NADP^+$, creating the energy-rich NADPH.

3-D Animation
Light Reactions

Apply It **Now**

Weed Killers

No plant can survive for very long in the dark. One low-tech way to kill an unwanted plant, therefore, is to deprive it of light. Gardeners who want to convert a lawn into a garden, for example, might kill the grass by covering it with layers of newspaper for several weeks. The light reactions of photosynthesis cannot occur in the dark; the plants die.

Another way to kill plants is to apply chemicals called herbicides. These plant poisons work by a variety of mechanisms, some of which are not directly related to photosynthesis. At least two herbicides, however, stop the light reactions (figure 5.A). For example, DCMU (short for 3-(3,4-dichlorophenyl)-1,1-dimethylurea and known by the name diuron) blocks electron flow in photosystem II. Paraquat, noted for its use in destroying marijuana plants, diverts electrons from photosystem I. Either way, blocking electron flow prevents the production of ATP and NADPH. Without these critical products, photosynthesis cannot continue.

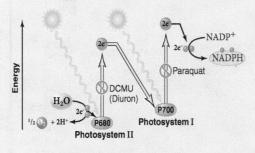

Figure 5.A Blocking the Light Reactions.

Pigment molecules in photosystem II absorb light and transfer the energy to a chlorophyll *a* reaction center, where it boosts two electrons to an orbital with a higher energy level. The "excited" electrons, now packed with potential energy, are ejected from the reaction center chlorophyll *a* and grabbed by the first protein in the electron transport chain that links the two photosystems (figure 5.8, step 1). ⓘ *electron orbitals*, p. 22

How does the reaction center chlorophyll *a* replace these two electrons? They come from water (H_2O), which donates two electrons when it splits into oxygen gas and two protons (H^+). Chlorophyll *a* picks up the electrons. The protons are released into the thylakoid space, and the O_2 is either used in the plant's respiration or released to the environment (step 2).

Meanwhile, the chloroplast uses the potential energy in the electrons to create a proton gradient (step 3). As the electrons

pass along the electron transport chain, the energy they lose drives the active transport of protons from the stroma into the thylakoid space. The resulting proton gradient across the thylakoid membrane represents a form of potential energy. ⓘ *active transport*, p. 83

An enzyme complex called **ATP synthase** transforms the gradient's energy into chemical energy in the form of ATP (step 4). A channel in ATP synthase allows protons trapped inside the thylakoid space to return to the chloroplast's stroma. As the gradient dissipates, energy is released. The ATP synthase enzyme uses this energy to add phosphate to ADP, generating ATP.

This mechanism is similar to using a dam to produce electricity. Water accumulating behind a dam represents potential energy, like the proton gradient across a thylakoid membrane. To harness this potential energy, the dam's operators allow water to pour through a large pipe at the dam's base. The gushing water turns massive blades that spin an electric generator. Likewise, ATP synthase generates ATP as it allows accumulated protons to pass from the thylakoid space into the stroma.

The coupling of ATP formation to the release of energy from a proton gradient is called **chemiosmotic phosphorylation** because it is the addition of a phosphate to ADP (phosphorylation) using energy from the movement of protons across a membrane (chemiosmosis). As described in chapter 6, the same process also occurs in cellular respiration: An electron transport chain provides the energy to create a proton gradient, and ATP synthase uses the gradient's potential energy to produce ATP.

B. Electrons from Photosystem I Reduce NADP⁺ to NADPH

Photosystem I functions much as photosystem II does. Photon energy strikes energy-absorbing antenna pigment molecules, which pass the energy to the reaction center chlorophyll *a*. The reactive chlorophyll molecule ejects electrons to an electron carrier molecule in a second electron transport chain (figure 5.8, step 5). The boosted electrons in photosystem I are then replaced with electrons passing down the first electron transport chain from photosystem II.

The second electron transport chain, however, does not generate a proton gradient, nor does it pass its electrons to yet another photosystem. Instead, the electrons reduce a molecule of $NADP^+$ to NADPH (step 6). This NADPH is the electron carrier that will reduce carbon dioxide in the carbon reactions, while ATP will provide the energy. (The Apply It Now box explains how blocking the light reactions quickly leads to a plant's demise.)

5.4   **MASTERING CONCEPTS**

1. Describe how light striking photosystem II leads to the production of ATP.

2. What is water's role in the light reactions?

3. What happens after light strikes photosystem I?

4. How are the electrons from photosystem I replaced?

98   UNIT ONE   Science, Chemistry, and Cells

5.5 The Carbon Reactions Produce Carbohydrates

Tutorial
Calvin Cycle

The carbon reactions, also called the Calvin cycle, occur in the chloroplast's stroma. The **Calvin cycle** is the metabolic pathway that uses NADPH and ATP to assemble CO_2 molecules into three-carbon carbohydrate molecules (figure 5.9). These products are eventually assembled into glucose and other sugars. (The pathway is named in honor of its discoverer, American biochemist Melvin Calvin.)

The first step of the Calvin cycle is **carbon fixation**—the initial incorporation of carbon from CO_2 into an organic compound. Specifically, CO_2 combines with **ribulose bisphosphate (RuBP),** a five-carbon sugar with two phosphate groups.

The enzyme that catalyzes this essential first reaction is RuBP carboxylase/oxygenase, also known as **rubisco.** As an essential component of every plant, rubisco is one of the most abundant and important proteins on Earth.

The six-carbon product of the initial reaction immediately breaks down into two three-carbon molecules called phosphoglycerate (PGA). Further steps in the cycle convert PGA to phosphoglyceraldehyde (PGAL), which is the carbohydrate product that leaves the Calvin cycle. The cell can use PGAL to build larger carbohydrate molecules such as glucose and sucrose. Some of the PGAL, however, is rearranged to form additional RuBP, perpetuating the cycle.

ATP and NADPH produced in the light reactions provide the potential energy and electrons necessary to reduce CO_2. As long as ATP and NADPH are plentiful, the Calvin cycle continuously "fixes" the carbon from CO_2 into small organic molecules.

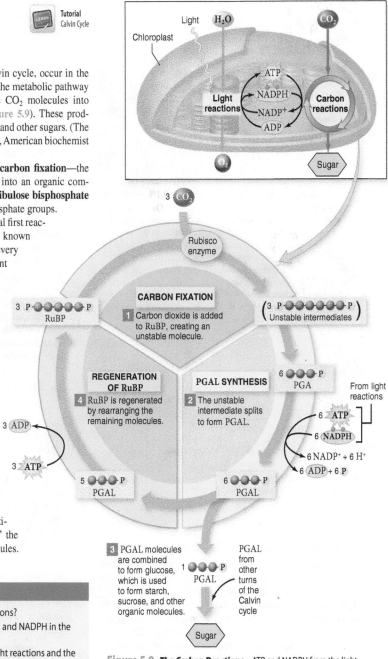

Figure 5.9 **The Carbon Reactions.** ATP and NADPH from the light reactions power the Calvin cycle, which occurs in the stroma of a chloroplast. This figure shows that three CO_2 molecules build one three-carbon molecule, PGAL, which is used to build larger carbohydrate molecules such as glucose.

Animation
Calvin Cycle

5.5   MASTERING CONCEPTS

1. What is the product of the carbon reactions?
2. What are the roles of rubisco, RuBP, ATP, and NADPH in the Calvin cycle?
3. What is the relationship between the light reactions and the carbon reactions?
4. Use figure 5.9 to determine how many ATP and NADPH molecules are used to produce a six-carbon glucose molecule.

5.6 C₃, C₄, and CAM Plants Use Different Carbon Fixation Pathways

The Calvin cycle is also known as the **C_3 pathway** because a three-carbon molecule, PGA, is the first stable compound in the pathway. Although all plants use the Calvin cycle, C_3 plants use *only* this pathway to fix carbon from CO_2. About 95% of plant species are C_3, including cereals, peanuts, tobacco, spinach, sugar beets, soybeans, most trees, and some lawn grasses.

C_3 photosynthesis is obviously a successful adaptation, but it does have a weakness: inefficiency. Photosynthesis has a theoretical efficiency rate of about 30% in ideal conditions, but a plant's efficiency in nature is typically as low as 0.1% to 3%.

How do plants waste so much solar energy? One contributing factor is a metabolic pathway called **photorespiration,** a series of reactions that begin when rubisco adds O_2 instead of CO_2 to RuBP. The product of this reaction does not continue in the Calvin cycle. The plant therefore loses CO_2 that it fixed in previous turns of the cycle, wasting both ATP and NADPH.

A plant with open stomata minimizes the photorespiration rate. This is because CO_2 and O_2 compete for rubisco's active site; when stomata are open, CO_2 from the atmosphere enters the leaf, and O_2 produced in the light reactions diffuses out. But plants in hot, dry climates face a trade-off. If the stomata remain open too long, a plant may lose water, wilt, and die. If the plant instead closes its stomata, CO_2 runs low, and O_2 builds up in the leaves. Under those conditions, photorespiration becomes much more likely, and photosynthetic efficiency plummets. Plants may lose as much as 30% of their fixed carbon to this pathway.

In hot climates, plants that minimize photorespiration may therefore have a significant competitive advantage. One way to improve efficiency is to ensure that rubisco always encounters high CO_2 concentrations. The C_4 and CAM pathways are two adaptations that do just that.

C_4 plants physically separate the light reactions and the carbon reactions into different cells. The light reactions occur in mesophyll cells, as does a carbon-fixation reaction called the C_4 pathway. In the **C_4 pathway,** CO_2 combines with a three-carbon "ferry" molecule to form the four-carbon compound, oxaloacetate (hence the name C_4). The oxaloacetate is usually reduced to malate, another four-carbon molecule.

Malate then moves via plasmodesmata into adjacent **bundle-sheath cells** that surround the leaf veins. The CO_2 is liberated inside these cells, where the Calvin cycle fixes the carbon a second time. Meanwhile, at the cost of two ATP molecules, the three-carbon "ferry" returns to the mesophyll to pick up another CO_2.

C_4 plants owe their efficiency to the arrangement of cells in their leaves (figure 5.10). Bundle-sheath cells are isolated from the O_2-rich air spaces in the leaf. Moreover, unlike chloroplasts in

mesophyll cells, those in bundle-sheath cells have adaptations that reduce the amount of O_2 they generate. Because CO_2 is abundant, the rubisco in bundle-sheath cells is therefore much more likely to bind CO_2 instead of O_2, reducing photorespiration.

As a bonus, unlike rubisco, the enzyme that first fixes CO_2 in the C_4 pathway does not bind O_2 at all. C_4 plants can therefore acquire the CO_2 they need with fewer, smaller stomata than C_3 plants. Since water loss occurs primarily through stomata, C_4 plants require about half as much water as C_3 plants.

About 1% of plants use the C_4 pathway. All are flowering plants growing in hot, sunny environments, including crabgrass and crop plants such as sugarcane and corn. C_4 plants are less abundant, however, in cooler, moister habitats. In those environments, the ATP cost of ferrying each CO_2 from a mesophyll cell to a bundle-sheath cell apparently exceeds the benefits of reduced photorespiration.

Another energy- and water-saving strategy, called crassulacean acid metabolism (CAM), was first discovered in desert plants in the Crassulaceae family. Plants that use the **CAM pathway** add a new twist: they open their stomata only at night, fix CO_2, then fix it again in the Calvin cycle during the day. Unlike C_4 plants, however, both fixation reactions occur in the same cell.

A CAM plant's stomata open at night, when the temperature drops and humidity rises. CO_2 diffuses in. Mesophyll cells incorporate the CO_2 into malate, which they store in large vacuoles. The stomata close during the heat of the day, but the stored malate moves from the vacuole to a chloroplast and releases its CO_2. The chloroplast then fixes the CO_2 in the Calvin cycle. The

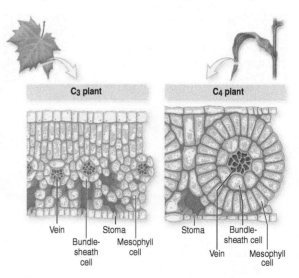

Figure 5.10 **C_3 and C_4 Leaf Anatomy.** In C_3 plants, the light reactions and the Calvin cycle occur in mesophyll cells. In C_4 plants, the light reactions occur in mesophyll, but the inner ring of bundle-sheath cells houses the Calvin cycle.

CAM pathway reduces photorespiration by generating high CO_2 concentrations inside chloroplasts.

About 3% to 4% of plant species, including pineapple and cacti, use the CAM pathway. All CAM plants are adapted to dry habitats. In cool environments, however, CAM plants cannot compete with C_3 plants. Their stomata are open only at night, so CAM plants have much less carbon available to their cells for growth and reproduction.

Figure 5.11 compares and contrasts C_3, C_4, and CAM plants.

5.6   MASTERING CONCEPTS

1. Why is the Calvin cycle also called the C_3 pathway?
2. How does photorespiration counter photosynthesis?
3. What conditions maximize photorespiration?
4. Describe how a C_4 plant minimizes photorespiration.
5. How is the CAM pathway similar to C_4 metabolism, and how is it different?

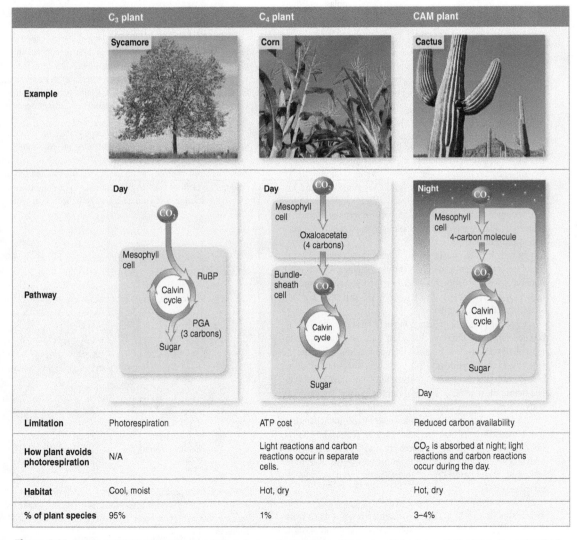

	C_3 plant	C_4 plant	CAM plant
Example	Sycamore	Corn	Cactus
Pathway			
Limitation	Photorespiration	ATP cost	Reduced carbon availability
How plant avoids photorespiration	N/A	Light reactions and carbon reactions occur in separate cells.	CO_2 is absorbed at night; light reactions and carbon reactions occur during the day.
Habitat	Cool, moist	Hot, dry	Hot, dry
% of plant species	95%	1%	3–4%

Figure 5.11 C_3, C_4, and CAM Pathways Compared. Most plants use the C_3 pathway, which is vulnerable to photorespiration in hot, dry weather. The C_4 and CAM pathways are adaptations that minimize photorespiration.

INVESTIGATING LIFE

5.7 Solar-Powered Sea Slugs

Most animals have an indirect relationship with photosynthesis. Plants and other autotrophs use the sun's energy in photosynthesis, and the food they make goes on to feed the animals.

But *Elysia chlorotica* is an unusual animal by all accounts (figure 5.12). This sea slug lives in salt marshes along the eastern coast of North America. As mentioned in this chapter's opening essay, *E. chlorotica* is solar-powered: it harbors chloroplasts in the lining of its gut.

These invertebrate animals do not inherit their solar panels from their parents; instead, they acquire the chloroplasts by eating algae called "water felt." As a young sea slug grazes, it punctures the yellow-green filaments of the algae and sucks out the cell's contents. The animal digests most of the nutrients, but cells lining the slug's gut absorb the chloroplasts. The organelles stay there for the rest of the animal's life, carrying out photosynthesis as if they were still in the alga's cells. Like a plant, the solar-powered sea slug can live on sunlight and air.

A chloroplast requires a few thousand genes to carry out photosynthesis. Although chloroplasts contain their own DNA, these genes encode less than 10% of the required proteins. DNA in a plant cell's nucleus makes up the difference. But slugs are animals, and the nuclei inside their cells presumably lack these critically important genes. How can the chloroplasts operate inside their mollusk partners?

Mary E. Rumpho, of the University of Maine, collaborated with James R. Manhart, of Texas A&M University, to find out the answer. They considered two possibilities. Either the chloroplasts can work inside the host slug's digestive tract without the help of supplemental genes, or the slug's own cells provide the necessary proteins.

The researchers tested the first possibility by searching the chloroplast's DNA for genes that are essential for photosynthesis. They discovered that a gene called *psbO* was missing from the chloroplast. The *psbO* gene encodes a protein that is an

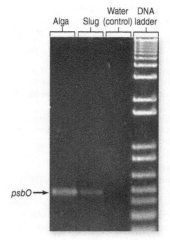

Water   DNA
Alga   Slug   (control)   ladder

psbO →

Figure 5.13
Photosynthesis Gene. Both algae and the "solar-powered" sea slug contain *psbO*, a gene required for photosynthesis. This electrophoresis gel sorts DNA fragments by size as they migrate from the top to the bottom of the gel. The "ladder" contains DNA pieces of known size, allowing the researchers to estimate the size of the DNA being studied.

essential part of photosystem II. Without *psbO*, photosynthesis is impossible. The researchers therefore rejected the hypothesis that the chloroplasts are autonomous.

That left the second possibility, which suggested that the slug's cells contain the DNA necessary to support the chloroplasts. The team looked for the *psbO* gene in the animal's DNA, and they found it (figure 5.13). Moreover, when they sequenced the *psbO* gene from the slug's genome, it was identical to the same gene in algae.

How could a gene required for photosynthesis have moved from a filamentous yellow-green alga to the genome of a sea slug? No one knows, but the researchers speculate that cells in a slug's digestive tract may have taken up fragments of algal DNA that spilled from partially eaten filaments.

Biologists do know that bacterial species often swap genes in a process called horizontal gene transfer. Rumpho and Manhart's study provides convincing evidence that horizontal gene transfer can and does occur between distantly related eukaryotes, too. Moreover, genetic evidence from many organisms suggests that horizontal gene transfer may have been extremely common throughout life's long history. As a result, many biologists are discarding the notion of a tidy evolutionary "tree" in favor of a messier, but perhaps more fascinating, evolutionary thicket.

Rumpho, Mary E., and seven colleagues, including James R. Manhart. 2008. Horizontal gene transfer of the algal nuclear gene *psbO* to the photosynthetic sea slug *Elysia chlorotica*. *Proceedings of the National Academy of Sciences*, vol. 105, pages 17867–17871.

5.7 MASTERING CONCEPTS

1. Explain the most important finding of this study, and describe the evidence the researchers used to arrive at their conclusion.

2. The researchers also looked for the *psbO* gene in pufferfish (a vertebrate animal) and slime molds (a nonphotosynthetic protist). The gene was absent in both species. How was this finding important to the interpretation of the results of this study?

Figure 5.12 A Slug with Solar Panels. The leaflike body of the sea slug *Elysia chlorotica* is typically 2 to 3 centimeters long.

Head

Digestive tract

CHAPTER SUMMARY

5.1 Life Depends on Photosynthesis

 3-D Animation
Photosynthesis

- **Autotrophs** are organisms that produce organic compounds from inorganic starting materials such as CO_2 and water. **Heterotrophs** rely on organic molecules as a carbon source.

A. Photosynthesis Builds Carbohydrates Out of Carbon Dioxide and Water

- **Photosynthesis** converts kinetic energy in light to potential energy in the covalent bonds of carbohydrates such as glucose. It is a redox reaction in which water is oxidized and CO_2 is reduced.
- Plants, algae, and some bacteria are photosynthetic.

B. Plants Use Carbohydrates in Many Ways

- Plants use glucose and other sugars to grow, generate ATP, nourish nonphotosynthetic plant parts, and produce cellulose and many other biochemicals. Most store excess carbohydrates as starch or sucrose.

C. The Evolution of Photosynthesis Changed Planet Earth

- Before photosynthesis evolved, organisms were heterotrophs. The first autotrophs made new food sources available.
- Over billions of years, oxygen produced in photosynthesis changed Earth's climate and the history of life.

5.2 Sunlight Is the Energy Source for Photosynthesis

A. What Is Light?

- Visible light is a small part of the **electromagnetic spectrum.**
- **Photons** move in waves. The shorter the **wavelength,** the more kinetic energy per photon. Visible light occurs in a spectrum of colors representing different wavelengths.

B. Photosynthetic Pigments Capture Light Energy

- **Chlorophyll** *a* is the primary photosynthetic pigment in plants. **Accessory pigments** absorb wavelengths of light that chlorophyll *a* cannot absorb.

C. Chloroplasts Are the Sites of Photosynthesis

- Plants exchange gases with the environment through **stomata.**
- Leaf **mesophyll** cells contain abundant **chloroplasts.**
- A chloroplast contains a gelatinous matrix called the **stroma. Grana** are stacks of **thylakoid** membranes. Photosynthetic pigments are embedded in the thylakoid membranes, which enclose the **thylakoid space.**
- A **photosystem** consists of **antenna pigments** and a **reaction center.**

5.3 Photosynthesis Occurs in Two Stages

- The **light reactions** of photosynthesis produce ATP and **NADPH;** these molecules provide energy and electrons for the sugar-producing **carbon reactions** (figure 5.14).

5.4 The Light Reactions Begin Photosynthesis

A. Light Striking Photosystem II Provides the Energy to Produce ATP

- Photosystem II captures light energy and sends electrons from reactive chlorophyll *a* to an **electron transport chain.**
- Electrons from chlorophyll are replaced with electrons from water. O_2 is the waste product.
- The energy released in the electron transport chain drives the active transport of protons into the thylakoid space. The protons diffuse out through channels in **ATP synthase.** This movement powers the phosphorylation of ADP to ATP.
- The coupling of the proton gradient and ATP formation is called **chemiosmotic phosphorylation.**

B. Electrons from Photosystem I Reduce NADP+ to NADPH

- Photosystem I receives electrons from the first electron transport chain. Light provides the energy to send the electrons to a second chain, which uses them to reduce NADP+. The product is NADPH.

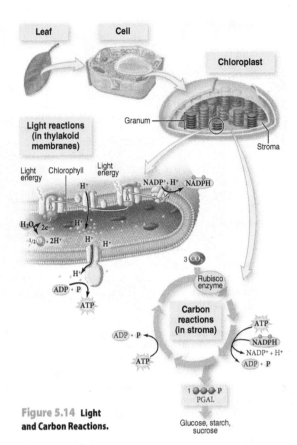

Figure 5.14 Light and Carbon Reactions.

5.5 The Carbon Reactions Produce Carbohydrates

- The carbon reactions use energy from ATP and electrons from NADPH in **carbon fixation** reactions that add CO_2 to organic compounds.
- In the **Calvin cycle, rubisco** catalyzes the reaction of CO_2 with **ribulose bisphosphate** (RuBP) to yield two molecules of PGA. These are converted to PGAL, the immediate product of photosynthesis. PGAL later becomes glucose and other carbohydrates.

5.6 C₃, C₄, and CAM Plants Use Different Carbon Fixation Pathways

- The Calvin cycle is also called the C_3 **pathway.** Most plant species are C_3 plants, which use only this pathway to fix carbon.
- **Photorespiration** wastes carbon and energy when rubisco reacts with O_2 instead of CO_2.
- The C_4 **pathway** reduces photorespiration by separating the light and carbon reactions into different cells. In mesophyll cells, CO_2 is fixed as a four-carbon molecule, which moves to a **bundle-sheath cell** and liberates CO_2 to be fixed again in the Calvin cycle.
- In the **CAM pathway,** desert plants such as cacti open their stomata and take in CO_2 at night, storing the fixed carbon in vacuoles. During the day, they split off CO_2 and fix it in chloroplasts in the same cells.

5.7 Investigating Life: Solar-Powered Sea Slugs

- The sea slug *Elysia chlorotica* contains chloroplasts acquired from its food, a filamentous alga. The slug's DNA includes a gene required for photosynthesis.

MULTIPLE CHOICE QUESTIONS

1. Where does the energy come from to drive photosynthesis?
   a. A chloroplast   c. The sun
   b. ATP   d. Glucose

2. Photosynthesis is an example of an _____ chemical reaction because _____.
   a. exergonic; energy is released by the reaction center pigment
   b. endergonic; light energy is used to build chemical bonds
   c. exergonic; light energy is captured by pigment molecules
   d. endergonic; the reactions occur inside a cell

3. The evolution of photosynthesis resulted in
   a. an increase in the amount of O_2 in the atmosphere.
   b. the initial appearance of heterotrophs.
   c. global warming.
   d. an increase in the amount of CO_2 in the atmosphere.

4. Only high-energy light can penetrate the ocean and reach photosynthetic organisms in coral reefs. What color of light would you predict these organisms use?
   a. Red   c. Blue
   b. Yellow   d. Orange

5. Identify the *second*-smallest structure in the following list: *photosystem, chlorophyll, granum, thylakoid*
   a. Photosystem   c. Granum
   b. Chlorophyll   d. Thylakoid

6. The light reactions and the carbon reactions are connected by the participation of which molecules?
   a. ATP and ADP   c. Glucose
   b. NADPH and NADP   d. Both a and b are correct.

7. Photorespiration becomes more likely when
   a. CO_2 concentrations are high in leaf cells.
   b. stomata remain closed in C_3 plants.
   c. glucose concentrations are low in leaf cells.
   d. ATP binds to rubisco.

8. A plant that opens its stomata only at night is a
   a. C_2 plant.   c. C_4 plant.
   b. C_3 plant.   d. CAM plant.

Answers to these questions are in appendix A.

WRITE IT OUT

1. Imagine that multiple simultaneous volcanic eruptions send black ash into Earth's atmosphere, making photosynthesis impossible anywhere on Earth for many years. What would be the consequence to plants? To animals? To microbes?

2. Other stars in the galaxy emit light at different wavelengths than the sun. If photosynthesis evolved on a planet around one of these stars, how might it be different from and similar to photosynthesis on Earth?

3. In some ways, chlorophyll can be thought of as a solar panel like the ones used to generate electricity at power plants. Using terms such as *granum, photosystem, ATP,* and *chlorophyll,* explain this comparison.

4. Would a plant grow better in a room painted blue or in a room painted green? Explain your answer.

5. Explain why some scientists call the light reactions the "energy converting reactions" and the carbon reactions the "energy storage reactions." Include ATP, NADPH, and sugar in your explanation.

6. Of the many groups of photosynthetic bacteria, only cyanobacteria use chlorophyll *a.* How does this observation support the hypothesis that cyanobacteria gave rise to the chloroplasts of today's plants and algae?

7. One of the classic experiments in photosynthesis occurred in 1771, when Joseph Priestley found that if he placed a mouse in an enclosed container with a lit candle, the mouse would die. But if he also added a plant to the container, the mouse could live. Priestley concluded that plants "purify" air, allowing animals to breathe. What is the biological basis for this observation?

8. When vegetables and flowers are grown in greenhouses in the winter, their growth rate greatly increases if the CO_2 concentration is raised to two or three times the level in the natural environment. What is the biological basis for the increased rate of growth?

9. Over the past decades, the CO_2 concentration in the atmosphere has increased.
   a. Predict the effect of increasing carbon dioxide concentrations on photorespiration.
   b. Scientists suggest that increasing CO_2 concentrations are leading to higher average global temperatures. If temperatures are increasing, does this change your answer to part (a)?

10. How does photosynthesis help compensate for increasing atmospheric CO_2? Where does the CO_2 go? Does cutting down forests likely increase or decrease the rate of CO_2 accumulation in the atmosphere?

11. How is the CAM pathway adaptive in a desert habitat?

12. Explain how C_4 photosynthesis is based on a spatial arrangement of structures, whereas CAM photosynthesis is temporally based.

13. Explain why each of the following misconceptions about photosynthesis is false:
    a. Only plants are autotrophs.
    b. Plants do not need cellular respiration because they carry out photosynthesis.
    c. Chlorophyll is the only plant pigment.

PULL IT TOGETHER

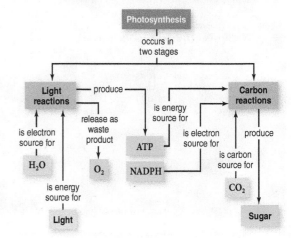

Figure 5.15 Pull It Together: Photosynthesis.

Refer to figure 5.15 and the chapter content to answer the following questions.

1. Where do electron transport chains fit into this concept map?

2. How would you incorporate the Calvin cycle, rubisco, C_3 plants, C_4 plants, and CAM plants into this concept map?

3. Where do humans and other heterotrophs fit into this concept map?

4. Build another small concept map showing the relationships among the terms *chloroplast, stroma, grana, thylakoid, photosystem,* and *chlorophyll.*

5. Add a connecting phrase to the concept map to show what happens to sugar after it is produced.

CHAPTER

6

How Cells Release Energy

Huge Meal. This African rock python is consuming a Thomson's gazelle.

Enhance your study | **BIOLOGY**
of this chapter with practice quizzes,
animations and videos, answer keys,
and downloadable study tools.
www.mhhe.com/hoefnagels

Eating for Life

THE AFRICAN ROCK PYTHON LAY IN WAIT FOR THE LONE GAZELLE. When the gazelle came close, the snake moved suddenly, positioning the victim's head and holding it in place while swiftly entwining its 9-meter-long body snugly around the mammal. Each time the gazelle exhaled, the snake squeezed, shutting down the victim's heart and lungs in less than a minute.

Thanks to the adaptations of its digestive system, the snake can swallow and digest a meal over half its own size. The reptile begins by opening its jaws at an angle of 130 degrees (compared with 30 degrees for the most gluttonous human) and places its mouth over the gazelle's head, using strong muscles to gradually envelop and push along the carcass. Saliva coats the prey, easing its journey to the snake's stomach. After several hours, the huge meal arrives at the stomach, and the remainder of the digestive tract readies itself for several weeks of dismantling the gazelle. Hydrochloric acid (HCl) builds up in the snake's stomach, and the output of digestive enzymes in the intestines increases 60-fold.

As the gazelle passes through the snake's digestive system, it breaks into clumps of cells. These cells disintegrate, releasing proteins, carbohydrates, and lipids. After the snake digests these macromolecules, the component parts are small enough to enter the blood and move to the body's tissues. The animal's cells absorb these smaller nutrient molecules. Then, in cellular respiration, energy in the bonds of the food molecules is transferred to the high-energy phosphate bonds of ATP. Afterward, only a few chunks of hair and bone will remain to be eliminated.

Our own eating habits may not seem to have much in common with those of the African rock python. After all, we typically eat many small meals a day; our bodies are not adapted to digest enormous prey in a single gulp. Nevertheless, the fruits, vegetables, meats, eggs, dairy products, and other foods that we consume are doing for us precisely what the gazelle's body is doing for the snake: The food molecules break down into nutrients that the cells use to make ATP.

In humans, snakes, and every other organism, nearly all activities depend on energy stored in ATP. Yet no organism eats ATP directly. This chapter describes how cells convert what we do eat—glucose and other food molecules—into those little ATP molecules that nothing can live without.

LEARNING OUTLINE

 6.1 Cells Use Energy in Food to Make ATP

6.2 Cellular Respiration Includes Three Main Processes

6.3 In Eukaryotic Cells, Mitochondria Produce Most ATP

6.4 Glycolysis Breaks Down Glucose to Pyruvate

 6.5 Aerobic Respiration Yields Abundant ATP

    A. Pyruvate Is Oxidized to Acetyl CoA

    B. The Krebs Cycle Produces ATP and Electron Carriers

    C. The Electron Transport Chain Drives ATP Formation

 6.6 How Many ATPs Can One Glucose Molecule Yield?

6.7 Other Food Molecules Enter the Energy-Extracting Pathways

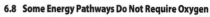 **6.8** Some Energy Pathways Do Not Require Oxygen

    A. Anaerobic Respiration Uses an Electron Acceptor Other than O_2

    B. Fermenters Acquire ATP Only from Glycolysis

 6.9 Photosynthesis and Respiration Are Ancient Pathways

6.10 Investigating Life: Hot Plants Offer Heat Reward

LEARN HOW TO LEARN
Don't Skip the Figures

As you read the narrative in the text, pay attention to the figures; they are there to help you learn. Some figures summarize the narrative, making it easier for you see the "big picture." Other illustrations show the parts of a structure or the steps in a process; still others summarize a technique or help you classify information. Also, remember that students use illustrations in different ways. Once you encounter a figure's callout, you may prefer to stop reading to absorb the entire figure, or you may switch back and forth between the narrative and the figure's parts. Being attentive to your preferences will help you to be more systematic as you study.

6.1 Cells Use Energy in Food to Make ATP

No cell can survive without **ATP**—adenosine triphosphate. Without this energy carrier, you could not have developed from a fertilized egg into an adult. You could not breathe, chew, talk on the phone, circulate your blood, blink your eyes, walk, or listen to music. Without ATP, a plant could not take up soil nutrients, grow, or produce flowers, fruits, and seeds. A fungus could not acquire food or produce mushrooms. A bacterial cell could not move or divide. Like a car without gasoline, a cell without ATP would simply die. ⓘ *ATP,* p. 76

ATP is essential because it powers nearly every activity that requires energy input in the cell: synthesis of DNA, RNA, proteins, carbohydrates, and lipids; active transport across the membranes surrounding cells and organelles; separation of duplicated chromosomes during cell division; movement of cilia and flagella; muscle contraction; and many others. This constant need for ATP explains the need for a steady food supply. All organisms, from giant redwood trees to whales to bacteria and archaea, use the potential energy stored in food to make ATP.

Where does the food come from in the first place? Chapter 5 explains the answer: In most ecosystems, plants and other autotrophs use photosynthesis to make organic molecules such as glucose ($C_6H_{12}O_6$) out of carbon dioxide (CO_2) and water (H_2O). Light supplies the energy. The carbohydrates produced in photosynthesis feed not only autotrophs but also all of the animals, fungi, and microbes that share the ecosystem.

All cells need ATP, but they don't all produce it in the same way. The pathways that generate ATP from food fall into three categories. In aerobic cellular respiration, the main subject of this chapter, a cell uses oxygen gas (O_2) and glucose to generate ATP. Plants, animals, and most microbes (including protists, fungi, bacteria, and archaea) use aerobic respiration. The other two pathways, anaerobic respiration and fermentation, generate ATP from glucose without using O_2. Section 6.8 describes these two processes, both of which are most common in microorganisms.

The overall equation for **aerobic respiration** is essentially the reverse of photosynthesis:

$$\text{glucose} + \text{oxygen} \longrightarrow \text{carbon dioxide} + \text{water} + \text{ATP}$$
$$C_6H_{12}O_6 + 6O_2 \longrightarrow 6CO_2 + 6H_2O + 36ATP$$

This equation reveals that aerobic cellular respiration requires organisms to acquire O_2 and get rid of CO_2 (figure 6.1). These gases simply diffuse across the cell membranes of single-celled organisms, but more complex organisms have specialized organs of gas exchange such as gills or lungs. In humans and many other animals, O_2 from inhaled air diffuses into the bloodstream across the walls of microscopic air sacs in the lungs. The circulatory system carries the inhaled O_2 to cells, where gas exchange occurs. O_2 diffuses into the cell's mitochondria, the sites of respiration. Meanwhile, CO_2 diffuses out of the cells and into the bloodstream. After moving from the blood into the lungs, the CO_2 is exhaled.

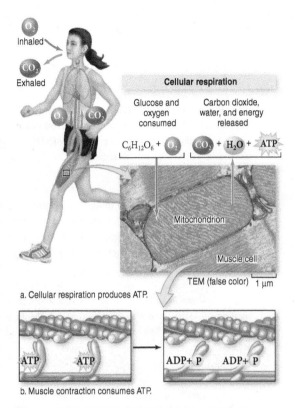

a. Cellular respiration produces ATP.

b. Muscle contraction consumes ATP.

Figure 6.1 Breathing and Cellular Respiration. (a) The athlete breathes in O_2, which is distributed to all cells. In mitochondria, O_2 participates in the reactions of cellular respiration. CO_2, a metabolic waste, is exhaled. (b) Energy-rich ATP generated in cellular respiration is used in muscle contraction, among many other cellular activities.

Many people mistakenly believe that plants do not use cellular respiration because they are photosynthetic. In fact, plants use O_2 to respire about half of the glucose they produce. Why do plants have a reputation for producing O_2, if they also consume it? The reason is that plants incorporate much of the remaining glucose into cellulose, starch, and other stored organic molecules. Therefore, they absorb much more CO_2 in photosynthesis than they release in respiration, and they release more O_2 than they consume.

The rest of this chapter describes how cells use the potential energy in food to generate ATP. Like photosynthesis, the journey entails several overlapping metabolic pathways and many different chemicals. But if we consider energy release in major stages, the logic emerges.

6.1 MASTERING CONCEPTS

1. Why do all organisms need ATP?
2. What are the three general ways to generate ATP from food, and which organisms use each pathway?
3. How do organisms get O_2 to their cells?
4. How can plants release more O_2 in photosynthesis than they consume in respiration?

6.2 Cellular Respiration Includes Three Main Processes

The chemical reaction that generates ATP is straightforward: an enzyme tacks a phosphate group onto ADP, yielding ATP. As described in chapter 4, however, ATP synthesis requires an input of energy. The metabolic pathways of respiration harvest potential energy from food molecules and use it to make ATP. This section briefly introduces these pathways; later sections explain them in more detail.

Like photosynthesis, respiration is an oxidation–reduction reaction. The pathways of aerobic respiration oxidize (remove electrons from) glucose and reduce (add electrons to) O_2. Because of oxygen's strong attraction for electrons, this reaction is "easy," like riding a bike downhill. It therefore releases energy, which the cell traps in the bonds of ATP. ⓘ *redox reactions*, p. 75

This reaction does not happen all at once. If a cell released all the potential energy in glucose's chemical bonds in one uncontrolled step, the sudden release of heat would destroy the cell; in effect, it would act like a tiny bomb. Rather, the chemical bonds and atoms in glucose are rearranged one step at a time, releasing a tiny bit of energy with each transformation. According to the second law of thermodynamics, some of this energy is lost as heat. But much of it is stored in the chemical bonds of ATP.

Biologists organize the intricate biochemical pathways of respiration into three main groups: glycolysis, the Krebs cycle, and electron transport (figure 6.2). In **glycolysis** (literally, "breaking sugar"), a six-carbon glucose molecule splits into two three-carbon **pyruvate** molecules. This process harvests energy in two forms. First, some of the electrons from glucose are transferred to an electron carrier molecule called **NADH** (nicotine adenine dinucleotide). Second, glycolysis generates two molecules of ATP.

Additional reactions, including a "transition step" and the **Krebs cycle,** oxidize the pyruvate and release CO_2. Enzymes rearrange atoms and bonds in ways that transfer the pyruvate's potential energy and electrons to ATP, NADH, and another electron carrier molecule—**FADH$_2$** (flavin adenine dinucleotide).

By the time the Krebs cycle is complete, the carbon atoms that made up the glucose are gone—liberated as CO_2. The cell has generated a few molecules of ATP, but most of the potential energy from glucose now lingers in the high-energy electron carriers, NADH and FADH$_2$. The cell uses them to generate more ATP.

The **electron transport chain** transfers energy-rich electrons from NADH and FADH$_2$ through a series of membrane proteins. As electrons pass from carrier to carrier in the electron transport chain, the energy is used to create a gradient of hydrogen ions. (Recall from chapter 2 that a hydrogen ion is simply a hydrogen atom stripped of its electron, leaving just a proton.) The mitochondrion uses the potential energy stored in this proton gradient to generate ATP. An enzyme called **ATP synthase** forms a channel in the membrane, releasing the protons and using their

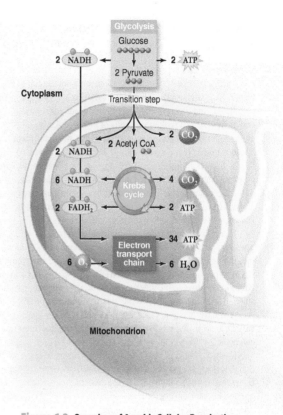

Figure 6.2 Overview of Aerobic Cellular Respiration.
A six-carbon glucose molecule is broken down to six molecules of carbon dioxide in three main stages: glycolysis, the Krebs cycle, and the electron transport chain. Along the way, energy is harvested as ATP. Except for glycolysis, these reactions occur inside the mitochondria of eukaryotic cells.

Tutorial
Overview of Respiration

potential energy to add phosphate to ADP. (As described in section 5.4, the same enzyme generates ATP in the light reactions of photosynthesis.) In the meantime, the "spent" electrons are transferred to O_2, generating water as a waste product.

A common misconception is that any ATP-generating pathway in a cell is considered "respiration." In fact, however, all forms of respiration, aerobic and anaerobic, use an electron transport chain. As you will see in section 6.8, fermentation is not respiration because it generates ATP from glycolysis only.

6.2 MASTERING CONCEPTS

1. Why do the reactions of respiration occur step-by-step instead of all at once?
2. What occurs in each of the three stages of cellular respiration?

116

GENERAL BIOLOGY

108   UNIT ONE   Science, Chemistry, and Cells

6.3 In Eukaryotic Cells, Mitochondria Produce Most ATP

Glycolysis always occurs in the cytoplasm, but the location of the other pathways in aerobic respiration depends on the cell type. In bacteria and archaea, the enzymes of the Krebs cycle are in the cytoplasm, and electron transport proteins are embedded in the cell membrane. The eukaryotic cells of protists, plants, fungi, and animals, however, contain organelles called **mitochondria** that house the other reactions of cellular respiration (figure 6.3).

A mitochondrion is bounded by two membranes, an outer membrane and a highly folded inner membrane. **Cristae** are folds of the inner membrane. The **intermembrane compartment** is the area between the two membranes, and the mitochondrial **matrix** is the space enclosed within the inner membrane.

In a eukaryotic cell, the two pyruvate molecules produced in glycolysis cross both of the mitochondrial membranes and move into the matrix. Here, enzymes cleave pyruvate and carry out the Krebs cycle. Then, $FADH_2$ and NADH from glycolysis and the Krebs cycle move to the inner mitochondrial membrane, which is studded with many copies of the electron transport proteins and ATP synthase. The inner membrane's cristae greatly increase the surface area on which the reactions of the electron transport chain can occur.

Electron transport chains and ATP synthase also occur in the thylakoid membranes of chloroplasts, which generate ATP in the light reactions of photosynthesis (see chapter 5). Similar enzymes operate in respiring bacteria and archaea, making ATP synthase one of the most highly conserved proteins over evolutionary time.

Mitochondria and chloroplasts share another similarity, too: Both types of organelles contain DNA and ribosomes. Mitochondrial DNA encodes ATP synthase and most of the proteins of the electron transport chain. Not surprisingly, a person with abnormal versions of these genes may be very ill or even die. The worst mitochondrial diseases affect the muscular and nervous systems. Muscle and nerve cells are especially energy-hungry: Each one may contain as many as 10,000 mitochondria. When their mitochondria fail, these cells cannot carry out their functions.

6.3   MASTERING CONCEPTS

1. What are the parts of a mitochondrion?
2. Which respiratory reactions occur in each part of the mitochondrion?

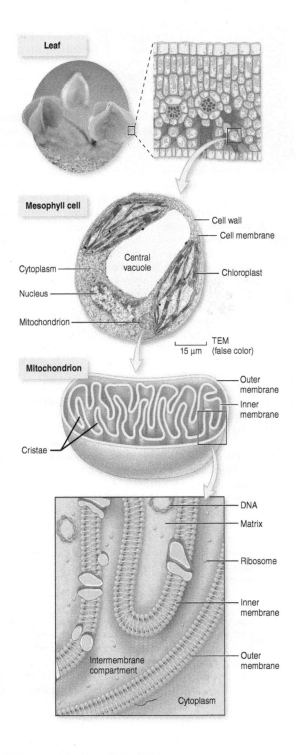

Figure 6.3   Anatomy of a Mitochondrion. Eukaryotic cells, such as the ones that make up leaves, contain mitochondria that provide most of the cell's ATP. Each mitochondrion includes two membranes. The inner membrane encloses fluid called the mitochondrial matrix, and the space between the inner and outer membranes is the intermembrane compartment.

6.4 Glycolysis Breaks Down Glucose to Pyruvate

Glycolysis is a more-or-less universal metabolic pathway that splits glucose into two three-carbon pyruvate molecules. The name of the pathway reflects its function: *glyco-* means sugar, and *-lysis* means to break.

The entire process of glycolysis requires 10 steps, all of which occur in the cell's cytoplasm (figure 6.4). None of the steps requires O_2, so cells can use glycolysis in both oxygen-rich and anaerobic environments.

The reactions of glycolysis are divided into two stages, the first of which is labeled "energy investment" in figure 6.4. The cell spends two molecules of ATP to activate glucose, redistributing energy in the molecule and splitting it in half. Then, in the "energy harvest" stage, the cell generates a return on its initial investment, producing two molecules of NADH plus four molecules of ATP. Overall, the net gain is two NADHs and two ATPs per molecule of glucose.

The ATP produced in glycolysis is formed by **substrate-level phosphorylation,** which means that an enzyme transfers a phosphate group directly from a high-energy "donor" molecule to ADP. Unlike chemiosmotic phosphorylation, which is described in section 6.5, this method of producing ATP does not require a proton gradient or the ATP synthase enzyme.

Glucose contains considerable bond energy, but cells recover only a small portion of it as ATP and NADH during glycolysis. Most of the potential energy of the original glucose molecule remains in the two pyruvate molecules. As you will see, the pathways of aerobic respiration extract much more of that energy.

6.4 | MASTERING CONCEPTS

1. Overall, what happens in glycolysis?
2. How is substrate-level phosphorylation different from chemiosmotic phosphorylation?
3. What is the net gain of ATP and NADH for each glucose molecule undergoing glycolysis?

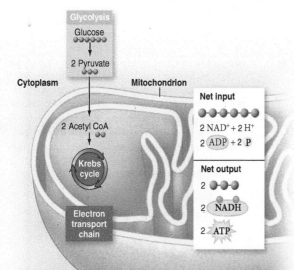

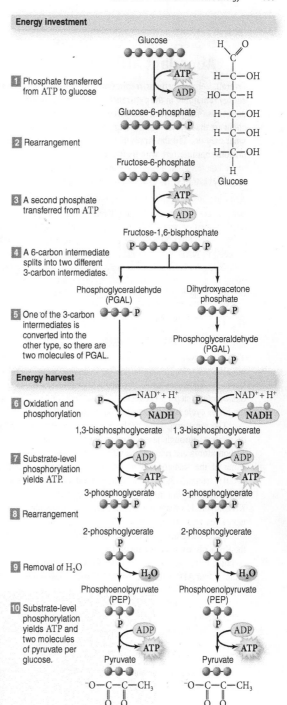

Figure 6.4 Glycolysis. Glucose splits into two pyruvate molecules, producing a net yield of two ATPs and two NADHs. These reactions occur in the cytoplasm. The illustration to the left shows an overview of glycolysis, and the entire 10-step process appears above. (Each gray sphere represents a carbon atom.)

3-D Animation Glycolysis

6.5 Aerobic Respiration Yields Abundant ATP

Overall, aerobic cellular respiration taps much of the potential energy remaining in the pyruvate molecules that emerge from the pathways of glycolysis. The Krebs cycle and electron transport chain are the key ATP-generating processes. This section explains what they do, and the Apply It Now box on page 112 describes poisons that interfere with their work.

A. Pyruvate Is Oxidized to Acetyl CoA

After glycolysis, pyruvate moves into the mitochondrial matrix, but it is not directly used in the Krebs cycle. Instead, a preliminary "transition step" further oxidizes each pyruvate molecule (figure 6.5). First, a molecule of CO_2 is removed, and NAD^+ is reduced to NADH. The remaining two-carbon molecule, called an acetyl group, is transferred to a coenzyme to form acetyl coenzyme A (abbreviated acetyl CoA). **Acetyl CoA** is the compound that enters the Krebs cycle. ⓘ *coenzymes*, p. 79

B. The Krebs Cycle Produces ATP and Electron Carriers

The Krebs cycle completes the oxidation of each acetyl group, releasing CO_2 (figure 6.6). The cycle begins when acetyl CoA sheds the coenzyme and combines with a four-carbon molecule, oxaloacetate (step 1). The resulting six-carbon molecule is citrate; the Krebs cycle is therefore also called the citric acid cycle.

The remaining steps in the Krebs cycle rearrange and oxidize citrate through several intermediates. Along the way, two carbon atoms are released as CO_2 (steps 2 and 3). In addition, some of the transformations transfer electrons to NADH and $FADH_2$ (steps 2, 3, 5, and 6); others produce ATP by substrate-level phosphorylation (step 4). Eventually, the molecules in the Krebs cycle re-create the original acceptor molecule, oxaloacetate. The cycle can now repeat.

Since one glucose molecule yields two acetyl CoA molecules, the Krebs cycle turns twice for each glucose. Thus, the combined net output to this point (glycolysis, acetyl CoA formation, and the Krebs cycle) is four ATP molecules, 10 NADH molecules, and two $FADH_2$ molecules. All six carbon atoms are gone, released as CO_2.

Besides continuing the breakdown of glucose, the Krebs cycle also has another function not directly related to respiration. The cell uses intermediate compounds formed in the Krebs cycle to manufacture other organic molecules, such as amino acids or fats. Section 6.7 explains that the reverse process also occurs; amino acids and fats can enter the Krebs cycle to generate energy from food sources other than carbohydrates.

C. The Electron Transport Chain Drives ATP Formation

The products generated so far are CO_2, ATP, NADH, and $FADH_2$. The cell ejects the CO_2 as waste and uses ATP to fuel essential

Tutorial
Electron Transport Chain

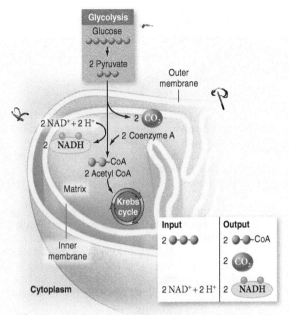

Figure 6.5 Transition Step. After pyruvate moves into a mitochondrion, it is oxidized to form an acetyl group, CO_2, and NADH. The acetyl group joins with coenzyme to form acetyl CoA, the molecule that enters the Krebs cycle.

processes. But what becomes of the NADH and $FADH_2$? An electron transport chain in the inner mitochondrial membrane harnesses the potential energy of these electron carriers as well.

The electron transport chain uses the energy from NADH and $FADH_2$ in stages (figure 6.7). The first protein in the chain accepts electrons from NADH; $FADH_2$ donates its electrons to the second protein. The electrons then pass to the next protein in the chain, and the next, and so on. The final electron acceptor is O_2, which combines with hydrogen ions to form water. Along the way, some of the proteins in the electron transport chain use energy from the electrons to pump hydrogen ions (H^+) from the matrix into the intermembrane compartment.

The electron transport chain therefore uses the energy in NADH and $FADH_2$ to establish a proton gradient across the inner mitochondrial membrane. As explained in chapter 4, a gradient represents a form of potential energy. The mitochondrion harvests this energy as ATP in the final stage of cellular respiration, with the help of the ATP synthase enzyme. In **chemiosmotic phosphorylation,** protons move down their gradient through ATP synthase back into the matrix, and ADP is phosphorylated to ATP. The ATP synthase enzyme therefore captures the potential energy of the proton gradient and saves it in a form the cell can use: ATP.

6.5 MASTERING CONCEPTS

1. Pyruvate has three carbon atoms; an acetyl group has only two. What happens to the other carbon atom?
2. How does the Krebs cycle generate CO_2, ATP, NADH, and $FADH_2$?
3. How do NADH and $FADH_2$ power ATP formation?
4. What is the role of O_2 in the electron transport chain?

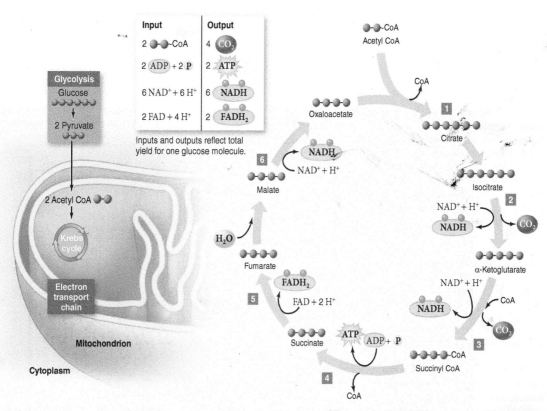

Figure 6.6 Krebs Cycle. In the mitochondrial matrix, (1) acetyl CoA enters the Krebs cycle and (2, 3) is oxidized to two molecules of CO_2. (4, 5, 6) In the rest of the Krebs cycle, potential energy is trapped as ATP, NADH, and $FADH_2$. The left half of this figure summarizes the inputs, outputs, and location of the Krebs cycle; the right half shows the entire cycle, step-by-step.

3-D Animation
Krebs Cycle

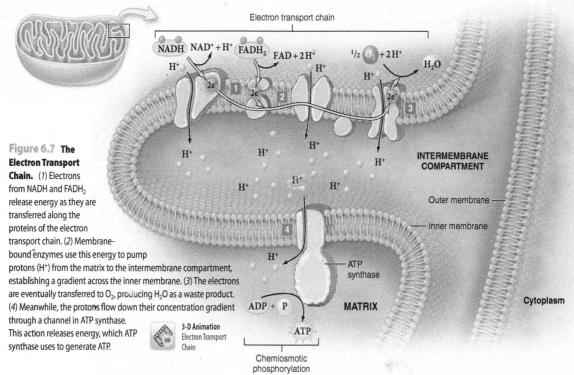

Figure 6.7 The Electron Transport Chain. (1) Electrons from NADH and $FADH_2$ release energy as they are transferred along the proteins of the electron transport chain. (2) Membrane-bound enzymes use this energy to pump protons (H^+) from the matrix to the intermembrane compartment, establishing a gradient across the inner membrane. (3) The electrons are eventually transferred to O_2, producing H_2O as a waste product. (4) Meanwhile, the protons flow down their concentration gradient through a channel in ATP synthase. This action releases energy, which ATP synthase uses to generate ATP.

3-D Animation
Electron Transport Chain

6.6 How Many ATPs Can One Glucose Molecule Yield?

To estimate the yield of ATP produced from every glucose molecule that enters aerobic cellular respiration, we can add the maximum number of ATPs generated in glycolysis, the Krebs cycle, and the electron transport chain (figure 6.8).

Substrate-level phosphorylation yields two ATPs from glycolysis and two ATPs from the Krebs cycle (one ATP each from two turns of the cycle). These are the only steps that produce ATP directly. In addition, each glucose yields two NADH molecules from glycolysis and two more from acetyl CoA production. Two turns of the Krebs cycle yield an additional six NADHs and two FADH$_2$s.

In theory, the ATP yield from electron transport is three ATPs per NADH and two ATPs per FADH$_2$. Electrons from the 10 NADHs from glycolysis and the Krebs cycle therefore yield up to 30 ATPs; electrons from the two FADH$_2$ molecules yield four more. Add the four ATPs from substrate-level phosphorylation, and the total is 38 ATPs per glucose. However, NADH from glycolysis must be shuttled into the mitochondrion, usually at a cost of one ATP for each NADH. This reduces the net theoretical production of ATPs to 36.

In reality, some protons leak across the inner mitochondrial membrane on their own, and the cell spends some energy to move pyruvate and ADP into the matrix. These "expenses" reduce the actual ATP yield to about 30 per glucose. The number of calories stored in 30 ATPs is about 32% of the total calories stored in the glucose bonds; the rest of the potential energy in glucose is lost as heat. This may seem wasteful, but for a biological process, it is reasonably efficient. To put this energy yield into perspective, an automobile uses only about 20% to 25% of the energy contained in gasoline's chemical bonds; the rest is lost as heat.

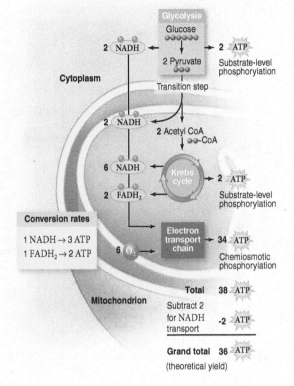

Figure 6.8 Energy Yield of Respiration. Breaking down glucose to carbon dioxide can yield as many as 36 ATPs, mostly from chemiosmotic phosphorylation.

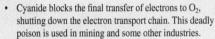

6.6 MASTERING CONCEPTS

1. Explain how to arrive at the estimate that each glucose molecule theoretically yields 36 ATPs.

2. How does the actual ATP yield compare to the theoretical yield?

Apply It **Now**

Some Poisons Inhibit Respiration

Many toxic chemicals kill by blocking one or more reactions in respiration. Poisons are therefore the tools of murderous villains—and of biochemists. The judicious use of poisons in isolated cells (or even isolated mitochondria) can reveal much about the chemistry of the Krebs cycle and electron transport chain. The following lists a few examples of chemicals that inhibit respiration:

Krebs cycle inhibitor:
- Arsenic interferes with several essential chemical reactions. For example, arsenic binds to part of a biochemical needed for the formation of acetyl CoA. It therefore blocks the Krebs cycle.

Electron transport inhibitors:
- Some mercury compounds are toxic because they stop an oxidation–reduction reaction early in the electron transport chain. Mercury is used in some thermometers, in fluorescent lights, and in many industrial applications.

- Cyanide blocks the final transfer of electrons to O_2, shutting down the electron transport chain. This deadly poison is used in mining and some other industries.

- Carbon monoxide (CO) blocks electron transport at the same point as cyanide. This colorless, odorless gas is a byproduct of incomplete fuel combustion. CO from unvented heaters, stoves, and fireplaces can accumulate to deadly levels in homes. Car exhaust and cigarette smoke are other sources of CO.

Chemiosmotic phosphorylation inhibitors:
- The insecticide 2,4-dinitrophenol (DNP) kills by making the inner mitochondrial membrane permeable to protons, blocking formation of the proton gradient necessary to drive ATP synthesis.

- Oligomycin blocks the phosphorylation of ADP by inhibiting the part of the ATP synthase enzyme that lets the protons through. Oligomycin is mostly used in laboratory studies of respiration.

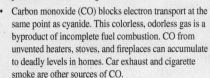

6.7 Other Food Molecules Enter the Energy-Extracting Pathways

So far, we have focused on the complete oxidation of glucose. But food also includes starch, proteins, and lipids that contribute calories to the diet. These molecules also enter the energy pathways (figure 6.9).

The digestion of starch from potatoes, wheat, and other carbohydrate-rich food begins in the mouth and continues in the small intestine. Enzymes snip the long starch chains into individual glucose monomers, which generate ATP as described in this chapter. Another polysaccharide, glycogen, follows essentially the same path as starch. ⓘ *carbohydrates*, p. 31

Proteins are digested into monomers called amino acids. The cell does not typically use these amino acids to produce ATP; instead, most of them are incorporated into new proteins. When an organism depletes its immediate carbohydrate supplies, however, cells may use amino acids as an energy source. First, nitrogen is stripped from the amino acid and excreted, often as urea. The remainder of each molecule enters the energy pathways as pyruvate, acetyl CoA, or an intermediate of the Krebs cycle, depending on the amino acid. ⓘ *amino acids*, p. 32

Meanwhile, enzymes in the small intestine digest fat molecules from food into glycerol and three fatty acids, which enter the bloodstream and move into the body's cells. (The Burning Question on page 114 describes a diet pill that blocks this

process.) Enzymes convert the glycerol to pyruvate, which then proceeds through the rest of cellular respiration as though it came directly from glucose. The fatty acids enter the mitochondria, where they are cut into many two-carbon pieces that are released as acetyl CoA. From here, the pathways continue as they would for glucose. ⓘ *lipids*, p. 36

Figure It Out

Suppose that each of a fat molecules's three fatty acid chains contains 16 carbon atoms. How many acetyl CoA molecules can a cell generate from this fat molecule?

Answer: 24 (8 acetyl CoA per chain x 3 chains)

Fats contain more calories per gram than any other food molecule; after all, a single fat molecule may yield dozens of two-carbon acetyl CoA groups for the Krebs cycle. Conversely, the body can also store excess energy from either carbohydrates or fat by doing the reverse: diverting acetyl CoA away from the Krebs cycle and using the two-carbon fragments to build fat molecules. These lipids are stored in fat tissue that the body can use for energy if food becomes scarce.

6.7 MASTERING CONCEPTS

1. At which points do digested polysaccharides, proteins, and fats enter the energy pathways?
2. How does the body store extra calories as fat?

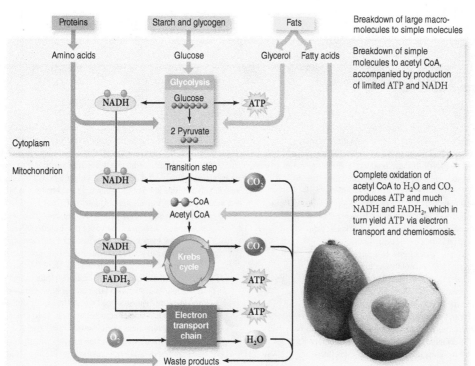

Figure 6.9 How Other Foods Enter the Energy Pathways. Most cells use carbohydrates as a primary source of energy, but cells can also use amino acids and lipids to generate ATP.

6.8 Some Energy Pathways Do Not Require Oxygen

Most of the known organisms on Earth, including humans, use aerobic cellular respiration. Nevertheless, life thrives without O_2 in waterlogged soils, deep puncture wounds, sewage treatment plants, and your own digestive tract, to name just a few places. In the absence of O_2, the microbes in these habitats generate ATP using anaerobic metabolic pathways. Two examples are anaerobic respiration and fermentation (figure 6.10).

A. Anaerobic Respiration Uses an Electron Acceptor Other than O_2

Anaerobic respiration is essentially the same as aerobic respiration, except that an inorganic molecule other than O_2 is the electron acceptor at the end of the electron transport chain. Alternative electron acceptors include NO_3^- (nitrate), SO_4^{2-} (sulfate), and CO_2. The number of ATPs generated per molecule of glucose depends on the electron acceptor, but it is always lower than the ATP yield for aerobic respiration.

Many bacteria and archaea generate ATP by anaerobic respiration, and they play starring roles in nutrient cycles wherever O_2 is scarce. For example, in waterlogged, oxygen-poor soils, bacteria that use NO_3^- as an electron acceptor begin a chain reaction

Figure 6.10 Alternative Metabolic Pathways. If O_2 is available, most organisms generate ATP in aerobic respiration. Two other pathways, anaerobic respiration and fermentation, can occur in the absence of O_2. Both alternatives yield less ATP than does aerobic respiration.

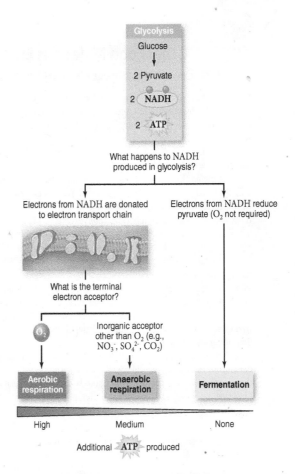

Glycolysis
Glucose
2 Pyruvate
2 NADH
2 ATP

What happens to NADH produced in glycolysis?

Electrons from NADH are donated to electron transport chain

Electrons from NADH reduce pyruvate (O_2 not required)

What is the terminal electron acceptor?

O_2

Inorganic acceptor other than O_2 (e.g., NO_3^-, SO_4^{2-}, CO_2)

| Aerobic respiration | Anaerobic respiration | Fermentation |

High | Medium | None

Additional ATP produced

Burning Question

How do diet pills work?

Ads for diet pills are everywhere. Some are for weight-loss drugs that the U.S. Food and Drug Administration (FDA) has approved as safe and effective. Others are for dietary supplements that are not subject to FDA approval at all. All of these products, and their promises of effortless weight loss, may seem to be a dream come true. How do they work?

The FDA has approved three prescription weight-loss drugs. One is orlistat (Xenical); the over-the-counter drug Alli is a low-dose version of the same medicine. This drug interferes with lipase, the enzyme that digests fat in the small intestine. Undigested fat leaves the body in feces; orlistat therefore reduces calorie intake by reducing the body's absorption of high-energy fat molecules. The other two prescription weight-loss drugs are sibutramine (Meridia) and phentermine (Adipex-P). These medicines also reduce calorie intake, but in a different way: they suppress appetite.

All three prescription drugs can help a person lose weight but only if combined with exercise, a low-calorie diet, and behavior modification. Each also has side effects.

Dietary supplements greatly outnumber prescription weight-loss drugs. The FDA does not require the manufacturers of dietary supplements to show that the remedies are either safe or effective. Ads for "natural" supplements such as hoodia, green tea extract, and fucoxanthin make extraordinary promises of rapid weight loss, but the claims remain largely untested in scientific studies. The mechanism by which they work (if they work at all) usually remains unclear.

Unfortunately, some dietary supplements have serious side effects. Ephedra is one example. Before 2004, ephedra was marketed as a weight-loss aid and energy booster, but studies eventually linked it to fatal seizures, strokes, and heart attacks. The FDA therefore banned the sale of ephedra in the United States in 2004. An herb called bitter orange has taken its place in many "ephedra-free" weight-loss aids. But bitter orange has side effects that are similar to ephedra's, and its safety remains unknown.

Submit your burning question to
Marielle.Hoefnagels@mheducation.com

that ends with the production of nitrogen gas (N_2). This gas drifts into the atmosphere, leaving the soil less fertile for plant growth. Bacteria that live in wetlands may use SO_4^{2-}, producing smelly hydrogen sulfide (H_2S) as a byproduct. And archaea living inside the intestines of cattle use CO_2 as an electron acceptor, generating methane gas (CH_4). The methane, which the cattle emit as belches and flatulence, is one of the greenhouse gases implicated in global climate change. ⓘ *carbon cycle,* p. 780; *nitrogen cycle,* p. 781

Figure It Out

Compare the number of molecules of ATP generated from 100 glucose molecules undergoing aerobic respiration versus fermentation.

Answer: 3600 (theoretical yield) for aerobic respiration; 200 for fermentation

B. Fermenters Acquire ATP Only from Glycolysis

Tutorial
Fermentation

Some microorganisms, including many inhabitants of your digestive tract, use fermentation. In these organisms, glycolysis still yields two ATPs, two NADHs, and two molecules of pyruvate per molecule of glucose. But the NADH does not donate its electrons to an electron transport chain, nor is the pyruvate further oxidized.

Instead, in **fermentation,** electrons from NADH reduce pyruvate. This process regenerates NAD^+ so that glycolysis can continue, but it generates no additional ATP. Fermentation is therefore far less efficient than respiration. Not surprisingly, fermentation is common among microorganisms that live in sugar-rich environments where food is essentially unlimited.

Some microorganisms make their entire living by fermentation. An example is *Entamoeba histolytica,* a protist that causes a form of dysentery in humans. Others, including the gut-dwelling bacterium *Escherichia coli,* use O_2 when it is available but switch to fermentation when it is not. Most multicellular organisms, however, require too much energy to rely on fermentation exclusively.

Of the many fermentation pathways that exist, one of the most familiar produces ethanol (an alcohol). In **alcoholic fermentation,** pyruvate is converted to CO_2 and ethanol, while NADH is oxidized to produce NAD^+ (figure 6.11a). Alcoholic fermentation produces wine from grapes, beer from barley, and cider from apples.

In **lactic acid fermentation,** a cell uses NADH to reduce pyruvate, but in this case, the products are NAD^+ and lactic acid or its close relative, lactate (figure 6.11b). The bacterium *Lactobacillus,* for example, ferments the lactose in milk, producing lactic acid that gives yogurt its sour taste. Bacteria can also ferment sugars in cabbage to produce the acids in sauerkraut.

Fermentation also occurs in human muscle cells. During vigorous exercise, muscles work so strenuously that they consume their available oxygen supply. In this "oxygen debt" condition, the muscle cells can acquire ATP only from glycolysis. The cells use fermentation to generate NAD^+ so that glycolysis can continue. Lactate concentrations therefore rise. After the race, when the circulatory system catches up with the muscles' demand for O_2, liver cells convert lactate back to pyruvate. Mitochondria then process the pyruvate as usual. ⓘ *fermentation in muscle cells,* p. 602

Many people believe that lactic acid buildup causes a pH drop in muscle cells, provoking soreness a day or two after intense exercise. Two lines of evidence, however, suggest that this idea is a myth. First, muscle cells produce lactate (not lactic acid); lactate does not change the cytoplasm's pH. Second, cells consume the lactate shortly after the workout ends, so it is unlikely to cause pain days later. Microscopic tears in muscle tissue are now thought to be the culprit responsible for delayed muscle soreness.

6.8   MASTERING CONCEPTS

1. What are some examples of alternative electron acceptors used in anaerobic respiration?
2. How many ATPs per glucose does fermentation produce?
3. What are two examples of fermentation pathways?

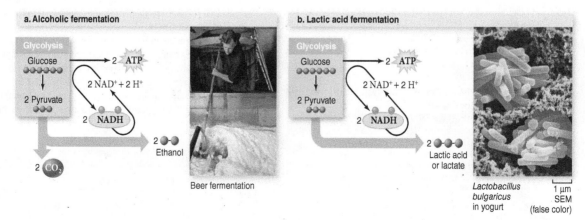

Figure 6.11 Fermentation. In fermentation, ATP comes only from glycolysis. (a) Yeasts produce ethanol and carbon dioxide by alcoholic fermentation. The man in the photograph is stirring a large vat of fermenting beer. (b) Lactic acid fermentation occurs in some bacteria and, occasionally, in mammalian muscle cells. The photograph shows *Lactobacillus* bacteria in yogurt.

6.9 Photosynthesis and Respiration Are Ancient Pathways

As you may have noticed, photosynthesis, glycolysis, and cellular respiration are intimately related (table 6.1 and figure 6.12). The carbohydrate product of photosynthesis—glucose—is the starting material for glycolysis. The O_2 released in photosynthesis becomes the final electron acceptor in aerobic respiration. CO_2 generated in respiration enters the carbon reactions in chloroplasts. Finally, photosynthesis splits water produced by aerobic respiration. Together, these energy reactions sustain life. How might they have arisen?

Glycolysis is probably the most ancient of the energy pathways because it occurs in virtually all cells. Glycolysis evolved when the atmosphere lacked or had very little O_2. These reactions enabled the earliest organisms to extract energy from simple organic compounds in the nonliving environment. Photosynthesis, in turn, may have evolved from glycolysis; some of the reactions of the Calvin cycle are the reverse of some of those of glycolysis. ⓘ Calvin cycle, p. 98

The first photosynthetic organisms could not have been plants, because such complex organisms were not present on the early Earth. Rather, photosynthesis may have originated in an anaerobic cell that used hydrogen sulfide (H_2S) instead of water as an electron donor. These first photosynthetic microorganisms would have released sulfur, rather than O_2, into the environment. Eventually, changes in pigment molecules enabled some of these organisms to use water instead of H_2S as an electron source. Fossil evidence of cyanobacteria shows that oxygen-generating photosynthesis arose at least 3.5 billion years ago. Once this pathway started, the accumulation of O_2 in the primitive atmosphere altered life on Earth forever (see section 5.1).

Later, in a process called endosymbiosis, a large "host" cell engulfed one of those ancient cyanobacteria and thereby transformed itself into a eukaryotic-like cell, complete with chloroplasts. Mitochondria evolved in a similar way, when larger cells engulfed bacteria capable of using O_2.

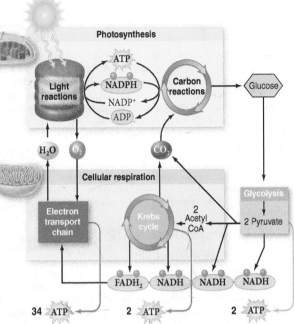

Figure 6.12 Connections Between Photosynthesis and Respiration. An overview of metabolism illustrates how biological energy reactions are interrelated.

The double membranes of both chloroplasts and mitochondria are a consequence of endosymbiosis. The engulfed bacterium's cell membrane developed into each organelle's inner membrane, and the vesicle membrane remained as the outer membrane. Endosymbiosis therefore explains why the electron transport chain is in the bacterial cell membrane but in the inner mitochondrial membrane of a eukaryotic cell. The observation that both mitochondria and chloroplasts contain DNA and ribosomes lends additional support to the endosymbiosis theory. ⓘ endosymbiosis, p. 311

As time went on, different types of complex cells probably diverged, leading to the evolution of a great variety of eukaryotic organisms. Today, the interrelationships among photosynthesis, glycolysis, and aerobic respiration, along with the great similarities of these reactions in diverse species, demonstrate a unifying theme of biology: All types of organisms are related at the biochemical level.

TABLE **6.1** **Photosynthesis and Respiration Compared**

	Photosynthesis	Respiration
Food	Produced	Consumed
Energy	Stored as glucose	Released from glucose
Light	Required	Not required
H_2O	Consumed	Released
CO_2	Consumed	Released
O_2	Released	Consumed

6.9   MASTERING CONCEPTS

1. Which energy pathway is probably the most ancient? What is the evidence?
2. Why must the first metabolic pathways have been anaerobic?
3. What is the evidence that photosynthesis may have evolved from glycolysis?

6.10 Hot Plants Offer Heat Reward

Think of an organism that feels warm. Did you think of yourself? A puppy? Your cat? Chances are you thought of a mammal or perhaps a bird, but certainly not a plant. Yet some plants, including *Philodendron,* do warm themselves (or at least their reproductive parts) to several degrees above ambient temperature (figure 6.13). How do they do it and, more important, what do they get out of it?

Philodendron flowers generate heat with a metabolic pathway involving the electron transport chain. As described in section 6.5, electrons from NADH and $FADH_2$ pass along a series of proteins embedded in the inner mitochondrial membrane. Along the way, the proteins pump H^+ into the space between the two mitochondrial membranes; ATP synthase uses the resulting proton gradient to generate ATP. The last protein in the electron transport chain dumps the electrons on O_2, yielding water as a waste product.

Plants and a few other types of organisms have another pathway, dubbed "alternative oxidase," that diverts electrons from the electron transport chain. NADH and $FADH_2$ still donate electrons to a protein in the chain, but that electron acceptor transfers them immediately to O_2 instead of to the next carrier. The pathway therefore does not help the mitochondrion generate ATP. It does, however, generate more heat than conventional respiration—after all, potential energy that is not harvested as ATP must be lost as heat.

So what does *Philodendron* gain by warming its flowers? One clue comes from the observation that the plant heats *just* its flowers and not its leaves, stem, or roots. Since flowers are reproductive parts, could the hot blooms somehow improve the plant's reproductive success?

In many plants, reproduction depends on animals that carry pollen from flower to flower. The plants may give away free meals of sweet nectar that lure pollinators such as insects, birds, and mammals. As the animal collects the offering, it brushes against the pollen-producing (male) flower parts. It then deposits the pollen on the female part of the next flower it visits.

Australian researcher Roger Seymour and his colleagues wondered whether heat from the flowers of *Philodendron solimoesense* helped the plant attract pollinators. They did a simple set of experiments to find out. First, they measured the temperature of *Philodendron* flowers. The central spike peaked at 40°C, about 15° above ambient

**Figure 6.13
Hot Bloom.**
The central part of this *Philodendron solimoesense* flower generates heat.

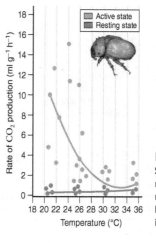

Figure 6.14 Energy Saver. Resting beetles respired at the same rate no matter what the temperature, but active beetles saved energy in warmer surroundings.

temperature, while the floral chamber was consistently a few degrees warmer than the surrounding air.

Next, the researchers turned their attention to beetles known to pollinate the flowers. The team used a device called a respirometer to measure the amount of CO_2 generated by active and resting beetles at a range of temperatures from 20°C to 35°C. Since respiration generates CO_2 as a waste product, the respirometer indirectly measures how much energy an organism uses. Resting beetles emitted approximately the same amount of CO_2 at all temperatures, but active ones (such as those that would visit flowers) produced only about one tenth as much CO_2 at 30°C as they did at 20°C (figure 6.14). This observation made sense, since warm flight muscles use energy more efficiently than cold ones.

Finally, the researchers used their data to calculate the "energy-saving factor" attributed to floral heat. They concluded that the beetles used 2.0 to 4.8 times more energy at ambient temperature than at the temperature of the warmed flower, depending on time of night. The beetles therefore save energy simply by loitering on or near the flowers, energy that they can use to find food or lure mates even as they pollinate the plant. The hot flowers—courtesy of the seemingly wasteful alternative oxidase pathway—therefore enhance the reproductive success of both *Philodendron* and the beetles.

Seymour, Roger S., Craig R. White, and Marc Gibernau. November 20, 2003. Heat reward for insect pollinators. *Nature,* vol. 426, pages 243–244.

6.10 MASTERING CONCEPTS

1. What hypothesis were the researchers testing, and what experiments did they design to help them test the hypothesis?

2. Suppose you hold one group of active beetles at 20°C and another group at 30°C. After several hours, you place each beetle in a device that measures how far the animal can fly at 20°C. Which group of beetles do you predict will fly farther?

118   **UNIT ONE**   Science, Chemistry, and Cells

CHAPTER SUMMARY

6.1 Cells Use Energy in Food to Make ATP

- Every cell requires **ATP** to power reactions that require energy input.
- **Aerobic respiration** is a biochemical pathway that produces ATP by extracting energy from glucose in the presence of oxygen.
- In humans, lungs acquire the oxygen used in aerobic cellular respiration.
- Autotrophs such as plants also use aerobic respiration to generate ATP.
- Some organisms use anaerobic respiration or fermentation.

6.2 Cellular Respiration Includes Three Main Processes

3-D Animation
Cellular Respiration

- **Glycolysis** is the first step in harvesting energy from glucose. In respiration, the **Krebs cycle** and an **electron transport chain** follow.
- The electron transport chain establishes a proton gradient that powers ATP production by the enzyme **ATP synthase.**

6.3 In Eukaryotic Cells, Mitochondria Produce Most ATP

- The Krebs cycle and electron transport chain occur in **mitochondria.**
- Each mitochondrion has two membranes enclosing a central **matrix.**
- Electron transport chain proteins are embedded in **cristae:** folds of the inner membrane. These proteins pump protons into the **intermembrane compartment.** ATP synthase also spans the inner membrane.

6.4 Glycolysis Breaks Down Glucose to Pyruvate

- In glycolysis, glucose is broken into three-carbon molecules of **pyruvate.**
- During these reactions, electrons are added to NAD^+, forming **NADH.** Two ATPs are formed by **substrate-level phosphorylation** (figure 6.15).

6.5 Aerobic Respiration Yields Abundant ATP

A. Pyruvate Is Oxidized to Acetyl CoA
- Pyruvate moves into a mitochondrion. In the matrix, pyruvate is broken down into **acetyl CoA** and CO_2. This reaction also produces NADH.

B. The Krebs Cycle Produces ATP and Electron Carriers
- Acetyl CoA enters the Krebs cycle. This series of oxidation–reduction reactions occurs in the matrix and produces ATP, NADH, **FADH$_2$,** and CO_2. Substrate-level phosphorylation produces ATP in the Krebs cycle.

C. The Electron Transport Chain Drives ATP Formation
- Energy-rich electrons from NADH and FADH$_2$ fuel an electron transport chain in the inner mitochondrial membrane. Electrons move along a series of proteins that release energy at each step. O_2 accepts the electrons at the end of the chain, producing water.
- The proteins of the electron transport chain pump protons from the mitochondrial matrix into the intermembrane compartment. As protons diffuse back into the matrix through channels in ATP synthase, their potential energy drives **chemiosmotic phosphorylation** of ADP to ATP.

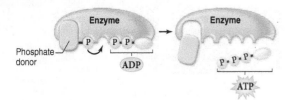

Figure 6.15 Substrate-Level Phosphorylation.

6.6 How Many ATPs Can One Glucose Molecule Yield?

- In aerobic respiration, each glucose molecule theoretically yields 36 ATP molecules (figure 6.16). The actual yield is about 30 ATP per glucose.

6.7 Other Food Molecules Enter the Energy-Extracting Pathways

- Polysaccharides are digested to glucose before undergoing cellular respiration. Amino acids enter the energy pathways as pyruvate, acetyl CoA, or an intermediate of the Krebs cycle. Fatty acids enter as acetyl CoA, and glycerol enters as pyruvate.

6.8 Some Energy Pathways Do Not Require Oxygen

A. Anaerobic Respiration Uses an Electron Acceptor Other than O_2
- Some organisms can use nitrate or sulfate as an electron acceptor.

B. Fermenters Acquire ATP Only from Glycolysis
- **Fermentation** pathways oxidize NADH to NAD^+, which is recycled to glycolysis. **Alcoholic fermentation** converts pyruvate to ethanol and carbon dioxide. **Lactic acid fermentation** reduces pyruvate to lactic acid.

6.9 Photosynthesis and Respiration Are Ancient Pathways

- Photosynthesis and respiration are interrelated, with common intermediates and some reactions that mirror those of other pathways.
- Eukaryotes may have arisen by endosymbiosis, in which cells engulfed bacteria that were forerunners to mitochondria and chloroplasts.

6.10 Investigating Life: Hot Plants Offer Heat Reward

- *Philodendron* plants use a modified respiratory pathway, creating a "heat reward" for their insect pollinators.

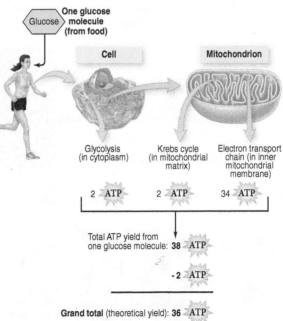

Figure 6.16 ATP Yield for One Glucose Molecule.

MULTIPLE CHOICE QUESTIONS

1. Which of the following is required for aerobic respiration to occur?
   a. Light   c. CO_2
   b. O_2 d. H_2O

2. Which stage in cellular respiration produces the most ATP?
   a. Glycolysis   c. Krebs cycle
   b. Pyruvate oxidation   d. Electron transport

3. What is the role of ATP synthase?
   a. It uses ATP to make glucose.
   b. It uses a hydrogen ion gradient to make ATP.
   c. It uses ATP to make a hydrogen ion gradient.
   d. It synthesizes ATP directly from glucose.

4. Where in a eukaryotic cell does glycolysis occur?
   a. The cytoplasm
   b. The outer membrane of the mitochondria
   c. The inner membrane of the mitochondria
   d. The mitochondrial matrix

5. Which molecule has the greatest amount of potential energy?
   a. Pyruvate   c. Glucose
   b. Acetyl CoA   d. CO_2

6. Fats can be broken down into acetyl CoA for use in the Krebs cycle. Fats can also
   a. be built from excess acetyl CoA for energy storage.
   b. function as an electron carrier in the electron transport chain.
   c. be broken down directly into ATP.
   d. be broken down directly into NADH.

7. Why is it important to regenerate NAD^+ during fermentation?
   a. It helps maintain the reactions of glycolysis.
   b. So it can transfer an electron to the electron transport chain
   c. To maintain the concentration of pyruvate in a cell
   d. To produce alcohol or lactic acid for the cell

8. What is endosymbiosis?
   a. A type of fermentation
   b. The transport of pyruvate into the matrix of the mitochondria
   c. A possible explanation for the origin of mitochondria
   d. The movement of electrons along the electron transport chain

Answers to these questions are in appendix A.

WRITE IT OUT

1. *Respiration* contains the Latin word root *spiro*, which means "to breathe." Why is the process described in this chapter called cellular respiration? What might your answer indicate about what scientists already knew when they first observed cellular respiration?

2. All steps of cellular respiration are closely connected. Describe the problems that would occur if glycolysis, the Krebs cycle, or the electron transport chain were not working.

3. How does aerobic respiration yield so much ATP from each glucose molecule, compared with glycolysis alone?

4. How might a mitochondrion's double membrane make cellular respiration more efficient than if it had a single membrane?

5. Health-food stores sell a product called "pyruvate plus," which supposedly boosts energy. Why is this product unnecessary? What would be a much less expensive substitute that would accomplish the same thing?

6. In a properly functioning mitochondrion, is the pH in the matrix lower than, higher than, or the same as the pH in the intermembrane space? If

you apply on
box, how do

7. Describe the
absence of (

8. A chemical
membranes
would the i

9. Some types
carbonated at bottling, but if you open them a few weeks later they will bubble. Explain the source of this carbonation.

10. Describe how aerobic respiration occurs in bacteria. How does this relate to how aerobic respiration occurs in mitochondria? Explain the relationship between bacteria and mitochondria.

11. Under what conditions might your cells shift from aerobic respiration to fermentation? In what habitats might an organism rely solely on fermentation?

12. Compare the number of ATP molecules required to produce one glucose molecule in photosynthesis (see figure 5.9) with the number of ATP molecules generated per glucose in aerobic respiration (see figure 6.8). How do these numbers compare to the ATP yield from fermentation?

PULL IT TOGETHER

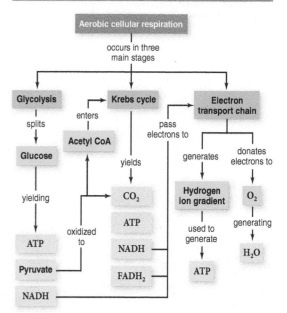

Figure 6.17 Pull It Together: How Cells Release Energy.

Refer to figure 6.17 and the chapter content to answer the following questions.

1. Add the locations of each stage of respiration to this map.

2. How many ATP, NADH, CO_2, $FADH_2$, and H_2O molecules are produced at each stage of respiration?

3. What do cells do with the ATP they generate in respiration?

4. Where would photosynthesis, fermentation, anaerobic respiration, and ATP synthase fit into this concept map?

DNA, Inheritance, and Biotechnology

CHAPTER

7

DNA Structure and Gene Function

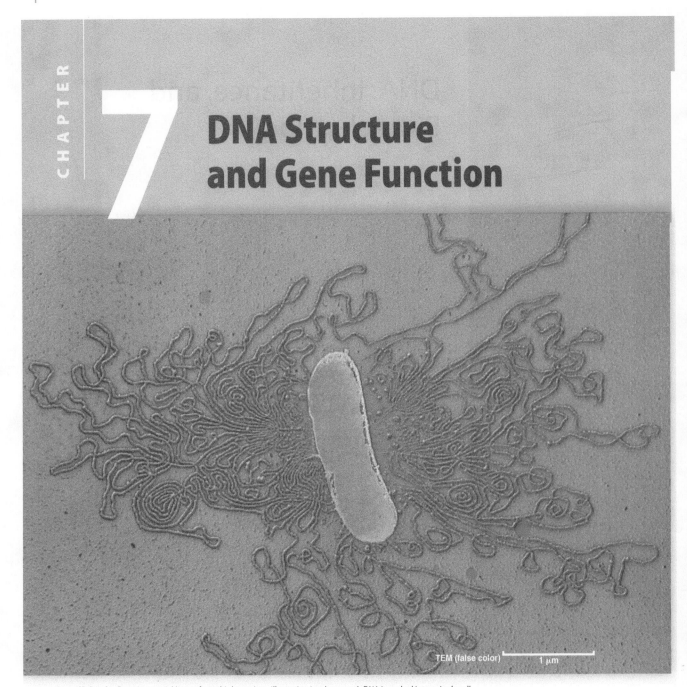

TEM (false color) 1 μm

Long Molecule. Genetic material bursts from this bacterium, illustrating just how much DNA is packed into a single cell.

connect plus+

Enhance your study BIOLOGY
of this chapter with practice quizzes,
animations and videos, answer keys,
and downloadable study tools.
www.mhhe.com/hoefnagels

UNIT 2

Our DNA Sequence Is Just the Beginning

ALL LIFE REQUIRES DNA, THE STRINGY SUBSTANCE SPILLING OUT OF THE CELL ON THE FACING PAGE. Your own cells contain DNA, as do the cells of fruit flies, polar bears, and all other animals. Protists, fungi, and plants have DNA too.

We know much more about DNA now than we did a generation ago. The technology needed to sequence DNA was in its infancy in the 1970s, but by the 1990s it had ignited a scientific revolution. Biologists began cranking out the first of hundreds of complete DNA sequences representing viruses and organisms from all three of life's domains. The 1990s also saw the dawn of the Human Genome Project. ⓘ *DNA sequencing*, p. 222

In a way, the Human Genome Project is old news. The completion of the DNA sequence in 2003, and the subsequent fanfare, might have led an outsider to conclude that science had learned all there was to know about human DNA. News stories suggested that parents would soon be able to screen their unborn children for every trait imaginable. Talk soon turned to "designer babies," whose genes would be artificially altered to boost health, attractiveness, intelligence, athletic ability, and other desirable characteristics.

The truth is that we have a long way to go before we understand what all of that DNA actually does in our cells. Of course, we understand DNA's overall function: a gene's nucleotide sequence encodes a protein. But just knowing a gene's sequence does not provide instant insight into everything needed to make a human. By itself, a DNA sequence does not explain how the cell turns each gene on and off, the function of the protein, or what happens if the gene mutates. Nor does it explain the function of the huge swaths of DNA that do not code for protein.

We do know, however, that only a 0.1% difference separates any two individuals. Investigating these differences will likely answer such questions as why some people get cancer and others do not or why a medication helps some people but harms others. Even within an individual, cells express different combinations of genes. Understanding how the proteins produced in breast cancer cells differ from those in normal cells, for example, may reveal new targets for anticancer drugs. ⓘ *tale of two drugs*, p. 45

We begin this genetics unit with a look at the intimate relationship between DNA and proteins. Subsequent chapters describe how cells copy DNA just before they divide, how cell division leads to the fascinating study of inheritance, and how researchers find practical applications for knowledge about DNA.

LEARN HOW TO LEARN
Pause at the Checkpoints

As you read, get out a piece of paper and see if you can answer the Figure It Out and Mastering Concepts questions. If not, you may want to study a bit more before you move on. Each section builds on the material that came before, and mastering one chunk at a time will make it much easier to learn whatever comes next.

🍁 7.1 Experiments Identified the Genetic Material

The nucleic acid DNA is one of the most familiar molecules, the subject matter of movies and headlines (figure 7.1). Criminal trials hinge on DNA evidence; the idea of human cloning raises questions about the role of DNA in determining who we are; and DNA-based discoveries are yielding new diagnostic tests, medical treatments, and vaccines.

More important than DNA's role in society is its role in life itself. DNA is a molecule with a remarkable function: it stores the information that each cell needs to produce proteins. These instructions make life possible. In fact, before a cell divides, it first makes an exact replica of its DNA. This process, described in chapter 8, copies the precious information that will enable the next generation of cells to live.

The discovery of DNA's role in life required many decades of research. By the early 1900s, biologists had recognized the connection between inheritance and protein. For example, English physician Archibald Garrod noted that people with inherited "inborn errors of metabolism" lacked certain enzymes. Other researchers linked abnormal or missing enzymes to unusual eye color in fruit flies and nutritional deficiencies in bread mold. But how were enzyme deficiencies and inheritance linked? Experiments in bacteria would answer the question.

A. Bacteria Can Transfer Genetic Information

In 1928, English microbiologist Frederick Griffith contributed the first step in identifying DNA as the genetic material (figure 7.2). Griffith studied two strains of a bacterium,

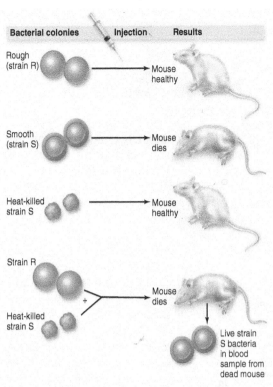

Figure 7.2 **A Tale of Two Microbes.** Griffith's experiments showed that a molecule in a lethal strain of bacteria (type S) could transform harmless type R bacteria into killers. Additional experiments showed that the molecule was DNA.

Figure 7.1 **DNA—The Molecule in the Media.** *Jurassic Park* was a movie in which fictional scientists re-created dinosaurs. The dinosaur DNA came from blood found in ancient mosquitoes entombed in amber.

Streptococcus pneumoniae. Type R bacteria, named for their "rough" colonies, do not cause pneumonia when injected into mice. Type S ("smooth") bacteria, on the other hand, cause pneumonia. The smooth polysaccharide capsule that encases type S bacteria is apparently necessary for infection.

Griffith found that heat-killed type S bacteria did not cause pneumonia in mice. However, when he injected mice with a mixture of live type R bacteria plus heat-killed type S bacteria, neither of which could cause pneumonia alone, the mice died. Moreover, their bodies contained live type S bacteria encased in polysaccharide. Something in the heat-killed type S bacteria transformed the normally harmless type R strain into a killer.

How had the previously harmless bacteria acquired the ability to cause disease? In the 1940s, U.S. physicians Oswald Avery, Colin MacLeod, and Maclyn McCarty finally learned the identity of the "transforming principle." When the researchers treated the solution from the type S strain with a protein-destroying enzyme, the type R strain still changed into a killer. Therefore, a protein was not transmitting the killing trait. But when they treated the solution with a DNA-destroying enzyme, the type R bacteria remained harmless. The conclusion: DNA from type S cells altered the type R bacteria, enabling them to manufacture the smooth coat necessary to cause infection.

B. Hershey and Chase Confirmed the Genetic Role of DNA

Animation
Hershey-Chase
Experiment

At first, biologists hesitated to accept DNA as the molecule of heredity. They knew more about proteins than about nucleic acids. They also thought that protein, with its 20 building blocks, could encode many more traits than DNA, which includes just four types of building blocks. In 1950, however, U.S. microbiologists Alfred Hershey and Martha Chase conclusively showed that DNA—not protein—is the genetic material.

Hershey and Chase used a very simple system. They infected the bacterium *Escherichia coli* with a bacteriophage, which is a virus that infects only bacteria. The virus consisted of a protein coat surrounding a DNA core. We now know that when the virus infects a bacterial cell, it injects its DNA, but the protein coat remains loosely attached to the outside of the bacterium. The viral DNA directs the bacterium to use its own energy and raw materials to manufacture more virus particles, which then burst from the cell. But much of this information was not available in 1950. In fact,

Figure 7.3 DNA's Role Confirmed.
Hershey and Chase used radioactive isotopes to distinguish a bacteriophage's protein coat from its DNA. They showed that the virus transfers DNA (not protein) to the bacterium, and this viral DNA causes bacterial cells to produce viruses. The photo at right shows several bacteriophages.

Virus

Bacterium (*E. coli*)

50 nm
TEM (false color)

Hershey and Chase wanted to know which part of the virus controls its replication: the DNA or the protein coat. ⓘ *bacteriophages*, p. 332; *E. coli*, p. 354

To answer the question, the researchers "labeled" two batches of viruses, one with radioactive sulfur that marked protein and the other with radioactive phosphorus that marked DNA. They used each type of labeled virus to infect a separate batch of bacteria (figure 7.3). Then they agitated each mixture in a blender, which removed the unattached viruses and empty protein coats from the surfaces of the bacteria. They poured the mixtures into test tubes and spun them at high speed. The infected bacteria settled to the bottom of each test tube because they were heavier than the liberated viral protein coats.

Hershey and Chase examined the bacteria and the fluid in each tube. In the test tube containing sulfur-labeled viral proteins, the bacteria were not radioactive, but the fluid portion of the material in the tube was. In the other tube, where the virus contained DNA marked with radioactive phosphorus, the infected bacteria were radioactive, but the fluid was not.

The "blender experiments" therefore showed that the part of the virus that could enter the bacteria and direct them to mass-produce viruses was the part with the phosphorus label—namely, the DNA. The genetic material, therefore, was DNA and not protein.

7.1 MASTERING CONCEPTS

1. How did Griffith's research, coupled with the work of Avery and his colleagues, demonstrate that DNA, not protein, is the genetic material?

2. How did the Hershey–Chase "blender experiments" confirm Griffith's results?

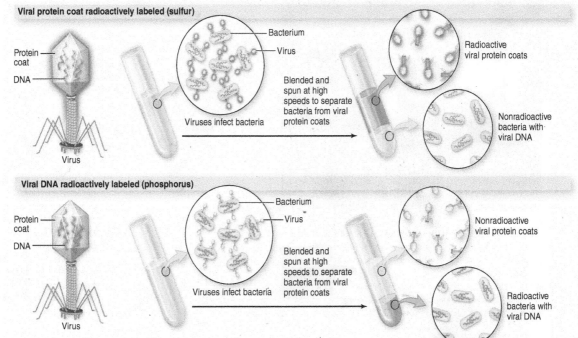

Viral protein coat radioactively labeled (sulfur)

Protein coat

DNA

Virus

Bacterium

Virus

Viruses infect bacteria

Blended and spun at high speeds to separate bacteria from viral protein coats

Radioactive viral protein coats

Nonradioactive bacteria with viral DNA

Viral DNA radioactively labeled (phosphorus)

Protein coat

DNA

Virus

Bacterium

Virus

Viruses infect bacteria

Blended and spun at high speeds to separate bacteria from viral protein coats

Nonradioactive viral protein coats

Radioactive bacteria with viral DNA

124   **UNIT TWO**   DNA, Inheritance, and Biotechnology

7.2 DNA Is a Double Helix of Nucleotides

 Animation
DNA Structure

The early twentieth century also saw advances in the study of the structure of DNA. By 1929, biochemists had discovered the distinction between **RNA (ribonucleic acid)** and **DNA (deoxyribonucleic acid),** the two types of nucleic acid. They also had determined that **nucleotides** are the building blocks of nucleic acids. Finally, researchers knew that each nucleotide includes a sugar (ribose for RNA; deoxyribose for DNA), one of several nitrogen-containing bases, and one or more phosphorus-containing groups. But how were those nucleotides arranged?

In the early 1950s, biochemists raced to discover DNA's chemical structure. Two lines of evidence were considered critical. Austrian-American biochemist Erwin Chargaff showed that the amount of the base guanine (G) in a DNA molecule always equals the amount of cytosine (C), and the amount of adenine (A) always equals the amount of thymine (T). English physicist

Maurice Wilkins and chemist Rosalind Franklin bombarded DNA with X-rays, using a technique called X-ray diffraction to determine the three-dimensional shape of the molecule. The X-ray diffraction pattern revealed a regularly repeating structure of building blocks (figure 7.4a and b).

Video
Rosalind Franklin

Early in 1953, chemist Linus Pauling proposed a triple-helix model of DNA; he was soon proved incorrect. But by April of 1953, U.S. biochemist James Watson and English physicist Francis Crick, working at the Cavendish laboratory in Cambridge in the United Kingdom, had solved the mystery. They used the "Chargaff rule" and Franklin's X-ray diffraction pattern to build a ball-and-stick model of the now-familiar DNA double helix. Watson, Crick, and Wilkins won the 1962 Nobel Prize in Physiology or Medicine for their discovery (figure 7.4c).

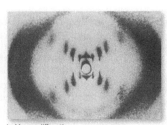

a. Rosalind Franklin   b. X–ray diffraction

c.

Figure 7.4 **Discovery of DNA's Structure.** (a) Rosalind Franklin produced (b) X-ray images of DNA that were crucial in the discovery of DNA's structure. (c) Maurice Wilkins, Francis Crick, and James Watson (first, third, and fifth from the left) shared the 1962 Nobel Prize in Physiology or Medicine for their discovery. Franklin had died in 1958, and by the rules of the award, she could not be included. (The other three men in the photo won Nobel Prizes in other disciplines.)

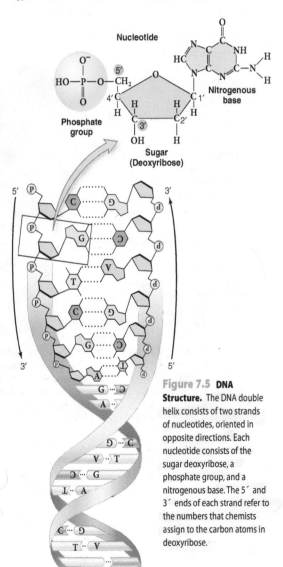

Figure 7.5 **DNA Structure.** The DNA double helix consists of two strands of nucleotides, oriented in opposite directions. Each nucleotide consists of the sugar deoxyribose, a phosphate group, and a nitrogenous base. The 5′ and 3′ ends of each strand refer to the numbers that chemists assign to the carbon atoms in deoxyribose.

Figure 7.6 Complementary Base Pairing.
(a) Adenine and guanine are purines; cytosine and thymine are pyrimidines. (b) Purines pair with complementary pyrimidines: cytosine with guanine, and adenine with thymine. Dotted lines represent hydrogen bonds; all other bonds are covalent.

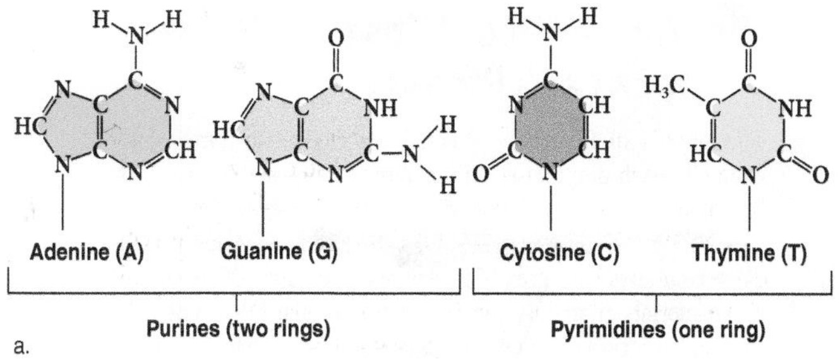

Adenine (A)   Guanine (G)   Cytosine (C)   Thymine (T)

Purines (two rings)   Pyrimidines (one ring)

a.

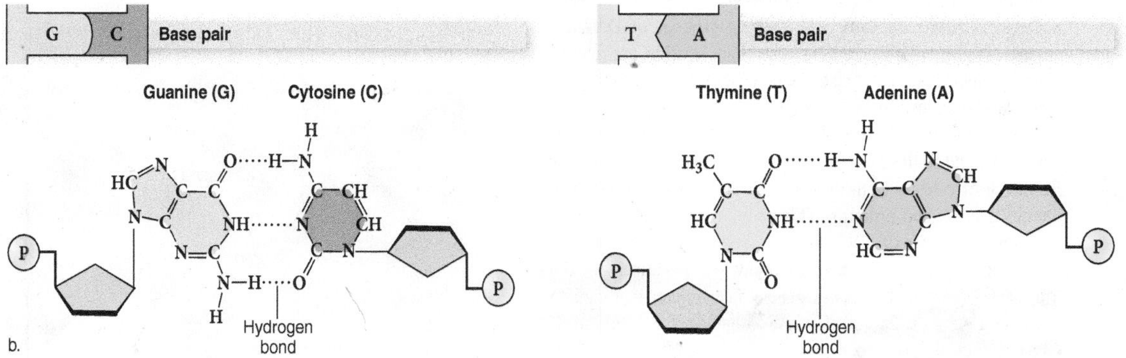

Guanine (G)   Cytosine (C)   Thymine (T)   Adenine (A)

Hydrogen bond   Hydrogen bond

b.

The DNA double helix resembles a twisted ladder (figure 7.5). The twin rails of the ladder, also called the sugar–phosphate "backbones," are alternating units of deoxyribose and phosphate joined with covalent bonds. ⓘ *covalent bonds*, p. 24

Although the two chains of the DNA double helix are parallel to each other, they are oriented in opposite directions, like the northbound and southbound lanes of a highway. This head-to-tail ("antiparallel") arrangement is apparent when the carbon atoms in deoxyribose are numbered. When the nucleotides are joined into a chain, opposite ends of the strand are designated "**3 prime**" (3′) and "**5 prime**" (5′). At the same end of the double helix, one chain therefore ends with a free (unbound) 3′ carbon, while the other chain ends with a free 5′ carbon.

The ladder's rungs are A–T and G–C base pairs joined by hydrogen bonds. These base pairs arise from the chemical structures of the nucleotides (figure 7.6). Adenine and guanine are purines, bases with a double ring structure. Cytosine and thymine are pyrimidines, which have a single ring. Each A–T pair is the same width as a C–G pair because each includes a purine and a pyrimidine.

The two strands of a DNA molecule are **complementary** to each other; that is, the sequence of each strand defines the sequence of the other. An A on one strand means a T on the opposite strand, and a G on one strand means a C on the other. The two strands are therefore somewhat like a photograph and its negative, since each is sufficient to define the other.

Why does A pair with T but not with C, even though both T and C have similar shapes? The explanation relates to the positions

Figure It Out

Write the complementary DNA sequence of the following:

3′-ATCGGATCGCTACTG-5′

Answer: 5′-TAGCCTAGCGATGAC-3′

of the atoms in each nucleotide. Recall from section 2.2 that hydrogen bonds form between atoms carrying opposite partial charges (in this case, between H atoms with partial positive charges and oxygen or nitrogen atoms with partial negative charges). As you examine figure 7.6, note that cytosine and guanine can form three hydrogen bonds. On the other hand, adenine and thymine can only form two. This difference accounts for the specificity of the A-T and C-G base pairs. ⓘ *hydrogen bonds*, p. 25

You may also remember from section 2.2 that hydrogen bonds are weak compared to covalent bonds. While it is true that each hydrogen bond is weak, a DNA molecule consisting of millions of base pairs also has millions of hydrogen bonds. Collectively, these bonds are strong enough to hold the two strands together yet weak enough to pull apart when the cell needs to use its DNA.

7.2   MASTERING CONCEPTS

1. What are the components of DNA and its three-dimensional structure?

2. What evidence enabled Watson and Crick to decipher the structure of DNA?

3. Identify the 3′ and 5′ ends of a DNA strand.

7.3 DNA Contains the "Recipes" for a Cell's Proteins

The amount of DNA in any cell is enormous. In humans, for example, each pinpoint-sized nucleus contains some 6.4 billion base pairs of genetic information.

An organism's **genome** is all of the genetic material in its cells. Genomes vary greatly in size and packaging. The genome of a bacterial cell mainly consists of one circular DNA molecule. In a eukaryotic cell, however, the majority of the genome is divided among multiple chromosomes housed inside the cell's nucleus; each **chromosome** is a discrete package of DNA and associated proteins (figure 7.7). The mitochondria and chloroplasts of eukaryotic cells also contain DNA and therefore have their own genomes.

What does all of that DNA do? As described in more detail toward the end of this chapter, much of it has no known function. But some of it has a well-known role, which is to encode all of the cell's RNA and proteins. This section introduces the **gene,** which is a sequence of DNA nucleotides that codes for a specific protein or RNA molecule. Because many proteins are essential to life, each organism has many genes. The human genome, for example, includes 20,000 to 25,000 genes scattered on its 23 pairs of chromosomes.

A. Protein Synthesis Requires Transcription and Translation

Animation
Gene Function
Overview

In the 1940s, biologists working with the fungus *Neurospora crassa* deduced that each gene somehow controls the production of one protein. In the next decade, Watson and Crick described this relationship between nucleic acids and proteins as a flow of information they called the "central dogma." (i) *Neurospora,* p. 407

Figure 7.8 summarizes the process of protein production. First, in **transcription,** a cell copies a gene's DNA sequence to a complementary RNA molecule. Then, in **translation,** the information in RNA is used to manufacture a protein by joining a specific sequence of amino acids into a polypeptide chain.

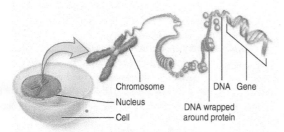

Figure 7.7 From Cell to Chromosome to Gene. A eukaryotic cell's nucleus contains chromosomes, which consist of DNA wrapped around specialized proteins. A gene is a segment of DNA that encodes a protein.

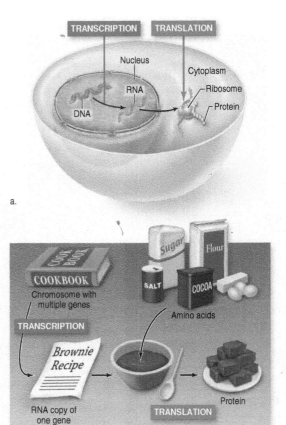

Figure 7.8 DNA to RNA to Protein. (a) The central dogma of biology states that information stored in DNA is copied to RNA (transcription), which is used to assemble proteins (translation). (b) DNA stores the information used to make proteins, just as a recipe stores the information needed to make brownies.

According to this model, a gene is therefore somewhat like a recipe in a cookbook. A recipe specifies the ingredients and instructions for assembling one dish, such as spaghetti sauce or brownies. Likewise, a protein-encoding gene contains the instructions for assembling a protein, amino acid by amino acid. A cookbook that contains many recipes is analogous to a chromosome, which is an array of genes. A person's entire collection of cookbooks, then, would be analogous to a genome.

To illustrate DNA's function with a concrete example, suppose a cell in a female mammal's breast is producing milk to feed an infant (see figure 3.13). One of the many proteins in milk is albumin. The following steps summarize the production of albumin, starting with its genetic "recipe":

1. Inside the nucleus, an enzyme first transcribes the albumin gene's DNA sequence to a complementary sequence of RNA.
2. After some modification, the RNA emerges from the nucleus and binds to a ribosome.
3. At the ribosome, amino acids are assembled in a specific order to produce the albumin protein.

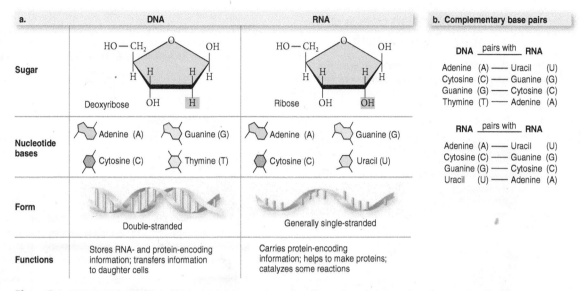

Figure 7.9 DNA and RNA Compared. (a) The two nucleic acids, DNA and RNA, differ in chemical structure, overall form, and function. (b) RNA contains uracil, not thymine. Like thymine, however, uracil pairs with adenine in complementary base pairs.

The amino acid sequence in albumin is dictated by the sequence of nucleotides in the RNA molecule. The RNA, in turn, was transcribed from DNA. In this way, DNA provides the recipe for albumin and every other protein in the cell.

B. RNA Is an Intermediary Between DNA and a Polypeptide Chain

RNA is a multifunctional nucleic acid that differs from DNA in several ways (figure 7.9). First, its nucleotides contain the sugar ribose instead of deoxyribose. Second, RNA has the nitrogenous base uracil, which behaves similarly to thymine; that is, uracil binds with adenine in complementary base pairs. Third, unlike

DNA, RNA can be single-stranded, although it often folds into loops. Finally, RNA can catalyze chemical reactions, a role not known for DNA.

RNA is central to the flow of genetic information. Three types of RNA interact to synthesize proteins (table 7.1):

- **Messenger RNA (mRNA)** carries the information that specifies a protein. Each group of three mRNA bases in a row forms a **codon,** which is a genetic "code word" that corresponds to one amino acid.

- **Ribosomal RNA (rRNA)** combines with proteins to form a **ribosome,** the physical location of protein synthesis. Some rRNAs help to correctly align the ribosome and mRNA, and others catalyze formation of the bonds between amino acids in the developing protein.

- **Transfer RNA (tRNA)** molecules are "connectors" that bind an mRNA codon at one end and a specific amino acid at the other. Their role is to carry each amino acid to the ribosome at the correct spot along the mRNA molecule.

The function of each type of RNA is further explained later in this chapter, beginning in section 7.4 with the first stage in protein production: transcription.

TABLE 7.1 Three Major Types of RNA

Molecule	Typical Number of Nucleotides	Function
mRNA	500–3000	Encodes amino acid sequence
rRNA	100–3000	Associates with proteins to form ribosomes, which structurally support and catalyze protein synthesis
tRNA	75–80	Binds mRNA codon on one end and an amino acid on the other, linking a gene's message to the amino acid sequence it encodes

7.3 MASTERING CONCEPTS

1. What is the relationship between a gene and a protein?

2. What are the two main stages in protein synthesis?

3. What are the three types of RNA, and how does each contribute to protein synthesis?

7.4 Transcription Uses a DNA Template to Create RNA

Transcription produces an RNA copy of one gene. If a gene is analogous to a recipe for a protein, then transcription is like opening a cookbook to a particular page and copying just the recipe for the dish you want to prepare. After the copy is made, the book can return safely to the shelf. Just as you would then use the instructions on the copy to make your meal, the cell uses the information in RNA—and not the DNA directly—to make each protein.

A. Transcription Occurs in Three Steps

Tutorial
Transcription

Complementary base pairing underlies transcription, just as it does DNA replication (see chapter 8). In fact, transcription resembles DNA replication, with two main differences: (1) the product of transcription is RNA, not DNA; and (2) transcription copies just one gene from one DNA strand, rather than copying both strands of an entire chromosome.

In transcription, RNA nucleotide bases bind with exposed complementary bases on the **template strand,** which is the strand in the DNA molecule that is actually copied to RNA (figure 7.10). The process occurs in three stages:

1. **Initiation:** Enzymes unzip the DNA double helix, exposing the template strand. **RNA polymerase** (the enzyme that builds an RNA chain) binds to the **promoter,** a DNA sequence that signals the gene's start.
2. **Elongation:** RNA polymerase moves along the DNA template strand in a 3′-to-5′ direction, adding nucleotides only to the 3′-end of the growing RNA molecule.
3. **Termination:** A **terminator** sequence signals the end of the gene. Upon reaching the terminator sequence, the RNA polymerase enzyme separates from the DNA template and releases the newly synthesized RNA. The DNA molecule then resumes its usual double-helix shape.

As the RNA molecule is synthesized, it curls into a three-dimensional shape dictated by complementary base pairing within the molecule. The final shape determines whether the RNA functions as mRNA, tRNA, or rRNA.

The observation that the cell's DNA encodes all types of RNA—not just mRNA—has led to debate over the definition of the word *gene*. Originally, a gene was defined as any stretch of DNA that encodes one protein. More recently, however, biologists have expanded the definition to include any DNA sequence that is transcribed. The phrase *gene expression* can therefore mean the production of either a functional RNA molecule or a protein.

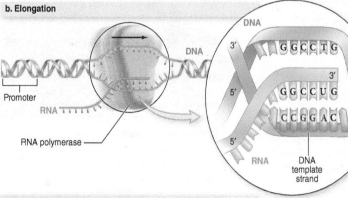

a. Initiation

b. Elongation

c. Termination and release

Figure 7.10 Transcription Creates mRNA. (a) During initiation, RNA polymerase binds to DNA. (b) During elongation, RNA polymerase adds nucleotides to the mRNA strand. (c) Termination occurs at the terminator sequence in the gene; RNA polymerase and mRNA detach from the DNA, which then returns to its double helix form.

Figure It Out

Write the sequence of the mRNA molecule transcribed from the following DNA template sequence: 3′-TTACACTTGCAAC-5′

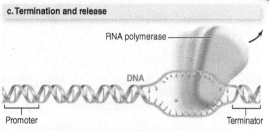

Answer: 5′-AAUGUGAACGUUG-3′

B. mRNA Is Altered in the Nucleus of Eukaryotic Cells

In bacteria and archaea, ribosomes may begin translating mRNA to a protein before transcription is even complete. In eukaryotic cells, however, the presence of the nuclear membrane prevents one mRNA from being simultaneously transcribed and translated. Moreover, in eukaryotes, mRNA is usually altered before it leaves the nucleus to be translated (figure 7.11).

5′ Cap and Poly A Tail After transcription, a short sequence of modified nucleotides, called a cap, is added to the 5′ end of the mRNA molecule. At the 3′ end, 100 to 200 adenines are added, forming a "poly A tail." Together, the cap and poly A tail enhance translation by helping ribosomes attach to the 5′ end of the mRNA molecule. The length of the poly A tail may also determine how long an mRNA lasts before being degraded.

Intron Removal In archaea and in eukaryotic cells, only part of an mRNA molecule is translated into an amino acid sequence. Figure 7.11 shows that an mRNA molecule consists of alternating sequences called introns and exons. **Introns** are portions of the mRNA that are removed before translation. The word *intron* is short for *intra*genic regions, where *intra-* means "within" and -*genic* refers to the gene. Small catalytic RNAs and proteins remove the introns from the mRNA.

The remaining portions, the **exons,** are spliced together to form the mature mRNA that leaves the nucleus to be translated. (A tip for remembering this is that *ex*ons are the portions of an mRNA molecule that are actually *ex*pressed or that *ex*it the nucleus.)

The amount of genetic material devoted to introns can be immense. The average exon is 100 to 300 nucleotides long, whereas the average intron is about 1000 nucleotides long. Some mature mRNA molecules consist of 70 or more spliced-together exons; the cell therefore simply discards much of the RNA created in transcription. Although introns may seem wasteful, section 7.6 explains that this cutting and pasting is important in the regulation of gene expression.

7.4 MASTERING CONCEPTS

1. What happens during each stage of transcription?
2. Where in the cell does transcription occur?
3. What is the role of RNA polymerase in transcription?
4. What are the roles of the promoter and terminator sequences in transcription?
5. How is mRNA modified before it leaves the nucleus of a eukaryotic cell?

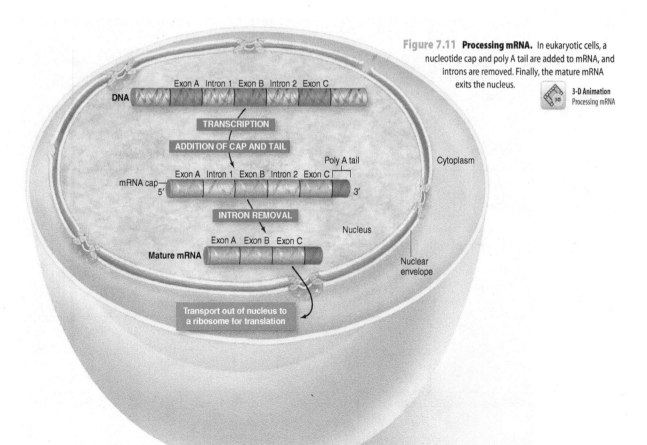

Figure 7.11 Processing mRNA. In eukaryotic cells, a nucleotide cap and poly A tail are added to mRNA, and introns are removed. Finally, the mature mRNA exits the nucleus.

3-D Animation
Processing mRNA

7.5 Translation Builds the Protein

Transcription copies the information encoded in a DNA base sequence into the complementary language of mRNA. Once transcription is complete and mRNA is processed, the cell is ready to translate the mRNA "message" into a sequence of amino acids. If mRNA is like a copy of a recipe, then translation is like preparing the dish.

A. The Genetic Code Links mRNA to Protein

The **genetic code** is the set of "rules" by which a cell uses the nucleotides in mRNA to assemble amino acids into a protein (figure 7.12). Each codon is a group of three mRNA bases corresponding either to one amino acid or to a "stop" signal.

In the 1960s, however, researchers did not yet understand exactly how the genetic code worked. One early question was the number of RNA bases that specify each amino acid. Researchers reasoned that RNA contains only four different nucleotides, so a genetic code with a one-to-one correspondence of mRNA bases to amino acids could specify only four different amino acids—far fewer than the 20 amino acids that make up biological proteins. A code consisting of two bases per codon could specify only 16 different amino acids. A code with three bases per codon, however, yields 64 different combinations, more than enough to specify the 20 amino acids in life. Experiments later confirmed the triplet nature of the genetic code.

A second, and more difficult, problem was to determine which codons correspond to which amino acids. In the 1960s, researchers answered this question by synthesizing mRNA molecules in the laboratory. They added these synthetic mRNAs to test tubes containing all the ingredients needed for translation, extracted from *E. coli* cells. Analyzing the resulting polypeptides allowed scientists to finish deciphering the genetic code in less than a decade—a monumental task. Chemical analysis eventually showed that the genetic code also contains directions for starting and stopping translation. AUG is typically the first codon in mRNA, and the codons UGA, UAA, and UAG each signify "stop."

Nearly all species use the same mRNA codons to specify the same amino acids, although mitochondria and a handful of

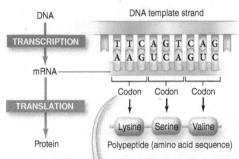

Figure 7.12 The Genetic Code. In translation, mRNA codons are matched with amino acids as specified in the genetic code.

The Genetic Code				
Second letter of codon				
	U	**C**	**A**	**G**	
U	UUU ⌐ Phenylalanine (Phe; F) UUC ⌐ UUA ⌐ Leucine (Leu; L) UUG ⌐	UCU ⌐ Serine (Ser; S) UCC UCA UCG	UAU ⌐ Tyrosine (Tyr; Y) UAC UAA Stop UAG Stop	UGU ⌐ Cysteine (Cys; C) UGC UGA Stop UGG Tryptophan (Trp; W)	U C A G
C	CUU ⌐ Leucine (Leu; L) CUC CUA CUG	CCU ⌐ Proline (Pro; P) CCC CCA CCG	CAU ⌐ Histidine (His; H) CAC CAA ⌐ Glutamine (Gln; Q) CAG	CGU ⌐ Arginine (Arg; R) CGC CGA CGG	U C A G
A	AUU ⌐ Isoleucine (Ile; I) AUC AUA AUG Start Methionine (Met; M)	ACU ⌐ Threonine (Thr; T) ACC ACA ACG	AAU ⌐ Asparagine (Asn; N) AAC AAA ⌐ Lysine (Lys; K) AAG	AGU ⌐ Serine (Ser; S) AGC AGA ⌐ Arginine (Arg; R) AGG	U C A G
G	GUU ⌐ Valine (Val; V) GUC GUA GUG	GCU ⌐ Alanine (Ala; A) GCC GCA GCG	GAU ⌐ Aspartic acid (Asp; D) GAC GAA ⌐ Glutamic acid (Glu; E) GAG	GGU ⌐ Glycine (Gly; G) GGC GGA GGG	U C A G

First letter of codon (left margin) / Third letter of codon (right margin)

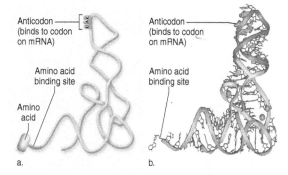

a.   b.

Figure 7.13 **Transfer RNA.** (a) A simplified tRNA molecule shows the anticodon at one end and the amino acid binding region at the opposite end. (b) Three-dimensional view of tRNA.

species use alternative codes that differ slightly from the code in figure 7.12. The best explanation for the (nearly) universal genetic code is that all life evolved from a common ancestor.

B. Translation Requires mRNA, tRNA, and Ribosomes

Translation—the actual construction of the protein—requires the following participants:

- **mRNA:** This product of transcription carries the genetic information that encodes a protein, with each three-base codon specifying one amino acid.

- **tRNA:** This "bilingual" molecule binds to an mRNA codon and to an amino acid (figure 7.13). The **anticodon** is a three-base loop that is complementary to one mRNA codon. The other end of the tRNA molecule forms a covalent bond

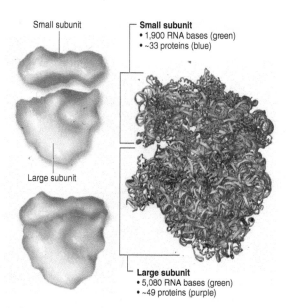

Figure 7.14 **The Ribosome.** A ribosome from a eukaryotic cell has two subunits containing a total of 82 proteins and four rRNA molecules.

to the amino acid corresponding to that codon. For example, a tRNA with the anticodon sequence AAG always picks up the amino acid phenylalanine.

- **Ribosome:** The ribosome, built of rRNA and proteins, anchors mRNA during translation. Each ribosome has one large and one small subunit that join at the initiation of protein synthesis (figure 7.14). Ribosomes may be free in the cytoplasm or attached to the rough endoplasmic reticulum (see figure 3.15).

Apply It **Now**

Some Poisons Disrupt Protein Synthesis

We learned in chapter 6 that some poisons kill by interfering with respiration. Here we list a few poisons that inhibit protein synthesis; a cell that cannot make proteins quickly dies.

- **Amanatin:** This toxin occurs in the "death cap mushroom," *Amanita phalloides* (pictured at right). Amanatin inhibits RNA polymerase, making transcription impossible.

- **Diphtheria toxin:** A respiratory illness called diphtheria is caused by bacteria that secrete the diphtheria toxin. This compound inhibits an elongation factor, a protein that helps add amino acids to a polypeptide chain during translation.

- **Antibiotics**: Clindamycin, chloramphenicol, tetracyclines, and gentamicin are all antibiotics that bind to bacterial ribosomes. When its ribosomes are disrupted, a cell cannot make proteins, and it dies.

- **Ricin:** Derived from seeds of the castor bean plant, ricin is a potent natural poison that consists of two parts. One part binds to

a cell, and the other enters the cell and inhibits protein synthesis by an unknown mechanism. Interestingly, the part of the molecule that enters the cell is apparently more toxic to cancer cells than to normal cells, making ricin a potential cancer treatment.

- **Trichothecenes:** Fungi in the genus *Fusarium* produce toxins called trichothecenes. During World War II, thousands of people died after eating bread made from moldy wheat, and many researchers believe trichothecenes were used as biological weapons during the Vietnam War. The mode of action is unclear, but the toxins seem to interfere somehow with ribosomes.

C. Translation Occurs in Three Steps

Tutorial
Translation

The process of translation can be divided into three stages, during which mRNA, tRNA molecules, and ribosomes come together, link amino acids into a chain, and then dissociate again (figure 7.15).

1. **Initiation:** The leader sequence at the 5′ end of the mRNA molecule bonds with a small ribosomal subunit. The first mRNA codon to specify an amino acid is usually AUG, which attracts a tRNA that carries the amino acid methionine. This methionine signifies the start of a polypeptide. A large ribosomal subunit attaches to the small subunit to complete initiation.

2. **Elongation:** A tRNA molecule carrying the second amino acid (glycine in figure 7.15) then binds to the second codon, GGA in this case. The two amino acids, methionine and glycine, align, and a covalent bond forms between them. With that peptide bond in place, the ribosome releases the first tRNA. The cell may now reuse this "empty" tRNA; that is, the tRNA will pick up another methionine that may be incorporated into another new protein. ① *peptide bond*, p. 32

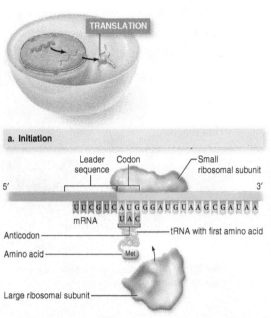

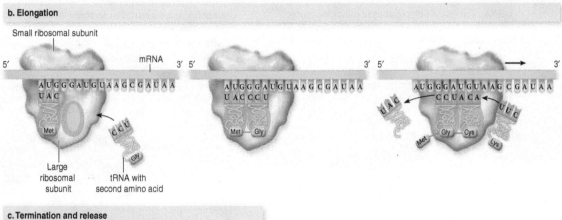

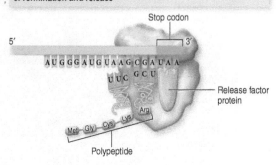

Figure 7.15 **Translation Creates the Protein.** Translation occurs in three stages. (a) Initiation brings together the ribosomal subunits, mRNA, and the tRNA carrying the first amino acid. (b) As elongation begins, a tRNA molecule bearing the second amino acid binds to the second codon. The first amino acid forms a covalent bond with the second amino acid. Additional tRNAs bring subsequent amino acids encoded in the mRNA. (c) Termination occurs when a release factor protein binds to the stop codon. All components of the translation machine are released, along with the completed polypeptide.

Next, the ribosome moves down the mRNA by one codon. A third tRNA enters, carrying its amino acid. This third amino acid aligns with the other two and forms a covalent bond to the second amino acid in the growing chain. The tRNA attached to glycine is released and recycled. With the help of proteins called elongation factors, the polypeptide grows one amino acid at a time, as tRNAs continue to deliver their cargo.

3. **Termination:** Elongation halts at a "stop" codon (UGA, UAG, or UAA). No tRNA molecules correspond to these stop codons. Instead, proteins called release factors bind to the stop codon, prompting the participants of protein synthesis to separate from one another. The ribosome releases the last tRNA, the ribosomal subunits separate and are recycled, and the new polypeptide is released.

Figure It Out

If a DNA sequence is 3′-AAAGCAGTACTA-5′, what would be the corresponding amino acid sequence?

Answer: Phe-Arg-His-Asp

Protein synthesis can be very speedy. A plasma cell in the human immune system can manufacture 2000 identical antibody proteins per second, helping the body quickly respond to infections. How can protein synthesis occur fast enough to meet all of a cell's needs? One way the cell maximizes efficiency is by producing multiple copies of each mRNA, giving the cell more than one genetic "recipe" for the ribosomes to read. In addition, dozens of ribosomes may simultaneously bind along the length of one mRNA molecule, following each other from the 5′ end to the 3′ end (figure 7.16). These ribosomes zip along the mRNA, incorporating some 15 amino acids per second. Thanks to this fast-moving "assembly line," a cell can make many copies of a protein from the same mRNA.

Because proteins are essential to life, chemicals that disrupt protein production can be lethal. The Apply It Now box on page 131 describes a few examples of poisons that kill cells by blocking one or more steps in protein synthesis.

D. Proteins Must Fold Correctly after Translation

The newly synthesized protein cannot do its job until it folds into its final shape (see figure 2.19). Some regions of the amino acid chain attract or repel other parts, contorting the polypeptide's overall shape. Enzymes catalyze the formation of chemical bonds, and "chaperone" proteins stabilize partially folded regions.

Proteins can fold incorrectly if the underlying DNA sequence is altered (see section 7.7), because the encoded protein may have the wrong sequence of amino acids. Serious illness may result. In some forms of cystic fibrosis, for example, a membrane transport protein does not fold correctly into its final form. The absence of

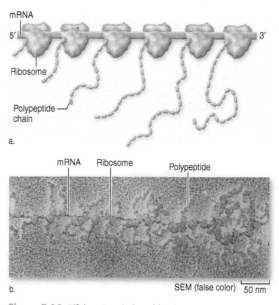

Figure 7.16 Efficient Translation. (a) Multiple ribosomes can simultaneously translate one mRNA. (b) This micrograph shows about two dozen ribosomes producing proteins from the same mRNA.

the membrane protein causes sticky mucus to accumulate in the lungs and other organs.

Errors in protein folding can occur even if the underlying genetic sequence remains unchanged. Alzheimer disease, for example, is associated with a protein called amyloid that folds improperly and then forms an abnormal mass in brain cells. Likewise, mad cow disease and similar conditions in sheep and humans are caused by abnormal clumps of misfolded proteins called prions in nerve cells. ⓘ *prions*, p. 340

In addition to folding, some proteins must be altered in other ways before they become functional. For example, insulin, which is 51 amino acids long, is initially translated as the 80-amino-acid polypeptide proinsulin. Enzymes cut proinsulin to form insulin. A different type of modification occurs when polypeptides join to form larger protein molecules. The oxygen-carrying blood protein hemoglobin, for example, consists of four polypeptide chains (two alpha and two beta) encoded by separate genes.

7.5 MASTERING CONCEPTS

1. How did researchers determine that the genetic code is a triplet and learn which codons specify which amino acids?
2. What happens in each stage of translation?
3. Where in the cell does translation occur?
4. How are polypeptides modified after translation?

7.6 Cells Regulate Gene Expression

Producing proteins costs tremendous amounts of energy. For example, an *E. coli* cell spends 90% of its ATP on protein synthesis. Transcription and translation require energy, as does the synthesis of nucleotides, enzymes, ribosomal proteins, and other molecules that participate in protein synthesis. Removing the introns and making other modifications to the mRNA require still more energy. ⓘ *ATP*, p. 76

Cells constantly produce essential proteins, such as the enzymes involved in the energy pathways described in chapters 5 and 6. Considering the high cost of making protein, however, it makes sense that cells save energy by not producing unneeded proteins.

Beyond energy savings, cells have many additional reasons to regulate gene expression. First, multicellular organisms consist of many types of specialized cells. Humans, for example, have at least 200 different cell types. If each cell contains the same complete set of genes, how does it acquire its unique function? The answer is that each type of cell expresses a different subset of genes. A hair follicle cell, for example, produces a lot of keratin (the protein that makes up hair) but never makes hemoglobin. Conversely, a red blood cell produces a lot of hemoglobin but leaves the keratin gene turned off. Each cell's function is unique because it produces a unique combination of proteins. These specialized cells are analogous to a chef's owning one set of cookbooks but using unique combinations of recipes when preparing breakfast, lunch, and dinner.

Second, regulating gene expression gives cells flexibility to respond to changing conditions. For example, the python pictured on page 105 ramps up its production of digestive enzymes shortly after it begins to swallow the gazelle. The genes encoding those enzymes turn off once the meal is gone. Likewise, specialized immune system cells churn out antibodies in response to an infection. Once the threat is gone, antibody production halts.

Third, an intricate set of genetic instructions orchestrates the growth and development of a multicellular organism. Early in an animal embryo's development, for example, protein signals "tell" cells whether they are at the head end of the body, the tail end, or somewhere in between. These signals, in turn, regulate the expression of unique combinations of genes that enable cells in each location to specialize. Similarly, in a flowering plant, genes that were silent early in the plant's life become active when external signals trigger flower formation.

These examples illustrate the idea that cells produce many proteins only under certain conditions. This section describes some of the mechanisms that regulate gene expression in cells.

A. Operons Are Groups of Bacterial Genes That Share One Promoter

Soon after the discovery of DNA's structure, researchers began to unravel the controls of gene expression. In 1961, French biologists François Jacob and Jacques Monod described how and when *E. coli* bacteria produce the three enzymes that degrade the sugar lactose. The bacteria produce the proteins only when lactose is present in the cell's surroundings. What signals "tell" a simple bacterial cell to transcribe all three genes at precisely the right time? ⓘ *E. coli*, p. 354

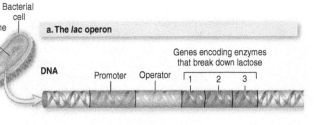

a. The *lac* operon

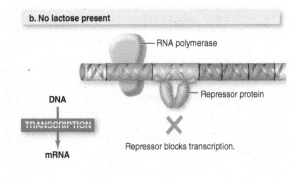

b. No lactose present

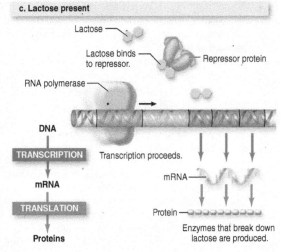

c. Lactose present

Figure 7.17 The *Lac* Operon. (a) An operon consists of a promoter, an operator, and a group of related genes. (b) In the absence of lactose, a repressor protein binds to the operator and prevents transcription. The enzymes are not produced. (c) If lactose is present, it binds to the repressor, which subsequently releases the operator. Transcription proceeds.

Jacob and Monod showed that in *E. coli* and other bacteria, related genes are organized as operons. An **operon** is a group of genes plus a promoter and an operator that control the transcription of the entire group at once (figure 7.17a). The promoter, as described earlier, is the site to which RNA polymerase attaches to begin transcription. The **operator** is a DNA sequence located between the promoter and the protein-encoding regions. If a protein called a **repressor** binds to the operator, it prevents the transcription of the genes.

E. coli's *lac* **operon** consists of the three genes that encode lactose-degrading proteins, plus a promoter and operator. To understand how the *lac* operon works, first imagine an *E. coli* cell in an environment lacking lactose. Expressing the three genes would be a waste of energy. The repressor protein therefore binds to the operator, preventing RNA polymerase from transcribing the genes (figure 7.17b). The genes are effectively "off."

When lactose is present, however, the sugar attaches to the repressor, which changes its shape so that it detaches from the DNA. RNA polymerase is now free to transcribe the genes (figure 7.17c). After translation, the resulting enzymes enable the cell to absorb and degrade the sugar. Lactose, in a sense, causes its own dismantling.

Soon, geneticists discovered other groups of genes organized as operons. Some, like the *lac* operon, negatively control transcription by removing a block. Others produce factors that turn on transcription. As Jacob and Monod stated in 1961, "The genome contains not only a series of blueprints, but a coordinated program of protein synthesis and means of controlling its execution."

B. Eukaryotic Organisms Use Transcription Factors

In eukaryotic cells, groups of proteins called **transcription factors** bind DNA at specific sequences that regulate transcription. RNA polymerase cannot bind to a promoter or initiate transcription of a gene in the absence of transcription factors. A transcription factor may bind to a gene's promoter or to an **enhancer,** a regulatory DNA sequence that lies outside the promoter. An enhancer may be located near the gene (or even within it), but often they are thousands of base pairs away. ⓘ *enhancers and wing spots*, p. 273

Figure 7.18 shows how transcription factors prepare a promoter to receive RNA polymerase. The first transcription factor to bind is attracted to a part of the promoter called the TATA box. The TATA binding protein attracts other transcription factors, including proteins bound to an enhancer. Finally, RNA polymerase joins the complex, binding just in front of the start of the gene sequence. With RNA polymerase in place, transcription can begin.

Transcription factors respond to external stimuli that signal a gene to turn "on." Once a signaling molecule binds to the outside of a target cell, a series of chemical reactions occurs inside the cell. The last step in the series can be the activation or deactivation of a transcription factor. Moreover, one stimulus may trigger many simultaneous changes in the cell. An example

is the series of events that follows the fusion of egg and sperm (see chapter 35). The fertilized egg cell immediately begins its journey toward embryonic development, a process that requires the activation of many genes that were silent before the sperm reached the egg.

The ability to digest lactose provides an excellent example of the importance of transcription factors and enhancers in gene regulation. All infants produce lactase, the enzyme that digests the lactose in milk. But many adults are lactose intolerant because their lactase-encoding gene remains turned off after infancy. Without the enzyme, lactose is indigestible. Some people, however, can continue to digest milk into adulthood. In these lactose-tolerant adults, an enhancer is modified in a way that promotes transcription of the lactase gene throughout life.

One gene can have multiple enhancers, each of which regulates transcription in a different cell type. For example, cells in the kidneys, lungs, and brain all produce a membrane protein called Duffy, as do red blood cells. Each cell type uses a different enhancer to control expression of Duffy. Most people from western Africa lack Duffy on their red blood cells, even though their

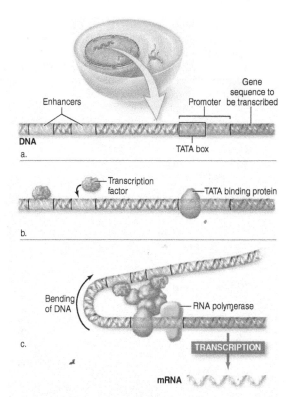

Figure 7.18 How Transcription Factors Work. RNA polymerase initiates transcription only if proteins called transcription factors are also present. (a) Enhancers and promoters are DNA sequences that regulate transcription. (b) Transcription factors, including TATA binding proteins, bind to enhancers and promoters. (c) DNA bends, bringing the transcription factors together with RNA polymerase.

other cells do produce the protein. The explanation is a change in the enhancer that controls Duffy production in just the red blood cells. The "Duffy-negative" blood cells apparently protect against malaria but increase a person's susceptibility to HIV.

Defects in transcription factors underlie some diseases. Cancer, for example, is a family of illnesses in which cells divide out of control. Proteins provide the signals that normally regulate cell division. Since transcription factors help turn genes on and off, defective transcription factors can cause these fine-tuned signals to be disrupted. Cancer develops because the cells are unable to stop dividing. ① *cancer*, p. 156

In addition, some drugs interfere with transcription factors. The "abortion pill" RU486, for example, indirectly blocks transcription factors needed for the development of an embryo.

C. Eukaryotic Cells Also Use Additional Regulatory Mechanisms

As we have already seen, protein production costs a tremendous amount of energy. Eukaryotic cells have several ways to control whether each gene is "on" or "off" (figure 7.19).

DNA Availability A chromosome's DNA must be unwound for its genes to be expressed (figure 7.19, part 1). In addition, a cell can "tag" unneeded DNA with methyl groups ($-CH_3$). Proteins inside the cell bind to the tagged DNA, preventing gene expression and signaling the cell to fold that section of DNA more tightly. These modifications turn off the genes. Interestingly, the placement of these tags—not just the DNA itself—can pass from generation to generation. The study of these and other heritable changes in gene expression is part of a field of research called epigenetics. Abnormalities in epigenetic mechanisms can lead to cancer and other illnesses.

 Video Epigenetics

Transcription Factors Specialized proteins called transcription factors bind to each gene's promoter and determine whether or not RNA polymerase can transcribe the gene (figure 7.19, part 2). Section 7.6B described transcription factors in detail.

RNA Processing One gene can encode multiple proteins if different combinations of exons are included in the final mRNA. For example, if exon B were excluded in figure 7.19 (step 3), exons A and C would be spliced together. The mRNA would then encode a different protein. For mRNA molecules with dozens of exons, the number of alternative proteins is huge. Researchers know of a gene in fruit flies that can theoretically be spliced into more than 38,000 different configurations!

Figure 7.19 Regulating Gene Expression. Eukaryotic cells have many ways to control whether each gene is turned on or off.

 Animation Regulating Gene Expression

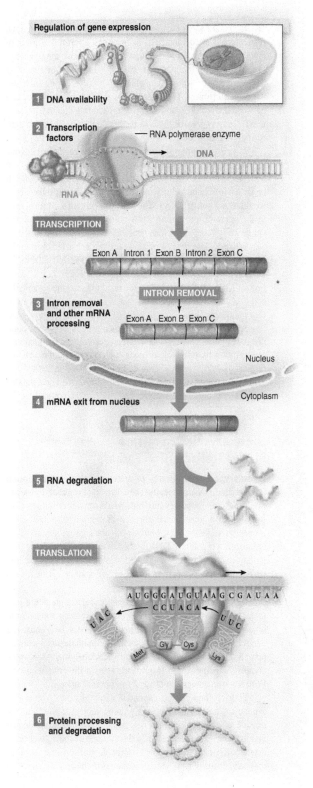

Regulation of gene expression

1 DNA availability

2 Transcription factors — RNA polymerase enzyme

DNA

RNA

TRANSCRIPTION

Exon A Intron 1 Exon B Intron 2 Exon C

INTRON REMOVAL

3 Intron removal and other mRNA processing

Exon A Exon B Exon C

Nucleus

4 mRNA exit from nucleus

Cytoplasm

5 RNA degradation

TRANSLATION

AUGGGAUGUAAGCGAUAA
CCUACA
UAC   UUC
Met Gly Cys Lys

6 Protein processing and degradation

BurningQuestion

Is there a gay gene?

Despite periodic headlines about newly discovered genes "for" homosexuality, the reality is a bit more complex.

Linking a human behavior to one or more genes is difficult for several reasons. First, the question of a "gay gene" is somewhat misleading. Genes encode RNA and proteins, not behaviors, so any relationship between DNA and sexual behavior is necessarily indirect. Second, to establish a clear link to DNA, a researcher must be able to define and measure a behavior. This in itself is difficult, because people disagree about what it means to be homosexual. Third, an individual who possesses a gene version that contributes to a trait will not necessarily express the gene; many genes in each cell remain "off" at any given time. Fourth, multiple genes and a strong environmental influence are likely to be involved in anything as complex as sexual orientation.

Despite these complications, research has yielded some evidence of a biological component to homosexuality, at least in males. For example, a male homosexual's identical twin is much more likely to also be homosexual than is a nonidentical twin, indicating a strong genetic contribution. In addition, the more older brothers a male has, the more likely he is to be homosexual. This "birth order" effect occurs only for siblings with the same biological mother; having older stepbrothers does not increase the chance that a male is homosexual. Events before birth, not social interactions with brothers, are therefore apparently responsible for the effect.

Other research has produced ambiguous results. Anatomical studies of cadavers have revealed differences in the size of a particular brain structure between heterosexual and homosexual men, but the relative contribution of genes and environment to this structure is unknown. One study linked homosexuality in males, but not in females, to part of the X chromosome; a subsequent study did not support this conclusion.

So is there a gay gene? The short answer is no, because there is unlikely to be a single gene that "causes" homosexuality. At the same time, research suggests a genetic contribution to sexual orientation. Sorting out the complex interactions between multiple genes and the environment, however, remains a formidable challenge.

Submit your burning question to
Marielle.Hoefnagels@mheducation.com

mRNA Exit from Nucleus   For a protein to be produced, mRNA must leave the nucleus and attach to a ribosome (figure 7.19, part 4). If mRNA fails to leave, the gene is silenced.

RNA Degradation   Not all mRNA molecules are equally stable. Some are rapidly destroyed, perhaps before they can be translated, whereas others persist longer (figure 7.19, part 5).

Moreover, tiny RNA sequences called microRNAs can play a role in regulating gene expression. Each microRNA is only about 21 to 23 nucleotides long, and it does not encode a protein. Instead, a cell may produce a microRNA that is complementary to a coding mRNA. If the microRNA attaches to the mRNA, the resulting double-stranded RNA cannot be translated at a ribosome and is likely to be destroyed. Medical researchers are actively studying microRNAs; the ability to silence harmful genes may help treat illnesses ranging from cancer to influenza and HIV.

Protein Processing and Degradation   Some proteins must be altered before they become functional (figure 7.19, part 6). Dozens of modifications are possible, including the addition of sugars or an alteration in the protein's structure. Producing insulin, for example, requires a precursor protein to be cut in two places. If these modifications fail to occur, the insulin protein cannot function.

In addition, to do its job, a protein must move from the ribosome to where the cell needs it. For example, a protein secreted in milk must be escorted to the Golgi apparatus and be packaged for export (see figure 3.13). A gene is effectively silenced if its product never moves to the correct destination.

Finally, like RNA, not all proteins are equally stable. Some are degraded shortly after they form, whereas others persist longer.

A human cell may express hundreds to thousands of genes at once. Unraveling the complex regulatory mechanisms that control the expression of each gene is an enormous challenge. Biologists now have the technology to begin navigating this regulatory maze. The payoff will be a much better understanding of cell biology, along with many new medical applications. The same research may also help scientists understand how external influences on gene expression contribute to complex traits, such as the one described in this chapter's Burning Question.

7.6   MASTERING CONCEPTS

1. What are some reasons that cells regulate gene expression?
2. How do proteins determine whether a bacterial operon is expressed?
3. How do enhancers and transcription factors interact to regulate gene expression?
4. What are some other ways that a cell controls which genes are expressed?

7.7 Mutations Change DNA Sequences

Virtual Lab
Mutations

A **mutation** is a change in a cell's DNA sequence, either in a protein-coding gene or in noncoding DNA such as an enhancer. Many people think that mutations are always harmful, perhaps because some of them cause such dramatic changes (figure 7.20). Although some mutations do cause illness, they also provide the variation that makes life interesting (and makes evolution possible).

To continue the cookbook analogy introduced earlier, a mutation in a gene is similar to an error in a recipe. A small typographical error might be barely noticeable. A minor substitution of one ingredient for another might hurt (or improve) the flavor. But serious errors such as missing ingredients or truncated instructions are likely to ruin the dish.

A. Mutations Range from Silent to Devastating

A mutation may change one or a few base pairs or affect large portions of a chromosome. Some are not detectable except by DNA sequencing, while others may be lethal. The rest of this section describes the major types of mutations in detail. ⓘ *DNA sequencing*, p. 222

Substitution Mutations A substitution mutation is the replacement of one DNA base with another. Such a mutation is "silent" if the mutated gene encodes the same protein as the original gene version. Mutations can be silent because more than one codon encodes most amino acids.

Often, however, a substitution mutation changes a base triplet so that it specifies a different amino acid. This change is called a missense mutation. The substituted amino acid may drastically alter the protein's shape, changing its function. Sickle cell disease results from this type of mutation (figure 7.21).

In other cases, called nonsense mutations, a base triplet specifying an amino acid changes into one that encodes a "stop"

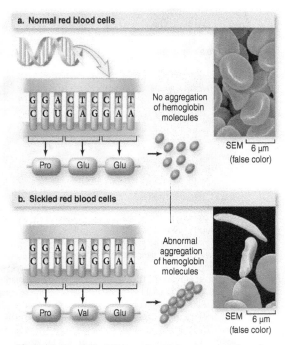

Figure 7.21 **Sickle Cell Mutation.** The most common form of sickle cell anemia results from a mutation in one of two hemoglobin genes. (a) Normal hemoglobin molecules do not aggregate, enabling the red blood cell to assume a rounded shape. (b) A substitution mutation causes one amino acid (glutamic acid) to be replaced with a different one (valine). Hemoglobin molecules clump into rods that deform the red blood cell.

codon. This shortens the protein product, which can profoundly influence the organism. At least one of the mutations that give rise to cystic fibrosis, for example, is a nonsense mutation. Instead of the normal 1480 amino acids, the faulty protein has only 493 and·therefore cannot function.

Base Insertions and Deletions An insertion mutation adds one or more nucleotides to a gene; a deletion mutation removes

Animation
Frameshift
Mutations

nucleotides. In a **frameshift mutation,** nucleotides are added or deleted by a number other than a multiple of three. Because triplets of DNA bases specify amino acids, such an addition or deletion disrupts the codon reading frame (figure 7.22). Frameshift mutations are therefore likely to alter the sequence of amino acids (missense) or cause premature stop codons (nonsense). Either way, a frameshift usually devastates a protein's function. Some mutations that cause cystic fibrosis, for example, reflect the addition or deletion of just one or two nucleotides.

Even if a small insertion or deletion does not shift the reading frame, the effect might still be significant if the change drastically alters the protein's shape. The most common mutation that causes severe cystic fibrosis deletes a single group of three

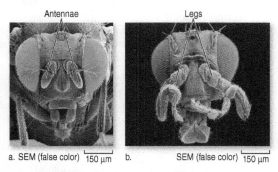

Figure 7.20 **Legs on the Head.** Mutations in some genes can cause parts to form in the wrong places. (a) A normal fruit fly. (b) This fly has legs growing where antennae should be; it has a mutation that affects development.

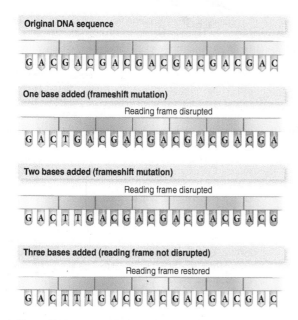

Original DNA sequence

One base added (frameshift mutation)
Reading frame disrupted

Two bases added (frameshift mutation)
Reading frame disrupted

Three bases added (reading frame not disrupted)
Reading frame restored

Figure 7.22 Frameshift Mutations. Inserting one or two nucleotides dramatically alters a gene's codons. Adding three nucleotides restores the reading frame, although the extra codon may still alter the encoded protein's shape.

TABLE 7.2 Types of Mutations

Type	Illustration
Wild type	THE ONE BIG FLY HAD ONE RED EYE
Substitution (missense)	TH**Q** ONE BIG FLY HAD ONE RED EYE
Nonsense	THE ONE BIG
Insertion	THE ONE BIG **WET** FLY HAD ONE RED EYE
Insertion (frameshift)	THE ONE **Q**BI GFL YHA DON ERE DEY
Deletion	THE ONE BIG HAD ONE RED EYE
Expanding repeat	Generation 1: THE ONE BIG FLY HAD ONE RED EYE
	Generation 2: THE ONE BIG FLY **FLY FLY** HAD ONE RED EYE
	Generation 3: THE ONE BIG FLY FLY **FLY FLY FLY FLY** HAD ONE RED EYE

Figure It Out

Suppose that a substitution mutation replaces the first A in the following mRNA sequence with a U:

  5'-AAAGCAGUACUA-3'.

How many amino acids will be in the polypeptide chain?

Answer: Zero

nucleotides. The resulting protein lacks just one amino acid, but it cannot function.

Expanding Repeats In an **expanding repeat mutation,** the number of copies of a three- or four-nucleotide sequence increases over several generations. With each generation, the symptoms begin earlier or become more severe (or both). Expanding genes underlie several inherited disorders, including fragile X syndrome and Huntington disease. In Huntington disease, expanded repeats of GTC cause extra glutamines (an amino acid) to be incorporated into the gene's protein product. The abnormal protein forms fibrous clumps in the nuclei of some brain cells, which causes the symptoms of uncontrollable movements and personality changes.

Large-Scale Mutations Some mutations affect extensive regions of DNA (see figure 9.14). For example, a large part of a chromosome may be mistakenly deleted or duplicated during meiosis. One region of a chromosome may also become inverted or fused with a different chromosome. Either event can bring together gene segments that were not previously joined. When part of chromosome 9 breaks off and fuses with chromosome 22, for example, the resulting chromosome has a fused gene whose protein product causes a type of leukemia.

Table 7.2 illustrates some of the major types of mutations, using three-letter words to represent codons.

B. What Causes Mutations?

Some mutations occur spontaneously (without outside causes). A spontaneous substitution mutation usually originates as a DNA replication error. Replication errors can also cause insertions and deletions, especially in genes with repeated base sequences, such as GCG CGC . . . . It is as if the molecules that guide and carry out replication become "confused" by short, repeated sequences, as a proofreader scanning a manuscript might miss the spelling errors in the words "happpiness" and "bananana." ⓘ *DNA replication, p. 150*

The average rate of replication errors for most genes is about 1 in 100,000 bases, but it varies among organisms and among genes. The larger a gene, the more likely it is to mutate. In addition, the more frequently DNA replicates, the more it mutates. Bacteria accumulate mutations faster than cells of complex organisms simply because their DNA replicates more often. Likewise, rapidly dividing skin cells tend to have more mutations than the nervous system's neurons, which divide slowly if at all.

Exposure to harmful chemicals or radiation may also damage DNA. A **mutagen** is any external agent that induces mutations. Examples include the ultraviolet radiation in sunlight, X-rays, radioactive fallout from atomic bomb tests and nuclear accidents, chemical weapons such as mustard gas, and chemicals in tobacco. The more contact a person has with mutagens, the higher the risk for cancer. Coating skin with sunscreen, wearing a lead "bib" during dental X-rays, and avoiding tobacco all lower cancer risk by reducing exposure to mutagenic chemicals and radiation.

Movable DNA sequences are yet another source of mutations. A **transposable element,** or transposon for short, is a DNA sequence that can "jump" within the genome. A transposon can insert itself randomly into chromosomes. If it lands within a gene, the transposon can disrupt the gene's function; it can also leave a gap in the gene when it leaves.

C. Mutations May Pass to Future Generations

A **germline mutation** is a DNA sequence change that occurs in the cells that give rise to sperm and eggs. Germline mutations are heritable because the mutated DNA will be passed down in at least some of the sex cells that the organism produces. As a result, every cell of the organism's affected offspring will carry the mutation. Such mutations may run in families, or they can appear suddenly. For example, two healthy people of normal height may have a child with a form of dwarfism called achondroplasia. The child's achondroplasia arose from a new mutation that occurred by chance in the mother's or father's germ cell.

Most mutations, however, do not pass from generation to generation. A **somatic mutation** occurs in nonsex cells, such as those that make up the skin, intestinal tract, or lungs. All cells derived from the altered one will also carry the mutation, but the mutation does not pass to the organism's offspring. The children of a cigarette smoker with mutations that cause lung cancer, for example, do not inherit the parent's damaged genes.

D. Mutations Are Important

A mutation in a gene sometimes changes the structure of its encoded protein so much that the protein can no longer do its job. Inherited diseases, including cystic fibrosis and sickle cell anemia, stem from such DNA sequence changes. Some of the most harmful mutations affect the genes encoding the proteins that repair DNA. Additional mutations then rapidly accumulate in the cell's genetic material, which can kill the cell or lead to cancer.

Mutations are also extremely important because they produce genetic variability. They are the raw material for evolution because they create new **alleles,** or variants of genes. Except for identical twins, everyone has a different combination of alleles for the 25,000 or so genes in the human genome. The same is true for any genetically variable group of organisms.

Some of these new alleles are "neutral" and have no effect on an organism's fitness. Your reproductive success, for example, does not ordinarily depend on your eye color or your shoe size. As unit 3 explains, however, variation has important evolutionary consequences. In every species, individuals with some allele combinations reproduce more successfully than others. Natural selection "edits out" the less favorable allele combinations.

Homeotic genes illustrate the importance of mutations in evolution. These genes encode transcription factors that are expressed during the development of an embryo; they control the formation of the organism's body parts. The flies in figure 7.20 show what happens when homeotic genes are mutated. Having parts in the wrong places is usually harmful. But studies of many species reveal that mutations in homeotic genes have profoundly influenced animal evolution (see section 13.5). Limb modifications such as arms, wings, and flippers trace their origins to homeotic mutations.

Mutations sometimes enhance an organism's reproductive success. Consider, for example, the antibiotic drugs that kill bacteria by targeting membrane proteins, enzymes, and other structures. Random mutations in bacterial DNA encode new versions of these targeted proteins. The descendants of some of the mutated cells become new strains that are unaffected by these antibiotics. The medical consequences are immense. Antibiotic-resistant bacteria have become more and more common, and many people now die of bacterial infections that once were easily treated with antibiotics.

Mutations can also be enormously useful in science and agriculture. Geneticists frequently induce mutations to learn how genes normally function. For example, biologists discovered how genes control flower formation by studying mutant *Arabidopsis* plants in which flower parts form in the wrong places. Plant breeders also induce mutations to create new varieties of many crop species (figure 7.23). Some kinds of rice, grapefruit, oats, lettuce, begonias, and many other plants owe their existence to breeders treating cells with radiation and then selecting interesting new varieties from the mutated individuals. ⓘ *Arabidopsis,* p. 393

7.7 MASTERING CONCEPTS

1. What is a mutation?
2. What are the types of mutations, and how does each alter the encoded protein?
3. What causes mutations?
4. What is the difference between a germline mutation and a somatic mutation?
5. How are mutations important?

a.   b.   c.

Figure 7.23 Useful Mutants. (a) Rio Red grapefruits and several types of (b) rice and (c) cotton are among the many plant varieties that have been created by using radiation to induce mutations.

INVESTIGATING LIFE

🍁 7.8 Clues to the Origin of Language

As you chat with your friends and study for your classes, you may take language for granted. Communication is not unique to humans, but a complex spoken language does set us apart from other organisms. Every human society has language. Without it, people could not transmit information from one generation to the next, so culture could not develop. Its importance to human evolutionary history is therefore incomparable. But how and when did such a crucial adaptation arise?

One clue emerged in the early 1990s, when scientists described a family with a high incidence of an unusual language disorder. Affected family members had difficulty controlling the movements of their mouth and face, so they could not pronounce sounds properly. They also had lower intelligence compared with unaffected individuals, and they had trouble applying simple rules of grammar.

Researchers traced the language disorder to one mutation in a single gene on chromosome 7. Further research revealed that the gene belongs to the large *forkhead box* family of genes, abbreviated *FOX*. All members of the *FOX* family encode transcription factors, proteins that bind to DNA and control gene expression. The "language gene" on chromosome 7, eventually named *FOXP2*, is not solely responsible for language acquisition. But the fact that the gene encodes a transcription factor explains how it can simultaneously affect both muscle control and the brain.

To learn more about the evolution of *FOXP2*, scientists Wolfgang Enard, Svante Pääbo, and colleagues at Germany's Max Planck Institute and at the University of Oxford compared the sequences of the 715 amino acids that make up the FOXP2 protein in humans, several other primates, and mice (figure 7.24). Chimpanzees, gorillas, and the rhesus macaque monkey all have identical FOXP2 proteins; their version differs from the mouse's by only one amino acid. The human version differs from the mouse's by three amino acids.

This result showed that in the 70 million or so years since the mouse and primate lineages split, the FOXP2 protein changed by only one amino acid. Yet in the 5 or 6 million years since humans split from the rest of the primates, the *FOXP2* gene changed twice.

Initially, the new, human-specific *FOXP2* version would have been rare, as are all mutations. Today, however, nearly everyone has the same allele of *FOXP2*. The human-specific *FOXP2* allele evidently conferred such improved language skills that individuals with the allele consistently produced more offspring than those without it. That is, natural selection "fixed" the new, beneficial allele in the growing human population.

The research team used mathematical models to estimate that the original mutation happened within the past 200,000 years. A subsequent study, however, revealed that Neandertal DNA contains the same two changes as those observed in mod-

Species	Number of Differences Relative to Mouse Protein
Rhesus monkey	1
Gorilla	1
Chimpanzee	1
Human	3

Figure 7.24 FOXP2 Protein Compared. The mouse version of the FOXP2 protein differs from that of nonhuman primates by just one amino acid out of 715 in the protein. The human version has three differences when compared with that of the mouse.

ern humans. The mutations therefore must have occurred before modern humans and Neandertals split from their last common ancestor, some 300,000 to 400,000 years ago.

The study of *FOXP2* is important because it helps us understand a critical period in human history. The gene changed after humans diverged from chimpanzees, and then individuals with the new, highly advantageous allele produced more offspring than those with any other version. By natural selection, the new allele quickly became fixed in the human population. Without those events, human communication and culture (including everything you chat about with your friends) might never have happened.

Enard, Wolfgang, Molly Przeworski, Simon E. Fisher, and five coauthors, including Svante Pääbo. August 22, 2002. Molecular evolution of *FOXP2*, a gene involved in speech and language. *Nature*, vol. 418, pages 869–872.

Krause, Johannes, Carles Lalueza-Fox, Ludovic Orlando, and 10 coauthors, including Svante Pääbo. November 6, 2007. The derived *FOXP2* variant of modern humans was shared with Neandertals. *Current Biology*, vol. 17, pages 1908–1912.

7.8 MASTERING CONCEPTS

1. What question about the *FOXP2* gene were the researchers trying to answer?
2. What insights could scientists gain by intentionally mutating the *FOXP2* gene in a developing human? Would such an experiment be ethical?

CHAPTER SUMMARY

7.1 Experiments Identified the Genetic Material

A. Bacteria Can Transfer Genetic Information

- Frederick Griffith determined that an unknown substance transmits a disease-causing trait between two types of bacteria.
- With the help of protein- and DNA-destroying enzymes, scientists subsequently showed that Griffith's "transforming principle" was DNA.

B. Hershey and Chase Confirmed the Genetic Role of DNA

- Using viruses that infect bacteria, Alfred Hershey and Martha Chase confirmed that the genetic material is DNA and not protein.

7.2 DNA Is a Double Helix of Nucleotides

- Erwin Chargaff discovered that A and T, and G and C, occur in equal proportions in DNA. Maurice Wilkins and Rosalind Franklin provided X-ray diffraction data. James Watson and Francis Crick combined these clues to propose the double-helix structure of **DNA.**
- DNA is made of building blocks called **nucleotides.** The rungs of the DNA "ladder" consist of **complementary** base pairs (A with T; C with G).
- The two chains of the DNA double helix are antiparallel, with the **3′** end of one strand aligned with the **5′** end of the complementary strand.

7.3 DNA Contains the "Recipes" for a Cell's Proteins

- An organism's **genome** includes all of its genetic material. Most of the genome is divided among multiple **chromosomes,** which are discrete packages of DNA and associated proteins.

A. Protein Synthesis Requires Transcription and Translation

- A **gene** is a stretch of DNA that is transcribed to **RNA.** To produce a protein, a cell **transcribes** the gene's information to mRNA, which is **translated** into a sequence of amino acids.

B. RNA Is an Intermediary Between DNA and a Polypeptide Chain

- Three types of RNA (**mRNA, rRNA,** and **tRNA**) participate in gene expression (figure 7.25).

7.4 Transcription Uses a DNA Template to Create RNA

A. Transcription Occurs in Three Steps

- Transcription begins when the **RNA polymerase** enzyme binds to a **promoter** on the DNA **template strand.** RNA polymerase then builds an RNA molecule. Transcription ends when RNA polymerase reaches a **terminator** sequence in the DNA.

B. mRNA Is Altered in the Nucleus of Eukaryotic Cells

- After transcription, the cell adds a cap and poly A tail to mRNA. **Introns** are cut out of RNA, and the remaining **exons** are spliced together.

7.5 Translation Builds the Protein

A. The Genetic Code Links mRNA to Protein

- The correspondence between codons and amino acids is the **genetic code.**
- Each group of three consecutive mRNA bases is a **codon** that specifies one amino acid (or a stop codon).

B. Translation Requires mRNA, tRNA, and Ribosomes

- mRNA carries a protein-encoding gene's information. rRNA associates with proteins to form **ribosomes,** which support and help catalyze protein synthesis.
- On one end, tRNA has an **anticodon** sequence complementary to an mRNA codon; the corresponding amino acid binds to the other end.

C. Translation Occurs in Three Steps

- Translation begins with initiation, when mRNA joins with a small ribosomal subunit and a tRNA carrying an amino acid. A large ribosomal subunit then joins the small one.
- In the elongation stage, additional tRNA molecules carrying amino acids bind to subsequent mRNA codons.
- Termination occurs when the ribosome reaches a "stop" codon. The ribosome is released, and the new polypeptide breaks free.

D. Proteins Must Fold Correctly After Translation

- Chaperone proteins help fold the polypeptide, which may be shortened or combined with others to form the finished protein.

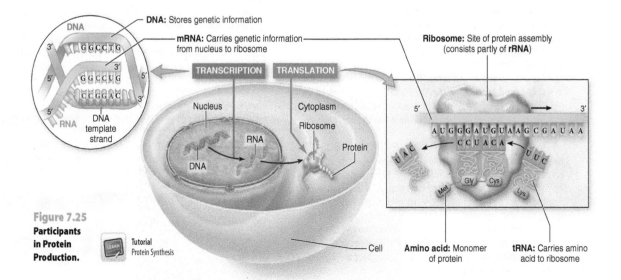

Figure 7.25

Participants in Protein Production.

Tutorial
Protein Synthesis

DNA: Stores genetic information

mRNA: Carries genetic information from nucleus to ribosome

Ribosome: Site of protein assembly (consists partly of **rRNA**)

DNA template strand

Amino acid: Monomer of protein

tRNA: Carries amino acid to ribosome

7.6 Cells Regulate Gene Expression

- Protein synthesis requires substantial energy input.

A. Operons Are Groups of Bacterial Genes That Share One Promoter

- In bacteria, **operons** coordinate expression of grouped genes whose encoded proteins participate in the same metabolic pathway. *E. coli*'s **lac operon** is a well-studied example. Transcription does not occur if a **repressor** protein binds to the **operator** sequence of the DNA.

B. Eukaryotic Organisms Use Transcription Factors

- In eukaryotic cells, proteins called **transcription factors** bind to promoters and **enhancers,** which are DNA sequences that regulate which genes a cell transcribes.

C. Eukaryotic Cells Also Use Additional Regulatory Mechanisms

- Other regulatory mechanisms include inactivating regions of a chromosome; alternative splicing; controls over mRNA stability and translation; and controls over protein folding and movement.
- Table 7.3 lists some of the most common regulatory mechanisms in the context of the steps in protein production.

7.7 Mutations Change DNA Sequences

- A **mutation** adds, deletes, alters, or moves nucleotides in DNA.

A. Mutations Range from Silent to Devastating

- A substitution mutation may result in an mRNA that encodes the wrong amino acid or that substitutes a "stop" codon for an amino acid–coding codon. Substitution mutations can also be "silent."
- In a **frameshift mutation**, inserting or deleting nucleotides disrupts the reading frame and changes the sequence of the encoded protein. Insertions or deletions in groups of three nucleotides do not alter the reading frame.
- **Expanding repeat mutations** cause some inherited illnesses.

B. What Causes Mutations?

- A gene can mutate spontaneously, especially during DNA replication.
- **Mutagens** such as chemicals or radiation induce some mutations.
- Problems in meiosis can cause mutations if portions of chromosomes are deleted, inverted, or moved.

C. Mutations May Pass to Future Generations

- A **germline mutation** originates in cells that give rise to gametes and therefore appears in every cell of an offspring that inherits the mutation. A **somatic mutation,** which occurs in nonsex cells, affects a subset of cells in the body but does not affect the offspring.

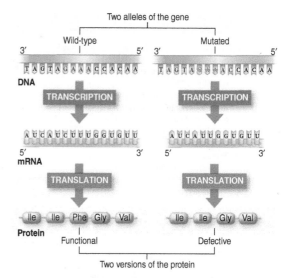

Figure 7.26 Mutations Create New Alleles.

D. Mutations Are Important

- Mutations create new alleles, which are the raw material for evolution (figure 7.26).
- Induced mutations help scientists deduce gene function and help plant breeders produce new varieties of fruits and flowers.

7.8 Investigating Life: Clues to the Origin of Language

- A family with a language disorder led researchers to discover a gene that is apparently involved in the acquisition of language.
- Comparing the human version of the gene with that in other primates and in mice suggests that the gene apparently began evolving rapidly soon after modern humans arose. Eventually one allele became fixed in the human population.

TABLE 7.3   Regulated Points in Protein Production

Event	Description	Location in Eukaryotic Cell	Regulatory Mechanism(s)
Transcription	RNA polymerase enzyme uses DNA template to produce mRNA	Nucleus	DNA availability; transcription factors
mRNA processing (eukaryotic cells)	Cap and tail are added; introns are removed	Nucleus	Selection of introns to be removed; exit of mRNA from nucleus
Translation	Information in mRNA is used to assemble protein	Ribosome	mRNA degradation before translation
Protein modification	Protein is folded and may be shortened or combined with other polypeptides	Anywhere in cell	Availability of proteins needed for processing; tagging for correct location in cell; protein degradation

MULTIPLE CHOICE QUESTIONS

1. A nucleotide is composed of all of the following EXCEPT a
   a. sugar.
   b. nitrogen-containing group.
   c. sulfur-containing group.
   d. phosphorus-containing group.

2. If one strand of DNA has the sequence ATTGTCC, then the sequence of the complementary strand will be
   a. TAACAGG.   c. ACCTCGG.
   b. CGGAGTT.   d. CCTGTTA.

3. Transcription copies a _____ to a complementary _____ molecule.
   a. chromosome; DNA   c. gene; RNA
   b. genome; RNA   d. DNA sequence; ribosome

4. Choose the DNA sequence from which this mRNA sequence was transcribed: 5'-AUACGAUUA-3'.
   a. 3'-TATGCTAAT-5'   c. 3'-UAUCGUAAU-5'
   b. 3'-UTUGCUTTU-5'   d. 3'-CTCAGCTTC-5'

5. The segments of eukaryotic mRNA that are translated into proteins are called
   a. promoters.   c. exons.
   b. introns.   d. caps.

6. How many different three-codon sequences encode the amino acid sequence Phe-Val-Ala? Hint: Refer to figure 7.12.
   a. 1   c. 8
   b. 4   d. 32

7. What is the job of the tRNA during translation?
   a. It carries amino acids to the mRNA.
   b. It triggers the formation of a covalent bond between amino acids.
   c. It binds to the small ribosomal subunit.
   d. It triggers the termination of the protein.

8. How does the *lac* operon regulate lactose digestion in bacteria?
   a. The repressor protein becomes a lactose-digesting enzyme only when lactose is present.
   b. The repressor protein binds to the *lac* operon when lactose is present, blocking transcription.
   c. When lactose is present, it binds to the operator region of the *lac* operon, activating transcription of the repressor protein gene.
   d. The repressor protein falls off the *lac* operon when lactose is present, and lactose-digesting genes are expressed.

9. If adenine in the 10th nucleotide position of a gene mutates to cytosine, then the _____ amino acid in the protein encoded by this gene could change.
   a. 1st   c. 10th
   b. 4th   d. 30th

10. Are mutations harmful?
    a. Yes, because the DNA is damaged.
    b. No, because changes in the DNA result in better alleles.
    c. Yes, because mutated proteins don't function.
    d. It depends on how the mutation affects the protein's function.

Answers to these questions are in appendix A.

WRITE IT OUT

1. Explain how Griffith's experiment and Avery, MacLeod, and McCarty's experiment determined that DNA in bacteria transmits a trait that kills mice.

2. Describe the three-dimensional structure of DNA.

3. Explain Chargaff's observation that a DNA molecule contains equal amounts of A and T and equal amounts of G and C.

4. Write the complementary DNA sequence of each of the following base sequences:
   a. AGGCATACCTGAGTC
   b. GTTTAATGCCCTACA
   c. AACACTACCGATTCA

5. Put the following in order from smallest to largest: nucleotide, genome, nitrogenous base, gene, nucleus, cell, codon, chromosome.

6. What is the function of DNA?

7. Use figure 7.9 to describe the structural and functional differences between RNA and DNA.

8. Explain how information in DNA is transcribed and translated into amino acids.

9. Some people compare DNA to a blueprint stored in the office of a construction company. Explain how this analogy would extend to transcription and translation.

10. List the three major types of RNA and their functions.

11. List the sequences of the mRNA molecules transcribed from the following template DNA sequences:
    a. TGAACTACGGTACCATAC
    b. GCACTAAAGATC

12. How many codons are in each of the mRNA molecules that you wrote for question 11?

13. Refer to the figure to answer these questions:

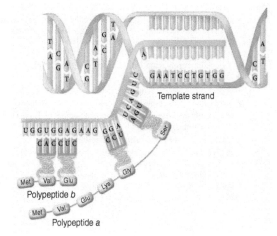

Template strand

Polypeptide *b*

Polypeptide *a*

a. Add labels for mRNA (including the 5' and 3' ends) and tRNA. In addition, draw in the RNA polymerase enzyme and the ribosomes, including arrows indicating the direction of movement for each.

b. What are the next three amino acids to be added to polypeptide *b*?

c. Fill in the nucleotides in the mRNA complementary to the template DNA strand.

d. What is the sequence of the DNA complementary to the template strand (as much as can be determined from the figure)?

e. Does this figure show the entire polypeptide that this gene encodes? How can you tell?

f. What might happen to polypeptide *b* after its release from the ribosome?

g. Does this figure depict a prokaryotic or a eukaryotic cell? How can you tell?

14. Is changing the first nucleotide in a codon *more likely* or *less likely* to change the encoded amino acid than changing the third nucleotide in a codon?

15. Titin is a muscle protein whose gene has the largest known coding sequence: 80,781 DNA bases. How many amino acids long is titin?

16. If a protein is 1259 amino acids long, what is the minimum size of the gene that encodes the protein? Why might the gene be longer than the minimum?

17. How did researchers reason that a combination of at least three RNA bases must specify each amino acid?

18. The roundworm *C. elegans* has 556 cells when it hatches. Each cell contains the entire genome but expresses only a subset of the genes. Therefore, the cells "specialize" in particular functions. List all of the ways that a roundworm cell might silence the unneeded genes.

19. The genome of the human immunodeficiency virus (HIV) includes nine genes. Two of the genes encode four different proteins each. How is this possible?

20. The shape of a finch's beak reflects the expression of a gene that encodes a protein called calmodulin. A cactus finch has a long, pointy beak; its cells express the gene more than a ground finch, which has a short, deep beak. When researchers boosted gene expression in a ground finch embryo, the bird's upper beak was longer than normal. Develop a hypothesis that explains this finding.

21. If a gene is like a cake recipe, then a mutation is like a cake recipe containing an error. List the major types of mutations, and describe an analogous error in a cake recipe.

22. A protein-encoding region of a gene has the following DNA sequence:
TTTCATCAGGATGCAACA

Determine how each of the following mutations alters the amino acid sequence:
a. substitution of an A for the T in the first position
b. substitution of a G for the C in the 17th position
c. insertion of a T between the fourth and fifth DNA bases
d. insertion of a GTA between the 12th and 13th DNA bases
e. deletion of the first DNA nucleotide

23. Explain how a mutation in a protein-encoding gene, an enhancer, or a gene encoding a transcription factor can all have the same effect on an organism.

24. How can a mutation alter the sequence of DNA bases in a gene but not produce a noticeable change in the gene's polypeptide product? How can a mutation alter the amino acid sequence of a polypeptide yet not alter the organism?

25. Describe the mutation shown in figure 7.26 and explain how the mutation affects the amino acid sequence encoded by the gene.

26. Parkinson disease causes rigidity, tremors, and other motor symptoms. Only 2% of cases are inherited, and these tend to have an early onset of symptoms. Some inherited cases result from mutations in a gene that encodes the protein parkin, which has 12 exons. Indicate whether each of the following mutations in the parkin gene would result in a smaller protein, a larger protein, or no change in the size of the protein:
a. deletion of exon 3
b. deletion of six consecutive nucleotides in exon 1
c. duplication of exon 5
d. disruption of the splice site between exon 8 and intron 8
e. deletion of intron 2

27. Consult the genetic code to write codon changes that could account for the following changes in amino acid sequence:
a. tryptophan to arginine
b. glycine to valine
c. tyrosine to histidine

28. Researchers use computer algorithms that search DNA sequences for indications of specialized functions. Explain the significance of detecting the following sequences:
a. a promoter
b. a sequence of 75 to 80 nucleotides that folds into a shape resembling a backwards letter *L*
c. RNAs with poly A tails

29. In a disorder called gyrate atrophy, cells in the retina begin to degenerate in late adolescence, causing night blindness that progresses to total blindness. The cause is a mutation in the gene that encodes an enzyme, ornithine aminotransferase (OAT). Researchers sequenced the *OAT* gene for five patients with the following results:

- Patient A: A change in codon 209 of UAU to UAA
- Patient B: A change in codon 299 of UAC to UAG
- Patient C: A change in codon 426 of CGA to UGA
- Patient D: A two-nucleotide deletion at codons 64 and 65 that results in a UGA codon at position 79
- Patient E: Exon 6, including 1071 nucleotides, is entirely deleted.

a. Which patient(s) have a frameshift mutation?
b. How many amino acids is patient E missing?
c. Which patient(s) will produce a shortened protein?

PULL IT TOGETHER

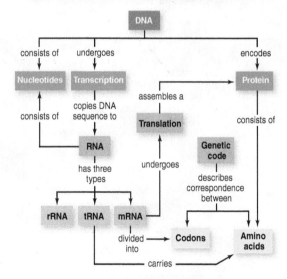

Figure 7.27 Pull It Together: DNA Structure and Gene Function.

Refer to figure 7.27 and the chapter content to answer the following questions.

1. Why is protein production essential to cell function?

2. Where do promoters, terminators, stop codons, transcription factors, RNA polymerase, and enhancers fit into this concept map?

3. Use the concept map to explain how DNA nucleotides are related to amino acids.

4. Use the concept map to explain why a mutation in DNA sometimes causes protein function to change.

CHAPTER

8

DNA Replication, Binary Fission, and Mitosis

Big Man. One of the world's tallest men, Bao Xishun, stands at 2.36 meters (7 feet, 9 inches). Rapid cell division during adolescence explains his extreme height.

connect plus+

Enhance your study |BIOLOGY
of this chapter with practice quizzes,
animations and videos, answer keys,
and downloadable study tools.
www.mhhe.com/hoefnagels

The Tallest and the Shortest

A QUICK GLANCE AT ANY CROWD REVEALS THAT NOT EVERYONE IS THE SAME HEIGHT. In the United States, the average height is about 1.78 meters (5 feet, 10 inches) for men and about 1.62 m (5 feet, 4 inches) for women. But those statistics hide a great deal of variation; many people are much taller or shorter than average.

A person's adult height reflects cell division during childhood and adolescence, especially in the ends of the bones. During cell division, one cell becomes two. The next round of division yields four cells, and the following round produces eight. Each new cell grows as it produces proteins and takes in water and other nutrients. If the thousands of cells at each end of a bone are all actively dividing, then the bone tissue quickly expands, and the person gets taller. ⓘ *bone growth*, p. 596

Chemical signals regulate bone growth. The most important signal is human growth hormone, which is secreted by the pituitary gland. Human growth hormone "tells" bone cells to divide. The more growth hormone, the greater the rate of cell division. Small changes in the abundance of growth hormone may therefore profoundly affect development.

For example, gigantism results from an overproduction of growth hormone early in life. Over many years of bone growth, a small excess in growth hormone may produce bones that are much longer than normal. The tallest person known to have lived, Robert Wadlow, had gigantism (see figure 28.5). He never stopped growing, and he was 2.72 meters (nearly 9 feet) tall when he died.

At the other extreme, a growth hormone deficiency produces a type of dwarfism. In this disorder, bone cells do not receive enough signals to divide during childhood. While the brain develops normally, other body parts remain small. One person with this disorder is Chandra Bahadur Dangi of Nepal. At only about 0.55 m (1 foot, 9 inches) tall, he is the shortest known adult.

Dwarfism has other causes as well. The most common form of dwarfism, called achondroplasia, reflects a problem with the cells of the limb bones. Even though human growth hormone is present, the bone cells fail to divide, and the arms and legs remain abnormally short.

The natural variation in human height shines the spotlight on a larger message: Tissue growth and repair rely on cell division, the subject of this chapter. As you learn more about how cells divide, think back on this essay and remember that faulty signals can produce surprisingly large—or small—effects.

LEARNING OUTLINE

 8.1 Cells Divide and Cells Die
  A. Sexual Life Cycles Include Mitosis, Meiosis, and Fertilization
  B. Cell Death Is Part of Life

 8.2 DNA Replication Precedes Cell Division

8.3 Prokaryotes Divide by Binary Fission

 8.4 Replicated Chromosomes Condense as a Eukaryotic Cell Prepares to Divide

8.5 Mitotic Division Generates Exact Cell Copies
  A. Interphase Is a Time of Great Activity
  B. Chromosomes Divide During Mitosis
  C. The Cytoplasm Splits in Cytokinesis

 8.6 Cancer Arises When Cells Divide Out of Control
  A. Chemical Signals Regulate Cell Division
  B. Cancer Cells Break Through Cell Cycle Controls
  C. Cancer Cells Differ from Normal Cells in Many Ways
  D. Cancer Treatments Remove or Kill Abnormal Cells
  E. Inheritance and Environment Both Can Cause Cancer

 8.7 Apoptosis Is Programmed Cell Death

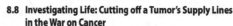 **8.8 Investigating Life: Cutting off a Tumor's Supply Lines in the War on Cancer**

LEARN HOW TO LEARN
Explain It, Right or Wrong

As you work through the multiple choice questions at the end of each chapter, make sure you can explain why each correct choice is right. You can also test your understanding by taking the time to explain why each of the other choices is wrong.

8.1 Cells Divide and Cells Die

Your cells are too small to see without a microscope, so it is hard to appreciate just how many you lose as you sleep, work, and play. Each minute, for example, you shed tens of thousands of dead skin cells. If you did not have a way to replace these lost cells, your body would literally wear away. Instead, cells in your deep skin layers divide and replace the ones you lose. Each new cell lives an average of about 35 days, so you will gradually replace your entire skin in the next month or so—without even noticing!

Cell division produces a continuous supply of replacement cells, both in your skin and everywhere else in your body. But cell division has other functions as well. No living organism can reproduce without cell division, and the growth and development of a multicellular organism also require the production of new cells.

This chapter explores the opposing but coordinated forces of cell division and cell death, and considers what happens if either process goes wrong. We begin by exploring cell division's role in reproduction, growth, and development.

A. Sexual Life Cycles Include Mitosis, Meiosis, and Fertilization

Organisms must reproduce—generate other individuals like themselves—for a species to persist. The most straightforward and ancient way for a single-celled organism to reproduce is **asexually,** by replicating its genetic material and splitting the contents of one cell into two. Except for the occasional mutation, asexual reproduction generates genetically identical offspring. Bacteria and archaea, for example, reproduce asexually via a simple type of cell division called binary fission (see section 8.3). Many protists and multicellular eukaryotes also reproduce asexually.

Sexual reproduction, in contrast, is the production of offspring whose genetic makeup comes from two parents. Each parent contributes a sex cell, and the fusion of these cells signals the start of the next generation. Because sexual reproduction mixes up and recombines traits, the offspring are genetically different from each other and their parents.

Figure 8.1 illustrates how two types of cell division, meiosis and mitosis, interact in a sexual life cycle. In humans and many other species, the male parent provides sperm cells, and a female produces egg cells; these sex cells are collectively called **gametes**. A specialized type of cell division called **meiosis** gives rise to gametes, which are genetically different from one another (see chapter 9). This variation among gametes explains why the offspring of two parents usually look different from one another (except for identical twins).

Fertilization is the union of the sperm and the egg cell, producing a zygote (the first cell of the new offspring). Immediately after fertilization, the other type of cell division—mitotic—takes over. **Mitosis** divides a eukaryotic cell's genetic information

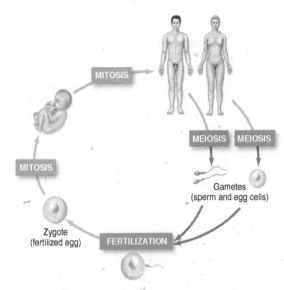

Figure 8.1 Sexual Reproduction. In the life cycle of humans and many other organisms, adults produce gametes by meiosis. Fertilization unites sperm and egg, and mitotic cell division accounts for the growth of the new offspring.

into two identical nuclei. Mitotic cell division explains how you grew from a single-celled zygote into an adult (figure 8.2), how you repair damage after an injury, and how you replace the cells that you lose every day. Likewise, mitotic cell division accounts for the growth and development of plants, mushrooms, and other multicellular eukaryotes.

Each of the trillions of cells in your body retains the genetic information that was present in the fertilized egg. Inspired by the astonishing precision with which this occurs, geneticist Herman J. Müller wrote in 1947:

In a sense we contain ourselves, wrapped up within ourselves, trillions of times repeated.

This quotation eloquently expresses the powerful idea that every cell in the body results from countless rounds of cell division, each time forming two genetically identical cells from one.

B. Cell Death Is Part of Life

The development of a multicellular organism requires more than just cell division. Cells also die in predictable ways, carving distinctive structures. **Apoptosis** is cell death that is a normal part of development. Like cell division, it is a precise, tightly regulated sequence of events (see section 8.7). Apoptosis is therefore also called "programmed cell death."

During early development, both cell division and apoptosis shape new structures. For example, the feet of both ducks and chickens start out as webbed paddles when the birds are embryos

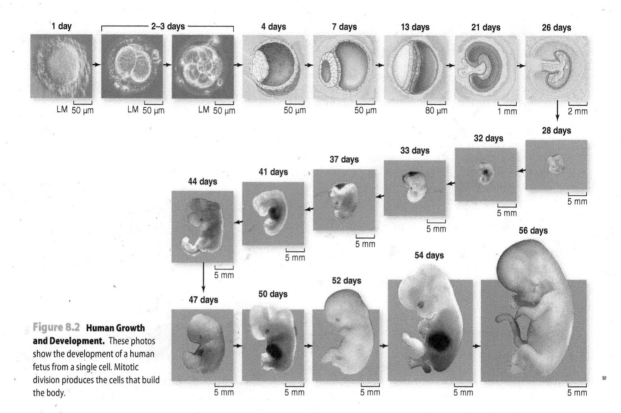

Figure 8.2 Human Growth and Development. These photos show the development of a human fetus from a single cell. Mitotic division produces the cells that build the body.

Figure 8.3 Apoptosis Carves Toes. The feet of embryonic ducks and chickens have webbing between the digits. (a) A duck's foot retains this webbing. (b) In a developing chicken foot, the toes take shape when the cells between the digits die.

(figure 8.3). The webs of tissue remain in the duck's foot throughout life. In the chicken, however, individual toes form as cells between the digits die. Likewise, cells in the tail of a tadpole die as the young frog develops into an adult.

Throughout an animal's life, cell division and cell death are in balance, so tissue neither overgrows nor shrinks. Cell division compensates for the death of skin and blood cells, a little like adding new snow (cell division) to a snowman that is melting (apoptosis). Both cell division and apoptosis also help protect the organism. For example, cells divide to heal a scraped knee; apoptosis peels away sunburnt skin cells that might otherwise become cancerous.

Before learning more about mitosis and apoptosis, it is important to understand how the genetic material in a eukaryotic cell copies itself and condenses in preparation for cell division. Sections 8.2 and 8.4 explain these events.

8.1 MASTERING CONCEPTS

1. Explain the roles of mitotic cell division, meiosis, and fertilization in the human life cycle.

2. Why are both cell division and apoptosis necessary for the development of an organism?

8.2 DNA Replication Precedes Cell Division

Tutorial DNA Replication

Before any cell divides—by binary fission, mitotically, or meiotically—it must first duplicate its entire **genome,** which consists of all of the cell's genetic material. The genome may consist of one or more **chromosomes,** which are individual molecules of DNA with their associated proteins. Chapter 7 describes the cell's genome as a set of "cookbooks" (chromosomes), each containing "recipes" (genes) that encode tens of thousands of proteins. In DNA replication, the cell copies all of this information, letter by letter. Without a full set of instructions, a new cell might die.

Recall from figure 7.5 that DNA is a double-stranded nucleic acid. Each strand of the double helix is composed of nucleotides.

Animation DNA Structure

Hydrogen bonds between the nitrogenous bases of the nucleotides hold the two strands together. The base adenine (A) pairs with its complement, thymine (T); similarly, cytosine (C) forms complementary base pairs with guanine (G).

Figure It Out

Write the complementary strand for the following DNA sequence:
5'-TCAATACCGATTAT-3'

Answer: 3'-AGTTATGGCTAATA-5'

When Watson and Crick reported DNA's structure, they understood that they had uncovered the key to DNA replication. Their paper ends with the tantalizing statement, "It has not escaped our notice that the specific pairing we have postulated immediately suggests a possible copying mechanism for the genetic material." They envisioned DNA unwinding, exposing unpaired bases that would attract their complements, and neatly knitting two double helices from one. This route to replication, which turned out to be essentially correct, is called semiconservative because each DNA double helix conserves half of the original molecule (figure 8.4).

DNA does not, however, replicate by itself. Instead, an army of enzymes copies DNA just before a cell divides (figure 8.5). Enzymes called helicases unwind and "unzip" the DNA, while binding proteins prevent the two single strands from rejoining each other. Other enzymes then guide the assembly of new DNA strands. **DNA polymerase** is the enzyme that adds new DNA nucleotides that are complementary to the bases on each exposed strand. As the new DNA strands grow, hydrogen bonds form between the complementary bases.

Curiously, DNA polymerase can add nucleotides only to an existing strand. A primase enzyme therefore must build a short complementary piece of RNA, called an RNA primer, at the start of each DNA segment to be replicated. The RNA primer attracts the DNA polymerase enzyme. Once the new strand of DNA is in place, another enzyme removes each RNA primer. DNA polymerase then fills the gap with the correct DNA nucleotides. This enzyme cannot, however, join the existing strand

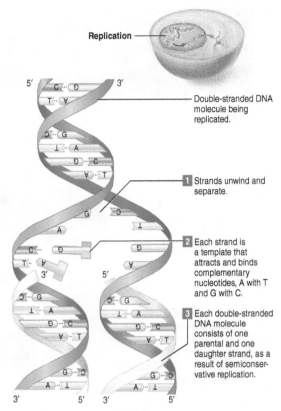

Replication

Double-stranded DNA molecule being replicated.

1 Strands unwind and separate.

2 Each strand is a template that attracts and binds complementary nucleotides, A with T and G with C.

3 Each double-stranded DNA molecule consists of one parental and one daughter strand, as a result of semiconservative replication.

Figure 8.4 DNA Replication: A Simplified View. (1) DNA strands unwind and separate. (2) New nucleotides form complementary base pairs with each exposed strand. (3) The process ends with two identical double-stranded DNA molecules.

Animation DNA Replication Simplified

with the last nucleotide to be placed in the gap. Enzymes called **ligases** form the covalent bonds that seal these nicks.

Furthermore, like the RNA polymerase enzyme described in section 7.4, DNA polymerase can add new nucleotides only to the exposed 3' end—never the 5' end—of a growing strand. Replication therefore proceeds continuously on only one new DNA strand, called the leading strand. On the other strand, called the lagging strand, replication occurs in short 5' to 3' pieces. These short pieces, each preceded by its own RNA primer, are called Okazaki fragments.

Replication enzymes work simultaneously at hundreds of points, called origins of replication, on each DNA molecule (figure 8.6). This arrangement is similar to the way that hurried office workers might split a lengthy report into short pieces and then divide the sections among many copy machines operating at the same time. Thanks to this division of labor, copying the billions of DNA nucleotides in a human cell takes only 8 to 10 hours.

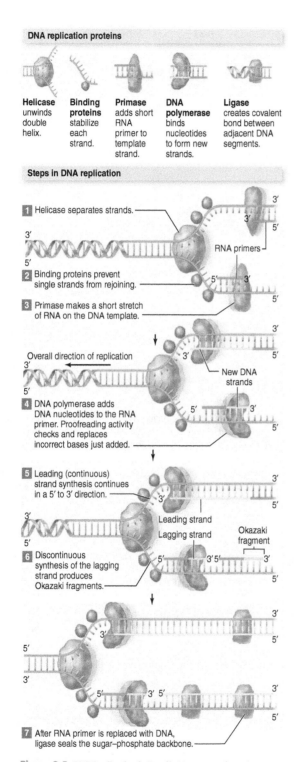

DNA replication proteins

Helicase	Binding proteins	Primase	DNA polymerase	Ligase
unwinds double helix.	stabilize each strand.	adds short RNA primer to template strand.	binds nucleotides to form new strands.	creates covalent bond between adjacent DNA segments.

Steps in DNA replication

1 Helicase separates strands.

2 Binding proteins prevent single strands from rejoining.

3 Primase makes a short stretch of RNA on the DNA template.

RNA primers

Overall direction of replication

New DNA strands

4 DNA polymerase adds DNA nucleotides to the RNA primer. Proofreading activity checks and replaces incorrect bases just added.

5 Leading (continuous) strand synthesis continues in a 5' to 3' direction.

Leading strand

Lagging strand

Okazaki fragment

6 Discontinuous synthesis of the lagging strand produces Okazaki fragments.

7 After RNA primer is replaced with DNA, ligase seals the sugar–phosphate backbone.

Figure 8.5 DNA Replication in Detail. Many types of proteins participate in DNA replication. Although they are depicted separately for clarity, in reality they form a cluster that moves along the DNA molecule.

Animation
DNA Replication
In Detail

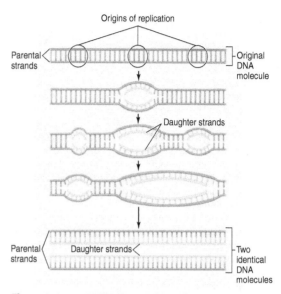

Origins of replication

Parental strands

Original DNA molecule

Daughter strands

Parental strands

Daughter strands

Two identical DNA molecules

Figure 8.6 Origins of Replication. DNA replication occurs simultaneously at many points along a chromosome.

DNA replication is incredibly accurate. DNA polymerase "proofreads" as it goes, backtracking to discard mismatched nucleotides and insert correct ones. After proofreading, DNA polymerase incorrectly incorporates only about one in a billion nucleotides. Other repair enzymes help ensure the accuracy of DNA replication by cutting out and replacing incorrect nucleotides.

Nevertheless, mistakes occasionally remain. The result is a **mutation,** which is any change in a cell's DNA sequence. To extend the cooking analogy, a mutation is similar to a mistake in one of the recipes in a cookbook. Section 7.7 describes the many ways that a mutation can affect the life of a cell.

Overall, DNA replication requires a great deal of energy because a large, organized nucleic acid contains much more potential energy than do many individual nucleotides. Energy from ATP is required to synthesize nucleotides and to create the covalent bonds that join them together in the new strands of DNA. Many of the enzymes that participate in DNA replication, including helicase and ligase, also require energy to catalyze their reactions. (i) *ATP,* p. 76

8.2   MASTERING CONCEPTS

1. Why does DNA replicate?
2. What is semiconservative replication?
3. What are the steps of DNA replication?
4. Could DNA replication occur if primase were not present in a cell? Explain your answer.
5. What happens if DNA polymerase fails to correct an error?

8.3 Prokaryotes Divide by Binary Fission

Like all organisms, bacteria and archaea transmit DNA from generation to generation as they reproduce. In prokaryotes, reproduction occurs by **binary fission,** an asexual process that replicates DNA and distributes it (along with other cell parts) into two daughter cells (figure 8.7).

Each prokaryotic cell contains one circular chromosome. As the cell prepares to divide, its DNA replicates. The chromosome and its duplicate attach to the inner surface of the cell. The cell membrane grows between the two DNA molecules, separating them. Then the cell pinches in half to form two daughter cells from the original one.

In optimal conditions, some bacterial cells can divide every 20 minutes. The few microbes that remain after you brush your teeth therefore easily repopulate your mouth as you sleep; their metabolic activities produce the foul-smelling "morning breath."

8.3 | MASTERING CONCEPTS

1. Which cell types divide by binary fission?
2. What are the events of binary fission?

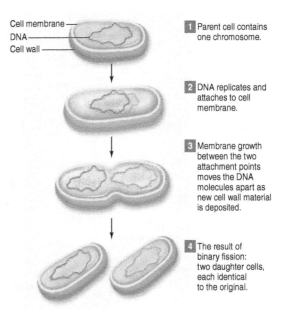

Cell membrane
DNA
Cell wall

1 Parent cell contains one chromosome.

2 DNA replicates and attaches to cell membrane.

3 Membrane growth between the two attachment points moves the DNA molecules apart as new cell wall material is deposited.

4 The result of binary fission: two daughter cells, each identical to the original.

Figure 8.7 Binary Fission. A dividing prokaryotic cell replicates its DNA, grows, and then indents, separating one cell into two.

 ## 8.4 Replicated Chromosomes Condense as a Eukaryotic Cell Prepares to Divide

Binary fission is relatively uncomplicated because the genetic material in prokaryotic cells consists of a single circular DNA molecule. In a eukaryotic cell, however, distributing DNA into daughter cells is more complex because the genetic information consists of multiple chromosomes inside a nucleus.

Each species has a characteristic number of chromosomes. A mosquito's cell has 6 chromosomes; grasshoppers, rice plants, and pine trees all have 24; humans have 46; dogs and chickens have 78; a carp has 104. Each of these numbers is even because sexually reproducing organisms inherit one set of chromosomes from each parent. Human sperm and egg cells, for example, each contain 23 chromosomes; fertilization therefore yields an offspring with 46 chromosomes in every cell.

With so much genetic material, a eukaryotic cell must balance two needs. On the one hand, the cell must have access to the information in its DNA. On the other hand, a dividing cell must package its DNA into a portable form that can easily move into the two daughter cells (figure 8.8). To learn how cells maintain this balance, we must look closely at a chromosome's structure.

Eukaryotic chromosomes consist of **chromatin,** which is a collective term for all of the cell's DNA and its associated proteins. These proteins include the many enzymes that help replicate the DNA and transcribe it to a sequence of RNA (see chapter 7). Others serve as scaffolds around which DNA entwines, helping to pack the DNA efficiently inside the cell.

To illustrate the importance of DNA packing, consider this fact: Stretched end to end, the DNA in one human cell would form a thread some 2 meters long. If the DNA bases of all 46 human chromosomes were typed as A, C, T, and G, the several billion letters would fill 4000 books of 500 pages each! How can a cell only 100 microns in diameter contain so much material?

The explanation is that chromatin is organized into units called **nucleosomes,** each consisting of a stretch of DNA wrapped around eight proteins (histones). A continuous thread of DNA connects nucleosomes like beads on a string (figure 8.9). When the cell is not dividing, chromatin is barely visible because the nucleosomes are loosely packed together. The cell can therefore access the information in the DNA to produce the proteins that it needs for its metabolic activities. DNA replication in preparation for cell division also requires that the cell's DNA be unwound.

LM   30 µm

Figure 8.8 Two Views of DNA. In the cell on the left, the material resembling a solid disk is unwound DNA. Before a cell divides, the DNA coils into the compact chromosomes visible in the cell on the right.

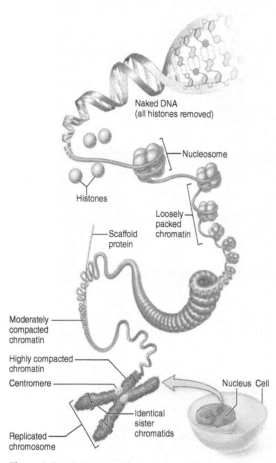

Figure 8.9 **Parts of a Chromosome.** DNA replicates just before a cell divides, and then the chromatin condenses into its familiar, compact form.

The chromosome's appearance changes shortly after DNA replication. The nucleosomes gradually fold into progressively larger structures, until the chromosome takes on its familiar, compact shape. DNA packing is somewhat similar to winding a long thread around a spool. Just as spooled thread occupies less space and is more portable than a pile of loose thread, condensed DNA is easier for the cell to manage than is unwound chromatin.

Once condensed, a chromosome has readily identifiable parts (see figure 8.9). A replicated chromosome consists of two **chromatids,** each with a DNA sequence identical to the other. These paired chromatids are therefore called "sister chromatids." The **centromere** is a small section of DNA and associated proteins that attaches the sister chromatids to each other. As a cell's genetic material divides, the centromere splits, and the sister chromatids move apart. At that point, each chromatid becomes an individual chromosome.

8.4 MASTERING CONCEPTS

1. How are chromosomes and chromatin related?

2. What might happen to a cell if DNA packing fails?

8.5 Mitotic Division Generates Exact Cell Copies

Tutorial Mitosis

Suppose you scrape your leg while sliding into second base during a softball game. At first, the wound bleeds, but the blood soon clots and forms a scab. Underneath the dried crust, cells of the immune system clear away trapped dirt and dead cells. At the same time, undamaged skin cells bordering the wound begin to divide repeatedly, producing fresh, new daughter cells that eventually fill the damaged area.

Those actively dividing skin cells illustrate the **cell cycle,** which describes the events that occur from one cell division until the next. Biologists divide the cell cycle into stages (figure 8.10). During **interphase,** the cell is not dividing, but protein synthesis, DNA replication, and many other events occur. Immediately following interphase is mitosis, during which the contents of the nucleus divide. **Cytokinesis** is the splitting of the cell itself. After cytokinesis is complete, the daughter cells enter interphase, and the cell cycle begins anew.

Mitotic cell division occurs some 300 million times per minute in your body, replacing cells lost to abrasion or cell death.

Video Animal Cells Dividing

In each case, the products are two daughter cells, each receiving complete, identical genetic instructions and the molecules and organelles they need to maintain metabolism.

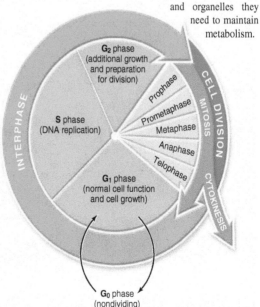

Figure 8.10 **The Cell Cycle.** Interphase includes gap phases (G_1 and G_2), when the cell grows and some organelles duplicate. Nondividing cells can leave G_1 and enter G_0 indefinitely. During the synthesis phase (S) of interphase, DNA replicates. Mitosis divides the replicated genetic material between two nuclei. Cytokinesis then splits the cytoplasm in half, producing two identical daughter cells.

A. Interphase Is a Time of Great Activity

3-D Animation
Interphase

Biologists once mistakenly described interphase as a time when the cell is at rest. The chromatin is unwound and therefore barely visible, so the cell appears inactive. However, interphase is actually a very active time. The cell carries out its basic functions, from muscle contraction to insulin production to bone formation. DNA replication also occurs during this stage.

Interphase is divided into "gap" phases (designated G_1, G_0, and G_2), separated by a "synthesis" (S) phase. During **G_1 phase,** the cell grows, carries out basic functions, and produces molecules needed to build new organelles and other components it will require if it divides. A cell in G_1 may enter a nondividing stage called G_0.

In **G_0 phase**, a cell continues to function, but it does not replicate its DNA or divide. At any given time, most cells in the human body are in G_0. Nerve cells in the brain are permanently in G_0, which explains both why the brain does not grow after it reaches its adult size and why brain damage is often irreparable.

During **S phase,** enzymes replicate the cell's genetic material and repair damaged DNA (see section 8.2). As S phase begins, each chromosome includes one DNA molecule. By the end of S phase, each chromosome consists of two identical, attached DNA molecules.

Another event that occurs during S phase is the duplication of the centrosome in an animal cell. **Centrosomes** are structures that organize the proteins that will move the chromosomes during mitosis. Each centrosome includes proteins enclosing a pair of barrel-shaped centrioles. Most plant cells lack centrosomes; they organize their chromosome-moving proteins throughout the cell.

In **G_2 phase,** the cell continues to grow but also prepares to divide, producing the proteins that will help coordinate mitosis. The DNA winds more tightly, and this start of chromosome condensation signals impending mitosis. Interphase has ended.

Figure It Out

A cell that has completed interphase contains __ times as much DNA as a cell at the start of interphase.

Answer: two

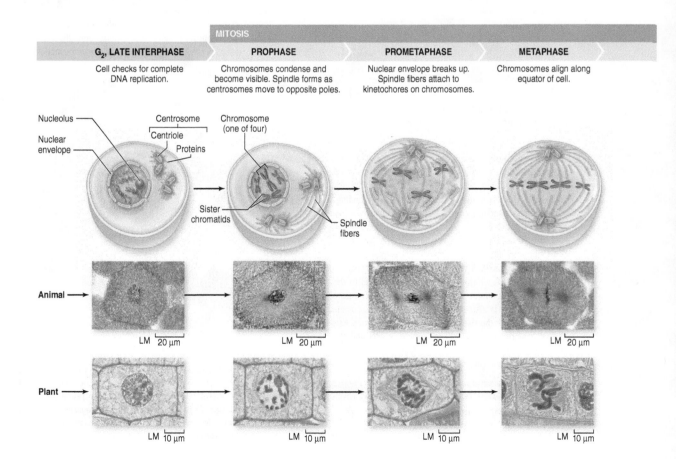

MITOSIS			
G_2, LATE INTERPHASE	**PROPHASE**	**PROMETAPHASE**	**METAPHASE**
Cell checks for complete DNA replication.	Chromosomes condense and become visible. Spindle forms as centrosomes move to opposite poles.	Nuclear envelope breaks up. Spindle fibers attach to kinetochores on chromosomes.	Chromosomes align along equator of cell.

Nucleolus
Nuclear envelope
Centrosome
Centriole
Proteins
Chromosome (one of four)
Sister chromatids
Spindle fibers

Animal

LM 20 μm   LM 20 μm   LM 20 μm   LM 20 μm

Plant

LM 10 μm   LM 10 μm   LM 10 μm   LM 10 μm

B. Chromosomes Divide During Mitosis

Overall, mitosis separates the genetic material that replicated during S phase. For the chromosomes to be evenly distributed, they must line up in a way that enables them to split equally into two sets that are then pulled to opposite poles of the cell.

Mitosis is a continuous process, but biologists divide it into stages for ease of understanding. Figure 8.11 summarizes the key events of mitosis; you may find it helpful to consult this figure as you read on.

During **prophase,** DNA coils very tightly, shortening and thickening the chromosomes (see figure 8.9). As the chromosomes condense, they become visible when stained and viewed under a microscope. For now, the chromosomes remain randomly arranged in the nucleus. The nucleolus (the dark area in the nucleus) also disappears.

Also during prophase, the two centrosomes migrate toward opposite poles of the cell, and the spindle begins to form. The mitotic **spindle** is the set of microtubule proteins that coordinate

the movements of the chromosomes during mitosis. In animal cells, centrosomes organize the microtubules that make up the spindle. ⓘ *microtubules,* p. 63

Prometaphase occurs immediately after the formation of the spindle. The nuclear envelope and associated endoplasmic reticulum break into small pieces, enabling the spindle fibers to reach the chromosomes. Meanwhile, proteins called **kinetochores** begin to assemble on each centromere; these proteins attach the chromosomes to the spindle.

As **metaphase** begins, the spindle aligns the chromosomes down the center, or equator, of the cell. This alignment ensures that each cell will contain one copy of each chromosome.

In **anaphase,** the centromeres split, and the sister chromatids (now chromosomes) move toward opposite poles of the cell. This movement results from interactions between the spindle and the kinetochores. As some of the microtubules in the spindle shorten, they pull the chromosomes toward the poles. Meanwhile, spindle fibers slide past one another, pushing the poles farther apart and stretching the dividing cell.

Figure 8.11   Stages of Mitosis. Mitotic cell division includes similar stages in all eukaryotes, including animals and plants. Notice that the cell entering mitosis has four chromosomes (two red and two blue), as does each of the two resulting daughter cells.

3-D Animation
Mitosis

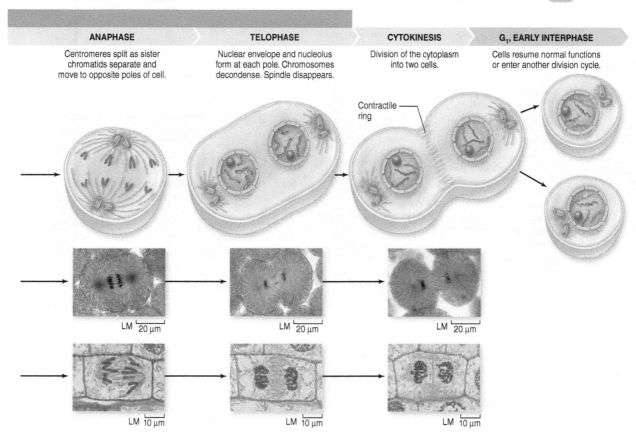

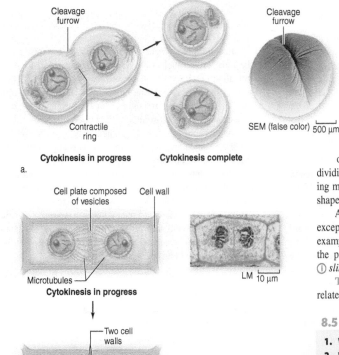

Figure 8.12 **Cytokinesis.** (a) In an animal cell, the first sign of cytokinesis is an indentation called a cleavage furrow, which is formed by a contractile ring consisting of actin and myosin proteins. (b) In plant cells, the cell plate is the first stage in the formation of a new cell wall.

3-D Animation Cytokinesis

Telophase, the final stage of mitosis, essentially reverses the events of prophase and prometaphase. The spindle disassembles, and the chromosomes begin to unwind. In addition, a nuclear envelope and nucleolus form at each end of the stretched-out cell. As telophase ends, the division of the genetic material is complete, and the cell contains two nuclei—but not for long.

C. The Cytoplasm Splits in Cytokinesis

In cytokinesis, organelles and macromolecules are distributed into the two forming daughter cells, which then physically separate. The process differs somewhat between animal and plant cells (figure 8.12).

In an animal cell, the first sign of cytokinesis is the **cleavage furrow,** a slight indentation around the middle of the cell. This indentation results from a contractile ring of actin and myosin proteins that forms beneath the cell membrane. The proteins contract like a drawstring, separating the daughter cells.

Unlike animal cells, plant cells are surrounded by cell walls. A dividing plant cell must therefore construct a new wall that separates the two daughter cells. The first sign of cell wall construction is a line, called a **cell plate,** between the forming cells. Vesicles from the Golgi apparatus travel along microtubules, delivering structural materials such as cellulose fibers, other polysaccharides, and proteins to the midline of the dividing cell. The layer of cellulose fibers embedded in surrounding material makes a strong, rigid wall that gives a plant cell its shape. ⓘ *cell wall,* p. 64

Although cytokinesis typically follows mitosis, there are exceptions. Some types of green algae and slime molds, for example, exist as enormous cells containing thousands of nuclei, the products of many rounds of mitosis without cytokinesis. ⓘ *slime molds,* p. 368

Table 8.1 on page 159 summarizes some of the vocabulary related to chromosomes and the cell cycle.

8.5 MASTERING CONCEPTS

1. What are the three main events of the cell cycle?
2. What happens during interphase?
3. Suppose a centromere does not split during anaphase. Describe the chromosomes in the daughter cells.
4. Distinguish between mitosis and cytokinesis.

8.6 Cancer Arises When Cells Divide Out of Control

 Virtual Lab Cell Cycle and Cancer

Some cells divide more or less constantly. The cells at a plant's root tips, for example, may divide throughout the growing season, exploring soil for water and nutrients. Likewise, stem cells in bone marrow constantly produce new blood cells. On the other hand, skin cells quit dividing once a scrape has healed; mature brain cells rarely divide. How do any of these cells "know" what to do?

A. Chemical Signals Regulate Cell Division

 Animation Cell Cycle Checkpoints

Cells divide in response to a variety of chemical signals, many of which originate outside the cell. **Growth factors** are proteins that stimulate cell division. These proteins bind to receptors on a receiving cell's membrane, and then a cascade of chemical reactions inside the cell initiates division. For example, a growth factor stimulates our cells to produce new skin underneath a scab; in plants, growth factors induce the formation of galls (see the Burning Question on page 158).

In addition, several internal "checkpoints" ensure that a cell does not enter one stage of the cell cycle until the previous stage is complete. Figure 8.13 illustrates a few cell cycle checkpoints:

- The G_1 checkpoint screens for DNA damage. If the DNA is damaged, a protein called p53 promotes the expression of genes encoding DNA repair enzymes. Badly damaged DNA prompts p53 to trigger apoptosis, and the cell dies.

- Several S phase checkpoints ensure that DNA replication occurs properly. If the cell does not have enough nucleotides to complete replication or if a DNA molecule breaks, the cell cycle may pause or stop at this point.

- The G_2 checkpoint is the last one before the cell begins mitosis. If the cell does not contain two full sets of identical DNA or if the spindle-making machinery is not in place, the cell cycle may be delayed. Alternatively, the p53 protein may trigger apoptosis.

- The metaphase checkpoint ensures that all chromosomes are aligned and that the spindle fibers attach correctly to the chromosomes. If everything checks out, the cell proceeds to anaphase.

Two groups of internal signaling proteins guide a cell's progress through these checkpoints. The concentrations of proteins called cyclins fluctuate in predictable ways during each stage. For example, cyclin E peaks between the G_1 and S phases of interphase, whereas cyclin B is essentially absent at that time but has its highest concentration between G_2 and mitosis. Proteins that bind to each cyclin, in turn, translate these fluctuations into action by activating the transcription factors that stimulate entry into the next stage of the cell cycle. ① *regulation of gene expression*, p. 134

A cell that fails to pass a checkpoint correctly will not undergo the change in cyclin concentrations that allows it to progress to the next stage. These checkpoints are therefore somewhat like the guards that check passports at border crossings, denying entry to travelers without proper documentation.

Precise timing of the many chemical signals that regulate the cell cycle is essential. Too little cell division, and an injury may go unrepaired; too much, and an abnormal growth forms. Understanding these signals may therefore help reveal how diseases such as cancer arise.

B. Cancer Cells Break Through Cell Cycle Controls

What happens when the body loses control over the balance between cell division and cell death? Sometimes, a **tumor**—an abnormal mass of tissue—forms. Biologists classify tumors into two groups (see figure 8.14 on page 158). **Benign tumors** are usually slow-growing and harmless, unless they become large enough to disrupt nearby tissues or organs. A tough capsule surrounding the tumor prevents it from invading nearby tissues or spreading to other parts of the body. Warts and moles are examples of benign tumors of the skin.

In contrast, a **malignant tumor** invades adjacent tissue. Because it lacks a surrounding capsule, a malignant tumor is likely to **metastasize,** meaning that its cells can break away from the original mass and travel in the bloodstream or lymphatic system to colonize other areas of the body. **Cancer** is a class of diseases characterized by malignant cells.

Solid tumors of the breast, lung, skin, and other major organs are the most familiar forms of cancer. But cells in the blood-forming tissues of the bone marrow can also divide out of control. Leukemia is a group of cancers characterized by the excessive production of the wrong kinds of blood cells.

Whatever its form, cancer begins when a single cell accumulates genetic mutations that cause it to break through its death and division controls. As the cell continues to divide, a tumor may develop. All tumors grow slowly at first, because only a few cells are dividing. However, not all tumors continue to grow at the same rate. In one study, for example, researchers measured how long it took for tumors in lung cancer patients to double in size. For patients with the fastest-growing tumors, the doubling time was about 68 days; the slowest-growing masses took about 225 days to double. In general, the slower a tumor's growth rate, the better the patient's prognosis.

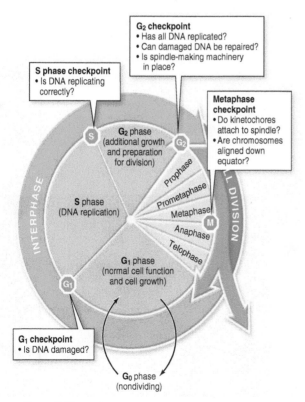

Figure 8.13 Cell Cycle Control Checkpoints. These checkpoints ensure that a cell completes each stage of the cell cycle correctly before proceeding to the next.

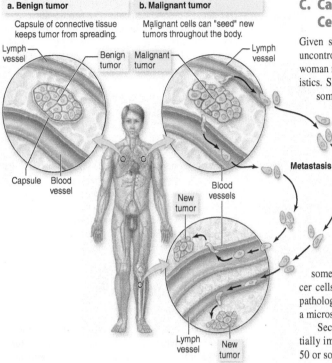

a. Benign tumor

Capsule of connective tissue keeps tumor from spreading.

Lymph vessel

Benign tumor

Capsule   Blood vessel

b. Malignant tumor

Malignant cells can "seed" new tumors throughout the body.

Malignant tumor

Lymph vessel

Metastasis

Blood vessels

New tumor

New tumor

Lymph vessel   New tumor

Figure 8.14 Benign and Malignant Tumors. (a) A capsule of connective tissue prevents a benign tumor from invading adjacent tissues. (b) A malignant tumor lacks a capsule and therefore can spread throughout the body in blood and lymph.

C. Cancer Cells Differ from Normal Cells in Many Ways

Given sufficient nutrients and space, cancer cells can divide uncontrollably and eternally. The cervical cancer cells of a woman named Henrietta Lacks vividly illustrate these characteristics. Shortly before Lacks died in 1951, researchers removed some of her cancer cells and began to grow them in a laboratory at Johns Hopkins University. Lacks's cells grew so well, dividing so often, that they quickly became a favorite of cell biologists seeking cells to culture that would divide indefinitely. Still used today, "HeLa" (for *Henrietta La*cks) cells replicate so vigorously that if just a few of them contaminate a culture of other cells, within days they completely take over.

In addition to uncontrolled division, cancer cells have other unique characteristics as well. First, a cancer cell looks different from a normal cell (figure 8.15). Its shape may be different, and it may lose some of the specialized features of its parent cells. Some cancer cells have multiple nuclei. These visible differences allow pathologists to detect cancerous cells by examining tissue under a microscope.

Second, unlike normal cells, many cancer cells are essentially immortal, ignoring the "clock" that limits normal cells to 50 or so divisions. This cellular clock resides in **telomeres,** the noncoding DNA at the tips of eukaryotic chromosomes. Telomeres consist of hundreds to thousands of repeats of a specific DNA sequence. At each cell division, the telomeres lose nucleotides from their ends, so the chromosomes gradually become shorter. After about 50 divisions, the cumulative loss of telomere DNA signals division to cease in a normal cell. Cells that produce an enzyme called **telomerase,** however, can

BurningQuestion

What are the galls that form on plants?

Galls are abnormal growths that often form on plants. The growths may be smooth and perfectly round, as in the leaf gall shown here. They may also cause grotesque deformities on stems, flowers, roots, and other plant parts.

Many organisms cause plants to form galls, including fungi, bacteria, and even parasitic plants. The most common galls, however, are traced to a distinctive group of wasps. A female gall wasp lays an egg in the vein of a stem or leaf. When the egg hatches and develops into a larva, it secretes growth factors or other chemicals that stimulate the plant's cells to divide. The resulting gall does not usually hurt or help the tree, but it does form a protective shell that houses and feeds the young wasp until adulthood.

Submit your burning question to
Marielle.Hoefnagels@mheducation.com

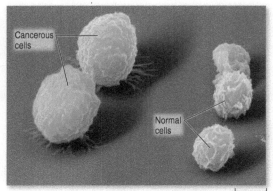

Cancerous cells

Normal cells

SEM (false color)   4 µm

Figure 8.15 Cancer Cells Are Abnormal. The two cancerous leukemia cells on the left are larger than the normal marrow cells on the right.

TABLE **8.1** **Miniglossary of Cell Division Terms**

Term	Definition
Chromatin	Collective term for all of the DNA and associated proteins in a cell
Chromosome	A discrete, continuous molecule of DNA wrapped around protein. Eukaryotic cells contain multiple linear chromosomes, whereas bacterial cells each contain one circular chromosome.
Chromatid	One of two identical attached copies that make up a replicated chromosome
Centromere	A small part of a chromosome that attaches sister chromatids to each other
Interphase	Stage of the cell cycle in which chromosomes replicate and the cell grows
G_1 phase	Gap stage of interphase in which the cell grows and carries out its functions
G_0 phase	Gap stage of interphase in which the cell functions but does not divide
G_2 phase	Gap stage of interphase in which the cell produces membrane components and spindle proteins
S phase	Synthesis stage of interphase when DNA replicates
Mitosis	Division of a cell's chromosomes into two identical nuclei
Prophase	Stage of mitosis when chromosomes condense and the spindle begins to form (*pro-* = before)
Prometaphase	Stage of mitosis when the nuclear membrane breaks up and spindle fibers attach to kinetochores
Metaphase	Stage of mitosis when chromosomes are aligned down the center of the cell (*meta-* = middle)
Anaphase	Stage of mitosis when the spindle pulls sister chromatids toward opposite poles of the cell
Telophase	Stage of mitosis when chromosomes arrive at opposite poles and nuclear envelopes form (*telo-* = end)
Cytokinesis	Distribution of cytoplasm to daughter cells following division of a cell's chromosomes
Cleavage furrow	Indentation in cell membrane of an animal cell undergoing cytokinesis
Cell plate	Material that forms the beginnings of the cell wall in a plant cell undergoing cytokinesis
Centrosome	Structure that organizes the microtubules that make up the spindle in animal cells
Spindle	Array of microtubule proteins that move chromosomes during mitosis
Kinetochore	Protein complex to which the spindle fibers attach on a chromosome's centromere

continually add DNA to chromosome tips. Their telomeres stay long, which enables them to divide beyond the 50-or-so division limit. Cancer cells have high levels of telomerase; inactivating this enzyme could therefore have tremendous medical benefits.

A third difference between normal cells and cancer cells lies in growth factors, the chemical signals that stimulate cell division. Normal cells stop dividing once external growth factors are depleted. Many cancer cells, however, divide even in the absence of growth factors.

Fourth, normal cells growing in culture exhibit **contact inhibition,** meaning that they stop dividing when they touch one another in a one-cell-thick layer. Cancer cells lack contact inhibition, so they tend to pile up in culture. In addition, normal cells divide only when attached to a solid surface, a property called anchorage dependence. The observation that cancer cells lack anchorage dependence helps explain how metastasis occurs.

Cancer cells have other unique features, too. For example, a normal cell dies (undergoes apoptosis) when badly damaged, but many cancer cells do not. Cancer cells also send signals that stimulate a process called **angiogenesis,** the development of new blood vessels. The newly sprouted blood vessels boost tumor growth by delivering nutrients and removing wastes. Disrupting angiogenesis is a possible cancer-fighting strategy (see section 8.8).

D. Cancer Treatments Remove or Kill Abnormal Cells

Medical professionals describe the spread of cancer cells as a series of stages. In one system used to classify colon cancer, for example, a stage I cancer has started invading tissue layers adjacent to the tumor's origin, but cancerous cells remain confined to the colon. At stage II, the tumor has spread to tissues around the colon but has not yet reached nearby lymph nodes. Stage III cancers have spread to organs and lymph nodes near the cancer's origin, and stage IV cancers have spread to distant sites. The names and criteria for each stage vary among cancers. In general, however, the lower the stage, the better the prospect for successful treatment.

Physicians use many techniques to estimate the stage of a patient's cancer. For example, X-rays, CAT scans, MRIs, PET scans, ultrasound, and other imaging tests are noninvasive ways to detect and measure tumors inside the body. A physician can also use an endoscope to inspect the inside of some organs, such as the esophagus or intestines. The same tool can also collect a biopsy sample; pathologists then use microscopes to search the tissue for suspicious cells. Blood tests can reveal more clues, including an abnormal number of white blood cells or a high level of a "tumor marker" such as prostate-specific antigen

(PSA). Combining many such lines of evidence helps medical professionals diagnose cancer and determine the stage, which in turn helps guide treatment decisions.

Traditional cancer treatments include surgical tumor removal, drugs (chemotherapy), and radiation. Chemotherapy drugs, usually delivered intravenously, are intended to stop cancer cells anywhere in the body from dividing. Radiation therapy uses directed streams of energy from radioactive isotopes to kill tumor cells in limited areas. ⓘ *isotopes*, p. 21

Chemotherapy and radiation are relatively "blunt tools" that target rapidly dividing cells, whether cancerous or not. Examples of cells that divide frequently include those in the bone marrow, digestive tract, and hair follicles. The death of these cells accounts for the most notorious side effects of cancer treatment: fatigue, nausea, and hair loss. Fortunately, the healthy cells usually return after the treatment ends. Some patients, especially those who receive high doses of chemotherapy or radiation, also have bone marrow transplants to speed the replacement of healthy blood cells.

Basic research into the cell cycle has yielded new cancer treatments with fewer side effects. For example, drugs that target a cancer cell's unique molecules have been very successful in treating some forms of breast cancer and leukemia (see the opening essay for chapter 3). Drugs called angiogenesis inhibitors block a tumor's ability to recruit blood vessels, starving the cancer cells of their support system. In the future, cancer patients may receive gene therapy treatments that add functional genes to cells with faulty versions. ⓘ *gene therapy*, p. 230

The success of any cancer treatment depends on many factors, including the type of cancer and the stage in which it is detected. Surgery can cure cancers that have not spread or that have only invaded local lymph nodes. Once cancer metastasizes, however, it becomes difficult to locate and treat all of the tumors. Moreover, DNA replication errors introduce mutations in rapidly dividing cancer cells (see section 8.8). Treatments that shrank the original tumor may have no effect on this new, changed growth.

Video Targeting Cancer

E. Inheritance and Environment Both Can Cause Cancer

Proteins control both the cell cycle and apoptosis. Genes encode proteins, so genetic mutations (changes in genes) play a key role in causing cancer. So far, researchers know of hundreds of genes that contribute to cancer. Two classes of cancer-related genes, oncogenes and tumor suppressor genes, are in a perpetual "tug of war" in determining whether cancer develops (figure 8.16).

Genes called proto-oncogenes encode many types of cell cycle–related proteins, from the receptors that bind growth factors outside the cell to any of the participants in the series of reactions that trigger cell division. These proteins normally stimulate cell division (*onkos* is the Greek word for "mass" or "lump"). **Oncogenes** are mutated variants of proto-oncogenes. A mutation in a proto-oncogene might cause the encoded protein to be abnormally active or expressed at too high a concentration. In that case, the cell cycle will be accelerated, and cancer may develop. Oncogenes cause some cancers of the cervix, bladder, and liver.

Recall from section 8.4 that our cells contain 23 pairs of chromosomes, with one member of each pair coming from each parent. Oncogenes are especially dangerous because only one of the two versions in a cell needs to be damaged for cancer to develop. The oncogene's abnormal protein is an "accelerator" that overrides the normal protein encoded by the proto-oncogene.

The other class of cancer-related genes, **tumor suppressor genes,** encode proteins that normally block cancer development; that is, they promote apoptosis or prevent cell division. Inactivating, deleting, or mutating these genes therefore eliminates crucial limits on cell division. Unlike oncogenes, usually both of a cell's versions of a tumor suppressor gene must be damaged for cancer to develop. That is, as long as one tumor-suppressor gene is functioning, the cell continues to produce the protective proteins.

One example of a tumor suppressor gene is *p53*, which encodes a protein that participates in the cell cycle control checkpoints described earlier. Biologists suspect that mutations in *p53* cause about half of all human cancers.

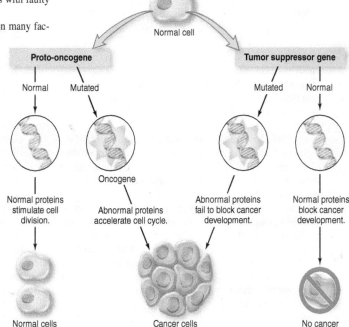

Figure 8.16 Cancer-Related Genes. Oncogenes and tumor suppressor genes both influence the cell cycle. When proto-oncogenes are mutated, they form oncogenes that accelerate cell division. Tumor suppressor genes encode proteins that normally inhibit cell division, but when the genes are mutated, cancer can develop.

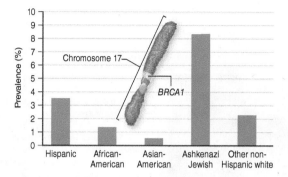

Figure 8.17 *BRCA1* **Mutations by Ethnic Group.** The likelihood that a woman with breast cancer has a mutation in *BRCA1* depends on her ethnicity. People of Ashkenazi Jewish descent are especially at risk.

A different tumor suppressor gene is associated with an unusually high risk for breast cancer. Ethnic groups vary widely in their risk of inheriting mutations in the gene, which is called *BRCA1* (figure 8.17). People of Ashkenazi Jewish descent have a much higher than average chance of carrying a particularly harmful *BRCA1* mutation. An evolutionary mechanism called the "founder effect" explains this observation. According to genetic studies, the mutation arose among Ashkenazi Jews many generations ago. Because Ashkenazi Jews historically avoided marrying outside their group, the mutation remains more frequent within this subgroup than in the human population at large. ⓘ *founder effect*, p. 254

The more oncogenes or mutated tumor suppressor genes in a person's cells, the higher the probability of cancer. Where do these mutations come from? Sometimes, a person inherits mutated DNA from one or both parents. The mutations may run in families, as in the case of many *BRCA1* mutations, or they may have arisen spontaneously in a parent's sperm- or egg-producing cells. Often, however, people acquire the cancer-causing mutations throughout their lifetimes.

Figure 8.18 depicts some choices a person can make to reduce cancer risk. Some of these strategies are straightforward. For example, UV

radiation and many chemicals in tobacco are mutagens, which means they damage DNA. Reducing sun exposure and avoiding tobacco therefore directly reduce cancer risk (see the Apply It Now box on page 162). Likewise, condoms can help prevent infection with cancer-causing viruses that are sexually transmitted. ⓘ *mutagens*, p. 139

Other risk factors illustrated in figure 8.18 are less obvious. Obesity, for example, greatly increases the risk of death from cancers of the breast, cervix, uterus, and ovaries in women; obese men have an elevated risk of dying from prostate cancer. High-calorie foods that are rich in animal fats and low in fiber, coupled with a lack of exercise, contribute to high body weight. But scientists remain uncertain why obesity itself is a risk factor for cancer. Perhaps fat tissue secretes hormones that contribute to metastasis, or maybe obesity reduces immune system function. Research into the cancer–obesity connection is increasingly important as obesity rates continue to climb.

One thing is clear: an enormous variety of illnesses are grouped under the category of "cancer," and each is associated with a unique suite of risk factors. It therefore pays to be skeptical of claims that any one product can miraculously fight cancer. A healthy lifestyle remains the best way to reduce cancer risk.

8.6   MASTERING CONCEPTS

1. What prevents normal cells from dividing when they are not supposed to?
2. What happens at cell cycle checkpoints?
3. What is the difference between a benign and a malignant tumor?
4. How do cancer cells differ from normal cells?
5. Distinguish among the treatments for cancer.
6. What is the relationship between mutations and cancer?
7. How does a person acquire the mutations associated with cancer?

To avoid or reduce the risk of cancer

Figure 8.18 **Cancer Risk.** Many aspects of a person's lifestyle influence the risk of cancer.

| Reduce dietary animal fat. | Avoid obesity. | Eat lots of fruits and vegetables. | Get regular vigorous exercise. | Stop using tobacco, or better yet, never start. | Avoid UV radiation from sunlight and tanning beds. | Use self tests and medical exams for early detection. | Avoid exposure to viruses known to cause cancer. |

Apply It **Now**

Detecting and Preventing Skin Cancer

Cancer has many forms, some inherited and others caused by radiation or harmful chemicals. Exposure to ultraviolet radiation from the sun or from tanning beds, for example, increases the risk of skin cancer because UV radiation damages DNA. If genetic mutations occur in genes encoding proteins that control the pace of cell division, cells may begin dividing out of control, forming a malignant tumor on the skin.

How might a person determine whether a mole, sore, or growth on the skin is cancerous? The abnormal skin may vary widely in appearance, and only a physician can tell for sure. Nevertheless, most cancers have a few features in common. "ABCD" is a shortcut for remembering these four characteristics:

- **Asymmetry:** Each half of the area looks different from the other.
- **Borders:** The borders of the growth are irregular, not smooth.
- **Color:** The color varies within a patch of skin, from tan to dark brown to black. Other colors, including red, may also appear.

- **Diameter:** The diameter of a cancerous area is usually greater than 6 mm, which is about equal to the size of a pencil eraser.

Skin cancer is the most common form of cancer in the United States. Several types of skin cancer exist, including basal cell carcinoma, squamous cell carcinoma, and melanoma. Basal cell carcinoma is the most common, but melanoma causes the most deaths because the cancerous cells quickly spread to other parts of the body.

The highest risk for skin cancer occurs among people who have light-colored skin and eyes, and who spend a lot of time in the sun. Avoiding exposure to UV radiation, both in the sun and in tanning beds, can help minimize this risk. Sunscreen is a must when outdoors. In addition, medical professionals recommend that people pay attention to changes in their skin. Carcinomas and melanomas are treatable if detected early.

8.7 Apoptosis Is Programmed Cell Death

Development relies on a balance between cell division and programmed cell death, or apoptosis (see figure 8.3). Apoptosis is different from necrosis, which is the "accidental" cell death that follows a cut or bruise. Whereas necrosis is sudden, traumatic, and disorderly, apoptosis results from a precisely coordinated series of events that dismantle a cell.

The process begins when a "death receptor" protein on a doomed cell's membrane receives a signal to die (figure 8.19). Within seconds, apoptosis-specific "executioner" proteins begin to cut apart the cell's proteins and destroy the cell. Immune system cells descend, and the cell is soon gone.

Apoptosis has two main functions in animals. First, apoptosis eliminates excess cells, carving out functional structures such as fingers, toes, nostrils, and ears as an animal grows. The second function of apoptosis is to weed out aging or defective cells that otherwise might harm the organism. A good example is the peeling skin that follows a sunburn. Sunlight contains UV radiation that can cause cancer by damaging the DNA in skin cells. Apoptosis helps protect against skin cancer by eliminating severely damaged cells, which die and simply peel away.

Plant cells die, too, but not in precisely the way that animal cells meet their programmed fate. Instead, plant cells are digested by enzymes in their own vacuoles; when the vacuole bursts, the cell dies. Plants also use a form of cell death to kill cells infected by fungi or bacteria, limiting the spread of the pathogen.

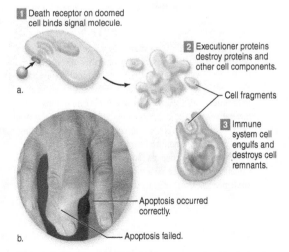

1 Death receptor on doomed cell binds signal molecule.

2 Executioner proteins destroy proteins and other cell components.

Cell fragments

3 Immune system cell engulfs and destroys cell remnants.

a.

Apoptosis occurred correctly.

Apoptosis failed.

b.

Figure 8.19 Death of a Cell. (a) Enzymes trigger apoptosis shortly after a cell's death receptor receives the signal to die. Afterwards, immune system cells mop up the debris. (b) Two fingers on this woman's hand appear fused together, thanks to a failure of apoptosis during development.

8.7 MASTERING CONCEPTS

1. What events happen in a cell undergoing apoptosis?
2. Describe two functions of apoptosis.

8.8 Cutting off a Tumor's Supply Lines in the War on Cancer

When Charles Darwin proposed natural selection as a mechanism of evolutionary change, he envisioned selective forces operating on tortoises, flowering plants, and other whole organisms. But the power of natural selection extends to a much smaller scale, including the individual cells that make up a tumor. The advance, retreat, resurgence, and death of these renegade cells command dramatic headlines in the war on cancer.

Our weapons against cancer include powerful chemotherapy drugs, but drug-resistant tumor cells are a significant barrier to successful treatment. Rapidly dividing tumor cells develop resistance to drugs because frequent cell division produces abundant opportunities for mutations. An alternative cancer-fighting strategy, therefore, might be to launch an indirect attack on a tumor's slower-growing support tissues instead.

Any tumor larger than 1 or 2 cubic millimeters needs a blood supply to carry nutrients, oxygen, and wastes. Blood travels throughout the body in vessels lined with endothelial tissue. For a blood vessel to grow, its endothelial cells must divide, which happens only rarely in adults. Cancer cells, however, secrete molecules that stimulate endothelial cells to divide and form new blood vessels. This sprouting of new "supply lines" is called angiogenesis.

Fortunately, biologists have discovered a class of drugs that stops blood vessel growth. One such drug, called endostatin, keeps endothelial cells from dividing but does not kill resting endothelial cells or other cells in the body. It should therefore choke off a tumor's supply lines without toxic side effects. But do cancer cells develop resistance to endostatin? Cancer researchers Thomas Boehm, Judah Folkman, and their colleagues at the Dana Farber Cancer Center and Harvard Medical School set out to answer this question.

The researchers first induced cancer in mice by "seeding" each animal with one of three types of cancer cells. After tumors developed, the researchers injected the mice with endostatin. Injections continued for several days, until the tumors in endostatin-treated mice were barely detectable. When the tumors regrew, the researchers repeated the treatments.

The results were astounding: the tumors never developed resistance (figure 8.20a). With each dose of endostatin, the tumors shriveled. Moreover, after two to six treatments with endostatin, the tumors never grew back, and the mice remained healthy. Standard chemotherapy drugs could temporarily shrink a tumor or delay its growth. But resistant cells would soon take over, and the tumor would regrow (figure 8.20b).

The results of subsequent clinical trials with human cancer patients, however, were mixed. Endostatin shrank tumors in a handful of people. But the drug was ineffective in most patients, and its U.S. manufacturer eventually stopped making it.

What does endostatin have to do with evolution? The logic behind its use as an anticancer drug relies on natural selection.

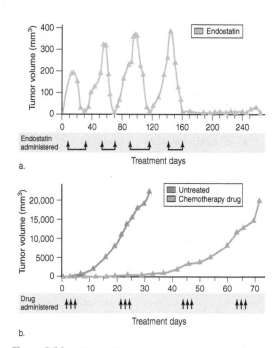

Figure 8.20   No Resistance. (a) Endostatin repeatedly shrank tumors in mice, and the tumors never developed resistance to the drug. (b) In contrast, a traditional chemotherapy drug delayed but did not prevent tumor growth in mice.

Because DNA may mutate every time it replicates, rapidly dividing cancer cells are genetically different from one another. A conventional chemotherapy drug may kill most cancer cells in a tumor, but a few have mutations that let them survive. These cells divide; over time, the entire tumor is resistant to the drug. Unlike other drugs, however, endostatin does not target the tumor; instead, it affects a blood vessel's endothelial cells. These cells rarely divide and therefore accumulate mutations slowly, reducing the chance that they will become resistant to endostatin.

This may seem comforting, but evolution will not stand still for our convenience. New mutations may still enable tumor cells to inactivate or break down endostatin. Understanding natural selection helps researchers know what to look for—and perhaps even launch new offensives in the war on cancer.

Boehm, Thomas, Judah Folkman, Timothy Browder, and Michael S. O'Reilly. November 27, 1997. Antiangiogenic therapy of experimental cancer does not induce acquired drug resistance. *Nature*, vol. 390, pages 404–407.

8.8   MASTERING CONCEPTS

1. Why doesn't endostatin select for drug-resistant cancer cells, as other chemotherapy drugs do?

2. Suppose you learn of a study in which ginger slowed tumor growth in mice for 30 days. What questions would you ask before deciding whether to recommend that a cancer-stricken relative eat more ginger?

164   UNIT TWO   DNA, Inheritance, and Biotechnology

CHAPTER SUMMARY

8.1 Cells Divide and Cells Die

A. Sexual Life Cycles Include Mitosis, Meiosis, and Fertilization
- In **sexual reproduction,** two parents produce genetically variable **gametes** by **meiosis. Fertilization** produces a zygote.
- **Mitotic** cell division produces identical eukaryotic cells used in growth, tissue repair, and **asexual reproduction.**

B. Cell Death Is Part of Life
- **Apoptosis** is programmed cell death.

8.2 DNA Replication Precedes Cell Division

- A dividing cell must first duplicate its **genome,** which may consist of one or more **chromosomes.**
- Helicase enzymes unwind and unzip the DNA; binding proteins keep the strands separate. **DNA polymerase** adds DNA nucleotides to an RNA primer. **Ligase** seals nicks after the primer is replaced with DNA.
- DNA replication errors produce **mutations.**

8.3 Prokaryotes Divide by Binary Fission

- During **binary fission,** DNA first replicates, then the two chromosomes attach to the cell membrane. Cell growth between the attachment points separates the chromosomes into two identical daughter cells.

8.4 Replicated Chromosomes Condense as a Eukaryotic Cell Prepares to Divide

- A chromosome consists of **chromatin** (DNA plus protein). In eukaryotic cells, chromatin is organized into **nucleosomes.**
- A replicated chromosome consists of two identical sister **chromatids** attached at a section of DNA called a **centromere** (figure 8.21).

8.5 Mitotic Division Generates Exact Cell Copies

- The **cell cycle** (summarized in figure 8.22) is a sequence of events in which a cell is preparing to divide (**interphase**), dividing its genetic material (**mitosis**), and dividing its cytoplasm (**cytokinesis**).

A. Interphase Is a Time of Great Activity
- Interphase includes gap periods, G_1 **phase** and G_2 **phase,** when the cell grows and produces molecules required for cell function and division. DNA replicates during the synthesis period (**S phase**). A cell that is not dividing is in G_0 **phase.**
- In animal cells, the **centrosome** duplicates during interphase.

B. Chromosomes Divide During Mitosis
- In **prophase,** the chromosomes condense and the **spindle** forms. In **prometaphase,** the nuclear envelope breaks up, and spindle fibers attach to **kinetochores.** In **metaphase,** replicated chromosomes align along the cell's equator. In **anaphase,** the chromatids of each replicated

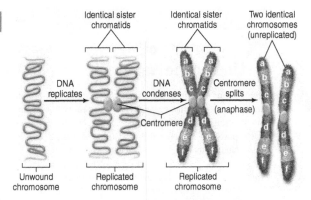

Figure 8.21 Chromosomes and Chromatids Compared.

chromosome separate. In **telophase,** the spindle breaks down, and nuclear envelopes form.

C. The Cytoplasm Splits in Cytokinesis
- In animal cells, contractile ring forms a **cleavage furrow,** dividing the cell in two. Plant cells divide as a **cell plate** forms between daughter cells.

8.6 Cancer Arises When Cells Divide Out of Control

A. Chemical Signals Regulate Cell Division
- External signals called **growth factors** stimulate cell division.
- Cell division may pause or halt at multiple checkpoints during the cell cycle.

B. Cancer Cells Break Through Cell Cycle Controls
- **Tumors** can result from excess cell division or deficient apoptosis. A **benign tumor** does not spread, but a **malignant tumor** invades nearby tissues and **metastasizes** if it reaches the bloodstream or lymph.
- **Cancer** is a family of diseases characterized by malignant cells.

C. Cancer Cells Differ from Normal Cells in Many Ways
- A cancer cell divides uncontrollably.
- When **telomeres** become very short, division ceases. Cancer cells produce an enzyme called **telomerase,** which adds DNA to telomeres.
- Cancer cells may continue to divide even after growth factors are depleted.
- A cancer cell lacks **contact inhibition** and anchorage dependence, may not undergo apoptosis, and secretes chemicals that stimulate **angiogenesis** (the growth of new blood vessels).

D. Cancer Treatments Remove or Kill Abnormal Cells
- Surgery, chemotherapy, and radiation are common cancer treatments.

E. Inheritance and Environment Both Can Cause Cancer
- **Oncogenes** speed cell division, and mutated **tumor suppressor genes** fail to stop excess cell division. Mutations in cancer-related genes may be inherited or acquired during a person's lifetime.

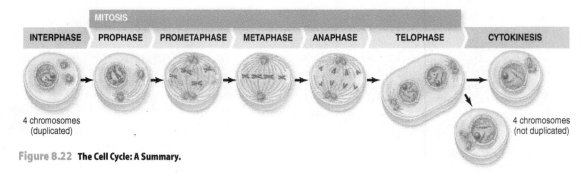

Figure 8.22 The Cell Cycle: A Summary.

8.7 Apoptosis Is Programmed Cell Death

- Apoptosis shapes structures and kills cells that could become cancerous.
- After a cell receives a signal to die, enzymes destroy the cell's components. Immune system cells dispose of the remains.

8.8 Investigating Life: Cutting off a Tumor's Supply Lines in the War on Cancer

- Natural selection occurs inside tumors. As chemotherapy drugs eliminate susceptible cells, resistant ones survive and divide to regrow the tumor.
- Endostatin starves tumors by stopping the growth of blood vessels.

MULTIPLE CHOICE QUESTIONS

1. A pancreas cell has a different function and structure from a brain cell
   a. because the cells contain different genes.
   b. because the cells contain different chromosomes.
   c. because the cells have different replication proteins.
   d. but the cells have identical DNA.

2. A DNA molecule is placed in a test tube containing fluorescently tagged nucleotides. DNA replication is induced. After replication,
   a. only one DNA molecule would have two fluorescent strands.
   b. both strands of each DNA molecule would be half-fluorescent.
   c. each DNA molecule would have one fluorescent strand.
   d. both DNA molecules would be completely fluorescent.

3. If you were to look at a sample of actively dividing leaf cells, in what stage of the cell cycle would you find most of the cells?
   a. Interphase   c. Metaphase
   b. Prophase   d. Telophase

4. Predict how excess telomerase activity would affect a cell.
   a. It would cause the telomeres to rapidly shrink.
   b. It would reduce the number of chromosomes in the cell.
   c. It would increase the number of times the cell could divide.
   d. It would inhibit growth of the organism.

5. What is the role of executioner proteins in apoptosis?
   a. They kill the cell by destroying its proteins.
   b. They function as the "death receptor" on the surface of the cell.
   c. They are part of the immune response that eliminates the cells.
   d. They cause the cell to swell and burst.

Answers to these questions are in appendix A.

WRITE IT OUT

1. Explain how cell division and cell death work together to form a functional multicellular organism.

2. Why does DNA replication precede cell division?

3. Write and explain an analogy for each of these DNA replication enzymes: helicase, binding proteins, ligase.

4. Tightly packed DNA cannot be used for protein synthesis. Why has evolution favored the histones and other proteins that help DNA fold into visible chromosomes?

5. Obtain a rubber band and twist it as many times as you can. What happens to the overall shape of the rubber band? How is this similar to what happens to chromosomes as a cell prepares to divide? How is it different?

6. If a cell somehow skipped G_1 of interphase during multiple cell cycles, how would the daughter cells change?

7. Why is G_1 a crucial time in the life of

8. Does a cell in G_1 contain more, less, or t. cell in G_2? Explain your answer.

9. Describe what will happen to a cell if interph. does not.

10. List the ways that binary fission is similar to and di ᴍnitotic cell division.

11. List the ways that cancer cells differ from normal cells.

12. How might the observation that more advanced cancer cells have higher telomerase activity be developed into a test that could help physicians treat cancer patients?

13. In the early 1900s, scientists began to experiment with radiation as a cancer treatment. Many physicians who administered the treatment subsequently died of cancer. Why?

14. Scientists sometimes compare the genes that influence cancer development to the controls of a car. In this comparison, oncogenes are like an accelerator stuck in the "full throttle" position, and mutated tumor suppressor genes are like brakes that don't work. How do the roles of proto-oncogenes and tumor suppressor genes relate to this analogy?

15. List the three most common categories of cancer treatments. Why do many cancer treatments have unpleasant side effects?

PULL IT TOGETHER

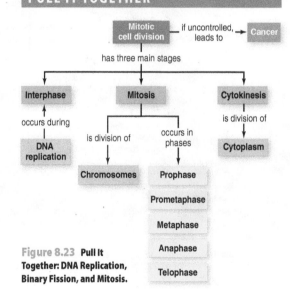

Figure 8.23 Pull It Together: DNA Replication, Binary Fission, and Mitosis.

Refer to figure 8.23 and the chapter content to answer the following questions.

1. Add *DNA polymerase, nucleotides,* and *complementary base pairing* to this concept map.

2. Add *cell growth* and *tissue repair* to the concept map.

3. What is the relationship between mitotic cell division and apoptosis?

9 Sexual Reproduction and Meiosis

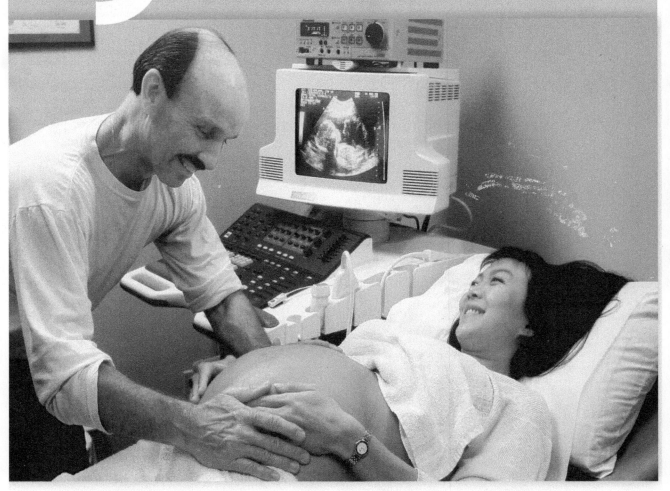

Ultrasound. A couple enjoys seeing an image of their unborn baby, which started developing months earlier. The sperm and egg cells that came together to make the child were the products of meiosis.

Prenatal Diagnosis Highlights Ethical Dilemmas

BARBARA IS PREGNANT. Like many women, she periodically has her fetus examined by ultrasound. Barbara delights in seeing her unborn child, but her latest scan has revealed a possible abnormality. Her physician cannot be sure of the diagnosis without ordering a test of the fetus's chromosomes.

How is it possible to see chromosomes hidden inside the cells of a fetus, which is itself tucked into the mother's uterus? A technician begins by extracting a small amount of the fluid or tissue surrounding the developing fetus. Fetal cells in the fluid can then be used to prepare a photograph of the fetus's chromosomes.

The image may reveal several types of abnormalities, including extra chromosomes, missing chromosomes, or the movement of genetic material from one chromosome to another. If the physician detects a chromosomal abnormality, Barbara may consult a counselor who can advise her on how best to prepare for the birth of her baby. In the case of a severe abnormality, Barbara may decide to seek an abortion, ending the pregnancy. But this choice raises many difficult issues.

Prenatal diagnosis illustrates one of many intersections between morality and science. Few people would argue against Barbara's use of prenatal diagnosis to learn more about a possible illness. But should parents have the right to expose a fetus to the small risks of prenatal screening simply to determine its sex? Should parents be allowed to abort a fetus of the "wrong" sex? What if an expectant mother lives in a country where having a second female child can bring economic ruin?

Furthermore, what constitutes a "severe" abnormality? Clearly, many chromosomal defects are not survivable, and the child will die shortly after birth (if not before). On the other hand, the symptoms of many conditions range from mild to severe, and a karyotype cannot always predict the severity. And what if a mother or family lacks the resources to care for a child with special needs? These are difficult questions without scientific answers.

Science can, however, help us understand the origin of chromosomal abnormalities. Many of them trace to errors that occur during a specialized form of cell division called meiosis. In humans and many other organisms, meiosis plays a starring role in the production of sperm and egg cells, which lie at the heart of sexual reproduction. This chapter explains the chromosomal choreography of meiosis.

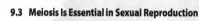

LEARN HOW TO LEARN
Write It Out—Really!

Get out a pen and a piece of scratch paper, and answer the open-ended Write It Out questions at the end of each chapter. This tip applies even if the exams in your class are multiple choice. Putting pen to paper (as opposed to just saying the answer in your head) forces you to organize your thoughts and helps you discover the difference between what you know and what you only THINK you know.

9.1 Why Sex?

Humans are so familiar with our way of reproducing that it can be hard to remember that there is any other way to make offspring. In fact, however, reproduction occurs in two main forms: asexual and sexual (figure 9.1). In **asexual reproduction,** an organism simply copies its DNA and splits the contents of one cell into two. Some genetic material may mutate during DNA replication, but the offspring are virtually identical. Examples of asexual organisms include bacteria, archaea, and single-celled eukaryotes such as the amoeba in figure 9.1a. Many plants, fungi, and other multicellular organisms also reproduce asexually.

Sexual reproduction, in contrast, requires two parents. The male parent contributes sperm cells, one of which fertilizes a female's egg cell to begin the next generation. Later in this chapter, you will learn that each time the male produces sperm, he scrambles the genetic information that he inherited from his own parents. A similar process occurs as the female produces eggs. The resulting variation among sex cells ensures that the offspring from two parents are genetically different from one another.

How did sexual reproduction evolve? Clues emerge from studies of reproduction and genetic exchange in diverse organisms. The earliest process that combines genes from two individuals appeared about 3.5 billion years ago. In **conjugation,** one bacterial cell uses an outgrowth called a sex pilus to transfer genetic material to another bacterium (see figure 17.9). This ancient form of bacterial gene transfer is still prevalent today. The unicellular eukaryote *Paramecium* uses a variation on this theme, exchanging nuclei via a bridge of cytoplasm.

Thanks to conjugation, bacteria and *Paramecium* can acquire new genetic information from their neighbors, even though they reproduce asexually. Unicellular green algae of the genus *Chlamydomonas,* however, exhibit a simple form of true sexual reproduction in which two genetically different cells fuse to form a new individual. The earliest sexual reproduction, which may have begun about 1.5 billion years ago, may have been similar to that of *Chlamydomonas.*

Attracting mates takes a lot of energy, as does producing and dispersing sperm and egg cells. Yet the persistence of sexual reproduction over billions of years and in many diverse species attests to its success. Why does such a costly method of reproducing persist, and why is asexual reproduction comparatively rare?

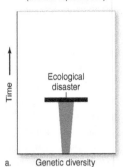 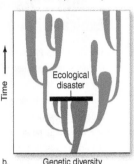

Figure 9.2 Why Sex? (a) In asexually reproducing organisms, the members of a population are usually very similar to one another; a single change in the environment can wipe out the population. (b) Sexual reproduction generates genetic variability, which boosts the chance that at least some members of the population *(blue)* will survive in a changing environment.

Although no one knows the full answer to this question, many studies point to the benefit of genetic diversity in a changing environment (figure 9.2). The mass production of identical offspring makes sense in habitats that never change, but conditions rarely remain constant in the real world. Temperatures rise and fall, prey species disappear, and new parasites emerge (see section 9.9). Genetic variability increases the chance that at least some individuals will have a combination of traits that allows them to survive and reproduce, even if some poorly suited individuals die. Asexual reproduction typically cannot create or maintain this genetic diversity, but sexual reproduction can.

9.1 MASTERING CONCEPTS

1. How do asexual and sexual reproduction differ?
2. How can asexually reproducing organisms acquire new genetic information?
3. Why does sexual reproduction persist even though it requires more energy than asexual reproduction?

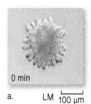 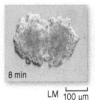 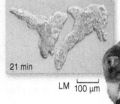 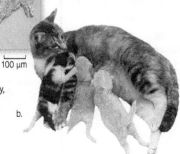

Figure 9.1 Asexual and Sexual Reproduction. (a) A single-celled *Amoeba* reproduces asexually, generating identical offspring by splitting in two. (b) These three kittens were conceived sexually. They differ from one another because each received different combinations of their parents' alleles.

9.2 Diploid Cells Contain Two Homologous Sets of Chromosomes

Before exploring sexual reproduction further, a quick look at a cell's chromosomes is in order. Recall from chapters 7 and 8 that a **chromosome** is a single molecule of DNA and its associated proteins.

A sexually reproducing organism consists mostly of **diploid cells** (abbreviated 2*n*), which contain two full sets of chromosomes; one set is inherited from each parent. Each diploid human cell, for example, contains 46 chromosomes (figure 9.3). The photo in figure 9.3 illustrates a **karyotype,** a size-ordered chart of all the chromosomes in a cell. Notice that the 46 chromosomes are arranged in 23 pairs; your mother and your father each contributed one member of each pair.

Of the 23 chromosome pairs in a human cell, 22 pairs are **autosomes**—chromosomes that are the same for both sexes. The remaining pair is made up of the two **sex chromosomes,** which determine whether an individual is female or male. Females have two X chromosomes, whereas males have one X and one Y chromosome.

The two members of most chromosome pairs are homologous to each other. A **homologous pair** of chromosomes is a matching pair of chromosomes that look alike and have the same sequence of genes. (The word *homologous* means "having the same basic structure.") The physical similarities between any two homologous chromosomes are evident in figure 9.3: They share the same size, centromere position, and pattern of light- and dark-staining bands. The karyotype does not, however, show that the two members of a homologous pair of chromosomes also carry the same sequence of genes. Chromosome 21, for example, includes 367 genes, always in the same order.

Homologous chromosomes, however, are not identical—after all, nobody has two identical parents! Instead, the two homologs differ in the combination of **alleles,** or versions, of the genes they carry (figure 9.4). As described in chapter 7, each allele of a gene encodes a different version of the same protein. A chromosome typically carries exactly one allele of each gene, so a person inherits one allele per gene from each parent. Depending on the parents' chromosomes, the two alleles may be identical or different. Overall, however, the members of each homologous pair of chromosomes are at least slightly different from each other.

Unlike the autosome pairs, the X and Y chromosomes are not homologous to each other. X is much larger than Y, and its genes are completely different. Nevertheless, in males, the sex chromosomes behave as homologous chromosomes during meiosis.

9.2 MASTERING CONCEPTS

1. What are autosomes and sex chromosomes?
2. Draw a hypothetical karyotype for a cell with a diploid number of 8.

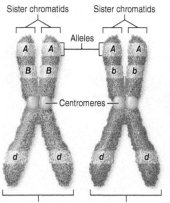

10 μm   LM

Figure 9.3 A Human Karyotype.
A diploid human cell contains 23 pairs of chromosomes, with one member of each pair inherited from each parent. The chromosomes numbered 1 through 22 are autosomes; X and Y are sex chromosomes. The two insets show the sex chromosomes for a female (XX) and a male (XY).

SEM (false color) 3 μm

Replicated chromosome   Replicated chromosome
(inherited from mother)   (inherited from father)

Homologous pair of chromosomes

Figure 9.4 Homologous Chromosomes. On these homologous chromosomes, both alleles for gene *A* are the same, as are those for gene *D*. The two alleles for gene *B*, however, are different.

9.3 Meiosis Is Essential in Sexual Reproduction

Sexually reproducing species range from humans to ferns to the mold that grows on bread. This section describes some of the features that all sexual life cycles share.

A. Gametes Are Haploid Sex Cells

Sexual reproduction poses a practical problem: maintaining the correct chromosome number. We have already seen that most cells in the human body contain 46 chromosomes. If a baby arises from the union of a man's sperm and a woman's egg, then why does a human baby not have 92 chromosomes per cell (46 from each parent)? And if that offspring later reproduced, wouldn't cells in the next generation have 184 chromosomes?

In fact, the normal chromosome number does not double with each generation. The explanation is that the

special cells required for sexual reproduction, sperm cells and egg cells, are not diploid. Rather, they are **haploid cells** (abbreviated n); that is, they contain only one full set of genetic information instead of the two sets that characterize most cells.

These haploid cells, called **gametes,** are sex cells that combine to form a new offspring. **Fertilization** merges the gametes from two parents, creating a new cell: the diploid **zygote,** which is the first cell of the new organism (figure 9.5). The zygote has two full sets of chromosomes, one set from each parent. In most species, including plants and animals, the zygote begins dividing mitotically shortly after fertilization.

Thus, the life of a sexually reproducing, multicellular organism requires two ways to package DNA into daughter cells. **Mitosis,** described in chapter 8, divides a eukaryotic cell's chromosomes into two identical daughter nuclei. Mitotic cell division produces the cells needed for growth, development, and tissue repair. **Meiosis,** the subject of this chapter, forms genetically variable sex cells used in reproduction, with each gamete containing half as many chromosomes as the organism's diploid cells.

B. Specialized Germ Cells Undergo Meiosis

Only some cells can undergo meiosis and produce gametes. In humans and other animals, these specialized diploid cells, called **germ cells,** occur only in the ovaries and testes. Plants don't have the same reproductive organs as animals, but they do have specialized gamete-producing cells in flowers and other reproductive parts.

The rest of the body's diploid cells, called **somatic cells,** do not participate directly in reproduction. Leaf cells, root cells, skin cells, muscle cells, and neurons are examples of somatic cells. Most somatic cells can divide mitotically, but they do not undergo meiosis.

To make sense of this, consider your own life. It began when a small, swimming sperm cell carrying 23 chromosomes from your father wriggled toward your mother's comparatively enormous egg cell, also containing 23 chromosomes. You were conceived when the sperm fertilized the egg cell. At that moment, you were a one-celled zygote, with 46 chromosomes. That first cell then began dividing, generating identical copies of itself to form an embryo, then a fetus, infant, child, and eventually an adult (see figure 8.2). Once you reached reproductive maturity, diploid cells in your testes or ovaries produced haploid gametes of your own, perpetuating the cycle.

The human life cycle is of course most familiar to us, and many animals reproduce in essentially the same way. Gametes are the only haploid cells in our life cycle; all other cells are diploid. Sexual reproduction, however, can take many other forms as well. In some organisms, including plants, both the haploid and the diploid stages are multicellular. Section 9.8 describes the life cycle of a sexually reproducing plant in more detail.

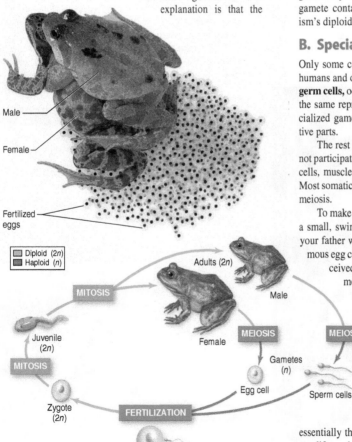

Male
Female
Fertilized eggs

☐ Diploid (2n)
☐ Haploid (n)

Adults (2n)

MITOSIS   Male

Juvenile (2n)   Female   MEIOSIS   MEIOSIS

MITOSIS   Gametes (n)

Zygote (2n)   Egg cell   Sperm cells

FERTILIZATION

Figure 9.5 Sexual Reproduction. All sexual life cycles include meiosis and fertilization; mitotic cell division enables the organism to grow. The photo shows a male frog clasping his mate as he fertilizes her eggs.

C. Meiosis Halves the Chromosome Number and Scrambles Alleles

No matter the species, meiosis has two main outcomes. First, the resulting gametes contain half as many chromosomes as the rest of the body's cells. They therefore ensure that the chromosome number does not double with every generation. The second function of meiosis is to scramble genetic information, so that two parents can generate offspring that are genetically different from the parents and from one another. As described in section 9.1, genetic variability is one of the evolutionary advantages of sexual reproduction.

Figure It Out

A type of fish called a carp has gametes containing 52 chromosomes. How many chromosomes are in a carp's somatic cells?

Answer: 104

Although meiosis has unique functions, many of the events are similar to those of mitosis. As you work through the stages of meiosis, it may therefore help to think of what you already know about mitotic cell division. For example, a cell that is preparing to divide mitotically undergoes interphase, followed by the overlapping phases of mitosis and then cytokinesis (see figure 8.10).

Similarly, interphase occurs just before meiosis; the names of the phases of meiosis are similar to those in mitosis; and cytokinesis occurs after the genetic material is distributed.

Despite these similarities, meiosis has two unique outcomes, highlighted in figure 9.6. First, meiosis includes two divisions, which create four haploid cells from one specialized diploid cell. Second, meiosis shuffles genetic information, setting the stage for each haploid nucleus to receive a unique mixture of alleles.

Sections 9.4 and 9.5 explain in more detail how meiosis simultaneously halves the chromosome number and produces genetically variable nuclei. We then turn to problems that can occur in meiosis and describe how humans package haploid nuclei into individual sperm or egg cells.

9.3 | MASTERING CONCEPTS

1. What is the difference between somatic cells and germ cells?
2. How do haploid and diploid nuclei differ?
3. What are the roles of meiosis, gamete formation, and fertilization in a sexual life cycle?
4. What is a zygote?

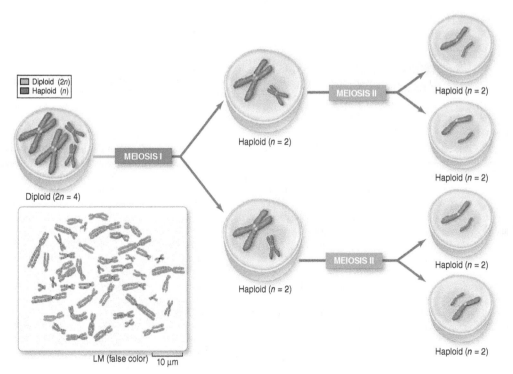

Figure 9.6 Summary of Meiosis. In meiosis, a diploid nucleus gives rise to four haploid nuclei with a mix of chromosomes from each parent. This illustration summarizes meiosis in a nucleus containing four chromosomes (two homologous pairs). A diploid human cell, however, contains 46 chromosomes (23 homologous pairs, as shown in the inset).

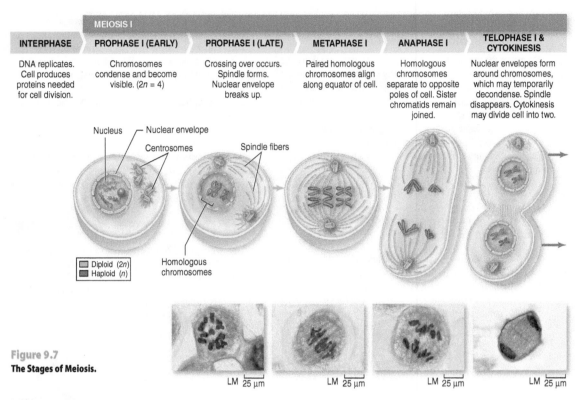

	MEIOSIS I				
INTERPHASE	PROPHASE I (EARLY)	PROPHASE I (LATE)	METAPHASE I	ANAPHASE I	TELOPHASE I & CYTOKINESIS
DNA replicates. Cell produces proteins needed for cell division.	Chromosomes condense and become visible. (2n = 4)	Crossing over occurs. Spindle forms. Nuclear envelope breaks up.	Paired homologous chromosomes align along equator of cell.	Homologous chromosomes separate to opposite poles of cell. Sister chromatids remain joined.	Nuclear envelopes form around chromosomes, which may temporarily decondense. Spindle disappears. Cytokinesis may divide cell into two.

Nucleus — Nuclear envelope

Centrosomes — Spindle fibers

☐ Diploid (2n)
☐ Haploid (n)

Homologous chromosomes

LM 25 µm   LM 25 µm   LM 25 µm   LM 25 µm

Figure 9.7
The Stages of Meiosis.

9.4 In Meiosis, DNA Replicates Once, but the Nucleus Divides Twice

Tutorial
Meiosis

Before meiosis occurs, a diploid cell first undergoes interphase. The cell grows during G₁ of interphase and synthesizes the molecules necessary for division. All of the cell's DNA replicates during S phase, after which each of the cell's chromosomes consists of two identical sister chromatids attached at a centromere. The cell also produces proteins and other enzymes necessary to divide the cell. Finally, in G₂, the chromatin begins to condense, and the cell produces the spindle proteins that will eventually move the chromosomes. ⓘ *DNA replication,* p. 150

The cell is now ready for meiosis to begin. During meiosis I, each chromosome physically aligns with its homolog. The homologous pairs split into two cells toward the end of meiosis I. Meiosis II then partitions the genetic material into four haploid nuclei. Figure 9.7 diagrams the entire process; you may find it helpful to refer to it as you read the rest of this section.

A. In Meiosis I, Homologous Chromosomes Pair Up and Separate

Homologous pairs of chromosomes find each other and then split up during the first meiotic division.

Prophase I During prophase I (that is, the prophase of meiosis I), replicated chromosomes condense. A **spindle** begins to form from microtubules assembled at the centrosomes, and spindle attachment points called **kinetochores** assemble on each centromere. Meanwhile, the nuclear envelope breaks up; once it is gone, the spindle fibers can reach the chromosomes.

The events described so far resemble those of prophase of mitosis, but something unique happens during prophase I of meiosis: The homologous chromosomes line up next to one another. (Mules are sterile because their cells cannot complete this stage, as described in this chapter's Burning Question.) Section 9.5 describes how this arrangement allows for an allele-shuffling mechanism called crossing over.

Metaphase I In metaphase I, the spindle aligns the paired homologs down the center "equator" of the cell. Each member of a homologous pair attaches to a spindle fiber stretching to one pole. The stage is therefore set for the homologous pairs to be separated.

Anaphase I, Telophase I, and Cytokinesis Spindle fibers pull the homologous pairs apart in anaphase I, although the sister chromatids that make up each chromosome remain joined. The chromosomes complete their movement to opposite poles in telophase I. In most species, cytokinesis occurs after telophase I, splitting the original cell into two.

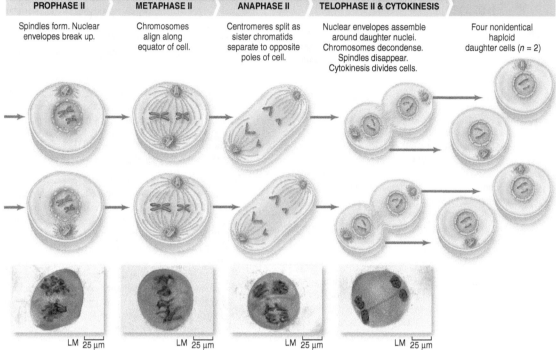

MEIOSIS II				
PROPHASE II	**METAPHASE II**	**ANAPHASE II**	**TELOPHASE II & CYTOKINESIS**	
Spindles form. Nuclear envelopes break up.	Chromosomes align along equator of cell.	Centromeres split as sister chromatids separate to opposite poles of cell.	Nuclear envelopes assemble around daughter nuclei. Chromosomes decondense. Spindles disappear. Cytokinesis divides cells.	Four nonidentical haploid daughter cells (n = 2)

LM ⊢ 25 μm   LM ⊢ 25 μm   LM ⊢ 25 μm   LM ⊢ 25 μm

B. Meiosis II Yields Four Haploid Cells

A second interphase precedes meiosis II in many species. During this time, the chromosomes unfold into very thin threads. The cell manufactures proteins, but the genetic material does not replicate a second time.

Meiosis II strongly resembles mitosis. The process begins with prophase II, when the chromosomes again condense and become visible. In metaphase II, the spindle aligns the chromosomes down the center of each cell. In anaphase II, the centromeres split, and the separated sister chromatids move to opposite poles. In telophase II, nuclear envelopes form around the separated sets of chromosomes. Cytokinesis then separates the nuclei into individual cells. The overall result: one diploid cell has divided into four haploid cells.

Figure It Out

A cell that is entering prophase I contains ___ times as much DNA as one daughter cell at the end of meiosis.

Answer: Four

9.4 MASTERING CONCEPTS

1. What happens during interphase?
2. How do the events of meiosis I and meiosis II produce four haploid cells from one diploid cell?

BurningQuestion

If mules are sterile, then how are they produced?

A mule is the hybrid offspring of a mating between a male donkey and a female horse. The opposite cross (female donkey with male horse) yields a hybrid called a hinny.

Mules and hinnies may be male or female, but they are usually sterile. Why?

A peek at the parents' chromosomes reveals the answer. Donkeys have 31 pairs of chromosomes, whereas horses have 32 pairs. When gametes from horse and donkey unite, the resulting hybrid zygote has 63 chromosomes (31+32). The zygote divides mitotically to yield the cells that make up the mule or hinny.

These hybrid cells cannot undergo meiosis for two reasons. First, they have an odd number of chromosomes, which disrupts meiosis because at least one chromosome lacks a homologous partner. Second, donkeys and horses have slightly different chromosome structures, so the hybrid's parental chromosomes cannot align properly during prophase I. The result: an inability to produce sperm and egg cells. The only way to produce more mules and hinnies is to again mate horses with donkeys. ⓘ *hybrid infertility*, p. 285

Submit your burning question to
Marielle.Hoefnagels@mheducation.com

 9.5 Meiosis Generates Enormous Variability

 Tutorial
Gamete
Variability

By creating new combinations of alleles, meiosis generates astounding genetic variety among the offspring from just two parents. This section describes three mechanisms that account for this diversity.

A. Crossing Over Shuffles Alleles

Crossing over is a process in which two homologous chromosomes exchange genetic material (figure 9.8). During prophase I, the homologs align themselves precisely, gene by gene, in a process called synapsis. The chromosomes are attached at a few points along their lengths, called chiasmata (singular: chiasma), where the homologs exchange chromosomal material.

Consider what takes place in your own cells. You inherited one member of each homologous pair from your mother; the other came from your father. Crossing over means that pieces of these homologous chromosomes physically change places.

Suppose, for instance, that one chromosome carries genes that dictate hair color, eye color, and finger length. Perhaps the version you inherited from your father has the alleles that specify blond hair, blue eyes, and short fingers. The homolog from your mother is different; its alleles dictate black hair, brown eyes, and long fingers. Now, suppose that crossing over occurs between the homologous chromosomes. Afterward, one chromatid might carry alleles for blond hair, brown eyes, and long fingers; another would

specify black hair, blue eyes, and short fingers. These two chromatids are termed "recombinant" because they combine alleles from your two parents. The two chromatids that did not form chiasmata, however, would remain unchanged and are termed "parental." Note that although all of the alleles in your ovaries or testes came from your parents, half of the chromatids—the recombinant ones—now contain new allele *combinations*.

The result of crossing over is four unique chromatids in place of two pairs of identical chromatids. Each chromatid will end up in a separate haploid cell. Thus, crossing over ensures that each haploid cell will be genetically different from the others.

B. Chromosome Pairs Align Randomly During Metaphase I

Figure 9.9 reveals a second way that meiosis creates genetic variability. At metaphase I, pairs of homologous chromosomes line up at the cell's center. Examine the orientation of the chromosomes in the cell labeled "Alternative 1." All of the blue chromosomes are on top, whereas the red homologs are on the bottom. In anaphase I, the chromosomes separate, and the resulting nuclei contain either all blue or all red chromosomes.

The next time a cell in the same individual undergoes meiosis, the orientation of the chromosomes may be the same, or it may not be. The alignment of chromosomes at metaphase I is a random process, and all four alternatives shown in figure 9.9 are equally probable. Most of the time, the arrangement will yield gametes with a mix of genetic material from both parents.

The number of possible arrangements is related to the number of chromosomes. For two pairs of homologs, each resulting gamete may have any of four (2^2) unique chromosome

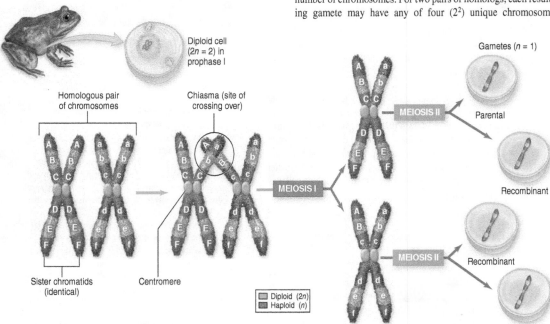

Figure 9.8 Crossing Over. Crossing over between homologous chromosomes generates genetic diversity by mixing up parental traits, creating recombinant chromatids. The capital and lowercase letters represent different alleles of six genes.

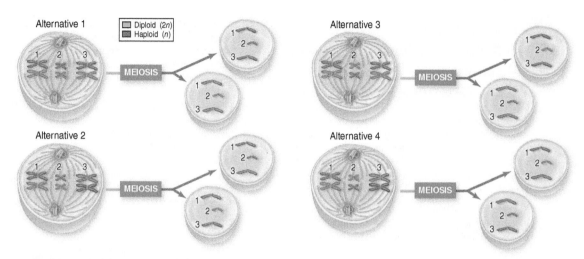

Figure 9.9 **Random Orientation.** A diploid cell containing three homologous pairs of chromosomes ($2n = 6$) has four possible unique configurations in metaphase I. The result is eight possible unique gametes ($n = 3$). Note that this number does not include the effects of crossing over.

Animation
Random Orientation

configurations. For three pairs of homologs, as shown in figure 9.9, eight (2^3) unique configurations can occur in the gametes. Extending this concept to humans, with 23 chromosome pairs, each gamete contains one of 8,388,608 (2^{23}) possible chromosome combinations—all equally likely.

C. Fertilization Multiplies the Diversity

We have already seen that every diploid cell undergoing meiosis is likely to produce haploid nuclei with different combinations of chromosomes. Furthermore, it takes two to reproduce. In one mating, any of a woman's 8,388,608 possible egg cells can combine with any of the 8,388,608 possible sperm cells of a partner. One couple could therefore theoretically create more than 70 trillion (8,388,608^2) genetically unique individuals! And this enormous number is an underestimate, because it does not take into account the additional variation from crossing over.

With so much potential variability, the chance of two parents producing genetically identical individuals seems exceedingly small. How do the parents of identical twins defy the odds? The answer is that identical twins result from just one fertilization event. The resulting zygote or embryo splits in half, creating separate, identical babies (figure 9.10). Identical twins are called *monozygotic* because they derive from one zygote. In contrast, nonidentical (fraternal) twins occur when two sperm cells fertilize two separate egg cells. The twins are therefore called *dizygotic*. See the Apply It Now box on page 183 for more on multiple births.

9.5   MASTERING CONCEPTS

1. How does crossing over shuffle alleles?
2. Explain how to arrive at the estimate that one human couple can produce over 70 trillion unique offspring.
3. How are identical twins different from fraternal twins?

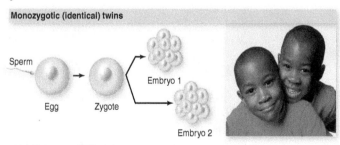

Monozygotic (identical) twins

Sperm   Egg   Zygote   Embryo 1   Embryo 2

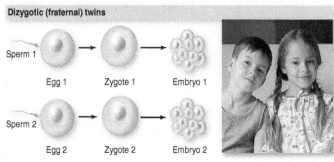

Dizygotic (fraternal) twins

Sperm 1   Egg 1   Zygote 1   Embryo 1

Sperm 2   Egg 2   Zygote 2   Embryo 2

Figure 9.10 **Two Origins for Twins.** Monozygotic twins are genetically identical because they come from the same zygote. Dizygotic, or fraternal, twins are no more alike than nontwin siblings because they start as two different zygotes.

9.6 Mitosis and Meiosis Have Different Functions: A Summary

Tutorial Mitosis and Meiosis Compared

Mitosis and meiosis are both mechanisms that divide a eukaryotic cell's genetic material (figure 9.11). The two processes share many events, as revealed by the similar names of the stages. The cell copies its DNA during an interphase stage that precedes both mitosis and meiosis, after which the chromosomes condense. Moreover, spindle fibers orchestrate the movements of the chromosomes in both mitosis and meiosis.

However, the two processes also differ in many ways:

- Mitosis occurs in somatic cells throughout the body, and it occurs throughout the life cycle. In contrast, meiosis occurs only in germ cells and only at some stages of life (see section 9.8).
- Homologous chromosomes do not align with each other during mitosis, as they do in meiosis. This alignment allows for crossing over, which also occurs only in meiosis.

- Mitotic division yields identical daughter cells for growth, repair, and asexual reproduction. Meiotic division generates genetically variable daughter cells used in sexual reproduction. The variation among gametes results from crossing over and the random orientation of chromosome pairs during metaphase I.
- Following mitosis, cytokinesis occurs once for every DNA replication event. The product of mitotic division is therefore two daughter cells. In meiosis, cytokinesis occurs twice, although the DNA has replicated only once. One cell therefore yields four daughter cells.
- After mitosis, the chromosome number in the daughter cells is the same as in a parent cell. Depending on the species, either haploid or diploid cells can divide mitotically. In contrast, only diploid cells divide meiotically, producing four haploid daughter cells.

9.6 MASTERING CONCEPTS

1. In what ways are mitosis and meiosis similar?
2. In what ways are mitosis and meiosis different?

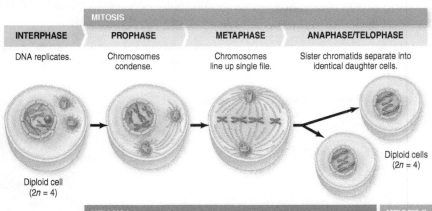

Figure 9.11 Mitosis and Meiosis Compared. Mitotic division adds and replaces identical cells, whereas meiosis produces haploid nuclei with new genetic combinations. (Some stages are omitted for clarity.)

MITOSIS

INTERPHASE	PROPHASE	METAPHASE	ANAPHASE/TELOPHASE
DNA replicates.	Chromosomes condense.	Chromosomes line up single file.	Sister chromatids separate into identical daughter cells.

Diploid cell (2n = 4)

Diploid cells (2n = 4)

MEIOSIS I | **MEIOSIS II**

INTERPHASE	PROPHASE I	METAPHASE I	ANAPHASE I /TELOPHASE I	METAPHASE II	ANAPHASE II /TELOPHASE II
DNA replicates.	Crossing over occurs. Paired chromosomes condense.	Homologous chromosomes line up double file.	Homologs separate into haploid daughter cells; sister chromatids remain joined.	Chromosomes line up single file.	Sister chromatids separate into nonidentical haploid cells.

Diploid cell (2n = 4)

☐ Diploid (2n)
■ Haploid (n)

Haploid cells (n = 2)

9.7 Errors Sometimes Occur in Meiosis

When meiosis takes a wrong turn, the result can be gametes with extra or missing chromosomes. Even small chromosomal abnormalities can have devastating effects on health.

A. Polyploidy Means Extra Chromosome Sets

An error in meiosis, such as the failure of the spindle to form properly, can produce a **polyploid cell** with one or more complete sets of extra chromosomes (*polyploid* means "many sets"). For example, if a sperm with the normal 23 chromosomes fertilizes an abnormal egg cell with two full sets (46), the resulting zygote will have three copies of each chromosome (69 total), a type of polyploidy called triploidy. Most human polyploids cease developing as embryos or fetuses.

In contrast to humans, about 30% of flowering plant species tolerate polyploidy well. Many crop plants are polyploids; durum wheat in pasta, for example, is tetraploid (it has four sets of seven chromosomes). As described in section 14.3C, polyploidy can be an important force in the evolution of new plant species.

B. Nondisjunction Results in Extra or Missing Chromosomes

Some gametes have just one extra or missing chromosome. The cause of the abnormality is an error called **nondisjunction,** which occurs when chromosomes fail to separate at either anaphase I or anaphase II (figure 9.12). The result is a sperm or egg cell with two copies of a particular chromosome or none at all. When such a gamete fuses with another at fertilization, the resulting zygote has either 45 or 47 chromosomes instead of the normal 46.

Most embryos with incorrect chromosome numbers cease developing before birth. Extra genetic material, however, causes fewer problems than missing material. This is why most children with the wrong number of chromosomes have an extra one—a trisomy—rather than a missing one. (i) *when a pregnancy ends,* p. 719

Following is a look at some syndromes in humans resulting from too many or too few chromosomes.

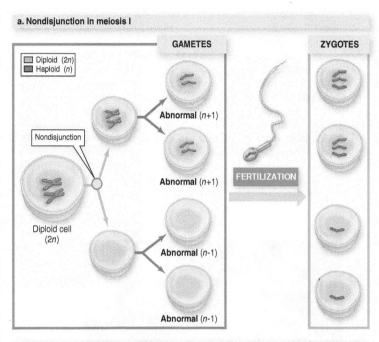

a. Nondisjunction in meiosis I

□ Diploid (2n)
■ Haploid (n)

GAMETES

ZYGOTES

Nondisjunction

Diploid cell (2n)

Abnormal (n+1)

Abnormal (n+1)

FERTILIZATION

Abnormal (n-1)

Abnormal (n-1)

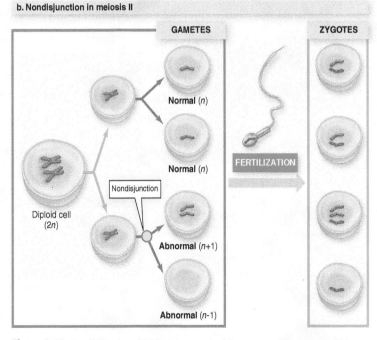

b. Nondisjunction in meiosis II

GAMETES

ZYGOTES

Normal (n)

Normal (n)

Nondisjunction

Diploid cell (2n)

FERTILIZATION

Abnormal (n+1)

Abnormal (n-1)

Figure 9.12 Nondisjunction. (a) A homologous pair of chromosomes fails to separate during the first division of meiosis. The result: two nuclei with two copies of the chromosome and two nuclei that lack the chromosome. (b) Sister chromatids fail to separate during the second meiotic division. One nucleus has an extra chromosome, and one is missing the chromosome. (All chromosomes other than the ones undergoing nondisjunction are omitted for clarity.)

Tutorial Nondisjunction

Extra Autosomes: Trisomy 21, 18, or 13 A person with trisomy 21, the most common cause of Down syndrome, has three copies of chromosome 21 (figure 9.13). An affected person has distinctive facial features and a unique pattern of hand creases. Intelligence varies greatly; some children have profound mental impairment, whereas others learn well. Many affected children die before their first birthdays, often because of congenital heart defects. People with Down syndrome also have an above-average risk for leukemia and Alzheimer disease.

The probability of giving birth to a child with trisomy 21 increases dramatically as a woman ages. For women younger than 30, the chances of conceiving a child with the syndrome are 1 in 3000. For a woman of 48, the incidence jumps to 1 in 9. An increased likelihood of nondisjunction in older females may

account for this age association, but no one knows for sure why older women might have problems completing meiosis.

Trisomy 21 is the most common autosomal trisomy, but that is only because the fetus is most likely to remain viable. Trisomies 18 and 13 are the next most common, but few infants with these genetic abnormalities survive infancy. Trisomies undoubtedly occur with other chromosomes, but the embryos fail to develop.

Extra or Missing Sex Chromosomes: XXX, XXY, XYY, and XO Nondisjunction can produce a gamete that contains two X or Y chromosomes instead of only one. Fertilization then produces a zygote with too many sex chromosomes: XXX, XXY, or XYY. A gamete may also lack a sex chromosome altogether. If one gamete contains an X chromosome and the other gamete has neither X nor Y, the resulting zygote is XO. Interestingly, medical researchers have never reported a person with one Y and no X chromosome. Table 9.1 summarizes some of the sex chromosome abnormalities.

C. Smaller-Scale Chromosome Abnormalities Also Occur

Animation
Chromosomal
Mutations

Parts of a chromosome may be deleted, duplicated, inverted, or even moved to a new location (figure 9.14). Because each chromosome includes hundreds or thousands of genes, even small changes in a chromosome's structure can affect an organism.

A chromosomal **deletion** results in the loss of one or more genes. Cri du chat syndrome (French for "cat's cry"), for example, is associated with deletion of several genes on chromosome 5. The illness is named for the odd cry of an affected child, similar to the mewing of a cat. The gene deletion also causes severe mental retardation and developmental delay.

In the opposite situation, a **duplication** produces multiple copies of part of a chromosome. Fragile X syndrome, for example, results from repeated copies of a three-base sequence (CGG) on the X chromosome. The disorder can produce a range of symptoms, including mental retardation. The number of repeats can range from fewer than 10 to more than 200. Individuals with the most copies of the repeat are the most severely affected.

The duplication of entire genes sometimes plays an important role in evolution. If one copy of the original gene continues to do its old job, then a mutation in a "spare" copy will not be harmful. Although these mutations often ruin the gene, they can also lead to new functions. As just one example, biologists have studied a gene that was originally required for the secretion of calcium in tooth enamel in vertebrates. Mutations in duplicate genes created new functions, including the production of calcium-rich breast milk.

In an **inversion,** part of a chromosome flips and reinserts, changing the gene sequence. Unless inversions break genes, they are usually less harmful than deletions, because all the genes are still present. Fertility problems can arise, however, if an adult has an inversion in one chromosome but its homolog is normal. During crossing over, the inverted chromosome and its noninverted

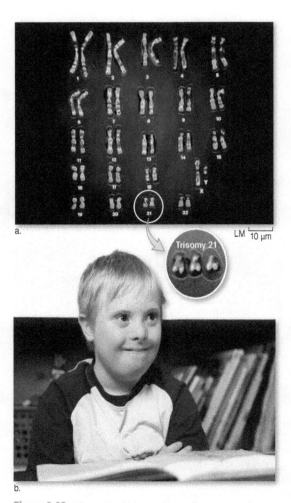

a.

LM 10 μm

Trisomy 21

b.

Figure 9.13 Trisomy 21. (a) A normal human karyotype reveals 46 chromosomes, in 23 pairs. (b) A child with three copies of chromosome 21 has Down syndrome.

TABLE **9.1**   **Examples of Sex Chromosome Abnormalities**

Chromosomes	Name of Condition	Incidence	Symptoms
XXX	Triplo-X	1 in every 1000 to 2000 females	Symptoms are tall stature, menstrual irregularities, and a normal-range IQ that is slightly lower than that of other family members. A woman with triplo-X may produce some egg cells bearing two X chromosomes, which increases her risk of giving birth to triplo-X daughters or XXY sons.
XXY	Klinefelter or XXY syndrome	1 in every 500 to 1000 males	The syndrome varies greatly. Often, however, affected individuals are sexually underdeveloped, with rudimentary testes and prostate glands and no pubic or facial hair. They also have very long limbs and large hands and feet, and they may develop breast tissue. Individuals with XXY syndrome may be slow to learn, but they are usually not mentally retarded unless they have more than two X chromosomes, which is rare.
XYY	Jacobs or XYY syndrome	One in every 1000 males	The vast majority of XYY males are apparently normal, although they may be very tall. They may also have acne and problems with speech and reading.
XO	Turner syndrome	1 in every 2000 females	Young women with only one X chromosome are short and sexually undeveloped. They are usually of normal intelligence. Although women with Turner syndrome are infertile, treatment with hormone supplements can promote growth and sexual development.

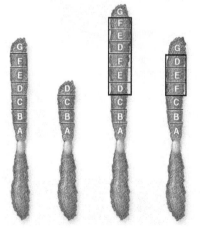

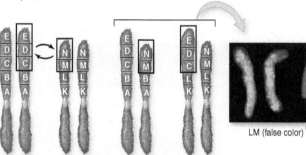

Figure 9.14 Chromosomal Abnormalities. Portions of a chromosome can be (a) deleted, (b) duplicated, or (c) inverted. (d) In translocation, two nonhomologous chromosomes exchange parts. The micrograph shows a portion of chromosome 5 (larger pair) that has switched places with part of chromosome 14 (smaller pair).

LM (false color)   5 μm

Normal   a. Deletion   b. Duplication   c. Inversion   d. Translocation (before)   Translocation (after)

partner may twist around each other in a way that generates chromosomes with deletions or duplications. Because the gametes will have extra or missing genes, the result may be a miscarriage or birth defects.

In a **translocation,** nonhomologous chromosomes exchange parts. Translocations often break genes, sometimes causing leukemia or other cancers. In about 95% of people with chronic myelogenous leukemia, for example, parts of chromosomes 9 and 22 switch places. The translocation creates a combined gene on chromosome 22; this gene, in turn, encodes a protein that speeds cell division and suppresses normal cell death (apoptosis). The result is leukemia, a form of cancer in which blood cells divide out of control. ① *apoptosis,* p. 162

If no genes are broken in a translocation, then the person has the normal amount of genetic material; it is simply rearranged.

Such a person is healthy but may have fertility problems. Some sperm or egg cells will receive one of the translocated chromosomes but not the other, causing a genetic imbalance—some genes are duplicated, and others are deleted. The consequences may be mild or severe, depending on which genes are disrupted.

9.7   MASTERING CONCEPTS

1. Draw a diagram to show how nondisjunction of all chromosomes during meiosis I in one parent could lead to polyploid offspring. (Use 2*n* = 6 for the starting cells; assume the others parent's gamete contributes the normal number of chromosomes.)

2. How can deletions, duplications, inversions, and translocations cause illness?

180   UNIT TWO   DNA, Inheritance, and Biotechnology

9.8 Haploid Nuclei Are Packaged into Gametes

The events of meiosis explain how a diploid cell produces four genetically different haploid nuclei. The same process occurs in both sexes, yet sperm and egg cells typically look very different from each other (figure 9.15). Usually, a sperm is lightweight and can swim; an egg cell is huge by comparison and packed with nutrients and organelles. How do males and females package those haploid nuclei into such different-looking gametes?

A. In Humans, Gametes Form in Testes and Ovaries

The formation and specialization of sperm cells is called spermatogenesis (figure 9.16). Inside the testes, spermatogonia are diploid germ cells that divide mitotically to produce two kinds of cells: more spermatogonia and specialized cells called primary spermatocytes. During interphase, primary spermatocytes accumulate cytoplasm and replicate their DNA. The first meiotic division yields two equal-sized haploid cells called secondary spermatocytes.

Each secondary spermatocyte then completes its second meiotic division. The products are four equal-sized spermatids, each of which specializes into a mature, tadpole-shaped sperm cell. The entire process, from spermatogonium to sperm, takes about 74 days.

In comparison to a sperm cell, an egg cell is massive. The female produces these large cells by unequally packaging the

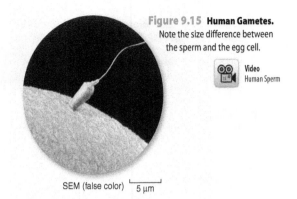

Figure 9.15 **Human Gametes.** Note the size difference between the sperm and the egg cell.

Video
Human Sperm

SEM (false color)   5 μm

cytoplasm from the two meiotic divisions. The egg cell gets most of the cytoplasm, and the other products of meiosis are tiny.

The formation of egg cells is called oogenesis (figure 9.17). It occurs in the ovaries and begins with a diploid germ cell, an oogonium. This cell can divide mitotically to produce more oogonia or a cell called a primary oocyte. In meiosis I, the primary oocyte divides into a small haploid cell with very little cytoplasm, called a polar body, and a much larger haploid cell called a secondary oocyte. In meiosis II, the secondary oocyte divides unequally to produce another polar body and the mature egg cell, or ovum, which contains a large amount of cytoplasm. The tiny polar bodies normally play no further role in reproduction.

Chapter 35 explores human reproduction and development in more detail.

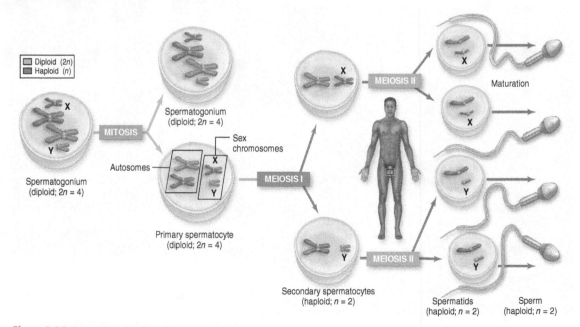

Diploid (2n)
Haploid (n)

Spermatogonium
(diploid; 2n = 4)

MITOSIS

Sex chromosomes

Autosomes

Spermatogonium
(diploid; 2n = 4)

Primary spermatocyte
(diploid; 2n = 4)

MEIOSIS I

MEIOSIS II

MEIOSIS II

X

X

Y

Y

Maturation

Secondary spermatocytes
(haploid; n = 2)

Spermatids
(haploid; n = 2)

Sperm
(haploid; n = 2)

Figure 9.16 **Sperm Formation (Spermatogenesis).** In humans, diploid primary spermatocytes undergo meiosis, yielding four equal-sized, haploid sperm. Of the normal 23 pairs of chromosomes, only one pair of autosomes and one pair of sex chromosomes are shown.

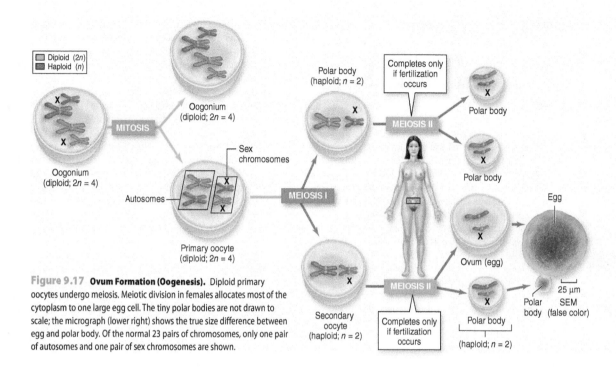

Figure 9.17 Ovum Formation (Oogenesis). Diploid primary oocytes undergo meiosis. Meiotic division in females allocates most of the cytoplasm to one large egg cell. The tiny polar bodies are not drawn to scale; the micrograph (lower right) shows the true size difference between egg and polar body. Of the normal 23 pairs of chromosomes, only one pair of autosomes and one pair of sex chromosomes are shown.

B. In Plants, Gametophytes Produce Gametes

Plant life cycles include an **alternation of generations** between multicellular haploid and diploid individuals (figure 9.18). A diploid zygote divides mitotically and develops into a mature sporophyte. Germ cells in the diploid sporophyte undergo meiosis to produce haploid cells called spores. The spores germinate, dividing mitotically to produce a multicellular haploid plant called a gametophyte. The gametophyte, in turn, produces haploid sperm or egg cells by mitotic cell division. A sperm fertilizes an egg cell to form a zygote; the cycle begins anew.

In mosses and ferns, the gametophytes are small green plants that are visible with the unaided eye. In flowering plants, however, the gametophyte is microscopic and relies on the sporophyte for nutrition. The egg-producing female gametophyte, for example, is buried deep within a flower.

Some plants produce swimming sperm cells. In mosses and ferns, the male gametes use flagella to swim in a film of water to the stationary egg cell. The sperm cells of conifers and flowering plants, however, do not swim. Instead, these plants produce pollen grains—male gametophytes—that travel in wind or on animals to reach female plant parts. Pollen germination delivers sperm cells directly to the stationary egg cell. Chapters 19 and 24 further describe plant reproduction.

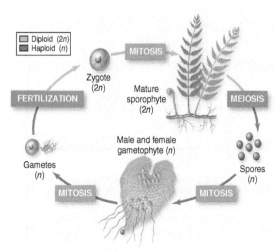

Figure 9.18 Plant Reproduction. Plant life cycles include an alternation of multicellular haploid and diploid generations.

9.8   MASTERING CONCEPTS

1. What are the stages of sperm development in humans?
2. What are the stages of development of an egg cell in humans?
3. How does gamete production in plants differ from that in animals?

INVESTIGATING LIFE

9.9 Hermaphrodites and Parasites Meet the Red Queen

Sexual reproduction is a hassle. Why spend energy to attract mates when you could just make identical copies of yourself and ensure that your genome makes it to the next generation?

Some scientists suggest that parasites explain the evolution and persistence of sexual reproduction. Parasites often reproduce much faster than their hosts, so mutations frequently produce new variants. Perhaps sexually reproducing hosts, which generate new allele combinations in each generation, have the best chance to survive in an environment full of constantly changing parasites.

The predicted endless evolutionary battle between host and parasite gives this proposition its common name: the Red Queen hypothesis. In Lewis Carroll's book *Through the Looking Glass*, the Red Queen remarks to Alice, "It takes all the running you can do, to keep in the same place." Sexual reproduction may give a species just enough variation to hold its own against rapidly evolving parasites. Does any evidence support this idea?

A team of Indiana University researchers, led by Levi Morran and Curtis Lively, tested the predictions of the Red Queen hypothesis by studying disease-causing bacteria and their host, the microscopic roundworm *Caenorhabditis elegans* (figure 9.19). These worms are convenient laboratory workhorses. Hundreds of them can be reared, with or without bacteria, in a single petri dish. ⓘ *C. elegans*, p. 430

Roundworms also have another trait that makes them ideal for research on reproduction: they can be hermaphrodites. Meiosis in hermaphrodites generates both male and female sex cells. A hermaphrodite worm can reproduce sexually with a male, or it can self-reproduce. Sexual reproduction between a male and a hermaphrodite generates variation, but when gametes from the same individual combine, the resulting offspring have genetic material identical to that of the parent. ⓘ *hermaphrodites*, p. 718

These two reproductive strategies allowed the researchers to study how a single population of *C. elegans* can shift toward or away from sexual reproduction when parasites are present. In one experiment, the research team exposed a population containing both sexually reproducing and self-reproducing *C. elegans* to three experimental conditions. One group of worms was allowed to reproduce in petri dishes with a "fixed" (unchanging) strain of disease-causing bacteria. A second group was reared with bacteria that had successfully infected and reproduced in hosts of the previous generation—in other words, these bacteria were evolving with the hosts. The remaining worms (the control group) were placed in petri dishes containing dead bacteria. In all three treatments, each generation of worm offspring was moved to fresh petri dishes (with live or dead bacteria) and allowed to reproduce.

The researchers documented the rate of sexual reproduction in each of the three *C. elegans* groups over 30 generations (figure 9.20). At the start of the experiment, sexual reproduction was rare in all three groups. But the rate of sexual reproduction increased within a few generations for both populations exposed to bacteria. Roundworms exposed to a fixed bacterial strain eventually shifted back toward self-reproduction, presumably because disease-resistance traits became more common. In contrast, the population exposed to evolving bacteria entered an evolutionary

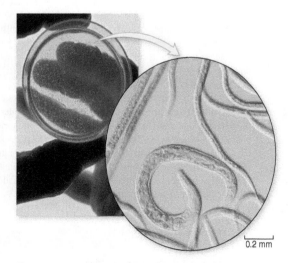

Figure 9.19 Microscopic Worms. The roundworm *C. elegans* replicates quickly in small petri dishes, making this species ideally suited for laboratory research.

0.2 mm

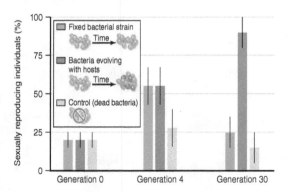

Figure 9.20 Shift to Sexual Reproduction. Researchers measured the rate of sexual reproduction in *C. elegans* populations exposed to a fixed bacterial strain, bacteria evolving with the worms, or dead bacteria (control). Over 30 generations of worms, the evolving bacteria selected for sexual reproduction in their hosts. (Error bars represent two standard errors; see appendix B.)

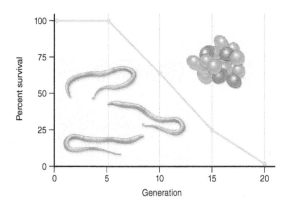

Figure 9.21 Hermaphrodite Extinction. When a completely hermaphroditic roundworm population is exposed to an evolving strain of disease-causing bacteria over multiple generations, the population eventually goes extinct.

race like the one the Red Queen hypothesis predicts. As each generation of bacteria got better at infecting familiar hosts, the worms became more likely to shuffle the genetic deck and produce a greater proportion of unfamiliar offspring.

In another experiment, a population consisting entirely of identical, hermaphroditic *C. elegans* was exposed to bacteria that evolved with their hosts throughout the experiment. The bacteria quickly became effective at infecting the roundworms. Meanwhile, each generation of identical offspring became more vulnerable to the evolving bacteria. After 20 generations, the roundworm population was extinct (figure 9.21). Evidently, without the ability to generate genetically unique offspring, the roundworms lost the evolutionary race against the bacteria.

These experiments reveal that parasites select for sexual reproduction in their hosts. In the evolutionary race between organisms and their parasites, sexual reproduction produces new allele combinations, boosting the chance that the host species will evade extinction in a rapidly changing pool of parasites. Sex costs time and energy, but the alternative—easy reproduction of a doomed allele combination—may be even costlier.

Morran, Levi, Olivia Schmidt, Ian Gelarden, Raymond Parrish II, and Curtis Lively. July 8, 2011. Running with the Red Queen: Host-parasite coevolution selects for biparental sex. *Science,* vol. 333, pages 216–218.

9.9 MASTERING CONCEPTS

1. Why are the offspring of a male and a hermaphrodite more variable than the offspring of a self-reproducing hermaphrodite?

2. Under what conditions does evolution select for sexual reproduction in *C. elegans*?

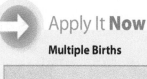

Apply It **Now**

Multiple Births

As you learned in section 9.5, twins can be fraternal (no more alike genetically than siblings born singly) or identical. But how do triplets, quadruplets, and higher-order multiple births arise?

Triplets come about in several ways. The least common route is for a single embryo to split and develop into three genetically identical babies (monozygotic triplets). Alternatively, if three sperm fertilize three separate egg cells, the triplets will all be fraternal (trizygotic). Most commonly, however, an embryo splits and forms two identical babies, and another embryo develops into an additional, nonidentical baby.

Identical quadruplets are exceedingly rare, occurring perhaps once in 11 million deliveries. Monozygotic quintuplets are even more unusual, with only one set ever known to have been born. Just as for triplets, higher-order multiples usually are combinations of identical and fraternal siblings.

Multiple births have become more common since the 1980s for two reasons. First, older women are more likely to have multiple births, and childbearing among these women has become more common. Second, treatment for infertility has increased. Some fertility drugs stimulate a woman to release more than one egg cell. If sperm fertilize all of them, a multiple birth could result. Another infertility therapy is *in vitro* fertilization, in which sperm fertilize egg cells harvested from a woman's ovaries in the lab. One or more embryos judged most likely to result in a live birth are then implanted into the woman's uterus. Multiple births often result.

A notable example occurred in 2009, when a woman gave birth to octuplets conceived by *in vitro* fertilization. The children represent only the second full set of octuplets born alive in U.S. history.

CHAPTER SUMMARY

9.1 Why Sex?

- **Asexual reproduction** is reproduction without sex. **Sexual reproduction** produces offspring by mixing traits from two parents.
- **Conjugation** is a form of gene transfer in some microorganisms.
- Asexual reproduction can be successful in a stable environment, but a changing environment selects for sexual reproduction.

9.2 Diploid Cells Contain Two Homologous Sets of Chromosomes

- **Diploid cells** have two full sets of **chromosomes**, one from each parent.
- In humans, the **sex chromosomes** (X and Y) determine whether an individual is male or female. The 22 **homologous pairs** of **autosomes** do not determine sex.
- Homologous chromosomes share the same size, banding pattern, and centromere location, but they differ in the **alleles** they carry.

9.3 Meiosis Is Essential in Sexual Reproduction

Animation
Meiosis
Overview

A. Gametes Are Haploid Sex Cells

- **Meiosis** halves the genetic material to produce **haploid cells**. **Fertilization** occurs when **gametes** fuse, forming the diploid **zygote**. **Mitotic cell division** produces the body's cells during growth and development. Figure 9.22 summarizes the events of a sexual life cycle.

B. Specialized Germ Cells Undergo Meiosis

- **Somatic** cells do not participate in reproduction, whereas diploid **germ cells** produce haploid sex cells.

C. Meiosis Halves the Chromosome Number and Scrambles Alleles

- The events of meiosis ensure that gametes are haploid and genetically variable (figure 9.23).

9.4 In Meiosis, DNA Replicates Once, but the Nucleus Divides Twice

- Interphase (including DNA replication) happens before meiosis.
- During meiosis, **spindle** fibers attached to **kinetochores** move the chromosomes.

A. In Meiosis I, Homologous Chromosomes Pair Up and Separate

- Homologous pairs of chromosomes align during prophase I, then split apart during anaphase I.

B. Meiosis II Yields Four Haploid Cells

- In meiosis II, the two products of meiosis I divide, producing four cells that each contain half as many chromosomes as a diploid cell.

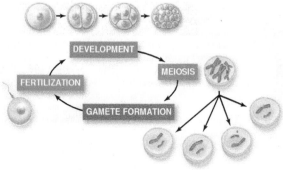

Figure 9.22 Sexual Life Cycle Events.

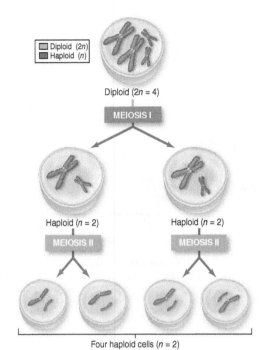

Diploid (2n = 4)

MEIOSIS I

Haploid (n = 2)   Haploid (n = 2)

MEIOSIS II   MEIOSIS II

Four haploid cells (n = 2)

Figure 9.23 Summary of Meiosis.

9.5 Meiosis Generates Enormous Variability

Animation
Genetic
Variation

A. Crossing Over Shuffles Alleles

- **Crossing over**, which occurs in prophase I, produces variability when portions of homologous chromosomes switch places.

B. Chromosome Pairs Align Randomly During Metaphase I

- Every possible orientation of homologous pairs of chromosomes at metaphase I is equally likely. As a result, gametes have many possible unique combinations of paternal and maternal chromosomes.

C. Fertilization Multiplies the Diversity

- Because any sperm can fertilize any egg cell, a human couple can produce trillions of genetically different offspring.
- Identical (monozygotic) twins arise when a zygote splits into two embryos. Fraternal (dizygotic) twins develop from separate zygotes.

9.6 Mitosis and Meiosis Have Different Functions: A Summary

- Mitotic division makes identical cell copies and occurs throughout life.
- Meiosis produces genetically different haploid cells. It occurs only in specialized cells and only during some parts of the life cycle.

9.7 Errors Sometimes Occur in Meiosis

A. Polyploidy Means Extra Chromosome Sets

- **Polyploid cells** have one or more extra sets of chromosomes.

B. Nondisjunction Results in Extra or Missing Chromosomes

- **Nondisjunction** is the failure of chromosomes to separate in meiosis, and it causes gametes to have incorrect chromosome numbers. A sex chromosome abnormality is typically less severe than an incorrect number of autosomes.

C. Smaller-Scale Chromosome Abnormalities Also Occur

- Chromosomal rearrangements can **delete** or **duplicate** genes. An **inversion** flips gene order; in a **translocation**, two nonhomologs exchange parts. Inversions and translocations may disrupt vital genes.

9.8 Haploid Nuclei Are Packaged into Gametes

A. In Humans, Gametes Form in Testes and Ovaries

- Spermatogenesis begins in the testes. Diploid germ cells undergo mitosis and then meiosis I and II before differentiating into four sperm cells.
- In oogenesis, diploid germ cells called oogonia divide mitotically and then meiotically, yielding a large egg cell and three small cells called polar bodies. Oogenesis occurs in the ovaries.

B. In Plants, Gametophytes Produce Gametes

- In plants, sexual reproduction involves an **alternation of generations** with multicellular haploid and diploid phases.

9.9 Investigating Life: Hermaphrodites and Parasites Meet the Red Queen

- In lab experiments, populations of roundworms were more likely to reproduce sexually when exposed to disease-causing bacteria.

MULTIPLE CHOICE QUESTIONS

1. Compared to other forms of reproduction, the unique feature of sex is
   a. the ability of a cell to divide.
   b. the production of offspring.
   c. the ability to generate new genetic combinations.
   d. All of the above are correct.

2. Fertilization results in the formation of a
   a. diploid zygote.   c. diploid somatic cell.
   b. haploid gamete.   d. haploid zygote.

3. Meiosis explains why
   a. you inherited half of your DNA from each of your parents.
   b. the sister chromatids in a chromosome are identical to each other.
   c. each of your somatic cells contains the same DNA.
   d. zygotes contain half as much DNA as somatic cells.

4. How many chromatids are visible in a human cell at the start of anaphase I?
   a. 23   c. 92
   b. 46   d. 184

5. Which of the following is *not* a mechanism that contributes to diversity among the offspring from two parents?
   a. Random fertilization
   b. Crossing over
   c. Cytokinesis
   d. Chromosome alignment during metaphase I

6. What process might produce a gamete with one extra chromosome?
   a. Nondisjunction   c. Translocation
   b. Crossing over   d. Independent assortment

7. Why can a gametophyte produce gametes by mitosis?
   a. Because a plant's gametes are diploid
   b. Because the gametophyte's cells are already haploid
   c. Because the gametes will go through meiosis later
   d. Because spores function like germ cells

Answers to these questions are in appendix A.

WRITE IT OUT

1. Explain why evolution often selects traits that promote genetic diversity.
2. Describe a situation in which asexual reproduction might be more likely than sexual reproduction.
3. Most cells in a sexually reproducing organism have two sets of chromosomes. Explain this observation and describe its significance to meiosis.

4. Sketch the relationship between mitosis, meiosis, and fertilization in a sexual life cycle.
5. What is the difference between haploid and diploid cells? Are your skin cells haploid or diploid? What about germ cells? Gametes?
6. Some male veterans of the Gulf War in Iraq claim that their children have birth defects that were caused by toxic substances contaminating the war zone. What types of cells would a toxin have to have affected in these men to cause birth defects years later? Explain your answer.
7. How does crossing over produce variation among gametes?
8. Draw all possible metaphase I chromosomal arrangements for a cell with a diploid number of 8. How many unique gametes are possible for this species? Is this number an underestimate or an overestimate? Why?
9. Is it possible for a boy–girl pair of twins to be genetically identical? Why or why not?
10. List some examples of chromosomal abnormalities, and explain how each relates to an error in meiosis.
11. Could nondisjunction occur during mitosis? Compare and contrast the likely consequence of nondisjunction in mitosis vs. meiosis.
12. How does spermatogenesis differ from oogenesis, and how are the processes similar?
13. Provide examples to support or refute this statement: The products of meiosis are always haploid cells, whereas the products of mitotic division are always diploid cells.

PULL IT TOGETHER

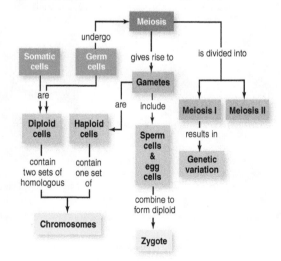

Figure 9.24 Pull It Together: Sexual Reproduction and Meiosis.

Refer to figure 9.24 and the chapter content to answer the following questions.

1. Fit the following terms into this concept map: *chromatid, centromere, nondisjunction, fertilization,* and *mitosis.*
2. Create a separate concept map that includes these terms: *crossing over, synapsis, gamete, autosome,* and *homologous pair.* You may add other terms to the map as well.
3. What two processes in meiosis I generate genetic variation among gametes?

CHAPTER

10 Patterns of Inheritance

Family Photo. Former University of Oklahoma basketball player Blake Griffin (second from left) walks with his brother and parents after a news conference announcing his intention to play in the professional leagues.

Enhance your study |BIOLOGY
of this chapter with practice quizzes,
animations and videos, answer keys,
and downloadable study tools.
www.mhhe.com/hoefnagels

LEARN HOW TO LEARN
Be a Good Problem Solver

This chapter is about the principles of inheritance, and you will find many sample problems within its pages; in addition, "Activity" icons indicate interactive problems available online. Need help? The "How to Solve a Genetics Problem" guide at the end of this chapter shows a systematic, step-by-step approach to answering the most common types of questions. Keep using the guide until you feel comfortable solving any problem type.

From Mendel to Medical Genetics

STUDY THE FAMILY PORTRAIT ON THE OPPOSITE PAGE. It is hard to resist scrutinizing the faces, searching for similarities and differences between parent and offspring. Our inherent interest in heredity is probably as old as humankind itself. But of all the people who have studied inheritance, one nineteenth-century investigator, Gregor Mendel, made the most lasting impression on what would become the science of genetics.

Mendel was born in 1822 and spent his early childhood in a small village in what is now the Czech Republic, where he learned how to tend fruit trees. After finishing school, Mendel became a priest at a monastery where he could teach and do research in natural science. The young man eagerly learned how to artificially pollinate crop plants to control their breeding. The monastery sent him to earn a college degree at the University of Vienna, where courses in the sciences and statistics fueled his interest in plant breeding. Mendel began to think about experiments to address a compelling question for plant breeders: Why did some traits disappear, only to reappear a generation later?

From 1857 to 1863, Mendel crossed and cataloged some 24,034 plants through several generations. He observed consistent ratios of traits in the offspring and deduced that the plants transmitted distinct units, or "elementen" (now called genes). Mendel described his work to the Brno Medical Society in 1865 and published it in the organization's journal the next year.

Interestingly, Charles Darwin puzzled over natural selection and evolution at the same time that Mendel was tending his plants. No one knew it at the time, but each scientist was exploring genetic variation from a different point of view. Mendel focused on the fate of specific traits from generation to generation; Darwin studied larger-scale shifts in variation within populations. Thanks to another century of biological research, we now know that all variation traces to mutations in DNA. That insight ties together the ideas of Mendel, Darwin, and many other scientists. The so-called "modern evolutionary synthesis" integrates genetic variation, inheritance, and natural selection to explain evolutionary changes in populations. We take up this idea again in unit 3.

Biology has made great strides since Mendel and Darwin's time. Today, genetics and DNA are familiar to nearly everyone, and the entire set of genetic instructions to build a person—the human genome—has been deciphered. Even so, every family encounters the same principles of heredity that Mendel derived in his experiments with peas. Our look at genetics begins the traditional way, with Gregor Mendel, but we can now appreciate his genius in light of what we know about DNA.

LEARNING OUTLINE

 10.1 Chromosomes Are Packets of Genetic Information: A Review

 10.2 Mendel's Experiments Uncovered Basic Laws of Inheritance
  A. Why Peas?
  B. Dominant Alleles Appear to Mask Recessive Alleles
  C. For Each Gene, a Cell's Two Alleles May Be Identical or Different
  D. Every Generation Has a Name

 10.3 The Two Alleles of a Gene End Up in Different Gametes
  A. The Simplest Punnett Squares Track the Inheritance of One Gene
  B. Meiosis Explains Mendel's Law of Segregation

 10.4 Genes on Different Chromosomes Are Inherited Independently
  A. Tracking Two-Gene Inheritance May Require Large Punnett Squares
  B. Meiosis Explains Mendel's Law of Independent Assortment
  C. The Product Rule Replaces Complex Punnett Squares

 10.5 Genes on the Same Chromosome May Be Inherited Together
  A. Genes on the Same Chromosome Are Linked
  B. Studies of Linked Genes Have Yielded Chromosome Maps

 10.6 Gene Expression Can Alter Phenotypic Ratios
  A. Incomplete Dominance and Codominance Add Phenotype Classes
  B. Some Inheritance Patterns Are Especially Difficult to Interpret

 10.7 Sex-Linked Genes Have Unique Inheritance Patterns
  A. X and Y Chromosomes Carry Sex-Linked Genes
  B. X-Linked Recessive Disorders Affect More Males Than Females
  C. X Inactivation Prevents "Double Dosing" of Proteins

 10.8 Pedigrees Show Modes of Inheritance

 10.9 Most Traits Are Influenced by the Environment and Multiple Genes
  A. The Environment Can Alter the Phenotype
  B. Polygenic Traits Depend on More Than One Gene

 10.10 Investigating Life: Heredity and the Hungry Hordes

10.1 Chromosomes Are Packets of Genetic Information: A Review

A healthy young couple, both with family histories of cystic fibrosis, visits a genetic counselor before deciding whether to have children. The counselor suggests genetic tests, which reveal that both the man and the woman are carriers of cystic fibrosis. The counselor tells the couple that each of their future children has a 25% chance of inheriting this serious illness. How does the counselor arrive at that one-in-four chance? This chapter will explain the answer. ⓘ *genetic testing,* p. 230

First, however, it may be useful to review some concepts from previous chapters in this unit. Chapter 7 explained that cells contain DNA, a molecule that encodes all of the information needed to sustain life. Human DNA includes some 25,000 genes. A **gene** is a portion of DNA whose sequence of nucleotides (A, C, G, and T) encodes a protein. When a gene's nucleotide sequence mutates, the encoded protein may also change. Each gene can therefore exist as one or more **alleles,** or alternative forms, each arising from a different mutation.

The DNA in the nucleus of a eukaryotic cell is divided among multiple **chromosomes,** which are long strands of DNA associated with proteins. Recall that a **diploid cell** contains two sets of chromosomes, with one set inherited from each parent. The human genome consists of 46 chromosomes, arranged in 23 pairs (figure 10.1a). Of these, 22 pairs are **autosomes,** which are the chromosomes that are the same for both sexes. The single pair of **sex chromosomes** determines each person's sex: A female has two X chromosomes, whereas a male has one X and one Y.

With the exception of X and Y, the chromosome pairs are homologous (figure 10.1b). As described in chapter 9, the two members of a **homologous pair** of chromosomes look alike and have the same sequence of genes in the same positions. (A gene's *locus* is its physical place on the chromosome.) But the two homologs may or may not carry the same alleles. Since each homolog comes from a different parent, each person inherits two alleles for each gene in the human genome.

An analogy may help clarify the relationships among these terms. If each chromosome is like a cookbook, then the human genome is a "library" that consists of 46 such volumes, arranged in 23 pairs of similar books. The entire cookbook library includes about 25,000 recipes, each analogous to one gene.

The two alleles for each gene, then, are comparable to two of the many ways to prepare brownies; some recipes include nuts, for example, whereas others use different types of chocolate. The two "brownie recipes" in a cell may be exactly the same, slightly different, or very different from each other. Furthermore, with the exception of identical twins, everyone inherits a unique combination of alleles for all of the genes in the human genome.

Another important idea to review from chapter 9 is the role of meiosis and fertilization in a sexual life cycle (see figure 9.5). **Meiosis** is a specialized form of cell division that occurs in diploid germ cells and gives rise to **haploid cells,** each containing just one

Tutorial
Homologous
Chromosomes

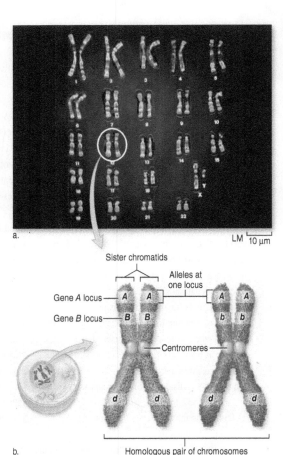

a.   LM [10 μm]

Sister chromatids

Alleles at one locus

Gene *A* locus — A   A   A   A
Gene *B* locus — B   B   b   b

— Centromeres —

d   d   d   d

b.   Homologous pair of chromosomes

Figure 10.1 Homologous Chromosomes. (a) A human diploid cell contains 23 pairs of chromosomes. (b) Each chromosome has one allele for each gene. For the chromosome pair in this figure, both alleles for gene *A* are identical. The same is true for gene *D*, but the chromosomes carry different alleles for gene *B*.

set of chromosomes. In humans, these haploid cells are **gametes**—sperm or egg cells. **Fertilization** unites the gametes from two parents, producing the first cell of the next generation. Gametes are the cells that convey chromosomes from one generation to the next, so they play a critical part in the study of inheritance.

No one can examine a gamete and say for sure which allele it carries for every gene. As we shall see in this chapter, however, for some traits, we can use knowledge of a person's characteristics and family history to say that a gamete has a 100% chance, 50% chance, or 0% chance of carrying a specific allele. With this information for both parents, it is simple to calculate the probability that a child will inherit the allele.

10.1 MASTERING CONCEPTS

1. Describe the relationships among chromosomes, DNA, genes, and alleles.
2. How do meiosis, fertilization, diploid cells, and haploid cells interact in a sexual life cycle?

🍁 10.2 Mendel's Experiments Uncovered Basic Laws of Inheritance

Gregor Mendel, the nineteenth-century researcher who discovered the basic principles of genetics (see the chapter-opening essay), knew nothing about DNA, genes, chromosomes, or meiosis. But he nevertheless discovered how to calculate the probabilities of inheritance, at least for some traits. This section explains how he used careful observations of pea plants to draw his conclusions.

A. Why Peas?

As Mendel discovered, the pea plant is a good choice for studying heredity. Pea plants are easy to grow, develop quickly, and produce many offspring. Moreover, peas have many traits that appear in two easily distinguishable forms. For example, seeds may be round or wrinkled, yellow or green. Pods may be inflated or constricted. Stems may be tall or short.

Pea plants also have another advantage for studies of inheritance: it is easy to control which plants mate with which (figure 10.2). An investigator can take pollen from the male flower parts of one plant and apply it to the female part of the same plant (self-fertilization) or another plant (cross-fertilization). The resulting offspring are seeds that develop inside pods; each pea represents a genetically unique offspring, analogous to you and your siblings. Traits such as seed color or seed shape are evident right away; for other characteristics, such as plant height or flower color, the investigator must sow the seeds and observe each plant that develops.

B. Dominant Alleles Appear to Mask Recessive Alleles

Mendel's first experiments with peas dealt with single traits that have two expressions, such as yellow or green seed colors. He noted that some plants were always **true breeding;** that is, self-fertilization always produced offspring identical to the parent plant. Plants derived from green seeds, for example, always

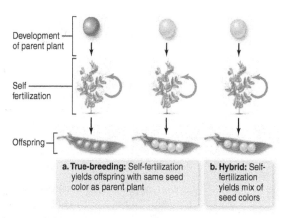

a. True-breeding: Self-fertilization yields offspring with same seed color as parent plant

b. Hybrid: Self-fertilization yields mix of seed colors

Figure 10.3 **True-Breeding and Hybrid Plants.** Pea plants derived from green seeds were always true breeding. In contrast, plants grown from yellow seeds could be true breeding or hybrids.

produced green seeds when self-fertilized. But crosses involving plants grown from yellow seeds were more variable. Sometimes these plants were true breeding, but others were **hybrids:** their offspring were mixed, including both yellow and green peas (figure 10.3).

Cross-fertilization experiments yielded other intriguing results. For example, Mendel crossed plants derived from green seeds with plants grown from yellow seeds. Sometimes, the pods contained only yellow seeds; the green trait seemed to vanish, although it might reappear in the next generation. Other times, the pods contained green and yellow seeds (see figure 10.4 on page 190). Mendel noticed a similar mode of inheritance when he studied other pea plant characteristics: one trait seemed to obscure the other. Mendel called the masking trait *dominant;* the trait being masked is called *recessive.* The yellow-seed trait, for example, is dominant to the green trait.

Although Mendel referred to *traits* as dominant or recessive, modern biologists reserve these terms for *alleles.* A **dominant allele** is one that exerts its effects whenever it is present; a **recessive allele** is one whose effect is masked if a dominant allele is also present. When a gene has only two alleles, it is common to

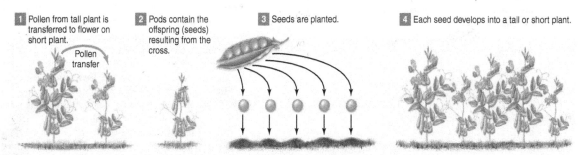

1 Pollen from tall plant is transferred to flower on short plant.

Pollen transfer

2 Pods contain the offspring (seeds) resulting from the cross.

3 Seeds are planted.

4 Each seed develops into a tall or short plant.

Figure 10.2 **Mendel's Experimental Approach.** Gregor Mendel used this technique to set up carefully designed crosses of pea plants, so he could observe the appearance of traits in the next generation.

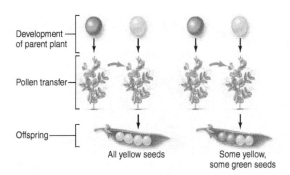

Figure 10.4 Yellow Is Dominant. When Mendel crossed a plant derived from a green seed with a plant grown from a yellow seed, the offspring could be all yellow, or they could be a mix of green and yellow peas. Crosses such as these led Mendel to conclude that yellow seed color is dominant over green.

Genotype	Phenotype
Homozygous dominant (*GG*)	Yellow
Heterozygous (*Gg*)	Yellow
Homozygous recessive (*gg*)	Green

Figure 10.5 Genotypes and Phenotypes Compared. A pea's genotype for the "seed color" gene consists of the two alleles that the seed inherited from its parents. Its phenotype is its outward appearance: yellow or green.

symbolize the dominant allele with a capital letter (such as *G* for yellow) and the recessive allele with the corresponding lowercase letter (*g* for green).

The "dominance" of an allele may seem to imply that it "dominates" in the population as a whole. The most common allele, however, is not always the dominant one. In humans, the allele that causes a form of dwarfism called achondroplasia is dominant, but it is very rare—as is the dominant allele that causes Huntington disease. Conversely, blue eyes are the norm in people of northern European origin, but the alleles that produce this eye color are recessive.

The term *dominant* may also conjure images of a bully that forces a weak, recessive allele into submission. After all, the recessive allele seems to hide when a dominant allele is present, emerging from its hiding place only if the dominant allele is absent. How does the recessive allele "know" what to do? In fact, alleles cannot hide, emerge, or know anything. A recessive allele remains a part of the cell's DNA, regardless of the presence of a dominant allele. It only seems to hide because it typically encodes a nonfunctional protein. If a dominant allele is also present, the organism usually has enough of the functional protein to maintain its normal appearance (although section 10.6 describes some exceptions). It is only when both alleles are recessive that the lack of the functional protein becomes noticeable. This chapter's first Burning Question, on page 191, describes a health-related consequence of a nonfunctional protein encoded by a recessive allele.

C. For Each Gene, a Cell's Two Alleles May Be Identical or Different

Mendel chose traits encoded by genes with only two alleles, but some genes have hundreds of forms. Regardless of the number of possibilities, however, a diploid cell can have only two alleles for each gene. After all, each diploid individual has inherited one set of chromosomes from each parent, and each chromosome carries only one allele per gene.

For a given gene, a diploid cell's two alleles may be identical or different. The **genotype** expresses the genetic makeup of an individual, and it is written as a pair of letters representing the alleles (figure 10.5). An individual that is **homozygous** for a gene has two identical alleles, meaning that both parents contributed the same gene version. If both of the alleles are dominant, the individual's genotype is homozygous dominant (written as *GG,* for example). If both alleles are recessive, the individual is homozygous recessive *(gg).* An individual with a **heterozygous** genotype, on the other hand, has two different alleles for the gene *(Gg).* That is, the two parents each contributed different genetic information.

The organism's genotype is distinct from its **phenotype,** or observable characteristics (see figure 10.5). Seed color, flower color, and stem length are examples of pea plant phenotypes that Mendel studied. Your own phenotype includes not only your height, eye color, shoe size, number of fingers and toes, skin color, and hair texture but also other characteristics that are not readily visible, such as your blood type or the specific shape of your hemoglobin proteins. As described in section 10.9, most phenotypes result from a complex interaction between genes and environment. Mendel, however, chose traits controlled exclusively by genes.

Mendel's observation that only some yellow-seeded pea plants were true breeding arises from the two possible genotypes for the yellow phenotype (homozygous dominant and heterozygous). All homozygous plants are true breeding because all of their gametes contain the same allele. Heterozygous plants, however, are not true breeding because they may pass on either the dominant or the recessive allele. These plants are hybrids.

Today, biologists use additional terms to describe organisms. A **wild-type** allele, genotype, or phenotype is the most common form or expression of a gene in a population. Wild-type fruit flies, for example, have two antennae and one pair of wings. A **mutant** allele, genotype, or phenotype is a variant that arises when a gene undergoes a mutation. Mutant phenotypes for fruit flies include having multiple pairs of wings or having legs instead of antennae growing out of the head (see figure 7.20).

D. Every Generation Has a Name

Part of Mendel's genius was that he kept careful tallies of the offspring from countless crosses, which required a systematic accounting of multiple generations of plants. Biologists still use Mendel's system of standardized names to keep track of inheritance patterns.

The purebred **P generation** (for "parental") is the first set of individuals being mated; the **F$_1$ generation,** or first filial generation, is the offspring from the P generation (*filial* derives from the Latin word for "child"). The **F$_2$ generation** is the offspring of the F$_1$ plants, and so on. Although these terms are applicable only to lab crosses, they are analogous to human family relationships. If

TABLE 10.1   Miniglossary of Genetic Terms

Term	Definition
Generations	
P	The parental generation
F$_1$	The first filial generation; offspring of P generation
F$_2$	The second filial generation; offspring of F$_1$ generation
Chromosomes and genes	
Chromosome	A continuous molecule of DNA plus associated proteins
Gene	A sequence of DNA that encodes a protein
Locus	The physical location of a gene on a chromosome
Allele	One of the alternative forms of a specific gene
Dominant and recessive	
Dominant allele	An allele that is expressed if present in the genotype
Recessive allele	An allele whose expression is masked by a dominant allele
Genotypes and phenotypes	
Genotype	An individual's allele combination for a particular gene
Homozygous	Possessing identical alleles of one gene
Heterozygous	Possessing different alleles of one gene
Phenotype	An observable characteristic
True breeding	Homozygous; self-fertilization yields offspring identical to self for a given trait
Hybrid	Heterozygous; self-fertilization yields a mix of offspring for a given trait
Wild type	The most common phenotype, genotype, or allele in a population
Mutant	A phenotype, genotype, or allele resulting from a mutation in a gene

Burning Question

Why does diet soda have a warning label?

Foods containing the artificial sweetener aspartame carry a warning label that says "Contains phenylalanine." Since other sugar substitutes lack similar words of caution, aspartame must pose a unique threat. What is it?

A peek at aspartame's biochemistry reveals the answer. Aspartame contains an amino acid called phenylalanine. In most people, an enzyme converts phenylalanine into another amino acid. A mutated allele of the gene encoding this enzyme, however, results in the production of an abnormal, nonfunctional enzyme. People who have just one copy of this recessive allele are healthy because the cell has enough of the normal enzyme, thanks to the dominant allele. The recessive allele therefore seems to "vanish," just as in Mendel's pea plants.

Individuals who inherit two copies of the recessive allele, however, have a metabolic disorder called phenylketonuria (abbreviated PKU). These people cannot produce the normal enzyme. Phenylalanine accumulates to toxic levels, causing mental retardation and other problems. Avoiding foods containing phenylalanine helps minimize the effects of the disease—hence the warning.

Submit your burning question to
Marielle.Hoefnagels@mheducation.com

you consider your grandparents the P generation, your parents are the F$_1$ generation, and you and your siblings are the F$_2$ generation.

Table 10.1 summarizes the important terms encountered so far. The remainder of the chapter uses this basic vocabulary to integrate Mendel's findings with what biologists now know about genes, chromosomes, and reproduction.

10.2   MASTERING CONCEPTS

1. Why did Gregor Mendel choose pea plants as his experimental organism?
2. Distinguish between dominant and recessive; heterozygous and homozygous; phenotype and genotype; wild type and mutant.
3. Define the P, F$_1$, and F$_2$ generations.

10.3 The Two Alleles of a Gene End Up in Different Gametes

Tutorial Using Punnett Squares

Mendel used a systematic series of crosses to deduce the rules of inheritance, beginning with single genes.

A. The Simplest Punnett Squares Track the Inheritance of One Gene

Virtual Lab Punnett Squares

Mendel began with a P generation consisting of true-breeding plants derived from yellow seeds *(GG)* and true-breeding green-seeded plants *(gg)*. The F_1 offspring produced in this cross had yellow seeds (genotype *Gg*). The green trait therefore seemed to disappear in the F_1 generation.

Next, he used the F_1 plants to set up a **monohybrid cross:** a mating between two individuals that are both heterozygous for the same gene. The resulting F_2 generation had both yellow and green phenotypes, in a ratio of 3:1; that is, for every three yellow seeds, Mendel observed one green seed.

A diagram called a **Punnett square** uses the genotypes of the parents to reveal which allele combinations the offspring may inherit. The Punnett square in figure 10.6, for example, shows how the green phenotype reappeared in the F_2 generation. Both parents are heterozygous *(Gg)* for the seed color gene. Each

therefore produces some gametes carrying the *G* allele and some gametes carrying *g*. All three possible genotypes may therefore appear in the F_2 generation, in the ratio 1 *GG* : 2 *Gg* : 1 *gg*. The corresponding phenotypic ratio is three yellow seeds to one green seed, or 3:1. Mendel saw similar results for all seven traits that he studied (figure 10.7).

Figure It Out

If Mendel mated a true-breeding tall plant with a heterozygous tall plant, what percent of the offspring would also be tall?

Answer: 100%

Mendel could tally the plants with each phenotype, but he also needed to keep track of each genotype. He knew that the green-seeded plants were always homozygous recessive *(gg)*.

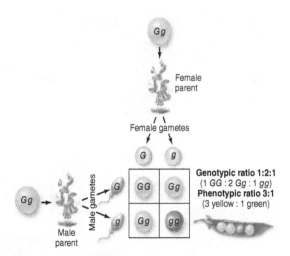

Figure 10.6 Punnett Square. This diagram depicts a cross between two heterozygous plants grown from yellow seeds *(Gg)*. The two possible types of female gametes are listed along the top of the square; the male gametes are listed on the left-hand side. The four compartments within the Punnett square contain the genotypes and phenotypes of all possible offspring.

Activity One-Gene Punnett Square

Trait	Dominant allele	Recessive allele
Seed color	Yellow (G)	Green (g)
Seed form	Round (R)	Wrinkled (r)
Pod color	Green (D)	Yellow (d)
Pod form	Inflated (V)	Constricted (v)
Flower color	Purple (P)	White (p)
Flower position	Axial (A)	Terminal (a)
Stem length	Tall (L)	Short (l)

Figure 10.7 Pea Traits. Mendel's breeding studies helped him to deduce the inheritance patterns of these seven pea plant characteristics.

If plant is homozygous dominant (GG):

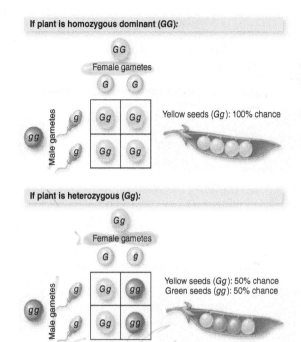

If plant is heterozygous (Gg):

Figure 10.8 **Testcross.** A pea plant grown from a yellow seed may be homozygous dominant *(GG)* or heterozygous *(Gg)*. To determine the genotype, the plant is mated with a homozygous recessive *(gg)* plant. If the unknown plant is *GG*, all offspring of the testcross will be yellow; if the unknown plant is *Gg*, about half the offspring are likely to be green.

But what was the genotype of each yellow seed, *GG* or *Gg*? He had no way to tell just by looking, so he set up breeding experiments called testcrosses to distinguish between the two possibilities. A **testcross** is a mating between an individual of unknown genotype and a homozygous recessive individual (figure 10.8). If a yellow-seeded plant crossed with a *gg* plant produced only yellow seeds, Mendel knew the unknown genotype was *GG;* if the cross produced seeds of both colors, he knew it must be *Gg*.

B. Meiosis Explains Mendel's Law of Segregation

All of Mendel's breeding experiments and calculations added up to a brilliant description of basic genetic principles. Without any knowledge of chromosomes or genes, Mendel used his data to conclude that genes occur in alternative versions (which we now call alleles). He further determined that each individual inherits two alleles for each gene and that these alleles may be the same or different. Finally, he deduced his **law of segregation,** which states that the two alleles of each gene are packaged into separate gametes; that is, they "segregate," or move apart from each other, during gamete formation. (In science, a *law* is a statement about a phenomenon that is invariable, at least as far as anyone knows. Unlike a theory, a law does not necessarily explain the phenomenon.)

Mendel's law of segregation makes perfect sense in light of what we now know about reproduction. During meiosis I, homologous pairs of chromosomes separate and move to opposite poles of the cell. After a plant of genotype *Gg* undergoes meiosis, half the gametes carry *G* and half carry *g* (figure 10.9). A *GG* plant,

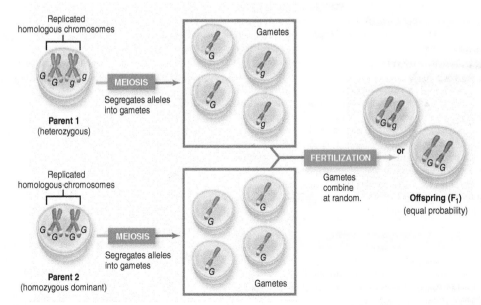

Figure 10.9 **Mendel's Law of Segregation.** During anaphase I of meiosis, homologous pairs of chromosomes (and the genes they carry) segregate from one another and are packaged into separate gametes. At fertilization, gametes combine at random to form the next generation (in this figure, red and blue denote different parental origins of the chromosomes).

Mother: healthy carrier
Female gametes

Father: healthy carrier
Male gametes

	F	f
F	FF Healthy non-carrier	Ff Healthy carrier
f	Ff Healthy carrier	ff Affected

Healthy noncarrier (*FF*): 25% chance
Healthy carrier (*Ff*): 50% chance
Affected (*ff*): 25% chance

Figure 10.10 Inheritance of Cystic Fibrosis. This Punnett square shows the possible results of a mating between two carriers of cystic fibrosis. The siblings in the photo have cystic fibrosis; the masks deliver medicine to treat their lung problems.

on the other hand, can produce only *G* gametes. When gametes from the two plants meet at fertilization, they combine at random. About 50% of the time, both gametes carry *G;* the other 50% of the time, one contributes *G* and the other, *g.*

This principle of inheritance applies to all diploid species, including humans. Return for a moment to the couple and their genetic counselor introduced in section 10.1. Cystic fibrosis arises when a person has two recessive alleles for a particular gene on chromosome 7 (see section 4.6). Genetic testing revealed that the man and the woman are both carriers. In genetic terms, this means that although neither has the disease, both are heterozygous for the gene that causes cystic fibrosis. Just as in Mendel's monohybrid crosses, each of their children has a 25% chance of inheriting two recessive alleles (figure 10.10). Each child also has a 50% chance of being a carrier (heterozygous) and a 25% chance of inheriting two dominant alleles.

Note that Punnett squares, including the one in figure 10.10, show the *probabilities* that apply to each offspring. That is, if the couple has four children, there will not necessarily be exactly one with genotype *FF*, two with *Ff*, and one with *ff*. Similarly, the chance of tossing a fair coin and seeing "heads" is 50%, but two tosses will not necessarily yield one head and one tail. If you toss the coin 1000 times, however, you will likely approach the expected 1:1 ratio of heads to tails. As Mendel discovered, pea plants are ideal for genetics studies in part because they produce many offspring in each generation.

10.3 MASTERING CONCEPTS

1. What is a monohybrid cross, and what are the genotypic and phenotypic ratios expected in the offspring of the cross?
2. How are Punnett squares helpful in following inheritance of single genes?
3. What is a testcross, and why is it useful?
4. How does the law of segregation reflect the events of meiosis?

10.4 Genes on Different Chromosomes Are Inherited Independently

Mendel's law of segregation arose from his studies of the inheritance of single traits. He next asked himself whether the same law would apply if he followed two characters at the same time. Mendel therefore began another set of breeding experiments in which he simultaneously examined the inheritance of pea shape and pea color.

A. Tracking Two-Gene Inheritance May Require Large Punnett Squares

A pea's shape may be round or wrinkled (determined by the *R* gene, with the dominant allele specifying round shape). At the same time, its color may be yellow or green (determined by the *G* gene, with the dominant allele specifying yellow).

As he did before, Mendel began with a P generation consisting of true-breeding parents (figure 10.11a). He crossed plants grown from wrinkled, green seeds with plants derived from round, yellow seeds. All F_1 offspring were heterozygous for both genes (*Rr Gg*) and therefore had round, yellow seeds.

Next, Mendel crossed F_1 plants with each other (figure 10.11b). A **dihybrid cross** is a mating between individuals that are each heterozygous for two genes. Each *Rr Gg* individual in the F_1 generation produced equal numbers of gametes of four different types: *RG, Rg, rG,* and *rg*. After Mendel completed the crosses, he found four phenotypes in the F_2 generation, reflecting all possible combinations of seed shape and color. The Punnett square predicts that the four phenotypes will occur in a ratio of 9:3:3:1. That is, nine of 16 offspring should have round, yellow seeds; three should have round, green seeds; three should have wrinkled, yellow seeds; and just one should have wrinkled, green seeds. This prediction almost exactly matches Mendel's results.

Figure It Out

In a cross between an *Rr Gg* plant and an *rr gg* plant, what proportion of the offspring is homozygous recessive for both seed shape and seed color?

Answer: 25%.

B. Meiosis Explains Mendel's Law of Independent Assortment

Based on the results of the dihybrid cross, Mendel proposed what we now know as the **law of independent assortment.** It states that during gamete formation, the segregation of the alleles for one gene does not influence the alleles for another gene (provided the genes are on separate chromosomes). That is, alleles for two different genes are randomly packaged into gametes with respect to each other. With this second set of experiments, Mendel had again inferred a principle of inheritance based on meiosis (figure 10.12).

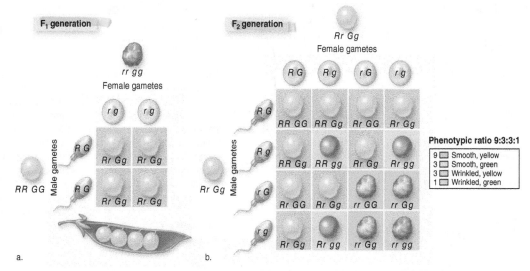

Figure 10.11 **Generating a Dihybrid Cross.** (a) In the parental generation, one parent is homozygous recessive for two genes; the other is homozygous dominant. The F₁ generation is therefore heterozygous for both genes. (b) A dihybrid cross is a mating between two plants from the F₁ generation. Phenotypes occur in a distinctive ratio in the resulting F₂ generation.

Activity Two-Gene Punnett Square

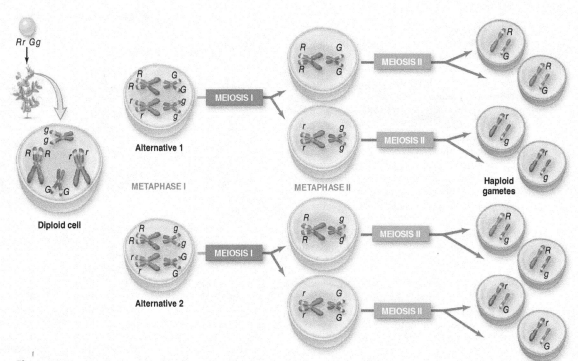

Figure 10.12 **Mendel's Law of Independent Assortment.** Homologous chromosome pairs align at random during metaphase I of meiosis. The exact allele combination in a gamete depends on which chromosomes happen to be packaged together. An individual of genotype *Rr Gg* therefore produces approximately equal numbers of four types of gametes: *RG, rg, Rg,* and *rG*.

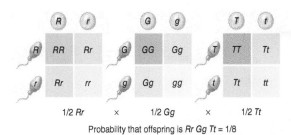

1/2 Rr   ×   1/2 Gg   ×   1/2 Tt

Probability that offspring is *Rr Gg Tt* = 1/8

Figure 10.13   The Product Rule. What is the chance that two parents that are heterozygous for three genes *(Rr Gg Tt)* will give rise to an offspring with that same genotype? To find out, multiply the individual probabilities for each gene.

Interestingly, Mendel found some trait combinations for which a dihybrid cross did not yield the expected phenotypic ratio. Mendel could not explain this result. No one could, until Thomas Hunt Morgan's work led to the chromosomal theory of inheritance. As you will see in section 10.5, the law of independent assortment does not apply to genes that are close together on the same chromosome.

C. The Product Rule Replaces Complex Punnett Squares

Punnett squares become cumbersome when analyzing more than two genes. A Punnett square for three genes has 64 boxes; for four genes, 256 boxes. An easier way to predict genotypes and phenotypes is to use the rules of probability on which Punnett squares are based. The **product rule** states that the chance that two independent events will both occur (for example, an offspring inheriting specific alleles for two genes) equals the product of the individual chances that each event will occur.

The product rule can predict the chance of obtaining wrinkled, green seeds *(rr gg)* from dihybrid *(Rr Gg)* parents. The probability that two *Rr* plants will produce *rr* offspring is 25%, or ¼, and the chance of two *Gg* plants producing a *gg* individual is ¼. According to the product rule, the chance of dihybrid parents *(Rr Gg)* producing homozygous recessive *(rr gg)* offspring is therefore ¼ multiplied by ¼, or ¹⁄₁₆. Now consult the 16-box Punnett square for Mendel's dihybrid cross (see figure 10.11). As expected, only one of the 16 boxes contains *rr gg*. Figure 10.13 applies the product rule to three traits.

10.4   MASTERING CONCEPTS

1. What is a dihybrid cross, and what is the phenotypic ratio expected in the offspring of the cross?
2. How does the law of independent assortment reflect the events of meiosis?
3. How can the product rule be used to predict the results of crosses in which multiple genes are studied simultaneously?

10.5   Genes on the Same Chromosome May Be Inherited Together

Biologists did not appreciate the significance of Gregor Mendel's findings during his lifetime, but his careful observations laid the foundation for modern genetics. In 1900, three botanists working independently each rediscovered the principles of inheritance. They eventually found the paper that Mendel had published in 1866, and other scientists demonstrated Mendel's ratios again and again in several species. At about the same time, advances in microscopy were allowing chromosomes to be observed and described for the first time.

It soon became apparent that what Mendel called "elementen" (later renamed "genes") had much in common with chromosomes. Both genes and chromosomes, for example, come in pairs. In addition, alleles of a gene are packaged into separate gametes, as are the members of a homologous pair of chromosomes. Finally, both genes and chromosomes are inherited in random combinations.

As biologists cataloged traits and the chromosomes that transmit them in several species, it soon became clear that the number of traits far exceeded the number of chromosomes. Fruit flies, for example, have only four pairs of chromosomes, but they have dozens of different bristle patterns, body colors, eye colors, wing shapes, and other characteristics. How might a few chromosomes control so many traits? The answer: each chromosome carries many genes.

A. Genes on the Same Chromosome Are Linked

Linked genes are carried on the same chromosome; they are therefore inherited together. Unlike genes on different chromosomes, they do not assort independently during meiosis. The seven traits that Mendel followed in his pea plants were all transmitted on separate chromosomes. Had the same chromosome carried these genes, Mendel's dihybrid crosses would have generated markedly different results.

The inheritance pattern of linked genes was first noticed in the early 1900s, when William Bateson and R. C. Punnett observed offspring ratios in pea plants that were different from the ratios predicted by Mendel's laws. The researchers crossed true-breeding plants that had purple flowers and long pollen grains (genotype *FF LL*) with true-breeding plants that had red flowers and round pollen grains (genotype *ff ll*). Then they crossed the heterozygous F₁ plants, of genotype *Ff Ll*, with each other.

Surprisingly, the F₂ generation did not show the expected phenotypic ratio for an independently assorting dihybrid cross (figure 10.14). Two types of F₂ offspring—those with the same phenotypes as the P generation—were more abundant than predicted. The other two classes of offspring, with a mix of phenotypes (genotypes *ff L_* and *F_ ll*) were less common. Bateson and Punnett hypothesized that this pattern reflected two genes located on the same chromosome, as depicted in figure 10.14b.

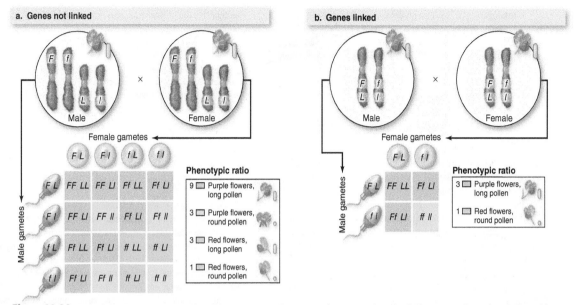

Figure 10.14 Gene Linkage. (a) When genes do not occur on the same chromosome, they assort independently. The gametes then represent all possible allele combinations, and the cross yields the expected phenotypic ratio. (b) If genes are linked on the same chromosome, only two allele combinations are expected in the gametes, and the number of phenotypes is reduced.

While Bateson and Punnett were studying linkage in peas, Thomas Hunt Morgan at Columbia University was breeding fruit flies and studying the inheritance of pairs of traits. The data began to indicate four **linkage groups,** collections of genes that tended to be inherited together. Within each linkage group, dihybrid crosses did not produce the proportions of offspring that Mendel's law of independent assortment predicts. Because the number of linkage groups was the same as the number of homologous pairs of chromosomes, scientists eventually realized that each linkage group was simply a set of genes transmitted together on the same chromosome. ⓘ *Drosophila*, p. 430

Nevertheless, the researchers did sometimes see offspring with trait combinations not seen in either parent. How could this occur? The answer turned out to involve yet another event in meiosis: **crossing over,** an exchange of genetic material between homologous chromosomes during prophase I (see figure 9.8). After crossing over, no two chromatids in a homologous pair of chromosomes are identical (figure 10.15).

Figure 10.15 Crossing Over. Linkage between two alleles is interrupted if crossing over occurs at a point between the two genes. As a result, some gametes contain recombinant arrangements of the alleles.

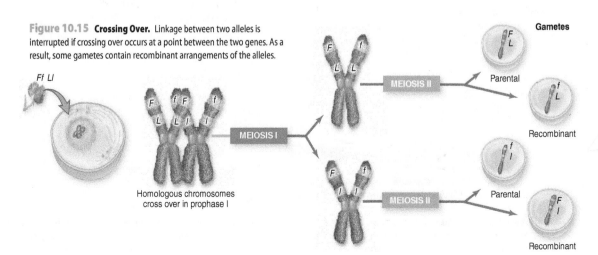

Crossing over is a random process, and it might or might not occur between two linked genes. For any pair of genes on the same chromosome, then, most offspring inherit a **parental chromatid,** which retains the allele combination from each parent. But whenever crossing over happens between the two genes, some of the offspring inherit a **recombinant chromatid** with a mix of maternal and paternal alleles.

B. Studies of Linked Genes Have Yielded Chromosome Maps

Morgan wondered why some crosses produced a higher proportion of recombinant offspring than others. Might the differences reflect the physical relationships between the genes on the chromosome? Alfred Sturtevant, Morgan's undergraduate assistant, explored this idea. In 1911, Sturtevant proposed that the farther apart two alleles are on the same chromosome, the more likely crossing over is to separate them—simply because more space separates the genes (figure 10.16a).

Sturtevant's idea became the basis for mapping genes on chromosomes. By determining the percentage of recombinant offspring, investigators can infer how far apart the genes are on one chromosome. Crossing over frequently separates alleles on opposite ends of the same chromosome, so recombinant offspring occur frequently. In contrast, a crossover would rarely separate alleles lying very close together on the chromosome, and the proportion of recombinant offspring would be small. Geneticists use this correlation between crossover frequency and the distance between genes to construct **linkage maps,** which are diagrams of gene order and spacing on chromosomes.

In 1913, Sturtevant published the first genetic linkage map, depicting the order of five genes on the X chromosome of the fruit fly (figure 10.16b). Researchers then rapidly mapped genes on all four fruit fly chromosomes. Linkage maps for human chromosomes followed over the next half century.

At one time, phenotypes were the basis for linkage maps. Now, however, genetic marker technology can associate a known, detectable DNA sequence with a specific phenotype. The marker does not have to be part of the gene that controls the phenotype; the two must simply be located close enough

together that the presence of the marker correlates strongly with the phenotype.

Figure It Out

Genes A, B, and D are on the same chromosome. The crossover frequency between B and D is 0.25, between A and B is 0.12, and between D and A is 0.13. Which two genes are farthest apart?

Answer: Genes B and D are farthest apart.

Figure It Out

Use the crossover frequencies in the question above to create a linkage map of genes A, B, and D. What is the order of the genes on the chromosome?

Answer: B-A-D

Genetic markers are useful tools for predicting the chance that a person will develop a particular inherited illness, even if the actual disease-causing gene is unknown. The first such use of genetic markers occurred in the 1980s. An extensive study of a small Venezuelan village with a high incidence of Huntington disease revealed that all family members with the disorder also carried a unique marker on chromosome 4. Healthy relatives did not have this sequence. Like a flag, the marker indicates the presence of the disease-causing allele to which it is closely linked. The actual gene was not identified until the 1990s, but in the meantime, researchers could identify who was likely to carry the Huntington disease–causing allele long before the symptoms developed.

The linkage maps of the mid–twentieth century provided the rough drafts to which DNA sequence information was added later in the century. Today, entire genomes are routinely sequenced using powerful computers that assemble many short, overlapping DNA sequences. ⓘ *DNA sequencing,* p. 222

10.5   MASTERING CONCEPTS

1. How do patterns of inheritance differ for unlinked versus linked pairs of genes?
2. What is the difference between recombinant and parental chromatids, and how do they arise?
3. How do biologists use crossover frequencies to map genes on chromosomes?

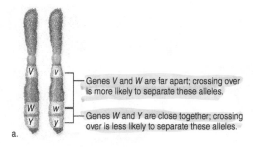
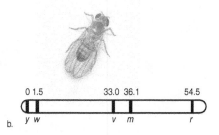

Genes V and W are far apart; crossing over is more likely to separate these alleles.

Genes W and Y are close together; crossing over is less likely to separate these alleles.

a.   b.

Figure 10.16 Breaking Linkage. (a) Crossing over is more likely to separate the alleles of genes V and W (or V and Y) than to separate the alleles of genes W and Y, because there is more room for an exchange to occur. (b) A linkage map of a fruit fly chromosome, showing the locations of five genes. The numbers represent crossover frequencies relative to the leftmost gene, y.

10.6 Gene Expression Can Alter Phenotypic Ratios

Mendel's crosses yielded easily distinguishable offspring. A pea is either yellow or green, round or wrinkled; a plant is either tall or short. Often, however, offspring traits do not occur in the proportions that Punnett squares or probabilities predict. It may appear that Mendel's laws do not apply—but they do. The underlying genotypic ratios are there, but the nature of the phenotype, other genes, or the environment alter how traits appear. Sections 10.6 and 10.7 describe some situations that may produce phenotypic ratios other than those Mendel observed.

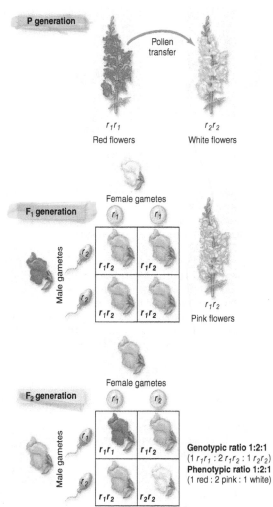

Figure 10.17 Incomplete Dominance. In snapdragons, a cross between a plant with red flowers (r_1r_1) and a plant with white flowers (r_2r_2) produces a heterozygous plant with pink flowers (r_1r_2). The red and white phenotypes reappear in the F$_2$ generation.

Activity
Incomplete
Dominance

A. Incomplete Dominance and Codominance Add Phenotype Classes

For the traits Mendel studied, one allele is completely dominant and the other is completely recessive. The phenotype of a heterozygote is therefore identical to that of a homozygous dominant individual. For many genes, however, heterozygous offspring do not share the phenotype of either parent. As you will see, biologists apply unique notation to alleles for these traits. Designating the alleles with capital and lowercase letters does not work, because neither allele is necessarily dominant over the other.

When a gene shows **incomplete dominance,** the heterozygote has a third phenotype that is intermediate between those of the two homozygotes. For example, a red-flowered snapdragon of genotype r_1r_1 crossed with a white-flowered r_2r_2 plant gives rise to an r_1r_2 plant with pink flowers (figure 10.17). The single copy of allele r_1 in the pink heterozygote directs less pigment production than the two copies in a red-flowered r_1r_1 plant. Although the red color seems to be "diluted" in the all-pink F$_1$ generation, the Punnett square shows that crossing two of these pink plants can yield F$_2$ offspring with red, white, or pink flowers.

In **codominance,** two different alleles are fully expressed in the phenotype. For example, the ABO blood typing system is important in determining which blood a person can receive in a transfusion. A person's ABO blood type is determined by the I gene, which has three possible alleles: I^A, I^B, and i (figure 10.18). The I gene encodes an enzyme that inserts either an "A" or a "B" molecule onto the surfaces of red blood cells. Allele i is recessive, so a person with genotype ii produces neither molecule A

Genotypes	Phenotypes		
	Surface molecules	ABO blood type	
I^AI^A I^Ai	Only A	Type A	
I^BI^B I^Bi	Only B	Type B	
I^AI^B	Both A and B	Type AB	
ii	None	Type O	

Figure 10.18 Codominance. The I^A and I^B alleles of the I gene are codominant, meaning that both are fully expressed in a heterozygote. Allele i is recessive.

Activity
Codominance

nor molecule B and therefore has type O blood. A person who produces only molecule A (genotype $I^A I^A$ or $I^A i$) has type A blood; likewise, someone with only molecule B (genotype $I^B I^B$ or $I^B i$) has type B blood. But genotype $I^A I^B$ yields type AB blood. The I^A and I^B alleles are codominant because both are equally expressed when both are present. ⓘ *ABO blood groups*, p. 613

What is the difference between the recessive *i* allele and the codominant I^A and I^B alleles? Recall that a recessive allele encodes a nonfunctional protein. Both alleles I^A and I^B code for functional proteins, so people of blood type AB have both molecules A and B on the surfaces of their red blood cells. Neither allele is silent.

The ABO blood type example also illustrates what can happen when one gene has more than two possible alleles: The number of possible phenotypes increases. In this case, two codominant alleles (I^A and I^B) and one recessive allele (*i*) produce six possible genotypes ($I^A I^A$, $I^A i$, $I^B I^B$, $I^B i$, $I^A I^B$ and *ii*) and four possible phenotypes (blood types A, B, AB, and O).

Figure It Out

A woman with type AB blood has children with a man who has type O blood. What is the probability that a child they conceive will have type B blood?

Answer: 50%; each child has an equal chance of inheriting $I^B i$ or $I^A i$

B. Some Inheritance Patterns Are Especially Difficult to Interpret

Some conditions are especially difficult to trace through families. For example, one gene may influence the phenotype in many ways; conversely, multiple genes may contribute to one phenotype. Although the basic rules of inheritance apply to each gene, the patterns of phenotypes that appear in grandparents, parents, and siblings may be hard to interpret.

Pleiotropy In **pleiotropy,** one gene has multiple effects on the phenotype (the word root *pleio-* comes from a Greek word meaning "very many"). Pleiotropy arises when one protein is important in different biochemical pathways or affects more than one body part or process. Although Mendelian rules of inheritance apply to pleiotropic genes, the conditions they cause can be difficult to trace through families because individuals with different subsets of symptoms may appear to have different disorders.

A collection of disorders called Marfan syndrome offers one example of pleiotropy. In Marfan syndrome, a mutated gene on chromosome 15 encodes a defective version of a protein that normally occurs in connective tissue. This tissue type is widespread throughout the body, and the normal protein is especially abundant in bones, lungs, the ligaments of the eye, and the aorta (a major blood vessel extending from the heart). The defective protein therefore affects many organ systems, with symptoms including long limbs, spindly fingers, a caved-in chest, a weakened aorta,

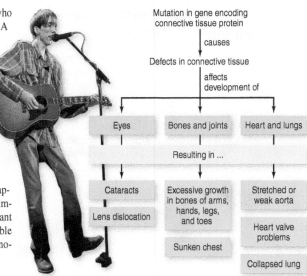

Figure 10.19 Pleiotropy. In Marfan syndrome, a single mutated gene encodes a defective connective tissue protein. The resulting effects on the body are widespread. Singer Bradford Cox was born with Marfan syndrome.

lens dislocation, and other conditions (figure 10.19). Abraham Lincoln may have had Marfan syndrome. Like achondroplasia and Huntington disease, Marfan syndrome is an example of an uncommon disorder caused by a dominant allele. ⓘ *connective tissue*, p. 524

Cystic fibrosis offers another example of pleiotropy. A defective gene on chromosome 7 encodes misshapen membrane channel proteins. The abnormal protein blocks the movement of water into and out of cells. As a result, sticky mucus accumulates in the lungs, digestive tract, and sweat glands. The mucus, in turn, causes a variety of conditions, including increased susceptibility to lung infections, weight loss, fatigue, and salty sweat.

Protein Interactions With thousands of genes active in a cell, it is not surprising that many proteins can interact to contribute to a single phenotype. These interactions can complicate the analysis of inheritance patterns because mutations in different genes can produce similar or identical phenotypes.

Some interactions occur among multiple proteins involved in the same biochemical pathway. For example, blood clot formation requires 11 separate biochemical reactions. A different gene encodes each enzyme in the pathway, and clotting disorders may result from abnormalities in any of these genes. The phenotypes are the same (poor blood clotting), but the genotypes differ.

Another type of interaction is **epistasis,** which occurs when one gene's product affects the expression of another gene. As a familiar example of epistasis, consider male pattern baldness and the "widow's peak" hairline, both of which are controlled by

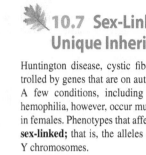

Genotypes: $I^A I^A$ or $I^A i$; HH or Hh — **Phenotype**

Surface molecule encoded by I^A

"Connector" molecule encoded by H

Type A blood

Genotypes: $I^A I^A$ or $I^A i$; hh — **Phenotype**

Surface molecule encoded by I^A

"Connector" molecule absent

Type O blood

Figure 10.20 Epistasis. The H gene encodes a protein that normally attaches molecule A or B to the red blood cells of a person with alleles I^A or I^B. If the genotype for the H gene is hh, then the molecule has nothing to attach to. The person's blood will test as type O, even though allele I^A or I^B is still present.

genes. The hair loss associated with male pattern baldness hides the effects of the "widow's peak" allele.

Epistasis is also responsible for some ABO blood type inconsistencies between parents and their children. Rarely, a child whose blood type tests as O has parents whose genotypes indicate that type O offspring are not possible. Does this mean that the child does not belong with the parents? Not necessarily.

Most people with alleles I^A or I^B have blood type A, B, or AB. However, a protein must physically link the A and B molecules to the blood cell's surface. If a gene called H is mutated, then that protein is nonfunctional, and A and B cannot attach (figure 10.20). A person with the extremely rare genotype hh therefore has blood that always tests as type O, even though he or she may have a genotype indicating type A, B, or AB blood. The interaction is epistatic because the H gene product affects the expression of the I gene product.

Moreover, a person with genotype hh can only receive blood from other hh individuals. The explanation is that the intact H protein in normal blood can induce an immune reaction in a person whose blood lacks that protein.

10.6 MASTERING CONCEPTS

1. How do incomplete dominance and codominance increase the number of phenotypes?
2. Differentiate between pleiotropy and epistasis.
3. How can the same phenotype stem from many different genotypes?
4. How can epistasis decrease the number of phenotypes observed in a population?

10.7 Sex-Linked Genes Have Unique Inheritance Patterns

Huntington disease, cystic fibrosis, and other conditions controlled by genes that are on autosomes affect both sexes equally. A few conditions, including red–green color blindness and hemophilia, however, occur much more frequently in males than in females. Phenotypes that affect one sex more than the other are **sex-linked;** that is, the alleles controlling them are on the X or Y chromosomes.

A. X and Y Chromosomes Carry Sex-Linked Genes

In many species, including humans, the sexes have equal numbers of autosomes but differ in the types of sex chromosomes they have. Females have two X chromosomes, whereas males have one X and one much smaller Y chromosome (figure 10.21). People who seek to increase the odds of conceiving a boy or a girl can exploit this size difference between X and Y chromosomes, as described in this chapter's Apply It Now box.

The Y chromosome plays the largest role in human sex determination. All human embryos start with rudimentary female structures (see figure 35.17). An embryo having a working copy of a Y-chromosome gene called *SRY* (for *sex-determining region*

Figure 10.21 Inheritance of Sex. In humans, each egg contains 23 chromosomes, one of which is a single X chromosome. A sperm cell's 23 chromosomes include either an X or a Y chromosome. If a Y-bearing sperm cell fertilizes an egg, the baby will be a male (XY). If an X-bearing sperm cell fertilizes an egg, the baby will be a female (XX).

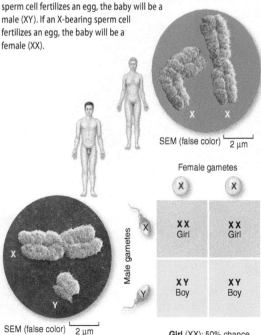

SEM (false color) 2 μm

Female gametes

	X	X
X	**X X** Girl	**X X** Girl
Y	**X Y** Boy	**X Y** Boy

Male gametes

SEM (false color) 2 μm

Girl (XX): 50% chance
Boy (XY): 50% chance

of the *Y*) develops into a male. *SRY* encodes a protein that switches on other genes that direct the undeveloped testes to secrete testosterone. Cascades of other gene activities promote the development of male sex organs. The SRY protein also turns on a gene encoding a protein that dismantles embryonic female structures. (*SRY*'s effects illustrate pleiotropy; see section 10.6B.)

Despite this critical role, the Y chromosome carries fewer than 100 genes. Scientists therefore know of very few **Y-linked** disorders; most involve defects in sperm production. The human X chromosome, on the other hand, carries more than 1000 protein-encoding genes, most of which have nothing to do with sex determination. Most human sex-linked traits are therefore **X-linked;** that is, they are controlled by genes on the X chromosome.

B. X-Linked Recessive Disorders Affect More Males Than Females

Thomas Hunt Morgan was the first to unravel the unusual inheritance patterns associated with genes on the X chromosome (figure 10.22). The eyes of fruit flies are normally red, but one

day Morgan discovered a male with white eyes. To study the inheritance of this odd phenotype, he created true-breeding lines of flies with each eye color. When he mated a parental generation of red-eyed females with white-eyed males, the F$_1$ flies were all red-eyed. The F$_2$ flies had a 3:1 ratio of red-eyed to white-eyed flies—but all the flies with white eyes were male. Morgan also did the reverse cross, mating a P generation of white-eyed females with red-eyed males. That time, all the males of the F$_1$ generation had white eyes, and all the females had red eyes.

Morgan reasoned that the recessive white-eye allele must be on the X chromosome. Because X and Y carry different genes, a male fly can never "mask" the white-eye allele on his X chromosome with a corresponding dominant allele. A female, however, has two X chromosomes. She will express the white-eye phenotype only if *both* of her X chromosomes carry the recessive eye color allele. X-linked inheritance therefore explained why white eyes appeared more frequently in males than in females.

Recessive alleles cause most X-linked disorders in humans, although a few are associated with dominant alleles (table 10.2). As in fruit flies, a human female inherits an X chromosome from

Figure 10.22 Fly Eye Color: An X-Linked Trait. (a) In a cross between a red-eyed female and a white-eyed male, white eyes reappear only in some males of the F$_2$ generation. (b) In the opposite cross, white eyes appear in all the F$_1$ males and in half of the F$_2$ males and females. If eye color were on an autosome rather than on the X chromosome, males and females would be equally likely to inherit each eye color.

Activity
Fly Eye Color

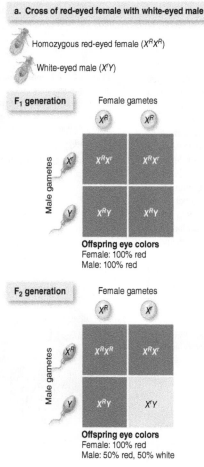
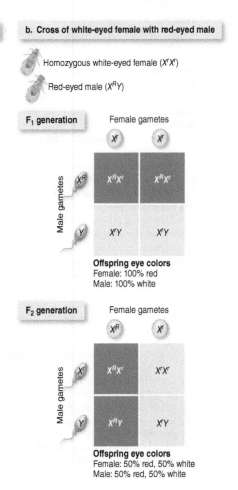

TABLE **10.2** **Some X-Linked Disorders in Humans**

Disorder	Genetic Explanation	Characteristics
X-linked recessive inheritance		
Duchenne muscular dystrophy	Mutant allele for gene encoding dystrophin	Rapid muscle degeneration early in life
Fragile X syndrome	Unstable region of X chromosome has unusually high number of CCG repeats.	Most common form of inherited mental retardation
Hemophilia A	Mutant allele for gene encoding blood clotting protein (factor VIII)	Uncontrolled bleeding, easy bruising
Red–green color blindness	Mutant alleles for genes encoding receptors for red or green (or both) wavelengths of light	Reduced ability to distinguish between red and green
Rett syndrome	Mutant allele for gene required for development of nerve cells	Severe developmental disorders. Almost all affected children are female; affected male embryos cease development before birth.
X-linked dominant inheritance		
Extra hairiness (congenital generalized hypertrichosis; some forms)	Mechanism unknown	Many more hair follicles than normal
Hypophosphatemic rickets (some forms)	Mutant allele for gene involved in phosphorus absorption	Low blood phosphorus level causes defective bones
Retinitis pigmentosa (some forms)	Mutant allele for cell-signaling protein; mechanism unknown	Defects in retina cause partial blindness

both parents; a male inherits his X chromosome from his mother (see figure 10.21). A female therefore exhibits an X-linked recessive disorder only if she inherits the recessive alleles from both parents. A male, in contrast, expresses every allele on his single X chromosome, whether dominant or recessive.

Figure 10.23 shows the inheritance of hemophilia A, a disorder with an X-linked recessive mode of inheritance. In hemophilia, a protein called a clotting factor is missing or defective. Blood therefore clots very slowly, and bleeding is excessive. The heterozygous female in the Punnett square does not exhibit symptoms because her dominant allele encodes a functional blood-clotting protein. When she has children with a normal male, however, each son has a 50% chance of being affected, and each daughter has a 50% chance of being a carrier.

Figure It Out

A woman who is heterozygous for the X-linked gene associated with color blindness marries a color-blind man. What is the probability that their first child will be a son who is color-blind?

Answer: 25%.

C. X Inactivation Prevents "Double Dosing" of Proteins

As we have already seen, each diploid cell has two versions of every autosome, and the two alleles of each autosomal gene can be different (heterozygous) or the same (homozygous). But the sex chromosomes are different. Relative to males, female mammals have a "double dose" of every gene on the X chromosome.

Cells balance this inequality by **X inactivation,** in which a cell shuts off all but one X chromosome in each cell. This process happens early in the embryonic development of a mammal.

X inactivation is directly observable because a turned-off X chromosome absorbs a stain much more readily than an active X chromosome does; the inactivated X forms a Barr body that is visible with a microscope. A normal male cell has no Barr bodies because the single X chromosome remains active.

Which X chromosome becomes inactivated—the one inherited from the father or the one from the mother—is a random

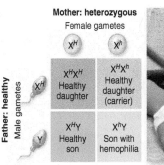
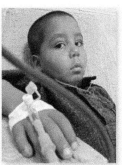

Healthy daughter, noncarrier ($X^H X^H$): 25% chance
Healthy daughter, carrier ($X^H X^h$): 25% chance
Healthy son ($X^H Y$): 25% chance
Affected son ($X^h Y$): 25% chance

Figure 10.23 **Inheritance of Hemophilia.** In a cross between a heterozygous female (a "carrier" of hemophilia A) and a healthy male, the chance of having a son with hemophilia is 25%. The boy in the photo is receiving treatment for hemophilia.

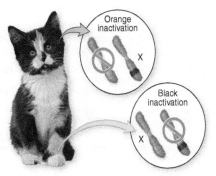

Figure 10.24 X Inactivation. In cats, the X chromosome carries a coat color gene with alleles for black or orange coloration. Calico cats are heterozygous for this gene; one of the two X chromosomes is inactivated in each colored patch. (A different gene accounts for the white background.) Can you explain why calico cats are almost always female?

Activity
X Inactivation

event. As a result, a female expresses the paternal X chromosome alleles in some cells and the maternal alleles in others. Moreover, when a cell with an inactivated X chromosome divides mitotically, all of the daughter cells have the same X chromosome inactivated. Because the inactivation occurs early in development, females have patches of tissue that differ in their expression of X-linked alleles. Figure 10.24 shows how inactivation of an X-linked coat color gene causes the distinctive orange and black fur patterns in calico and tortoiseshell cats, which are always female (except for rare XXY males).

X chromosome inactivation also explains another interesting observation: X-linked dominant disorders are typically less severe in females than in males. Thanks to X chromosome inactivation, a female who is heterozygous for an X-linked gene will express a dominant disease-causing allele in only some of her

cells. As a result, she experiences less severe symptoms than an affected male, who expresses the dominant allele in every cell.

An X-linked neurological disorder called Rett syndrome, for example, may be mild or severe in a girl, depending on how many of her cells express the Rett allele (figure 10.25). Male offspring who inherit the Rett allele typically die before birth. Nearly all people with Rett syndrome are therefore female.

MASTERING CONCEPTS

1. What determines a person's sex?
2. What is the role of the *SRY* gene in sex determination?
3. Why do males and females express recessive X-linked alleles differently?
4. Why does X inactivation occur in female mammals?

Apply It **Now**

Choosing the Sex of Your Baby

Scientists have used the size difference between the X and Y chromosomes to develop technologies that may help people choose the sex of their babies. Some techniques use dyes to differentiate sperm carrying the X from those carrying the Y. Others use swimming speeds or centrifuges to sort the slower, heavier X-containing sperm from the faster, lighter sperm carrying the Y chromosome.

After Y-carrying sperm are separated from X-carrying sperm, the woman is inseminated with the desired fraction of the sperm. Alternatively, if a woman is using *in vitro* fertilization, the egg is fertilized in the laboratory with the sperm most likely to give a baby of the desired sex. None of the methods, however, works all the time; at best, the sperm samples are enriched in sperm that favor one sex over the other.

What about "natural" ways to boost the odds of having a boy or a girl? Folk wisdom includes advice on the mother's diet (including lists of "boy foods" and "girl foods"), the timing of intercourse, the sexual position, and even what objects to place under the pillow during intercourse. Some of these ideas may have a biological basis, and it may be possible to give a slight edge to X- or Y-containing sperm in the race to fertilize the egg.

But the evidence for all of these "do-it-yourself" techniques relies heavily on anecdotes. Testimonials like "It worked for me!" may seem compelling, but the odds of having a baby with the desired sex are near 50% no matter what a person does. In reality, all such methods are difficult or impossible to test using controlled experiments, so it is hard to know for sure what (if anything) works.

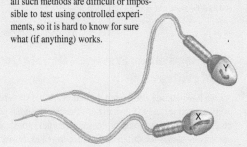

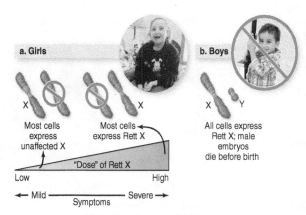

Figure 10.25 Rett Syndrome. In girls, symptoms of Rett syndrome depend on the proportion of cells expressing the normal allele (yellow) versus the Rett allele (orange). In males, every cell expresses the Rett allele, so affected male offspring typically die before birth.

10.8 Pedigrees Show Modes of Inheritance

Although Gregor Mendel did not study human genetics, our species nevertheless has some "Mendelian traits": those determined by single genes with alleles that are either dominant or recessive. For these traits, how do we know whether each phenotype is associated with a dominant or a recessive allele?

We have already seen in chapter 9 that karyotypes are useful for diagnosing chromosomal abnormalities. The same tool is useless in determining the inheritance of single-gene disorders, however, because different alleles look exactly alike under a microscope. To discover the inheritance pattern of an individual gene, researchers therefore track its incidence over multiple generations, much as Mendel did with his pea plants more than a century ago.

Genes on autosomes exhibit two modes of inheritance: autosomal dominant and autosomal recessive (table 10.3). An **autosomal dominant** disorder is expressed in heterozygotes and therefore typically appears in every generation. Because the allele is dominant and located on an autosome, one or both of the affected

Activity
Huntington Disease

individual's parents must also have the disorder (unless the disease-causing allele arose by a new mutation). If a generation arises in which no individuals inherit the allele by chance, transmission of the disorder stops in that family.

Inheriting an **autosomal recessive** disorder requires that a person receive the disease-causing allele from both parents. Each parent must therefore have at least one copy of the allele, either because they are homozygous recessive and have the disease or because they are heterozygotes ("carriers"). If both parents are carriers, autosomal recessive conditions may seem to disappear in one generation, only to reappear in the next.

Activity
Cystic Fibrosis

X-linked recessive conditions such as hemophilia produce unique inheritance patterns. Such disorders mostly affect males in a family; females are rarely affected, but many are heterozygous "carriers" for the disease-causing allele. Each child of a carrier has a 50% chance of inheriting the recessive allele from the mother. If a son receives the recessive allele, he will have the condition. Any daughter who inherits the recessive allele from the mother, however, will be a carrier—unless she also inherits the same allele from her father.

Activity
Hemophilia

TABLE 10.3   Some Autosomal Dominant and Autosomal Recessive Disorders in Humans

Disorder	Genetic Explanation	Characteristics
Autosomal dominant inheritance		
Achondroplasia	Mutant allele of gene on chromosome 4 causes deficiency of receptor protein for growth factor.	Dwarfism with short limbs; head and trunk sizes are normal
Familial hypercholesterolemia	Mutant allele of gene on chromosome 2 encodes faulty cholesterol-binding protein.	High cholesterol, heart disease
Huntington disease	Mutant allele of gene on chromosome 4 encodes protein with extra amino acids that cause it to misfold and form clumps in brain cells.	Progressive uncontrollable movements and personality changes, beginning in middle age
Marfan syndrome	Mutant allele of gene on chromosome 15 causes connective tissue disorder.	Long limbs, sunken chest, lens dislocation, spindly fingers, weakened aorta
Neurofibromatosis (type 1)	Mutant allele of gene on chromosome 17 encodes faulty cell signaling protein.	Brown skin marks (café-au-lait spots), benign tumors beneath skin
Polydactyly	Multiple genes on multiple chromosomes; mechanism is unknown.	Extra fingers or toes or both
Autosomal recessive inheritance		
Albinism	Mutant allele of gene on chromosome 11 encodes faulty gene in biochemical pathway required for pigment production.	Lack of pigmentation in skin, hair, and eyes
Cystic fibrosis	Mutant allele of gene on chromosome 7 encodes faulty chloride channel protein.	Lung infections and congestion, infertility, poor fat digestion, poor weight gain, salty sweat
Phenylketonuria (PKU)	Mutant allele of gene on chromosome 12 causes enzyme deficiency in biochemical pathway that breaks down the amino acid phenylalanine.	Buildup of phenylalanine and related compounds causes mental retardation
Tay-Sachs disease	Mutant allele of gene on chromosome 15 causes deficiency of lysosome enzyme.	Buildup of byproducts causes nervous system degeneration

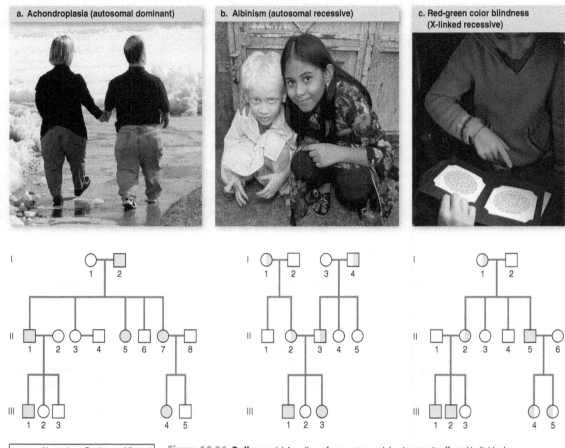

Figure 10.26 **Pedigrees.** (a) A pedigree for an autosomal dominant trait; affected individuals are homozygous dominant or heterozygous. (b) A pedigree for an autosomal recessive trait; affected individuals are homozygous recessive. (c) A pedigree for an X-linked recessive trait. Males are affected if they inherit the allele on their single X chromosome; females are typically carriers.

Pedigree charts depicting family relationships and phenotypes are useful for determining the mode of inheritance (figure 10.26). In a pedigree chart, squares indicate males and circles denote females. Colored shapes indicate individuals with the disorder, and half-filled shapes represent known carriers. Horizontal lines connect parents. Siblings connect to their parents by vertical lines and to each other by an elevated horizontal line.

Figure 10.26 shows typical pedigrees for genes carried on autosomes and the X chromosome. In studying the differences among these three pedigrees, notice especially the patterns of the colored shapes. For example, affected individuals appear in every generation for autosomal dominant traits, whereas recessive conditions often skip generations. (Remember, however, that a recessive allele does not vanish from a "skipped" generation; it remains in carriers, who may pass it to the next generation.) Carriers appear only in pedigrees depicting the inheritance of recessive traits. Also, note that males are most commonly affected with X-linked recessive disorders.

Despite their utility, pedigrees can be difficult to construct and interpret for several reasons. People sometimes hesitate to supply information because they are embarrassed or want to protect their privacy. Adoption, children born out of wedlock, serial marriages, blended families, and assisted reproductive technologies all can complicate efforts to trace family ties. Moreover, as medical and family records are lost, many people simply lack the information to construct an accurate pedigree.

10.8   MASTERING CONCEPTS

1. How are pedigrees helpful in determining a disorder's mode of inheritance?
2. How do the pedigrees differ for autosomal dominant, autosomal recessive, and X-linked recessive conditions?

10.9 Most Traits Are Influenced by the Environment and Multiple Genes

Mendel's data were clear enough for him to infer principles of inheritance because he observed characteristics determined by single genes with two easily distinguished alleles. Moreover, the traits he selected are unaffected by environmental conditions. A genetic counselor can likewise be confident in telling two cystic fibrosis carriers that each of their children has a 25% probability of getting the disease.

But the counselor cannot calculate the probability that the child will be an alcoholic, have depression, be a genius, or wear size 9 shoes. The reason is that multiple genes and the environment control these and most other traits.

A. The Environment Can Alter the Phenotype

The external environment can profoundly affect gene expression; that is, a gene may be active in one circumstance but inactive in another. As a simple example, temperature influences the quantity of pigment molecules in the fur of some animals. Siamese cats and Himalayan rabbits have light-colored bodies but dark extremities, thanks to differences in gene expression between warm and cool body parts (figure 10.27). In crocodiles, the incubation temperature of the egg determines whether the baby will develop as a male or a female. Different combinations of genes are activated at each temperature, greatly altering the phenotype of the offspring.

In humans, fetal alcohol syndrome is an example of the effect of environment on phenotype: Prenatal exposure to alcohol can cause a developing baby to develop facial abnormalities or epilepsy. Likewise, personal circumstances ranging from hormone levels to childhood experiences to diet influence a person's susceptibility to depression, alcoholism, and type II diabetes.

These three diseases have a genetic component as well, but sorting out the relative contributions of nature and nurture is difficult. Studies of twins are often helpful, as are careful observations of everything from family composition to brain structures. The Burning Question in chapter 7, for example, explains some strategies that researchers use to explore the genetic connection to homosexuality. Discovering the exact mechanism by which genes interact with external stimuli is a very active area of research.

Even human diseases with single-gene inheritance patterns can have an environmental component. Cystic fibrosis, for example, is a single-gene disorder. Because cystic fibrosis patients are so susceptible to infection, however, the course of the illness depends on which infectious agents a person encounters.

Figure 10.27 Temperature and Fur Color. Siamese cats have a mutation in a gene encoding an enzyme required for pigment production. The enzyme is active only at the relatively cool temperatures of the paws, ears, snout, and tail; these areas are darkly pigmented. At higher temperatures, the enzyme is inactive. Pigment production is therefore reduced where the skin is warmest.

Burning Question

Is obesity caused by genes or the environment?

At first glance, the cause of obesity seems simple: If a person eats more calories than he or she expends, the body stores the excess calories as fat. As fat accumulates, body weight climbs. According to this view, a person's genes are irrelevant to his or her body weight. In reality, however, obesity reflects the combined action of genes and the environment.

Several genes are associated with obesity. One example is the gene that encodes leptin, a hormone that helps curb appetite. Individuals who inherit mutant alleles for this gene never feel full, leading to overeating and obesity.

The environment can also influence the expression of the genes that a person inherits. For example, scientists have found that mothers who ingest low amounts of carbohydrates—sugars and starches—give birth to children who are especially likely to become obese later in life. Evidence suggests that the womb environment permanently alters gene expression patterns in the developing child.

Fetuses presumably use the mother's diet to "prepare for" the environment that they will be born into. These changes occur before birth, giving a newborn the best chance for survival. But if a fetus prepared for a low-calorie life is born into an environment where food is actually plentiful, then obesity is likely.

Submit your burning question to
Marielle.Hoefnagels@mheducation.com

B. Polygenic Traits Depend on More Than One Gene

Unlike cystic fibrosis, most inherited traits are **polygenic;** that is, the phenotype reflects the activities of more than one gene. Eye color is a familiar example of a polygenic trait. The production of pigments in the eye's iris is influenced by multiple enzymes, which are encoded by multiple genes. Male pattern baldness is another example; multiple genes influence the interactions between male sex hormones and hair follicle cells.

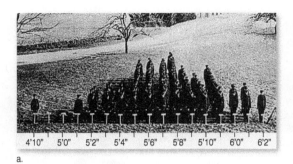
a.

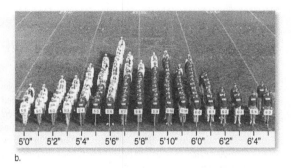
b.

Figure 10.28 **Variation in Human Height.** (a) These students from the University of Connecticut at Storrs lined up by height in 1920, demonstrating the characteristic bell-shaped distribution of polygenic traits. (b) A similar photo taken 57 years later reveals more tall students than the earlier lineup, illustrating the influence of improved health care and nutrition on height. In 1920, the tallest student was 6'2"; in the later photo, the tallest was 6'5".

To complicate matters, the environment often profoundly affects the expression of both single-gene and polygenic traits (see section 32.5 and the Burning Question on page 207). For example, in plants, polygenic traits typically include flower color, the density of leaf pores (stomata), and crop yield. But these traits do not remain static throughout a plant's life. Soil pH can affect flower color, CO_2 concentration can change the number of stomata per square centimeter, and nutrient and water availability greatly influence crop production. ⓘ *stomata*, p. 468

When the frequencies of all the phenotypes associated with a polygenic trait are plotted on a graph, they form a characteristic bell-shaped curve. Figure 10.28 shows a bell curve for height, which is a product of genetics, childhood nutrition, and health care. Figure 10.29 shows a continuum of gene expression for skin color, a trait that is affected by genes and exposure to sunlight. Body weight and intelligence are other traits that are both polygenic and influenced by the environment.

10.9 MASTERING CONCEPTS

1. How can the environment affect a phenotype?
2. What is a polygenic trait?

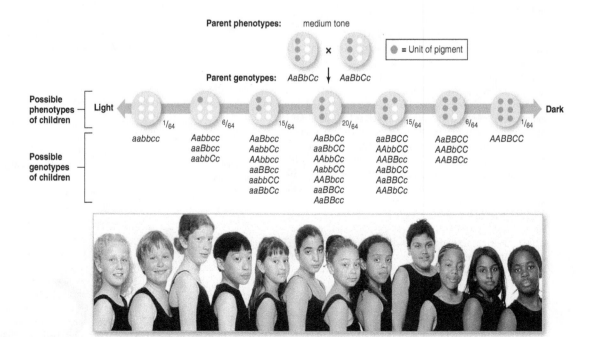

Figure 10.29 **Variation in Human Skin Color.** Multiple genes interact to determine the quantity of pigment in skin cells.

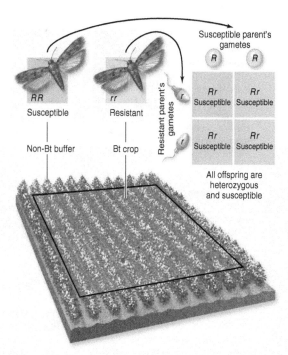

Figure 10.31 Buffers for Bt Crops. This Punnett square shows the logic of using buffer strips around Bt crops to help keep the incidence of recessive alleles low.

INVESTIGATING LIFE

10.10 Heredity and the Hungry Hordes

Agriculture provides a steady food supply, but not just to humans. Hungry insects and other animals can devastate crops by eating the leaves, roots, seeds, and fruits of the plants we grow for food or fiber. Farmers continually seek new ways to kill these competitors, but each tactic selects for new adaptations in the insects. It is a long-standing, and seemingly unavoidable, evolutionary arms race.

The larvae of butterflies and moths are especially voracious. A good example is the pink bollworm (figure 10.30). The adults of this species are moths that lay eggs on cotton bolls. When the eggs hatch, the pink caterpillars tunnel into the boll and eat the seeds, damaging the cotton fibers.

One tool that keeps bollworms and other caterpillars at bay is a soil bacterium called *Bacillus thuringiensis*, abbreviated Bt. This microbe produces a toxic protein that pokes holes in a caterpillar's intestinal tract, leaving the animal vulnerable to infection and unable to digest food. Bt is among the few insecticides that organic farmers can spray on their plants. Bt does not affect humans, because we lack the specific molecule to which the toxin binds.

But Bt sprays cannot reach every insect. Some caterpillars, such as those that tunnel inside an ear of corn, escape death because they never eat the Bt sprayed on a plant's surface. In the 1990s, biotechnology solved this problem when scientists inserted the bacterial gene for the Bt toxin into plant cells. Every cell in these genetically modified "Bt plants" produces the toxin. Nibbling on any hidden or exposed plant part spells death to the caterpillar. Genetically modified Bt corn and cotton are therefore enormously popular with farmers in the United States. ⓘ *transgenic organisms*, p. 219

Bt plants, however, pose a new problem: They greatly increase the selection pressure for Bt resistance in insect populations. When Bt was available only as a spray, insect populations

rarely encountered it. In contrast, genetically modified crops produce the toxin throughout their lives, so caterpillars are exposed from the moment they begin feeding. Bt plants kill most of the susceptible caterpillars, leaving the resistant individuals to produce the next generation.

To combat this selective pressure, farmers growing Bt crops must agree to surround each field with a refuge—that is, a buffer strip planted with a conventional (non-Bt) variety of the same crop. The success of the refuge strategy relies on the assumption that most Bt resistance alleles are recessive. A homozygous recessive, resistant moth emerging from the Bt crop has a good chance of encountering a susceptible mate from the buffer strip (figure 10.31). All of their heterozygous offspring are susceptible and therefore will die if they eat the Bt plants. A ready pool of susceptible mates from the refuge should therefore keep the recessive allele rare.

How can scientists test whether refuges really do keep recessive alleles rare in the real world? One solution is to find a way to measure a bollworm's genotype directly. Biologists Shai Morin, Bruce Tabashnik, and their colleagues at the University of Arizona tackled this problem by studying Bt resistance in several populations of pink bollworms. One population, reared for decades in a lab without exposure to Bt, was susceptible. Other groups, originally collected in Arizona and Texas, were artificially selected for resistance by feeding them Bt-laced meals and allowing the survivors to reproduce. ⓘ *artificial selection*, p. 241

Figure 10.30 Hungry Caterpillar. Pink bollworms cost cotton producers tens of millions of dollars each year.

Figure 10.32

Bt Resistance Is Recessive. When a heterozygous, susceptible insect is bred with a resistant mate, half the offspring should be resistant and half should be susceptible. Tests with Bt toxin show that this is indeed the case: half of the larvae thrived in the presence of Bt toxin, while the susceptible ones died or were very small.

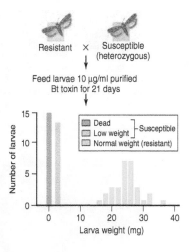

Resistant × Susceptible (heterozygous)

Feed larvae 10 µg/ml purified Bt toxin for 21 days

Legend:
- Dead — Susceptible
- Low weight — Susceptible
- Normal weight (resistant)

Number of larvae (y-axis), Larva weight (mg) (x-axis)

Laboratory experiments confirmed that alleles conferring Bt resistance are indeed recessive (figure 10.32). In addition, from previous studies, the researchers knew that Bt resistance comes from changes in a protein called cadherin, which is the target molecule to which the toxin binds. The recessive allele encodes a defective version of cadherin, rendering the Bt toxin harmless.

Further studies suggested that bollworm populations harbor three unique resistance alleles, each encoding a different variation on the cadherin protein's shape. An insect with two such resistance alleles is immune to the toxin. Furthermore, the unique DNA sequence associated with each allele is a useful "tag" for identifying Bt resistance in pink bollworms. Researchers can simply extract an insect's DNA and test for the presence of the recessive alleles.

As a result, we can now spy on the pink bollworm's evolution as it happens. The stakes are high. If the resistance alleles become very common, Bt may become useless as a control measure. Growers will then switch back to broad-spectrum pesticides that kill many more types of insects—even beneficial ones that do not harm corn or cotton. Careful monitoring will be crucial as we continue to wage war against the insects that will forever compete for our crops.

Morin, Shai, Robert W. Biggs, Mark S. Sisterson, and 10 other authors (including Bruce E. Tabashnik). April 29, 2003. Three cadherin alleles associated with resistance to *Bacillus thuringiensis* in pink bollworm. *Proceedings of the National Academy of Sciences*, vol. 100, pages 5004–5009.

10.10 MASTERING CONCEPTS

1. How did researchers in this study use a breeding experiment to demonstrate that Bt resistance alleles in pink bollworms are recessive?
2. What do you predict will happen to the incidence of resistance alleles in pink bollworm populations if farmers choose not to plant the required refuge?

CHAPTER SUMMARY

10.1 Chromosomes Are Packets of Genetic Information: A Review

- **Genes** encode proteins; mutations create new **alleles** (figure 10.33a).
- A **chromosome** is a continuous molecule of DNA with associated proteins. A **diploid** human cell contains 22 **homologous pairs** of **autosomes** and one pair of **sex chromosomes**.
- **Meiosis** is a type of cell division that gives rise to **haploid gametes**. **Fertilization** unites gametes and restores the diploid number.

10.2 Mendel's Experiments Uncovered Basic Laws of Inheritance

A. Why Peas?
- Gregor Mendel studied inheritance in pea plants because they develop quickly, produce abundant offspring, and are easy to breed.

B. Dominant Alleles Appear to Mask Recessive Alleles
- An individual is **true breeding** for a trait if self-fertilization yields only offspring identical to the parent. A **hybrid** individual produces a mix of offspring when self-fertilized.
- A **dominant** allele is always expressed if it is present; a **recessive** allele is masked by a dominant allele. Figure 10.34 uses a light bulb analogy to illustrate the difference between dominant and recessive alleles.

a. Mutations produce new alleles.

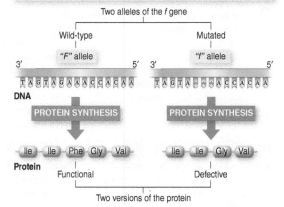

Two alleles of the *f* gene

Wild-type "F" allele / Mutated "f" allele

PROTEIN SYNTHESIS / PROTEIN SYNTHESIS

Ile Ile Phe Gly Val — Functional / Ile Ile Gly Val — Defective

Two versions of the protein

b. A Punnett square tracks the inheritance of these alleles among all possible offspring.

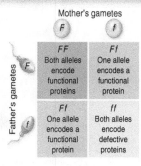

Mother's gametes: F, f
Father's gametes: F, f

	Mother's gametes F	Mother's gametes f
Father's gametes F	**FF** Both alleles encode functional proteins	**Ff** One allele encodes a functional protein
Father's gametes f	**Ff** One allele encodes a functional protein	**ff** Both alleles encode defective proteins

Figure 10.33 From Mutation to Punnett Square.

Homozygous dominant
(Lots of light)

Heterozygous
(Still plenty of light)

Homozygous recessive
(No light)

Figure 10.34 Mendelian Inheritance Patterns: An Analogy.

C. For Each Gene, a Cell's Two Alleles May Be Identical or Different
- An individual's **genotype** may be **heterozygous** (two different alleles for a gene) or a **homozygous** (both alleles are the same).
- A **phenotype** is any observable characteristic of an organism.
- A **wild-type** allele is the most common in a population. A change in a gene is a **mutation** and may result in a **mutant** phenotype.

D. Every Generation Has a Name
- In genetic crosses, the purebred parental generation is designated **P**; the next generation is F_1; and the next is F_2.

10.3 The Two Alleles of a Gene End Up in Different Gametes

A. The Simplest Punnett Squares Track the Inheritance of One Gene
- A **monohybrid cross** is a mating between two individuals that are heterozygous for the same gene.
- **Punnett squares** are useful for predicting the allele combinations that the offspring of a cross might inherit (see figure 10.33b).
- A **testcross** reveals an unknown genotype by breeding the individual to a homozygous recessive individual.

B. Meiosis Explains Mendel's Law of Segregation
- Mendel's **law of segregation** states that the two alleles of the same gene separate into different gametes.

10.4 Genes on Different Chromosomes Are Inherited Independently

A. Tracking Two-Gene Inheritance May Require Large Punnett Squares
- A **dihybrid cross** is a mating between individuals that are heterozygous for two genes.

B. Meiosis Explains Mendel's Law of Independent Assortment
- According to Mendel's **law of independent assortment,** the inheritance of one gene does not affect the inheritance of another gene on a different chromosome. Independent assortment occurs because homologous pairs of chromosomes align randomly during metaphase I of meiosis.

C. The Product Rule Replaces Complex Punnett Squares
- The **product rule** is an alternative to Punnett squares for following the inheritance of two or more traits at a time.

10.5 Genes on the Same Chromosome May Be Inherited Together

A. Genes on the Same Chromosome Are Linked
- **Linked genes** are located on the same chromosome. **Linkage groups** are collections of genes that are often inherited together.
- The farther apart two linked genes are on a chromosome, the more likely **crossing over** is to separate their alleles. If crossing over occurs between two alleles, some offspring will have **recombinant** genotypes; otherwise, offspring will have **parental** genotypes for the two genes.

B. Studies of Linked Genes Have Yielded Chromosome Maps
- Breeding studies reveal the crossover frequencies used to create **linkage maps**—diagrams that show the order of genes on a chromosome.

10.6 Gene Expression Can Alter Phenotypic Ratios

A. Incomplete Dominance and Codominance Add Phenotype Classes
- Heterozygotes for alleles with **incomplete dominance** have phenotypes intermediate between those of the two homozygotes. **Codominant** alleles are both expressed in a heterozygote. Figure 10.35 extends the light bulb analogy to incomplete dominance and codominance.

B. Some Inheritance Patterns Are Especially Difficult to Interpret
- A **pleiotropic** gene affects multiple phenotypes.
- When multiple proteins participate in a biochemical pathway, mutations in genes encoding any of the proteins can produce the same phenotype.
- In **epistasis,** one gene masks the effect of another.

10.7 Sex-Linked Genes Have Unique Inheritance Patterns

- Genes controlling **sex-linked** traits are on the X or Y chromosomes.

A. X and Y Chromosomes Carry Sex-Linked Genes
- In humans, the male has X and Y sex chromosomes, and the female has two X chromosomes.

B. X-Linked Recessive Disorders Affect More Males Than Females
- An **X-linked** gene passes from mother to son because the male inherits his X chromosome from his mother and his Y chromosome from his father. Scientists know of many more X-linked than **Y-linked** disorders.

C. X Inactivation Prevents "Double Dosing" of Proteins
- **X inactivation** shuts off all but one X chromosome in female mammals.

10.8 Pedigrees Show Modes of Inheritance

- **Pedigrees** trace phenotypes in families and reveal modes of inheritance.
- An **autosomal dominant** disorder can be inherited from one affected parent. An **autosomal recessive** disorder must be inherited from both parents. X-linked recessive disorders affect mostly males.

10.9 Most Traits Are Influenced by the Environment and Multiple Genes

A. The Environment Can Alter the Phenotype
- Most traits have environmental as well as genetic influences.

B. Polygenic Traits Depend on More Than One Gene
- A **polygenic trait** varies continuously in its expression.

10.10 Investigating Life: Heredity and the Hungry Hordes

- Researchers have developed a genetic test to monitor caterpillars for resistance to Bt, an insecticidal toxin produced in genetically modified cotton.

Incomplete dominance

Codominance

Heterozygous
(One nonfunctional bulb significantly reduces light level in room)

Heterozygous
(Functional lights of two colors)

Figure 10.35 Non-Mendelian Inheritance Patterns: An Analogy.

MULTIPLE CHOICE QUESTIONS

1. In the list of four terms below, which term is the *second* most inclusive?
   a. Genome
   b. Allele
   c. Chromosome
   d. Gene

2. According to Mendel, if an individual is *heterozygous* for a gene, the phenotype will correspond to that of
   a. the recessive trait alone.
   b. the dominant trait alone.
   c. a blend of the dominant and recessive traits.
   d. a wild-type trait.

3. An organism with a wild-type phenotype has
   a. the most common expression of a gene in a population.
   b. only the dominant allele for a gene.
   c. only the recessive allele for a gene.
   d. an appearance different from others in the population.

4. Each letter below represents an allele. Which of the following is an example of a dihybrid cross?
   a. $R \times R$
   b. $Rr \times Rr$
   c. $Rr Yy \times Rr Yy$
   d. $RR\ yy \times rr\ YY$

5. Which of the following is a possible gamete for an individual with the genotype $PP\ rr$?
   a. PP
   b. Pr
   c. pr
   d. rr

6. Use the product rule to determine the chance of obtaining an offspring with the genotype $Rr\ Yy$ from a dihybrid cross between parents with the genotype $Rr\ Yy$.
   a. ½
   b. ¼
   c. ⅛
   d. 1/16

7. Refer to the linkage map in figure 10.16b. A crossover event is most likely to occur between which pair of genes?
   a. w and v
   b. y and r
   c. y and w
   d. v and m

8. White cats have at least one dominant allele of the W gene, which masks the expression of all other genes that contribute to coat color. The W gene is an example of
   a. pleiotropy.
   b. incomplete dominance.
   c. codominance.
   d. epistasis.

9. Suppose a woman is a symptomless carrier of a recessive X-linked disease. If her husband has the disease, what is the chance that their first child is a girl who also has the disease?
   a. 100%
   b. 50%
   c. 25%
   d. 0

10. How does X inactivation contribute to a person's phenotype?
    a. It controls the number and kind of genes inherited on an X chromosome.
    b. It determines which X chromosome is expressed in a male.
    c. It allows for the expression of either the maternal or the paternal X in different cells.
    d. It enhances the expression of Y-linked genes in males.

Answers to these questions are in appendix A.

WRITE IT OUT

1. What advantages do pea plants and fruit flies have for studies of inheritance? Why aren't humans equally suitable?

2. Some people compare a homologous pair of chromosomes to a pair of shoes. Explain the similarity. How would you extend the analogy to the sex chromosomes for females and for males?

3. In an attempt to breed winter barley that is resistant to barley mild mosaic virus, agricultural researchers cross a susceptible domesticated strain with a resistant wild strain. The F_1 plants are all susceptible, but when the F_1 plants are crossed with each other, some of the F_2 individuals are resistant. Is the resistance allele recessive or dominant? How do you know?

4. How did Mendel use evidence from monohybrid and dihybrid crosses to deduce his laws of segregation and independent assortment? How do these laws relate to meiosis?

5. How does crossing over "unlink" genes?

6. Consider two genes that are near each other on a chromosome. After a germ cell undergoes meiosis, are the gametes likely or unlikely to contain a recombinant chromatid for these two genes? Explain.

7. Springer spaniels often suffer from canine phospho-fructokinase (PFK) deficiency. The dogs lack an enzyme that is crucial in extracting energy from glucose molecules. Affected pups have extremely weak muscles and die within weeks. A DNA test is available to identify male and female dogs that are carriers. Why would breeders wish to identify carriers if these dogs are not affected?

8. Explain how each of the following produces phenotypic ratios other than those Mendel observed: incomplete dominance, codominance, pleiotropy, epistasis.

9. Which gene on the Y chromosome triggers the development of male characteristics? What would happen if a male inherited a nonfunctional allele for this gene?

10. An individual that is genetically male develops as a female. Is this individual more or less likely to express an X-linked recessive disorder than an average female?

11. Would you expect dominant X-linked traits to affect women as often as men? Explain your answer.

12. What does X inactivation accomplish?

13. A family has an X-linked dominant form of congenital generalized hypertrichosis (excessive hairiness). Although the allele is dominant, males are more severely affected than females. Moreover, the women in the family often have asymmetrical, hairy patches on their bodies. How does X chromosome inactivation explain this observation?

14. X inactivation explains the large color patches in calico cat fur and the smaller patches in tortoiseshell cat fur. In which type of cat do you expect X inactivation occurs earlier in development? Why?

15. In the following pedigree, is the disorder's mode of inheritance autosomal dominant, autosomal recessive, or X-linked recessive? Explain your reasoning.

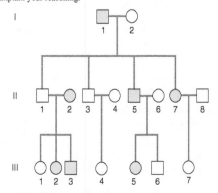

16. Explain the following "equation":

Genotype + Environment = Phenotype

17. How do heart disease and cancer illustrate diseases that reflect both genetic and environmental influences?

18. Design an experiment using twins to determine the degree to which autism is genetic or environmental.

GENETICS PROBLEMS

See pages 214 and 215 for a step-by-step guide to solving genetics problems.

1. In rose bushes, red flowers (*FF* or *Ff*) are dominant to white flowers (*ff*). A true-breeding red rose is crossed with a white rose; two flowers of the F_1 generation are subsequently crossed. What will be the most common genotype of the F_2 generation?

2. In Mexican hairless dogs, a dominant allele confers hairlessness. However, inheriting two dominant alleles is lethal; the fetus dies before birth. Suppose a breeder mates two dogs that are heterozygous for the hair allele. Draw a Punnett square to predict the genotypic and phenotypic ratios of the puppies that are born.

> **Activity**
> Lethal Alleles

3. A species of ornamental fish comes in two colors; red is dominant and gray is recessive. Emily owns a red fish, and she wants to know its genotype. Therefore, she mates her pet with a gray fish. If 50 of the 100 babies are red, what is the genotype of Emily's fish?

4. Two lizards have green skin and large dewlaps (genotype *GgDd*). (a) If 32 offspring are born, how many of the offspring are expected to be homozygous recessive for both genes? (b) What proportion of the offspring will have the dominant phenotype for both traits? (Assume that the traits assort independently.)

5. A fern with genotype *AABbCcddEe* mates with another fern with genotype *aaBbCCDdee*. What proportion of the offspring will be heterozygous for all genes? (Assume the genes assort independently.) Hint: Use the product rule.

6. Genes *Q*, *R*, and *S* are on the same chromosome. The crossover frequency between *S* and *Q* is 5%, the crossover frequency between *Q* and *R* is 30%, and the crossover frequency between *R* and *S* is 35%. Use this information to create a linkage map for the chromosome.

7. Three babies are born in the hospital on the same day. Baby X has type B blood; Baby Y has type AB blood; Baby Z has type O blood. Use the information in the following table to determine which baby belongs to which couple. (Assume that all individuals are homozygous dominant for the *H* gene.)

Couple	Father	Blood type	Mother	Blood type
1	Logan	B	Leslie	AB
2	Sam	A	Casey	A
3	Jordan	O	Taylor	B

8. In fraggles, males are genotype XY and females are XX. Silly, a male fraggle, has a rare X-linked recessive disorder that makes him walk backwards. He mates with Lilly, who is a carrier for the disorder. What proportion of their male offspring will walk backwards?

9. A woman is a carrier for red–green color blindness. Her genotype is X^cX, where X^c indicates the chromosome with the allele conferring

color blindness and X indicates the chromosome with the normal color vision allele. Very early in development, the X^c chromosome was inactivated in the first cell of her right eye. At the same time, the normal X chromosome was inactivated in the first cell of her left eye. Is she color blind in her left eye, her right eye, both eyes, or neither eye?

PULL IT TOGETHER

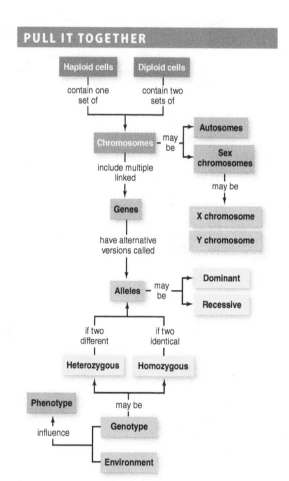

Figure 10.36 Pull It Together: Patterns of Inheritance.

Refer to figure 10.36 and the chapter content to answer the following questions.

1. Which cells in the human body are haploid? Which cells are diploid?

2. Explain the effects of a mutation, using *allele, dominant, recessive, genotype,* and *phenotype* in your answer.

3. Add *meiosis, gametes, incomplete dominance, codominance, pleiotropy,* and *epistasis* to this concept map.

HOW TO SOLVE A GENETICS PROBLEM

One Gene

Sample problem: Phenylketonuria (PKU) is an autosomal recessive disorder. If a man with PKU marries a woman who is a symptomless carrier, what is the probability that their first child will be born with PKU?

1. **Write a key.** Pick ONE letter to represent the gene in your problem. Use the capital form of your letter to symbolize the dominant allele; use the lowercase letter to symbolize the recessive allele.

   Sample: The dominant allele is *K;* the recessive allele is *k.*

2. **Summarize the problem's information.** Make a table listing the phenotypes and genotypes of both parents.

   Sample:

	Male	Female
Phenotype	Has PKU	No PKU (carrier)
Genotype	*kk*	*Kk*

3. **Sketch the parental chromosomes and gametes.** Use the genotypes in your table to draw the alleles onto chromosomes. Then draw short arrows to show the homologous chromosomes moving into separate gametes for each parent.

   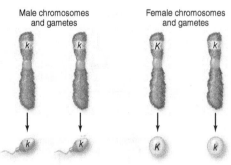

   Male chromosomes and gametes

   Female chromosomes and gametes

4. **Make a Punnett square.** Arrange the gametes you sketched in step 3 along the edges of the square, and fill in the genotypes of the offspring.

   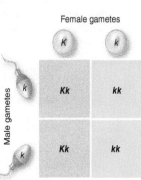

   Female gametes

   Male gametes

	K	k
k	Kk	kk
k	Kk	kk

5. **Calculate the genotypic ratio.** Count the number of squares that contain each offspring genotype.

   Sample: 2 *Kk* : 2 *kk*

6. **Calculate the phenotypic ratio.** Count the number of squares that contain each offspring phenotype.

   Sample: 2 PKU carriers : 2 PKU sufferers

7. **Calculate the probability of each phenotype.** Divide each number in step 6 by 4 (the total number of squares) and multiply by 100.

   Sample: 50% probability that a child will be a carrier; 50% probability that a child will have PKU

Two Genes (Punnett Square)

Sample problem: A student collects pollen (male sex cells) from a pea plant that is homozygous recessive for the genes controlling seed form and seed color. She uses the pollen to fertilize a plant that is heterozygous for both genes. What is the probability that an offspring plant has the same genotype and phenotype as the male parent? Assume the genes are not linked.

1. **Write a key.** Pick ONE letter to represent each of the genes in your problem. Use the capital form of your letter to symbolize the dominant allele; use the lowercase letter to symbolize the recessive allele.

   Sample: For seed form, the dominant allele (round) is *R;* the recessive allele (wrinkled) is *r;* for seed color, the dominant allele (yellow) is *G;* the recessive allele (green) is *g.*

2. **Summarize the problem's information.** Make a table listing the phenotypes and genotypes of both parents.

   Sample:

	Male	Female
Phenotype	Wrinkled, green	Round, yellow
Genotype	*rr gg*	*Rr Gg*

3. **Sketch the parental chromosomes and gametes.** Use the genotypes in your table to draw the alleles onto two sets of chromosomes, one for each parent. The law of independent assortment means that you need to draw all possible configurations. So redraw the chromosomes, this time switching the order of the alleles in one pair. Then draw short arrows to show the chromosomes separating, and sketch the four possible gametes for each parent. Depending on the parents' genotypes, some of the gametes produced by a parent may have the same genotype.

   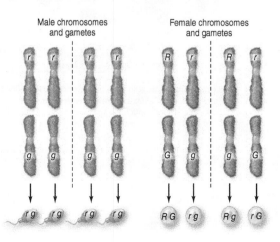

   Male chromosomes and gametes

   Female chromosomes and gametes

Activity
Genetics Problems

CHECK OUT the entire collection of interactive genetics problems online!

4. **Make a Punnett square.** Arrange the gametes you sketched in step 3 along the edges of the square, and fill in the genotypes of the offspring.

Female gametes

	R G	r g	R g	r G
r g	Rr Gg	rr gg	Rr gg	rr Gg
r g	Rr Gg	rr gg	Rr gg	rr Gg
r g	Rr Gg	rr gg	Rr gg	rr Gg
r g	Rr Gg	rr gg	Rr gg	rr Gg

Male gametes

5. **Calculate the genotypic ratio.** Count the number of squares that contain each offspring genotype.

Sample: 4 *Rr Gg* : 4 *rr gg* : 4 *Rr gg* : 4 *rr Gg*

6. **Calculate the phenotypic ratio.** Count the number of squares that correspond to each possible phenotype combination.

Sample: 4 round, yellow : 4 wrinkled, green : 4 round, green : 4 wrinkled, yellow

7. **Calculate the probability of each phenotype.** Divide each number in step 6 by 16 (the total number of squares) and multiply by 100.

Sample: 25% probability that an offspring has the same genotype and phenotype as the male parent.

Two Genes (Product Rule)

The product rule is a simpler way to solve a multi-gene problem and eliminates the need for a large Punnett square. To use the product rule in this case, first calculate the probability that the parents (*rr* × *Rr*) produce an offspring with genotype *rr* (½, or 50%). Then calculate the chance that *gg* × *Gg* parents produce a *gg* offspring (½, or 50%). Multiply the two probabilities to calculate the probability that both events occur simultaneously: ½ × ½ = ¼, or 25%. See section 10.4 for more on the product rule.

X-Linked Gene

Sample problem: Hemophilia is caused by an X-linked recessive allele. If a man who has hemophilia marries a healthy woman who is not a carrier, what is the chance that their child will have hemophilia?

1. **Write a key.** Pick ONE letter to represent the gene in your problem. Use the capital form of your letter to symbolize the dominant allele; use the lowercase letter to symbolize the recessive allele.

Sample: The dominant allele is *H;* the recessive allele is *h*. Because these alleles are on the X chromosome, inheritance will differ between males and females. It is therefore best to designate the chromosomes and alleles together as X^H and X^h.

2. **Summarize the problem's information.** Make a table listing the phenotypes and genotypes of both parents.

Sample:

	Male	**Female**
Phenotype	Has hemophilia	Healthy
Genotype	$X^h Y$	$X^H X^H$

3. **Sketch the parental chromosomes and gametes.** Use the genotypes in your table to draw the alleles onto chromosomes. Then draw short arrows to show the chromosomes moving into separate gametes for each parent.

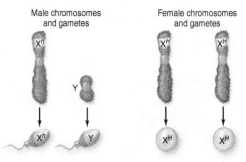

Male chromosomes and gametes   Female chromosomes and gametes

4. **Make a Punnett square.** Arrange the gametes you sketched in step 3 along the edges of the square; fill in the genotypes of the offspring.

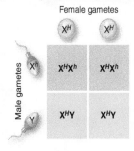

Female gametes

	X^H	X^H
X^h	$X^H X^h$	$X^H X^h$
Y	$X^H Y$	$X^H Y$

Male gametes

5. **Calculate the genotypic ratio.** Count the number of squares that contain each offspring genotype.

Sample: 2 $X^H X^h$: 2 $X^H Y$

6. **Calculate the phenotypic ratio.** Count the number of squares that correspond to each possible phenotype.

Sample: 2 female carriers : 2 healthy males

7. **Calculate the probability of each phenotype.** Divide each number in step 6 by 4 (the total number of squares) and multiply by 100.

Sample: 50% probability that a child will be a female carrier; 50% probability that a child will be a healthy male. No child, male or female, will have hemophilia.

DNA Technology

Carbon Copies. Tabouli, left, plays with her sibling, Baba Ganoush. In an effort to publicize its pet gene banking and cloning services, a private company produced the kittens by cloning a one-year-old cat.

Enhance your study |BIOLOGY
of this chapter with practice quizzes,
animations and videos, answer keys,
and downloadable study tools.
www.mhhe.com/hoefnagels

The Clones Are Here

IMAGINE BEING ABLE TO GROW A NEW INDIVIDUAL, GENETICALLY IDENTICAL TO YOURSELF, FROM A BIT OF SKIN OR THE ROOT OF A HAIR. Although humans cannot reproduce in this way, many organisms do the equivalent. They develop parts of themselves into genetically identical individuals—clones—that then detach and live independently.

Cloning, or asexual reproduction, has been a part of life since the first cell arose billions of years ago. Long before sex evolved, each individual simply reproduced by itself, without a partner to contribute half the offspring's genetic information.

In its simplest form, cloning consists of the division of a single cell. In bacteria, archaea, and other single-celled organisms, the cell's DNA replicates, and then the cell splits into two identical, individual organisms (see chapter 8).

Cloning is also a natural part of life for many species of plants, fungi, and animals. Hobbyists and commercial plant growers clone everything from fruit trees to African violets by cultivating cuttings from a parent plant's stems, leaves, and roots. Many fungi also are phenomenal breeders, asexually producing countless microscopic spores on bread, cheese, and every other imaginable food supply. Asexual reproduction is much less common in animals, but it does occur. For example, sponges and jellyfishes "bud" genetically identical clones that break away from the parent.

Mammals, however, normally reproduce only sexually. That is why biologists attracted worldwide attention in the 1990s by creating a lamb called Dolly, the first clone of an adult mammal (see section 11.3B). Since that time, many other mammals—but not humans—have been cloned.

As you will see, cloning is just one of many practical applications arising from knowledge of DNA's structure and function. Biologists have also created genetically modified organisms that have countless uses but raise controversial ethical issues. Other technologies allow us to compare the DNA sequences of hundreds of species, including our closest relatives, the chimpanzees (see section 11.5); such studies help us better understand our own genes. DNA profiling has given the criminal justice system a powerful tool for proving a suspect's guilt or innocence. Medical professionals can detect genetic diseases with unprecedented accuracy. This chapter describes all of these examples, along with a sampling of the many other uses of DNA technology.

LEARNING OUTLINE

 11.1 DNA Technology Is Changing the World

 11.2 DNA Technology's Tools Apply to Individual Genes or Entire Genomes
- A. Transgenic Organisms Contain DNA from Other Species
- B. DNA Sequencing Reveals the Order of Bases
- C. PCR Replicates DNA in a Test Tube
- D. DNA Profiling Detects Genetic Differences

 11.3 Stem Cells and Cloning Add New Ways to Copy Cells and Organisms
- A. Stem Cells Divide to Form Multiple Cell Types
- B. Cloning Creates Identical Copies of an Organism

 11.4 Many Medical Tests and Procedures Use DNA Technology
- A. DNA Probes Detect Specific Sequences
- B. Preimplantation Genetic Diagnosis Can Help Prevent Some Diseases
- C. Genetic Testing Can Detect Existing Diseases
- D. Gene Therapy Uses DNA to Treat Disease
- E. Medical Uses of DNA Technology Raise Many Ethical Issues

 11.5 Investigating Life: What Makes Us Human?

LEARN HOW TO LEARN

Vary Your Study Plan for Healthy Learning

Your study sessions may become stale if you do the same things over and over. After all, it is difficult to focus after watching countless animations or listening to hours of podcasts. Instead, try switching between strategies that are passive (watching and listening) and those that are active (drawing and writing). You might watch a video on Punnett squares and then try to draw one yourself. Or you could listen to a podcast about cloning and then write a paragraph describing the process in your own words. Keeping variety in your study plan will help you stay engaged.

11.1 DNA Technology Is Changing the World

The title of this section is not an exaggeration: DNA-based technologies have affected nearly every imaginable facet of society. **DNA technology** is a broad term that usually means the manipulation of genes for some practical purpose. This chapter describes some of the ways in which DNA technology has become a powerful tool in research, medicine, agriculture, criminal justice, and many other fields.

DNA technology became possible only after biologists learned the structure and function of DNA. Recall from chapter 7 that the DNA double helix is composed of nucleotides and that the function of DNA is to provide the "recipes" for the cell's proteins (figure 11.1). As described in chapter 8, enzymes copy these recipes as a cell prepares to divide, so that nearly every cell in a multicellular organism carries the same DNA sequence.

We have also learned that each person inherits a unique DNA sequence from his or her parents. As a result, with the exception of identical twins, each person is genetically different. Yet chapter 10 showed how we can trace the inheritance of particular alleles from child to parent to grandparent, and so on. Using this same logic, it is easy to see the power of DNA as a tool for tracing evolutionary history. Throughout the billions of years of life's history, descent with modification has produced countless unique species, each with its own adaptations but still displaying its relationship to the others in its DNA.

DNA technology applies these facts (and many more) to open entirely new ways to learn about life's history, to prevent and relieve human suffering, to protect the environment, and to enforce the law. As you will see, many of the more familiar applications of DNA technology are in medicine. For example, technicians can test a person's DNA for many alleles associated with inherited illnesses, marking a huge advance in disease screening and diagnosis. Stem cells often make headlines as well, especially because the ability to manipulate gene expression in these cells may offer treatments for diseases that currently have no cure.

Many people also know that genetically modified organisms (often abbreviated GMOs) have made their way into the human food supply, mostly in the form of herbicide- and insect-resistant crop plants. Yet another familiar use of DNA technology is DNA profiling, which can help solve crimes or match parents with their offspring.

As helpful as DNA technology can be, the ability to manipulate DNA also carries both risks and ethical questions. This chapter describes not only some of the tools and applications but also some of the downsides of DNA technology.

11.1   MASTERING CONCEPTS

1. What is DNA technology?
2. In what fields is DNA technology useful?

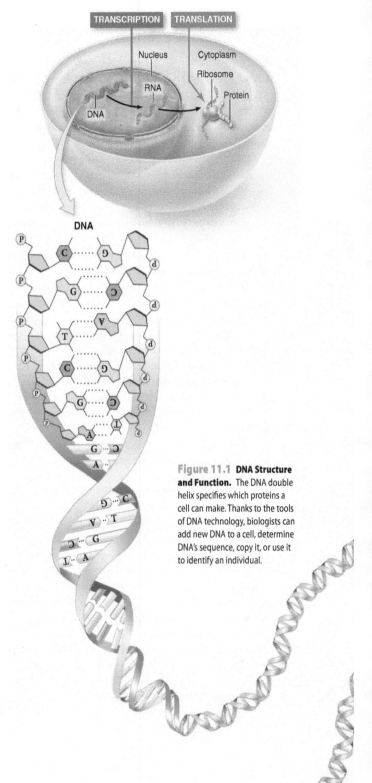

Figure 11.1 DNA Structure and Function. The DNA double helix specifies which proteins a cell can make. Thanks to the tools of DNA technology, biologists can add new DNA to a cell, determine DNA's sequence, copy it, or use it to identify an individual.

11.2 DNA Technology's Tools Apply to Individual Genes or Entire Genomes

Virtual Lab
Gene
Splicing

Some applications of DNA technology require moving a gene from one cell to another; others require comparisons among multiple genomes. This section explores a few of the tools that biologists use to manipulate everything from short stretches of DNA to the entire genetic makeup of a cell.

A. Transgenic Organisms Contain DNA from Other Species

As we saw in chapter 7, virtually all species use the same genetic code. It therefore makes sense that one type of organism can express a gene from another species, even if the two are distantly related. Biologists take advantage of this fact by coaxing cells to take up **recombinant DNA,** which is genetic material that has been spliced together from multiple organisms. A **transgenic** organism is an individual that receives recombinant DNA.

Scientists first accomplished this feat of "genetic engineering" in *E. coli* in the 1970s, but many microbes, plants, and animals have since been genetically modified. When cells containing the recombinant DNA divide, all of their daughter cells also harbor the new genes. These transgenic organisms express their new genes just as they do their own, producing the desired protein along with all of the others that they normally make. (Note that new varieties of animals and plants may also come from selective breeding. These organisms, however, are not transgenic, as described in the Burning Question on page 220.) ① *E. coli,* p. 354

Transgenic Bacteria and Yeasts   How do scientists create a transgenic organism? The first step is to obtain DNA from a source cell—usually a bacterium, plant, or animal (figure 11.2, step 1). The researcher may synthesize the DNA in the laboratory or extract it directly from the source cell. Extracting the DNA poses a problem, however, if the gene's source is a eukaryotic cell and the recipient will be a bacterium. Bacterial cells cannot remove introns from mRNA, so the DNA would encode a defective protein in bacteria.

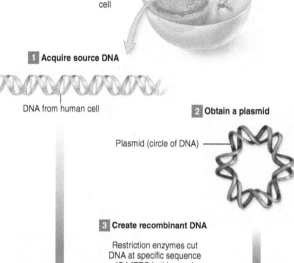

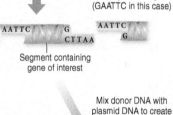

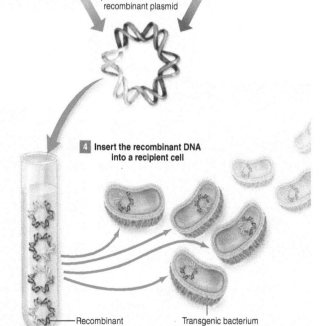

Figure 11.2 Creating Transgenic Bacteria. The first steps in creating a transgenic bacterium are to (*1*) isolate source DNA and (*2*) select a plasmid or other cloning vector. (*3*) Researchers use the same restriction enzyme to cut DNA from the donor cell and the plasmid. When the pieces are mixed, the "sticky ends" of the DNA fragments join, forming recombinant plasmids. (*4*) After the plasmid is delivered into a bacterium, it is mass-produced as the bacterium divides.

Animation
Transgenic Bacteria

Researchers therefore first isolate a mature mRNA molecule with the introns already removed. Then, they use an enzyme called **reverse transcriptase** to make a DNA copy of the mRNA. (As described in chapter 16, retroviruses such as HIV use this enzyme when they infect cells.) The resulting complementary DNA, or cDNA, encodes the eukaryotic protein but leaves out the introns.

Animation
cDNA

Next, the researcher chooses a **cloning vector,** a self-replicating genetic structure that will carry the source DNA into the recipient cell. (In molecular biology, "cloning" means to make many identical copies of a DNA sequence.) A common type of cloning vector is a **plasmid,** which is a small circle of double-stranded DNA separate from the cell's chromosome (figure 11.2, step 2). Viruses are also used as vectors. They are altered so that they transport DNA but cannot cause disease.

The next step is to create a recombinant plasmid (figure 11.2, step 3). To create DNA fragments that can be spliced together, researchers use **restriction enzymes,** which are proteins that cut double-stranded DNA at a specific base sequence. Some restriction enzymes generate single-stranded ends that "stick" to each other by complementary base pairing. The natural function of restriction enzymes is to protect bacteria by cutting up DNA from infecting viruses. Biologists, however, use them to cut and paste segments of DNA from different sources. When plasmid and donor DNA is cut with the same restriction enzyme and the fragments are mixed, the single-stranded sticky ends of some plasmids form base pairs with those of the donor DNA. Another enzyme, DNA ligase, seals the segments together.

Animation
Restriction
Enzymes

Next, the researchers move the cloning vector with its recombinant DNA into a recipient cell (figure 11.2, step 4). Zapping a bacterial cell with electricity opens temporary holes that admit naked DNA. Alternatively, "gene guns" shoot DNA-coated pellets directly into cells. DNA can also be packaged inside a fatty bubble called a liposome that fuses with the recipient cell's membrane, or it can be hitched to a virus that subsequently infects the recipient cell.

In the pharmaceutical industry, transgenic bacteria produce dozens of drugs, including human insulin to treat diabetes, blood clotting factors to treat hemophilia, immune system biochemicals, and fertility hormones. Other genetically modified bacteria produce the amino acid phenylalanine, which is part of the artificial sweetener aspartame. Still others degrade petroleum, pesticides, and other soil pollutants. ⓘ *artificial sweeteners,* p. 40

Single-celled fungi (yeasts) can also be genetically modified. For example, transgenic yeast cells produce a milk-curdling enzyme called chymosin used by many U.S. cheese producers. The baking, brewing, and wine industries, which rely on yeasts for fermentation, may increasingly use transgenic yeast cells in the future. ⓘ *fermentation,* p. 115

Transgenic Plants   One tool for introducing new genes into plant cells is a bacterium called *Agrobacterium tumefaciens* (figure 11.3). In nature, these bacteria enter the plant at a wound and inject a plasmid into the host's cells. The plasmid normally

encodes proteins that stimulate the infected plant cells to divide rapidly, producing a tumorlike gall where the bacteria live. (The name of the plasmid, Ti, stands for "tumor inducing.")

Scientists can replace some of the Ti plasmid's own genes with other DNA, such as a gene encoding a protein that confers herbicide resistance (figure 11.3, step 1). They allow the transgenic *Agrobacterium* to inject these recombinant plasmids into plant cells (step 2). All plants that grow from the infected cells should express the new herbicide-resistance gene (step 3). The farmer who plants the crop can therefore spray the field with herbicides, killing weeds without harming the genetically modified plants.

Biologists have used a similar technique to produce corn and cotton varieties that produce their own insecticides (see section 10.10). The insect-killing protein originated in a bacterium called *Bacillus thuringiensis*, abbreviated Bt. Any insect that nibbles on a plant expressing the Bt protein dies. These genetically modified

BurningQuestion

Is selective breeding the same as genetic engineering?

Simply put, the answer to this question is no. Selective breeding, also called artificial selection, yields new varieties of plants and animals by selecting for or against traits that already occur in a population. For example, consider the rainbow of carrot colors shown at left. To create a carrot variety lacking orange pigments, researchers allowed the rare plants with pale carrots to breed only among themselves. Over many generations, the result was a line of white carrots. Likewise, the researchers selected for purple or red carrots by breeding only those unusual plants with darkly pigmented roots. All of the carrots pictured are the products of selective breeding.

Introducing new DNA—genetic engineering—is a totally different way to create new plant and animal varieties. We have already seen, for instance, that Bt corn plants contain genes that were originally isolated from bacteria (see section 10.10). Likewise, some transgenic bacteria produce insulin and other human proteins, thanks to our ability to transfer DNA from one species to another.

One additional technique for developing new varieties of plants and animals is random mutagenesis. Researchers use chemicals or radiation to induce genetic mutations in an organism's DNA, which sometimes causes interesting new characteristics to arise. Figure 7.23 shows three plant varieties that owe their existence to mutagenesis. This technique falls somewhere in the middle of the spectrum between selective breeding and transgenic technology. It does not rely on preexisting mutations, as does selective breeding, but it is much less controlled than transgenic technology.

Submit your burning question to
Marielle.Hoefnagels@mheducation.com

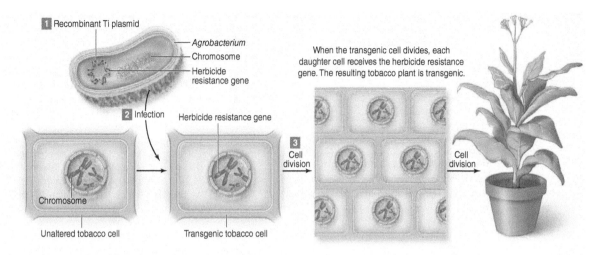

Figure 11.3 **Creating a Transgenic Plant.** (*1*) This genetically modified *Agrobacterium* cell contains a recombinant Ti plasmid encoding a gene that confers herbicide resistance. (*2*) The bacterium infects a tobacco plant cell, inserting the Ti plasmid into the plant cell's DNA. (*3*) The transgenic plant cells can be grown into tobacco plants that express the herbicide resistance gene in every cell.

Animation Transgenic Plants

Bt crops save farmers time and money because they greatly reduce the need for sprayed insecticides.

Besides tolerating herbicides or producing insecticides, transgenic crop plants may also resist viral infections, survive harsh environmental conditions, or contain nutrients that they otherwise wouldn't. Transgenic potato plants, for example, may someday be used to produce vaccines, and tobacco plants enhanced with bacterial enzymes may help degrade leftover explosives at contaminated military installations.

Video Using Transgenic Plants

Transgenic Animals
So far, we have described the use of DNA technology to genetically modify bacteria and plants. Biologists use a different technique to create transgenic mice and other animals. Typically, they pack recombinant DNA into viruses that can infect a gamete or fertilized egg. As the transgenic animal develops, it carries the foreign genes in every cell.

Video Transgenic Mice

Transgenic animals have many applications. A transgenic mouse "model" for a human gene can reveal how a disease begins, enabling researchers to develop drugs that treat the disease in its early stages. Transgenic farm animals can secrete human proteins in their milk or semen, yielding abundant, pure supplies of otherwise rare substances that are useful as drugs. Transgenic salmon have been engineered for rapid growth, so the fish can reach market faster than their wild relatives. On a more whimsical note, a glow-in-the-dark zebra fish was the first genetically modified house pet (figure 11.4).

Ethical Issues
Although transgenic organisms have many practical uses, some people question whether their benefits outweigh their potential dangers. Some object to the "unnatural" practice of combining genes from organisms that would never breed in nature. Others fear that ecological disaster could result if genetically modified organisms displace closely related species in the wild. Still others worry that unfamiliar protein combinations in transgenic crops could trigger food allergies. Finally, genetically modified seeds may be expensive, reflecting the high cost of developing and testing the plants. The farmers who stand to gain the most from transgenic plants are often unable to afford them.

 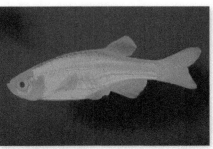

Figure 11.4 **Transgenic Animal.** Glow-in-the-dark zebra fish have been genetically altered to produce a fluorescent protein.

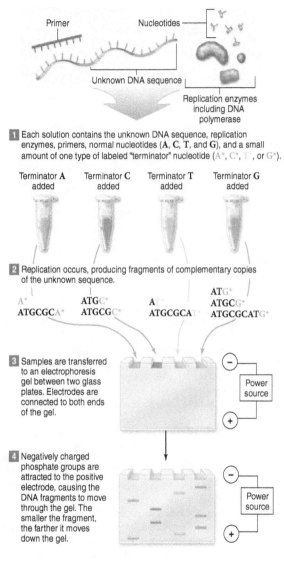

1 Each solution contains the unknown DNA sequence, replication enzymes, primers, normal nucleotides (**A**, **C**, **T**, and **G**), and a small amount of one type of labeled "terminator" nucleotide (A*, C*, T*, or G*).

2 Replication occurs, producing fragments of complementary copies of the unknown sequence.

3 Samples are transferred to an electrophoresis gel between two glass plates. Electrodes are connected to both ends of the gel.

4 Negatively charged phosphate groups are attracted to the positive electrode, causing the DNA fragments to move through the gel. The smaller the fragment, the farther it moves down the gel.

5 The fragments are read off by size, and the original sequence can be deduced.

Deduce original sequence from complement

Figure 11.5 DNA Sequencing. The DNA polymerase enzyme makes complementary copies of an unknown DNA sequence. But the copies are terminated early, thanks to chemically modified "terminator" nucleotides in the reaction mix. Placing the fragments in order by size reveals the sequence.

B. DNA Sequencing Reveals the Order of Bases

Scientists often want to know the nucleotide sequences of genes, chromosomes, or entire genomes. Researchers can use DNA sequence information to predict protein sequences, as described in chapter 7, or they can compare DNA sequences among species to determine evolutionary relationships. How do investigators get the DNA sequence information they need?

Modern DNA sequencing instruments use a highly automated version of a basic technique Frederick Sanger developed in 1977 (figure 11.5). Step 1 in the figure shows the components of the reaction mixture. The DNA polymerase enzyme generates a series of DNA fragments that are complementary to the DNA being sequenced. The reaction mixture also contains short, single-stranded pieces of DNA called primers, which are required by DNA polymerase to begin replication. Also included are normal nucleotides, supplemented with low concentrations of specially modified "terminator" nucleotides. Each time DNA polymerase incorporates one of these modified nucleotides instead of a normal one, the new DNA chain stops growing. ⓘ *DNA replication*, p. 150

Step 2 in figure 11.5 shows the products of the replication reactions: a group of fragments that differ in length from one another by one end base. Once a collection of such pieces is generated, a technique called **electrophoresis** can be used to separate the fragments by size. The researcher can deduce the sequence by "reading" the fragments from smallest to largest (steps 3 through 5).

Sanger used electrophoresis and radioactive labels to sort and visualize the fragments. Researchers today use a slightly different technique to sort the fragments by size, and fluorescent labels mark each of the four terminator nucleotides. The data appear as a sequential readout of the wavelengths of the fluorescence from the labels (figure 11.6).

The most famous application of DNA sequencing technology has been the Human Genome Project. This worldwide effort was aimed at sequencing all 3.2 billion base pairs of the human genome. This sequence, which was completed in 2003, revealed unexpected complexities. For example, although our genome includes approximately 25,000 protein-encoding genes, our cells can produce some 400,000 different proteins. Furthermore, only about 1.5% of the human genome actually encodes protein.

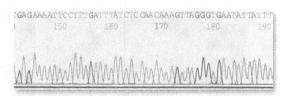

Figure 11.6 Modern Way to Read DNA. A computerized readout of a DNA sequence. The sequencing machine has sorted the DNA fragments by size and recorded the wavelength emitted by each nucleotide's fluorescent label.

How can so few genes specify so many proteins? Part of the answer lies in introns. By removing different combinations of introns from an mRNA molecule, a cell can produce several proteins from one gene—a departure from the old idea that each gene encodes exactly one protein. So far, no one understands exactly how a cell "decides" which introns to remove. ⓘ *introns*, p. 129

And what is the function of the 98.5% of our genome that does not encode proteins? Some of it is regulatory, such as the enhancers that control gene expression. In addition, much of our DNA is transcribed to rRNA, tRNA, and microRNA (see chapter 7). Chromosomes also contain many **pseudogenes,** DNA sequences that are very similar to protein-encoding genes and that are transcribed but whose mRNA is not translated into protein. Pseudogenes may be remnants of old genes that once functioned in our nonhuman ancestors; eventually they mutated too far from the normal sequence to encode a working protein.

The human genome is also riddled with highly repetitive sequences that have no known function. The most abundant types of repeats are transposons (see section 7.7B), DNA sequences that can "jump" within the genome. Transposons make up about 45% of human DNA. The genome also contains many tandem repeats (or "satellite DNAs"). These sequences consist of one or more bases repeated many times without interruption, such as CACACA or ATTCGATTCG. The exact number of repeats varies from person to person. As described in section 11.2D, DNA profiling technology measures variation in these areas.

Researchers are comparing the human genome to the DNA sequences of dozens of other species, from bacteria and archaea to protists, fungi, plants, and other animals. The similarities and differences have yielded unprecedented insights into the genes that unite all life and those that make each species unique. The Investigating Life essay in section 11.5 highlights one example of what biologists can learn by comparing the human genome with that of the chimpanzee, our closest living relative.

C. PCR Replicates DNA in a Test Tube

An extremely powerful and useful tool, the **polymerase chain reaction (PCR)** taps into a cell's DNA copying machinery to rapidly produce millions of copies of a DNA sequence of interest. Thanks to PCR, trace amounts of DNA extracted from a single hair or a few skin cells left at a crime scene can yield enough genetic material to reveal a person's unique DNA profile.

PCR replicates a selected sequence of DNA in a test tube. As illustrated in step 1 of figure 11.7, a PCR reaction tube includes the target DNA sequence to be replicated, DNA polymerase enzymes, a supply of the four types of DNA nucleotides, and two types of short, laboratory-made primers that are complementary to opposite ends of the target sequence.

PCR occurs in an automated device called a thermal cycler that controls key temperature changes. The reaction begins when heat separates the two strands of the target DNA (figure 11.7, step 2). Next, the temperature is lowered, and the short primers attach to the separated target strands by complementary base pairing (step 3). DNA polymerase adds nucleotides to the primers and builds sequences complementary to the target sequence

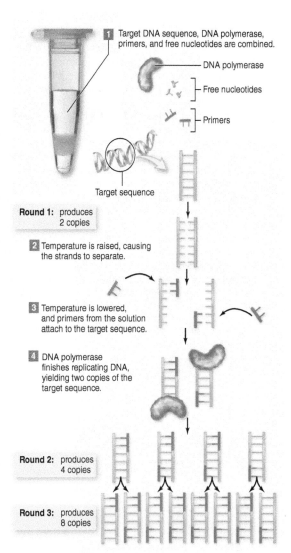

1 Target DNA sequence, DNA polymerase, primers, and free nucleotides are combined.

DNA polymerase

Free nucleotides

Primers

Target sequence

Round 1: produces 2 copies

2 Temperature is raised, causing the strands to separate.

3 Temperature is lowered, and primers from the solution attach to the target sequence.

4 DNA polymerase finishes replicating DNA, yielding two copies of the target sequence.

Round 2: produces 4 copies

Round 3: produces 8 copies

Figure 11.7 Polymerase Chain Reaction. A heat-stable DNA polymerase enzyme uses primers and plenty of nucleotides to produce millions of copies of the target sequence.

Animation PCR

(step 4). The new strands then act as templates in the next round of replication, which is initiated immediately by raising the temperature to separate the strands once more. The number of pieces of DNA doubles with every round of PCR.

Figure It Out

Suppose a researcher needs a million copies of a viral gene. She decides to use PCR on a sample of fluid containing one copy of the gene. If one round of PCR takes 2 minutes, how long will it take the researcher to obtain her million-fold amplification?

Answer: Producing 1 million copies would take 20 rounds, or 40 minutes.

The double-stranded DNA molecules become "unzipped" at about 95°C, which is nearly the boiling point of water. This temperature would denature most DNA polymerase enzymes, but PCR uses a heat-tolerant variety such as *Taq* polymerase. This enzyme is produced by *Thermus aquaticus,* a bacterium that inhabits hot springs.

Since its invention in the 1980s, PCR has found an enormous variety of applications (see the Burning Question on the facing page). Forensic scientists often work with DNA samples that are too tiny to analyze. With PCR, however, they can make thousands or millions of copies of a particular sequence. Once amplified, the DNA can easily be examined to help establish family relationships, identify human remains, convict criminals, and exonerate the falsely accused. When used to amplify the nucleic acids of microorganisms, viruses, and other parasites, PCR is important in agriculture, veterinary medicine, environmental science, and human health care. In genetics, PCR is both a crucial basic research tool and a way to identify known disease-causing genes in a cell's genome. Evolutionary biologists use PCR to amplify DNA from long-dead plants and animals. The list goes on and on.

PCR's greatest weakness, ironically, is its extreme sensitivity. A blood sample contaminated by leftover DNA from a previous run or by a stray eyelash dropped from the person running the reaction can yield a false result.

D. DNA Profiling Detects Genetic Differences

Tutorial
DNA Profiling

On average, each person's DNA sequence differs from that of a nonrelative by just one nucleotide out of 1000. Finding these small differences by sequencing and comparing entire genomes would be time-consuming, tedious, costly, and impractical. Instead, **DNA profiling** uses just the most variable parts of the genome to detect genetic differences between individuals.

The most common approach to DNA profiling is to examine **short tandem repeats (STRs),** which are sequences of a few nucleotides that are repeated in noncoding regions of DNA. People within a population have different numbers of these repeats. Figure 11.8 shows an STR site on chromosome 5 for three men. The first man has seven copies of the STR on the chromosome

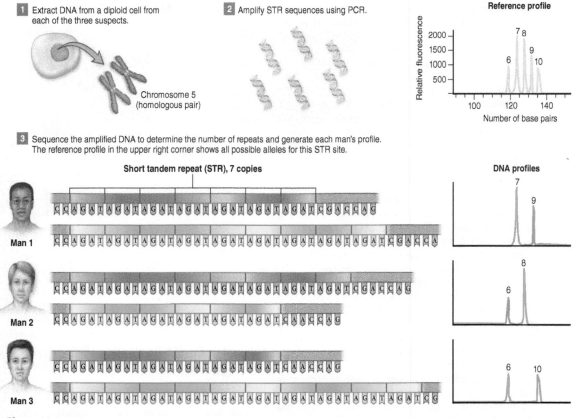

Figure 11.8   DNA Profiling. The human genome contains regions of short tandem repeats (STRs) that are genetically variable. DNA profiling techniques detect differences in the number of repeats at multiple STRs; this figure illustrates one STR site. [1] DNA extracted from cells of each man is [2] amplified using PCR. [3] Sequencing the DNA reveals each man's pattern at this STR site.

BurningQuestion

What are the uses of DNA testing?

DNA testing has so many practical applications that it is impossible to fully answer this question in a few paragraphs. Listed here, however, are a few uses that are not already described in the chapter.

In criminal justice, investigators sometimes use DNA profiling to generate leads when they have no suspects. They compare DNA collected from a crime scene with a database of DNA profiles. A partial match to someone whose DNA profile is on file can lead investigators to a close relative who committed the crime.

Many people also use DNA to learn more about their families. DNA testing can verify that a man is the father of a child or determine whether newborn twins are identical or fraternal. And genealogical DNA testing can use hundreds of thousands of variable DNA sequences in the human genome to paint a portrait of a family's ethnic history.

Food safety increasingly relies on DNA testing as well. In 2013, for example, DNA testing revealed that some products labeled as 100% beef in Europe actually contained ground horsemeat or pork. Researchers can also use DNA to verify other claims on food labels, notably the absence of potentially dangerous allergens such as peanuts.

Submit your burning question to:

Marielle.Hoefnagels@mheducation.com

that he inherited from one of his parents; he has nine copies on his other chromosome. His genotype for this STR is therefore "7, 9." The other two men have different genotypes.

To generate a DNA profile, a technician extracts DNA from a person's cells (figure 11.8, step 1) and uses PCR to amplify the DNA at each of 13 STR sites, leaving the rest of the DNA alone (step 2). A fluorescent label is incorporated into the DNA at the STR sites during the PCR reaction. The technician can then use electrophoresis and a fluorescence imaging system to determine the number of repeats at each site (step 3).

Statistical analysis plays a large role in DNA profiling. For example, suppose that DNA extracted from a hair found on a murder victim's body matches DNA from a suspect at all 13 STR sites. What is the probability that the two matching DNA

patterns come from the same person—the suspect—rather than from two individuals who happen to share the same DNA sequences? To find out, investigators consult databases that compile the frequency of each STR variant in the population. The statistical analysis suggests that the probability that any two unrelated individuals have the same pattern at all 13 STR markers is one in 250 trillion.

Conversely, a suspect can use dissimilar DNA profiles as evidence of his or her innocence. Since 1989, DNA analysis of stored evidence has proved the innocence of more than 300 people serving time in prison for violent crimes they did not commit (figure 11.9).

In addition to STRs in nuclear DNA, analysis of mitochondrial DNA is also sometimes useful. Mitochondrial DNA is typically only about 16,500 base pairs long, far shorter than the billions of nucleotides in nuclear DNA. But because each cell contains multiple mitochondria, each of which contains many DNA molecules, mitochondria can often yield useful information even when nuclear DNA is badly degraded. Investigators extract mitochondrial DNA from hair, bones, and teeth, then use PCR to amplify the variable regions for sequencing. ① *mitochondria,* p. 60

Because everyone inherits mitochondria only from his or her mother, this technique cannot distinguish among siblings. It is very useful, however, for verifying the relationship between woman and child. For example, children who were kidnapped during infancy can be matched to their biological mothers or grandmothers. The study of human evolution also has benefited from mitochondrial DNA analysis, which has revealed the genetic relationships among subpopulations from around the world.

11.2 MASTERING CONCEPTS

1. What are some uses for transgenic organisms?
2. What are the steps in creating a transgenic organism?
3. How do researchers determine a sequence of DNA?
4. What is the function of the 98.5% of the human genome that does not encode protein?
5. How does PCR work, and why is it useful?
6. How are short tandem repeats used in DNA profiling?
7. Why does mitochondrial DNA provide different information from nuclear DNA?

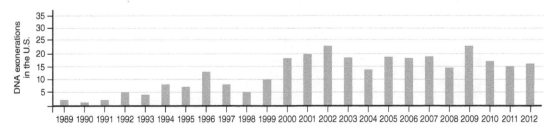

Figure 11.9 Proven Innocent. In the United States, DNA evidence has exonerated more than 300 prisoners who were serving time for crimes they did not commit. (Data are from the Innocence Project.)

11.3 Stem Cells and Cloning Add New Ways to Copy Cells and Organisms

The public debate over stem cells and cloning combines science, philosophy, religion, and politics in ways that few other modern issues do (figure 11.10). What is the biology behind the headlines?

A. Stem Cells Divide to Form Multiple Cell Types

A human develops from a single fertilized egg into an embryo and then a fetus—and eventually into an infant, child, and adult—thanks to mitotic cell division. As development continues, more and more cells become permanently specialized into muscle, skin, liver, brain, and other cell types. All contain the same DNA, but some genes become irreversibly "turned off" in specialized cells. Once committed to a fate, a mature cell rarely reverts to another type. ⓘ regulation of gene expression, p. 134

Animal development therefore relies on stem cells. In general, a stem cell is any undifferentiated cell that can give rise to specialized cell types. When a stem cell divides mitotically to yield two daughter cells, one remains a stem cell, able to divide again. The other specializes.

Animals have two general categories of stem cells: embryonic and adult (figure 11.11). **Embryonic stem cells** give rise

a.

b.

Figure 11.10 Stem Cell Controversy. Debates over stem cells often pit (a) people such as actor Michael J. Fox who advocate the use of embryonic stem cells in medicine against (b) people with moral objections.

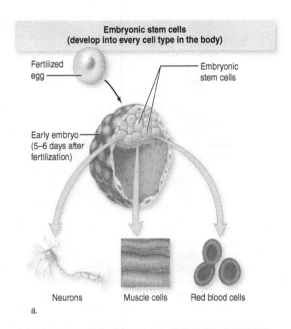

a.

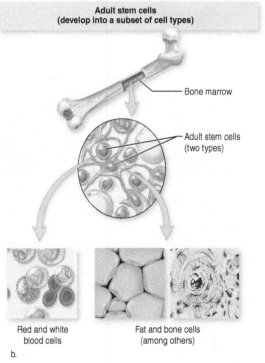

b.

Figure 11.11 Stem Cells. (a) Human embryonic stem cells are derived from a ball of cells that forms several days after fertilization. These stem cells give rise to all of the body's cell types. (b) The adult body also contains stem cells, but they may not have the potential to develop into as many different cell types as do embryonic stem cells.

to all cell types in the body (including adult stem cells) and are therefore called "totipotent"; *toti-* comes from the Latin word for "entire." **Adult stem cells** are more differentiated and produce a limited subset of cell types. For example, stem cells in the skin replace cells lost through wear and tear, and stem cells in the bone marrow produce all of the cell types that make up blood. Adult stem cells are "pluripotent"; *pluri-* means "many" in Latin.

Stem cells are important in biological and medical research. With the correct combination of chemical signals, **Video** Adult Stem Cells in Medicine
medical researchers should theoretically be able to coax stem cells to divide in the laboratory and produce blood cells, neurons, or any other cell type. Many people believe that stem cells hold special promise as treatments for neurological disorders such as Parkinson disease and spinal cord injuries, since neurons ordinarily do not divide to replace injured or diseased tissue. Stem cell therapies may also conquer diabetes, heart disease, and many other illnesses that are currently incurable.

The practical benefits would extend beyond treating illness. Currently, pharmaceutical companies test new drugs primarily on whole organisms, such as mice and rats. The ability to test on just kidney or brain cells, for example, would allow researchers to better predict the likely side effects of a new drug. It might also reduce the need for laboratory animals.

Both embryonic and adult stem cells have advantages and disadvantages for medical use. Embryonic stem cells are **Video** Embryonic Stem Cells in Medicine
extremely versatile, but a patient's immune system would probably reject tissues derived from another individual's cells. In addition, research on embryonic stem cells is controversial because of their origin. In fertility clinics, technicians fertilize eggs *in vitro,* and only a few of the resulting embryos are ever implanted into a woman's uterus. Researchers destroy some of the "spare" embryos at about 5 days old to harvest the stem cells. (The other embryos are either stored for possible later implantation or discarded.) Many people consider it unethical to use human embryos in medical research, even if those embryos would otherwise have been thrown away.

Biologists are also investigating adult stem cells in hair follicles, bone marrow, the lining of the small intestine, and other **Video** Stem Cells from Hair Follicles
locations in the body. A patient's immune system would not reject tissues derived from his or her own adult stem cells. These stem cells are less abundant than embryonic stem cells, however, and they usually give rise to only some cell types.

New laboratory techniques may eliminate some of these drawbacks. Researchers have discovered how to induce adult cells to behave like embryonic stem cells. This technique could allow differentiated cells taken from an adult to be turned into stem cells, which could then be coaxed to develop into any other cell type. Time will tell how useful these so-called "induced pluripotent stem cells" will be or whether they will match the medical potential of embryonic stem cells.

B. Cloning Creates Identical Copies of an Organism

Imagine being able to grow a new individual, genetically identical to yourself, from a bit of skin or the root of a hair. Although humans cannot reproduce in this way, many organisms do the equivalent. They develop parts of themselves into genetically identical individuals—clones—that then detach and live independently.

Cloning simply means asexual reproduction. In its simplest form, asexual reproduction consists of the division of a single cell. In bacteria, archaea, and single-celled eukaryotes such as *Amoeba,* the cell's DNA replicates, and then the cell splits into two identical, individual organisms. Although the details of cell division differ between prokaryotes and eukaryotes, the result is the same: one individual becomes two.

Most plants, fungi, and animals reproduce sexually, but at least some organisms in each kingdom also use asexual reproduction. This strategy is especially common in plants and fungi. Hobbyists and commercial plant growers clone everything from fruit trees to African violets in petri dishes (figure 11.12); cuttings from stems, leaves, and roots also can yield new plants. Many fungi produce countless microscopic spores on bread, cheese, and every other imaginable food supply (see figure 20.4). Asexual reproduction is much less common in animals, but sponges, coral animals, hydra, and jellyfishes all can "bud" new individuals that break away from the parent.

Lumps of undifferentiated plant cells

Clusters of identical plantlets   Agar containing nutrients and hormones

Figure 11.12 **Cloning in a Dish.** When plant tissue is cultured with the correct combination of hormones and nutrients, it gives rise to genetically identical plantlets.

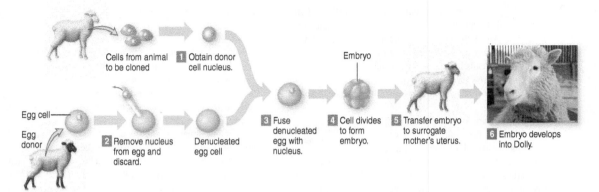

Figure 11.13 Creating Dolly. The first steps in cloning an adult female sheep were to (*1*) obtain a nucleus from a cell of the ewe's udder and (*2*) remove the nucleus from an egg cell. (*3*) Placing the adult cell's nucleus into the egg yielded a new cell genetically identical to the DNA donor. (*4*) This cell developed into an embryo, which (*5*) was implanted into a surrogate mother sheep and (*6*) eventually was born as Dolly.

Unlike many other organisms, mammals do not naturally clone themselves. In 1996, however, researcher Ian Wilmut and his colleagues in Scotland used a new procedure to create Dolly the sheep, the first clone of an adult mammal. The researchers used a technique called **somatic cell nuclear transfer** (figure 11.13). First, they obtained the nucleus from a cell removed from a donor sheep's mammary gland (figure 11.13, step 1). The name of the cloning technique derives in part from the fact that mammary glands consist of *somatic* cells, which are body cells that do not give rise to sperm or eggs. They then transferred this "donor" nucleus to a sheep's egg cell whose own nucleus had been removed (steps 2 and 3). The resulting cell divided mitotically to form an embryo (step 4), which the researchers implanted in a surrogate mother's uterus (step 5). The embryo then developed into a lamb, named Dolly (step 6).

Scientifically, this achievement was remarkable because it showed that the DNA from a differentiated somatic cell (in this case, from a mammary gland) could "turn back the clock" and revert to an undifferentiated state. Mitotic cell division then produced every cell in Dolly's body.

Dolly appeared normal, and she gave birth to six healthy lambs via sexual reproduction. But she had arthritis in her hind legs, and she died of lung disease in 2003 at age six. Normally, sheep of Dolly's breed live 11 or 12 years, and her early death fueled speculation that clones inevitably have an abnormally brief life span.

Since Dolly's birth, researchers have used somatic cell nuclear transfer to clone other mammals as well, including dogs, cats, mice, cattle, goats, and a champion horse that had been castrated (and therefore could not reproduce). Although some of the clones have had shorter-than-average life spans, others have not; the debate over clone longevity therefore continues.

Cloning may even help rescue endangered species or recover extinct species, using preserved DNA implanted into eggs from closely related species. So far, however, researchers have struggled to implement this strategy. One problem is the low success rate for cloning animals in general. Compounding this issue is the fact that scientists know few key details about reproduction in most endangered animals.

Many people wonder whether humans can and should be cloned. Reproductive cloning, as achieved with Dolly, could help infertile couples to have children. Scientists could also use cloned human embryos as a source of stem cells, which could be used to grow "customized" artificial organs that the patient's immune system would not reject. This application of cloning is called therapeutic cloning.

Despite the potential benefits, however, human cloning carries unresolved ethical questions. For example, most clones die early in development, presumably because the gene regulation mechanisms in an adult cell's nucleus are somehow incompatible with those in the egg cell. Even the tiny percentage of clones that make it to birth often have abnormalities. This difficulty emphasizes the ethical issues surrounding human reproductive cloning. In addition, therapeutic cloning still requires the destruction of an embryo to harvest the stem cells. As we have already seen, many people question the practice of creating human embryos only to destroy them. Finally, both reproductive and therapeutic cloning require unfertilized human eggs. The removal of eggs from a woman's ovaries is costly and poses medical risks.

11.3 MASTERING CONCEPTS

1. Describe the differences between embryonic, adult, and induced pluripotent stem cells.

2. What are the potential medical benefits of stem cells?

3. Summarize the steps scientists use to clone an adult mammal.

4. Why is the cloning technique called somatic cell nuclear transfer?

11.4 Many Medical Tests and Procedures Use DNA Technology

The list of human illnesses is long. Worldwide, the top causes of death include heart disease, stroke, cancer, and infection (see table 37.2); all of these diseases have environmental and genetic components. But some ailments, including cystic fibrosis, hemophilia, Tay-Sachs syndrome, sickle cell disease, and dozens of others, are entirely caused by mutated alleles of single genes. This section describes how the use of DNA technology can help prevent, detect, and treat genetic diseases. Although we use cystic fibrosis as an example, the same techniques are applicable (at least in theory) to any illness associated with a single gene.

A. DNA Probes Detect Specific Sequences

The ability to detect the alleles that cause cystic fibrosis and other genetic illnesses is crucial to the medical applications of DNA technology. At first glance, however, all DNA looks alike: a sequence of A, C, G, and T. With billions of nucleotides in a single cell, how can biologists search through an entire genome to find just the piece they need to "see"?

The answer is a **DNA probe,** a single-stranded sequence of nucleotides that is complementary to a particular known region of DNA (figure 11.14). A typical probe is a short, synthetic

strand of DNA that is labeled with either a radioactive isotope or a fluorescent tag. For example, a researcher can construct a probe that is complementary to part of an allele known to be associated with cystic fibrosis. A region of the DNA to be tested is separated into single strands and immobilized on a solid surface. If the DNA contains a nucleotide sequence that is complementary to the probe, then the probe binds to that region. The radioactivity or wavelength emitted by the probe reveals the presence of the cystic fibrosis allele.

B. Preimplantation Genetic Diagnosis Can Help Prevent Some Diseases

Imagine a young couple that wants a child. Both of the prospective parents know they are symptomless carriers of cystic fibrosis. Can DNA technology help the couple ensure that their baby is free of the disease? The answer is that no one can guarantee a cystic fibrosis–free baby, but a technique called **preimplantation genetic diagnosis (PGD)** can greatly reduce the odds of having an affected child.

The process begins with *in vitro* fertilization (literally, fertilization "in glass"), in which the man's sperm fertilize several of the woman's eggs in a laboratory dish. The resulting zygotes develop into embryos, each consisting of eight genetically identical cells. A technician then selects an embryo for PGD. He or she removes one cell from the embryo (figure 11.15); the loss of this cell will not affect the embryo's subsequent development. DNA extracted from that single cell undergoes PCR, amplifying the region of DNA where the cystic fibrosis gene is located. A DNA probe specific for one or more cystic fibrosis alleles can then determine whether the embryo's cells contain the disease-causing DNA sequences.

If the allele is detected, the embryo can be discarded, and others can be tested. Any embryo that lacks the disease-causing allele is a good candidate to be placed into the woman's body. If the embryo implants into the uterus and

Fluorescent label

T C T A T T C C G A G

Labeled probe complementary to cystic fibrosis allele

Cystic fibrosis allele

LM 4 μm

Sequence #1 (complementary to probe)

T C T A T T C C G A G

Binding occurs; cystic fibrosis allele detected

A A G C A G A T A A G G C T C A T C G

Sequence #2 (not complementary to probe)

T C T A T T C C G A G

No binding; cystic fibrosis allele not detected

T A T G C A T C G A T T A T G A T A C

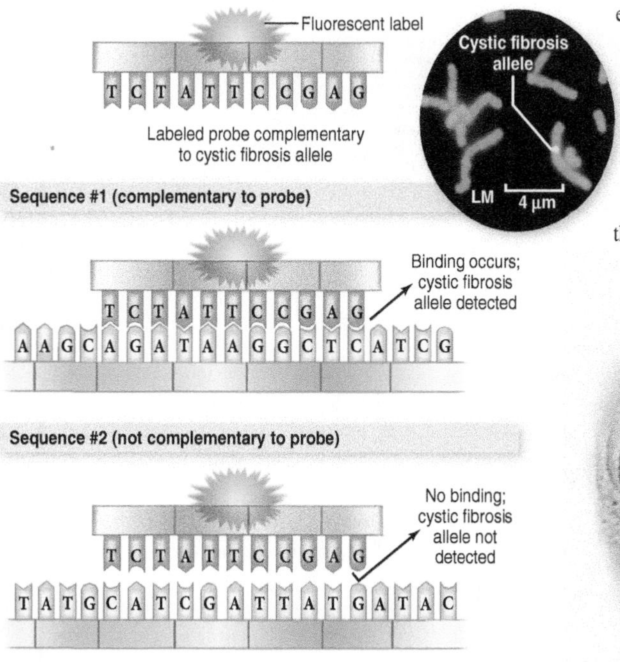

Figure 11.14 DNA Probe. A DNA probe is a labeled strand of single-stranded DNA that binds to a complementary target sequence. In this case, the probe reveals the presence of a cystic fibrosis allele.

Animation
DNA Probe

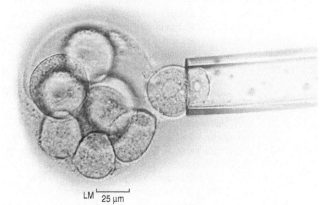

LM 25 μm

Figure 11.15 Preimplantation Genetic Diagnosis. A single cell is removed from a human embryo.

develops into a baby, the child is very likely to be born without cystic fibrosis.

There is a small chance, however, that the baby may be born with the disease despite PGD. Human error is one possible explanation. By amplifying DNA sequences that occur in just one or two copies from a single cell, PGD pushes PCR to its limits. As we have already seen, PCR is extremely sensitive to contamination; stray DNA that is accidentally amplified can lead to a false result. A second explanation relates to the fact that researchers have identified hundreds of mutations that can cause cystic fibrosis. PGD tests for the most common disease-causing alleles, but the baby may have inherited rare variants that the test cannot detect.

C. Genetic Testing Can Detect Existing Diseases

The same genetic tests used in PGD are also useful for testing fetuses, newborns, older children, and adults for disease-causing alleles. Instead of searching the DNA from an embryonic cell, however, the tests detect the alleles in DNA from cells taken from blood, saliva, or body tissues.

For example, newborns are routinely screened for a genetic disorder called phenylketonuria (PKU). Cells from unborn children can also be tested for disease-causing alleles; the parents can use the information to decide whether to terminate the pregnancy or to prepare for life with a special needs child.

Genetic testing has many applications in adults as well. People who suspect they may be heterozygous carriers of cystic fibrosis might choose to be tested for the disease-causing allele before deciding whether to have children. Likewise, a woman with a family history of breast cancer might be tested for damage to a gene called *BRCA1*, which is strongly associated with susceptibility to that disease. A positive test for the mutant allele might prompt the woman to have her breasts surgically removed to prevent the cancer from ever arising. And patients who already have breast cancer often have DNA from their tumors screened for genes encoding estrogen receptors. The results can indicate which treatments might be most promising.

D. Gene Therapy Uses DNA to Treat Disease

Cystic fibrosis and most other genetic illnesses currently have no cure, but **gene therapy** may someday provide new treatment options by adding healthy DNA to a person's cells. The new DNA supplements the function of a faulty gene (figure 11.16).

One variation on gene therapy is to use DNA to silence a gene whose activity is causing illness. For example, turning off cancer-associated genes might offer promising new cancer treatments. A technique called RNA interference can prevent the translation of mRNA from the cancer-related gene. In this strategy, researchers

▶ **Video** RNA Interference

introduce DNA encoding mRNA that is complementary to the cancer gene's mRNA. If both mRNA molecules are produced at the same time, they bind to each other and form double-stranded RNA that cannot be translated to a protein. The cancer-related gene is therefore silenced.

The gene therapy strategy illustrated in figure 11.16 shares some similarities with creating transgenic organisms (see section 11.2A) in that new DNA is introduced into existing cells. But the two techniques are also different in key ways. First, in gene therapy, the healthy gene introduced into a cell is from humans, not another species. Second, a typical transgenic organism can theoretically pass the foreign genes to the next generation, whereas a gene therapy patient would only receive new genes in the cell type that needs correction. Other cell

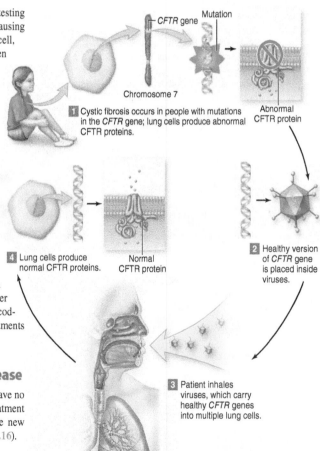

Chromosome 7

CFTR gene   Mutation

1 Cystic fibrosis occurs in people with mutations in the *CFTR* gene; lung cells produce abnormal CFTR proteins.

Abnormal CFTR protein

2 Healthy version of *CFTR* gene is placed inside viruses.

3 Patient inhales viruses, which carry healthy *CFTR* genes into multiple lung cells.

4 Lung cells produce normal CFTR proteins.

Normal CFTR protein

Figure 11.16 Gene Therapy. The overall goal of gene therapy is to supplement a faulty gene with a normal, healthy version. In this example, a genetically modified virus delivers a healthy *CFTR* gene to the lungs of a person with cystic fibrosis.

types, including the germline cells that produce sperm and egg cells, would be left alone.

Gene therapy is challenging for several reasons. The new gene must be delivered directly to only those cells that express the faulty allele. Viruses may be ideal for carrying DNA into target cells, because they typically infect only a limited range of cells. But for gene therapy to be safe, the viruses must not trigger an immune reaction, and the new DNA must not induce mutations that cause cancer. In addition, the gene therapy patient must express the repaired genes long enough for his or her health to improve.

Gene therapy trials in humans have proceeded slowly since 1999, when 18-year-old Jesse Gelsinger received a massive infusion of viruses carrying a gene to correct an inborn error of metabolism. He died in days from an overwhelming immune system reaction. Gelsinger's death prompted a temporary halt to several gene therapy studies and led to stricter rules for conducting experiments. Nevertheless, gene therapy research and clinical trials continue, with promising results for diseases including cystic fibrosis, sickle cell disease, and some forms of inherited blindness and immune disorders.

E. Medical Uses of DNA Technology Raise Many Ethical Issues

The use of DNA technology in medicine can prevent or reduce human suffering in many ways: by improving the chance of having healthy children, by detecting diseases early if they do occur, and by offering the prospect of new treatments for illnesses that currently have no cure.

But these techniques also present ethical dilemmas. A thorough treatment of ethics is beyond the scope of this book, but the rest of this section offers a small sampling of some questions that accompany the use of DNA technology in medicine.

In vitro fertilization and preimplantation genetic diagnosis, for example, are costly. Should these techniques be available only to the wealthy? And consider the diagnosis of a genetic disease in an unborn child. A woman who is pregnant with a fetus that carries a genetic abnormality may decide to end the pregnancy rather than carrying the child to term. Does the morality of her decision depend on the severity of the illness? In other words, should we reserve fetal screening for life-threatening illnesses, or is it morally permissible to use it for milder conditions as well? What about using genetic tests to select for or against embryos with traits that do not affect health at all, such as sex or eye color?

Genetic testing in older children and adults may also lead to sticky questions. For example, a genetic test that reveals a high risk for cancer may be beneficial if it leads to lifestyle changes that promote a longer, healthier life. On the other hand, the same test results may lead to depression or anxiety without improving the chance of treatment or a cure. The potential loss of health insurance coverage may also prevent people from seeking genetic testing, even if they might benefit from knowing the results.

Apply It **Now**

Gene Doping

If we can use genes to cure diseases, it must also be possible to use DNA to make a healthy person even "better." For example, it should be possible to inject genes that make an athlete stronger, faster, or better able to withstand the physical stress of competition.

"Gene doping" is the use of DNA to enhance the function of a healthy person. The techniques would be essentially the same as those used in gene therapy: new genes would be introduced into existing cells, and the proteins encoded by those genes would change the cells' function. The difference is that rather than curing a disease, the goal of gene doping is to give an athlete a competitive edge. An introduced gene might induce the growth of extra muscle, for example. Alternatively, an endurance athlete might use gene doping to boost the production of erythropoietin (EPO), a protein that stimulates red blood cell formation.

For now, technical difficulties and risks have kept gene doping from developing into a practical option for athletes seeking an edge. As the process improves, however, gene doping may become common. That prospect has led many sports organizations to simultaneously ban the practice and seek improved detection methods.

Gene therapy also comes with its share of dilemmas. This new form of treatment currently carries so many risks that its use is extremely limited. Once the technology is perfected, however, how should it be used? Only for debilitating diseases, or for less serious conditions as well? Is it right to use the techniques of gene therapy to enhance a person's appearance or athletic performance, as described in this chapter's Apply It Now box? What about using DNA technology to alter the DNA in a person's germline, so that future generations contain the new gene? The answer to this question is not trivial; tinkering with germline DNA could affect our future evolution in unforeseen ways.

11.4 MASTERING CONCEPTS

1. Explain how and why a researcher might use a DNA probe.
2. Compare and contrast preimplantation genetic diagnosis and genetic testing.
3. What is gene therapy?
4. What are some examples of ethical questions raised by the medical use of DNA technology?

INVESTIGATING LIFE

11.5 Investigating Life: What Makes Us Human?

Perhaps no scientific issue is more tantalizing and entangled with philosophy than the question of what makes us human. One way to look for answers is to study the similarities and differences between humans and chimpanzees, our closest living relatives on the evolutionary tree (figure 11.17). A team of scientists has sequenced the 3 billion or so DNA nucleotides that make up the chimpanzee genome and has begun comparing it with our own.

The story begins with the Chimpanzee Sequencing and Analysis Consortium, a group of 67 researchers in the United States, Europe, and Israel who collaborated to determine the genetic sequence of one chimpanzee *(Pan troglodytes)*. The scientists isolated DNA from the animal's blood cells, broke the genetic material into many small fragments, and inserted each fragment into a separate plasmid. Each plasmid that carried chimp DNA was placed into a different bacterial cell. The researchers allowed the bacteria to replicate on culture plates, producing countless copies of the plasmid. Then, when it was a fragment's "turn" to be processed, a technician simply retrieved a sample of the bacteria, extracted the plasmid, and determined the nucleotide sequence (see section 11.2B). Finally, powerful computers assembled the sequences from tens of millions of fragments.

Figure 11.17   Close Relative. Humans share 99% of our protein-encoding genes with chimpanzees. What are the differences that make us human?

Long before this project began, the startling genetic similarities between humans and chimps were well known. The chromosomes of the two species, for example, are extremely similar (figure 11.18). Although chimpanzees do have one more pair of chromosomes than do humans, a close look at figure 11.18 reveals why: our chromosome 2 formed when two smaller chromosomes fused. The other great apes (gorillas and orangutans) have the same chromosome number as chimpanzees, so this fusion event must have occurred after the human and chimpanzee lineages split.

The complete DNA sequences for both species, however, reveal exactly how much we have in common: The two genomes are 96% alike, with the differences concentrated in the noncoding regions. The coding regions (the sequences that specify proteins) are 99% alike.

Scientists must still scrutinize both genomes to identify the 25,000 or so coding regions. They must also sequence the genomes of additional individuals to locate the variable regions, and they must learn which alleles confer which traits. The result will be an unprecedented view of human biology and evolution. Here is a sampling of questions we may soon be able to answer:

- **Which genes define humans?** Previously, scientists could only compare the human genome with those of bacteria such as *E. coli,* plants such as *Arabidopsis,* and animals such as nematodes, fruit flies, and mice. Those comparisons gave important insights into the traits that are common to all animals, all eukaryotes, or all cells. With the chimp genome complete, we can finally determine precisely how human DNA *differs* from that of our closest relative. To answer this question, scientists are searching the two genomes for regions that have been duplicated, inserted, deleted, and otherwise changed since humans and chimps last shared a common ancestor.

- **What accounts for bipedalism, large brains, complex language, and other uniquely human features?** Considering how genetically similar humans and chimps are, we have strikingly different phenotypes. At least two hypotheses could explain this curious observation. Some scientists suggest that human and chimp proteins are essentially the same but that we turn the genes encoding those proteins on and off at different times. For example, section 7.8 illustrates how a small change in just one transcription factor can affect a person's ability to use language. A competing hypothesis is that after humans and chimps diverged, changes in the human lineage caused some previously functional genes to stop working. Such "degenerate" genes may make us less muscular and less hairy than chimpanzees. Comparing the chimp and human genotypes will help biologists test these hypotheses and yield insights into human evolution.

- **Why do humans and chimps have different diseases?** Our two species are very closely related, so it is reasonable to suppose that we suffer from the same illnesses. Yet the number of differences is surprising. For example, humans

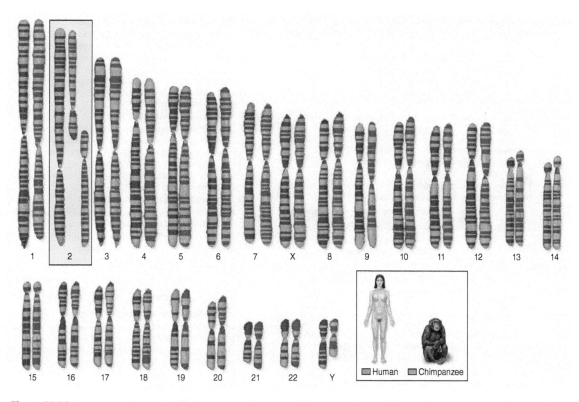

Figure 11.18 Chromosome Comparison. The chromosomes of humans and chimpanzees look virtually identical. The main exception is chromosome 2, which reflects a chromosomal fusion that occurred in humans after the human and chimp lineages diverged.

are susceptible to Alzheimer disease and carcinomas (cancers of the epithelium), but chimps are not. HIV progresses to AIDS in humans but not in chimps. At least some of the differences will certainly lie in our genes, and their discovery may yield new disease cures.

More recently, biologists have sequenced the genomes of orangutans and gorillas. The DNA sequences of these apes will reveal the answers to many questions that were previously impossible to approach. For example, researchers once suspected that a gene involved in hearing was one key to the human acquisition of complex language. The latest genome sequence, however, revealed that gorillas—which do not have complex language— have the same version of the gene as humans; other genes must therefore be responsible. The gorilla and orangutan genome sequences are sure to help researchers discover many additional details of our evolutionary history.

Whatever the source of our humanity, it is revealed partly in our ability to make reasoned decisions and in our compassion for others. Chimpanzees are endangered in the wild, where they succumb to habitat loss, hunting, the illegal pet trade, and biomedical research. The Chimpanzee Sequencing and Analysis Consortium's paper advocates the protection of chimpanzees in

the wild, and it ends with this statement: "We hope that elaborating how few differences separate our species will broaden recognition of our duty to these extraordinary primates that stand as our siblings in the family of life."

Chimpanzee Sequencing and Analysis Consortium. September 1, 2005. Initial sequence of the chimpanzee genome and comparison with the human genome. *Nature*, vol. 437, pages 69–87.

Locke, Devin P. and 100 coauthors. January 27, 2011. Comparative and demographic analysis of orang-utan genomes. *Nature*, vol. 469, pages 529–533.

Olson, Maynard V. and Ajit Varki. January 2003. Sequencing the chimpanzee genome: insights into human evolution and disease. *Nature Reviews Genetics*, vol. 4, pages 20–28.

Scally, Aylwyn and 70 coauthors. March 8, 2012. Insights into hominid evolution from the gorilla genome sequence. *Nature*, vol. 483, pages 169–175.

11.5 MASTERING CONCEPTS

1. What information can researchers gain by comparing the human and chimpanzee genome sequences?

2. How do the genome sequences of orangutans and gorillas help scientists further resolve the evolutionary history of humans?

CHAPTER SUMMARY

11.1 DNA Technology Is Changing the World

- Many disciplines benefit from **DNA technology,** the practical application of knowledge about DNA. Figure 11.19 summarizes some of the tools and techniques of DNA technology.

11.2 DNA Technology's Tools Apply to Individual Genes or Entire Genomes

A. Transgenic Organisms Contain DNA from Other Species

- **Transgenic organisms** are important in industry, research, and agriculture.
- **Restriction enzymes** and **plasmids** are tools that help researchers create **recombinant DNA** and introduce it to recipient cells.

Technology or Tool	Definition
Restriction enzyme	Protein that cuts double-stranded DNA at a specific base sequence
Recombinant DNA	Genetic material that has been cut with restriction enzymes and spliced with DNA from other organisms
Transgenic organism	An individual with recombinant DNA
DNA sequencing	Determines the nucleotide sequence of DNA fragments
PCR (polymerase chain reaction)	Amplifies DNA in a test tube using the cell's replication machinery
DNA profiling	Uses DNA sequencing and PCR to detect genetic differences among individuals
Stem cells	Cells found in embryos and some adult tissues that can give rise to other cell types
Cloning	Creates an identical copy of an organism
Somatic cell nuclear transfer	A type of cloning that combines a nucleus taken from one individual's body cell with a denucleated egg cell from another individual to produce the first cell of a new organism
DNA probe	A single-stranded sequence of DNA, labeled with a radioactive isotope or fluorescent tag, used to detect the presence of a known sequence of nucleotides
Preimplantation genetic diagnosis	Uses PCR and DNA probes to detect genetic diseases in embryos that might later be implanted in a woman's uterus
Genetic testing	Uses PCR and DNA probes to detect genetic diseases in fetuses, newborns, children, and adults
Gene therapy	Employs viruses to insert healthy genes into cells

Figure 11.19 Miniglossary of DNA Technology.

B. DNA Sequencing Reveals the Order of Bases

- The Sanger method uses modified nucleotides to generate DNA fragments of various lengths. Using **electrophoresis** to sort the fragments by size reveals the DNA sequence.
- Only 1.5% of the 3.2 billion base pairs of the human genome encode protein. The remaining 98.5% of the human genome encodes rRNA, tRNA, microRNA, regulatory sequences, pseudogenes, transposable elements, and other repeats.

C. PCR Replicates DNA in a Test Tube

- In the **polymerase chain reaction (PCR),** DNA separates into two strands, and DNA polymerase adds complementary nucleotides to each strand. Repeated cycles of heating and cooling allow for rapid amplification of the target DNA sequence.
- PCR finds many applications in research, forensics, medicine, agriculture, and other fields.

D. DNA Profiling Detects Genetic Differences

- Individuals vary genetically in single bases and **short tandem repeats (STRs). DNA profiling** detects these differences.
- Investigators can use known frequencies of alleles in the population to calculate the probability that two DNA samples match.
- Analysis of mitochondrial DNA can verify maternal relationships.

11.3 Stem Cells and Cloning Add New Ways to Copy Cells and Organisms

A. Stem Cells Divide to Form Multiple Cell Types

- **Embryonic stem cells** give rise to all cells in the body; **adult stem cells** produce only a limited subset of cell types.
- Induced pluripotent stem cells are adult cells that are converted to stem cells. They may eliminate some ethical issues associated with embryonic stem cells.

B. Cloning Creates Identical Copies of an Organism

- Researchers use a technique called **somatic cell nuclear transfer** to clone adult mammals.
- Human reproductive and therapeutic cloning have potential medical applications, but they also involve ethical dilemmas.

11.4 Many Medical Tests and Procedures Use DNA Technology

A. DNA Probes Detect Specific Sequences

- A **DNA probe** is a single-stranded fragment of DNA that is labeled. The probe binds to any complementary DNA, revealing its location.

B. Preimplantation Genetic Diagnosis Can Help Prevent Some Diseases

- In **preimplantation genetic diagnosis (PGD),** a human embryo can be tested for a variety of diseases before being implanted into a woman's uterus.

C. Genetic Testing Can Detect Existing Diseases

- With the help of DNA probes, genetic material extracted from cells of a fetus, child, or adult can be tested for the presence of disease-causing alleles.

D. Gene Therapy Uses DNA to Treat Disease

- **Gene therapy** places a functional gene into cells that are expressing a faulty gene.

E. Medical Uses of DNA Technology Raise Many Ethical Issues

- Because of its risks, high expense, and potential to alter human life, DNA technology raises a number of ethical questions.

11.5 Investigating Life: What Makes Us Human?

- Scientists completed the chimpanzee genome project in 2005. Comparing the chimp and human genomes will lead to unprecedented insight into the genes, phenotypes, and diseases that are unique to humans.

1. If a restriction enzyme cuts between the G and the A whenever it encounters the sequence GAATTC, how many fragments will be produced when the enzyme is digested with DNA with the following sequence? TGAGAATTCAACTGAATTCAAATTCGAATTCTTAGC

    a. Two
    b. Three
    c. Four
    d. Five

2. Which of the following is transgenic?

    a. A yeast cell that expresses a gene from a fish
    b. A human patient who receives gene therapy to repair a faulty cystic fibrosis gene
    c. A human embryo being tested for disease-causing alleles
    d. All of the above are transgenic.

3. What is an induced pluripotent stem cell?

    a. A cell from which the nucleus has been removed
    b. A cell extracted from an early embryo
    c. A specially treated somatic cell that can develop into any cell type
    d. A specially treated embryonic stem cell that develops into one specialized cell type

4. Tabouli, one of the kittens on page 216, is a clone produced by somatic cell nuclear transfer. Tabouli is genetically identical to the cat that

    a. gave birth to her.
    b. donated the egg that developed into her.
    c. donated her chromosomes.
    d. Tabouli is equally similar to all of these cats.

5. A DNA probe with sequence TCAGGCTTCAG would bind most strongly to which of the following DNA fragments?

    a. AGTCCGAAGTC
    b. TCAGGCTTCAG
    c. GACTTCGGACT
    d. UGAGGCUUGAG

6. Preimplantation genetic diagnosis would be least useful in detecting a ___ disease-causing allele.

    a. dominant
    b. recessive
    c. common
    d. rare

7. What is the role of a virus in gene therapy?

    a. It causes the disease that gene therapy is aiming to cure.
    b. It carries the healthy DNA into the patient's cells.
    c. It carries the faulty DNA out of the patient's cells.
    d. It reveals which cells carry the DNA causing the disease.

Answers to these questions are in appendix A.

1. What techniques might researchers use to create transgenic bacteria that produce human growth hormone (a drug used to treat extremely short stature)?

2. Transgenic crops often require fewer herbicides and insecticides than conventional crops. In that respect, they could be considered environmentally friendly. Use the Internet to research the question of why some environmental groups oppose transgenic technology.

3. Explain how the ingredients in a PCR reaction tube replicate DNA.

4. Compare and contrast the use of the DNA polymerase enzyme in DNA sequencing and PCR.

5. Why does DNA profiling require an understanding of probability?

6. Make a chart that lists the advantages and disadvantages of embryonic stem cells, adult stem cells, and induced pluripotent stem cells.

7. Unneeded genes in an adult animal cell are permanently inactivated, making it impossible for most specialized cells to turn into any other cell type. How does this arrangement save energy inside a cell? Why does the ability to clone an adult mammal depend on techniques for reactivating these "dormant" genes?

8. Search the Internet for examples of mammals that have been cloned (other than sheep). What ethical issues should people consider in deciding whether to clone plants, nonhuman animals, and humans?

9. This chapter's Apply It Now box (see page 231) describes some potential applications of gene doping. What are some examples of ethical issues that gene doping presents? What might the prospect of gene doping mean for the future of sports?

10. Describe gene therapy and explain the ethical issues that gene therapy presents.

11. If a cell's genome is analogous to a cookbook and a gene is analogous to a recipe, what is an analogy for preimplantation genetic diagnosis? For gene testing? For gene therapy?

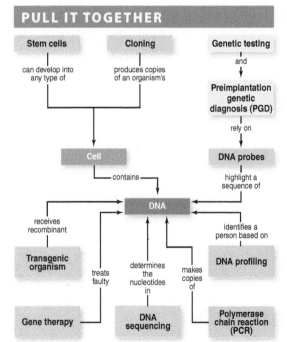

Figure 11.20 Pull It Together: DNA Technology.

Refer to figure 11.20 and the chapter content to answer the following questions.

1. What is recombinant DNA?

2. Add the terms *restriction enzyme, plasmid, virus, DNA polymerase,* and *short tandem repeat* to this concept map.

3. How is a patient who receives gene therapy similar to and different from a transgenic organism?

The Evolution of Life

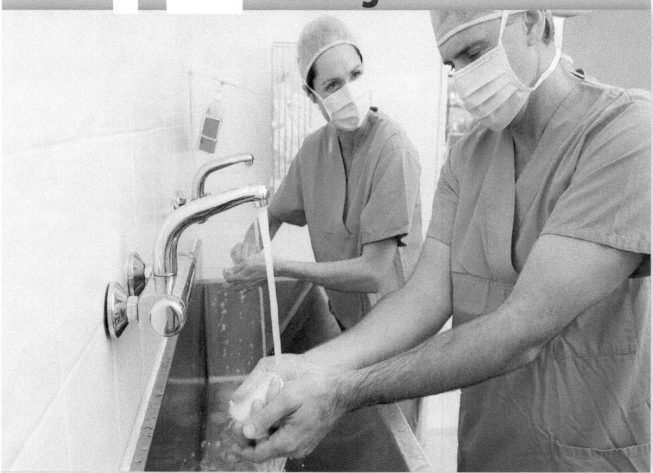

CHAPTER

12

The Forces of Evolutionary Change

Washing Off Bacteria. Hospitals are breeding grounds for antibiotic-resistant bacteria, which have become less susceptible to drugs in recent decades. Maintaining a bacteria-free environment is especially important during surgery, when a patient's skin is broken and cannot act as a barrier to infection.

Enhance your study |BIOLOGY
of this chapter with practice quizzes,
animations and videos, answer keys,
and downloadable study tools.
www.mhhe.com/hoefnagels

UNIT 3

The Unending War with Bacteria

DO YOU OWE YOUR LIFE TO ANTIBIOTICS? Even if you have never had a serious infection, chances are that one or more of your ancestors did, and antibiotics may have saved their lives. Had it not been for these "wonder drugs," you may never have been born.

Many antibiotics are naturally occurring chemicals. Soil fungi and bacteria secrete these compounds into their surroundings, giving them an edge against microbial competitors. Biologists discovered antibiotics in the early 1900s, but it took decades for chemists to figure out how to mass-produce them. Once that occurred, antibiotics revolutionized medical care in the twentieth century and enabled people to survive many once-deadly bacterial infections.

Unfortunately, the miracle of antibiotics is under threat, and many infections that once were easily treated are reemerging as killers. Ironically, the overuse and misuse of antibiotics is partly responsible for the problem. Physicians sometimes prescribe antibiotics for viral infections, even though the drugs kill only bacteria; moreover, many patients fail to take the drugs as directed. Agricultural practices contribute to the problem as well. Producers of cattle, chickens, and other animals use antibiotics to treat and prevent disease, even adding small amounts to the animals' feed to promote growth. Farmers also spray antibiotics on fruit- and vegetable-producing plants to treat bacterial infections.

By saturating the environment with antibiotics, we have profoundly affected the evolution of bacteria. Microbes that can defeat the drugs are becoming increasingly common, and the explanation is simple. Antibiotics kill susceptible bacteria and leave the resistant ones alone. The survivors multiply, producing a new generation of antibiotic-resistant bacteria. This is an example of natural selection in action, and the public health consequences are both widespread and severe. ⓘ *antibiotics,* p. 350

Antibiotic-resistant bacteria appeared just four years after these drugs entered medical practice in the late 1940s, and researchers responded by discovering new drugs. But the microbes kept pace. Today, 40% of hospital *Staphylococcus* infections resist all antibiotics but one. These so-called "superbugs" are called MRSA, which is short for methicillin-resistant *Staphylococcus aureus.* Worse, some laboratory strains are resistant to all antibiotics. Researchers fear that the discovery of new antibiotics will not keep up with the global proliferation of resistant strains.

Natural selection is just one mechanism of evolution, a process that occurs in every species and is obvious in many ways. This chapter explains how evolution occurs.

 LEARN HOW TO LEARN
Practice Your Recall

Here's an old-fashioned study tip that still works. When you finish reading a passage, close the book and write what you remember—in your own words. In this chapter, for example, you will learn about several forces of evolutionary change. After you read about them, can you list and describe them without peeking at your book? Try it and find out!

12.1 Evolution Acts on Populations

Scientific reasoning has profoundly changed thinking about the origin of species. Just 250 years ago, no one knew Earth's age. A century later, scientists learned that Earth is millions of years old (or older), but many believed that a creator made all species in their present form. Today's scientists, relying on a wide range of evidence, accept evolution as the explanation for life's diversity.

But what *is* evolution? A simple definition of **evolution** is descent with modification. "Descent" implies inheritance; "modification" refers to changes in traits from generation to generation. For example, we see evolution at work in the lions, tigers, and leopards that descended from one ancestral cat species.

Evolution has another, more specific, definition as well. Recall from unit 2 that a gene is a sequence of DNA that encodes a protein and that each gene can have multiple versions, or alleles. We have also seen that a **population** consists of interbreeding members of the same species (see figure 1.2). Biologists say that evolution occurs in a population when some alleles become more common, and others less common, from one generation to the next. A more precise definition of evolution, then, is genetic change in a population over multiple generations.

According to this definition, evolution is detectable by examining a population's **gene pool**—its entire collection of genes and their alleles. Evolution is a change in **allele frequencies;** one allele's frequency is calculated as the number of copies of that allele, divided by the total number of alleles in the population. Suppose, for example, that a gene has two possible alleles, *A* and *a*. In a population of 100 diploid individuals, the gene has 200 alleles. If 160 of those alleles are *a*, then the frequency of *a* is 160/200, or 0.8. In the next generation, however, *a* may become either more or less common. Because an individual's alleles do not change, *evolution occurs in populations, not in individuals.*

The allele frequencies for each gene determine the characteristics of a population (figure 12.1). Many people in Sweden, for example, have alleles conferring blond hair and blue eyes; a population of Asians would contain many more alleles specifying darker hair and eyes. If Swedes migrate to Asia and interbreed with the locals (or vice versa), allele frequencies change.

Some people use the term *microevolution* to refer to the small, generation-by-generation changes occurring in every population or species. It is remarkable to consider that over long periods, these same processes give rise to what are sometimes called "macroevolutionary" events, such as the appearance of new species. Chapter 14 explains this process in more detail.

Evolution does not, however, answer one compelling question: how did life begin in the first place? Because little evidence remains from life's ancient origin, this question is hard to answer scientifically; chapter 15 describes some of what we do know.

12.1   MASTERING CONCEPTS

1. What are two ways to define evolution?
2. Why can't evolution act on individuals?

Figure 12.1 Same Genes, Different Alleles. Human populations originating in different regions of the world have unique allele frequencies. Blond hair and blue eyes are typical of people from northern European countries, whereas people originating on the Asian continent usually have darker coloration.

12.2 Evolutionary Thought Has Evolved for Centuries

Although Charles Darwin typically receives credit for developing the theory of evolution, people began pondering life's diversity well before his birth. This section offers a brief glimpse into the history of evolutionary thought.

A. Many Explanations Have Been Proposed for Life's Diversity

People have tried to explain the diversity of life for a very long time (figure 12.2). In ancient Greece, Aristotle recognized that all organisms are related in a hierarchy of simple to complex forms, but he believed that all members of a species were created identical to one another. This idea influenced scientific thinking for nearly 2000 years.

Several other ideas were also considered fundamental principles of science well into the 1800s. Among them was the concept of a "special creation," the sudden appearance of organisms on Earth. People believed that this creative event was planned and purposeful, that species were fixed and unchangeable, and that Earth was relatively young.

What About Fossils? Scientists struggled to reconcile these beliefs with compelling evidence that species could in fact change. Fossils, which had been discovered at least as early as 500 BCE, were at first thought to be oddly shaped crystals or faulty attempts at life that arose spontaneously in rocks. But by the mid–1700s, the increasingly obvious connection between organisms and fossils argued against these ideas.

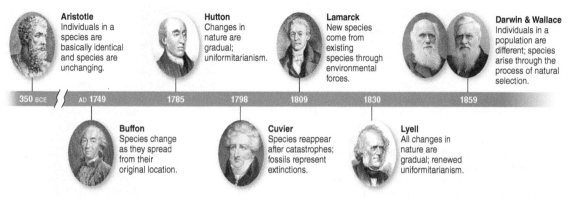

Aristotle Individuals in a species are basically identical and species are unchanging.

Hutton Changes in nature are gradual; uniformitarianism.

Lamarck New species come from existing species through environmental forces.

Darwin & Wallace Individuals in a population are different; species arise through the process of natural selection.

350 BCE / AD 1749   1785   1798   1809   1830   1859

Buffon Species change as they spread from their original location.

Cuvier Species reappear after catastrophes; fossils represent extinctions.

Lyell All changes in nature are gradual; renewed uniformitarianism.

Figure 12.2 **Early Evolutionary Thought.** Many scientists made significant contributions over the years, developing the foundation that Charles Darwin and Alfred Russel Wallace used to describe natural selection as the mechanism for evolution.

Scientists used religious stories to explain the existence of fossils without denying the role of a creator. Yet some of the fossils depicted organisms not seen before. Because people believed that species created by God could not become extinct, these fossils presented a paradox. The conflict between ideology and observation widened as geologists discovered that different rock layers revealed different groups of fossilized organisms, many of them now extinct.

New Ideas from Geology   In 1749, French naturalist Georges-Louis Buffon (1707–1788) became one of the first to openly suggest that closely related species arose from a common ancestor and were changing—a radical idea at the time. By moving the discussion into the public arena, he made possible a new consideration of evolution and its causes from a scientific point of view. Still no one had proposed how species might change.

Meanwhile, in the 1700s and 1800s, much of the study of nature focused on geology. In 1785, physician James Hutton (1726–1797) proposed the theory of **uniformitarianism,** which suggested that the processes of erosion and sedimentation that act in modern times have also occurred in the past, producing profound changes in Earth over time. On the other side, Georges Cuvier (1769–1832) was convinced of **catastrophism,** the theory that a series of brief, violent, global upheavals such as enormous floods, volcanic eruptions, and earthquakes were responsible for most geological formations.

Cuvier also used his knowledge of anatomy to identify fossils and to describe the similarities among organisms. He was the first to recognize the **principle of superposition**—the idea that lower layers of rock (and the fossils they contain) are older than those above them (figure 12.3). Although he had to accept that some species must have become extinct, he refused to believe that they were not originally formed through creation. He argued that catastrophes would destroy most of the organisms in an area, but then new life would arrive from surrounding areas.

Geologist Charles Lyell (1797–1875) renewed the argument for uniformitarianism in 1830. He suggested that natural processes are slow and steady, and that Earth is much older than 6000 years—perhaps millions or hundreds of millions of years

Newer rock layers

Older rock layers

Figure 12.3 **Earth's History Revealed in Rocks.** The colorful layers of sedimentary rock that form the Grand Canyon originated as sand, mud, and gravel that were deposited in ancient seas. Rock layers sometimes contain fossil evidence of organisms that lived (and died) when the layer was formed, providing clues about when the organism existed; layers near the bottom are older than those on top.

old. One obvious conclusion from his contribution is that gradual changes in some organisms could be represented in successive fossil layers. Lyell was so persuasive that many scientists began to reject catastrophism in favor of the idea of gradual geologic change.

Early Ideas About the Origin of Species   Once fossils were recognized as evidence of extinct life, it became clear that species could in fact change. Still, no one had proposed how this might happen. Then, in 1809, French taxonomist Jean Baptiste de Lamarck (1744–1829) proposed the first scientifically testable evolutionary theory. He reasoned that organisms that used one part of their body repeatedly would increase their abilities, very much like weight lifters developing strong arms. Conversely, disuse would weaken an organ until it disappeared. Lamarck surmised (incorrectly) that these changes would pass to future generations.

With these new theories and ideas, people were beginning to accept the concept of evolution but did not yet understand how it could result in the formation of new species. Ultimately, Charles Darwin recognized their application to the changing diversity of life on Earth.

B. Charles Darwin's Voyage Provided a Wealth of Evidence

Charles Darwin (1809–1882) was the grandson of Erasmus Darwin, a noted physician and poet who had anticipated evolutionary theory by writing in 1796 that all animals arose from a single "living filament."

Young Darwin attended Cambridge University in England and, at the urging of his family, completed studies to enter the clergy. Meanwhile, he also followed his own interests. He joined geological field trips and met several eminent geology professors.

Eventually, Darwin was offered a position as ship's naturalist aboard the HMS *Beagle*. Before the ship set sail for its 5-year voyage in 1831 (figure 12.4), the botany professor who had arranged Darwin's position gave the young man the first volume of Lyell's *Principles of Geology*. Darwin picked up the second and third volumes in South America. By the time he finished reading Lyell's works, Darwin was an avid proponent of uniformitarianism.

He recorded his observations as the ship journeyed around the coast of South America. He noted forces that uplifted new land, such as earthquakes and volcanoes, and the constant erosion that wore it down. He marveled at forest plant fossils interspersed with sea sediments and at shell fossils in a mountain cave. Darwin tried to reconstruct the past from contemporary observations and wondered how each fossil had arrived where he found it.

He was particularly aware of similarities and differences among organisms. If there had been a single special creation, then why was one sort of animal or plant created to live on a

mountaintop in one part of the world, yet another type was on mountains elsewhere? Even more puzzling was the resemblance between organisms living in similar habitats in different parts of the world. We now know that such species have undergone convergent evolution. That is, two species that live on opposite sides of the planet may nevertheless share characteristics because they evolved in similar environmental conditions. ⓘ *convergent evolution*, p. 271

In the fourth year of the voyage, the HMS *Beagle* spent five weeks in the Galápagos Islands, off the coast of Ecuador. The notes and samples Darwin brought back would form the seed of his theory of evolution by natural selection.

C. *On the Origin of Species* Proposed Natural Selection as an Evolutionary Mechanism

Toward the end of the voyage, Darwin began to assimilate all he had seen and recorded. Pondering the great variety of organisms in South America and their relationships to fossils and geology, he began to think that these were clues to how species originate.

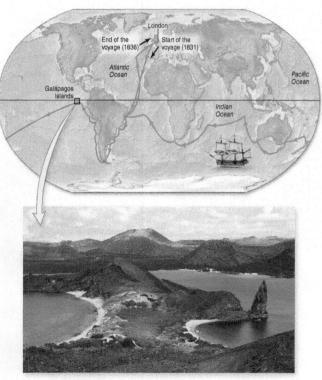

Figure 12.4   **The Voyage of the *Beagle*.** Darwin observed life and geology throughout the world during the journey of the HMS *Beagle*. Many of Darwin's ideas about natural selection and evolution had their origins in the observations he made on the Galápagos Islands.

Descent with Modification Darwin returned to England in 1836, and by 1837 he began assembling his notes in earnest. In March 1837, Darwin consulted ornithologist (bird expert) John Gould about the finches and other birds that the *Beagle* brought back from the Galápagos Islands. Gould could tell from bill structures that some of the finches ate small seeds, whereas others ate large seeds, fruits, or insects. In all, he described 13 distinct types of finches, each different from the birds on the mainland yet sharing some features.

Darwin thought that the different variet- **Video** Finch Beak Variation
ies of finches on the Galápagos had probably descended from a single ancestral type of finch that had flown to the islands and, finding a relatively unoccupied new habitat, flourished. Over the next 3 million years, the finch population gradually branched in several directions. Different groups ate insects, fruits, and seeds of different sizes, depending on the resources each island offered. Darwin also noted changes in other species, including Galápagos tortoises. He coined the phrase "descent with modification" to describe gradual changes from an ancestral type.

Malthus's Ideas on Populations In September 1838, Darwin read a work that helped him understand the diversity of finches on the Galápagos Islands. Economist and theologian Thomas Malthus's *Essay on the Principle of Population,* written 40 years earlier, stated that food availability, disease, and war limit the size of a human population. Wouldn't other organisms face similar limitations? If so, then individuals that could not obtain essential resources would die.

The insight Malthus provided was that **Video** Overproduction of Offspring
individual members of a population were not all the same, as Aristotle had taught. Instead, individuals better able to obtain resources were more likely to survive and reproduce. This would explain the observation that more individuals are produced in a generation than survive; they do not all obtain enough vital resources to live. Over time, environmental challenges would eliminate the more poorly equipped variants, and gradually, the population would change.

The Concept of Natural Selection Darwin used the term *natural selection* to describe "this preservation of favourable variations and the rejection of injurious variations." Biologists later modified the definition to add modern genetics terminology. We now say that **natural selection** occurs when environmental factors cause the differential reproductive success of individuals with particular genotypes.

Darwin got the idea of natural selection from thinking about artificial selection (also called selective breeding). In **artificial selection,** a human chooses one or a few desired traits, such as milk production or seed size, and then allows only the individuals that best express those qualities to reproduce (figure 12.5). Artificial selection is responsible not only for agriculturally important varieties of animals and plants but also for the many breeds

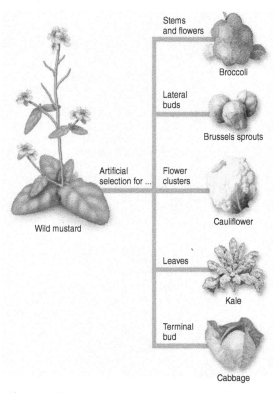

Figure 12.5 Artificial Selection. By selecting for different traits, plant breeders used one type of wild mustard to create all five of these vegetable varieties.

of domesticated cats and dogs (see the Apply It Now box on page 242). Darwin himself raised pigeons and developed several new breeds by artificial selection.

How did natural selection apply to the diversity of finch species on the Galápagos? Originally, some finches flew from the mainland to one island. Eventually that island population outgrew the supply of small seeds, and birds that could eat nothing else starved. But finches that could eat other things, perhaps because of an inherited difference in bill structure, survived and reproduced. Since their food was plentiful, these once-unusual birds gradually came to make up more of the population.

Darwin further realized that he could extend this idea to multiple islands, each of which had a slightly different habitat and therefore selected for different varieties of finches. A new species might arise when a population adapted to so many new conditions that its members could no longer breed with the original group (see chapter 14). In a similar way, new species have evolved throughout the history of life as populations have adapted to different resources. All species are therefore ultimately united by common ancestry.

Apply It **Now**

Dogs Are Products of Artificial Selection

People have been breeding dogs for thousands of years, beginning with domesticated wolves. Dog fanciers now recognize hundreds of breeds, each the product of artificial selection for a different trait that originally occurred as natural genetic variation. Bloodhounds, for example, are selected for their keen sense of smell. Border collies herd livestock (or anything else that moves), and the sleek greyhound is bred for speed.

Behind the carefully bred traits, however, lurk small gene pools and extensive inbreeding, which may harm the health of purebred show animals (table 12.A). Dog breeders can select for desired characteristics, but they can't always avoid the hereditary health problems associated with each breed.

Figure 12.A shows two examples. Pugs have broad heads and short snouts, which makes them gasp and snort for air when they become excited. Pugs' compressed bodies also may have misaligned vertebrae, sometimes leading to paralysis. At the other extreme, dachshunds have extended torsos. These dogs often suffer from painful degeneration of the discs between the vertebrae.

TABLE **12.A** **Purebred Plights**

Breed	Health Problem(s)
Cocker spaniel	Nervousness, ear infections, hernias, kidney problems
Collie	Blindness, bald spots, seizures
Dalmatian	Deafness
German shepherd	Hip dysplasia
Golden retriever	Lymphatic cancer, muscular dystrophy, skin allergies, hip dysplasia, absence of one testicle
Great Dane	Heart failure, bone cancer
Labrador retriever	Dwarfism, blindness
Shar-pei	Skin disorders

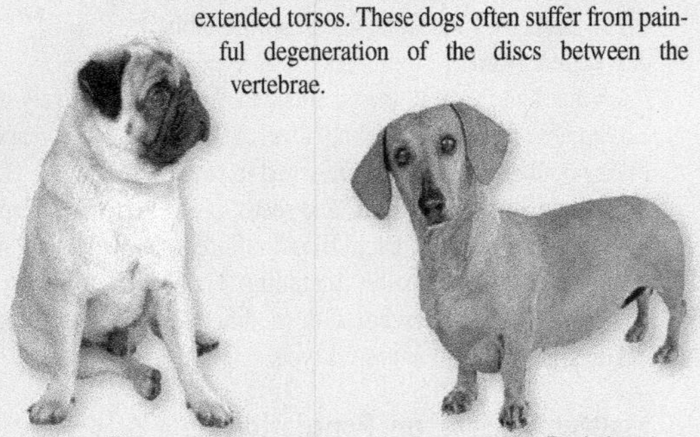

Pug   Dachshund

Figure 12.A **Artificial Selection in Dogs.** Whereas the small-statured pug was bred as a lap dog, the short legs and bold demeanor of dachshunds make them excellent hunters of badgers and other den-dwelling animals. These traits originally occurred as natural genetic variation in their wolf ancestors.

Publication of *On the Origin of Species* Darwin continued to work on his ideas until 1858, when he received a manuscript from British naturalist Alfred Russel Wallace (1823–1913). Wallace had observed the diverse insects, birds, and mammals of South America and southeast Asia, and his manuscript independently proposed that natural selection was the driving force of evolution.

Both Darwin's and Wallace's papers were presented at the Linnaean Society meeting later that year. In 1859, Darwin finally published the 490-page *On the Origin of Species by Means of Natural Selection, or Preservation of Favoured Races in the Struggle for Life.* It would form the underpinning of modern life science.

Table 12.1 summarizes Darwin's main arguments in support of natural selection. He observed that individuals in a species are different from one another and that at least some of this variation is heritable. If more individuals are born than can survive, then competition will determine which ones live long enough to reproduce. Darwin realized that those with the most adaptive traits would be most likely to "win" the competition, reproduce, and pass those favorable traits to the next generation. Over many generations, natural selection coupled with environmental change or a new habitat could change a population's characteristics or even give rise to new species. Darwin's own observations of ants, pigeons, orchids, and many other organisms provided abundant support for his ideas.

TABLE **12.1** **The Logic of Natural Selection: A Summary**

Observations of nature

1. **Genetic variation:** Within a species, no two individuals (except identical siblings) are exactly alike. Some of this variation is heritable.

2. **Limited resources:** Every habitat contains limited supplies of the resources required for survival.

3. **Overproduction of offspring:** More individuals are born than survive to reproduce.

Inferences from observations

1. **Struggle for existence:** Individuals compete for the limited resources that enable them to survive.

2. **Unequal reproductive success (natural selection):** The inherited characteristics of some individuals make them more likely to obtain resources, survive, and reproduce.

3. **Descent with modification:** Over many generations, natural selection can change the characteristics of populations, even giving rise to new species.

Some members of the scientific community happily embraced Darwin's efforts. Upon reading *On the Origin of Species,* his friend Thomas Henry Huxley remarked, "How stupid of me not to have thought of that." Others, however, were less appreciative. People in some religious denominations perceived a clash with their beliefs that all life arose from separate special creations, that species did not change, and that nature is harmonious and purposeful. Perhaps most disturbing to many people was the idea that humans were just one more species competing for resources.

D. Evolutionary Theory Continues to Expand

Although Charles Darwin's arguments were fundamentally sound, he could not explain all that he saw. For instance, he did not understand the source of variation within a population, nor did he know how heritable traits were passed from generation to generation. Ironically, Austrian monk Gregor Mendel was solving the puzzle of inheritance at the same time that Darwin was pondering natural selection (see the opening essay for chapter 10). Mendel's work, however, remained obscure until after Darwin's death.

Since Darwin's time, scientists have learned much more about genes, chromosomes, and the origin and inheritance of genetic variation (figure 12.6). In the 1930s, scientists finally recognized the connection between natural selection and genetics. They unified these ideas into the **modern evolutionary synthesis,** which suggests that genetic mutations create heritable variation and that this variation is the raw material upon which natural selection acts.

After the discovery of DNA's structure in the 1950s, the picture became clearer still. We now know that mutations are changes in DNA sequence (see chapter 7) and that mutations occur at random in all organisms. Sexual reproduction amplifies this variability by shuffling and reshuffling parental alleles to produce genetically different offspring (see chapter 9).

Today, overwhelming evidence supports the theory of evolution by natural selection; chapter 13 describes some of the data in detail. Contemporary biologists therefore accept evolution as the best explanation for the fact that diverse organisms use the same genetic code, the same chemical reactions to extract energy from nutrients, and many of the same (or very similar) enzymes and other proteins. Descent from a common ancestor explains both this great unity of life and the spectacular diversity of organisms today. Coupled with a wide variety of changing habitats and enormous amounts of time, the result of natural selection is a planet packed with millions of variations of the same underlying biochemical theme.

12.2 MASTERING CONCEPTS

1. How does the history of evolutionary thought illustrate the process of science?
2. What did Darwin observe that led him to develop his ideas about the origin of species?
3. How might artificial selection and natural selection produce the same result? Which process would be faster? Why?
4. What is the modern evolutionary synthesis?

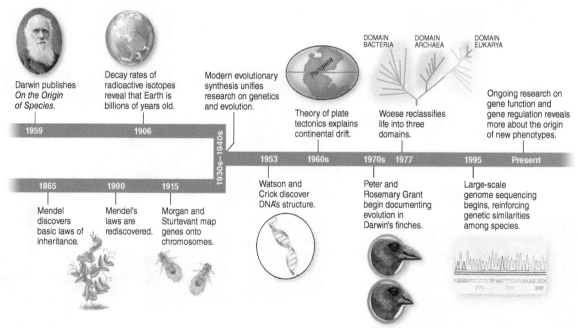

Figure 12.6 Evolutionary Theory Since Darwin. Charles Darwin and Gregor Mendel laid a foundation for evolutionary theory, but many scientists since that time have added to our understanding of how evolution works.

12.3 Natural Selection Molds Evolution

Natural selection is the most famous, and often the most important, mechanism of evolution. This section explains the basic requirements for natural selection to occur. The rest of this chapter describes natural selection and several others forces of evolutionary change in more detail.

A. Adaptations Enhance Reproductive Success

 3-D Animation Evolution

As Darwin knew, organisms of the same species are different from one another, and every population produces more individuals than resources can support (figure 12.7). Some members of any population will not survive to reproduce. A struggle for existence is therefore inevitable.

The variation inherent in each species means that some individuals in each population are better than others at obtaining nutrients and water, avoiding predators, tolerating temperature changes, attracting mates, or reproducing. The heritable traits conferring these advantages are **adaptations**—features that provide a selective advantage because they improve an organism's ability to survive and reproduce.

The word *adaptation* can be confusing because it has multiple meanings. For example, a student might say, "I have adapted well to college life," but short-term changes in an individual do not constitute evolution. Adaptations in the evolutionary sense include only those structures, behaviors, or physiological processes that are heritable and that contribute to reproductive success.

In any population, individuals with the best adaptations are most likely to reproduce and pass their advantage to their offspring. Because of this "differential reproductive success," a population changes over time, with the best available adaptations to the existing environment becoming more common with each generation (figure 12.8).

Natural selection requires preexisting genetic diversity. Ultimately, this diversity arises largely by chance. Nevertheless, it is important to realize that natural selection itself is not a random process. Instead, it selectively eliminates most of the individuals that are least able to compete for resources or cope with the prevailing environment.

One additional important note is that not all variation within a population is subject to natural selection. Some features are "selectively neutral," meaning that they neither increase nor decrease reproductive success. As a simple example, the shape of a person's earlobes has little to do with how many offspring he or she produces. Earlobe shape differences therefore represent neutral variation in the human population. Other types of neutral variation do not change an individual's characteristics at all. For example, a mutation may occur in a stretch of DNA that does not encode a protein. Even if a mutation occurs in a coding region of DNA, the protein's amino acid sequence may not change, thanks to redundancy in the genetic code. Natural selection neither favors nor selects against these "silent" mutations.

B. Natural Selection Eliminates Poorly Adapted Phenotypes

Recall from chapter 10 that an individual's phenotype is its observable properties, most of which arise from a combination

a.

b.

Figure 12.7 Requirements for Natural Selection. (a) This group of people illustrates genetic variation within the human population. (b) Dandelions produce many offspring, but few survive.

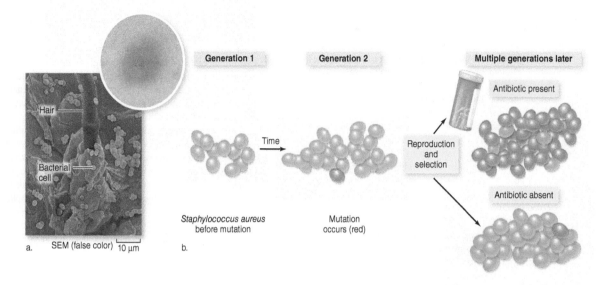

Generation 1   Generation 2   Multiple generations later

Time

Staphylococcus aureus before mutation

Mutation occurs (red)

Antibiotic present

Reproduction and selection

Antibiotic absent

Hair

Bacterial cell

a.   SEM (false color)   10 μm   b.

Figure 12.8 Natural Selection. (a) *Staphylococcus aureus* is a bacterium that causes skin infections. (b) By chance, a cell undergoes a random genetic mutation. The population is then exposed to an antibiotic. The drug kills most of the unmutated cells, but the mutated cell is unaffected and can reproduce. After many generations of exposure to the antibiotic, the mutation is common.

Tutorial Variation and Natural Selection

of environmental influences and the action of multiple genes. By "weeding out" individuals with poorly adapted phenotypes, natural selection indirectly changes allele frequencies in the population. The scientific literature contains countless examples, some of which are described in the Investigating Life sections of this book. For example, disease-causing bacteria select against sexual reproduction in nematode worms (see section 9.9); genetically modified cotton plants producing the Bt toxin eliminate Bt-susceptible moths from the population (see section 10.10); and exposure to the sun's ultraviolet radiation has selected against light skin pigmentation in our own species (see section 25.6).

Environmental conditions constantly change, so evolution never really stops. After all, the phenotype that is "best" depends entirely on the time and place; a trait that is adaptive in one set of circumstances may become a liability in another. Some orchids, for example, produce flowers that are pollinated by only one or a few species of wasp (figure 12.9). The orchids release chemicals that mimic a female wasp's pheromones. When a male wasp visits the flower, seeking a mate, pollen from the orchid sticks to its body. The insect later deposits the pollen on another orchid. As long as wasps are present, this exclusive relationship benefits the plants; they do not waste energy by attracting animals that are unlikely to visit another flower of the same species. But if the wasps went extinct, the orchids could no longer reproduce. In that case, having an exclusive relationship with one or a few pollinator species would doom the orchids.

Figure 12.9 Extremely Specialized. The intimate relationship between this hammer orchid and its pollinator (a wasp) is efficient for the plant. But if the insect goes extinct, the orchid pays the price, too.

C. Natural Selection Does Not Have a Goal

Because most species have become more complex over life's long evolutionary history, many people erroneously believe that natural selection leads to ever more "perfect" organisms or that evolution works toward some long-term goal. Explanations that use the words *need* or *in order to* typically reflect this misconception. For example, a person might say, "The orchids started producing pheromones because they needed to attract wasps" or "The orchids make pheromones in order to trick the male wasps into visiting their flowers."

Both explanations are incorrect because evolution does not have a goal. How could it? No known mechanism allows the environment to tell DNA how to mutate and generate the alleles needed to confront future conditions. Nor does natural selection strive for perfection; if it did, the vast majority of species in life's history would still exist. Instead, most are extinct.

Several factors combine to prevent natural selection from producing all of the traits that a species might find useful. First, every genome has limited potential, imposed by its evolutionary history. The structure of the human skeleton, for example, will not allow for the sudden appearance of wheels, no matter how useful they might be on paved roads. Second, no population contains every allele needed to confront every possible change in the environment. If the right alleles aren't available at the right time, an environmental change may wipe out a species (figure 12.10). Third, disasters such as floods and volcanic eruptions can indiscriminately eliminate the best allele combinations, simply by chance (see section 12.6). And finally, some harmful genetic traits are out of natural selection's reach, such as diseases that appear only after reproductive age.

"Need-based" evolution is among the most common misconceptions about biology; another is that traits automatically disappear when they are no longer needed. Blind cave fish, for example, lack eyes. Likewise, the protist that causes malaria can survive only inside a living host, having lost many features that allow independent living. Note, however, that "absence of need" is not a selective force. Instead, the environment selects against features that cost more than they are worth. Cells need energy to produce and maintain eyes or the proteins required for independent living. If an individual without that feature has more energy for gathering food or finding mates, it may have a reproductive edge. Over many generations, the feature may disappear.

In contrast to natural selection, artificial selection *does* have a goal: Humans select for specific, desired traits. However, we affect other species in so many ways that the distinction between artificial selection and human-influenced natural selection can be confusing. In general, if humans alter the environment but do not select which individuals breed, the term *natural selection* applies.

D. What Does "Survival of the Fittest" Really Mean?

Natural selection is often called "the survival of the fittest," but this phrase is not entirely accurate or complete. In everyday language, the "fittest" individual is the one in the best physical shape: the strongest, fastest, or biggest. Physical fitness, however, is not the key to natural selection (although it may play a part).

Rather, in an evolutionary sense, **fitness** refers to an organism's genetic contribution to the next generation. A large, quick, burly elk scores zero on the evolutionary fitness scale if poor eyesight makes it vulnerable to an early death in the jaws of a wolf. On the other hand, a mayfly that dies in the act of producing thousands of offspring is highly fit.

Paradoxically, natural selection promotes any trait that increases fitness, even if the trait virtually guarantees an individual's death. For example, a male praying mantis may not resist if the female begins to eat his head during copulation.

a.   2 cm   b.

Figure 12.10 Extinction. (a) Sea scorpions once thrived worldwide, but they died out during a mass extinction event some 250 million years ago. (b) These petrified trees in the Arizona desert are from a family of trees that is now extinct in the northern hemisphere, thanks to continental drift.

BurningQuestion

Why doesn't natural selection produce one superorganism?

Natural selection cannot produce one "perfect" organism that is supremely adapted to every possible habitat on Earth. The simple reason is that the adaptations that seem "perfect" in one habitat would be completely wrong in another. To take an extreme example, a trout's adaptations work well in a cold mountain stream but are useless in the sands of the Sahara. The variety of habitats on Earth—ocean, freshwater, tundra, prairie, desert, forest—is just too great for one species to be able to live everywhere.

Some people believe that evolution actually has produced a superorganism: humans. True, we have the intelligence, dexterity, and cultural background to occupy every continent on Earth. But humans can only make brief excursions into water and onto

the highest mountaintops, areas where other organisms thrive. And few organisms can live in the extreme heat of Earth's interior.

Nevertheless, organisms that can survive in a wide variety of habitats may threaten Earth's ecosystems. Weeds such as cheat grass and dandelions, along with animal pests such as cockroaches and rats, crowd out native species and appear to be able to live anywhere. Yet even they can't withstand conditions that are too hot, too cold, too dry, or too wet. Because different habitats have such different constraints, it seems unlikely that any organism will ever evolve with the combination of traits that would enable it to live everywhere.

Submit your burning question to
Marielle.Hoefnagels@mheducation.com

The male's passive behavior is adaptive because the extra food the female obtains in this way will enhance the chance of survival for their young. Likewise, section 35.7 describes a male spider that somersaults his abdomen into the jaws of his mate during copulation. Unlike the mantis, his body is too small to offer the female a nutritional benefit. Instead, the male's suicidal behavior prolongs copulation, so he sires the most possible offspring. As in the case of the mantis, the male spider does not survive—but his alleles will.

These examples illustrate an important point: *by itself, survival is not enough.* Because successful reproduction is the

only way for an organism to perpetuate its genes, fitness depends on the ability to survive just long enough to reproduce. Plants that germinate, grow, flower, produce seeds, and die within just a few weeks may have fitness equal to a redwood that lives for centuries (figure 12.11).

Many adaptations contribute to an organism's overall fitness. The ability to overcome poor weather conditions, combat parasites and other disease-causing organisms, evade predators, and compete for resources all enhance an organism's chances of reaching reproductive age. At that point, the ability to attract mates (or pollinators, in the case of many flowering plants) affects the number of offspring an organism produces.

Fitness includes not only the total number of offspring produced but also the proportion that reach reproductive age. Some organisms, **Video** Chick Competition
including humans, have few offspring but invest large amounts of energy in each one. Insects and many other species produce thousands of young but invest minimally in each. The optimal balance between "quality" and "quantity" may vary greatly, even among individuals within a population. Section 37.4 further describes this evolutionary trade-off.

Some people wonder whether evolution could produce one species that could thrive and reproduce in every habitat on Earth, outcompeting other species across the globe. This chapter's Burning Question discusses this possibility.

a.   b.

Figure 12.11 Fitness Is Reproductive Success. One key to fitness is living long enough to reproduce. (a) For a redwood, that may take centuries. (b) In an annual plant, it may take just a few weeks.

12.3 MASTERING CONCEPTS

1. What is an adaptation, and how do adaptations become more common within a population?
2. What is the role of genetic variation in natural selection?
3. How can natural selection favor different phenotypes at different times?
4. Why doesn't natural selection produce perfectly adapted organisms?
5. What is evolutionary fitness?

12.4 Evolution Is Inevitable in Real Populations

Tutorial
Hardy–Weinberg
Equilibrium

Shifting allele frequencies in populations are the small steps of change that collectively drive evolution. Given the large number of genes in any organism and the many factors that can alter allele frequencies (including but not limited to natural selection), evolution is not only possible but unavoidable. This section explains why.

A. At Hardy–Weinberg Equilibrium, Allele Frequencies Do Not Change

The study of population genetics relies on the intimate relationship between allele frequencies and **genotype frequencies.** Each genotype's frequency is the number of individuals with that genotype, divided by the total size of the population. For example, if 64 of the 100 individuals in a population are homozygous recessive, then the frequency of genotype *aa* is 64/100, or 0.64.

Hardy–Weinberg equilibrium is the highly unlikely situation in which allele frequencies and genotype frequencies do not change from one generation to the next. It occurs only in populations that meet the following assumptions: (1) natural selection does not occur; (2) mutations do not occur, so no new alleles arise; (3) the population is infinitely large, or at least large enough to eliminate random changes in allele frequencies; (4) individuals mate at random; and (5) individuals do not migrate into or out of the population.

Hardy–Weinberg equilibrium is named after mathematician Godfrey H. Hardy and physician Wilhelm Weinberg. They independently developed two simple equations representing the relationship between allele frequencies and genotype frequencies (figure 12.12). To understand their logic, begin by assuming that a gene has only two possible alleles, with frequencies p and q. The first equation, then, is the following expression:

$$p + q = 1$$

This equation represents the frequencies of both alleles in the population. For example, suppose that in a population of ferrets, the frequency of the dark fur allele *(D)* is 0.6; the frequency of the alternative allele *d*, which confers tan fur, is 0.4. The two frequencies add up to 1 because the two alleles represent all the possibilities in the population.

Assumptions of the Hardy–Weinberg model

1   Natural selection does not occur.

2   Mutations do not occur.

3   The population is infinitely large.

4   Individuals mate at random.

5   Individuals do not migrate into or out of the population.

Allele frequencies

Definition/equation	Example
p = frequency of dominant allele	p = frequency of D (dark fur) = 0.6
q = frequency of recessive allele	q = frequency of d (tan fur) = 0.4
$p + q = 1$	0.6 + 0.4 = 1

Genotype frequencies

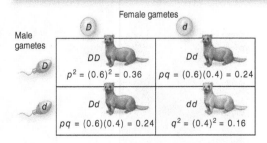

Female gametes

	D	d
Male gametes D	DD $p^2 = (0.6)^2 = 0.36$	Dd $pq = (0.6)(0.4) = 0.24$
d	Dd $pq = (0.6)(0.4) = 0.24$	dd $q^2 = (0.4)^2 = 0.16$

Equation	Example
$p^2 + 2pq + q^2 = 1$	$(0.6)^2 + (2 \times 0.6 \times 0.4) + (0.4)^2 = 1$

Figure 12.12 Hardy–Weinberg Equilibrium. At Hardy–Weinberg equilibrium, allele frequencies remain constant from one generation to the next; evolution does not occur. This figure depicts the random mating that underlies Hardy–Weinberg equilibrium. The sample population of ferrets shown in the figure contains only 25 individuals; one of the assumptions of Hardy–Weinberg equilibrium, however, is that a population must be very large.

Figure It Out

In a species of ladybug, one gene controls whether the beetle has spots or not, with the allele conferring spots being dominant. Suppose you find a swarm consisting of 1000 ladybugs; 250 of them lack spots. What are the frequencies of the dominant and recessive alleles?

Answer: $q^2 = 0.25$, so $q = 0.5$. Therefore, $p = 0.5$ as well.

At Hardy–Weinberg equilibrium, we can use allele frequencies to calculate genotype frequencies, according to the second equation in figure 12.12:

$$p^2 + 2pq + q^2 = 1$$

In this equation, the proportion of the population with genotype *DD* equals p^2, and the proportion of population members with genotype *dd* equals q^2. To calculate the frequency of the heterozygous class, multiply *pq* by 2. Since the homozygotes and the heterozygotes account for all possible genotypes in the population, the sum of their frequencies must add up to 1.

Figure It Out

A population of 100 starfish is in Hardy–Weinberg equilibrium. The trait for long arms is completely dominant to the trait for short arms. In this population, 40% of the alleles for this trait are dominant, and 60% are recessive. What is the frequency of the heterozygous genotype in this population?

Answer: $2 \times 0.4 \times 0.6 = 0.48$

When the conditions of Hardy–Weinberg equilibrium are met, allele and genotype frequencies will not change in future generations, and evolution will not occur. Conversely, a measurable change in genotype frequencies from one generation to the next is evidence that a population has evolved.

Besides providing a framework for determining whether evolution has occurred, these two equations are useful because they allow us to infer characteristics of a population based on limited information. One application is the use of known allele frequencies to estimate genotype frequencies in a population. DNA profiling, for example, relies on population databases that contain the known frequencies of each allele at 13 sites in the human genome. Forensic analysts can use this information to calculate the probability that two people share the same genotype across all 13 sites. ⓘ *DNA profiling*, p. 224

Usually, however, we do not know the exact frequency of every allele in a population. In that case, we can use the Hardy–Weinberg equations to estimate allele frequencies based on the known frequency of one genotype. But how do we get that information? Recall from chapter 10 that a distinctive phenotype is often associated with a homozygous recessive genotype. As a result, determining q^2 for some genes is relatively easy. Knowing *q*, in turn, makes it possible to calculate *p*. The values of *p* and *q* can then be plugged into the second equation to estimate the frequencies of homozygous dominant and heterozygous genotypes. For an example based on a genetic disease called cystic fibrosis, see the Figure It Out question below.

Figure It Out

Assume that one in 3000 Caucasian babies in the United States is born with cystic fibrosis, a disease caused by a recessive allele. The value of q^2 is therefore 1/3000 = 0.0003; *q* is the square root of 0.0003, or .018. Use this information to estimate the frequency of heterozygotes (symptomless carriers) in the American Caucasian population.

Answer: If $q = 0.018$, then $p = 0.982$; the frequency of heterozygotes is $2 \times 0.982 \times 0.018$ = 0.035, or 3.5%.

B. In Reality, Allele Frequencies Always Change

A population at Hardy–Weinberg equilibrium does not evolve. A real population, however, violates some or all of the assumptions of Hardy–Weinberg equilibrium. Allele frequencies change when any of the following occurs:

- some phenotypes are better adapted to the environment than others (natural selection);
- mutations introduce new alleles;
- allele frequencies change due to chance (genetic drift);
- individuals remain in closed groups, mating among themselves rather than with the larger population (nonrandom mating);
- individuals migrate among populations.

All of these events are common. If you think about the human population, for example, we can sometimes counter natural selection by medically correcting phenotypes that would otherwise prevent some of us from having children. But natural selection still acts to reduce the frequency of alleles that cause deadly childhood illnesses. After all, children who inherit these illnesses will not survive long enough to pass the alleles on.

Moreover, genetic mutations can and do occur. Some mutations happen randomly when DNA replicates. External agents, including harmful chemicals and radiation, can also cause mutations.

Finally, genetic drift, nonrandom mating, and migration all happen in real populations. The large size of the human population usually minimizes the chance of random changes in allele frequencies, but they occasionally occur (see section 12.7B). Humans are deliberate in our choices of mates and we may choose to live across the world from our parents; allele frequencies change as we move and mix.

These forces act on populations of other species as well, so allele frequencies always change over multiple generations. In other words, evolution is inevitable. Even though its assumptions do not apply to real populations, the concept of Hardy–Weinberg equilibrium does serve as a basis of comparison (a "null hypothesis") to reveal when evolution is occurring. Additional studies can then reveal which mechanism of evolution is acting on the population. Sections 12.5 through 12.7 describe these mechanisms of evolution in more detail.

12.4   MASTERING CONCEPTS

1. What are the five conditions required for Hardy–Weinberg equilibrium?
2. Why is the concept of Hardy–Weinberg equilibrium important?
3. Explain the components and meaning of the equation $p^2 + 2pq + q^2 = 1$.
4. Why doesn't Hardy–Weinberg equilibrium occur in real populations?

12.5 Natural Selection Can Shape Populations in Many Ways

Of all the mechanisms by which a population can evolve, natural selection is probably the most important. Natural selection changes the genetic makeup of a population by favoring the alleles that contribute to reproductive success and selecting against those that do not.

Natural selection, however, does not eliminate alleles directly. Instead, individuals with the "best" phenotypes are most likely to pass their alleles to the next generation; those with poorly suited phenotypes are less likely to survive long enough to reproduce. Three modes of natural selection—directional, disruptive, and stabilizing—are distinguished by their effects on the phenotypes in a population (figure 12.13).

In **directional selection,** one extreme phenotype is fittest, and the environment selects against the others. A change in tree trunk color from light to dark, for example, may select for dark-winged moths and against light-winged individuals. The rise of antibiotic resistance among bacteria, described in this chapter's opening essay, also reflects directional selection, as does the increase in pesticide-resistant insects (see section 10.10). The fittest phenotype may initially be rare, but its frequency increases over multiple generations as the environment changes—for example, after exposure to the antibiotic or insecticide.

In **disruptive selection** (sometimes called diversifying selection), two or more extreme phenotypes are fitter than the intermediate phenotype. Consider, for example, a population of marine snails that live among brown rocks encrusted with white barnacles. The white snails near the barnacles are camouflaged, and the dark brown ones on the bare rocks likewise blend in. The snails that are neither white nor dark brown are most often seen and eaten by predatory shorebirds.

In a third form of natural selection, called **stabilizing selection** (or normalizing selection), extreme phenotypes are less fit than the optimal intermediate phenotype. Human birth weight illustrates this tendency to stabilize. Very small or very large newborns are less likely to survive than babies of intermediate weight. By eliminating all but the individuals with the optimal phenotype, stabilizing selection tends to reduce the variation in a population. It is therefore most common in stable, unchanging environments.

These three models of natural selection might seem to suggest that, for each trait, only one or a few beneficial alleles ought to persist in the population. The harmful alleles should gradually become less common until they disappear, while the others become "fixed" in the population.

For some genes, however, natural selection maintains a **balanced polymorphism,** in which multiple alleles of a gene persist indefinitely in the population at more or less constant frequencies. (*Polymorphism* means "multiple forms.") In a balanced polymor-

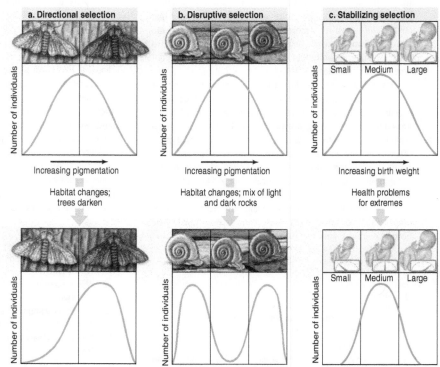

Figure 12.13 Types of Natural Selection.
(a) Directional selection results from selection against one extreme phenotype. (b) In disruptive selection, two extreme phenotypes each confer a selective advantage over the intermediate phenotype.
(c) Stabilizing selection maintains an intermediate expression of a trait by selecting against extreme variants.

a. Directional selection

Number of individuals

Increasing pigmentation

Habitat changes; trees darken

Number of individuals

b. Disruptive selection

Number of individuals

Increasing pigmentation

Habitat changes; mix of light and dark rocks

Number of individuals

c. Stabilizing selection

Small   Medium   Large

Number of individuals

Increasing birth weight

Health problems for extremes

Small   Medium   Large

Number of individuals

phism, even harmful alleles may remain in the population. This situation seems contrary to natural selection; how can it occur?

One circumstance that can maintain a balanced polymorphism is a **heterozygote advantage,** which occurs when an individual with two different alleles for a gene (a heterozygote) has greater fitness than those whose two alleles are identical (homozygotes). Heterozygotes can maintain a harmful recessive allele in a population, even if homozygous recessive individuals have greatly reduced fitness.

The best documented example of heterozygote advantage in humans is sickle cell disease. The disease-causing allele encodes an abnormal form of hemoglobin. The abnormal hemoglobin proteins do not fold properly; instead, they form chains that bend a red blood cell into a characteristic sickle shape (see figure 7.21). In a person who is homozygous recessive for the sickle cell allele, all the red blood cells are affected. Symptoms include anemia, joint pain, a swollen spleen, and frequent, severe infections; the person may not live long enough to reproduce. On the other hand, a person who is heterozygous for the sickle cell allele is only mildly affected. Some of his or her red blood cells may take abnormal shapes, but the resulting mild anemia is not usually harmful. Still, why doesn't natural selection eliminate the sickle cell allele from the population?

The answer is that heterozygotes also have a reproductive edge over people who are homozygous for the *normal* hemoglobin allele. Specifically, heterozygotes are resistant to a severe infectious disease, malaria. When a mosquito carrying cells of a protist called *Plasmodium* feeds on a human with normal hemoglobin, the parasite enters the red blood cells. Eventually, infected blood cells burst, and the parasite travels throughout the body. But the sickled red blood cells of an infected carrier halt the parasite's spread. ⓘ *malaria,* p. 373

The heterozygote advantage for the sickle cell allele is regional (figure 12.14). In malaria-free areas, anemia is the predominant selective force, and heterozygotes have no advantage. The sickle cell allele is therefore rare. Wherever malaria rages, however, the two opposing selective forces—anemia and malaria—maintain a balanced polymorphism for the sickle cell trait. In these areas, sickle cell carriers remain healthiest; they are resistant to malaria but not ill from sickle cell disease. The frequency of the sickle cell allele remains high because carriers have more children than people who are homozygous for either allele.

Unfortunately, as you can see in figure 12.14b, two carriers have a 25% chance of producing a child who is homozygous for the sickle cell allele. These children pay the evolutionary price for the genetic protection against malaria.

Cystic fibrosis provides another example of heterozygote advantage. This illness originates with a mutation in the gene encoding a membrane protein called CFTR; the mutated allele encodes a faulty (nonfunctional) version of the protein. People born with two mutated *CFTR* alleles have cystic fibrosis and are unlikely to reproduce. Heterozygotes, however, have an advantage in areas where an infectious disease called cholera is common. The cholera toxin overstimulates normal CFTR proteins in the

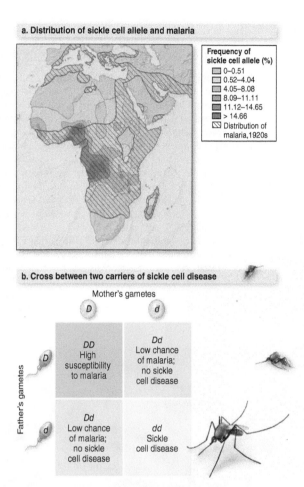

a. Distribution of sickle cell allele and malaria

Frequency of
sickle cell allele (%)
▢ 0–0.51
▢ 0.52–4.04
▢ 4.05–8.08
▢ 8.09–11.11
▢ 11.12–14.65
▢ > 14.66
▨ Distribution of
malaria,1920s

b. Cross between two carriers of sickle cell disease

Mother's gametes

	D	d
D	DD High susceptibility to malaria	Dd Low chance of malaria; no sickle cell disease
d	Dd Low chance of malaria; no sickle cell disease	dd Sickle cell disease

Father's gametes

Figure 12.14 Heterozygote Advantage. (a) The distribution of people with one copy of the sickle cell allele overlaps closely with the areas where malaria is prevalent. (b) Sickle cell anemia and malaria are opposing selective forces that maintain a balanced polymorphism for the two alleles of the hemoglobin gene. In regions where malaria thrives, heterozygotes for the sickle cell allele are most likely to survive long enough to reproduce.

intestines, causing watery diarrhea that can lead to dehydration and death. Carriers of the recessive allele are unlikely to die of dehydration from cholera because half of their CFTR proteins are abnormal. Heterozygotes therefore have a fitness advantage over both types of homozygotes, allowing the harmful allele to remain in the population (see section 4.6).

12.5 MASTERING CONCEPTS

1. Distinguish among directional, disruptive, and stabilizing selection.

2. How can natural selection maintain harmful alleles in a population?

12.6 Sexual Selection Directly Influences Reproductive Success

In many vertebrate species, the sexes look alike. The difference between a male and a female house cat, for example, is not immediately obvious. In some species, however, natural selection can maintain a **sexual dimorphism,** which is a difference in appearance between males and females. One sex may be much larger or more colorful than the other, or one sex may have distinctive structures such as horns or antlers.

Some of these sexually dimorphic features may seem to violate natural selection. For example, the vivid red feathers of male cardinals make the birds much more obvious to predators than their brown female counterparts, and the extravagant tail of a peacock is brightly colored and makes flying difficult. How can natural selection allow for traits that apparently reduce survival?

The answer is that a special form of natural selection is at work. **Sexual selection** is a type of natural selection resulting from variation in the ability to obtain mates. If female cardinals prefer bright red males, then showy plumage directly increases a male's chances of reproducing. Because the brightest males get

the most chances to reproduce, alleles that confer red plumage are common in the population.

Sexual selection has two forms. In **intrasexual selection,** the members of one sex compete among themselves for access to the opposite sex (figure 12.15). Mate choice plays no part in deciding the winner. Male bighorn sheep, for example, use their horns to battle for the right to mate with multiple females. The strongest rams are therefore the most likely to pass on their alleles. In **intersexual selection,** members of one sex choose their mates from among multiple members of the opposite sex (figure 12.16).

Why do males usually show the greatest effects of sexual selection? In most (but not all) vertebrate species, females spend more time and energy on producing and rearing offspring than do males. Because of this high investment in reproduction, females tend to be selective about their mates. Males are typically less choosy and must compete for access to females.

The evolutionary origin of the males' elaborate ornaments remains an open question. One possibility is that long tail feathers and bright colors are costly to produce and maintain; they are therefore indirect advertisements of good health or disease resistance. Likewise, the ability to win fights with competing males is also an indicator of good genes. A female who instinctively chooses a high-quality male will increase not only his fitness but also her own.

12.6   MASTERING CONCEPTS

1. How does sexual selection promote traits that would seem to decrease survival?
2. What is the difference between intrasexual selection and intersexual selection?

a.

b.

Figure 12.15   Intrasexual Selection. (a) Two bighorn sheep prepare to butt heads in the Rocky Mountains. (b) Western lowland gorillas in Africa fight for control of the family group.

a.

b.

Figure 12.16   Intersexual Selection. (a) Female weaver birds select mates based on the male's nest-building ability. (b) The male bird-of-paradise displays bright plumes that attract females.

12.7 Evolution Occurs in Several Additional Ways

Animation
Mechanisms of Evolution

Natural selection is responsible for adaptations that enhance survival and reproduction, but it is not the only mechanism of evolution. This section describes four more ways that a population can evolve: mutation, genetic drift, nonrandom mating, and gene flow. All occur frequently, and each can, by itself, disrupt Hardy–Weinberg equilibrium. The changes in allele frequencies that constitute evolution therefore occur nearly all the time.

A. Mutation Fuels Evolution

A change in an organism's DNA sequence introduces a new allele to a population. The new variant may be harmful, neutral, or beneficial, depending on how the mutation affects the sequence of the encoded protein. ⓘ *mutations*, p. 138

Mutations are the raw material for evolution because genes contribute to phenotypes, and natural selection acts on phenotypes. For example, random mutations in bacterial DNA may change the shapes of key proteins in the cell's ribosomes or cell wall. Exposure to antibiotics selects for some of the new phenotypes if they happen to make the cell resistant to the drug. In that case, the mutations will pass to the next generation.

As we saw in section 12.3C, one common misconception about evolution is that a mutation produces a novel adaptation precisely when a population "needs" it to confront a new environmental challenge. For example, many people mistakenly believe that antibiotics *create* resistance; that is, that resistance arises in bacteria *in response* to exposure to the drugs.

In reality, genes do not "know" when to mutate; the chance that a mutation will occur is independent of whether a new phenotype would benefit the organism. The only way antibiotic resistance arises is if some bacteria happen to have a mutation that confers antibiotic resistance *before* exposure to the drug. The drug creates a situation in which these variants can flourish. That trait will then become more common within the population by natural selection. If no bacteria start out resistant, the drug kills the entire population. Because bacterial populations are often enormous, however, it is likely that at least a few individuals carry such a mutation.

The rate at which mutations occur varies, both among different genes and within a gene. The average rate is around one DNA sequence change per 10^9 base pairs. At first, this number may seem too low to pose a significant force in evolution. Each genome, however, has an enormous number of base pairs, and a large number of cell divisions occur throughout life. Extensive cell division means ample opportunities for mutation.

A mutation affects evolution only if subsequent generations inherit it. In asexually reproducing organisms such as bacteria, each mutated cell gives rise to mutant offspring (if the mutation does not prevent reproduction). In a multicellular organism, however, a mutation can pass to the next generation only if it arises in a germ cell (i.e., one that will give rise to gametes; see chapter 9). For example, a cigarette smoker with lung cancer will not pass any smoking-induced mutations to her children, because her egg cells will not contain the altered DNA.

B. Genetic Drift Occurs by Chance

Animation
Genetic Drift

Genetic drift is a change in allele frequencies that occurs purely by chance. Unlike mutation, which increases diversity, genetic drift tends to eliminate alleles from a population.

All forms of genetic drift are rooted in sampling error, which occurs when a sample does not match the larger group from which it is drawn (figure 12.17). Suppose, for example, that one allele of a gene occurs at a very low frequency in a population. If, by chance, none of the individuals carrying the rare allele happens to reproduce, that variant will disappear from the population. Even if some do reproduce, the allele still might not pass to the next generation. After all, the events of meiosis ensure that each allele has only a 50% chance of passing to each offspring. A rare allele can therefore vanish from a population—not because it reduces fitness but simply by chance.

Genetic drift is inevitable; that is, allele frequencies for any gene will fluctuate at random from generation to generation.

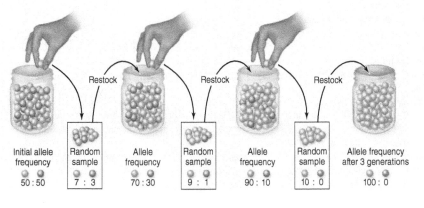

Figure 12.17 Sampling Error. Ten marbles are drawn at random from the jar on the left. Even though 50% of the marbles in the jar are blue, the random sample contains only 30% blue marbles. In the next "generation," 30% of the marbles are blue, but the random sample contains just one blue marble. The third sample contains no blue marbles and therefore eliminates the blue "allele" from the population, purely by chance.

Initial allele frequency
50 : 50

Random sample
7 : 3

Restock

Allele frequency
70 : 30

Random sample
9 : 1

Restock

Allele frequency
90 : 10

Random sample
10 : 0

Restock

Allele frequency after 3 generations
100 : 0

Significant sampling errors, however, are most likely to affect small populations. Hardy–Weinberg equilibrium requires populations to be very large (approaching infinity) to minimize the effects of these random changes in allele frequencies. In reality, of course, many populations are small, so genetic drift can be an important evolutionary force.

Random chance can eliminate rare alleles, but genetic drift can also operate in other ways. As described below, sampling errors (such as those illustrated in figure 12.17) can occur when a small population separates from a larger one or when a large population is reduced to a very small size.

The Founder Effect One cause of genetic drift is the **founder effect,** which occurs when a small group of individuals leaves its home population and establishes a new, isolated settlement. The small group's "allele sample" may not represent the allele frequencies of the original population. Some traits that were rare in the original population may therefore be more frequent in the new population. Likewise, other traits will be less common or may even disappear.

The Amish people of Pennsylvania provide a famous example of the founder effect. About 200 followers of the Amish denomination immigrated to North America from Switzerland in the 1700s. One couple, who immigrated in 1744, happened to carry the recessive allele associated with Ellis–van Creveld syndrome (figure 12.18). This allele is extremely rare in the population at large. Intermarriage among the Amish, however, has kept the disease's incidence high in this subgroup more than two centuries after the original immigrants arrived.

On a much broader scale, the history of human migration out of Africa has been a series of founder effects (see figure 15.27). A subset of people migrated from Africa to Asia about 40,000 to 70,000 years ago, and from there a smaller subset later migrated to the Americas. Meanwhile a different subset migrated from Africa to Europe. Each migration divided the genetic variation of the previous population. As populations became isolated in new environments, phenotypes diverged. These "serial founder effects" therefore explain the unique allele combinations among native occupants of each region (see figure 12.1).

The Bottleneck Effect Genetic drift also may result from a population **bottleneck,** which occurs when a population drops rapidly over a short period, causing the loss of many alleles that were present in the larger ancestral population (figure 12.19). Even if the few remaining individuals mate and eventually restore the population's numbers, the loss of genetic diversity is permanent.

Cheetahs are currently undergoing a population bottleneck. Until 10,000 years ago, these cats were common in many areas. Today, just two isolated populations live in South and East Africa, numbering only a few thousand animals. Inbreeding has made the South African cheetahs so genetically alike that even unrelated animals can accept skin grafts from each other. Researchers attribute the genetic uniformity of cheetahs to two bottlenecks:

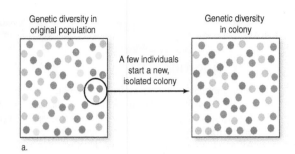

Genetic diversity in original population

A few individuals start a new, isolated colony

Genetic diversity in colony

a.

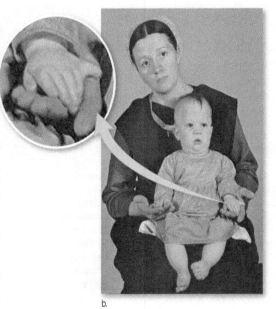

b.

Figure 12.18 The Founder Effect. (a) A few individuals leave one population and begin an isolated colony, which contains only some of the original population's diversity. (b) This Amish child from Lancaster County, Pennsylvania, has inherited Ellis–van Creveld syndrome, a condition characterized by short-limbed dwarfism, extra fingers, and other symptoms. This autosomal recessive disorder occurs in 7% of the people of this Amish community but is extremely rare elsewhere.

one that occurred at the end of the most recent ice age, when habitats changed drastically, and another when humans slaughtered many cheetahs during the nineteenth century.

North American species have undergone severe bottlenecks as well. Bison, for example, nearly went extinct because of overhunting in the 1800s. And habitat loss has caused the population of greater prairie chickens to plummet from about 100 million in 1900 to several hundred today. The loss of genetic diversity in cheetahs, bison, and prairie chickens presents a potential disaster: A single change in the environment might doom them all.

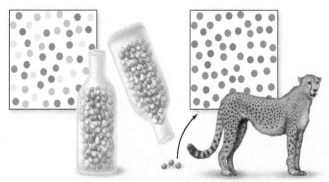

Original cheetah population contains 25 different alleles of a particular gene.

Cheetah population is drastically reduced.

Repopulation occurs. Only three different alleles remain.

Figure 12.19 The Bottleneck Effect. A population bottleneck occurs when the size of a population drastically falls, eliminating some alleles at random. Even if the population rebuilds, some genetic diversity is lost.

C. Nonrandom Mating Concentrates Alleles Locally

To achieve and maintain Hardy–Weinberg equilibrium, a population must have completely random mating, in which each individual has an equal chance of mating with any other member of the population.

In reality, however, mating is rarely random. Many factors influence mating, including geographical restrictions and physical access to the opposite sex. Most animal species also exhibit some form of preference in mate choice, including sexual selection (figure 12.20).

The practice of artificial selection is another way to reduce random mating. Humans select those animals or plants that have a desired trait and then prevent them from mating with those lacking that trait. The result is a wide variety of subpopulations (such as different breeds of dogs) that humans maintain by selective breeding.

D. Gene Flow Moves Alleles Between Populations

Under Hardy–Weinberg equilibrium, no alleles ever leave or enter a population. In reality, **gene flow** moves alleles among populations. Migration is one common way that gene flow occurs (figure 12.21). Departing members of a population take their alleles with them. Likewise, new members entering and interbreeding with an existing population may add new alleles. But gene flow does not require the movement of entire individuals. Wind can carry a plant's pollen for miles, for example, spreading one individual's alleles to a new population.

Gene flow can counteract the effects of both natural selection and genetic drift. At one time, isolated European populations had unique allele frequencies for many genetic diseases. Geographical barriers, such as mountain ranges and large bodies of water, historically restricted migration and kept the gene pools separate. Highways, trains, and airplanes, however, have eliminated physical barriers to migration. Eventually, gene flow should make these regional differences disappear.

12.7 | MASTERING CONCEPTS

1. How do mutations affect an organism's phenotype?
2. How does sampling error cause genetic drift?
3. What is the difference between the founder effect and a population bottleneck?
4. How do nonrandom mating and gene flow disrupt Hardy–Weinberg equilibrium?

Figure 12.20 Nonrandom Mating. If mating among toads were random, all individuals would have an equal chance of reproducing. Instead, a male mates only if his song attracts a willing female. This male toad inflates his throat pouch and generates a call.

Figure 12.21 Gene Flow. Immigration is one way for new alleles to enter a population.

INVESTIGATING LIFE

12.8 Size Matters in Fishing Frenzy

Studying the mechanisms of evolution helps us to understand life's history, but it also has practical consequences. A good example of natural selection is unfolding in fisheries worldwide. The selective force stems from a surprisingly mundane source—fishing regulations—but it affects everything from restaurant menus to the future of the ocean ecosystem.

The past several decades have seen devastating declines in the numbers of large predatory fishes such as swordfish, marlin, and **Video** Ocean Fishing Ban
sharks, as well as smaller animals including tuna, cod, and flounder. From a biological point of view, the reason for the fisheries decline is simple: The animals' death rate exceeds their reproductive rate. Industrial-scale fishing is the culprit. Since the 1950s, fishing fleets have employed larger ships and improved technologies in pursuit of their prey.

Fishing regulations usually allow the harvest of fish that exceed some minimum size. This strategy is logical, because the smallest fish are most likely to be juveniles. Protecting the young should permit the population to recover from the harvest of adult fish. Yet these regulations also have predictable evolutionary side effects. If humans harvest large individuals, fish that are small at maturity are the most likely to survive long enough to reproduce. Large fish may become more scarce over many generations. The same policy should also select for slow-growing fish, since they would be last to exceed the minimum allowed size.

Fish ecologists David Conover and Stephan Munch of Stony Brook University in New York tested these predictions by studying small coastal fish called Atlantic silversides (*Menidia menidia*). Conover and Munch randomly divided a large, captive population of Atlantic silversides into six tanks, each containing about 1100 juvenile fish. After about 6 months, the researchers assigned two tanks to each of the following treatments:

- **Large harvested:** Remove the largest 90% of the fish from two of the tanks, leaving the smallest 10% to reproduce.
- **Small harvested:** Remove the smallest 90% of the fish.
- **Random harvested (control):** Remove 90% of the fish, without size bias.

After the harvests, the 100 or so survivors in each tank reproduced, and their descendants were reared in identical conditions until it was again time to harvest 90% of each population. The researchers repeated the treatments over four generations.

Predictably, the weight of the average caught fish was initially highest for the large-harvested fish. Over four generations of size-biased fish removal, however, the small-harvested treatment favored both large size and rapid growth; the opposite was true in the large-harvested population (figure 12.22). The three treatments imposed different selective forces on the populations.

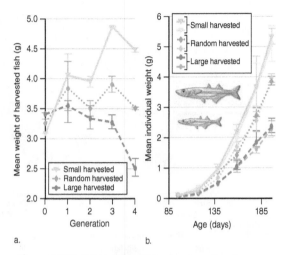

Figure 12.22 Fish Harvests. (a) Over four generations, the average fish in the large-harvested population weighed much less than in the small-harvested population. (b) Small-harvested fish grow faster than large-harvested fish.

The results in figure 12.22 represent only the first four years of a decade-long experiment. The fifth generation of fish was treated like the first four, but in years 6 through 10, Conover and his colleagues tested whether the evolutionary changes they observed could be reversed. For five generations they harvested 90% of the fish at random from all six tanks. The complete results suggested that the size of the fish in large-harvested populations might return to normal after about 12 generations.

Conover and Munch's experiment is more than a straightforward demonstration of natural selection in action; it also has economic and ecological applications. Revised regulations that protect the smallest and the largest fish would spare the juveniles that are critical to a species' future reproduction while also selecting for fast-growing fish. Imposing a maximum size limit would also have ecological benefits, restoring the feeding patterns and other "ecosystem services" of the largest fish. Moreover, the results of the second half of the experiment suggest that fish populations might rebound in coming decades if stocks are protected. This wide range of implications beautifully illustrates the powerful ideas that spring from understanding one fundamental idea: natural selection.

Conover, David O., and Stephan B. Munch. 2002. Sustaining fisheries yields over evolutionary time scales. *Science*, vol. 297, pages 94–96.

Conover, David O., Stephan B. Munch, and Stephen A. Arnott. 2009. Reversal of evolutionary downsizing caused by selective harvest of large fish. *Proceedings of the Royal Society B*, vol. 276, pages 2015–2020.

12.8 MASTERING CONCEPTS

1. What hypothesis did Conover and Munch test?
2. Draw how the graph in figure 12.22a might look once data from the second half of the experiment are added.

CHAPTER SUMMARY

12.1 Evolution Acts on Populations

- Biological **evolution** is descent with modification. One way to detect evolution is to look for a shift in the **gene pool** of a **population; allele frequencies** change from one generation to the next when evolution occurs.
- Microevolution is the small-scale genetic changes within a species. Over the long term, microevolutionary changes also explain macroevolutionary events such as the emergence of new species.

12.2 Evolutionary Thought Has Evolved for Centuries

A. Many Explanations Have Been Proposed for Life's Diversity

- Geology laid the groundwork for evolutionary thought. Some people explained the distribution of rock strata with the idea of **catastrophism** (a series of floods). The more gradual **uniformitarianism** (continual remolding of Earth's surface) became widely accepted.
- The **principle of superposition** states that lower rock strata are older than those above, suggesting an evolutionary sequence for fossils within them.
- Lamarck was the first to propose a testable mechanism of evolution, but it was based on use and disuse of traits during an organism's lifetime.

B. Charles Darwin's Voyage Provided a Wealth of Evidence

- During the voyage of the HMS *Beagle,* Darwin observed the distribution of organisms in diverse habitats and their relationships to geological formations. After much thought and consideration of input from other scientists, he developed his theory of the origin of species by means of **natural selection.**

C. *On the Origin of Species* Proposed Natural Selection as an Evolutionary Mechanism

- Natural selection is based on multiple observations: individuals vary for inherited traits; many more offspring are born than survive; and life is a struggle to acquire limited resources. The environment eliminates poorly adapted individuals, so only those with the best adaptations reproduce.
- **Artificial selection** is based on similar requirements, except that a human breeder takes the place of the environment.
- *On the Origin of Species* offered abundant evidence for descent with modification.

D. Evolutionary Theory Continues to Expand

- The **modern evolutionary synthesis** unifies ideas about DNA, mutations, inheritance, and natural selection.

12.3 Natural Selection Molds Evolution

- Natural selection is one mechanism of microevolution.

A. Adaptations Enhance Reproductive Success

- Individuals with the best **adaptations** to the current environment are most likely to leave fertile offspring, and therefore their alleles become more common in the population over time.
- Natural selection requires variation, which arises ultimately from random mutations.

B. Natural Selection Eliminates Poorly Adapted Phenotypes

- Natural selection weeds out some phenotypes, causing changes in allele frequencies over multiple generations.

C. Natural Selection Does Not Have a Goal

- Natural selection does not work toward a goal, nor can it achieve perfectly adapted organisms.

D. What Does "Survival of the Fittest" Really Mean?

- Organisms with the highest evolutionary **fitness** are the ones that have the greatest reproductive success. Many traits contribute to an organism's fitness.

12.4 Evolution Is Inevitable in Real Populations

- Calculations of allele frequencies and **genotype frequencies** allow biologists to detect whether evolution has occurred.

A. At Hardy–Weinberg Equilibrium, Allele Frequencies Do Not Change

- We can calculate the proportion of genotypes and phenotypes in a population by inserting known allele frequencies into an algebraic equation: $p^2 + 2pq + q^2 = 1$.
- If a population meets all assumptions of **Hardy–Weinberg equilibrium,** evolution does not occur because allele frequencies do not change from generation to generation.

B. In Reality, Allele Frequencies Always Change

- The conditions for Hardy–Weinberg equilibrium do not occur together in natural populations, suggesting that allele frequencies always change from one generation to the next. Figure 12.23 on page 258 summarizes the main mechanisms of evolution.

12.5 Natural Selection Can Shape Populations in Many Ways

- In **directional selection,** one extreme phenotype becomes more prevalent in a population.
- In **disruptive selection,** multiple extreme phenotypes survive at the expense of intermediate forms.
- In **stabilizing selection,** an intermediate phenotype has an advantage over individuals with extreme phenotypes.
- In **balanced polymorphism,** natural selection indefinitely maintains more than one allele for a gene.
- Harmful recessive alleles may remain in a population because of a **heterozygote advantage,** in which carriers have a reproductive advantage over homozygotes.

12.6 Sexual Selection Directly Influences Reproductive Success

- **Sexual dimorphisms** differentiate the sexes. They result from **sexual selection,** a form of natural selection in which inherited traits—even those that seem nonadaptive—make an individual more likely to mate.
- **Intrasexual selection** is competition that does not involve a choice by the opposite sex; **intersexual selection** reflects mate choice by members of the opposite sex.

12.7 Evolution Occurs in Several Additional Ways

A. Mutation Fuels Evolution

- Mutation alters allele frequencies by changing one allele into another, sometimes providing new phenotypes for natural selection to act on. Many mutations do not pass to the next generation.

B. Genetic Drift Occurs by Chance

- In **genetic drift,** allele frequencies change purely by chance events, especially in small populations. The **founder effect** and population **bottlenecks** are forms of genetic drift.

C. Nonrandom Mating Concentrates Alleles Locally

- Nonrandom mating causes some alleles to concentrate in subpopulations.

D. Gene Flow Moves Alleles Between Populations

- Allele movement between populations, as by migration, is **gene flow.**

12.8 Investigating Life: Size Matters in Fishing Frenzy

- Fishing regulations that spare only the smallest fish in a population select for small, slow-growing individuals. Studies of Atlantic silversides suggest that protecting the largest fish as well would increase fishery productivity in the long run.

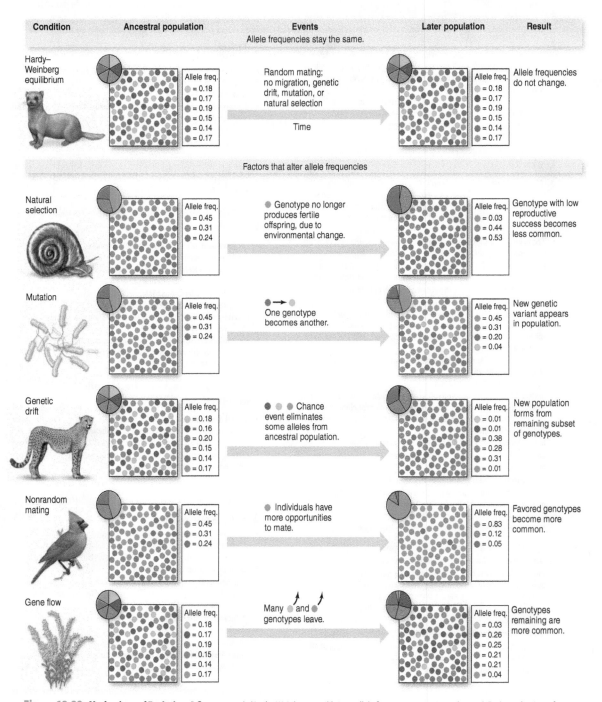

Figure 12.23 Mechanisms of Evolution: A Summary. At Hardy–Weinberg equilibrium, allele frequencies remain unchanged. Each mechanism of evolution—natural selection, mutation, genetic drift, nonrandom mating, and gene flow—changes allele frequencies. In these images, different colored dots represent the alleles for a particular gene. The left image of each pair shows the allele frequencies in the ancestral population; the right image shows the frequencies after evolutionary change has occurred.

Tutorial
Mechanisms
of Evolution

1. How are artificial selection and natural selection similar?
   a. They both rely on human intervention.
   b. They both work toward a predetermined goal.
   c. They both select for specific traits within a population.
   d. They are processes that only affect animals.

2. Biological evolution describes how _____ change from one generation to the next.
   a. individuals   c. phenotype frequencies
   b. allele frequencies   d. communities

3. Suppose a population of 200 individuals has a gene with two alleles (*G* and *g*). If 100 alleles in the population are *g*, then the frequency of the *g* allele in the population is
   a. 0.1   c. 0.5
   b. 0.25   d. 1.0

4. Which of the following is the best definition of fitness?
   a. The ability to increase the number of alleles in a gene pool
   b. The ability to survive for a long time
   c. The ability of an individual to adapt to a changing environment
   d. The ability to produce many offspring

5. After an environmental change, foxes with shorter legs than average are most likely to survive and reproduce. What type of selection will act on this population in the coming generations?
   a. Directional selection   c. Disruptive selection
   b. Stabilizing selection   d. Normalizing selection

6. Huntington disease is caused by a rare, lethal, dominant allele. Symptoms typically begin in mid-life. Which answer best explains why natural selection has not eliminated the Huntington allele?
   a. Females prefer males with the Huntington allele.
   b. The disease does not interfere with the ability to reproduce.
   c. New mutations generate the allele.
   d. Natural selection can eliminate only common alleles.

7. Assume that the dominant allele for the *D* gene occurs at a frequency of 0.8 in a population. What percentage of the population is heterozygous for the *D* gene, based on Hardy–Weinberg equilibrium?
   a. 80%   c. 32%
   b. 64%   d. 20%

8. Darwin observed that different types of organisms were found on either side of a geographic barrier. The barrier was preventing
   a. gene flow.   c. sexual selection.
   b. genetic drift.   d. mutation.

9. Which of the following processes is nonrandom?
   a. A population bottleneck   c. The founder effect
   b. Natural selection   d. Mutation

Answers to these questions are in appendix A.

1. How did James Hutton, Georges Cuvier, Georges-Louis Buffon, Jean Baptiste de Lamarck, Charles Lyell, and Thomas Malthus influence Charles Darwin's thinking?

2. Explain how understanding evolution is important to medicine, agriculture, and maintaining the diversity of organisms on Earth.

3. How does variation arise in an asexually reproducing population? A sexually reproducing population?

4. Influenza and smallpox are diseases caused by different types of viruses. Scientists must produce a new influenza vaccine each year, whereas the smallpox vaccine eradicated the disease. Explain these results from an evolutionary perspective.

5. Many articles about the rise of antibiotic-resistant bacteria claim that overuse of antibiotics creates resistant strains. How is this incorrect?

6. Explain how harmful recessive alleles can persist in populations, even though they prevent homozygous individuals from reproducing.

7. Fraggles are mythical, mouselike creatures that live underground beneath a large vegetable garden. Of the 100 Fraggles in this population, 84 have green fur, and 16 have gray fur. A dominant allele *F* confers green fur, and a recessive allele *f* confers gray fur. Assuming Hardy–Weinberg equilibrium is operating, answer the following questions. (a) What is the frequency of the gray allele *f*? (b) What is the frequency of the green allele *F*? (c) How many Fraggles are heterozygotes *(Ff)*? (d) How many Fraggles are homozygous recessive *(ff)*? (e) How many Fraggles are homozygous dominant *(FF)*?

8. One spring, a dust storm blankets the usually green garden of the Fraggles in gray. The green Fraggles therefore become visible to the Gorgs, who tend the gardens and try to kill the Fraggles to protect their crops. The gray Fraggles, however, blend easily into the dusty background. How might this event affect evolution in the Fraggles? What mode of natural selection does this represent?

9. Use the Internet to search for an example of the founder effect. Using your example, explain how allele frequencies in the new population differ from the allele frequencies in the original population.

10. Describe the competing selective forces acting on peacock tails. Together, do these selective forces produce disruptive, directional, or stabilizing selection?

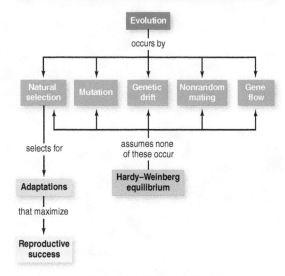

Figure 12.24 Pull It Together: The Forces of Evolutionary Change.

Refer to figure 12.24 and the chapter content to answer the following questions.

1. Describe a situation in which each of the five mechanisms of evolution shown in the concept map would occur.

2. Add the terms *genotype, phenotype, allele frequencies, founder effect, bottleneck effect,* and *sexual selection* to this concept map.

3. How does each mechanism of evolution change allele frequencies in a population?

13

Evidence of Evolution

Feathery Dinosaur. The theropod dinosaur *Protarchaeopteryx* lived about 145 million years ago (MYA) in China. It had downy feathers on its body and tail but also larger barbed feathers at the end of the tail and perhaps elsewhere. The model (left) shows what the animal might have looked like, based on evidence from fossils (right).

Enhance your study **BIOLOGY**
of this chapter with practice quizzes,
animations and videos, answer keys,
and downloadable study tools.
www.mhhe.com/hoefnagels

Are Birds Dinosaurs?

LIKE A PUZZLE WITH MANY PIECES MISSING, THE HIS-
TORY OF LIFE HAS MANY POSSIBLE INTERPRETATIONS.
But as more information surfaces, the pieces fit together, and the
story becomes clearer. Investigating the relationship between
birds and dinosaurs is one such story of life.

The idea that birds are closely related to small, meat-eating
dinosaurs called theropods began with the discovery of a
150-million-year-old fossil of a theropod with feathers in Bavaria.
It was 1860, the year after Darwin published *On the Origin of Species*. The animal, named *Archaeopteryx lithographica,* was the size
of a blue jay, with a mix of features seen in birds and nonavian
reptiles: wings and feathers, a toothed jaw, and a long, bony tail.

In 1870, Thomas Henry Huxley reported that he had identified
35 features that only ostriches and theropod skeletons shared, which
he interpreted as evidence of a close relationship. Others dismissed
Huxley's ideas. At the time, dinosaurs were not known to have
flown, and theropods were thought to lack bones needed for flight.

In the 1960s, however, Yale University paleontologist John
Ostrom strengthened the bird–dinosaur link with an exhaustive
comparison of bones discovered in the 1920s. Since then, the
similarities between dinosaurs and birds have added up. Many of
the structures that make flight possible were present in dinosaurs
that lived millions of years before birds. For example, some theropods had hollow bones, an upright stance in which they stood
on their toes, a horizontal back, long arms, and a short tail. Rare
finds of dinosaur nests reveal behavioral and reproductive similarities to birds.

Decades later, fossils of three types of feathered dinosaurs
were unearthed. Researchers discovered *Sinosauropteryx* in China
in 1996. This turkey-sized animal had a fringe of downlike structures along its neck, back, and flanks. Then, in 1998, a bonanza
fossil find introduced *Protarchaeopteryx* and *Caudipteryx*, both
even more feathery than *Sinosauropteryx*.

Still another piece of the puzzle fell into place in 2007, when
scientists revealed amino acid sequences of collagen protein molecules extracted from *Tyrannosaurus rex* fossils. Of all the vertebrate species studied, the *T. rex* collagen sequence was more
similar to that of a chicken than it was to other reptiles, including
alligators and lizards.

The surprising bird–dinosaur link illustrates the changeable
nature of science and reinforces the importance of evidence. Every
chapter of this textbook contains a section titled Investigating Life
that explains how biologists test hypotheses about evolution. This
chapter summarizes the main types of evidence they use.

LEARNING OUTLINE

 **13.1 Clues to Evolution Lie in the Earth, Body Structures,
and Molecules**

 13.2 Fossils Record Evolution
- A. Fossils Form in Many Ways
- B. The Fossil Record Is Often Incomplete
- C. The Age of a Fossil Can Be Estimated in Two Ways

 **13.3 Biogeography Considers Species' Geographical
Locations**
- A. The Theory of Plate Tectonics Explains Earth's
Shifting Continents
- B. Species Distributions Reveal Evolutionary Events

 13.4 Anatomical Comparisons May Reveal Common Descent
- A. Homologous Structures Have a Shared Evolutionary Origin
- B. Vestigial Structures Have Lost Their Functions
- C. Convergent Evolution Produces Superficial Similarities

 **13.5 Embryonic Development Patterns Provide
Evolutionary Clues**

 13.6 Molecules Reveal Relatedness
- A. Comparing DNA and Protein Sequences May Reveal Close
Relationships
- B. Molecular Clocks Help Assign Dates to Evolutionary Events

 13.7 Investigating Life: Limbs Gained and Limbs Lost

LEARN HOW TO LEARN
Make a Chart
One way to organize the information in a chapter is to make a
summary chart or matrix. The chart's contents will depend on the
chapter. For this chapter, for example, you might write the
following headings along the top of a piece of paper: "Type of
Evidence," "Definition," "How It Works," "What It Tells Us," and
"Example." Then you would list the lines of evidence for evolution
along the left edge of the chart. Start filling in your chart, using
the book at first to find the information you need. Later, you
should be able to re-create your chart from memory.

13.1 Clues to Evolution Lie in the Earth, Body Structures, and Molecules

The millions of species alive today did not just pop into existence all at once; they are the result of continuing evolutionary change in organisms that lived billions of years in the past. Many types of clues enable us to hypothesize about how modern species evolved from extinct ancestors and to understand the relationships among organisms that live today. (See the Burning Question on page 264.)

Tutorial
Evidence for Evolution

Comparisons among living organisms provided early evidence of the evolutionary relationships among species. Abundant additional data came from **paleontology,** the study of fossil remains or other clues to past life (figure 13.1). The discovery of many new types of fossils in the early 1800s created the climate that allowed Charles Darwin to make his tremendous breakthrough (see chapter 12). As people recognized that fossils must represent a history of life, scientists developed theories to explain that history. The geographical locations of fossils and modern species provided additional clues.

At Darwin's time, some scientists suspected that Earth was hundreds of millions of years old, but no one knew the exact age. We now know that Earth's history is about 4.6 billion years long, a duration that most people find nearly unimaginable. Scientists describe the events along life's long evolutionary path in the context of the **geologic timescale,** which divides Earth's history into a series of eons and eras defined by major geological or biological events such as mass extinctions (figure 13.2). ⓘ *mass extinctions*, p. 292

Fossils and biogeographical studies provided the original evidence for evolution, revealing when species most likely diverged from common ancestors in the context of other events happening on Earth. Comparisons of embryonic development and anatomical structures provided additional supporting data. An entirely new type of evidence emerged in the 1960s and 1970s, when scientists began analyzing the sequences of DNA, proteins, and other biological molecules. Since then, the explosion of molecular data has revealed in unprecedented detail how species are related to one another.

Chapter 12 explained how natural selection and other mechanisms of evolution account for changes within species. This chapter examines the different approaches to studying evolution in both living and extinct species. Chapter 14 explains how new species form and become extinct, ending with a description of how scientists assemble diverse clues into hypotheses of the relationships among species. Chapter 15 continues on this theme by offering a brief history of life on Earth.

13.1   MASTERING CONCEPTS

1. What is the geologic timescale?
2. What types of information provide the clues that scientists use in investigating evolutionary relationships?

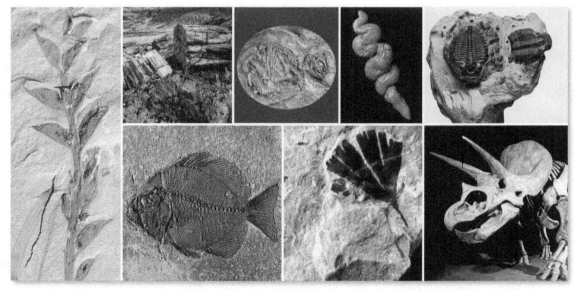

Figure 13.1   Diverse Fossils. Plants and animals have left a rich fossil record spanning hundreds of millions of years. Clockwise from left: *Archaefructus,* an early flowering plant that lived in China 138 million years ago; petrified wood; a 190-million-year-old dinosaur embryo encased in its egg; fossilized feces of an unidentified turtle from the Miocene epoch (between 5 million and 24 million years ago); trilobites, which were arthropods that became extinct some 250 million years ago; a skull of *Triceratops,* a dinosaur that lived in North America until 65 million years ago; a *Ginkgo* leaf; an exceptionally well-preserved fish.

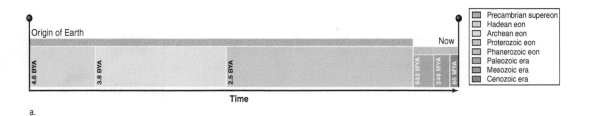

a.

Eon	Era	Period	Epoch	MYA	Important events
Phanerozoic eon / "Age of Mammals" / "Age of Reptiles" / "Age of Amphibians" / "Age of Fishes"	Cenozoic era	Quaternary	Recent		Human civilization
				0.01	
			Pleistocene		*Homo sapiens*, large mammals; ice ages
				1.8	
		Tertiary	Pliocene		Early humans; modern whales
				5.3	
			Miocene		First great apes; other mammals continue to diversify; modern birds; expansion of grasslands
				23.8	
			Oligocene		Elephants, horses; grasses
				33.7	
			Eocene		Mammals and flowering plants continue to diversify; first whales
				54.8	
			Paleocene		First primates; mammals, birds, and pollinating insects diversify
				65	
	Mesozoic era	Cretaceous			Widespread dinosaurs until extinction at end of Cretaceous; flowering plants diversify; present-day continents form
				144	
		Jurassic			First birds and mammals; cycads and ferns abundant; giant reptiles on land and in water; first flowering plants
				206	
		Triassic			First dinosaurs; first mammals; therapsids and thecodonts; forests of conifers and cycads
				248	
	Paleozoic era	Permian			First conifers; fewer amphibians, more reptiles; cotylosaurs and pelycosaurs; Pangaea supercontinent forms
				290	
		Carboniferous			First reptiles; ferns abundant; amphibians diversify; first winged insects
				354	
		Devonian			First bony fishes, corals, crinoids; first amphibians; land plants and arthropods diversify
				417	
		Silurian			First vascular plants and terrestrial invertebrates; first fish with jaws
				443	
		Ordovician			Algae, invertebrates, jawless fishes; first land plants
				490	
		Cambrian			"Explosion" of sponges, worms, jellyfish, "small shelly fossils"; ancestors of all modern animals appear; trilobites
				543	
Precambrian supereon	Proterozoic eon				O_2 from photosynthesis accumulates in atmosphere; first eukaryotes; first multicellular organisms; Ediacaran organisms
				2,500	
	Archean eon				Life starts; first bacteria and archaea
				3,800	
	Hadean eon				Earth forms
				4,600	

b.

Figure 13.2 The Geologic Timescale. (a) Scientists divide Earth's 4.6-billion-year history into four eons. The three earliest eons are combined into the Precambrian supereon, which lasted more than 4 billion years. The most recent eon, the Phanerozoic, started 543 MYA (million years ago). (b) Fossil evidence paints a detailed portrait of life's history during the Phanerozoic, which includes three eras (Paleozoic, Mesozoic, and Cenozoic). Red lines indicate the five largest mass extinction events of the Phanerozoic eon.

13.2 Fossils Record Evolution

A **fossil** is any evidence of an organism from more than 10,000 years ago (the end of the Pleistocene epoch). Fossils come in all sizes, documenting the evolutionary history of everything from microorganisms to dinosaurs to humans. These remains, the oldest of which formed more than 3 billion years ago, give us our only direct evidence of organisms that preceded human history. They occur all over the world and represent all major groups of organisms, revealing much about the geological past. For example, the abundant remains of extinct marine animals called ammonites in Oklahoma indicate that a vast, shallow ocean once submerged what is now the central United States (figure 13.3).

Fossils do more than simply provide a collection of ancient remains of plants, animals, and microbes. They also allow researchers to test predictions about evolution. Section 13.7 describes an excellent example: the discovery of *Tiktaalik*, an extinct animal with characteristics of both fishes and amphibians. Based on many lines of evidence showing the close relationship between these two groups, biologists had long predicted the existence of such an animal. *Tiktaalik*, described in 2006, finally provided direct fossil evidence of the connection.

A. Fossils Form in Many Ways

Evidence of past life comes in many forms (figure 13.4). Often, a fossil forms when an organism dies, becomes buried in sediments, and then is chemically altered. For example, coal, oil, and natural gas (also called fossil fuels) are the decomposed remains of plants and other organisms preserved by compression. Alternatively, minerals can replace the organic matter left by a

Figure 13.3 Big Change. Ammonite fossils such as these are common in land-locked Oklahoma, indicating that what is now the central United States was once covered by an ocean.

decaying organism, which literally turns to stone. Petrified wood forms in this way, as did the ammonite fossils in figure 13.3.

Impression fossils form when an organism presses against soft sediment, which then hardens, leaving an outline or imprint of the body. An impression fossil may also be evidence of an animal's movements, such as footprints. If the imprint later fills with mud that hardens into rock, the resulting cast is a rocky replica of the ancient organism. Teeth, bones, arthropod exoskeletons, and tree trunks often leave casts.

Burning Question

Is evolution really testable?

Some people believe that evolution cannot be tested because it happened in the past. Although no experiment can re-create the conditions that led to today's diversity of life, evolution is testable. In fact, its validity has been verified repeatedly over the past 150 years.

All scientific theories, including evolution, not only explain existing data but also predict future observations. Some other explanations for life's diversity, including intelligent design, are unscientific because they do not offer testable predictions; that is, no future observation can disprove the idea that an intelligent creator designed life on Earth. One strength of evolutionary theory, in contrast, is its ability to predict future discoveries.

For example, if vertebrate life started in the water and then moved onto land, an evolutionary biologist might predict that fishes should appear in the fossil record before reptiles or mammals. A newly found fossil that contradicts the prediction would require investigators to form a new hypothesis. On the other hand, fossils that confirm the prediction lend additional weight to the theory's validity.

Evaluating common descent is somewhat similar to solving a crime. The perpetrator may leave footprints, tire tracks, fingerprints,

and DNA at a crime scene. Detectives would develop hypotheses about possible suspects by piecing together the physical and biological evidence. Innocent suspects can exonerate themselves by providing additional information, such as a verified alibi, that contradicts the hypothesis. Ultimately, the best explanation is the one that is consistent with all available evidence.

A mountain of evidence supports the idea of common descent. Extinct organisms have left traces of their existence, both as fossils and as the genetic legacy that all current organisms have inherited. The distribution of life on Earth offers other clues, as does the study of everything from anatomical structures to protein sequences. Laboratory experiments and field observations of natural populations likewise suggest likely mechanisms for evolutionary change and have even documented the emergence of new species. No other scientifically testable hypothesis explains and unifies all of these observations as well as common descent.

Submit your burning question to
Marielle.Hoefnagels@mheducation.com

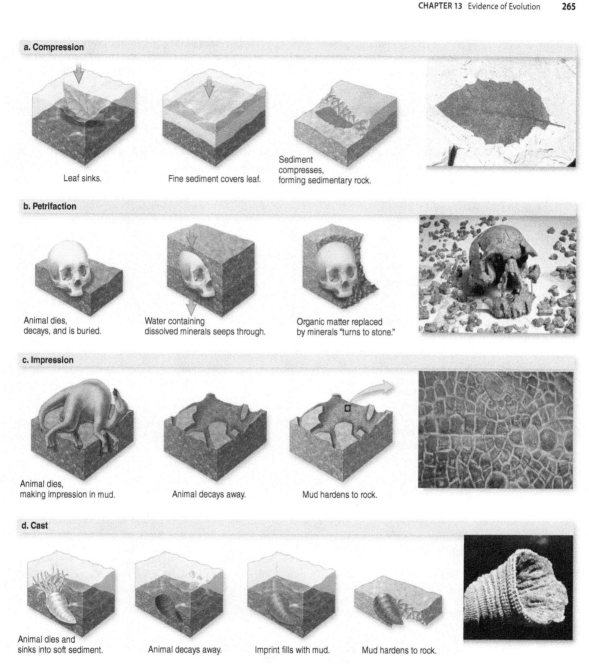

a. Compression

Leaf sinks.

Fine sediment covers leaf.

Sediment compresses, forming sedimentary rock.

b. Petrifaction

Animal dies, decays, and is buried.

Water containing dissolved minerals seeps through.

Organic matter replaced by minerals "turns to stone."

c. Impression

Animal dies, making impression in mud.

Animal decays away.

Mud hardens to rock.

d. Cast

Animal dies and sinks into soft sediment.

Animal decays away.

Imprint fills with mud.

Mud hardens to rock.

e. Intact preservation

Oozing sap traps an insect.

Figure 13.4 How Fossils Form. (a) A compression fossil of a leaf preserves part of the plant. (b) Most fossils of human ancestors consist of mineralized bones and teeth, usually found in fragments. (c) An impression fossil reveals an imprint of anatomical details, such as the scaly skin of a dinosaur. (d) This horn coral is a cast. Once-living material dissolved and was replaced by mud that hardened into rock. (e) Fossils can also be preserved intact in tree resin, which hardens to form amber.

Rarely, a whole organism is preserved intact. Fossil pollen grains in waterlogged lake sediments provide clues to long-ago climates. Sticky tree resin entraps plants and animals, hardening them in translucent amber tombs. The La Brea Tar Pits in Los Angeles have preserved more than 660 species of animals and plants that became stuck in the gooey tar thousands of years ago.

The most striking fossils have formed when sudden catastrophes, such as mud slides and floods, rapidly buried organisms in an oxygen-poor environment. Decomposition and tissue damage were minimal in the absence of oxygen; scavengers could not reach the dead. In those conditions, even delicate organisms have left detailed anatomical portraits (figure 13.5).

B. The Fossil Record Is Often Incomplete

Occasionally, researchers find fossils that document, step-by-step, the evolution of one species into another. For example, biologists have found many fossils revealing intermediate stages in the evolution of whales and dolphins from land animals. Usually, however, the fossil record is incomplete, meaning that some of the features marking the transition from one group to another are not recorded in fossils.

Several explanations account for this partial history. First, the vast majority of organisms never leave a fossil trace. Soft-bodied organisms, for example, are much less likely to be preserved than are those with teeth, bones, or shells. Organisms that decompose or are eaten after death, rather than being buried in sediments, are also unlikely to fossilize. Second, erosion or the movements of Earth's continental plates have destroyed many fossils that did form. Third, scientists are unlikely to ever discover the many fossils that must be buried deep in the Earth or submerged under water.

C. The Age of a Fossil Can Be Estimated in Two Ways

Virtual Lab
Radiometric
Dating

Scientists use two general approaches to estimate when a fossilized organism lived: relative dating and absolute dating.

Relative Dating   Relative dating places a fossil into a sequence of events without assigning it a specific age. It is usually based on the principle of superposition, with lower rock strata presumed to be older than higher layers (see figure 12.3). The farther down a fossil is, therefore, the longer ago the organism it represents lived—a little like a memo at the bottom of a stack of papers being older than a sheet near the top. Relative dating therefore places fossils in order from "oldest" to "most recent."

Absolute Dating and Radioactive Decay   Researchers use **absolute dating** to assign an age to a fossil by testing either the fossil itself or the sediments above and below the fossil. Either way, the dates usually are expressed in relation to the present. For example, scientists studying fossilized *Archaeopteryx* showed that this animal lived about 150 million years ago (MYA). Although the term *absolute dating* seems to imply pinpoint accuracy, absolute dating techniques typically return a range of likely dates.

Radiometric dating is a type of absolute dating that uses radioactive isotopes as a "clock." Recall from chapter 2 that each isotope of an element has a different number of neutrons. Some isotopes are naturally unstable, which causes them to emit radiation as they radioactively decay. Each radioactive isotope decays at a characteristic and unchangeable rate, called its half-life. The **half-life** is the time it takes for half of the atoms in a sample of a radioactive substance to decay. If an isotope's half-life is 1 year, for example, 50% of the radioactive atoms in a sample will have decayed in a year. In another year, half of the remaining radioactive atoms will decay, leaving 25%, and so on. If we measure the amount of a radioactive isotope in a sample, we can use the isotope's known half-life to deduce when the fossil formed. ⓘ *isotopes, p. 21*

One radioactive isotope often used to assign dates to fossils is carbon-14 (^{14}C; figure 13.6), which forms in the atmosphere when cosmic rays from space bombard nitrogen gas. Carbon-14 has a half-life of 5730 years; it decays to the more stable nitrogen-14 (^{14}N). Organisms accumulate ^{14}C during photosynthesis or by eating organic matter. One in every trillion carbon atoms present in living tissue is ^{14}C; most of the rest are ^{12}C, a nonradioactive (stable) isotope. When an organism dies, however, its intake of carbon, including ^{14}C, stops. As the body's ^{14}C decays without being replenished, the ratio of ^{14}C to ^{12}C decreases.

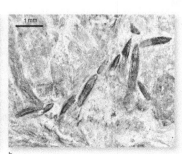

Figure 13.5 Doomed Dinosaur Embryos.
(a) Thousands of dinosaur eggs containing about-to-hatch babies were buried in mud in present-day Argentina about 89 MYA. The newborns would have been only 40 centimeters long but would have grown to an adult length of over 13 meters. (b) Preserved embryonic teeth were about 1 mm long. (c) The skin from some of the embryos was remarkably well preserved.

a.   b.   c.

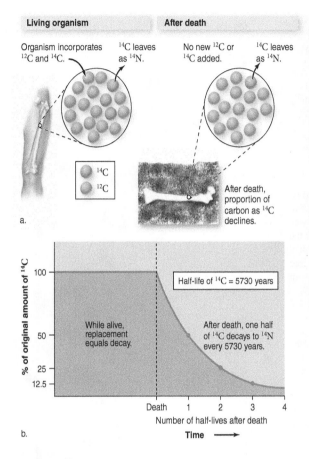

a.

b.

Living organism

Organism incorporates ¹²C and ¹⁴C.

¹⁴C leaves as ¹⁴N.

After death

No new ¹²C or ¹⁴C added.

¹⁴C leaves as ¹⁴N.

^{14}C

^{12}C

After death, proportion of carbon as ¹⁴C declines.

Half-life of ¹⁴C = 5730 years

While alive, replacement equals decay.

After death, one half of ¹⁴C decays to ¹⁴N every 5730 years.

% of original amount of ¹⁴C

100

50

25

12.5

Death   1   2   3   4

Number of half-lives after death

Time ⟶

c.

Figure 13.6 Carbon-14 Dating. (a) Living organisms accumulate radioactive carbon-14 (¹⁴C) by photosynthesis or eating other organisms. During life, ¹⁴C is replaced as fast as it decays to nitrogen-14 (¹⁴N). After death, no new ¹⁴C enters the body, so the proportion of ¹⁴C to ¹²C declines. (b) During one half-life, 50% of the remaining radioactive atoms in a sample decay. (c) Measuring the proportion of ¹⁴C to ¹²C allows scientists to determine how long ago a fossilized organism—such as this woolly mammoth—died.

Tutorial
Radiometric Dating

This ratio is then used to determine when death occurred, up to about 40,000 years ago.

For example, radioactive carbon dating determined the age of fossils of vultures that once lived in the Grand Canyon. The birds' remains have about one fourth the ¹⁴C-to-¹²C ratio of a living organism. Therefore, about two half-lives, or about 11,460 years, passed since the animals died. It took 5730 years for half of the ¹⁴C to decay, and another 5730 years for half of what was left to decay to ¹⁴N.

Another widely used radioactive isotope, potassium-40 (⁴⁰K), decays to argon-40 (⁴⁰Ar) with a half-life of 1.3 billion years, so it is valuable in dating very old rocks containing traces of both isotopes. Chemical analysis can detect the accumulation of ⁴⁰Ar in amounts corresponding to fossils that are about 300,000 years old or older.

One limitation of ¹⁴C and potassium–argon dating is that they leave a gap, resulting from the different half-lives of the radioactive isotopes. To cover the missing years, researchers use isotopes with intermediate half-lives or turn to other techniques, such as tree-ring comparisons. ⓘ *tree rings*, p. 476

Figure It Out

Kennewick Man is a human whose remains were found in 1996 in Washington state. Radiometric dating of a bone fragment suggests that he lived about 9300 years ago. At the time scientists dated the bone, about what percent of the original amount of ¹⁴C remained in his bones?

Answer: Approximately 30%.

13.2 MASTERING CONCEPTS

1. What are some of the ways that fossils form?
2. Why will the fossil record always be incomplete?
3. Distinguish between relative and absolute dating of fossils.
4. How does radiometric dating work?

13.3 Biogeography Considers Species' Geographical Locations

Geographical barriers greatly influence the origin of species (see chapter 14). It is therefore not surprising that the studies of geography and biology overlap in one field, **biogeography,** the study of the distribution of species across the planet.

A. The Theory of Plate Tectonics Explains Earth's Shifting Continents

Animation
Continental
Drift

Despite the occasional volcanic eruptions and earthquakes, Earth's geological history might seem rather uneventful. Not so. Fossils tell the story of ancient seafloors rising all the way to Earth's "ceiling": the Himalayan Mountains. Littering the Kali Gandaki River in the mountains of Nepal are countless fossilized ammonites, large mollusks similar to the chambered nautilus. How did fossils of marine animals end up more than 3600 meters above sea level?

The answer is that Earth's continents are in motion, an idea called "continental drift" (figure 13.7). According to the theory of **plate tectonics,** Earth's surface consists of several rigid layers, called tectonic plates, that move in response to forces acting deep within the planet. In some places where plates come together, one plate dives beneath another, forming a deep trench. In other areas, mountain ranges form as the plates become wrinkled and distorted. Long ago, the Indo-Australian plate (which includes the subcontinent of India) moved slowly north and eventually collided with the Eurasian plate. The mighty Himalayas—once an ancient seafloor—rose at the boundary, lifting the marine fossils toward the sky.

Meanwhile, at areas where plates move apart, molten rock seeps to Earth's surface and forms new plate material at the seafloor. As a result, oceans now separate continents that were once joined together. This slow-motion dance of the continental plates has dramatically affected life's history as oceans shifted, land bridges formed and disappeared, and mountain ranges emerged.

It may seem hard to imagine that Earth's continents have not always been located where they are now. But a wealth of evidence, including the distribution of some key fossils, indicates that the continents were once united (figure 13.8). Deep-sea probes that measure seafloor spreading, along with the locations of the world's earthquake-prone and volcanic "hot spots," reveal that the continents continue to move today.

B. Species Distributions Reveal Evolutionary Events

Biogeographical studies have shed light on past evolutionary events. The rest of this section describes three examples.

The Case of the Missing Marsupials   Marsupials are pouched mammals such as kangaroos, koalas, and sugar gliders. The newborns are tiny, hairless, blind, and helpless. As soon as

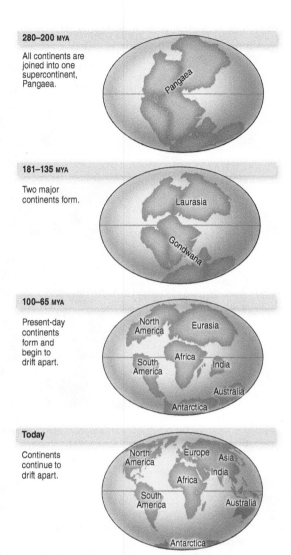

Figure 13.7   A Changing World. The locations of Earth's continents have changed with time, due to shifting tectonic plates.

they are born, they crawl along the mother's fur to tiny, milk-secreting nipples inside her pouch.

Marsupials were once the most widespread land mammals on Earth. About 110 MYA, however, a second group, the placental mammals, had evolved. The young of placental mammals develop within the female's body, nourished in the uterus by the placenta. Baby placental mammals are born more fully developed than are marsupials, giving them a better chance of survival after birth. Because of this reproductive advantage, placental mammals soon displaced marsupials on most continents, including North America. ⓘ *mammals,* p. 451

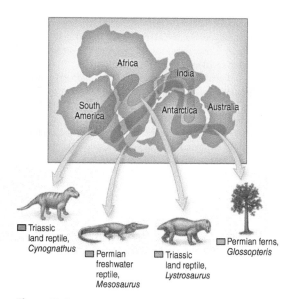

Figure 13.8 Growing Apart. Continental drift explains the modern-day distributions of fossils representing life in the southern hemisphere at the time of Pangaea.

Nevertheless, fossil evidence suggests that marsupials were diverse and abundant in South America until about 1 or 2 MYA, long after their counterparts on most other continents had disappeared. The reason is that water separated South America from North America until about 3 MYA. But sediments that eroded from both continents eventually created a new land bridge, the isthmus of Panama, which permitted migration between North and South America. The resulting invasion of the placental mammals eventually spelled extinction for most South American marsupials.

Australia's marsupials remained isolated from competition with placental mammals for much longer. Until about 140 MYA, Antarctica and Australia were part of Gondwana (see figure 13.7). Then, about 60 or 70 MYA, Australia separated from Antarctica and began drifting toward Eurasia. The isolation from the other continents meant marsupials remained free of competition from placentals. In fact, Australia remains unique in that most of its native mammals are still marsupials.

Wallace's Line Biogeography figured prominently in the early history of evolutionary thought. Alfred Russel Wallace, the British naturalist who independently discovered natural selection along with Charles Darwin, had noticed unique assemblages of birds and mammals on either side of an imaginary line in the Malay Archipelago (figure 13.9). The explanation for what came to be called "Wallace's line" turned out to be a deep-water trench that has separated the islands on either side of the line, even as sea levels rose and fell over tens of millions of years. The watery barrier prevented the migration of most species, so evolution produced a unique variety of organisms on each side of Wallace's line.

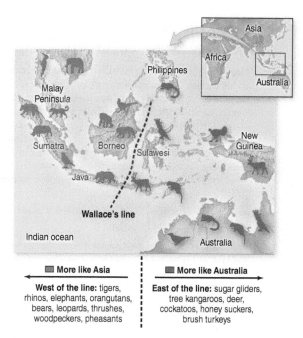

More like Asia	More like Australia
West of the line: tigers, rhinos, elephants, orangutans, bears, leopards, thrushes, woodpeckers, pheasants	**East of the line:** sugar gliders, tree kangaroos, deer, cockatoos, honey suckers, brush turkeys

Figure 13.9 Wallace's Line. As Alfred Russel Wallace traveled around the Malay archipelago, he noticed distinct patterns of animal life on either side of an imaginary boundary, which eventually came to be called Wallace's line.

Island Biogeography A smaller-scale application of biogeography is the study of species on island chains. Hawaii, the Galápagos, and other island groups house many unique species that appear nowhere else on Earth. Some of these organisms are downright bizarre; see, for example, the photo that accompanies chapter 14's opening essay.

Although an island's inhabitants may have unusual features, they are typically closely related to species on the nearest mainland. The explanation is that the only organisms that can colonize a newly formed, isolated island are those that can swim, fly, or raft from an inhabited location. Such colonization events may be extremely rare. Those organisms that do reach the island encounter conditions that are different from those on the mainland. With limited migration between the island and the ancestral populations, the relocated organisms have evolved and diversified into multiple new species, a process called adaptive radiation. Just as they did for the marsupials and the species near Wallace's line, geographical barriers have influenced the course of evolution on island chains as well. ⓘ *adaptive radiation*, p. 290

13.3 MASTERING CONCEPTS

1. How have the positions of Earth's continents changed over the past 200 million years?

2. How does biogeography provide evidence for evolution?

13.4 Anatomical Comparisons May Reveal Common Descent

Many clues to the past come from the present. As unit 1 explains, all life is made of cells, and eukaryotic cells are very similar in the structure and function of their membranes and organelles. On a molecular scale, cells share many similarities in their enzymes, signaling proteins, and metabolic pathways. Unit 2 describes another set of common features: the relationship between DNA and proteins, and the mechanisms of inheritance. We now turn to the whole-body scale, where comparisons of anatomy and physiology reveal still more commonalities among modern species.

A. Homologous Structures Have a Shared Evolutionary Origin

Two structures are termed **homologous** if the similarities between them reflect common ancestry. (Recall from chapter 9 that two chromosomes are homologous if they have the same genes, though not necessarily the same alleles, arranged in the same order.) Homologous genes, chromosomes, anatomical structures, or other features are similar in their configuration, position, or developmental path.

The organization of the vertebrate skeleton illustrates homology. All vertebrate skeletons support the body, are made of the same materials, and consist of many of the same parts. Amphibians, birds and other reptiles, and mammals typically have four limbs, and the numbers and positions of the bones that make up those appendages are strikingly similar (figure 13.10). The simplest explanation is that modern vertebrates descended from a common ancestor that originated this skeletal organization. Each group gradually modified the skeleton as species adapted to different environments.

Note that homologous structures share a common evolutionary origin, but they may not have the same function. The middle ear bones of mammals, for example, originated as bones that

supported the jaws of primitive fishes, and they still exist as such in some vertebrates. These bones are homologous and reveal our shared ancestry with fishes. Likewise, the forelimbs pictured in figure 13.10 have varying functions.

Homology is a powerful tool for discovering evolutionary relationships. For example, as described in section 13.6, a newly sequenced gene or genome can be compared with homologous genes from other species to infer how closely related any two species are. Similarly, fossilized structures are often compared with homologous parts in known species. Comparative studies can also provide clues to the origin of human features, including the hiccups (see the Apply It Now box on page 276).

B. Vestigial Structures Have Lost Their Functions

Evolution is not a perfect process. As environmental changes select against some structures, others persist even if they are not used. A **vestigial** structure has no apparent function in one

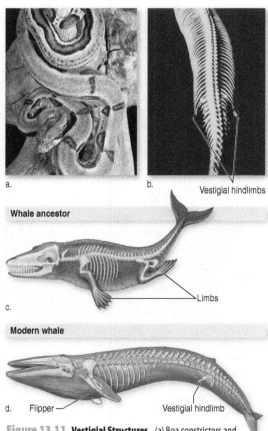

a.   b.   Vestigial hindlimbs

Whale ancestor

c.   Limbs

Modern whale

d.   Flipper   Vestigial hindlimb

Figure 13.11 Vestigial Structures. (a) Boa constrictors and some other snakes have vestigial hindlimbs. (b) These tiny limbs are visible in a python's skeleton. (c) Whales descended from mammals with four limbs. (d) Some modern whales retain a vestigial pelvis and hindlimbs.

Figure 13.10 Homologous Limbs. Although their forelimbs have different functions, all of these vertebrates have skeletons that are similarly organized and composed of the same type of tissue.

species, yet it is homologous to a functional organ in another. (Darwin compared vestigial structures to silent letters in a word, such as the "g" in *night;* they are not pronounced, but they offer clues to the word's origin.)

Figure 13.11 shows the vestigial limb bones in snakes and whales. Like all snakes, boa constrictors and pythons lack external limbs, but their skeletons reveal the bones of tiny hindlimbs. (See sections 13.5 and 13.7 for more on snake evolution.) Whales also have vestigial hindlimbs, retained from vertebrate ancestors that used legs to walk on land. Their aquatic habitat, meanwhile, selected for forelimbs modified into flippers.

Humans have several vestigial organs. The tiny muscles that make hairs stand on end helped our furry ancestors conserve heat or show aggression; in us, they apparently serve only as the basis of goose bumps. Human embryos have tails, which usually disintegrate long before birth; in other vertebrates, tails persist into adulthood. Above our ears, a trio of muscles (which most of us can't use) helps other mammals move their ears in a way that improves hearing. Each vestigial structure links us to other animals that still use these features.

Some plants also have vestigial structures. Dandelions, for example, produce seeds asexually, yet their flowers have male and female parts that do not participate in reproduction.

C. Convergent Evolution Produces Superficial Similarities

Some anatomical parts have similar functions and appear superficially similar among different species, but they are not homologous. Rather, they are **analogous,** meaning that the structures evolved independently. Flight, for example, evolved independently in birds and in insects. The bird's wing is a modification of vertebrate limb bones, whereas the insect's wing is an outgrowth of the exoskeleton that covers its body (figure 13.12). The wings have the same function—flight—and enhance fitness in the face of similar environmental challenges. The differences in structure, however, indicate they do not have a common developmental pathway. (In evolutionary biology, *homoplasy* is the technical term for a similarity between structures that evolved independently.)

a. Cave animals

b. Desert plants

Figure 13.13 **Convergent Evolution.** (a) The blind cave salamander, from Slovenia (left), and the cave crayfish, from Florida (right), both lack eyes and pigment. (b) Cacti from the desert in Mexico (left) have adaptations similar to those of *Euphorbia* plants from the Namib Desert in Africa (right).

Analogous structures are often the product of **convergent evolution,** which produces similar adaptations in organisms that do not share the same evolutionary lineage. The loss of pigmentation and eyes in cave animals provides a compelling example of convergent evolution, as does the similar appearance of unrelated desert plants from Mexico and Africa (figure 13.13).

Likewise, the similarities between sharks and dolphins illustrate the power of selective forces in shaping organisms. A shark is a fish, whereas a dolphin is a mammal that evolved from terrestrial ancestors. The two animals are not closely related; their last common ancestor lived hundreds of millions of years ago. Nevertheless, their marine habitat and predatory lifestyle have selected for many shared adaptations, including the streamlined body and the shape and locations of the fins or flippers.

13.4 MASTERING CONCEPTS

1. What can homologous structures reveal about evolution?
2. What is a vestigial structure? What are some examples of vestigial structures in humans and other animals?
3. What is convergent evolution?

Figure 13.12 **Analogous Structures.** The wings of birds and butterflies both function in flight, but they are analogous structures because they are not made of the same materials, nor are they organized in the same way. They are not inherited from a recent common ancestor.

13.5 Embryonic Development Patterns Provide Evolutionary Clues

Because related organisms share many physical traits, they must also share the processes that produce those traits. Developmental biologists study how the adult body takes shape from its single-celled beginning. Careful comparisons of developing body parts can be enlightening. As just one example, figure 13.14 shows that similar-looking skulls can develop in different ways, depending on how each part grows in proportion to the others.

Developmental biologists have also photographed embryos and fetuses of a variety of vertebrate species (figure 13.15). The images reveal homologies in the overall structure of the embryonic bodies and in specific features such as the tail.

More recently, the discovery of genes that contribute to development has spawned the field of evolutionary developmental biology (or "evo-devo" for short). Recall from chapter 7 that a

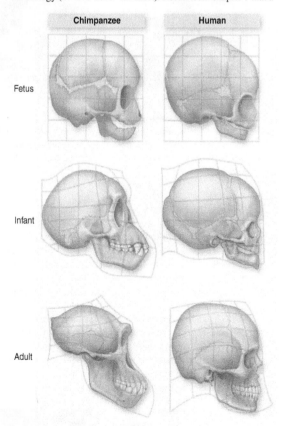

Figure 13.14 Same Parts, Different Proportions. The fetuses of humans and chimpanzees have very similar skulls, but the two species follow different developmental pathways. The grids superimposed on the images show the relative growth of each skull part over time. In an adult human, the brain is larger and the jaw is smaller than in chimpanzees.

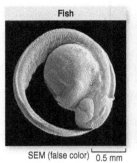

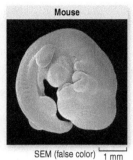

Fish — SEM (false color) 0.5 mm

Mouse — SEM (false color) 1 mm

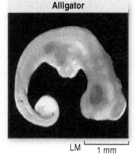

Alligator — LM 1 mm

Figure 13.15 Embryo Resemblances. Vertebrate embryos appear alike early in development. As development continues, parts grow at different rates in different species, and the embryos begin to look less similar.
Source: Fish © Dr. Richard Kessel/ Visuals Unlimited, Inc.

gene is a region of DNA that encodes a protein. Some genes encode proteins that dictate how an organism will develop. One goal of evo-devo research is to identify these genes and determine how mutations can give rise to new body forms.

A basic question in developmental biology, for example, is how a clump of identical cells transforms into a body with a distinct head, tail, segments, and limbs. One way to learn more about this process is to study genes encoding proteins that regulate development. Mutations in these genes can produce dramatic new phenotypes—see, for example, the fruit fly with legs growing out of its head in figure 7.20.

Homeotic is a general term describing any gene that, when mutated, leads to organisms with structures in abnormal or unusual places. Many homeotic genes encode proteins that regulate the expression of other genes. These genes occur in all animal phyla studied to date, as well as in plants and fungi, and they provide important clues about development.

Consider, for example, a pair of homeotic genes that influence limb formation in vertebrates (figure 13.16). In the chick embryo in figure 13.16a, the gene labeled A prompts wing development, whereas the gene labeled B stimulates formation of the legs. No limbs occur where both genes are expressed, such as in the midsection of the body. Now compare the chick with the pattern of gene expression in the python (figure 13.16b). The same two genes are expressed along most of the snake's body; as a result, the animal never develops forelimbs at all. (Another gene prevents the development of the python's vestigial hindlimbs.)

Researchers have also discovered that new phenotypes can come from mutations in DNA that does not encode proteins. As described in chapter 7, eukaryotic cells require proteins

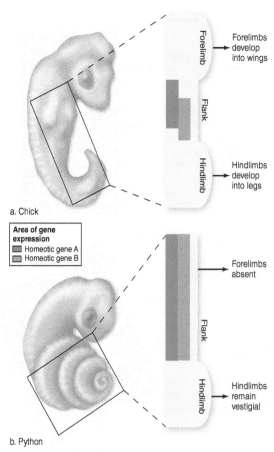

a. Chick

Area of gene expression
- Homeotic gene A
- Homeotic gene B

b. Python

Figure 13.16 Homeotic Genes. (a) Two homeotic genes are expressed unequally along the length of a chicken embryo. Where both genes are expressed, no limbs form. (b) The same pair of homeotic genes prevents the development of forelimbs in a python embryo.

called transcription factors for gene expression. The transcription factors bind to areas of DNA called enhancers, signaling a gene to turn on. Figure 13.17 shows that mutations in these enhancers can cause new features such as wing spots to develop in fruit flies. Perhaps more interesting is the observation that changes in other enhancers can cause the loss of a trait (in this case, pigmentation), even though the gene encoding the pigment remains intact.

Video
Fly Wing Spots

Evo-devo studies can even help biologists peer hundreds of millions of years into the past. For example, sponges—the simplest animals—contain the same developmental genes as do much more complex animals. If this genetic "toolbox" was already in place at the dawn of animal evolution, it may explain how diverse phyla arose so quickly during the Cambrian period (see section 21.17).

These examples only scratch the surface of the types of information about evolution that biologists can learn by studying development. The relatively new evo-devo field is sure to yield much more insight into evolution in the future.

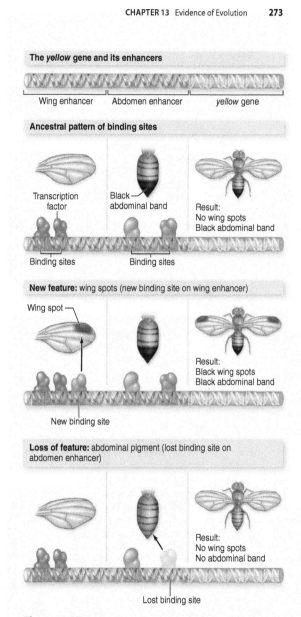

Figure 13.17 Gene Regulation. In fruit flies, a gene called *yellow* is required for the production of black pigment. Different combinations of transcription factors bound to enhancers determine whether *yellow* is activated in a fly's wings and abdomen.

13.5 MASTERING CONCEPTS

1. How does the study of embryonic development reveal clues to a shared evolutionary history?
2. Why are evolutionary biologists interested in how genes influence development?

13.6 Molecules Reveal Relatedness

The evidence for evolution described so far in this chapter is compelling, but it is only the beginning. Since the 1970s, biologists have compiled a wealth of additional data by comparing the molecules inside the cells of diverse organisms. The results have not only confirmed many previous studies but have also added unprecedented detail to our ability to detect and measure the pace of evolutionary change.

The molecules that are most useful to evolutionary biologists are nucleic acids (DNA and RNA) and proteins. As described in chapter 2, nucleic acids are long chains of subunits called nucleotides, whereas proteins are composed of amino acids. Cells use the information in nucleic acids to produce proteins.

This intimate relationship between nucleic acids and proteins is itself a powerful argument for common ancestry. All species use the same genetic code in making proteins, and cells use the same 20 amino acids. The fact that biologists can move DNA among species to create transgenic organisms is a practical reminder of the universal genetic code. (i) *transgenic organisms*, p. 219

A. Comparing DNA and Protein Sequences May Reveal Close Relationships

To study molecular evolution, biologists compare nucleotide and amino acid sequences among species. It is highly unlikely that two unrelated species would evolve precisely the same DNA and protein sequences by chance. It is more likely that the similarities were inherited from a common ancestor and that differences arose by mutation after the species diverged. Thus, an underlying assumption of molecular evolution studies is that the greater the similarity between two modern species, the closer their evolutionary relationship. One advantage of molecular comparisons is that they are less subjective than deciding whether two anatomical structures are homologous or analogous.

DNA   The ability to rapidly sequence DNA has led to an explosion of information. DNA differences can be assessed for a few bases, for one gene, for families of genes with related structures or functions, or for whole genomes. Biologists routinely locate a gene in one organism, then scan huge databases to study homologous genes in other species. (i) *DNA sequencing*, p. 222

Most of a cell's genetic material is in its nucleus, but the cell's numerous mitochondria also contain DNA. Mitochondrial DNA (mtDNA) presents unique possibilities because each cell contains many mitochondria, each containing many DNA molecules. Some of those mtDNA copies often remain intact in extinct organisms and museum specimens, even if the nuclear DNA is badly degraded. It is therefore sometimes easier to trace long-term evolutionary events with mtDNA than with nuclear DNA. (i) *mitochondria*, p. 60; *crossing over*, p. 174

For example, many studies show that people from Africa have the most diverse mtDNA sequences. Because mutations take time to accumulate, these results suggest that Africans have

existed longer than other modern populations. The idea that early humans originated in Africa and then migrated to the other continents is called the single origin ("out of Africa") hypothesis. (i) *human evolution*, p. 320

The Y chromosome, which passes only from father to son, has also been useful in tracking human migration. Because the Y chromosome does not exchange much genetic material with the X chromosome during meiosis, it accumulates changes much more slowly than do the other chromosomes.

Biologists have also sequenced noncoding DNA, including transposons and pseudogenes (see section 11.2B). Neither transposons nor pseudogenes have any known function, yet their sequences are similar in closely related species. The best explanation for these observations is common descent.

To make a large-scale tree that incorporates all life, researchers consider slowly evolving DNA sequences common to all organisms. The genes encoding ribosomal RNA fit the bill. Carl Woese used these genes to deduce the existence of the three domains (Archaea, Bacteria, and Eukarya).

The recent explosion of genetic information has also helped explain how evolution works. We now know that cells may add new **Animation** Gene Duplication functions by acquiring DNA from other organisms (see section 5.7) and by duplicating genes (figure 13.18). And we have already seen that studying gene expression can reveal differences among closely related species (see figure 13.17). The list of additional applications is endless, ranging from studies pinpointing

Chimp DNA

Salivary amylase gene

Human DNA

Copy 1   Copy 2

Salivary amylase genes (multiple copies)

Figure 13.18 Gene Duplication. Chimpanzees consume little starch compared to humans. This dietary difference apparently selected for additional copies of the gene encoding amylase, the starch-digesting enzyme.

Cytochrome c Evolution	
Organism	Number of amino acid differences from humans
Chimpanzee	0
Rhesus monkey	1
Rabbit	9
Cow	10
Pigeon	12
Bullfrog	18
Fruit fly	25
Yeast	40

Figure 13.19

Cytochrome c Comparison. The more recent the shared ancestor with humans, the fewer the differences in the amino acid sequence for the respiratory protein cytochrome c.

the origin of diseases (see sections 16.7 and 17.6) to monitoring the evolution of pesticide-resistant insects (see section 10.10).

Proteins Like DNA, homologous protein sequences also often support fossil and anatomical evidence of evolutionary relationships. One study, for example, found seven of 20 proteins to be identical in humans and chimps, our closest relatives. Many other proteins have only minor sequence differences from one species to another. The keratin of sheep's wool, for example, is virtually identical to that of human hair. The similarity reflects the shared evolutionary history of all mammals.

To study even broader groups of organisms, biologists use proteins that are present in all species. One example is cytochrome c, which is part of the electron transport chain in respiration (see section 6.5C). Figure 13.19 shows that the more closely related two species are, the more alike is their cytochrome c.

B. Molecular Clocks Help Assign Dates to Evolutionary Events

Animation
Molecular
Clock

A biological molecule such as DNA can act as a "clock." If biologists know the mutation rate for a gene, plus the number of differences in the DNA sequences for that gene in two species, they can use the DNA as a **molecular clock** to estimate the time when the organisms diverged from a common ancestor (figure 13.20).

For example, many human and chimpanzee genes differ in about 4% to 6% of their nucleotides, and substitutions occur at an estimated rate of 1% per 1 million years. Therefore, about 4 million to 6 million years have passed since the two species diverged.

Researchers can use either nuclear DNA or mtDNA as a molecular clock. Mitochondrial DNA is especially valuable in tracking recent evolutionary events because its molecular clock "ticks" 5 to 10 times faster than the nuclear DNA clock.

Molecular clock studies, however, are not quite as straightforward as glancing at a wristwatch. DNA replication errors occur in different regions of a chromosome at different rates, and some genes affect phenotypes more than others. Researchers must account for these differences when using molecules to estimate how much time has passed since two species last shared a common ancestor.

13.6 MASTERING CONCEPTS

1. How does analysis of DNA and proteins support other evidence for evolution?
2. What is an advantage of using mtDNA instead of nuclear DNA in tracing evolution?
3. What is the basis of using a molecular clock to determine when two species diverged from a common ancestor?

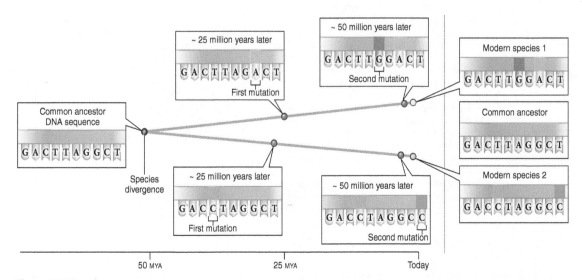

Figure 13.20 Molecular Clock. If a sequence of DNA accumulates mutations at a regular rate, then the number of sequence changes can act as a "clock" that tells how much time has passed since two species last shared a common ancestor. In this example, mutations occur about once every 25 million years.

INVESTIGATING LIFE

13.7 Limbs Gained and Limbs Lost

Every now and then, a spectacular fossil grabs headlines worldwide. That is exactly what happened—twice—in April 2006, when fossils shed light on two important questions in vertebrate evolutionary biology: how did terrestrial vertebrates gain four limbs as they evolved from their fish ancestors, and how did snakes lose their limbs?

Early amphibians crawled onto land some 375 MYA, and the descendants of those early colonists are today's amphibians, reptiles, and mammals. Fossils discovered over the past half-century, including *Acanthostega* and *Ichthyostega,* have clarified the fish–amphibian transition (see figure 15.15). Still, some details of this fascinating event remain poorly understood.

Scientists Edward B. (Ted) Daeschler of Philadelphia's Academy of Natural Sciences, Neil Shubin of the University of Chicago, and Harvard University's Farish Jenkins added new insights when they published back-to-back papers in the journal *Nature* in April 2006. The articles described fossils of an extinct animal, *Tiktaalik roseae,* that the researchers had unearthed in Arctic Canada (figure 13.21). *Tiktaalik* either crawled or paddled in shallow tropical streams about 380 MYA, during the late Devonian period. (Although today's Canada is anything but tropical, the entire North American continent was near the equator during the Devonian.)

The animal has an uncanny mix of characteristics from fish and terrestrial vertebrates. Like a fish, *Tiktaalik* had scales and gills. Like a land animal, it had lungs, and its ribs were robust enough to support its body. It could also move its head independently of its shoulders, something that a fish cannot do. But the appendages got the most attention. *Tiktaalik* had moveable wrist bones that were sturdy enough to support the animal in shallow water or on short excursions to land. Although the bones were clearly limblike, the "limbs" were fringed with fins, not toes.

The *Tiktaalik* fossils caught the world's eye because they were extraordinarily complete and exquisitely preserved. Scientifically, *Tiktaalik* is important for two reasons. First, it adds to our knowledge about the evolution of terrestrial vertebrates. Second, it highlights the predictive power of evolutionary biology.

Apply It **Now**

An Evolutionary View of the Hiccups

It happens to everyone: We eat or drink too fast, or we laugh too hard, and then the hiccups begin. During a hiccup, an involuntary muscle spasm causes us to inhale sharply. At the same time, the epiglottis blocks the airway to the lungs, producing the classic "hic" sound. The events are familiar, yet the very existence of hiccups poses a mystery. The quick intake of air apparently doesn't prevent or solve any known problem. So why do we get the hiccups at all?

Hiccups result from irritation of one or both phrenic nerves. These nerves trigger contraction of the diaphragm, which controls breathing. The distance between the origin of the phrenic nerves in the neck and the diaphragm offers many opportunities for irritation and, thus, hiccups. A more practical arrangement would be for the phrenic nerves to emerge from the spinal cord nearer the diaphragm. But we inherited our existing anatomy from our fishy ancestors, whose gills are near where their breathing-control nerves emerge (figure 13.A).

The second clue to the origin of hiccups comes from a close examination of young amphibians. Tadpoles have both lungs and gills, so they can gulp air or extract oxygen from water. In the latter case, they pump mouthfuls of water across their gills; at the same time, the glottis closes to keep water out of the lungs. The tadpole's breathing action almost exactly matches what happens in a human hiccup.

Together, these two lines of evidence suggest that the hiccup is an accident of evolution—a vestigial remnant of our shared evolutionary history with the vertebrates that came before us.

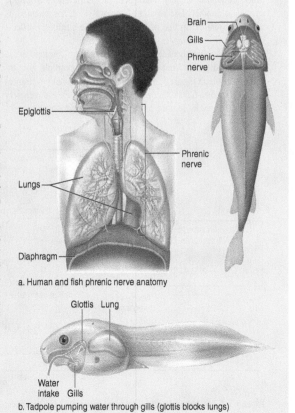

a. Human and fish phrenic nerve anatomy

b. Tadpole pumping water through gills (glottis blocks lungs)

Figure 13.A Hiccup Origins. (a) Humans have long phrenic nerves compared to those of fish. (b) When a tadpole breathes with its gills, its glottis closes. This action resembles a human hiccup.

Figure 13.21 Fossil "Fishapod." This photo shows a portion of the *Tiktaalik* fossil discovered in 2006.

The researchers did not simply stumble on *Tiktaalik* by accident. Instead, they were looking for a fossil representing the fish–amphibian transition, based on previous knowledge of how, when, and where vertebrates moved onto land hundreds of millions of years ago. Finding *Tiktaalik* confirmed the prediction.

Fossils have answered the question of how terrestrial vertebrates got their limbs, but until recently, the same was not true for another important issue in vertebrate evolution: how did snakes *lose* their limbs? Molecular and anatomical information, including vestigial legs in some snakes (see figure 13.11), clearly indicated that snakes evolved from lizards. Yet the precise four-legged ancestor remained elusive.

Scientists proposed two competing hypotheses to explain the origin of snakes. Noting that snakes resemble two existing groups of burrowing lizards, some scientists suggested that snakes evolved on land. Opposing scientists, citing skull and jaw similarities, contend that snakes descend from mosasaurs, marine reptiles that thrived during the Cretaceous period.

Argentinian paleontologist Sebastián Apesteguía, along with Brazilian colleague Hussam Zaher, added a critical clue to the debate over snake origins in April 2006, when they reported finding three fossilized snakes in the Patagonia region of Argentina (figure 13.22). The snakes, which they named *Najash rionegrina*, lived during the Upper Cretaceous period, about 90 MYA.

Najash is different from other ancient snakes for at least two reasons. First, it is the first snake ever found to have not only functional legs and a pelvis but also a sacrum—a bone connecting the pelvis to the spine. The sacrum is important because lizards and other terrestrial vertebrates have the same bone. *Najash* is therefore more primitive than any snake ever found (see figure 13.21b). Second, both the fossil's features and the rock where it was found suggest that it was terrestrial, not marine. Taken together, these two pieces of evidence seem to settle the matter: snakes originated on land.

Spectacular fossils such as *Tiktaalik* and *Najash* spark a flurry of excitement that obscures the countless hours of tedious, labor-intensive work needed to interpret fossils. Researchers scrutinize the scales, limbs, skull, jaw, teeth, vertebrae, and other parts of each new find to glean every possible piece of information about the animal and how it lived. In this way, fossils contribute immeasurably to our understanding of life's long history.

Apesteguía, Sebastián, and Hussam Zaher. April 20, 2006. A Cretaceous terrestrial snake with robust hindlimbs and a sacrum. *Nature,* vol. 440, pages 1037–1040.

Daeschler, Edward B., Neil H. Shubin, and Farish A. Jenkins, Jr. April 6, 2006. A Devonian tetrapod-like fish and the evolution of the tetrapod body plan. *Nature,* vol. 440, pages 757–763.

Shubin, Neil H., Edward B. Daeschler, and Farish A. Jenkins, Jr. April 6, 2006. A pectoral fin of *Tiktaalik roseae* and the origin of the tetrapod limb. *Nature,* vol. 440, pages 764–771.

13.7 MASTERING CONCEPTS

1. How might the ability to crawl on land for short periods have enhanced the reproductive fitness of *Tiktaalik*?
2. How might the loss of hindlimbs enhance the reproductive fitness of a burrowing animal such as *Najash*?

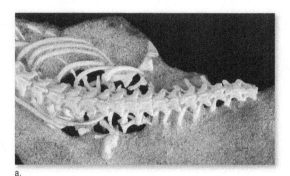

a.

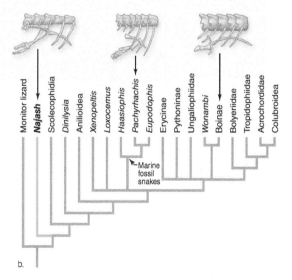

b.

Figure 13.22 *Najash,* the Fossil Snake. (a) *Najash* had hindlimbs, a pelvis, and a sacrum. (b) *Najash* was one of the most primitive snakes, whereas all three types of extinct marine snakes with legs arose later. This evidence suggests that snakes evolved on land and later colonized water.

CHAPTER SUMMARY

13.1 Clues to Evolution Lie in the Earth, Body Structures, and Molecules

- The **geologic timescale** divides Earth's history into eras defined by major events such as mass extinctions.
- Evidence for evolutionary relationships comes from **paleontology** (the study of past life) and from comparing anatomical and biochemical characteristics of species.

13.2 Fossils Record Evolution

- **Fossils** are the remains of ancient organisms.

A. Fossils Form in Many Ways

- Fossils may form when mineral replaces tissue gradually, or they may consist of footprints or feces. Rarely, organisms are preserved whole.

B. The Fossil Record Is Often Incomplete

- Many organisms that lived in the past have not left fossil evidence.

C. The Age of a Fossil Can Be Estimated in Two Ways

- The position of a fossil in the context of others provides a **relative date.**
- **Radiometric dating** uses a radioactive isotope to estimate the **absolute date** when an organism lived (figure 13.23). The length of an isotope's **half-life** determines whether it is useful for ancient or recent objects.

13.3 Biogeography Considers Species' Geographical Locations

- **Biogeography** is the study of the distribution of species on Earth.

A. The Theory of Plate Tectonics Explains Earth's Shifting Continents

- The **plate tectonics** theory indicates that forces deep inside Earth have moved the continents throughout much of life's history, creating and eliminating geographical barriers.

B. Species Distributions Reveal Evolutionary Events

- Biogeography provides insight into large- and small-scale evolutionary events.

13.4 Anatomical Comparisons May Reveal Common Descent

A. Homologous Structures Have a Shared Evolutionary Origin

- **Homologous** anatomical structures and molecules have similarities that indicate they were inherited from a shared ancestor.

B. Vestigial Structures Have Lost Their Functions

- **Vestigial** structures have no function in an organism but are homologous to functioning structures in related species.

C. Convergent Evolution Produces Superficial Similarities

- **Analogous** structures are similar in function but do not reflect shared ancestry. **Convergent evolution** can produce analogous structures.
- Figure 13.24 uses an evolutionary tree to illustrate the differences among homologous, analogous, and vestigial structures.

13.5 Embryonic Development Patterns Provide Evolutionary Clues

- Evolutionary developmental biology combines the study of development with the study of DNA sequences. Many genes, including **homeotic genes,** influence the development of an organism's body parts; mutations in homeotic genes therefore may lead to new phenotypes.

13.6 Molecules Reveal Relatedness

A. Comparing DNA and Protein Sequences May Reveal Close Relationships

- Similarities in molecular sequences are unlikely to occur by chance; descent from a shared ancestor is more likely.
- DNA sequence comparisons provide an indication of the relationships among species, as can the amino acid sequences of proteins.

B. Molecular Clocks Help Assign Dates to Evolutionary Events

- A **molecular clock** compares DNA sequences to estimate the time when two species diverged from a common ancestor.

13.7 Investigating Life: Limbs Gained and Limbs Lost

- Fossils of an extinct animal named *Tiktaalik roseae* reflect the transition between fishes and amphibians, which occurred about 375 MYA.
- Another fossil, *Najash rionegrina*, has helped researchers understand the origin of snakes. The features of *Najash* suggest that snakes arose on land from burrowing ancestors.

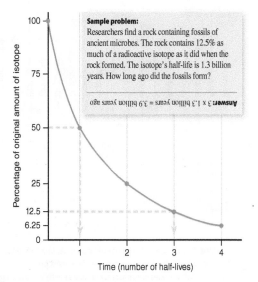

Sample problem:
Researchers find a rock containing fossils of ancient microbes. The rock contains 12.5% as much of a radioactive isotope as it did when the rock formed. The isotope's half-life is 1.3 billion years. How long ago did the fossils form?

Answer: 3 × 1.3 billion years = 3.9 billion years ago

Figure 13.23 Decay of a Radioactive Isotope.

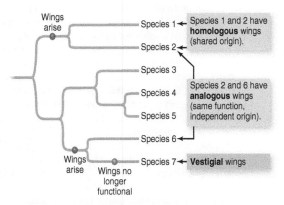

Figure 13.24 Homologous, Analogous, and Vestigial Structures Compared.

MULTIPLE CHOICE QUESTIONS

1. You discover that a 24,000-year-old fossil has one fourth the concentration of a radioactive isotope compared to a living organism. What is the half-life of this isotope?
   a. 3000 years   c. 8000 years
   b. 6000 years   d. 12,000 years

2. Fossils found in deeper layers of the Earth generally have ____ ^{14}C than fossils found in the upper layers.
   a. more   c. the same amount of
   b. less   d. different types of

3. Both octopuses and cuttlefish have a single-lens eye. Their common ancestor also had a single-lens eye. What word describes the relationship between the octopus eye and the cuttlefish eye?
   a. homologous   c. analogous
   b. vestigial   d. convergent

4. How does the activity of a homeotic gene relate to evolution?
   a. Homeotic genes serve as markers for convergent evolution.
   b. Organisms with similar homeotic genes have the same vestigial structures.
   c. Mutations in homeotic genes can produce new body plans.
   d. The presence of homeotic genes helps to identify a fossil as that of an animal.

5. Which of the following would be most useful for comparing ALL known groups of organisms?
   a. DNA encoding ribosomal RNA
   b. DNA encoding the keratin protein
   c. Mitochondrial DNA
   d. Y chromosome DNA

6. As described in chapter 7, the genetic code's redundancy means that a genetic mutation does not necessarily change the amino acid sequence of a protein. For a given gene, which molecule would you expect to change the most over evolutionary time?
   a. The DNA sequence.
   b. The protein sequence.
   c. The two should have exactly the same number of changes.
   d. The answer depends on the gene.

7. Mutations are known to arise in a certain gene once every 200 million years. If the gene sequences for two related species differ by six nucleotides, how long ago did these species last share an ancestor? *Hint:* Look at the number of nucleotide differences in figure 13.20.
   a. 33 million years   c. 600 million years
   b. 200 million years   d. 1200 million years

Answers to these questions are in appendix A.

WRITE IT OUT

1. Explain the significance of the geologic timescale in the context of evolution.

2. What types of information are used to hypothesize how species are related to one another by descent from a shared ancestor? Give an example of how multiple types of evidence can support one another.

3. Describe six types of fossils and how they form. What present environmental conditions might preserve today's organisms to form the fossils of the future?

4. Why are transitional fossils especially useful for understanding evolutionary relationships? Why might some transitional fossils never be found?

5. Index fossils represent organisms that were widespread but lived during relatively short periods of time. How might index fossils be useful in relative dating?

6. How did the discovery of Wallace's line demonstrate the predictive power of evolution?

7. How have geological events such as continental movements and the emergence of new volcanic islands influenced the history of life on Earth?

8. Why is it important for evolutionary biologists to be able to distinguish between homologous and analogous anatomical structures?

9. Suppose that plants in the San Francisco Bay area and in southern Chile share a common seed dispersal method. Scientists determine that the evolutionary divergence of these plants happened long before this seed dispersal method arose in each plant. What term relates the seed dispersal method of the San Francisco Bay plant to the seed dispersal method of the southern Chile plant? Explain your answer.

10. Explain why vestigial structures are important to evolutionary biologists.

11. Many species look similar as embryos. What causes them to appear different as adults? Why does the study of development give insights into evolutionary relationships?

12. Suggest a type of genetic change that could have a drastic effect on the evolution of a species.

13. How do biologists use sequences of proteins and genes to infer evolutionary relationships?

14. Some genes are more alike between human and chimp than other genes are from person to person. Does this mean that chimps are humans or that humans with different alleles are different species? What other explanation fits the facts?

15. Evolutionary biologists often try to assign an approximate date when two organisms last shared a common ancestor. Why do you think that molecular evidence often yields an earlier date than fossil evidence?

PULL IT TOGETHER

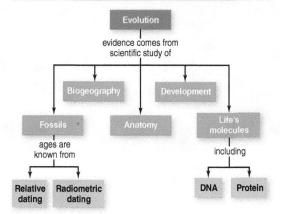

Figure 13.25 Pull It Together: Evidence of Evolution.

Refer to figure 13.25 and the chapter content to answer the following questions.

1. Write a phrase to connect *fossils* and *biogeography* and a separate phrase to connect *development* and *life's molecules*.

2. Add the following terms to this concept map: *homologous structures, vestigial structures, homeotic genes,* and *molecular clock.*

14 Speciation and Extinction

Bizarre Island Species. Socotra, an isolated island in the Indian ocean, is home to many strange organisms found nowhere else on Earth. In this plant, called the desert rose, the dry climate has selected for a thick trunk that stores water.

Enhance your study |BIOLOGY
of this chapter with practice quizzes,
animations and videos, answer keys,
and downloadable study tools.
www.mhhe.com/hoefnagels

Islands Provide Windows on Speciation and Extinction

OVER BILLIONS OF YEARS, MANY NEW SPECIES HAVE APPEARED ON EARTH IN A PROCESS CALLED SPECIATION. Yet most species that have ever lived are now extinct. The opposing, ongoing processes of speciation and extinction have defined life's history.

Islands provide ideal opportunities to study speciation. Their small land areas house populations that are relatively easy to monitor. In addition, few organisms can travel vast distances across oceans to reach isolated islands. The descendants of those that have done so have diversified and exploited multiple habitats. Islands located far from a mainland therefore often have groups of closely related species found nowhere else.

Many examples illustrate the spectacular diversity that islands may host. For example, about 800 species of *Drosophila* flies and their close relatives inhabit the Hawaiian Islands. Twenty-eight species of plants called silverswords thrive in every imaginable Hawaiian island habitat, yet all apparently descended from one ancestor that colonized Hawaii long ago. The same islands are also home to birds called honeycreepers, each with a bill adapted to a different food source.

At the same time, island species are especially vulnerable to extinction. Many factors conspire against them. A single hurricane, fire, or flood may destroy a small island population, as can the extinction of a prey species or the introduction of a new predator. Even random fluctuations in birth and death rates can doom a small population.

A volcanic island called Mauritius, in the Indian Ocean, illustrates how humans increase the extinction risk that island populations face. Until the sixteenth century, Mauritius teemed with tall forests, colorful birds, scurrying insects, and basking reptiles. One inhabitant was the large, flightless dodo bird, described by one scientist as "a magnificently overweight pigeon." When European sailors arrived in the 1500s, however, the men ate dodo meat; their pet monkeys and their pigs ate dodo eggs. Rats and mice swam ashore from ships and attacked native insects and reptiles. The sailors' Indian myna birds inhabited nests of the native echo parakeet, while imported plants crowded the seedlings of native trees. By the mid-1600s, only 11 of the original 33 species of birds remained. The dodo was exterminated by 1681, the first of many recorded extinctions caused by human activities.

Both speciation and extinction have likely been a part of evolution since life began. This chapter explains how these processes occur.

LEARNING OUTLINE

 14.1 The Definition of "Species" Has Evolved over Time
- A. Linnaeus Devised the Binomial Naming System
- B. Ernst Mayr Developed the Biological Species Concept

 14.2 Reproductive Barriers Cause Species to Diverge
- A. Prezygotic Barriers Prevent Fertilization
- B. Postzygotic Barriers Prevent Viable or Fertile Offspring

 14.3 Spatial Patterns Define Three Types of Speciation
- A. Allopatric Speciation Reflects a Geographic Barrier
- B. Parapatric Speciation Occurs in Neighboring Regions
- C. Sympatric Speciation Occurs in a Shared Habitat
- D. Determining the Type of Speciation May Be Difficult

 14.4 Speciation May Be Gradual or May Occur in Bursts
- A. Gradualism and Punctuated Equilibrium Are Two Models of Speciation
- B. Bursts of Speciation Occur During Adaptive Radiation

 14.5 Extinction Marks the End of the Line
- A. Many Factors Can Combine to Put a Species at Risk
- B. Extinction Rates Have Varied over Time

 14.6 Biological Classification Systems Are Based on Common Descent
- A. The Taxonomic Hierarchy Organizes Species into Groups
- B. A Cladistics Approach Is Based on Shared Derived Traits
- C. Cladograms Depict Hypothesized Evolutionary Relationships
- D. Many Traditional Groups Are Not Monophyletic

 14.7 Investigating Life: Birds Do It, Bees Do It

 LEARN HOW TO LEARN

Don't Neglect the Boxes

You may be tempted to skip the chapter-opening essays and boxed readings because they're not "required." Read them anyway. The contents should help you remember and visualize the material you are trying to learn. And who knows? You may even find them interesting.

14.1 The Definition of "Species" Has Evolved over Time

Throughout the history of life, the types of organisms have changed: new species have appeared, and existing ones have gone extinct. The term **macroevolution** describes these large, complex changes in life's panorama. Macroevolutionary events tend to span very long periods, whereas the microevolutionary processes described in chapter 12 happen so rapidly that we can sometimes observe them over just a few years (see the Burning Question on page 283). Nevertheless, the many small changes that accumulate in a population by microevolution eventually lead to large-scale macroevolution.

Evolution has produced an obvious diversity of life. A bacterium, for example, is clearly distinct from a tree or a bird (figure 14.1). At the same time, some organisms are more closely related than others, as the two cats in figure 14.2 illustrate. To make sense of these observations, biologists recognize the importance of grouping similar individuals into **species**—that is, distinct types of organisms. This task requires agreement on what the word *species* means. Perhaps surprisingly, the definition has changed considerably over time and is still the topic of vigorous debate among biologists.

A. Linnaeus Devised the Binomial Naming System

Swedish botanist Carolus Linnaeus (1707–1778) was not the first to ponder what constitutes a species, but his contributions last to this day. Linnaeus defined species as "all examples of creatures that were alike in minute detail of body structure." Importantly, he was the first investigator to give every species a two-word name. Each name combines the broader classification *genus* (plural: genera) with a second word that designates the species. The scientific name for humans, for example, is *Homo sapiens*.

Linnaeus also devised a hierarchical system for classifying species. He grouped similar genera into orders, classes, and kingdoms; scientists now use additional categories, as described in

Figure 14.2 **Similar Species.** These two species of felines—a leopard and a bobcat—have many characteristics in common.

section 14.6. Linnaeus's classifications organized the great diversity of life and helped scientists communicate with one another.

His system did not, however, consider the role of evolutionary relationships. Linnaeus thought that each species was created separately and could not change. Therefore, species could not appear or disappear, nor were they related to one another.

Charles Darwin (1809–1882) finally connected species diversity to evolution. He predicted that classifications would come to resemble genealogies, or extended "family trees." As the theory of evolution by natural selection became widely accepted in the nineteenth and twentieth centuries, scientists no longer viewed classifications merely as ways to organize life. They considered them to be hypotheses about the evolutionary history of life.

B. Ernst Mayr Developed the Biological Species Concept

In the 1940s, Harvard biologist Ernst Mayr amended the work of Linnaeus and Darwin by considering reproduction and genetics. Mayr defined a **biological species** as a population, or group of populations, whose members can interbreed and produce fertile

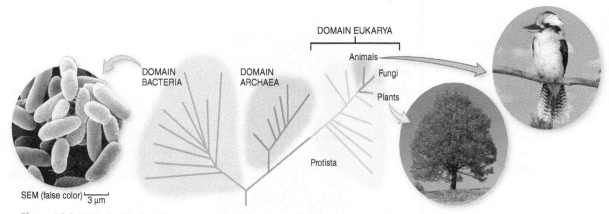

Figure 14.1 **Distinctive Species.** Bacteria, a tree, and a bird are about as dissimilar as three types of organisms can be.

Burning Question

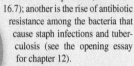

Can people watch evolution and speciation in action?

Evolution is ongoing in every species, so it is not surprising that biologists have documented many instances of evolution "in action." Medicine provides the most familiar context. One example is the discovery that HIV evolved from a virus that occurs in chimpanzees (see section 16.7); another is the rise of antibiotic resistance among the bacteria that cause staph infections and tuberculosis (see the opening essay for chapter 12).

The use of pesticides has provided ample examples as well. Many people know that populations of DDT-resistant insects skyrocketed shortly after people began using DDT to kill mosquito larvae. Likewise, section 10.10 describes the selection for moth larvae that are resistant to Bt, an insecticidal protein.

Speciation is observable as well. Mosquito populations that have been isolated for more than 100 years in the tunnels of the London Underground, for example, can no longer breed with their aboveground counterparts. Scientists have also witnessed the birth of new plant species in the genus *Tragopogon*, a plant group that was introduced to western North America decades ago.

Submit your burning question to
Marielle.Hoefnagels@mheducation.com

Figure 14.3 How Many Species? Linnaeus would have categorized these butterflies based on their physical appearance. Mayr's biological species definition, however, provides an objective rule for determining whether each group really is a separate species.

offspring. **Speciation,** the formation of new species, occurs when members of a population can no longer successfully interbreed.

How might this happen? A new species can form if a population somehow becomes divided. Recall from chapter 12 that a population's **gene pool** is its entire collection of genes and their alleles. An intact, interbreeding population shares a common gene pool. After a population splits in two, however, microevolutionary changes such as natural selection, genetic drift, and gene flow can lead to genetic divergence between the groups. With the accumulation of enough differences in their separate gene pools, the two groups can no longer produce fertile offspring even if they come into contact once again. In this way, microevolution becomes macroevolution.

The biological species definition does not rely on physical appearance, so it is much less subjective than Linnaeus's observations. Under the system of Linnaeus, it would be impossible to determine whether two similar-looking butterflies belong to different species (figure 14.3). Using Mayr's definition, however, if the two groups can produce fertile offspring together, they share a gene pool and therefore belong to one species.

Nevertheless, Mayr's species definition raises several difficulties. First, the biological species concept cannot apply to asexually reproducing organisms, such as bacteria, archaea, and many fungi and protists. Second, it is likewise impossible to

apply the biological species definition to extinct organisms known only from fossils. Third, some types of organisms have the *potential* to interbreed in captivity, but they do not do so in nature. Fourth, reproductive isolation is not always absolute. Closely related species of plants, for example, may occasionally produce fertile offspring together, even though their gene pools mostly remain separate.

As a result, the biological species concept does not provide a perfect way to determine the "boundaries" of each species. DNA sequence analysis has helped to fill in some of these gaps. Biologists working with bacteria and archaea, for example, use a stretch of DNA that encodes ribosomal RNA to define species. If the DNA sequences of two specimens are more than 97% identical, they are considered to be the same species. These genetic sequences, however, still present some ambiguity because they cannot reveal whether genetically similar organisms currently share a gene pool.

Despite these difficulties, reproductive isolation is the most common criterion used to define species. The rest of this chapter therefore uses the biological species concept to describe how speciation occurs.

14.1   MASTERING CONCEPTS

1. What is the relationship between macroevolution and microevolution?
2. How does the biological species concept differ from Linnaeus's definition?
3. What are some of the challenges in defining species?

14.2 Reproductive Barriers Cause Species to Diverge

In keeping with Mayr's biological species concept, a new species forms when one portion of a population can no longer breed and produce fertile offspring with the rest of the population. That is, the two separate groups no longer share a gene pool, and each begins to follow its own, independent evolutionary path.

Two parts of a population can become reproductively isolated in many ways, because successful reproduction requires so many complex events. Any interruption in courtship, fertilization, embryo formation, or offspring development can be a reproductive barrier.

Biologists divide the many mechanisms of reproductive isolation into two broad groups: prezygotic and postzygotic. Prezygotic reproductive barriers occur before the formation of the zygote, or fertilized egg; postzygotic barriers reduce the fitness of a hybrid offspring. (A hybrid, in this case, is the offspring of individuals from two different species.) Figure 14.4 summarizes the reproductive barriers; the rest of this section describes them in detail.

Barrier	Description	Example	Illustration
PREZYGOTIC REPRODUCTIVE ISOLATION			
Habitat isolation	Different environments	Ladybugs feed on different plants.	
Temporal isolation	Active or fertile at different times	Field crickets mature at different rates.	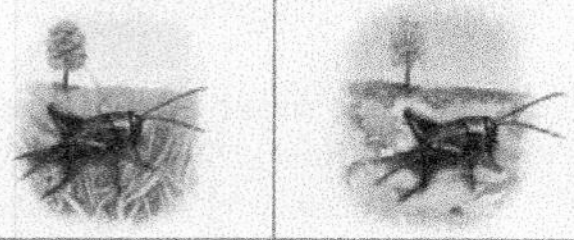
Behavioral isolation	Different courtship activities	Frog mating calls differ.	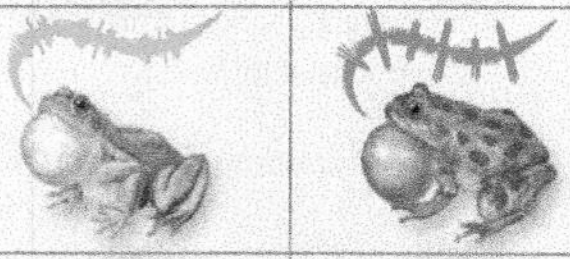
Mechanical isolation	Mating organs or pollinators incompatible	Sage species use different pollinators.	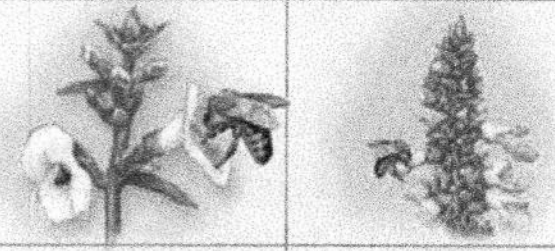
Gametic isolation	Gametes cannot unite.	Sea urchin gametes are incompatible.	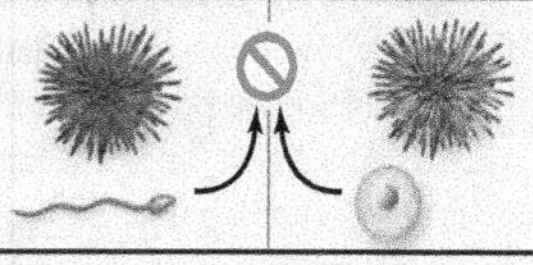
POSTZYGOTIC REPRODUCTIVE ISOLATION			
Hybrid inviability	Hybrid offspring fail to reach maturity.	Hybrid eucalyptus seeds and seedlings are not viable.	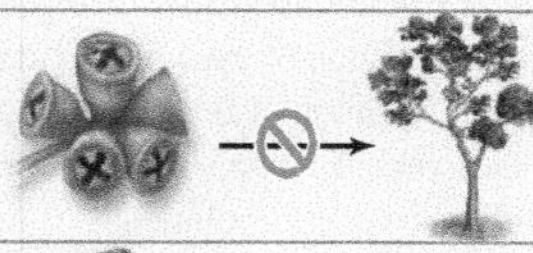
Hybrid infertility (sterility)	Hybrid offspring unable to reproduce	Lion-tiger cross (liger) is infertile.	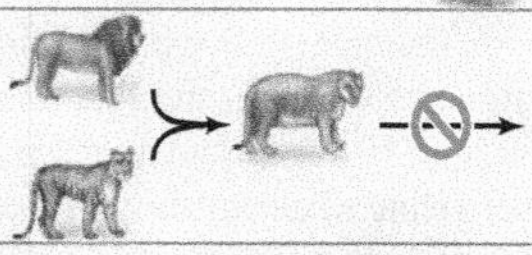
Hybrid breakdown	Second-generation hybrid offspring have reduced fitness.	Offspring of hybrid mosquitoes have abnormal genitalia.	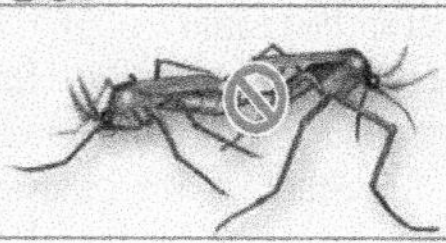

Figure 14.4   Reproductive Barriers. Prezygotic barriers prevent gametes from two species from combining to produce a hybrid offspring. Postzygotic barriers keep species separate by selecting against hybrid offspring.

A. Prezygotic Barriers Prevent Fertilization

Mechanisms of **prezygotic reproductive isolation** affect the ability of two species to combine gametes and form a zygote. These reproductive barriers include the following:

- **Ecological (or habitat) isolation:** A difference in habitat preference can separate two populations in the same geographic area. For example, one species of ladybird beetle eats one type of plant, while a closely related species eats a different plant. The two species never occur on the same host plant, although they interbreed freely in the laboratory. The different habitat preferences are the reproductive barrier that keeps the gene pools of the two species separate.

- **Temporal isolation:** Two species that share a habitat will not mate if they are active at different times of day or reach reproductive maturity at different times of year. Among field crickets in Virginia, for example, one species takes much longer to develop than another, so the adults of the two species may not meet until late in the season, if at all. Similarly, the different emergence schedules for 13- and 17-year periodical cicadas suggest that temporal isolation prevents interbreeding between these two species.

- **Behavioral isolation:** Behavioral differences may prevent two closely related species from mating. The males of two species of tree frogs, for instance, use distinct calls to attract mates. Female frogs choose males of their own species based on the unique calls. Likewise, sexual selection in many birds is based on intricate mating dances. Any variation in the ritual from one group to another could prevent them from being attracted to one another. ⓘ *sexual selection*, p. 252

- **Mechanical isolation:** In many animal species, male and female parts fit together almost like a key in a lock. Any change in the shape of the gamete-delivering or -receiving structures may prevent groups from interbreeding. In plants, males and females do not copulate, but mechanical barriers still apply. For example, although two species of sage plant in California can interbreed, in practice they rarely do because they use different pollinators. One species has flowers that attract large bees, whereas the other accommodates small to medium bees. The different pollinators effectively isolate the gene pools of the two plant species. Section 14.7 explores a similar reproductive barrier in another pair of plant species. ⓘ *pollination*, p. 501

- **Gametic isolation:** If a sperm cannot fertilize an egg cell, then no reproduction will occur. For example, many marine organisms, such as sea urchins, simply release sperm and egg cells into the water. These gametes display unique surface molecules that enable an egg to recognize sperm of the same species. In the absence of a "match," fertilization will not occur, and the gene pools will remain separate.

B. Postzygotic Barriers Prevent Viable or Fertile Offspring

Individuals of two different species may produce a hybrid zygote. Even then, **postzygotic reproductive isolation** may keep the species separate by selecting against the hybrid offspring, effectively preventing genetic exchange between the populations. Collectively, these postzygotic barriers are sometimes called hybrid incompatibility.

Postzygotic reproductive barriers include the following:

- **Hybrid inviability:** A hybrid embryo may die before reaching reproductive maturity, typically because the genes of its parents are incompatible. For example, two species of eucalyptus trees coexist in California forests, but hybrid offspring are rare. Either the hybrid seeds fail to germinate, or the seedlings die soon after sprouting. Since the hybrid offspring cannot reproduce, the gene pools of the parent species remain isolated from one another.

- **Hybrid infertility (sterility):** Some hybrids are infertile. A familiar example is the mule, a hybrid offspring of a female horse and a male donkey. Mules are infertile because a horse's egg has one more chromosome than a donkey's sperm cell. The animal can grow and develop, but meiosis does not occur in the mule's germ cells because the chromosomes are not homologous. Similarly, a liger is the hybrid offspring of a male lion and a female tiger; ligers are usually sterile. Although mules and ligers contain the mixed genes of two species, they cannot pass their genes back into either parent population. Therefore, genetic exchange between parent populations is not sustained. ⓘ *homologous chromosomes*, p. 169; *mules*, p. 173

- **Hybrid breakdown:** Some species produce hybrid offspring that are fertile. When the hybrids reproduce, however, their offspring may have abnormalities that reduce their fitness. Some second-generation hybrid offspring of the mosquito species *Aedes aegypti* and *Aedes mascarensis*, for example, have abnormal genitalia that make mating difficult. The strong selective pressure against hybrid offspring limits gene flow between the two mosquito species.

Successful hybridization is rare in animals, but it frequently occurs in plants. One of the problems with introducing nonnative species of plants into a region is the potential production of hybrids that displace the native plants. On the other hand, some food crops are the result of hybridization. A fruit called a tangelo, for example, is the hybrid offspring of a tangerine and a pomelo (grapefruit); a plumcot is a cross between a plum and an apricot.

14.2 MASTERING CONCEPTS

1. How do reproductive barriers lead to speciation?
2. Research and describe examples of each of the eight modes of reproductive isolation. Alternatively, make up your own examples.

14.3 Spatial Patterns Define Three Types of Speciation

Reproductive barriers keep related species apart, but how do these barriers arise in the first place? More specifically, how could two populations of the same species evolve along different pathways, eventually yielding two species?

The most obvious way is to physically separate the populations so that they do not exchange genes. Evolution would then act independently in the two populations. Eventually, the genetic differences between the populations would give rise to one or more reproductive barriers.

Yet speciation can also separate populations that have physical contact with each other. They may divide into new species even though they inhabit neighboring regions or even share a habitat. Biologists recognize these different circumstances by dividing the geographic setting of speciation into three categories: allopatric, parapatric, and sympatric (figure 14.5).

A. Allopatric Speciation Reflects a Geographic Barrier

In **allopatric speciation,** a geographic barrier physically separates a population into two groups that cannot interbreed (*allo-* means "other," and *patria* means "fatherland"). These barriers may take many forms. Rivers, deserts, or glaciers may divide a habitat. Rising sea levels may trap populations on isolated islands. New mountain ranges or large bodies of water may replace flat land. Humans may build dams, farms, and cities that block the movements of some species.

If two parts of a population cannot contact each other, gene flow between them stops. Meanwhile, the forces of microevolution continue to alter allele frequencies in each group. Mutations and genetic drift both occur at random, while natural selection favors different allele combinations in each habitat. Eventually, the result of these ongoing microevolutionary changes may be

one or more reproductive barriers. And when the descendants of the original two populations can no longer interbreed, one species has branched into two.

The Devil's Hole pupfish, which inhabits a warm spring at the base of a mountain near Death Valley, California, illustrates one way that allopatric speciation occurs (figure 14.6). The spring was isolated from other bodies of water about 50,000 years ago, preventing genetic exchange between the fish trapped in the spring and those in the original population. Generation after generation, different alleles have accumulated in each pupfish population. Without reproduction between the pupfish groups, changes in one population were not shared with the others; each population took its own evolutionary path. Since the time that the spring became isolated, the gene pool has shifted enough that a Devil's Hole pupfish cannot mate with fish from another spring. It has become a distinct species.

In addition to isolated springs, island archipelagos also offer opportunities for allopatric speciation. For example, 11 subspecies of tortoise occupy the various Galápagos islands. Researchers have compared the DNA collected from 161 individuals and used the sequences to reconstruct many of the events that occurred after tortoises first colonized the islands a couple of million years ago (figure 14.7).

According to the DNA analysis, a few newcomers from the South American mainland first colonized either San Cristóbal or Española (also called Hood Island). As the population grew, the tortoises migrated to nearby islands, where they encountered new habitats that selected for different adaptations, especially in shell shape. Dry islands with sparse vegetation have selected for notched shells that enable the tortoises to reach for higher food sources. The Hood Island tortoise in figure 14.7 illustrates this characteristic "saddleback" shape. On islands with lush, low-growing vegetation, the tortoises have domed shells; Isabela Island's Volcán Alcedo tortoise is an example.

Although many of the subspecies look distinctly different from one another, the tortoises can interbreed. They are not yet separate species, but the genetic similarities among tortoises on

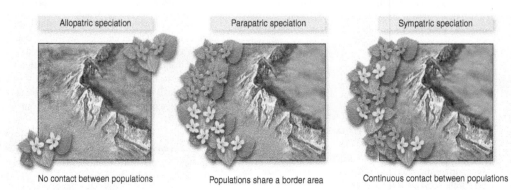

Allopatric speciation — No contact between populations

Parapatric speciation — Populations share a border area

Sympatric speciation — Continuous contact between populations

Figure 14.5 Speciation and Geography. The three modes of speciation are distinguished based on whether populations are separated by a physical barrier or mingle within a shared border area.

Figure 14.6 **Allopatric Speciation in Pupfish.** Devil's Hole is a pool in a cavern east of Death Valley National Park. The pupfish species that lives there is a product of allopatric speciation; it cannot breed with pupfish from nearby springs.

each island suggest that gene flow from island to island was historically rare. The Galápagos tortoises illustrate an ongoing process of allopatric speciation.

Separation by a geographic barrier has been considered the most common mechanism of speciation because the evidence for it is the most abundant and obvious. The diversification of plant and animal species on island archipelagos such as Hawaii and the Galápagos provide many striking examples. So do the world's fishes: of the 29,000 or so known species of fishes, 36% live in freshwater habitats, although these places account for only 1% of Earth's surface. Compared with the vast interconnected oceans, the countless springs, lakes, ponds, streams, and rivers provide diverse habitats and ample barriers to genetic exchange.

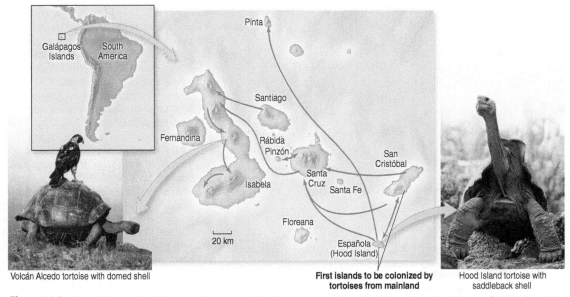

Volcán Alcedo tortoise with domed shell

First islands to be colonized by tortoises from mainland

Hood Island tortoise with saddleback shell

Figure 14.7 **Allopatric Speciation in Tortoises.** Descendants of the first tortoises to arrive on the Galápagos have colonized most of the islands, evolving into many subspecies. Unique habitats have selected for different sets of adaptations in the tortoises.

B. Parapatric Speciation Occurs in Neighboring Regions

In **parapatric speciation,** part of a population enters a new habitat bordering the range of the parent species (*para-* means "alongside"). Most individuals mate within their own populations, although gene flow may still occur among individuals that venture into the shared border zone.

Despite this limited gene flow, parapatric speciation can occur if the two habitats are different enough to drive disruptive selection. As described in section 12.5, disruptive selection occurs when individuals with intermediate forms have lower fitness than those at either extreme. Parapatric speciation might begin if one phenotype conferred high fitness in one habitat, but a different phenotype worked better in the neighboring area. As allele frequencies changed independently in each habitat, the two subpopulations would mingle less and less. Over time, the two populations would become genetically (and reproductively) isolated.

Consider the little greenbul, a small green bird that lives in the tropical rain forest of Cameroon, West Africa (figure 14.8). The birds also inhabit the isolated patches of forest that characterize the transitional areas (called ecotones) between rain forest and grassland. In one study, researchers captured birds from six tropical rain forest sites and six ecotone sites. The birds in the ecotone patches had greater weight, deeper bills, and longer legs and wings than their rain forest counterparts.

What forces might have selected for these differences? The researchers speculated that longer wings increase fitness in the ecotone by improving flight, since the little greenbuls are vulnerable to predation in the open grassland areas separating the patches of forest. Presumably, the foods available in the ecotone and rain forest habitats account for the difference in bill depth.

The little greenbuls from the ecotones can still mate with those from the rain forest, so speciation has not yet occurred. Nevertheless, the researchers concluded that the forces of natural selection are greater than the gene flow between the two populations, gradually taking the groups farther apart. We are likely seeing speciation in action.

C. Sympatric Speciation Occurs in a Shared Habitat

 Video Fish Sympatric Speciation

In **sympatric speciation,** populations diverge genetically while living in the same physical area (*sym-* means "together"). Among evolutionary biologists, the idea of sympatric speciation can be controversial. After all, how can a new species arise in the midst of an existing population?

Often sympatric speciation reflects the fact that a habitat that appears uniform actually consists of many microenvironments. Fishes called cichlids, for example, have diversified into many species within the same lakes in Africa. Figure 14.9 shows two cichlids in Cameroon's tiny Lake Ejagham. This 18-meter-deep lake has distinct ecological zones. Its bottom is muddy near the center, whereas leaves and twigs cover the sandy bottom near the shore.

Two closely related cichlids each specialize in a different zone. The larger fish consume insects near the shore, whereas the smaller cichlids eat tiny floating prey in deeper waters. The fish breed where they eat. The two forms therefore typically remain isolated and could be undergoing sympatric speciation.

In plants, a common mechanism of sympatric speciation is **polyploidy,** which occurs when the number of sets of chromosomes increases. Many major crops, including wheat, corn, sugar cane, potatoes, and coffee, are derived from polyploid plants. ⓘ *polyploidy,* p. 177

Polyploidy sometimes arises when gametes from two different species fuse. Cotton plants provide an example of polyploidy (figure 14.10). An Old World species of wild cotton has 26 large chromosomes, whereas one from Central and South America has 26 small chromosomes. The two species interbred, creating a diploid hybrid with 26 chromosomes (13 large and 13 small). This hybrid was sterile. But eventually the chromosome number doubled. The resulting cotton plant, *Gossypium hirsutum,* is a fertile polyploid with 52 chromosomes (26 large and 26 small). Farmers around the world cultivate this species to harvest cotton for cloth.

Polyploidy can also occur when meiosis fails. A diploid individual may occasionally produce diploid sex cells. Self-fertilization will produce tetraploid offspring (with four sets

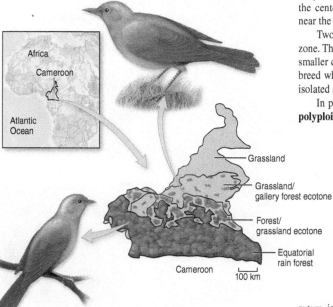

Africa
Cameroon
Atlantic Ocean

Grassland
Grassland/ gallery forest ecotone
Forest/ grassland ecotone
Equatorial rain forest

Cameroon
100 km

Figure 14.8 Parapatric Speciation. The little greenbul lives in the rain forest and in ecotones, which are patches of forest in the border zone with grasslands. Birds from the ecotone are larger than their rain forest counterparts.

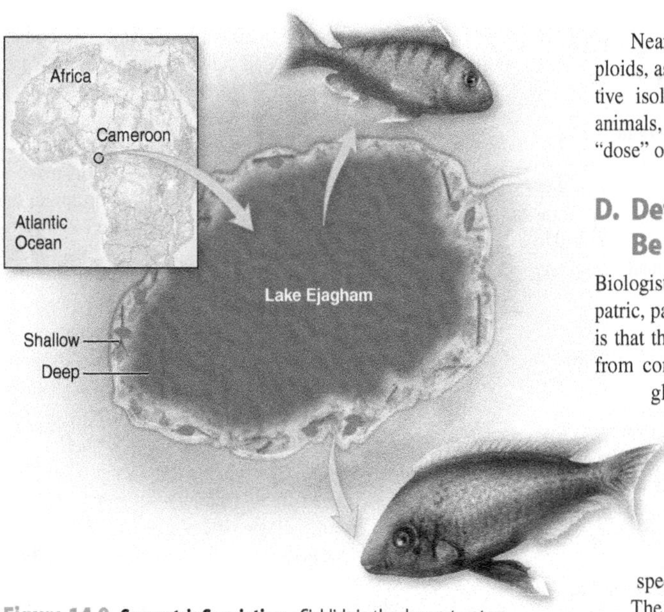

Nearly half of all flowering plant species are natural polyploids, as are about 95% of ferns. Clearly, this form of reproductive isolation is extremely important in plant evolution. In animals, however, polyploidy is rare, possibly because the extra "dose" of chromosomes is usually fatal.

D. Determining the Type of Speciation May Be Difficult

Biologists sometimes debate whether a speciation event is allopatric, parapatric, or sympatric. One reason for the disagreement is that the definitions represent three points along a continuum, from complete reproductive isolation to continuous intermingling. Another difficulty is that we may not be able to detect the barriers that are important to other species. For example, a researcher might perceive a patch of forest to be uniform and conclude that speciation events occurring are sympatric. But to an insect, the distance between the forest floor and the treetops may represent an insurmountable barrier. In that case, speciation would be considered allopatric.

The problem of perspective also leads to debate over the size of the geographic barrier needed to separate two populations, which depends on the distance over which a species can spread its gametes. A plant with windblown pollen or a fungus producing lightweight spores encounters few barriers to gene flow. Pollen and spores can travel thousands of miles in the upper atmosphere. On the other hand, a desert pupfish cannot migrate out of its aquatic habitat, so the isolation of its pool instantly creates a geographic barrier. The same circumstance would not deter gene flow in species that walk or fly between pools.

Figure 14.9 Sympatric Speciation. Cichlids in the deepest waters of Lake Ejagham have smaller bodies than do shallow-water fish.

of chromosomes). This organism represents an "instant species" because it is reproductively isolated from its diploid ancestors. After all, when the tetraploid plant's gametes (each containing two sets of chromosomes) combine with haploid gametes from the parent species, each offspring inherits three sets of chromosomes. This hybrid is infertile because it cannot complete meiosis: three chromosome sets cannot form the required homologous pairs.

14.3 MASTERING CONCEPTS

1. Distinguish among allopatric, parapatric, and sympatric speciation, and provide examples of each.
2. How can polyploidy contribute to sympatric speciation?
3. Why is it sometimes difficult to determine whether speciation is allopatric, parapatric, or sympatric?

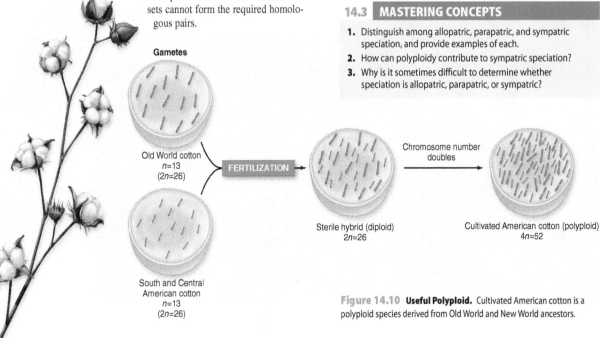

Gametes

Old World cotton
n=13
(2*n*=26)

South and Central
American cotton
n=13
(2*n*=26)

FERTILIZATION

Sterile hybrid (diploid)
2*n*=26

Chromosome number
doubles

Cultivated American cotton (polyploid)
4*n*=52

Figure 14.10 Useful Polyploid. Cultivated American cotton is a polyploid species derived from Old World and New World ancestors.

14.4 Speciation May Be Gradual or May Occur in Bursts

On a global level, Earth has seen times of relatively little change in the living landscape but also periods of rapid speciation and times of mass extinctions. Even within a short time, one species can evolve rapidly, while another hardly changes at all (the Burning Question on page 301 explains this disparity). As described in this section, speciation can happen quickly, gradually, or at any rate in between.

A. Gradualism and Punctuated Equilibrium Are Two Models of Speciation

Darwin envisioned one species gradually transforming into another through a series of intermediate stages. The pace as Darwin saw it was slow, although not necessarily constant. This idea, which became known as **gradualism,** held that evolution proceeds in small, incremental changes over many generations (figure 14.11a).

If the gradualism model is correct, "slow and steady" evolutionary change should be evident in the fossil record. In fact, however, many steps in species formation did not leave fossil evidence, and so we do not know of many intermediate or transitional forms between species. Much of the fossil record instead suggests the opposite: that a new species may appear relatively suddenly and evolve quickly, followed by long periods over which the species changed little.

What accounts for the "missing" transitional forms? One explanation is that the fossil record is incomplete, for many reasons: poor preservation of biological material, natural forces that destroyed fossils, and the simple fact that we haven't discovered every fossil on Earth. Chapter 13 explores these reasons in more detail.

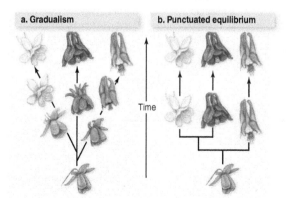

a. Gradualism   **b. Punctuated equilibrium**

Time

Figure 14.11 **Evolution—Both Gradual and Dramatic.** (a) In gradualism, three species arise from one ancestor by way of small, incremental steps. (b) Punctuated equilibrium produces the same result, except that the new species arise in rapid bursts followed by periods of little change.

Another explanation for the absence of some predicted transitional forms is that such "missing links" may have been too rare to leave many fossils. After all, periods of rapid biological changes would not leave much fossil evidence of transitional forms. In 1972, paleontologists Stephen Jay Gould and Niles Eldredge coined the term **punctuated equilibrium** to describe relatively brief bursts of rapid evolution interrupting long periods of little change (see figure 14.11b). The fossil record, they argued, lacks some transitional forms because they never existed in a particular location or because there were simply too few organisms to leave fossils.

The punctuated equilibrium model fits well with the concept of allopatric speciation. Consider the isolated population of desert pupfish that became genetically distinct from its ancestral population over 50,000 years (see figure 14.6). If the climate changed and the spring containing the new species rejoined its "old" spring, the fossil record might show that a new fish species suddenly appeared with its ancestors—after all, 50,000 years is a blink of an eye in geologic time. Afterward, unless the environment changed again, no new selective forces would drive the formation of new species. Thus, a period of stability would ensue.

The fossil record supports both punctuated equilibrium and gradualism. Microscopic protists such as foraminiferans and diatoms, for example, have evolved gradually. Vast populations of these asexually reproducing organisms span the oceans. Since isolated populations rarely form, it is perhaps not surprising that speciation has occurred only gradually among those protists. On the other hand, the fossils of animals such as bryozoans, mollusks, and mammals all reveal many examples of rapid evolution followed by periods of stability.

B. Bursts of Speciation Occur During Adaptive Radiation

Speciation can happen in rapid bursts during an **adaptive radiation,** in which a population inhabiting a patchy or heterogeneous environment gives rise to multiple specialized forms in a relatively short time. (In this context, the term *radiation* means spreading outward from a central source.)

In adaptive radiation, speciation typically occurs in response to the availability of new resources. For example, a few individuals might colonize a new, isolated habitat such as a mountaintop or island. Multiple food sources, such as plants with different-sized seeds, would simultaneously select for different adaptations. Over time, multiple species would develop.

Adaptive radiation is especially common in island groups. One stunning example occurred in the Caribbean islands of Cuba, Jamaica, Puerto Rico, and Hispaniola (figure 14.12). Adaptive radiation occurred separately on each island, where at least 150 species of small lizards called anoles have adapted in very similar ways to different parts of their habitats. Other examples of adaptive radiation occur on Hawaii (as described in this chapter's opening essay), the Galápagos, and the Malay archipelago, where Alfred Russel Wallace collected a multitude of beetles and butterflies.

Upper trunk/canopy

Large toe pads, can change color

Cuba—*Anolis porcatus*
Hispaniola—*A. chlorocyanus*
Jamaica—*A. grahami*
Puerto Rico—*A. evermanni*

A. evermanni

Midtrunk

Long forelimbs, vertically flattened body

Cuba—*Anolis loysiana*
Hispaniola—*A. distichus*
Jamaica—none found
Puerto Rico—none found

A. loysiana

Lower trunk/ground

Stocky body, long hind limbs

Cuba—*Anolis sagrei*
Hispaniola—*A. cybotes*
Jamaica—*A. lineatopus*
Puerto Rico—*A. cristatellus*

A. cristatellus

Grass/bush

Slender body, very long tail

Cuba—*Anolis alutaceus*
Hispaniola—*A. olssoni*
Jamaica—none found
Puerto Rico—*A. pulchellus*

A. pulchellus

Florida
GULF OF MEXICO
ATLANTIC OCEAN
CUBA
PUERTO RICO
JAMAICA HISPANIOLA

Figure 14.12 Adaptive Radiation. More than 150 anole lizard species have evolved on four Caribbean islands. Each island has a unique collection of species, yet the adaptations to each habitat are similar—a striking example of convergent evolution (see section 13.4C).

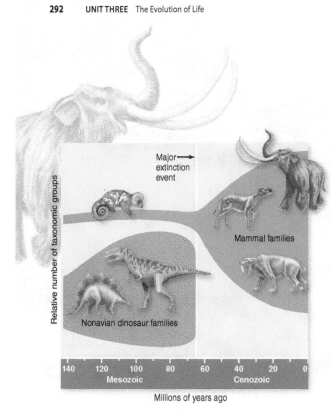

Figure 14.13 Speciation Following a Mass Extinction. With many ecological niches vacated when most dinosaurs became extinct about 65 million years ago, mammals flourished.

As another path to adaptive radiation, some members of a population may inherit a key adaptation that gives them an advantage. The first flowering plants, for example, appeared around 144 million years ago (in the late Jurassic period). Their descendants diversified rapidly during the Cretaceous, and all of today's major lineages were already in place 100 million years ago. Hundreds of thousands of flowering plant species now inhabit Earth. The new adaptation—the flower—apparently unleashed an entirely new set of options for reproduction, prompting rapid diversification.

A third type of adaptive radiation occurs when some members of a population have a combination of adaptations that enable them to survive a major environmental change. After the poorly suited organisms perish, the survivors diversify as they exploit the new resources in the changed environment. Mammals, for example, underwent an enormous adaptive radiation when dinosaur extinctions opened up many new habitats (figure 14.13).

14.4 MASTERING CONCEPTS

1. Describe the theories of gradualism and punctuated equilibrium. How can the fossil record support both?
2. What are three ways that adaptive radiation can occur?

14.5 Extinction Marks the End of the Line

A species goes **extinct** when all of its members have died. If speciation is the birth of a species, extinction represents its death.

A. Many Factors Can Combine to Put a Species at Risk

Extinctions have many causes. Habitat loss, new predators, or new diseases all can wipe out a species. Extinction may also be a matter of bad luck: sometimes no individual of a species survives a catastrophe such as a volcanic eruption or asteroid impact.

No matter what the external trigger of an extinction may be, the root cause is always the same: species die out if evolution fails to meet the pace of environmental change. Any species will eventually vanish if its gene pool does not contain the "right" alleles necessary for individuals to produce fertile offspring and sustain the population.

When faced with shifting conditions, what is the chance that a species will become extinct? The answer depends in part on the pace and scale of environmental change. Species such as elephants, which reach reproductive maturity at 30 years, are much less likely to survive a sudden change than are mice, which produce three generations a year. And if the environment changes on a massive scale—the climate changes from warm and wet to cool and dry, for example—extinctions are inevitable. Research suggests that plants rarely thrive in a habitat that is very different from that of their ancestors (see section 39.6).

In addition, the smaller the initial size of a population, the less likely it is to endure a major challenge. Small populations experience fewer genetic mutations, which are the ultimate source of new adaptations (see section 12.7). Low genetic diversity within a population, in turn, poses two problems. First, the population may contain too few beneficial alleles to withstand a new challenge. An emerging disease, for example, may wipe out most individuals, leaving too few survivors to maintain the population's size. Second, inbreeding in a small population tends to bring together lethal recessive alleles, which can weaken the organisms and make them less able to survive and reproduce.

B. Extinction Rates Have Varied over Time

Biologists distinguish between two different types of extinction events. The **background extinction rate** results from the gradual loss of species as populations shrink in the face of new challenges. Paleontologists have used the fossil record to calculate that most species exist from 1 million to 10 million years before becoming extinct. Thus, the background rate is roughly 0.1 to 1.0 extinctions per year per million species. Most extinctions overall occur as part of this background rate.

Earth has also witnessed several periods of **mass extinctions,** when a great number of species disappeared over relatively short expanses of time. The geologic timescale in figure 13.2 shows

Apply It **Now**

Recent Species Extinctions

Species extinctions have occurred throughout life's long history. They continue today, often accelerated by human activities (see chapter 40). Overharvesting, for example, caused the extinction of the passenger pigeon and many other species. Habitat loss to agriculture, urbanization, damming, or pollution also takes a toll. Introduced plants and animals can deplete native species by competing with or preying on them.

The International Union for Conservation of Nature keeps track of recent extinctions of animal and plant species (figure 14.A). Of the hundreds of documented extinctions over the past 500 years, most have occurred on islands. This chapter's opening essay explores some of the reasons that island species are especially vulnerable.

Table 14.A lists a few species of vertebrate animals that have disappeared during the past few centuries. This list is far from complete; many more species of animals and plants have become extinct during the same time. Countless others are threatened or endangered, meaning that they are at risk for extinction.

Dodo

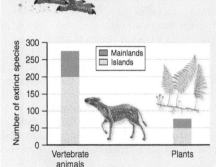

Figure 14.A Recent Extinctions. Island species of vertebrates and plants are most vulnerable to extinction.

TABLE 14.A   Recent Vertebrate Extinctions

Name	Cause of Extinction	Former Location
Fishes		
Chinese paddlefish (*Psephurus gladius*)	Habitat destruction	China
Las Vegas dace (*Rhinichthys deaconi*)	Habitat destruction	North America
Amphibians		
Palestinian painted frog (*Discoglossus nigriventer*)	Habitat destruction	Israel
Southern day frog (*Taudactylus diurnus*)	Undetermined	Australia
Monteverde golden toad (*Bufo periglenes*)	Habitat destruction, disease	Costa Rica
Reptiles		
Yunnan box turtle (*Cuora yunnanensis*)	Habitat destruction, overharvesting	China
Martinique lizard (*Leiocephalus herminieri*)	Undetermined	Martinique
Birds		
Dodo (*Raphus cucullatus*)	Habitat destruction, overharvesting	Mauritius
Moa (*Megalapteryx diderius*)	Overharvesting	New Zealand
Laysan honeycreeper (*Himatione sanguinea*)	Habitat destruction	Hawaii
Black mamo (*Drepanis funerea*)	Habitat destruction, introduced predators	Hawaii
Passenger pigeon (*Ectopistes migratorius*)	Overharvesting	North America
Great auk (*Alca impennis*)	Overharvesting	North Atlantic
Mammals		
Quagga (*Equus quagga quagga*)	Overharvesting	South Africa
Steller's sea cow (*Hydrodamalis gigas*)	Overharvesting	Bering Sea
Bali tiger (*Panthera tigris balica*)	Habitat destruction, overharvesting	Indonesia
Javan tiger (*Panthera tigris sondaica*)	Habitat destruction, overharvesting	Indonesia
Caspian tiger (*Panthera tigris virgata*)	Habitat destruction, overharvesting	Central Asia
Yangtze River dolphin (*Lipotes vexillifer*)	Habitat destruction, overharvesting	China

five major mass extinction events over the past 500 million years (red lines indicate mass extinctions). These events have had a great influence on Earth's history because they have periodically opened vast new habitats for adaptive radiation to occur.

Paleontologists study clues in Earth's sediments to understand the catastrophic events that contribute to mass extinctions. Two theories have emerged to explain these events, although several processes have probably contributed to mass extinctions.

The first explanation, called the **impact theory,** suggests that meteorites or comets have crashed to Earth, sending dust, soot, and other debris into the sky, blocking sunlight and setting into motion a deadly chain reaction. Without sunlight, plants died. The animals that ate plants, and the animals that ate those animals, then perished. Evidence for the impact theory of the extinction at the end of the Cretaceous period includes centimeter-thick layers of earth that are rich in iridium, an element rare on Earth but common in meteorites (figure 14.14).

A second theory is that movements of Earth's crust may explain some mass extinctions. The crust, or uppermost layer of the planet's surface, is divided into many pieces, called tectonic plates. During Earth's history, movement of tectonic plates caused continents to drift apart, then come back together. These continental wanderings have profoundly affected life, both on land and in water. Organisms that had thrived in their old habitats had new competitors. Climates changed as continents moved toward or away from the poles. Colliding continents caused shallow coastal areas packed with life to disappear; mountain ranges grew, destroying some habitats and creating new ones. ⓘ *plate tectonics,* p. 268

Many biologists warn that we are in the midst of a sixth mass extinction—this one caused entirely by human actions. Ecologists estimate that the current extinction rate is about 20 to 200 extinctions per million species per year. Habitat loss and habitat fragmentation, pollution, introduced species, and over-harvesting combine to imperil many species, with unknown consequences to global ecosystems (see chapter 40). This chapter's Apply It Now box, on page 293, lists a few of the many vertebrate species that have recently become extinct, but the problem extends throughout all kingdoms of life.

14.5   MASTERING CONCEPTS

1. What factors can cause or hasten extinction?
2. Distinguish between background extinction and mass extinctions.
3. How have humans influenced extinctions?

Figure 14.14   Impact Theory Evidence. This distinctive layer of rock marks the end of the Cretaceous period, about 65 million years ago.

14.6   Biological Classification Systems Are Based on Common Descent

Darwin proposed that evolution occurs in a branched fashion, with each species giving rise to other species as populations occupy and adapt to new habitats. As described in chapter 13, ample evidence has shown him to be correct.

The goal of modern classification systems is to reflect this shared evolutionary history. **Systematics,** the study of classification, therefore incorporates two interrelated specialties: taxonomy and phylogenetics. **Taxonomy** is the science of describing, naming, and classifying species; **phylogenetics** is the study of evolutionary relationships among species. This section describes how biologists apply the evidence for evolution to the monumental task of organizing life's diversity into groups.

A. The Taxonomic Hierarchy Organizes Species into Groups

Carolus Linnaeus, the biologist introduced at the start of this chapter, made a lasting contribution to systematics. He devised a way to organize life into a hierarchical classification scheme that assigned a consistent, scientific name to each type of organism.

Linnaeus's idea is the basis of the taxonomic hierarchy used today. Biologists organize life into nested groups of taxonomic levels, based on similarities (figure 14.15). The three domains—Archaea, Bacteria, and Eukarya—are the most inclusive levels. Each domain is divided into kingdoms, which in turn are divided into phyla, then classes, orders, families, genera, and species. A **taxon** (plural: taxa) is a group at any rank; that is, domain Eukarya is a taxon, as is the order Liliales and the species *Aloe vera.* Some disciplines also use additional ranks, such as superfamilies and subspecies.

The more features two organisms have in common, the more taxonomic levels they share (figure 14.16). A human, a squid, and a fly are all members of the animal kingdom, but their many differences place them in separate phyla. A human, rat, and pig are more closely related—all belong to the same kingdom, phylum, and class (Mammalia). A human, orangutan, and chimpanzee are even more closely related, sharing the same kingdom, phylum, class, order, and family (Order Primates, Family Hominidae). As humans, our full classification is Eukarya-Animalia-Chordata-Mammalia-Primates-Hominidae-*Homo*-*Homo sapiens.*

This hierarchy is useful, but it has a flaw: The ranks are not meaningful in an evolutionary context. That is, the eight main levels might give the impression that evolution took exactly eight "leaps" to produce each modern species. In reality, the ranks are arbitrary, leading to frequent disputes about whether collections of species should be lumped into one taxon or divided among many. Despite its imperfections, the system remains in use because biologists have not agreed on a better approach.

Taxonomic group	*Aloe vera* plant found in:	Number of species
Domain	Eukarya	Several million
Kingdom	Plantae	~375,000
Phylum	Anthophyta	~235,000
Class	Liliopsida	~65,000
Order	Liliales	~1200
Family	Asphodelaceae	785
Genus	*Aloe*	500
Species	*Aloe vera*	1

Figure 14.15 Taxonomic Hierarchy. Life is divided into three domains, which are subdivided into kingdoms. The kingdoms, in turn, contain numerous smaller categories. This diagram shows the complete classification for the plant *Aloe vera*.

Figure 14.16 More Similarities, More Shared Levels. (a) A squid and a fly are both eukaryotes classified in the animal kingdom, but they do not share other taxonomic levels. (b) A chimpanzee and an orangutan share enough similarities to be classified in the same family.

B. A Cladistics Approach Is Based on Shared Derived Traits

Animation
Phylogenetic Trees

Biologists illustrate life's diversity in the form of evolutionary trees, also called **phylogenies,** which depict species' relationships based on descent from shared ancestors. Systematists have long constructed phylogenetic trees, which are hypotheses about evolutionary relationships. (Charles Darwin included an example in *On the Origin of Species*.)

Biologists use multiple lines of evidence to construct phylogenetic trees. Anatomical features of fossils and existing organisms are useful, as are behaviors, physiological adaptations, and molecular sequences. In the past, systematists constructed phylogenetic tree diagrams by comparing as many characteristics as possible among species. Those organisms with the most characteristics in common would be neighbors on the tree's branches.

Basing a tree entirely on similarities, however, can be misleading. As just one example, many types of cave animals are eyeless and lack pigments. But these resemblances do not mean that the fish and snail species that occupy caves are closely related to one another; instead, they are the product of convergent evolution. If the goal of a classification system is to group related organisms together, attending only to similarities might lead to an incorrect classification.

A cladistics approach solves this problem. Widely adopted beginning in the 1990s, **cladistics** is a phylogenetic system that defines groups by distinguishing between ancestral and derived characters. **Ancestral characters** are inherited attributes that resemble those of the ancestor of a group; an organism with **derived characters** has features that are different from those found in the group's ancestor.

Cladistics therefore builds on the concept of homology, described in chapter 13. Homologous structures are inherited from a common ancestor; examples include the forelimbs of birds and mammals (see figure 13.10). We have already seen that natural selection can modify homologous structures (and genes) into a wide variety of new forms. In a cladistics analysis, an ancestral character has changed little from its state in a group's ancestor; a derived character, on the other hand, has changed more.

How does a researcher know which characters are ancestral and which are derived? They choose an **outgroup** consisting of comparator organisms that are not part of the group being studied. For example, in a cladistic analysis of land vertebrates, an appropriate outgroup might be lungfishes. Features that are present both in lungfishes and in land vertebrates are assumed to be ancestral. A segmented backbone and two eyes are therefore ancestral features. Derived features would include four limbs, feathers, fur, or other characteristics that appear only in some land vertebrates but not in a lungfish.

In a cladistics approach, biologists use shared derived characters to define groups. A **clade,** also called a **monophyletic** group, is a group of organisms consisting of a common ancestor and all of its descendants; in other words, it is a group of species united by a single evolutionary pathway. For example, birds form a clade because they all descended from the same group of reptiles. A clade may contain any number of species, as long as all of its members share an ancestor that organisms outside the clade do not share.

C. Cladograms Depict Hypothesized Evolutionary Relationships

Tutorial
Reading a Cladogram

The result of a cladistics analysis is a **cladogram,** a treelike diagram built using shared derived characteristics (figure 14.17). The emphasis in a cladogram is not similarities but rather historical relationships. To emphasize this point, imagine a lizard, a crocodile, and a chicken. Which resembles the lizard more closely: the crocodile or the chicken? Clearly, the most *similar* animals are the lizard and the crocodile. But these resemblances are only superficial. The shared derived characters tell a more complete story of evolutionary history. Based on the evidence, crocodiles are more closely related to birds than they are to lizards.

Figure It Out

How many clades are represented in figure 14.17?

Answer: 6

All cladograms have features in common. The tips of the branches represent the taxa in the group being studied. Existing species, such as birds and turtles, are at the tips of longer branches in figure 14.17; the nonavian dinosaurs are extinct and therefore occupy a shorter branch. Each node in a cladogram

indicates where two groups arose from a common ancestor. A branching pattern of lines therefore represents populations that diverge genetically, splitting off to form a new species. The branching pattern also implies the passage of time, as indicated by the arrow at the bottom of figure 14.17.

The evolutionary relationships in a cladogram are depicted as nested hierarchies, with small clades contained entirely within larger ones. You can therefore think of a cladogram as a tree with a trunk, main branches, smaller branches, and twigs. According to this analogy, a clade is the piece that would "fall off" if you made a single cut to any part of the tree. The larger the branch you cut, the more inclusive the clade.

Each clade can rotate on its branch without changing the meaning of the cladogram (figure 14.18). Moreover, biologists can use either diagonal lines or square brackets when drawing a cladogram. As a result, many equivalent cladograms can tell the same evolutionary story.

A common mistake in interpreting cladograms is to incorrectly assume that a taxon must be closely related to both groups that appear next to it on the tree. In figure 14.17, for example, mammals are adjacent to both turtles and amphibians. Does this mean that rabbits are as closely related to frogs as they are to turtles? To find out, trace the mammal and turtle lineages from right to left until they intersect. That node represents the most recent common ancestor of lizards and turtles. Similarly, trace the mammal and amphibian lineages backward to find their last common ancestor. Now compare the locations of the two nodes. Since the common ancestor of mammals and turtles was more recent than the common ancestor of mammals and amphibians, rabbits are more closely related to turtles than they are to frogs.

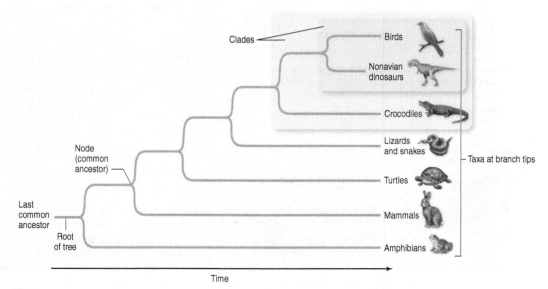

Time

Figure 14.17   Reading a Cladogram.   Each clade consists of a common ancestor (a node) and all of its descendants. The more recently any two groups share a common ancestor, the more closely related they are.

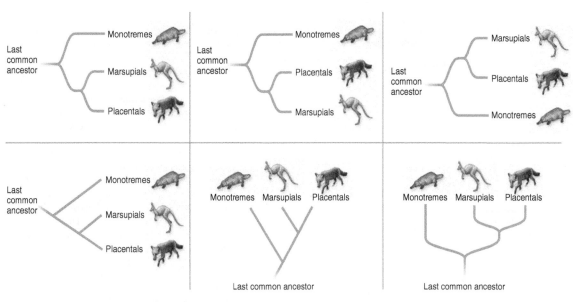

Figure 14.18 **Different Cladograms, Same Relationships.** All of these cladograms depict the same information about evolutionary relationships among mammals.

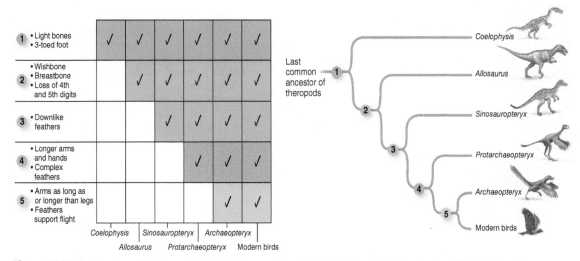

Figure 14.19 **Constructing a Cladogram.** To build a cladogram, tally up the derived characters that species share. Pairs that share the greatest number of derived characters are hypothesized to be most closely related. *Source:* Cladogram data based on Kevin Padian, June 25, 1998, When is a bird not a bird? *Nature,* vol. 393, page 729.

Figure 14.19 demonstrates how to construct a cladogram using the derived characters that were important in the evolution of birds. The first step is to select the traits to be studied in each species, such as the presence of feathers and lightweight bones. Next, the researcher collects the data and makes a chart showing which species have which traits. Then, in constructing the tree, species sharing the most derived characters occupy the branches farthest from the root. The resulting cladogram shows the hypothesized relationship between modern birds and their close relatives, the nonavian dinosaurs.

The cladogram in figure 14.19 is based on the physical features of not only existing birds but also the fossils of extinct dinosaurs. Molecular sequences are also extremely useful because they add many more characters on which to build cladograms and

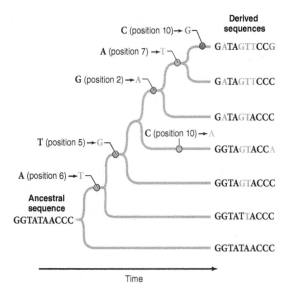

Figure 14.20 Cladogram Based on DNA. Mutations in DNA produce unique sequence variations, characters that can be used to build cladograms.

deduce evolutionary relationships. Figure 14.20 shows a simple cladogram based on mutations in a 10-nucleotide sequence of DNA. (In reality, cladograms are typically based on far longer DNA sequences.) Scientists can analyze DNA not only from living species but also from long-dead organisms preserved in museums, amber, and permafrost (see section 19.6).

Comparing molecular sequence differences among species also provides a way to assign approximate dates to the branching

points of a cladogram. If researchers can estimate the rate at which a selected stretch of DNA accumulates mutations, they can use "molecular clocks" to estimate how much time has passed since two species diverged from a common ancestor. ⓘ *molecular clocks,* p. 275

A problem with cladistics is that the analysis becomes enormously complicated when many species and derived characters are included. Mathematically, many trees can accommodate the same data set; for instance, just 10 taxa can be arranged into millions of possible trees. Sorting through all the possibilities requires tremendous computing power. How do researchers settle on the "best" tree? One strategy is to select the most **parsimonious** tree, which is the one that requires the fewest steps to construct. The most parsimonious tree therefore invokes the fewest evolutionary changes needed to explain the data.

All phylogenetic trees are based on limited and sometimes ambiguous information. They are therefore not peeks into the past but rather tools that researchers can use to construct hypotheses about the relationships among different types of organisms. These investigators can then add other approaches to test the hypotheses.

D. Many Traditional Groups Are Not Monophyletic

Contemporary scientists using a cladistics approach typically assign names only to clades; groups that reflect incomplete clades or that combine portions of multiple clades are not named. Many familiar groups of species, however, are not monophyletic. Instead, these groups may be paraphyletic or polyphyletic (figure 14.21).

For example, according to the traditional Linnaean classification system, class Reptilia includes turtles, lizards,

Figure 14.21 Paraphyletic and Polyphyletic Groups. The Linnaean class Reptilia is paraphyletic; it excludes birds and therefore does not form a clade. A group containing only endothermic animals is polyphyletic because it excludes the most recent common ancestor of these animals.

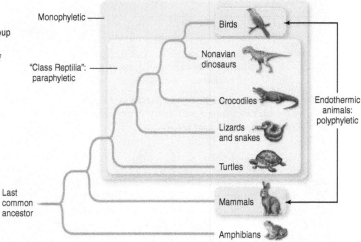

snakes, crocodiles, and the extinct dinosaurs, but it excludes birds. The cladogram, however, places birds in the same clade with the reptiles based on their many shared derived characteristics. Most biologists therefore now consider birds to be reptiles—living dinosaurs, actually—so they make a distinction between birds and nonavian ("non-bird") reptiles.

The traditional class Reptilia is considered **paraphyletic** because it contains a common ancestor and some, but not all, of its descendants. The kingdom Protista is also paraphyletic (figure 14.22). Protists include mostly single-celled eukaryotes that do not fit into any of the three eukaryotic kingdoms (plants, fungi, and animals). Yet all three of these groups share a common eukaryotic ancestor with the protists. Biologists are currently struggling to divide kingdom Protista into monophyletic groups, an immense task.

Polyphyletic groups exclude the most recent common ancestor shared by all members of the group. For example, a group consisting of endothermic (formerly called "warm-blooded") animals includes only birds and mammals. This group is polyphyletic because it excludes the most recent common ancestor of birds and mammals, which was an ectotherm (formerly called "cold-blooded"). Likewise, the term *algae* reflects a polyphyletic grouping of many unrelated species of aquatic organisms that carry out photosynthesis. In general, polyphyletic groups reflect characteristics—such as ectothermy or photosynthesis—that have evolved independently in multiple species.

Systematists try to avoid paraphyletic and polyphyletic groups, which do not reflect a shared evolutionary history. Nevertheless, many such group names remain in everyday usage.

Table 14.1 summarizes some of the terminology used in systematics.

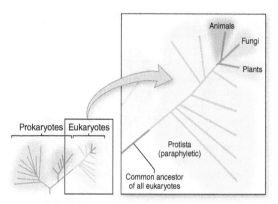

Figure 14.22 **Paraphyletic Protists.** Although domains Bacteria, Archaea, and Eukarya are all monophyletic, the group of eukaryotes called protists is paraphyletic because it excludes plants, fungi, and animals.

14.6   MASTERING CONCEPTS

1. Describe the taxonomic hierarchy.
2. What is the advantage of a cladistics approach over a more traditional approach to phylogeny?
3. Distinguish between ancestral and derived characters.
4. What sorts of evidence do biologists use in a cladistics analysis?
5. How is a cladogram constructed?
6. How do paraphyletic and polyphyletic groups differ from monophyletic groups?

TABLE **14.1**   **Miniglossary of Systematics Terms**

Term	Definition
Ancestral characters	Features present in the common ancestor of a clade
Clade	Group of organisms consisting of a common ancestor and all of its descendants; a monophyletic group
Cladistics	Phylogenetic system that groups organisms by characteristics that best indicate shared ancestry
Cladogram	Phylogenetic tree built on shared derived characters
Derived characters	Features of an organism that are different from those found in a clade's ancestors
Monophyletic group	Group of organisms consisting of a common ancestor and all of its descendants; a clade
Outgroup	Comparator organism outside the group being studied; useful for identifying ancestral traits
Paraphyletic group	Group of organisms consisting of a common ancestor and some, but not all, of its descendants
Phylogenetic tree	Diagram depicting hypothesized evolutionary relationships
Polyphyletic group	Group of species that excludes the most recent common ancestor
Systematics	The combined study of taxonomy and evolutionary relationships among organisms

INVESTIGATING LIFE

14.7 Birds Do It, Bees Do It

The origin of biological diversity has long intrigued biologists, especially after Charles Darwin published *On the Origin of Species*. According to Mayr's biological species concept, the formation of a reproductive barrier that divides a population is the event that signals the birth of a new species. It is easy to understand how mountains, glaciers, and other physical obstacles can prevent interbreeding. But how can a new reproductive barrier arise within a single population, creating two species from one?

Plants offer an ideal opportunity to answer this question. Many species of flowering plants depend on animals such as birds or bees as pollen carriers. Closely related plant species may employ different pollinators, thus creating a reproductive barrier. Consider two species of wildflowers native to the western United States (figure 14.23): the purple monkeyflower *(Mimulus lewisii)* and the scarlet monkeyflower *(Mimulus cardinalis)*. Bumblebees pollinate *M. lewisii*, whereas hummingbirds prefer the red-flowered *M. cardinalis*. If, by chance, a hummingbird carries *M. cardinalis* pollen to *M. lewisii*, the resulting hybrid offspring are viable. Such cross-breeding rarely happens in the wild, however, thanks to the more-or-less exclusive relationship between each plant and its pollinators.

Because the two monkeyflowers are so closely related, it is reasonable to suppose that, in the past, one ancestral *Mimulus* species gave rise to both types. The reproductive barrier that separates them may have arisen after the slow, constant buildup of mutations in many genes. Alternatively, a mutation in one or a few "major" genes (those that control flower form or color, for example) may have had the same effect. We know that a single mutation can dramatically alter an organism's appearance (see the fly with a homeotic mutation in figure 7.20). Can a single mutation in a plant species also create a reproductive barrier by attracting a new pollinator?

Biologist H. D. "Toby" Bradshaw, of the University of Washington, and Michigan State University's Douglas Schemske studied the two *Mimulus* species to find out. They knew that these plants have a gene locus (area of a chromosome) that controls the concentration of yellowish orange pigments called carotenoids in the flower petals. The locus, which may consist of one or a few genes, is called *YUP* (for *y*ellow *up*per petal). In the wild-type purple monkeyflower, the dominant allele prevents carotenoids from forming, leaving the pinkish-purple anthocyanin pigments to provide the petal color. Wild-type scarlet monkeyflowers have two copies of the recessive *yup* allele. In these plants, carotenoid pigments accumulate, turning the flowers red in the presence of anthocyanins (table 14.2).

Bradshaw and Schemske used selective breeding to create two new lineages of plants that mimicked the effect of a mutation in the *YUP* gene. They began by crossing the two species with each other; the resulting hybrid offspring were heterozygous for the *YUP* locus. They then repeatedly backcrossed the hybrids

Figure 14.23 Wild-Type and Selectively Bred *Mimulus*. By selective breeding, researchers created *Mimulus* plants that resembled their wild-type counterparts in every respect—except flower color. They used the wild-type and selectively bred plants to test hypotheses about reproductive barriers in *Mimulus*.

T A B L E **14.2**   Wild-Type Monkeyflower Characteristics

Species	Flower Color	Genotype at Flower Color Locus	Pollinator
Purple monkey-flower, *Mimulus lewisii*	Pink-purple	YUP/YUP or YUP/yup	Bumblebee
Scarlet monkey-flower, *Mimulus cardinalis*	Red	yup/yup	Hummingbird

with the wild-type parents, selecting each time for the desired allele. After four generations of backcrossing, the researchers had produced two new plant lineages: *M. lewisii* that were homozygous for the recessive *yup* allele and *M. cardinalis* plants that expressed the dominant *YUP* allele. Each was 97% identical to its parent strain but with one obvious difference—the flower colors. The new variety of *Mimulus lewisii* had pale yellow-orange petals, while the new *M. cardinalis* plants had dark pink blooms (see figure 14.23).

To test the hypothesis that a change in the *YUP* locus could prompt a pollinator shift, Bradshaw and Schemske planted all four *Mimulus* varieties (the two wild-type species and their selectively bred siblings) at a California location where both species normally occur. For about a week and a half, the researchers observed the plants from dawn until evening, recording the animal species that visited each flower. They found that the substituted *YUP* alleles did indeed alter pollinator preferences (table 14.3). The orange *M. lewisii* flowers attracted fewer bees but more hummingbirds than did their wild-type purple counterparts. *M. cardinalis* drew far more bumblebee visits with its new dark pink petals than did the wild-type red plants, while hummingbird visits stayed about the same.

In a subsequent experiment, Bradshaw and another researcher, Christina Owen, used chemicals to induce a single genetic mutation that eliminated the lower petals of *M. lewisii* flowers. The mutant flowers were missing the bumblebees' "landing platform" and therefore attracted only 29% as many bee visits as did the wild-type flowers.

These experiments support the hypothesis that a change in just one gene locus may have jump-started speciation in *Mimulus*. Additional mutations, coupled with natural selection, eventually sculpted the flower shapes and petal positions that define the purple and scarlet monkeyflower species. It is tempting to extend this finding to other species. Can a single mutation modify an

BurningQuestion

Why does evolution occur rapidly in some species but slowly in others?

Even though the same basic forces of microevolution operate on all populations, species evolve at different rates. This may seem like a paradox until you think of all the different ways that a population's gene pool can change over multiple generations (see chapter 12). In general, evolution occurs most quickly in:

- genes with high mutation rates
- small populations, which are most susceptible to genetic drift
- species with a high rate of polyploidy
- species that reproduce rapidly, such as bacteria and insects
- times of rapid environmental change
- populations with high rates of immigration or emigration
- species that reproduce sexually

Biologists have much to learn about evolution rates. One unsolved mystery is how a species's DNA can evolve rapidly, even as external appearances remain unchanged. Such is the case for the tuatara, a New Zealand reptile. When researchers compared DNA extracted from modern tuataras and from 8750-year-old fossils, they measured the fastest known molecular evolution rate. Yet the tuataras themselves have changed little. The solution to the mystery awaits further research.

Submit your burning question to:
Marielle.Hoefnagels@mheducation.com

animal's mating ritual just enough to create a new reproductive barrier? Or cause a flower to open its petals at a different time of day? Or enable an animal to exploit a new food source, extending its habitat? These experiments do not answer these questions. Every now and then, however, small mutations may fuel the birth of an entirely new species.

Bradshaw, H. D., Jr., and Douglas W. Schemske. November 13, 2003. Allele substitution at a flower colour locus produces a pollinator shift in monkeyflowers. *Nature*, vol. 426, pages 176–178.

Owen, Christina R. and H. D. Bradshaw. 2011. Induced mutations affecting pollinator choice in *Mimulus lewisii* (Phrymaceae). *Arthropod-Plant Interactions*, vol. 5, pages 235–244.

14.7 MASTERING CONCEPTS

1. What hypothesis were the investigators testing, and why did they choose these two plant species as experimental subjects?

2. If biologists could mutate the gene that controls carotenoid concentration, they could generate pairs of plants that differ only in that one gene, improving on the 97% similarity they achieved by backcrossing hybrids with wild-type plants. Explain why this improvement would help the researchers test their hypothesis.

TABLE **14.3** **Pollinator Visits**

		Number of Visits (10^{-3} visits/flower/hour)	
		Bumblebees	Hummingbirds
M. lewisii			
	Wild-type (pink-purple)	15.4	0.0212
	Selectively bred (yellow-orange)	2.63	1.44
M. cardinalis			
	Wild-type (red)	0.148	189
	Selectively bred (dark pink)	10.9	168

CHAPTER SUMMARY

14.1 The Definition of "Species" Has Evolved over Time

- **Macroevolution** refers to large-scale changes in life's diversity, including the appearance of new **species** and higher taxonomic levels.

A. Linnaeus Devised the Binomial Naming System

- Linnaeus's species designations and classifications helped scientists communicate. Darwin added evolutionary meaning.

B. Ernst Mayr Developed the Biological Species Concept

- Mayr added the requirement for reproductive isolation to define **biological species.**
- **Speciation** is the formation of a new species, which occurs when a population's **gene pool** is divided and each part takes its own evolutionary course.

14.2 Reproductive Barriers Cause Species to Diverge

A. Prezygotic Barriers Prevent Fertilization

- **Prezygotic reproductive isolation** occurs before or during fertilization. It includes obstacles to mating such as space, time, and behavior; mechanical mismatches between male and female; and molecular mismatches between gametes.

Barriers that maintain reproductive isolation between related species		
Prezygotic reproductive barriers prevent formation of zygote		
Name of barrier	Basis	
Habitat isolation	Space	No mating
Temporal isolation	Time	
Behavioral isolation	Mating rituals	
Mechanical isolation	Reproductive organs	Mating but no fertilization
Gametic isolation	Chemical signals on gametes	

Fertilization occurs if no prezygotic barriers are present; zygote forms

Postzygotic reproductive barriers prevent zygote from developing into fertile offspring	
Name of barrier	Basis
Hybrid inviability	Hybrid adult fails to develop.
Hybrid infertility (sterility)	Hybrid adult cannot reproduce.
Hybrid breakdown	Offspring of hybrid adult have reduced fertility.

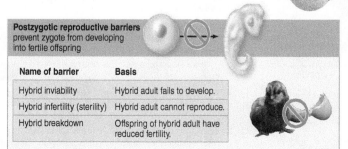

A viable, fertile offspring forms only if no reproductive barriers are present

Figure 14.24 Reproductive Barriers: A Summary.

B. Postzygotic Barriers Prevent Viable or Fertile Offspring

- **Postzygotic reproductive isolation** results in offspring that die early in development, are infertile, or produce a second generation of offspring with abnormalities.
- Figure 14.24 summarizes the main types of reproductive barriers.

14.3 Spatial Patterns Define Three Types of Speciation

A. Allopatric Speciation Reflects a Geographic Barrier

- **Allopatric speciation** occurs when a geographic barrier separates a population. The two populations then diverge genetically to the point that their members can no longer produce fertile offspring together.

B. Parapatric Speciation Occurs in Neighboring Regions

- **Parapatric speciation** occurs when two populations live in neighboring areas but share a border zone. Genetic divergence between the two groups exceeds gene flow, driving speciation.

C. Sympatric Speciation Occurs in a Shared Habitat

- **Sympatric speciation** enables populations that occupy the same area to diverge. **Polyploidy** (one or more extra chromosome sets) may create the reproductive barrier that triggers sympatric speciation.

D. Determining the Type of Speciation May Be Difficult

- The distinction between allopatric, parapatric, and sympatric speciation is not always straightforward, partly because it is difficult to define the size of a geographic barrier.

14.4 Speciation May Be Gradual or May Occur in Bursts

A. Gradualism and Punctuated Equilibrium Are Two Models of Speciation

- Evolutionary change occurs at many rates, from slow and steady **gradualism** to the periodic bursts that characterize **punctuated equilibrium.**

B. Bursts of Speciation Occur During Adaptive Radiation

- In **adaptive radiation,** an ancestral species rapidly branches into several new species.

14.5 Extinction Marks the End of the Line

- **Extinction** is the disappearance of a species.

A. Many Factors Can Combine to Put a Species at Risk

- Rapid environmental change, a slow reproductive rate, and low genetic diversity make species vulnerable to extinction.

B. Extinction Rates Have Varied over Time

- The **background extinction rate** reflects ongoing losses of species on a local scale.
- Historically, **mass extinctions** have resulted from global changes such as continental drift. The **impact theory** suggests that a meteorite or comet caused a mass extinction at the end of the Cretaceous period.
- Human activities are increasing the extinction rate.

14.6 Biological Classification Systems Are Based on Common Descent

- **Systematics** includes **taxonomy** (classification) and **phylogenetics** (species relationships).

A. The Taxonomic Hierarchy Organizes Species into Groups

- Biologists use a taxonomic hierarchy to classify life's diversity, with **taxa** ranging from domain to species.

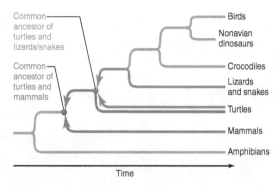

Figure 14.25 Finding Common Ancestors in a Cladogram.

B. A Cladistics Approach Is Based on Shared Derived Traits
- Cladistics defines groups using **ancestral** and **derived characters.** A **clade,** or **monophyletic** group, is an ancestor plus all of its descendants.
- An **outgroup** helps researchers detect ancestral characters.

C. Cladograms Depict Hypothesized Evolutionary Relationships
- A **cladogram** shows evolutionary relationships as a branching hierarchy with nodes representing common ancestors. Figure 14.25 shows how to use a cladogram to find the common ancestor shared by two groups.
- The most **parsimonious** cladogram is the simplest tree that fits the data.

D. Many Traditional Groups Are Not Monophyletic
- **Paraphyletic** groups exclude some descendants of a common ancestor; **polyphyletic** groups exclude the common ancestor of its members.

14.7 Investigating Life: Birds Do It, Bees Do It
- Changing the color of *Mimulus* flowers caused the plants to attract different pollinators. A shift in pollinators may have created the reproductive barrier that separates two *Mimulus* species.

MULTIPLE CHOICE QUESTIONS

1. The biological species concept defines species based on
   a. external appearance.
   b. the number of adaptations to the same habitat.
   c. ability to interbreed.
   d. DNA and protein sequences.

2. A mule is the offspring of a male donkey and a female horse. Mules are unable to produce offspring. What reproductive barrier separates horses and donkeys?
   a. Mechanical isolation   c. Hybrid inviability
   b. Gametic isolation   d. Hybrid infertility

3. A mountain range separates a population of gorillas. After many generations, the gorillas on different sides of the mountain range cannot produce viable, fertile offspring. What has happened?
   a. Sympatric speciation   c. Parapatric speciation
   b. Allopatric speciation   d. Adaptive radiation

4. Why is a species with a small population more likely than a large population to undergo an extinction?
   a. Because they cannot produce enough offspring
   b. Because there is less genetic diversity
   c. Because the individuals are isolated from one another
   d. Because they take too long to produce offspring

5. Flying animals have diverse evolutionary histories. They therefore form
   a. a monophyletic group.   c. a polyphyletic group.
   b. a paraphyletic group.   d. an outgroup.

Answers to these questions are in appendix A.

WRITE IT OUT

1. What type of reproductive barrier applies to each of these scenarios?
   a. Water buffalo and cattle can mate, but the embryos die early in development.
   b. Scientists try to mate two species of dragonfly that inhabit the same pond at the same time of day. However, females never allow males of the other species to mate with them.
   c. One species of reed warbler is active in the upper parts of the canopy while another species of reed warbler is active in the lower canopy. Both species are active during the day.
   d. Scientists mate two parrots from different populations to see if speciation has occurred. The parrots mate over and over again, but the male's sperm never fertilizes the female's egg.

2. How does natural selection predict a gradualistic mode of evolution? Does the presence of fossils that are consistent with punctuated equilibrium mean that natural selection does not occur?

3. Why do species become extinct? Choose a species that has recently become extinct and describe some possible evolutionary consequences to other species that interacted with that species before its extinction.

4. Figure 19.3 summarizes the hypothesized evolutionary relationships among living plants. Are the bryophytes monophyletic, polyphyletic, or paraphyletic? Explain your answer.

5. On figure 14.19, circle a monophyletic group, a paraphyletic group, and a polyphyletic group. Describe the qualities that define how each group is classified.

PULL IT TOGETHER

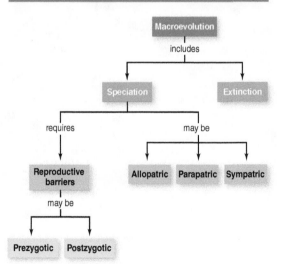

Figure 14.26 Pull It Together: Speciation and Extinction.

Refer to figure 14.26 and the chapter content to answer the following questions.

1. How do reproductive barriers relate to the biological species concept?

2. Add *fertilization* and *offspring* to the concept map.

3. Draw pictures of allopatric, parapatric, and sympatric speciation.

4. Add *gradualism* and *punctuated equilibrium* to this concept map.

5. How do species become extinct?

CHAPTER

15

The Origin and History of Life

Bombardment. Meteoroids enter Earth's atmosphere every day, as they have done for eons. Some scientists hypothesize that ancient objects from space carried the organic molecules needed for life to begin on Earth.

Enhance your study **|BIOLOGY**
of this chapter with practice quizzes,
animations and videos, answer keys,
and downloadable study tools.
www.mhhe.com/hoefnagels

Life from Space

IN A 1908 BOOK ENTITLED *WORLDS IN THE MAKING*, SWEDISH CHEMIST SVANTE ARRHENIUS SUGGESTED THAT LIFE CAME TO EARTH FROM THE COSMOS. He later broadened the idea, calling it "panspermia" and proposing that life-carrying spores (or the organic chemicals needed for life) arrived on interstellar dust, comets, asteroids, and meteorites.

What is the evidence for panspermia? Modern proponents point to several intriguing clues:

- Some microorganisms can survive under extreme conditions, which would be necessary to endure the high radiation and cold temperatures of space during a journey that could take millions of years. A bacterium called *Deinococcus radiodurans,* for example, tolerates a thousand times the radiation level that a person can; it even lives in nuclear reactors! Microbes also live in pockets of water within the ice of Antarctic lakes, surroundings not unlike the icy insides of a comet. In addition, researchers have revived some bacteria after a dormancy lasting millions of years.
- Meteorites that have fallen to Earth from space sometimes contain organic compounds such as amino acids.
- The surface of one of Jupiter's moons, Europa, is covered with a thick layer of ice. The frozen surface may conceal an ocean of liquid water, a prerequisite for life. ⓘ *essential water,* p. 26
- Canyons, shorelines, and other physical features of Mars leave little doubt that liquid water once flowed on the red planet. The Martian climate is now too cold for liquid water, but vast deposits of ice—and the possibility of life— remain below the planet's surface. In 2004, an orbiting spacecraft called *Mars Express* found high concentrations of water vapor and methane in the Martian atmosphere, suggesting that methane-producing microbes might live in liquid water beneath Mars's surface. The Mars lander *Phoenix* "tasted" Martian soil and verified the presence of subsurface ice in 2008. A second lander, *Curiosity,* was launched in 2011; one of the mission's objectives is to learn whether Mars ever supported life.

Panspermia is not widely accepted, in part because it sidesteps the question of life's ultimate origin in the universe. Instead, most scientists accept that life probably arose from simple chemical substances on Earth. This process and its astounding aftermath are the subjects of this chapter.

LEARNING OUTLINE

 15.1 Life's Origin Remains Mysterious
   A. The First Organic Molecules May Have Formed in a Chemical "Soup"
   B. Some Investigators Suggest an "RNA World"
   C. Membranes Enclosed the Molecules
   D. Early Life Changed Earth Forever

 15.2 Complex Cells and Multicellularity Arose over a Billion Years Ago
   A. Endosymbiosis Explains the Origin of Mitochondria and Chloroplasts
   B. Multicellularity May Also Have Its Origin in Cooperation

 15.3 Life's Diversity Exploded in the Past 500 Million Years
   A. The Strange Ediacarans Flourished Late in the Precambrian
   B. Paleozoic Plants and Animals Emerged onto Land
   C. Reptiles and Flowering Plants Thrived During the Mesozoic Era
   D. Mammals Diversified During the Cenozoic Era

 15.4 Fossils and DNA Tell the Human Evolution Story
   A. Humans Are Primates
   B. Molecular Evidence Documents Primate Relationships
   C. Hominin Evolution Is Partially Recorded in Fossils
   D. Environmental Changes Have Spurred Hominin Evolution
   E. Migration and Culture Have Changed *Homo sapiens*

 15.5 Investigating Life: Big Continents, Small Differences

LEARN HOW TO LEARN
Write Your Own Test Questions

Have you ever tried putting yourself in your instructor's place by writing your own multiple-choice test questions? It's a great way to pull the pieces of a chapter together. The easiest questions to write are based on definitions and vocabulary, but those will not always be the most useful. Try to think of questions that integrate multiple ideas or that apply the concepts in a chapter. Write 10 questions, and then let a classmate answer them. You'll probably both learn something new.

15.1 Life's Origin Remains Mysterious

Tutorial
Origin of Life

Reconstructing life's start is like reading all the chapters of a novel except the first. A reader can get some idea of the events and setting of the opening chapter from clues throughout the novel. Similarly, scattered clues from life through the ages reflect events that may have led to the origin of life.

Scientists describe the origin and history of life in the context of the **geologic timescale,** which divides time into eons, eras, periods, and epochs defined by major geological or biological events. Figure 15.1 shows a simplified geologic timescale; see figure 13.2 for a complete version.

The study of life's origin begins with astronomy and geology. Earth and the solar system's other planets formed about 4.6 BYA (billion years ago) as solid matter condensed out of a vast expanse of dust and gas swirling around the early Sun. The red-hot ball that became Earth cooled enough to form a crust by about 4.2 to 4.1 BYA, when the surface temperature ranged from 500°C to 1000°C, and atmospheric pressure was 10 times what it is now.

The geological evidence paints a chaotic picture of this Hadean eon, including volcanic eruptions, earthquakes, and ultraviolet radiation. Analysis of craters on other objects in the solar system suggests that comets, meteorites, and possibly asteroids bombarded Earth's surface during its first 500 million to 600 million years (figure 15.2). These impacts repeatedly boiled off the seas and vaporized rocks to carve the features of the fledgling world.

Still, protected pockets of the environment probably existed where organic molecules could aggregate and perhaps interact. So harsh and unsettled was the early environment of Earth that organized groups of chemicals may have formed many times and

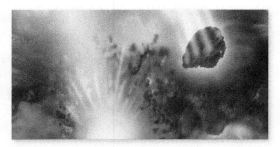

Figure 15.2 Early Earth. Intense bombardment by meteorites marked Earth's first 500 million to 600 million years.

at many places, only to be torn apart by heat, debris from space, or radiation. We can't know.

At some point, however, an entity arose that could survive, thrive, reproduce, and diversify. The clues from geology and paleontology suggest that early in the Precambrian supereon—sometime between 4.2 and 3.85 BYA—simple cells (or their precursors) arose.

This section describes some of the major steps in the chemical evolution that eventually led to the first cell; figure 15.3 summarizes one possible version of the process. (Today, however, new life is unlikely to originate from nonliving matter; the Burning Question on page 309 explains why.)

A. The First Organic Molecules May Have Formed in a Chemical "Soup"

Early Earth was different from today's planet, both geologically and chemically. The atmosphere today contains gases such as nitrogen (N_2), oxygen (O_2), carbon dioxide (CO_2), and water vapor (H_2O). What might it have been like 4 BYA?

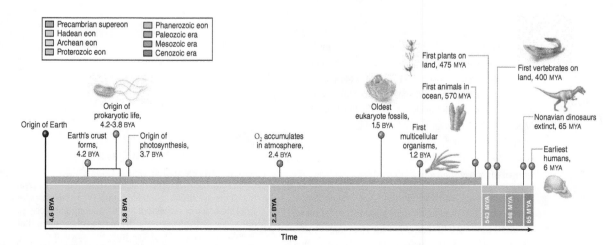

Figure 15.1 Highlights in Life's History. In this simplified geologic timescale, the size of each eon and era is proportional to its length in years. (BYA = billion years ago; MYA = million years ago)

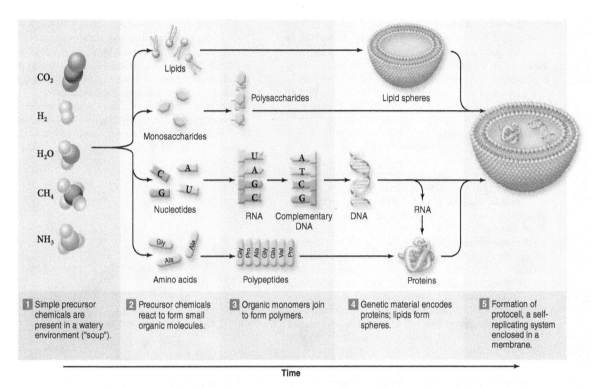

Time

Figure 15.3 Pathway to a Cell. The steps leading to the origin of life on Earth may have started with the formation of organic molecules from simple precursors. However it originated, the first cell would have contained self-replicating molecules enclosed in a phospholipid bilayer membrane.

Russian chemist Alex I. Oparin hypothesized in his 1938 book, *The Origin of Life,* that a hydrogen-rich, or reducing, atmosphere was necessary for organic molecules to form on Earth. Oparin thought that this long-ago atmosphere included methane (CH_4), ammonia (NH_3), water, and hydrogen (H_2), similar to the atmospheres of the outer planets today. These simple chemicals appear in step 1 of figure 15.3. Note that O_2 was not present in the atmosphere at the time life originated. In the absence of O_2, Oparin suggested, the chemical reactions that form amino acids and nucleotides could have occurred (see figure 15.3, step 2). ⓘ *organic molecules,* p. 30

Miller's Experiment In 1953, Stanley Miller, a graduate student in chemistry at the University of Chicago, and his mentor, Harold Urey, decided to test whether Oparin's atmosphere could indeed give rise to organic molecules. Miller built a sterile glass enclosure to contain Oparin's four gases, through which he passed electric discharges to simulate lightning (figure 15.4). He condensed the gases in a narrow tube; from there, the liquid passed into a flask. Boiling the fluid caused gases to evaporate back into the synthetic "atmosphere," completing the loop.

 Animation
Miller-Urey
Experiment

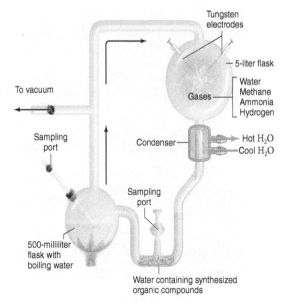

Figure 15.4 The First Prebiotic Simulation. When Stanley Miller passed an electrical spark through heated gases, the mixture generated amino acids and other organic molecules.

After a few failures and adjustments, Miller saw the condensed liquid turn yellowish. Chemical analysis showed that he had made glycine, the simplest amino acid in organisms. When he let the brew cook a full week, the solution turned varying shades of red, pink, and yellow-brown; he subsequently found a few more amino acids, some of which are found in life. (In fact, the solution contained even more chemicals than Miller realized; a 2008 reanalysis of material saved from one of Miller's experiments revealed 22 amino acids.)

A prestigious journal published the original work, which Urey gallantly refused to put his name on. The 25-year-old Miller made headlines in newspapers and magazines reporting (incorrectly) that he had created "life in a test tube."

Life is far more than just a few amino acids, but "the Miller experiment" went down in history as the first **prebiotic simulation,** an attempt to re-create chemical conditions on Earth before life arose. Miller and many others later extended his results by altering conditions or using different starting materials. For example, methane and ammonia could form clouds of hydrogen cyanide (HCN), which produced amino acids in the presence of ultraviolet light and water. Prebiotic "soups" that included phosphates yielded nucleotides, including the biological energy molecule ATP. Other experiments produced carbohydrates and phospholipids similar to those in biological membranes.

The experiment has survived criticisms that Earth's early atmosphere actually contained abundant CO_2, a gas not present in Miller's original setup. Organic molecules still form, even with an adjusted gas mixture.

Hydrothermal Vents as a Model

More recent prebiotic simulations mimic deep-sea hydrothermal vents. Here, in a zone where hot water meets cold water, chemical mixtures could have encountered a rich brew of minerals spewed from Earth's interior. One laboratory version combines mineral-rich lava with seawater containing dissolved CO_2; under high temperature and pressure, simple organic compounds form. In another vent model, nitrogen compounds and water mix with an iron-containing mineral under high temperature and pressure. The iron catalyzes reactions that produce ammonia—one of the components of the original Miller experiment. ⓘ *hydrothermal vents,* p. 789

The Possible Role of Clays

Once the organic building blocks of macromolecules were present, they had to have linked into chains (polymers). This process, depicted in step 3 of figure 15.3, may have happened on hot clays or other minerals that provided ample, dry surfaces.

Clays may have played an important role in early organic chemistry for at least three reasons. First, clays consist of sheet-like minerals. Their flat surfaces can therefore form templates on which chemical building blocks could have linked to build larger molecules. Second, some types of clay also contain minerals that can release electrons, providing energy to form chemical bonds. Third, these minerals may also have acted as catalysts to speed chemical reactions.

Prebiotic simulations demonstrate that the first RNA molecules could have formed on clay surfaces (figure 15.5). Not only do the positive charges on clay's surface attract and hold negatively charged RNA nucleotides, but clays also promote formation of the covalent bonds that link the nucleotides into chains. They even attract other nucleotides to form a complementary strand. About 4 BYA, clays might have been fringed with an ever-increasing variety of growing polymers. Some of these might have become the macromolecules that would eventually build cells.

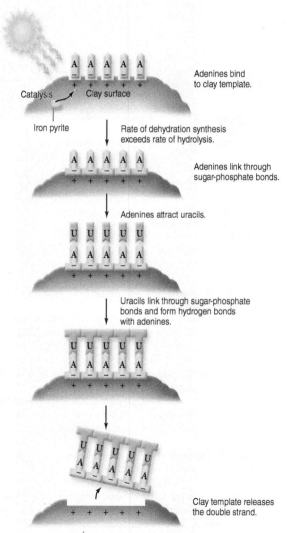

Adenines bind to clay template.

Catalysis   Clay surface

Iron pyrite   Rate of dehydration synthesis exceeds rate of hydrolysis.

Adenines link through sugar-phosphate bonds.

Adenines attract uracils.

Uracils link through sugar-phosphate bonds and form hydrogen bonds with adenines.

Clay template releases the double strand.

Figure 15.5 A Possible Role for Clay. Chains of nucleotides may have formed on clay templates. In this hypothesized scenario, iron pyrite ("fool's gold") was the catalyst for polymer formation, and sunlight provided the energy.

B. Some Investigators Suggest an "RNA World"

Life requires an informational molecule. That molecule may have been RNA, or something like it, because RNA is the most versatile molecule that we know of. It stores genetic information and uses it to manufacture proteins. RNA can also catalyze chemical reactions and duplicate on its own. As Stanley Miller summed it up, "The origin of life is the origin of evolution, which requires replication, mutation, and selection. Replication is the hard part. Once a genetic material could replicate, life would have just taken off."

Perhaps pieces of RNA on clay surfaces continued to form and accumulate, growing longer, becoming more complex in sequence, and changing as replication errors led to mutations. Some members of this accumulating community of molecules would have been more stable than others, leading to an early form of natural selection. The term **"RNA world"** has come to describe how self-replicating RNA may have been the first independent precursor to life on Earth.

At some point, RNA might have begun encoding proteins, just short chains of amino acids at first. An RNA molecule may eventually have grown long enough to encode the enzyme reverse transcriptase, which copies RNA to DNA. With DNA, the chemical blueprints of life found a much more stable home. Protein enzymes eventually took over some of the functions of catalytic RNAs. Step 4 in figure 15.3 shows this stage in life's origin.

C. Membranes Enclosed the Molecules

Meanwhile, lipids would have been entering the picture. Under the right temperature and pH conditions, and with the necessary precursors, phospholipids could have formed membranelike structures, some of which left evidence in ancient sediments. Laboratory experiments show that pieces of membrane can indeed grow on structural supports and break free, forming a bubble called a liposome. ⓘ *phospholipids*, p. 54

Perhaps an ancient liposome enclosed a collection of nucleic acids and proteins to form a cell-like assemblage, or protocell (see figure 15.3, step 5). Carl Woese, who described the domain Archaea, gave the term **progenotes** to these hypothetical, ancient aggregates of RNA, DNA, proteins, and lipids. Also called protocells or protobionts, these were precursors of cells but they were not nearly as complex.

The capacity of nucleic acids to mutate may have enabled progenotes to become increasingly self-sufficient, giving rise eventually to the reaction pathways of metabolism. No one knows what these first metabolic pathways were or how they eventually led to respiration, photosynthesis, and thousands of other chemical reactions that support life today. Despite intriguing similarities between glycolysis and some photosynthetic reactions (see section 6.9), these early stages of metabolism may not have left enough evidence for us ever to understand their origins.

Burning Question

Does new life spring from inorganic molecules now, as it did in the past?

It is intriguing to think of the possibility that new life could be forming from nonliving matter now, just as it did long ago in Earth's history. Although theoretically possible, scientists have never seen life emerging from a collection of simple chemicals. Such a finding would be a major blow to the cell theory, which says that cells come only from preexisting cells (see section 3.1B).

The emergence of new life from simple molecules, however, is improbable today. One reason is that when Earth was young, no life existed, so the first simple cells encountered no competition. Now, however, life thrives nearly everywhere on Earth (see chapter 17's Burning Question). Perhaps new life *is* forming, but before it has a chance to become established, a hungry microbe gobbles it up. Such an event would be extremely difficult to detect.

A second reason is that the chemical and physical environment on the young Earth was nothing like that of today's world. The conditions that allowed new life to develop billions of years ago simply no longer exist.

So does the ancient chemical origin for life on Earth violate the cell theory? The answer is no, because the cell theory applies to today's circumstances, which are very different from those on the early Earth. Scientists have never observed the formation of life from nonliving matter—but that does not mean that it did not happen in the distant past.

Submit your burning question to
Marielle.Hoefnagels@mheducation.com

D. Early Life Changed Earth Forever

Unfortunately, direct evidence of the first life is likely gone because most of Earth's initial crust has been destroyed. Erosion tears rocks and minerals into particles, only to be built up again into sediments, heated and compressed. Seafloor is dragged into Earth's interior at deep-sea trenches, where it is melted and recycled. The oldest rocks that remain today, from an area of Greenland called the Isua formation, date to about 3.85 BYA. They house the oldest hints of life: quartz crystals containing organic deposits rich in the carbon isotopes found in organisms. ⓘ *plate tectonics*, p. 268

Whatever they were, the first organisms were simpler than any cell known today. Several types of early cells probably prevailed for millions of years, competing for resources and sharing genetic material. Eventually, a type of cell arose that was the last shared ancestor of all life on Earth today.

These first cells lived in the absence of O_2 and probably used organic molecules as a source of both carbon and energy.

Another source of carbon, however, was the CO_2 in the atmosphere. Photosynthetic bacteria and archaea eventually evolved that could use light for energy and atmospheric CO_2 as a carbon source (see chapter 5). These microbes no longer relied on organic compounds in their surroundings for food.

Photosynthesis probably originated in aquatic bacteria that used hydrogen sulfide (H_2S) instead of water as an electron donor. These first photosynthetic microorganisms would have released sulfur, rather than O_2, into the environment. Eventually, changes in pigment molecules enabled some of the microorganisms to use H_2O instead of H_2S as an electron donor. Cells using this new form of photosynthesis released O_2 as a waste product.

Some of the oldest known fossils are from 3.7-billion-year-old rocks in Australia and South Africa. The fossils strongly resemble large formations of cyanobacteria called stromatolites. These ancient cyanobacteria, along with many others, would have consumed CO_2 and released O_2 over hundreds of millions of years (figure 15.6a). The O_2 would have bubbled out of the water and been released into the atmosphere.

Extensive iron deposits dating to about 2 billion years ago provide evidence of the changing atmosphere. As O_2 from photosynthesis built up in the oceans, iron that was previously dissolved in seawater reacted with the O_2 and sank to the bottom of the sea, producing distinctive layers of iron-rich sediments.

The evolution of photosynthesis forever altered life on Earth. Photosynthetic organisms formed the base of new food chains. In addition, natural selection began to favor aerobic organisms that could use O_2 in metabolism, while anaerobic species would persist in pockets of the environment away from oxygen. Ozone (O_3) also formed from O_2 high in the atmosphere, blocking the sun's damaging ultraviolet radiation. The overall result was an explosion of new life that eventually gave rise to today's microbes, plants, fungi, and animals (figure 15.6b).

Although most people associate photosynthesis only with plants, microbes living in water or along shorelines were the only photosynthetic organisms for most of life's history. Plants did not even colonize dry land until about 450 million years ago. Even today, about half of the O_2 generated in photosynthesis comes from aquatic organisms, mostly living in the oceans.

15.1 MASTERING CONCEPTS

1. How were conditions on Earth before life began different from current conditions?
2. What types of information can prebiotic simulations provide?
3. Why is RNA likely to have been pivotal in life's beginnings?
4. How did early life change Earth?

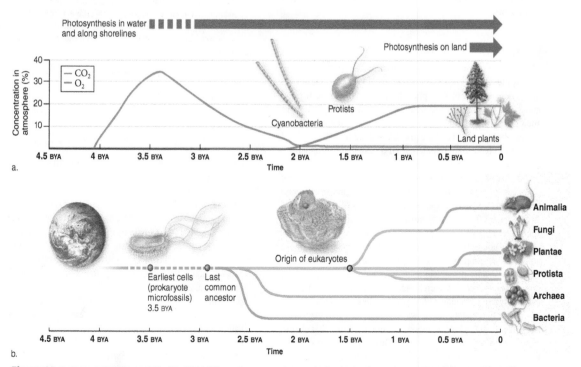

Figure 15.6 Oxygen Gas Changed the World. (a) Billions of years ago, photosynthetic microbes began to pump O_2 into the atmosphere. (b) As O_2 accumulated, life's diversity exploded.

15.2 Complex Cells and Multicellularity Arose over a Billion Years Ago

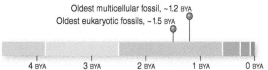

Oldest multicellular fossil, ~1.2 BYA
Oldest eukaryotic fossils, ~1.5 BYA

4 BYA   3 BYA   2 BYA   1 BYA   0 BYA

Until this point, we have considered the origin of prokaryotic cells. Fossil evidence shows that eukaryotic cells emerged during the Proterozoic era, at least 1.9 to 1.4 BYA. Australian fossils consisting of organic residue 1.69 billion years old are chemically similar to eukaryotic membrane components and may have come from a very early unicellular eukaryote.

Recall from chapter 3 that prokaryotic cells are structurally simple compared with compartmentalized eukaryotic cells. We may never know the origin of the nuclear envelope, endoplasmic reticulum, Golgi apparatus, and other membranes within the eukaryotic cell. The membranes of these organelles consist of phospholipids and proteins, as does the cell's outer membrane. Perhaps the outer membrane of an ancient cell repeatedly folded in on itself, eventually pinching off inside the cell to form a complex internal network of organelles (figure 15.7).

Unfortunately, that hypothesis is difficult or impossible to test, so we can only speculate about that aspect of eukaryotic cell evolution. Some details, however, are becoming clear. For example, the endosymbiont theory may explain the origin of two types of membrane-bounded organelles.

Animation
Origin of Eukaryotes

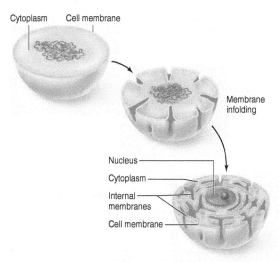

Cytoplasm   Cell membrane

Membrane infolding

Nucleus
Cytoplasm
Internal membranes
Cell membrane

Figure 15.7 Membrane Infolding. A highly folded cell membrane may have formed an internal membrane network as a possible step in the origin of eukaryotic cells.

A. Endosymbiosis Explains the Origin of Mitochondria and Chloroplasts

The **endosymbiont theory** proposes that mitochondria and chloroplasts originated as free-living bacteria that began living inside other prokaryotic cells (figure 15.8). The term *endosymbiont* derives from *endo-*, meaning "inside," and *symbiont*, meaning "to live together."

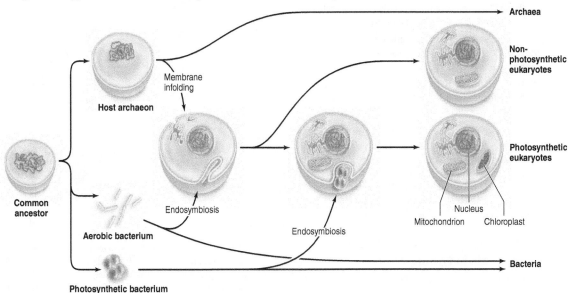

Archaea

Non-photosynthetic eukaryotes

Photosynthetic eukaryotes

Membrane infolding

Host archaeon

Common ancestor

Endosymbiosis

Aerobic bacterium

Endosymbiosis

Nucleus
Mitochondrion   Chloroplast

Bacteria

Photosynthetic bacterium

Figure 15.8 The Endosymbiont Theory. Mitochondria and chloroplasts may have originated from an ancient union of bacterial cells with archaean cells.

Tutorial
Endosymbiont Theory

Endosymbiosis has occurred multiple times in the history of eukaryotes. In the first endosymbiosis event shown in figure 15.8, a host cell engulfed one or more bacteria that could carry out aerobic respiration; this process would have been similar to endocytosis (see figure 4.20). These bacteria eventually developed into mitochondria. In a later endosymbiosis, some descendants of this early eukaryote took in photosynthetic bacteria that became chloroplasts. We know that mitochondria must have come first, because virtually all eukaryotes have these organelles. On the other hand, chloroplasts occur only in photosynthetic protists and plants.

After the ancient endosymbiosis events, many genes moved from the DNA of the organelles to the nuclei of the host cells. These genetic changes made the captured microorganisms unable to live on their own outside their hosts, as described in the Burning Question on page 313. Over time, they came to depend on one another for survival. The result of this biological interdependency, according to the endosymbiont theory, is the compartmentalized cells of modern eukaryotes.

Biologist Lynn Margulis proposed this theory in the late 1960s. Since that time, the evidence supporting the idea that mitochondria and chloroplasts originated as independent organisms has mounted. The evidence includes the following:

- similarities in size, shape, and membrane structure between the organelles and some types of bacteria;
- the double membrane surrounding mitochondria and chloroplasts, a presumed relic of the original engulfing event;
- the observation that mitochondria and chloroplasts are not assembled in cells but instead divide, as do bacterial cells;
- the similarity between the photosynthetic pigments in chloroplasts and those in cyanobacteria;
- the observation that mitochondria and chloroplasts contain DNA, RNA, and ribosomes, which are similar to those in bacterial cells; and
- DNA sequence analysis, which shows a close relationship between mitochondria and aerobic bacteria (proteobacteria), and between chloroplasts and cyanobacteria.

Endosymbiosis has been a potent force in eukaryote evolution. In fact, the chloroplasts of some types of photosynthetic protists apparently derive from a secondary endosymbiosis— that is, of a eukaryotic cell engulfing a eukaryotic red or green alga (figure 15.9; see also figure 18.2). In these species, three or four membranes surround the chloroplasts; some of their cells even retain remnants of the engulfed cell's nucleus.

B. Multicellularity May Also Have Its Origin in Cooperation

Another critical step leading to the evolution of plants, fungi, and animals was the origin of multicellularity, which occurred about 1.2 BYA. The earliest fossils of multicellular life are from a red alga that lived about 1.25 BYA to 950 MYA (million years

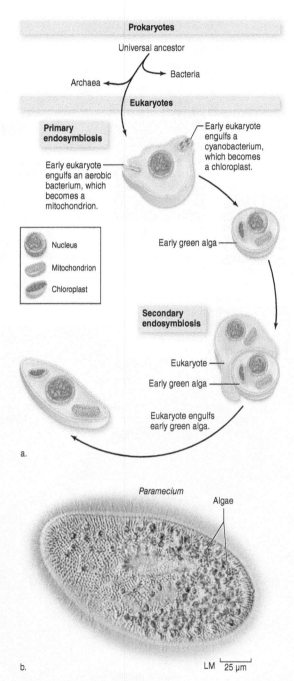

Figure 15.9 Secondary Endosymbiosis. (a) Many photosynthetic eukaryotes acquired chloroplasts by engulfing existing eukaryotic cells. (b) This protist, *Paramecium bursaria*, has engulfed eukaryotic algae, which live symbiotically inside its cytoplasm. This dual organism (and many others in similar partnerships) provide evidence for the endosymbiosis theory.

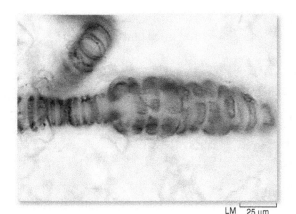

LM   25 μm

Figure 15.10 Early Multicellularity. This 1.2-billion-year-old fossil of a red alga offers some of the oldest evidence of multicellularity.

ago) in Canada (figure 15.10). Abundant fossil evidence of multicellular algae, dating from a billion years ago, also comes from eastern Russia.

No one knows how eukaryotes came to adopt a multicellular lifestyle. The fossil record is essentially silent on the transition, mostly because the first multicellular organisms lacked hard parts that fossilize readily. We do know, however, that multicellularity arose independently in multiple lineages. After all, genetic evidence clearly suggests that plants, fungi, and animals arose from different lineages of multicellular protists.

We also know that some multicellular organisms consist of cells that bear an uncanny resemblance to one-celled protists; figure 15.11 shows two examples. How might the transition to multicellularity have occurred? Perhaps many individual cells came together, joined, and took on specialized tasks to form a

BurningQuestion

Why can't mitochondria and chloroplasts survive on their own?

The idea that mitochondria and chloroplasts are derived from free-living bacteria is fascinating, and it raises the intriguing question of whether these organelles could be extracted from living cells and survive on their own.

The brief answer to this question is that they cannot. The endosymbiosis event that eventually gave rise to mitochondria occurred more than a billion years ago, and since that time the organelles lost most of the genes present in their bacterial ancestors.

Gene numbers tell the story. A typical chloroplast genome encodes about 100 genes; in humans and other mammals, the mitochondrial genome encodes a mere 37 genes. These numbers are tiny compared to the several thousand genes in a bacterial cell. Among the genes that mitochondria and chloroplasts have lost are those that encode defensive chemicals, many transport proteins, and other molecules that are essential to free-living bacteria.

Mitochondria and chloroplasts did, however, retain DNA encoding proteins that are essential to their present-day functions: aerobic cellular respiration for mitochondria, and photosynthesis for chloroplasts. They also have their own ribosomes, so they can produce these proteins without help from the rest of the cell. However, their limited set of genes is nowhere near enough to enable mitochondria and chloroplasts to regain their independence.

Submit your burning question to:
Marielle.Hoefnagels@mheducation.com

multicellular organism. The life cycle of modern-day protists called slime molds illustrates this possibility (see figure 18.13). Alternatively, a single-celled organism may have divided, and the daughter cells may have remained stuck together rather than separating. After many rounds of cell division, these cells may have begun expressing different subsets of their DNA. The result would be a multicellular organism with specialized cells—similar to the way in which modern animals and plants develop from a single fertilized egg cell. ⓘ *slime molds,* p. 368

Whichever way it happened, the origin of multicellularity ushered in the possibility of specialized cells, which allowed for new features such as attachment to a surface or an upright orientation. The resulting explosion in the variety of body sizes and forms introduced new evolutionary possibilities and opened new habitats for other organisms. The rest of this chapter describes the diversification of multicellular life.

15.2   MASTERING CONCEPTS

1. How might the endoplasmic reticulum, nuclear envelope, and other internal membranes have arisen?
2. What is the evidence that mitochondria and chloroplasts descend from simpler cells engulfed long ago?
3. What are two ways that multicellular organisms may have originated?

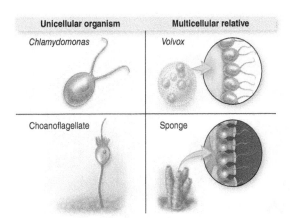

Unicellular organism	Multicellular relative
Chlamydomonas	*Volvox*
Choanoflagellate	Sponge

Figure 15.11 From One to Many. A single-celled green alga called *Chlamydomonas* shares many similarities with its close relative, the many-celled *Volvox*. Likewise, a protist called a choanoflagellate resembles a collar cell on the inner surface of a sponge.

15.3 Life's Diversity Exploded in the Past 500 Million Years

It would take many thousands of pages to capture all of the events that passed from the rise of the first cells to life today—if we even knew them. This section highlights a few key events in the history of multicellular, eukaryotic life.

As you read through this section, keep in mind what you have already learned about evolution, speciation, and extinction. Species have come and gone in response to major environmental changes such as rising and falling temperatures, the increasing concentration of O_2 in the atmosphere, the shifting continents, and the advance and retreat of glaciers. Short-term catastrophes such as floods, volcanic eruptions, and meteorite impacts have also taken their toll on some species and created new opportunities for others. ⓘ *mass extinctions, p. 292*

A. The Strange Ediacarans Flourished Late in the Precambrian

The "Precambrian" is an informal name for the eventful 4 billion years that preceded the Cambrian period of the Paleozoic era. During the Precambrian supereon, life originated, reproduced, and diversified into many forms. In addition, photosynthesis evolved, O_2 accumulated in Earth's atmosphere, and eukaryotes arose, as did the first multicellular algae and animals.

Perhaps the most famous Precambrian residents were the mysterious Ediacaran organisms, which left no known modern descendants (figure 15.12). One example, *Dickinsonia*, could reach 1 meter in diameter but was less than 3 millimeters thick. Biologists have interpreted these fossils as everything from worms to ferns to fungi. The Ediacarans vanished from the fossil record about 544 MYA. (In 2004, geologists named the last portion of the Precambrian, from 543 to about 600 MYA, the Ediacaran period in honor of these strange marine creatures.)

B. Paleozoic Plants and Animals Emerged onto Land

Cambrian Period (543 to 490 MYA)   Fossils of all major phyla of animals appeared within a few million years of one another in the Cambrian seas, a spectacular period of diversification sometimes called the "Cambrian explosion" (see chapter 21's opening essay). During this time, remnants of the Ediacaran world coexisted with abundant red and green algae, sponges, jellyfishes, and worms. Most notable were the earliest known organisms with hard parts, such as insectlike trilobites, nautiloids, scorpion-like eurypterids, and brachiopods, which resembled clams. Many of these invertebrates left remnants identified only as "small, shelly fossils." The early Cambrian seas were also home to diverse wormlike, armored animals, some of which would die out.

The Burgess Shale from the Canadian province of British Columbia preserves a glimpse of life from this time. A mid-Cambrian mud slide buried enormous numbers of organisms, including animals with skeletons and soft-bodied invertebrates not seen elsewhere. The Burgess Shale animals were abundant, diverse, and preserved in exquisite detail (figure 15.13).

Ordovician Period (490 to 443 MYA)   During the Ordovician period, the seas continued to support huge communities of algae and invertebrates such as sponges, corals, snails, clams, and cephalopods. The first vertebrates to leave fossil evidence, jawless fishes called ostracoderms, appeared at this time. Fossilized spores indicate that life had ventured onto land, in the form of primitive plants that may have resembled modern liverworts (see section 19.2).

Figure 15.12

Ediacarans Were . . . Different.

(a) *Dickinsonia* was an Ediacaran organism with segments, two different ends, and internal features that paleontologists have interpreted as a simple circulatory or digestive system. But just what it was remains unclear. (b) No one knows what type of animal *Spriggina* was, either.

a.

1 cm

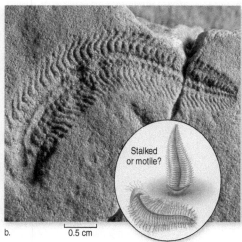

b.

0.5 cm

Stalked or motile?

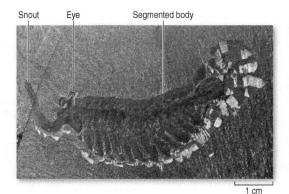

Snout   Eye   Segmented body

1 cm

Figure 15.13 Cambrian Life. *Opabinia* is one of many strange animals whose fossils have been discovered in the Burgess Shale. Its body was segmented, and its head sported stalked eyes and a long, flexible snout.

The Ordovician period ended with a mass extinction that killed huge numbers of marine invertebrates. Apparently the supercontinent of Gondwana drifted toward the South Pole, causing temperatures on the landmass to fall. Sea levels dropped as glaciers accumulated, destroying shoreline habitats.

Silurian Period (443 to 417 MYA)   The first plants with specialized water- and mineral-conducting tissues, the vascular plants, evolved during the Silurian (figure 15.14). These plants were larger than their ancestors, so they provided additional food and shelter for animals. The first terrestrial animals to leave fossils resembled scorpions, which may have preyed upon other small animals exploring the land. Fungi likely colonized land at the same time.

Aquatic life also continued to change. Fishes with jaws arose, as did the first freshwater fishes, but their jawless counterparts

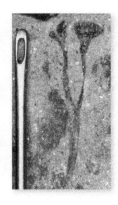

Figure 15.14 Early Land Plant. *Cooksonia*, which lived during the Silurian, is the oldest known vascular plant.

were still widespread during the Silurian. The oceans also contained abundant corals, trilobites, and mollusks.

Devonian Period (417 to 354 MYA)   The Devonian period was the "Age of Fishes." The seas continued to support more life than did the land. The now prevalent invertebrates were joined by fishes with skeletons of cartilage or bone. Corals and animals called crinoids that resembled flowers were abundant.

The fresh waters of the Devonian were home to the lobe-finned fishes (figure 15.15a). These animals had fleshy, powerful fins and could obtain O$_2$ through both gills and primitive lunglike structures. Toward the end of the Devonian period, about 360 MYA, the first amphibians appeared (figure 15.15b and c). *Acanthostega* had a fin on its tail like a fish and used its powerful tail to move underwater, but it also had hips, paddlelike legs, and toes. Preserved footprints indicate that the animal could venture briefly onto land. A contemporary of *Acanthostega*, called *Ichthyostega*, had more powerful legs and a rib cage strong enough to support the animal's weight on land, yet it had a skull shape and finned tail reminiscent of fish ancestors.

a. *Eusthenopteron*

b. *Acanthostega*

c. *Ichthyostega*

Figure 15.15 The Vertebrate Transition to Land. (a) This lobe-finned fish, *Eusthenopteron*, had fleshy fins with bones that closely resemble those of a terrestrial vertebrate's limbs. (b) *Acanthostega* stayed mostly in the water but had legs and other adaptations that permitted it to spend short periods on land. (c) *Ichthyostega* could spend longer periods on land because its rib cage was stronger.

Many fossils indicate that by this time, plants were diversifying to ferns, horsetails, and seed plants. Scorpions, millipedes, and other invertebrates lived on the land.

A mass extinction of marine life marks the end of the Devonian period. Warm-water invertebrates and jawless fishes were hit especially hard, and jawed fishes called placoderms became extinct. Life on land, however, was largely spared. The cause of this mass extinction remains unknown.

Carboniferous Period (354 to 290 MYA)
Amphibians flourished from about 350 to 300 MYA, giving this period the name the "Age of Amphibians." These animals spent time on land, but they had to return to the water to wet their skins and lay eggs. Although today's amphibians are small, some of their ancient relatives were huge—up to 9 meters long!

During the Carboniferous, some amphibians arose that coated their eggs with a hard shell. These animals branched from the other amphibians, eventually giving rise to reptiles. The first vertebrates capable of living totally on land, the primitive reptiles, appeared about 300 MYA.

Carboniferous swamps included ferns and early seed plants, some of which towered to 40 meters (figure 15.16). The air was alive with the sounds of grasshoppers, crickets, and giant dragonflies with 75-centimeter wingspans. Land snails and other invertebrates flourished in the sediments. By the end of the period, many of the plants had died, buried beneath the swamps to form coal beds during the coming millennia. In fact, the term *Carboniferous* means "coal-bearing"; see this chapter's Apply It Now box on page 319 for more on coal.

Meanwhile, in the oceans, the bony fishes and sharks were beginning to resemble modern forms, and protists called foraminiferans were abundant. Bryozoans and brachiopods were plentiful, but trilobites were becoming less common.

Permian Period (290 to 248 MYA)
During the Permian, seed plants called gymnosperms became more prominent. Reptiles were also becoming more prevalent. The reptile introduced a new adaptation, the amniote egg, in which an embryo could develop completely on dry land (see figure 21.29). Amniote eggs persist today in reptiles, birds, and a few mammals.

The Permian period foreshadowed the dawn of the dinosaur age. Cotylosaurs were early Permian reptiles that gave rise to the dinosaurs and all other reptiles. They coexisted with their immediate descendants, the pelycosaurs, or sailed lizards.

The Permian period ended with what paleontologists call "the mother of mass extinctions." It affected marine life the most, wiping out more than 90% of species in shallow areas of the sea. On the land, many types of insects, amphibians, and reptiles disappeared, paving the way for the age of dinosaurs.

Figure 15.16 Carboniferous Forest Life. (a) About 300 MYA, lush forests dominated the landscape. The fernlike plants in the foreground are ancient seed-bearing plants. Other plants and trees, also extinct, gave rise to modern club mosses and ground pines. (b) These forests were eventually preserved in massive coal beds containing the remains of Carboniferous plants, such as this fossilized fern frond.

Paleontologists hypothesize that the Permian extinctions were partly the result of a drop in sea level, which dried out coastline communities. Carbon dioxide from oxidation of organic molecules accumulated in the atmosphere, raising global temperature and depleting the sea's dissolved O_2. The loss of O_2, in turn, may have favored bacteria that produce toxic hydrogen sulfide (H_2S) as a waste. A long series of volcanic eruptions, beginning 255 MYA and lasting a few million years, further altered global climate. Finally, sea level rose again, drowning coastline communities.

C. Reptiles and Flowering Plants Thrived During the Mesozoic Era

Triassic Period (248 to 206 MYA) During the Triassic period, the first archosaurs flourished, ushering in the "Age of Reptiles" (as the Mesozoic era is sometimes called). These first archosaurs were the ancestors of the now-extinct dinosaurs and of modern birds and crocodiles. Early archosaurs shared the forest of cycads, ginkgos, and conifers with other animals called therapsids, which were the ancestors of mammals.

At the close of the Triassic period, yet another mass extinction affected life in the oceans and on land. Many marine animals were wiped out, as were many reptiles and amphibians on land. As a result, much larger animals began to infiltrate a wide range of habitats. These new, well-adapted animals were the dinosaurs, and they would dominate for the next 120 million years.

Jurassic Period (206 to 144 MYA) By the Jurassic period, giant reptiles were everywhere (figure 15.17). Ichthyosaurs, plesiosaurs, and giant marine crocodiles swam in the seas alongside sharks and rays, feasting on fish, squid, and ammonites. Apatosaurs and stegosaurs roamed the land. Carnivores, such as allosaurs, preyed on the herbivores. Pterosaurs glided through the air, as did *Protoarchaeopteryx* and then *Archaeopteryx*—the first birds (see chapter 13's opening essay).

At the same time, the first flowering plants (angiosperms) appeared on land. The forests, however, still consisted largely of tall ferns and conifers, ginkgos, club mosses, and horsetails. The first frogs and the first true mammals, which were no larger than rats, appeared as well.

Figure 15.17 Marine Reptile. Plesiosaurs were enormous carnivorous reptiles that swam in the Jurassic seas.

Cretaceous Period (144 to 65 MYA) The Cretaceous period was a time of great biological change. By around 100 MYA, flowering plants had spread in spectacular diversity; many modern insects arose at about the same time. Marine reptiles hunted mollusks and fish, and birds and pterosaurs roamed the skies. Duck-billed maiasaurs traveled in groups of thousands in what is now Montana. Huge herds of apatosaurs migrated from the plains of Alberta to the Arctic, northern Europe, and Asia, which were joined as one continent at the time. Near the end of the Cretaceous, *Tyrannosaurus* roamed in what is now western North America, and *Triceratops* was so widespread that some paleontologists call it the "cockroach of the Cretaceous."

The reign of the giant reptiles ended about 65 MYA, with the extinction of ichthyosaurs, plesiosaurs, mosasaurs, pterosaurs, and nonavian dinosaurs. Ammonites vanished too, as did many types of foraminiferans, sea urchins, and bony fishes. In all, nearly 75% of species perished. The mass extinction opened up habitats for many species that survived, including flowering plants, mollusks, amphibians, some smaller reptiles, birds, and mammals. Many of these groups, including the mammals that gave rise to our own species, subsequently flourished.

The mass extinction that ended the Mesozoic era coincides with an asteroid impact near the Yucatán peninsula. The asteroid, which was about 10 kilometers in diameter, left a debris- and clay-filled crater offshore and a huge semicircle of sinkholes onshore (figure 14.14 shows the distinctive iridium layer, an important piece of evidence for the impact theory). Biologists estimate that photosynthesis was almost nonexistent for 3 years, as debris that was thrown into the sky circulated in the atmosphere, blocking sunlight. Plankton, which provide microscopic food for many larger marine dwellers, died as well, causing a devastating chain reaction.

Figure It Out

Suppose that a 100-meter track represents Earth's 4.6 billion–year history. How close to the end of the track would you mark the Permian and Cretaceous extinctions?

Answer: 5.4 m (Permian) and 1.4 m (Cretaceous)

D. Mammals Diversified During the Cenozoic Era

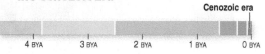

Tertiary Period (65 to 1.8 MYA)   The Cenozoic era, sometimes called the "Age of Mammals," began with the Tertiary period. The Tertiary was a time of great adaptive radiation for mammals, according to the fossil record (see figure 14.13). Within just 1.6 million years, 15 of the 18 modern orders of placental mammals arose. ⓘ *adaptive radiation*, p. 290

At the start of the Tertiary period, diverse hoofed mammals grazed the grassy Americas. Many may have been marsupials (pouched mammals) or egg-laying monotremes, ancestors of the platypus. Then placental mammals appeared, and fossil evidence indicates that they rapidly dominated the mammals.

Geology and the resulting climate changes molded the comings and goings of species throughout the Cenozoic. The era began with the formation of new mountains and coastlines as tectonic plates shifted. The wet warmth of the Paleocene epoch, which opened up many habitats for mammals, continued into the Eocene, providing widespread forests and woodlands. Grasslands began to replace the forests by the end of the Eocene, when the temperature and humidity dropped. Extinctions of some mammals paralleled the changing plant populations as the forests diminished, but grazing mammals thrived throughout the remaining three epochs of the Tertiary period.

Although the Cenozoic is best known for its spectacular assemblage of mammals, other types of animals diversified as well. One especially fruitful source of fossils from the Eocene epoch is the Green River formation in Wyoming (figure 15.18). Here, countless animals and plants were trapped in lake sediments that subsequently dried up and became exposed. Fossil collectors have scooped up millions of exquisitely preserved fish fossils similar to the one in figure 15.18a. In addition, the limestone of the Green River formation contains a rich fossil collection representing crocodiles, snakes, birds, mammals, snails, and insects. One particularly important example is the bat skeleton in figure 15.18b; this specimen is the oldest known fossilized bat. Leaves of ferns, sycamores, cattails, and other flowering plants were buried in the lake sediments as well. Amazingly, the Green River fossils not only cover a continuous six-million-year long

a.

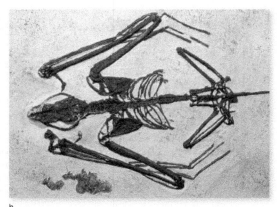

b.

Figure 15.18   Eocene Fossils. Wyoming's Green River formation has preserved a showcase of Eocene life from about 50 million years ago. (a) Freshwater fish are especially well represented in the fossil beds. (b) This skeleton is the oldest known fossil of a bat.

period but also reveal how life responded to the changing climate during the Eocene.

Quaternary Period (1.8 MYA to Present)   The Pleistocene epoch accounts for all but the last 10,000 years of the Quaternary period. During several Pleistocene ice ages, huge glaciers covered about 30% of Earth's surface and then withdrew again.

Many organisms of the time were similar to those that are familiar now, including flowering plants, insects, birds, and mammals. Some Pleistocene species, however, are extinct (figure 15.19). Camels and horses that were native to North America are gone (today's wild horses are descended from domesticated European horses). And the woolly mammoths, mastodons, saber-toothed cats, giant ground sloths, and other large mammals that once roamed North America, Asia, and Europe are known only from their fossils and the occasional DNA fragment (see section 19.6).

Apply It **Now**

Coal's Costs

The relationship between ancient plants and today's electronic gadgetry may seem remote, but it is not. Gadgets require electricity, and nearly half of the electricity in the United States comes from coal-fired power plants. Each lump of coal, in turn, is mined from the long-dead remains of the Carboniferous forests (figure 15.A).

The ferns and other plants in these forests produced their own food by photosynthesis. That is, they used water, energy from the sun, and CO_2 from the atmosphere to build the sugars and complex molecules that made up their bodies. Many of these leaves and stems did not decompose when the plants died; instead, they were buried under sediments. Heat and pressure eventually transformed the plant matter into coal. When we burn the coal, we release the potential energy and CO_2 that ancient plants trapped in photosynthesis hundreds of millions of years ago.

Burning coal to generate electricity is relatively inexpensive, compared to other energy sources. Coal powered the Industrial Revolution and continues to be economically important today. This fuel does not, however, come without costs.

First, coal mining has environmental and health consequences. Extracting coal from underground deposits can destroy soil, plants, and wildlife habitat. Water quality can suffer as exposed mountainsides erode away. And although coal mining in developed countries is safer than in times past, miners still risk injury and death in mine collapses and explosions.

Second, burning coal releases CO_2 into the atmosphere. This heat-trapping gas plays a large role in global climate change. Coal combustion also releases potentially harmful heavy metals such as mercury, which can accumulate in body tissues. Moreover, nitrogen- and

Figure 15.A   Coal Mining. Two miners extract coal deep within a mine shaft.

sulfur-rich gases from coal-fired power plants contribute to acid deposition. Chapter 40 describes these environmental issues in more detail.

Feeding the human population's voracious demand for energy requires enormous amounts of coal and other fossil fuels. As you consider the costs of coal, keep in mind that no energy source is free, not even renewable ones such as sunlight and wind; all require equipment, roads, power lines, and maintenance. The best way to avoid these costs is to reduce the overall demand for energy.

Figure 15.19   American Mastodon. These enormous, elephant-like mammals lived in North America from about 3.7 million years ago until they went extinct about 10,000 years ago.

The Pleistocene epoch was also eventful for our own branch of the mammal family tree, as multiple species of *Homo* came and went. Our species, *Homo sapiens* ("the wise human"), probably first appeared about 200,000 years ago in Africa and had migrated throughout most of the world by about 10,000 years ago. Other species of *Homo*, including Neandertals, vanished during the Pleistocene, leaving *Homo sapiens* as the sole human species.

The roots of our family tree, however, extend much deeper into history. We pick up the story of human evolution in more detail in section 15.4.

15.3   MASTERING CONCEPTS

1. When did the Ediacarans live, and what were they like?
2. What types of organisms flourished in the Cambrian?
3. How did Paleozoic life diversify during the Ordovician, Silurian, Devonian, Carboniferous, and Permian periods?
4. How did the Paleozoic era end?
5. Which organisms came and went during the Mesozoic era?
6. Which new organisms arose during the Cenozoic era?

15.4 Fossils and DNA Tell the Human Evolution Story

In many ways, humans are Earth's dominant species. True, we are not the most numerous—more microbes occupy one person's intestinal tract than there are people on Earth. But in the short time of human existence, we have colonized most continents, altered Earth's surface, eliminated many species, and changed many others to fit our needs. Where did we come from?

A. Humans Are Primates

If you watch the monkeys or apes in a zoo for a few minutes, it is almost impossible to ignore how similar they seem to humans. Young ones scramble about and play. They sniff and handle food. Babies cling to their mothers. Adults gather in small groups or sit quietly, snoozing or staring into space.

It is no surprise that we see ourselves reflected in the behaviors of monkeys and apes. All **primates**—including monkeys, apes, and humans—share a suite of physical characteristics (figure 15.20). First, primates have grasping hands with opposable thumbs that can bend inward to touch the pads of the fingers. Some primates also have grasping feet with opposable big toes. Second, a primate's fingers and toes have flat nails instead of claws. Third, eyes set in the front of the skull give primates binocular vision with overlapping fields of sight that produce excellent depth perception. Fourth, the primate brain is large by comparison with body size.

Compared with many other groups of mammals, primate anatomy is unusually versatile. For instance, bat wings are useful for flight but not much else; likewise, horse hooves are best for fast running. In contrast, primates have multipurpose fingers and toes that are useful not only for locomotion but also for grasping and manipulating small objects. Primate limbs are similarly versatile.

The Primate Lineage The primate lineage, which originated some 60 MYA, contains three main groups: prosimians, monkeys, and hominoids. **Prosimian** is an informal umbrella term for lemurs, aye-ayes, lorises, tarsiers, and bush babies. Monkeys are divided into two groups: Old World monkeys (native to Africa and Asia) and New World monkeys (native to South and Central America). The **hominoids** are apes, including humans.

Hominoids are further divided into two groups. One contains the gibbons, also called the "lesser apes." The other, the **hominids**, contains all of the "great apes": orangutans, gorillas, chimpanzees (including bonobos), and humans. Orangutans, however, are not as closely related to the other great apes. **Hominines** include only gorillas, chimpanzees, and humans, and **hominins** are extinct and modern humans. Table 15.1 summarizes the groups of primates.

Of the many sources of information indicating how these groups are related, paleontologists have used one the longest: the physical characteristics of skeletons (figure 15.21). Most human fossils consist of bones and teeth. Comparing these remains with existing primates reveals surprisingly detailed information about locomotion and diet. For this reason, knowledge of primate skeletal anatomy is essential to interpreting human fossils.

Dietary Adaptations in Primates Some of the most important skeletal characteristics, including the size and shape of the teeth, are related to diet (figure 15.22). Upper and lower molar teeth have ridges that fit together, much as the teeth of gears intermesh. Food caught between these surfaces is ground, crushed, and mashed. The size of these teeth is an adaptation that reflects the toughness of the diet.

As you examine the skulls in figure 15.22, notice the differences in the sagittal crests. This bony ridge runs lengthwise along

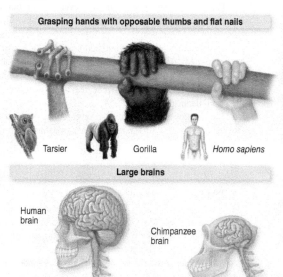

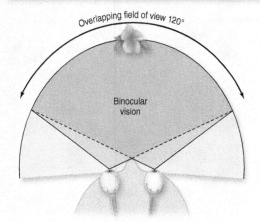

Figure 15.20 Primate Characteristics. Primates share several characteristics, including opposable thumbs, flattened nails, binocular vision, and large brains relative to body size.

TABLE **15.1** **Miniglossary of Primate Terminology**

Term	Animals Included in Group*
Primates	Prosimians, monkeys, and apes
Hominoids	"Lesser apes" (gibbons) and great apes
Hominids	"Great apes" (orangutans, gorillas, chimpanzees, humans)
Hominines	Gorillas, chimpanzees, humans
Hominins	Extinct and modern humans

*Each group also contains extinct representatives known only from fossils.

the top of the skull and is an attachment point for muscles. A prominent sagittal crest indicates particularly strong jaws, another clue to an animal's diet.

Other important features in primate skulls include the size of the jaw bones, the prominence of the ridge of bone above the eye, the degree to which the jaw protrudes, and the shape of the curve of the tooth row. All of these characteristics allow paleoanthropologists, the scientists who study human fossils, to identify hominid species.

Primate Locomotion   Additional important characteristics in hominoid skeletons are adaptations related to locomotion. Brachiation is swinging from one arm to the other while the body

Figure 15.21 **Clues from Bones.** The skeleton on the left, from a human, shares many similarities with the gorilla skeleton on the right.

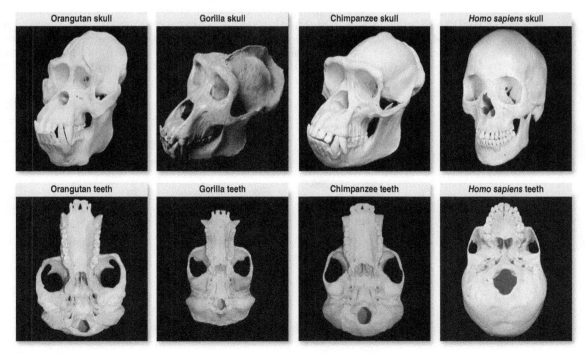

Figure 15.22 **Skulls and Teeth.** The skulls and teeth of an orangutan, gorilla, chimpanzee, and human reveal details about diet and jaw strength. Biologists compare fossils of extinct species to bones of existing primates to learn how our ancestors lived. The top row of photos shows side views; the bottom row shows skulls from underneath, revealing the hole through which the spinal cord enters the brain.

dangles below. Many hominoids move through the treetops in this way; in contrast, monkeys run on all fours along the tops of branches. Orangutans spend most of their lives in trees and move by brachiation when they are in treetops. Gibbons, the most superbly acrobatic hominoids, have long arms and hands. The size and opposability of the thumb are reduced, but their arms connect to the shoulders by ball-and-socket joints that allow free movement of the arms in 360 degrees. In addition, a long collarbone acts as a brace and keeps the shoulder from collapsing toward the chest.

Heavier-bodied chimpanzees and gorillas don't brachiate as much as gibbons and orangutans, but like humans, they can do so. Humans seldom brachiate, with the exception of small, light-bodied children playing on schoolyard "monkey bars." Adult human arms are too weak to support the heavy torso and legs.

Chimpanzees and gorillas move by knuckle-walking, a behavioral modification that allows an animal to run rapidly on the ground on all fours, with their weight resting on the knuckles. The proportionately longer arms of chimps and gorillas are an adaptation to knuckle-walking.

One important feature distinguishes humans from the other great apes: bipedalism, or the ability to walk upright on two legs. Adaptations to bipedalism include relatively short arms and longer, stronger leg bones. Foot bones form firm supports for walking, with the big toe fixed in place and not opposable. The bowl-shaped pelvis supports most of the weight of the body, and lumbar vertebrae are robust enough to bear some body weight.

Bipedalism is also reflected in the bones of the head. The foramen magnum is the large hole in the skull where the spinal cord leaves the brain (see figure 15.22). In modern humans, this hole is tucked beneath the skull. In gorillas and chimps, the foramen magnum is located somewhat closer to the rear of the skull; in animals that run on all fours, such as horses and dogs, the hole is at the back of the skull.

B. Molecular Evidence Documents Primate Relationships

Fossil evidence and anatomical similarities were once the only lines of evidence that paleoanthropologists could analyze in tracing the course of human evolution. Around 1960, however, scientists began to use molecular sequences to investigate relationships among primates. Studies of blood proteins and DNA presented a new picture of primate evolution, as it became clear that humans are a species of great ape. One of the astounding findings of these molecular studies was that the genes of humans and chimpanzees are 99% identical (see section 11.5).

Other research further eroded the distinctions between humans and other great apes. Previously, humans had been placed in a separate group, supposedly characterized by upright walking, tool-making, and language. Then, in the 1970s, chimpanzees and wild gorillas were observed to use tools, and captive great apes learned to use sign language to communicate with their trainers. The only characteristic that now remains unique to *Homo* is bipedal locomotion.

Video
Chimp Tool Use

As the new molecular evidence continued to pour in, scientists began to view primate relationships differently. Figure 15.23 shows an evolutionary tree that takes into account both the anatomical characteristics and the molecular data. As you examine this cladogram, keep in mind two important concepts. First, note that humans are not descended from other groups of modern apes. Instead, all living humans and chimpanzees share a common ancestor and diverged from that ancestor perhaps 7 MYA. Second, note that gibbons, orangutans, gorillas, and chimpanzees are not "less evolved" than humans. All living species are on an equal evolutionary footing, although some may belong to older lineages.

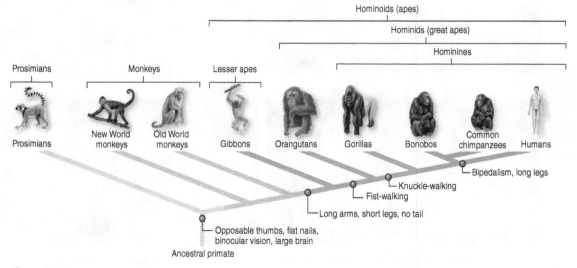

Figure 15.23 Primate Lineages. This cladogram shows the physical traits that differentiate the three main groups of primates: prosimians, monkeys, and hominoids. Molecular data support this hypothesis of the evolutionary relationships among primates.

C. Hominin Evolution Is Partially Recorded in Fossils

Tutorial
Evidence for
Human Evolution

Even though DNA and proteins provide overwhelming evidence of the relationships between living primates, these molecules deteriorate with time. Scientists therefore cannot usually use molecular data to establish relationships of prehistoric hominins. For this, we must turn to studies of fossilized remains.

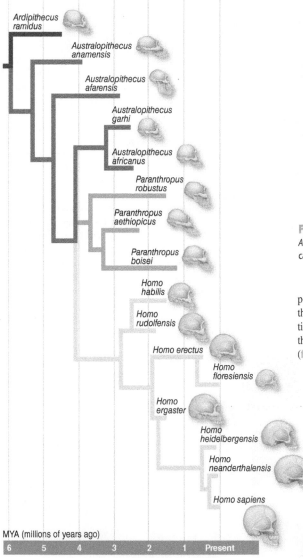

Figure 15.24 Human Family Tree. Fossilized remains place our close relatives into four main groups (*Ardipithecus, Australopithecus, Paranthropus,* and *Homo*). Skull sizes are approximately to scale and range from about 400 cm³ for *A. afarensis* to about 1450 cm³ for modern humans. The evolutionary relationships in this tree are hypothesized.

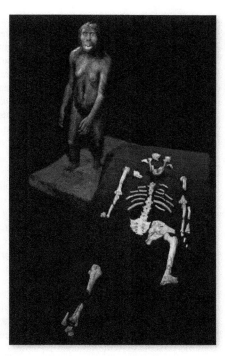

Figure 15.25 Early Human. This reconstruction of the *Australopithecus afarensis* specimen called "Lucy" was made from the casting of bones discovered in 1974.

To interpret fossils from the human family tree, paleoanthropologists compare details of the ancient skeletal features with those of modern primates and try to reconstruct as much information about diet and lifestyle as they can. So far, fossil hominins in the human family tree have fallen into the following groups (figure 15.24):

- **Ardipithecus.** In 2009, researchers revealed a detailed analysis of *Ardipithecus ramidus,* a human ancestor discovered in 1994 in Ethiopia. *Ardipithecus* (or "Ardi" for short) dates to about 4.4 MYA and is the oldest representative of the human lineage discovered to date. The 1994 discovery, coupled with dozens of other fossils from the same species, gives several clues about Ardi's life. The teeth indicate that Ardi was an omnivore. The pelvis supported both upright walking and powerful climbing, as did the feet, which had opposable big toes. The flexible hands had long, grasping fingers with which Ardi could have carried objects while walking upright.

- **Australopithecus.** Fossils of four or five species of extinct small apes have been assigned to the genus *Australopithecus,* meaning "Southern ape-man." The downward position of the foramen magnum indicates that these apes walked upright. *Australopithecus afarensis* (including the famous "Lucy" fossil in figure 15.25) and *A. africanus* are members of this group, which dates from about 4 to 2.5 MYA.

- **Paranthropus.** This extinct group, whose name literally means "beside humans," is characterized by extremely large teeth, protruding jaws, and skulls that have a sagittal crest. All of these specializations probably relate to the large jaw muscles needed to crush tough plants or crack nuts. Most researchers hypothesize that *Paranthropus* descended from *Australopithecus. Paranthropus aethiopicus, P. boisei,* and *P. robustus* are members of this group, which dates from about 3 to 1.5 MYA. *Paranthropus* seems to be an evolutionary dead end that gave rise to no other group.

- **Homo.** Fossils in this group are associated with stones thought to have been tools. *Homo* species tend to have larger bodies and larger brains than do australopiths. All members of genus *Homo* are considered humans, and *Homo habilis, H. ergaster,* and *H. erectus* belong to the cluster of extinct species that are called "early *Homo*." These species lived from about 2.5 MYA to about 500,000 years ago and gave rise to "recent *Homo*." Recent species of *Homo* have smaller teeth, lighter jaws, larger braincases, less protruding jaws, and lighter brow ridges. Their fossils are associated with evidence of culture (figure 15.26). Recent *Homo* species are *H. heidelbergensis, H. neanderthalensis, H. floresiensis,* and *H. sapiens.* The only human species alive today is *Homo sapiens.*

One interesting trend in human evolution has been an adaptive radiation of species, followed by extinctions. Fossil evidence shows that about 1.8 MYA, as many as five species of hominins lived together in Africa. About 200,000 years ago, three species of recent *Homo* coexisted in Europe. Today, however, all except *Homo sapiens* are extinct.

What happened to the other *Homo* species? No one knows, but many anthropologists wonder whether *H. sapiens* contributed to their extinction. Scientists have speculated that Neandertals interbred with *H. sapiens*, effectively causing the Neandertals to disappear from the fossil record about 30,000 years ago. Recent analyses of DNA from Neandertals and *H. sapiens* have supported that hypothesis, although the question remains unsettled.

D. Environmental Changes Have Spurred Hominin Evolution

What provoked the hominid ancestors of humans to abandon brachiation in favor of bipedal, upright walking? What allowed the large brains that are characteristic of recent *Homo* to develop? To find these answers, we have to consider a related question: Where did hominids evolve?

Charles Darwin was one of the first to speculate that humans evolved in Africa. About 12 MYA, tectonic movements caused a period of great mountain building. The continental plates beneath India and the Himalayan region collided and ground together, heaving up the Himalayas. The resulting climatic shift had enormous ecological consequences. Cooler temperatures reduced the thick tropical forests that had covered much of Europe, India, the Middle East, and East Africa. Open plains appeared, bringing new opportunities for species that could live there. These included less competition for food in the treetops, a new assortment of foods, and a different group of predators. Experts speculate that one type of small ape moved out of the trees and began life on the African savannas.

Perhaps at first this species alternated between running on all fours and bipedal walking. On open plains, however, there are advantages to bipedal walking, especially the elevated vantage point for sensing danger and spotting food and friends. This environment would have selected for apes with the best skeletal adaptations to bipedalism, and the trait would have been preserved and honed in the plains. Bipedalism also freed hominin hands to carry objects and use the tools that are so characteristic of *Homo* species.

No one knows what might have spurred the evolution of the large brain that characterizes humans. Some experts relate the development of a large brain to tool use; others relate it to life in social groups and language.

a.

b.

Figure 15.26   *Homo heidelbergensis.* (a) A skull replica [left] is paired with a model showing what *H. heidelbergensis* might have looked like [right]. (b) This hand axe, nicknamed "Excalibur," was discovered with a pit of 350,000-year-old *H. heidelbergensis* bones in Spain.

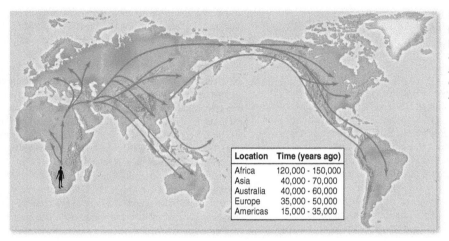

Figure 15.27 **Out of Africa.** Researchers used mitochondrial DNA sequences to deduce approximately when *Homo sapiens* originally settled each continent after migrating out of Africa.

Location	Time (years ago)
Africa	120,000 - 150,000
Asia	40,000 - 70,000
Australia	40,000 - 60,000
Europe	35,000 - 50,000
Americas	15,000 - 35,000

E. Migration and Culture Have Changed *Homo sapiens*

DNA sampled from people around the world has revealed a compelling portrait of human migration out of Africa (figure 15.27). Asia, Australia, and Europe all were colonized at least 40,000 years ago. (The Investigating Life essay in section 15.5 explores some of the genetic evidence for this "out of Africa" hypothesis.) Humans reached the Americas somewhat later, about 15,000 years ago.

As humans spread throughout the world, new habitats selected for different adaptations. Near the equator, for example, sunlight is much more intense than at higher latitudes. One component of sunlight is ultraviolet (UV) radiation, which is both harmful and beneficial. On the one hand, UV radiation damages DNA and causes skin cancer. On the other hand, some UV wavelengths help the skin produce vitamin D, which is essential to bone development and overall health.

These two counteracting selective pressures help explain why skin pigmentation is strongly correlated with the amount of ultraviolet radiation striking the Earth (see section 25.6). One pigment that contributes to skin color, melanin, blocks UV radiation. Intense UV radiation selects for alleles that confer abundant melanin. People whose ancestry is near the equator, such as in Africa and Australia, therefore tend to have very dark brown skin. In northern Europe and other areas with weak sunlight, however, heavily pigmented skin would block so much UV light that indigenous people would suffer from vitamin D deficiency. Northern latitudes are therefore correlated with a high frequency of alleles conferring pale, pinkish skin.

No matter where people roamed, one byproduct of the large human brain was **culture:** the knowledge, beliefs, and behaviors that we transmit from generation to generation. Among the earliest signs of culture are cave art from about 14,000 years ago, which indicates that our ancestors had developed fine hand coordination and could use symbols.

By 10,000 years ago, depending on which native plants and animals were available for early farmers to domesticate, agriculture began to replace a hunter–gatherer lifestyle in many places. Agriculture meant increased food production, which profoundly changed societies. Freed from the necessity of producing their own food, specialized groups of political leaders, soldiers, weapon-makers, religious leaders, scientists, engineers, artists, writers, and many other types of workers arose. These new occupations meant improved transportation and communication, better technologies, and the ability to explore the world for new lands and new resources.

Undoubtedly, humans are a special species. We can modify the environment much more than, for example, a slime mold or an earthworm can. We can also alter natural selection, in our own species and in others. Finally, culture allows each generation to build on information accumulated in the past. The knowledge, beliefs, and behaviors that shape each culture are constantly modified within a person's lifetime, in stark contrast to the millions of years required for biological evolution. Our species is therefore extremely responsive to short-term changes.

Despite our unique set of features, however, we are a species, descended from ancestors with which we share many characteristics. It is intriguing to think about where the human species is headed, which species will vanish, and how life will continue to diversify in the next 500 million years.

15.4 MASTERING CONCEPTS

1. Name and describe the three groups of contemporary primates. To which group do humans belong?
2. What can skeletal anatomy and DNA sequences in existing primates tell us about the study of human evolution?
3. What are the four groups of hominins in the human family tree, and which still exist today?
4. Which conditions may have contributed to the evolution of humans?

INVESTIGATING LIFE

15.5 Big Continents, Small Differences

On college applications or government forms you've probably been asked to indicate your race. You might have filled in a bubble next to "Asian," "African," "White," "Hispanic," or one of many other choices (figure 15.28). But do these race classifications mean anything from a biological perspective?

To answer this question, we must review the history of the human species. As described in section 15.4, many lines of evidence support the hypothesis that *Homo sapiens* originated in Africa. Then, by 40,000 years ago, a small subset of the African population began migrating to the European and Asian continents (see figure 15.27). As these groups became reproductively isolated, genotypes and phenotypes diverged.

At least two predictions follow from the "out of Africa" model of human evolution. One is that overall genetic diversity within Africa should be greater than the genetic diversity within any other continent. After all, evolution has acted on the populations within Africa for much longer than it has acted on the populations that migrated from Africa. A second prediction is related to the first: Since only a subset of Africans migrated, populations outside of Africa should be more genetically related to each other than to the African population.

A group of 10 scientists from across the world, led by the University of Chicago's Wen-Hsiung Li, tested these and other predictions. They compared DNA segments from 10 Africans, 10 Europeans, and 10 Asians to determine nucleotide diversity within and between continents. The individuals in each group were selected from different regions of the continent. For example, the European group consisted of people from 10 countries, including Finland, Spain, and Ukraine.

The researchers also used strict criteria when determining which DNA segments to compare: They randomly selected 50 nucleotide sequences that *do not* encode proteins. Why did the scientists not compare gene sequences? Differences in genes among populations reflect adaptations to unique environments. In contrast, differences in the nucleotide sequences of noncoding DNA are mostly due to random mutations that are not subject to

natural selection. Since mutations accumulate at a relatively constant rate for a given sequence of DNA, noncoding DNA sequences are more reliable indicators of evolutionary history than are genes.

After extracting DNA from each subject, the team isolated the target sequences, amplified them using the polymerase chain reaction, and put them in a DNA sequencer. Each sequence was then compared to the corresponding sequence in other subjects. For example, a sequence of nucleotides on chromosome 1 of the Finnish subject was compared with the corresponding chromosome 1 sequence of all European, Asian, and African subjects. The scientists used this process to make all possible person-to-person comparisons for each of the 50 sequences they selected. ⓘ *polymerase chain reaction*, p. 223; *DNA sequencing*, p. 222

Each comparison produced a value representing the percent difference between the two DNA sequences. If corresponding sequences were similar between two individuals, then the percent difference value would be low. Sequences that were less similar had higher percent difference values.

To estimate within-continent diversity, Li and his team averaged all of the difference values among the people from each continent (figure 15.29). The difference in DNA sequences among African subjects was nearly twice as high as among either Asian or European subjects. This finding supports the first prediction of the "out of Africa" model: The genetic diversity within Africa is greater than the genetic diversity outside of Africa.

The researchers then averaged the percent difference values for DNA sequence comparisons between continents (figure 15.30). Asians and Europeans are more closely related to one another than either group is to Africans, supporting the second prediction for the African origin of humans.

This study adds to the evidence that all modern humans evolved from a population in Africa. It also argues against the less-supported hypothesis that *Homo sapiens* evolved independently in several isolated populations (the "multiregional hypothesis"). If the multiregional hypothesis were true, then people from each region should have unique variants of DNA sequences. Instead, DNA variations outside of Africa are often a subset of the variation within Africa.

What does all of this have to do with race? The data certainly support the hypothesis that humans migrated out of Africa many generations ago. But the genetic differences between the races are extremely small. True, each continent has selected for some

Figure 15.28 Human Races. People native to Africa, northern Europe, and Asia belong to different races. They are genetically much more similar than their external appearances might suggest.

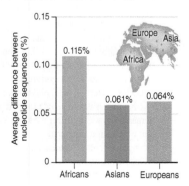

Figure 15.29
Within-Continent Genetic Diversity. Genetic variation among people sampled from Africa was greater than variation among people from Asia or Europe.

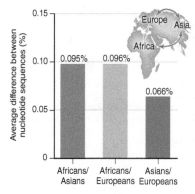

Figure 15.30 Between-Continent Genetic Diversity. Comparisons of people from one continent to another revealed that people from Asia and Europe were more similar to one another than either group was to people from Africa.

unique physical traits, including obvious differences in skin pigmentation (see section 25.6). Overall, however, race is less a biological concept than it is a social one; most of our differences really are only skin deep.

Yu, Ning and nine coauthors, including Wen-Hsiung Li. February 19, 2002. Larger genetic differences within Africans than between Africans and Eurasians. *Genetics*, vol. 161, pages 269–274.

15.5 MASTERING CONCEPTS

1. What criteria did the researchers use when choosing the subjects and the DNA sequences for their study?

2. Explain how the data in figures 15.29 and 15.30 support the "out of Africa" model of human evolution.

CHAPTER SUMMARY

15.1 Life's Origin Remains Mysterious

- The solar system formed about 4.6 BYA, and life first left evidence on Earth by about 3.7 BYA. The **geologic timescale** describes these and many other events in life's history.

Animation Overview of Life's History

A. The First Organic Molecules May Have Formed in a Chemical "Soup"

- **Prebiotic simulations** combine simple inorganic chemicals to form life's organic building blocks, including amino acids and nucleotides.
- These monomers may have linked together to form polymers on hot clay or mineral surfaces.

B. Some Investigators Suggest an "RNA World"

- The **RNA world** theory proposes that RNA preceded formation of the first cells. Proteins provided enzymes and structural features. Reverse transcriptase could have copied RNA's information into DNA.

C. Membranes Enclosed the Molecules

- Phospholipid sheets that formed bubbles around proteins and nucleic acids may have formed cell precursors, or **progenotes.**

D. Early Life Changed Earth Forever

- Early organisms permanently changed the physical and chemical conditions in which life continued to evolve.

15.2 Complex Cells and Multicellularity Arose over a Billion Years Ago

- The internal membranes of eukaryotic cells may have formed when the outer membrane folded in on itself repeatedly.

A. Endosymbiosis Explains the Origin of Mitochondria and Chloroplasts

- The **endosymbiont theory** proposes that chloroplasts and mitochondria originated as free-living bacteria that were engulfed by larger cells

B. Multicellularity May Also Have Its Origin in Cooperation

- The evolution of multicellularity, which occurred about 1.2 BYA, is poorly understood.
- Figure 15.31 summarizes the steps leading from the origin of life to today's diversity or prokaryotic and eukaryotic organisms.

15.3 Life's Diversity Exploded in the Past 500 Million Years

A. The Strange Ediacarans Flourished Late in the Precambrian

- The Ediacarans were soft, flat organisms that were completely unlike modern species. They lived during the late Precambrian and early Cambrian periods.

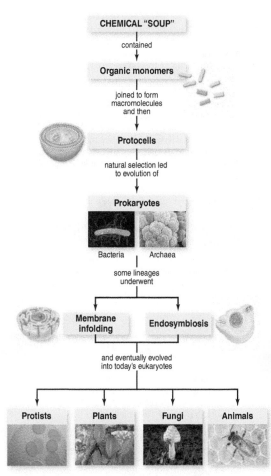

Figure 15.31 Origin and Diversification of Life: A Summary.

B. Paleozoic Plants and Animals Emerged onto Land

- The Cambrian explosion introduced many species, notably those with hard parts. Amphibian-like animals ventured onto land about 360 MYA, followed by reptiles, birds, and mammals. Invertebrates, ferns, and forests flourished.

C. Reptiles and Flowering Plants Thrived During the Mesozoic Era

- Dinosaurs prevailed throughout the Mesozoic era, when forests were largely cycads, ginkgos, and conifers. In the middle of the era, flowering plants became prevalent. When the nonavian dinosaurs died out 65 MYA, resources opened up for mammals.

D. Mammals Diversified During the Cenozoic Era

- Mammals diversified during the Tertiary period. Humans arose during the Pleistocene epoch of the Quaternary period. Repeated ice ages and the extinction of many large mammals also occurred during the Pleistocene.

15.4 Fossils and DNA Tell the Human Evolution Story

A. Humans Are Primates

- **Primates** have grasping hands, opposable thumbs, binocular vision, large brains, and flat nails. The three groups of primates are **prosimians,** monkeys, and **hominoids** (apes).
- **Hominids** are the "great apes," whereas **hominines** are gorillas, chimpanzees, and humans. **Hominins** are extinct and modern humans.
- Fossil bones and teeth reveal how extinct species moved and what they ate.

B. Molecular Evidence Documents Primate Relationships

- Protein and DNA analysis has altered how scientists draw the human family tree.

C. Hominin Evolution Is Partially Recorded in Fossils

- Three groups of hominins are australopiths, *Paranthropus,* and *Homo.*

D. Environmental Changes Have Spurred Hominin Evolution

- Millions of years ago, new mountain ranges arose, causing climate shifts. Savannas replaced tropical forests, and apes—the ancestors of humans—moved from the trees to the savanna.

E. Migration and Culture Have Changed *Homo sapiens*

- After migrating out of Africa, humans encountered new habitats that selected for new allele combinations.
- Humans owe our success to language and **culture.**

15.5 Investigating Life: Big Continents, Small Differences

- DNA sequences from diverse people reveal that Africans have the most genetic diversity and that Asians and Europeans are more similar to each other than they are to Africans. Both observations support the "out of Africa" model of human migration.

MULTIPLE CHOICE QUESTIONS

1. Which of the following events occurred earliest in Earth's history?
   a. Membrane-enclosed structures developed.
   b. O_2 gas accumulated in the atmosphere.
   c. Organic molecules formed.
   d. CO_2 gas appeared in the atmosphere.

2. Which of the following must be true for natural selection to occur in an "RNA world"?
   a. RNA molecules must turn into DNA molecules.
   b. RNA molecules must undergo mutations.
   c. RNA molecules must replicate.
   d Both b and c are correct.

3. Photosynthetic cells affected early Earth by
   a. adding O_2 to the atmosphere.
   b. increasing the amount of hydrogen sulfide in the early oceans.
   c. depleting the ozone layer.
   d. changing the pH of the early oceans.

4. Why is multicellularity adaptive?
   a. Multicellular organisms reproduce more quickly than unicellular organisms.
   b. Cells work together, each specializing in specific functions.
   c. Multicellular organisms are motile, whereas unicellular organisms are not.
   d. All of the above are correct.

5. Which of the following provides the strongest support for the idea that mitochondria were once independent organisms?
   a. Their size is similar to that of prokaryotes.
   b. They are surrounded by a membrane.
   c. They are shaped like a prokaryote.
   d. They have their own DNA and ribosomes.

6. What events preceded the "Cambrian explosion"?
   a. O_2 gas accumulated in Earth's atmosphere.
   b. Multicellularity arose.
   c. Cells with membrane-bounded organelles arose.
   d. All of the above are correct.

7. Why was the Mesozoic era extinction significant to the history of mammals?
   a. As photosynthesis slowed, meat-eating mammals prevailed.
   b. Fewer plankton species meant more open ocean ecosystems for large, aquatic mammals.
   c. Dinosaur extinctions opened up new habitats to mammals.
   d. Only the smartest primates knew how to survive the extinction.

8. Primates share all of the following characteristics except
   a. opposable thumbs.   c. bipedalism.
   b. excellent depth perception. d. flat fingernails.

9. Humans evolved from
   a. monkeys.
   b. chimpanzees.
   c. gorillas.
   d. an ancestor shared with chimpanzees.

10. DNA evidence suggests that modern humans
    a. share a single origin.
    b. arose independently in several isolated populations.
    c. have not evolved in the last 150,000 years.
    d. are evolving from chimpanzees today.

Answers to these questions are in appendix A.

WRITE IT OUT

1. Explain how the origin of self-replicating molecules was critical to life's origin.

2. List three ways that studying the history of life helps us understand life's current diversity, and predict how diversity might change in the future.

3. Review the structures of nucleic acids and proteins in chapter 2. What chemical elements had to have been in primordial "soup" to generate these organic molecules?

4. Describe the role of lipids in the origin of life.

5. The amoeba *Pelomyxa palustris* is a single-celled eukaryote with no mitochondria, but it contains symbiotic bacteria that can live in the presence of O_2. How does this observation support the endosymbiont theory?

6. The antibiotic streptomycin kills bacterial cells but not eukaryotic cells; diphtheria toxin kills eukaryotic cells but not bacteria. Which of these two substances do you predict would kill mitochondria and chloroplasts? Explain your answer.

7. List the major events of the Precambrian supereon and of the Paleozoic, Mesozoic, and Cenozoic eras.

8. Distinguish between the terms *primate, hominid, hominin,* and *Homo.*

9. Explain how opposable thumbs, large brains, and binocular vision are adaptive to primates.

10. What can scientists learn by comparing the fossilized skeletons of extinct primates with the bones of modern species?

11. How have DNA analyses changed how scientists study the evolutionary history of humans?

12. Use the Internet to learn about *National Geographic*'s Genographic Project. What are the main objectives and components of the project, and how are researchers using the information they gather to learn more about human evolution?

13. In what ways has culture been an important factor in human evolution?

14. At one time, several species of *Homo* existed at the same time. Propose at least two hypotheses that might explain why only *Homo sapiens* remains.

15. Compare culture to evolution by means of natural selection. How are they similar? How are they different? Can you think of examples of knowledge, beliefs, and behaviors that were appropriate in one set of conditions but that humans selected against as conditions changed?

16. The video game "Spore" invites players to design creatures and guide them through "five stages of evolution." Search the Internet for information about "Spore," then describe how evolution in this game is similar to, and different from, the evolution of life on Earth.

PULL IT TOGETHER

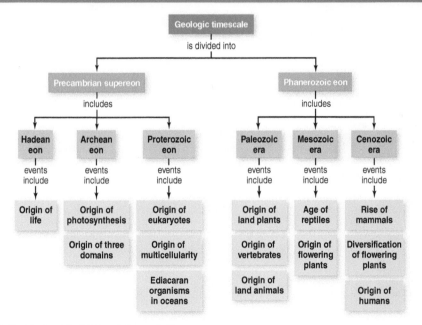

Figure 15.32 Pull It Together: The Origin and History of Life.

Refer to figure 15.32 and the chapter content to answer the following questions.

1. Arrange the 14 major events at the bottom of the concept map in chronological order, then indicate when the major extinction events occurred. What was the implication of each extinction?

2. How has the emergence of new species changed Earth's history?

3. Create an additional concept map that depicts the evolution of humans.

The Diversity of Life

CHAPTER

16 Viruses

Flu Protection. Protective masks help prevent the spread of influenza among passengers on this tram in western Ukraine.

Enhance your study |BIOLOGY
of this chapter with practice quizzes,
animations and videos, answer keys,
and downloadable study tools.
www.mhhe.com/hoefnagels

UNIT 4

Flu from the Farmyard

MOST VIRUSES INFECT ONLY A FEW, CLOSELY RELATED SPECIES. But some—including those that cause influenza—jump among more distant relatives such as birds, pigs, and humans.

Influenza, known as "flu" for short, probably began thousands of years ago in China, where the influenza virus moved from wild to domesticated ducks. In the seventeenth century, the Chinese brought domesticated ducks to live among rice paddies, where they were close to people, pigs (swine), and chickens.

Pigs contribute to influenza epidemics because cells that line a pig's throat carry receptors that bind to both the avian (bird) and human versions of flu viruses. Avian and human flu viruses infecting pigs commonly exchange segments of their genomes, generating new strains. These new viral varieties sometimes cause serious epidemics because most humans lack immunity against viruses that normally infect birds or pigs.

The "Spanish flu" pandemic of 1918 killed more people in the United States than World Wars I and II, the Korean War, and the Vietnam War combined. Unlike modern flu outbreaks, which typically kill children and the elderly, most victims of the 1918 flu were 20 to 40 years old. No one knows for sure whether this flu virus originated in chickens, swine, or other animals.

Video Killer Flu Recreated

Flu pandemics also occurred in 1957 and 1968. In 1997, epidemiologists feared yet another pandemic when a new flu variant appeared to jump from birds directly to humans. Panic set in. To avert an epidemic, the government killed every chicken in Hong Kong. Fortunately, the outbreak never went beyond 18 people, six of whom died.

Sporadic outbreaks of avian flu in Asia have occurred annually since 2003, infecting dozens of people each time. So far, however, the avian influenza virus has not spread directly from person to person. Outbreaks in humans are therefore limited. On the other hand, the flu virus that raced around the world in 2009—a mongrel containing genes of swine, avian, and human viruses—prompted health officials to declare an influenza pandemic. Fortunately, the fatality rate was less than 1%.

Flu viruses evolve rapidly. Epidemiologists therefore watch carefully for new variants that are both deadly and easily transmitted among humans. A new virus with both qualities might trigger an outbreak rivaling the disastrous 1918 flu pandemic.

Viruses infect every type of organism, not just humans, birds, and pigs. This chapter explains what viruses are, how they replicate and cause disease, and why they have proven so hard to defeat.

LEARNING OUTLINE

 16.1 Viruses Are Infectious Particles of Genetic Information and Protein
  A. Viruses Are Smaller and Simpler Than Cells
  B. A Virus's Host Range Consists of the Organisms It Infects
  C. Are Viruses Alive?

 16.2 Viral Replication Occurs in Five Stages

 16.3 Cell Death May Be Immediate or Delayed
  A. Some Viruses Kill Cells Immediately
  B. Viral DNA Can "Hide" in a Cell

 16.4 Effects of a Viral Infection May Be Mild or Severe
  A. Symptoms Result from Cell Death and the Immune Response
  B. Some Animal Viruses Linger for Years
  C. Drugs and Vaccines Help Fight Viral Infections

 16.5 Viruses Cause Diseases in Plants

 16.6 Viroids and Prions Are Other Noncellular Infectious Agents
  A. A Viroid Is an Infectious RNA Molecule
  B. A Prion Is an Infectious Protein

 16.7 Investigating Life: Scientific Detectives Follow HIV's Trail

 LEARN HOW TO LEARN
Take the Best Possible Notes

Some students take notes only on what they consider "important" during a lecture. Others write down words but not diagrams, or they write what's on the board but not what the instructor is saying. All of these strategies risk losing vital information and connections between ideas that could help in later learning. Instead, write down as much as you can during lecture, including sketches of the diagrams and notes on what the instructor is telling you about the main ideas. It will be much easier to study later if you have a complete picture of what happened in every class.

16.1 Viruses Are Infectious Particles of Genetic Information and Protein

Smallpox, influenza, the common cold, rabies, polio, chicken-pox, warts, AIDS—this diverse list includes illnesses that range from merely inconvenient to deadly. All have one thing in com-mon: they are infectious diseases caused by viruses.

Many people mistakenly lump viruses and bacteria together as "germs." Viruses, however, are not bacteria. Whereas a bacte-rium is a type of cell, a **virus** is simply genetic information enclosed in a protein coat. The 2000 or so known species of viruses therefore straddle the boundary between the chemical and the biological.

A. Viruses Are Smaller and Simpler Than Cells

A typical virus is much smaller than a cell (figure 16.1). At about 10 μm (microns) in diameter, an average human cell is perhaps one-tenth the diameter of a human hair. A bacterium is about one-tenth again as small, at about 1 μm (1000 nm) long. The average virus, with a diameter of about 80 nm, is more than 12 times smaller than a bacterium. However, not all viruses are quite so tiny: The largest known example, an ocean virus called pandora-virus, has a diameter of about 1 μm.

Viruses are simple structures that lack many of the character-istics of cells. A virus does not have a nucleus, organelles, ribo-somes, a cell membrane, or even cytoplasm. Only a few types of viruses contain enzymes. All viruses, however, have the follow-ing two features in common:

- **Genetic information.** All viruses contain genetic material (either DNA or RNA) that carries the "recipes" for their proteins (see chapter 7). The major criterion for classifying viruses is whether the genetic material is DNA or RNA. Either type of nucleic acid may be single- or double-stranded. ⓘ *nucleic acids,* p. 34

- **Protein coat.** The **capsid,** or protein coat, surrounds the genetic material. The capsid's shape determines a virus's overall form, which is another characteristic used in classification (figure 16.2). Many viruses are spherical or icosahedral (a 20-faced shape built of triangular sections). Others are rod-shaped, oval, or filamentous.

Some viruses have other features besides genetic material and a protein coat. For example, some have a lipid-rich **envelope,** an outer layer derived from the host cell's membrane. The pres-ence or absence of an envelope is another criterion for virus clas-sification. One example of an enveloped virus is the human immunodeficiency virus (HIV), which causes acquired immuno-deficiency syndrome (AIDS). The influenza virus also has an envelope.

Note that the viral envelope is derived from a cell membrane, but it does not share the membrane's function. That is, the enve-lope does not control what enters and leaves the virus. Instead, proteins embedded in the envelope help the virus invade a new host cell. ⓘ *cell membrane,* p. 54

Despite having relatively few components, a virus's over-all structure can be quite intricate and complex. For example, **bacteriophages** (sometimes simply called "phages") are viruses that infect bacteria. Some phages have parts that resem-ble tails, legs, and spikes; they look like the spacecrafts once used to land on the moon (see figure 16.2b).

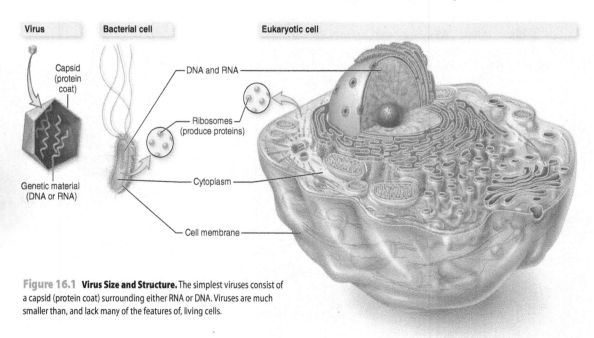

Figure 16.1 Virus Size and Structure. The simplest viruses consist of a capsid (protein coat) surrounding either RNA or DNA. Viruses are much smaller than, and lack many of the features of, living cells.

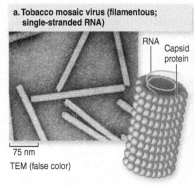

a. Tobacco mosaic virus (filamentous; single-stranded RNA)

RNA
Capsid protein

75 nm
TEM (false color)

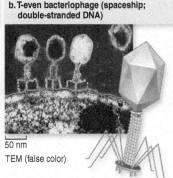

b. T-even bacteriophage (spaceship; double-stranded DNA)

50 nm
TEM (false color)

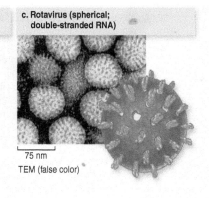

c. Rotavirus (spherical; double-stranded RNA)

75 nm
TEM (false color)

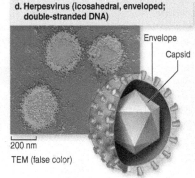

d. Herpesvirus (icosahedral, enveloped; double-stranded DNA)

Envelope
Capsid

200 nm
TEM (false color)

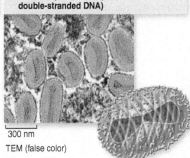

e. Poxvirus (oval, enveloped; double-stranded DNA)

300 nm
TEM (false color)

Figure 16.2 Virus Variety. Each type of virus has a characteristic structure, visible only with an electron microscope. (a) The capsid of the tobacco mosaic virus (TMV) is long and filamentous. (b) T-even viruses look like tiny spaceships. (c) Rotavirus causes severe diarrhea in young children. (d) Herpesviruses cause cold sores and rashes. (e) A poxvirus causes smallpox.

B. A Virus's Host Range Consists of the Organisms It Infects

Virtually all species of animals, fungi, plants, protists, and bacteria get viral infections. The **host range** of a virus is the kinds of organisms or cells that it can infect. A virus can enter only a cell that has a specific target attachment molecule, or receptor, on its surface. The reason a bacteriophage cannot attack human cells is that our cell surfaces lack the correct target molecules.

Some target molecules occur on a very small subset of cells in an organism, whereas others are more widespread. HIV, for example, infects only certain types of human immune system cells. The rabies virus, on the other hand, can infect the muscle and nerve cells of any mammal, including humans, skunks, foxes, raccoons, bats, and dogs. All of these animals have the target molecule that the rabies virus uses to recognize a potential host.

The **reservoir** of a virus is the site where it exists in nature. For many viruses that infect humans, the reservoir is a host animal that may or may not show symptoms of infection. A reservoir animal acts as a continual source of the virus to other host species. Examples of reservoirs for viruses that cause diseases in humans include wild birds (avian influenza and West Nile encephalitis), rodents (hantavirus pulmonary syndrome), mosquitoes (yellow fever), and raccoons (rabies).

Video
West Nile Virus

C. Are Viruses Alive?

Most biologists do not consider a virus to be alive because it does not metabolize, respond to stimuli, or reproduce on its own. Instead, a virus must enter a living host cell to manufacture more of itself. ⓘ *what is life?* p. 4

Nevertheless, viruses do have some features in common with life, including genetic material. Both DNA and RNA can mutate, which means that viruses evolve just as life does. Each time a virus replicates inside a host cell, random mutations occur. The genetic variability among the new viruses is subject to natural selection. That is, some variants are better than others at infecting host cells, replicating, and passing on their genes to a new crop of viruses.

Although viruses evolve, no one knows how they originated; their extreme diversity suggests that they do not share a single common ancestor. Viruses are therefore not included in the taxonomic hierarchy. Instead, scientists group viruses based on the type of nucleic acid, the structure of the virus, how it replicates, and the type of disease it causes. ⓘ *taxonomic hierarchy,* p. 294

16.1 MASTERING CONCEPTS

1. What features do all viruses share?
2. What determines a virus's host range?
3. How do viruses evolve?

16.2 Viral Replication Occurs in Five Stages

Tutorial
Viral
Replication

The production of new viruses is very different from cell division. When a cell divides, it doubles all of its components and splits in two. Virus production, on the other hand, more closely resembles the assembly of cars in a factory.

A cell infected with one virus may produce hundreds of new viral particles. Whatever the host species or cell type, the same basic processes occur during a viral infection (figure 16.3):

1. **Attachment:** A virus attaches to a host cell by adhering to a receptor molecule on the cell's surface. Generally, the virus can attach only to a cell within which it can reproduce. HIV cannot infect skin cells, for example, because its receptors occur only on certain white blood cells.

2. **Penetration:** The viral genetic material can enter the cell in several ways. Animal cells engulf virus particles and bring them into the cytoplasm via endocytosis. Viruses that infect plants often enter their host cells by hitching a ride on the mouthparts of herbivorous insects. Many bacteriophages inject their genetic material through a hole in the cell wall, somewhat like a syringe. ⓘ *endocytosis,* p. 84

3. **Synthesis:** The host cell produces multiple copies of the viral genome; mutations during this stage are the raw

material for viral evolution. In addition, the information encoded in viral DNA is used to produce the virus's proteins. The host cell provides all of the resources required for the production of new viruses: ATP, tRNA, ribosomes, nucleotides, amino acids, and enzymes.

4. **Assembly:** The subunits of the capsid join, and then genetic information is packed into each protein coat.

5. **Release:** Once the virus particles are assembled, they are ready to leave the cell. Some bacteriophages induce production of an enzyme that breaks down the host's cell wall, killing the cell as it releases the viruses. HIV and herpesviruses, on the other hand, bud from the host cell by exocytosis. The cell may die as enveloped viruses carry off segments of the cell membrane. ⓘ *exocytosis,* p. 84

The amount of time between initial infection and cell death varies. Bacteriophages need as little as half an hour to infect a cell and replicate. At the other extreme, for some animal viruses, years may elapse between initial attachment and the final burst of viral particles.

16.2   MASTERING CONCEPTS

1. Describe the five steps in viral replication.
2. What is the source of energy and raw materials for the synthesis of viruses in a host cell?

Figure 16.3   Viral Replication.
These five basic steps of viral replication apply to any virus, whether the host cell is prokaryotic or eukaryotic.

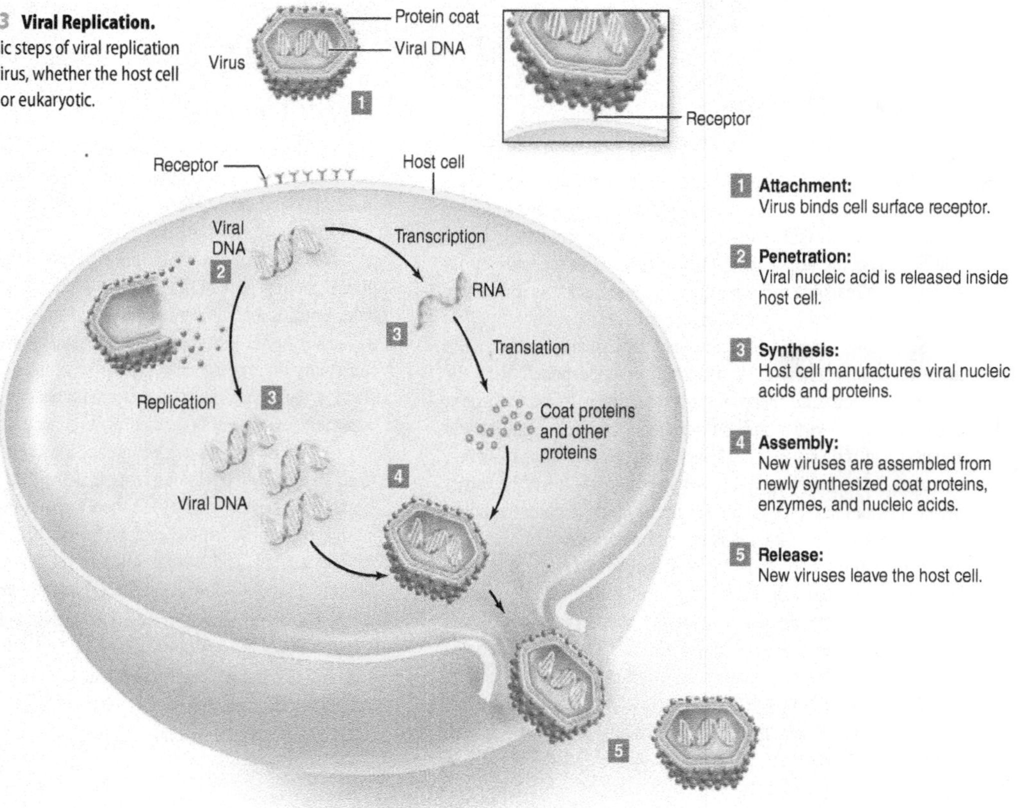

Protein coat
Viral DNA
Virus
Receptor

Receptor
Host cell
Viral DNA
Transcription
RNA
Translation
Replication
Coat proteins and other proteins
Viral DNA

1 Attachment:
Virus binds cell surface receptor.

2 Penetration:
Viral nucleic acid is released inside host cell.

3 Synthesis:
Host cell manufactures viral nucleic acids and proteins.

4 Assembly:
New viruses are assembled from newly synthesized coat proteins, enzymes, and nucleic acids.

5 Release:
New viruses leave the host cell.

16.3 Cell Death May Be Immediate or Delayed

Animation
Phage
Replication

Following attachment to the host cell and penetration of the viral genetic material, viruses may or may not immediately cause cell death. Bacteriophages, the viruses that infect bacteria, can do either. The two viral replication strategies in bacteriophages are called lytic and lysogenic infections (figure 16.4).

A. Some Viruses Kill Cells Immediately

In a **lytic infection,** a virus enters a bacterium, immediately replicates, and causes the host cell to burst (lyse) as it releases a flood of new viruses. The newly released viruses infect other bacteria, repeating the process until all of the cells are dead.

Video
Cell Lysis

Some researchers have investigated the possibility of using lytic bacteriophages to treat bacterial infections in people. This strategy, called "phage therapy," would have two main advantages over antibiotics (drugs that kill bacteria).

First, unlike drugs, viruses evolve along with their bacterial hosts, and they keep killing until all host cells are dead. Bacterial populations are therefore unlikely to acquire resistance to the phages. Second, each bacteriophage targets only one or a few types of bacteria, so the treatment is precisely tailored to the infection. Paradoxically, phage therapy's main weakness is related to this strength. Medical personnel must first identify the exact type of bacteria causing infection before beginning phage therapy. This delay could be deadly.

B. Viral DNA Can "Hide" in a Cell

In a **lysogenic infection,** the genetic material of a virus is replicated along with the bacterial chromosome, but the cell is not immediately destroyed. At some point, however, the virus reverts to a lytic cycle, releasing new viruses and killing the cell.

Many lysogenic viruses use enzymes to cut the host cell DNA and join their own DNA with the host's. A **prophage** is the DNA of a lysogenic bacteriophage that is inserted into the host chromosome. Other lysogenic viruses maintain their DNA apart from the chromosome. Either way, however, when the cell divides, the viral genes replicate, too. The virus gets a "free ride," infecting new cells without actually triggering viral production.

During a lysogenic stage, the viral DNA does not damage the host cell. Only a few viral proteins are produced, most functioning as a "switch" that determines whether the virus should become lytic. At some signal, such as stress from DNA damage or cell starvation, these viral proteins trigger a lytic infection cycle that kills the cell and releases new viruses that infect other cells. The next generation of viruses may enter a lytic or lysogenic replication cycle, depending on the condition of the host cells.

Much of what biologists know about viral replication comes from research on bacteriophages. The Focus on Model Organisms box on page 336 describes some of what scientists have learned from studies of one such bacteriophage, called lambda.

16.3 MASTERING CONCEPTS

1. What is a lytic viral infection?
2. How is a lysogenic viral infection similar to and different from a lytic cycle?

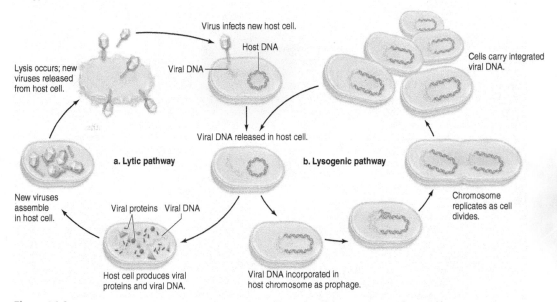

Figure 16.4 Lysis and Lysogeny. (a) In the lytic pathway, the host cell bursts (lyses) when new virus particles assemble and leave the cell. (b) In lysogeny, viral DNA replicates along with the cell, but new viruses are not immediately produced. An environmental change, such as stress in the host cell, may trigger a lysogenic virus to switch to the lytic pathway.

Tutorial Lytic and Lysogenic Cycles

16.4 Effects of a Viral Infection May Be Mild or Severe

A person can acquire a viral infection by inhaling the respiratory droplets of an ill person or by ingesting food or water contaminated with viruses. Some viruses, such as HIV and hepatitis B, enter a person's bloodstream via a blood transfusion, sexual contact, or the use of contaminated needles. The infected person often becomes ill (although some infections are symptomless).

A. Symptoms Result from Cell Death and the Immune Response

Once a viral infection is established, the death of infected cells produces a wide range of symptoms that reflect the types of host cells destroyed. If enough cells die, the disease may be severe.

To illustrate how symptoms develop, consider the flu. Influenza viruses infect cells lining the human airway. As cells produce and release new viruses, the infection spreads rapidly in the lungs, trachea, throat, and nose. The dead and damaged cells in the airway cause the respiratory symptoms of influenza, including cough and sore throat.

What about the other symptoms, such as fever and body aches? These classic signs of influenza do not directly involve the respiratory system, where the infected cells are located. Instead, these whole-body symptoms result from the immune system's response to the viral infection. Cells of the immune system

release signaling molecules called cytokines, which, in turn, induce fever; a high body temperature speeds other immune responses. Cytokines also trigger inflammation, which causes body ache and fatigue. These (and other) immune reactions usually defeat the influenza virus, but in the meantime, they can also make the host rather miserable! Chapter 33 describes the human immune system in more detail.

B. Some Animal Viruses Linger for Years

Like a lysogenic bacteriophage, a virus infecting an animal cell may remain dormant as a cell divides. In a **latent** infection, viral genetic information is inside the cell but is not expressed. As long as the infection remains latent, new viruses are not produced.

Many people harbor latent infections of the herpes simplex virus type I, which causes cold sores on the lips. After initial infection, the viral DNA remains in host cells indefinitely. When a cell becomes stressed or damaged, new viruses are assembled and leave the cell to infect other cells. Cold sores, which reflect the localized death of these cells, periodically recur at the site of the original infection.

Some latent viruses persist by signaling their host cells to divide continuously, so they may cause cancer. A latent infection by some strains of human papillomavirus can lead to cervical cancer (see the Burning Question on page 339). Epstein–Barr virus is another example. More than 80% of the human population carries this virus, which infects B cells of

FOCUS on Model Organisms

Bacteriophage Lambda

Although viruses are not organisms, they have nevertheless contributed enormously to the scientific understanding of life. This box focuses on a virus that has never made you sick because it does not infect human cells. Rather, it kills *Escherichia coli* bacteria that live in the intestines of humans and other mammals. Bacteriophage lambda (Greek letter λ) injects its genetic material into its host cell, which subsequently turns into a virus-making factory. In so doing, phage lambda has revealed many processes fundamental to all life.

Phage lambda's double-stranded DNA genome of 50,000 base pairs contains all the information it takes to make more phages, and its 60 or so genes must turn on and off in proper sequence for the new viruses to form properly. Biologists learn the functions of viral proteins by studying viral mutants—phages with missing proteins. These studies have revealed that phage lambda's proteins fall into three general groups:

- **Capsid proteins:** Phage lambda's protein coat consists of a nearly spherical head (enclosing the viral DNA) and a tube-shaped tail with proteins that bind to *E. coli*'s surface (figure 16.A). DNA enters the host cell through the tail.
- **Regulatory proteins:** Some of phage lambda's proteins bind to viral DNA and either promote or prevent transcription of particular genes. Other regulatory proteins stop the virus from entering the lysogenic pathway or prevent the replication of other viruses that may have also infected the cell.

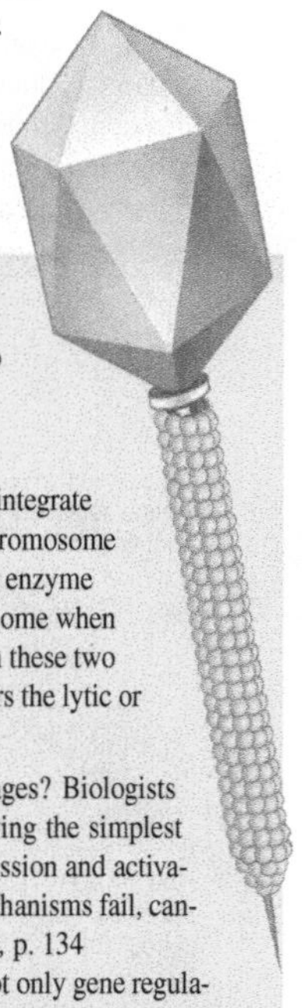

Figure 16.A Bacteriophage Lambda. This virus, deadly to the bacterium *E. coli*, is harmless to humans.

- **Enzymes:** A protein called integrase helps integrate phage lambda's DNA into the host cell's chromosome when it enters the lysogenic phase. Another enzyme cuts the viral DNA back out of the chromosome when the lytic phase begins. The balance between these two enzymes determines whether the virus enters the lytic or lysogenic phase of the life cycle.

Why study gene regulation in bacteriophages? Biologists can learn a lot about complex systems by studying the simplest models, since similar mechanisms of gene repression and activation also work in our own cells. When those mechanisms fail, cancer may result. ⓘ *regulation of gene expression, p. 134*

Phage lambda has taught scientists about not only gene regulation but also recombination and protein folding, both of which are fundamental life processes. In addition, this virus has become something of a laboratory workhorse. Phage lambda is unusual because it can complete its life cycle even if a large amount of foreign DNA is inserted into its genome. This discovery has made phage lambda an extremely important tool for ferrying recombinant DNA into *E. coli*. ⓘ *protein folding, p. 32; transgenic organisms, p. 219*

the immune system. A person who is initially exposed to the virus may develop mononucleosis (often called "mono"). The virus later maintains a latent infection in B cells. In a few people, especially those with weakened immune systems, the virus eventually causes a form of cancer called Burkitt lymphoma. ⓘ *cancer,* p. 156

HIV is another virus that can remain latent inside a human cell (figure 16.5). HIV belongs to a family of viruses called retroviruses, all of which have an RNA genome. The virus attaches to and penetrates a helper T cell, an essential type of white blood cell that helps coordinate the immune system. The virus's reverse transcriptase enzyme transcribes the viral RNA to DNA. The DNA then inserts itself into the host cell's DNA. Cells with active infections express the viral genes, producing and releasing many new HIV particles. These viruses go on to infect other T cells, so the number of helper T cells gradually declines. Eventually, the loss of T cells leaves the body defenseless against infections or cancer. AIDS is the result. ⓘ *T cells,* p. 683

In some of the body's T cells, however, HIV's genetic information remains dormant, forming a latent reservoir of infected but inactive cells. These latent infections are especially hard to treat with anti-HIV drugs, most of which work only in cells that are actively producing viruses (see the Apply It Now box on page 338 for more on anti-HIV drugs). Finding ways to coax the virus out of latency would greatly improve the efficacy of anti-HIV drugs; this is one of many active areas of HIV research.

C. Drugs and Vaccines Help Fight Viral Infections

Halting a viral infection is a challenge, in part because viruses invade living cells. Some antiviral drugs interfere with enzymes or other proteins that are unique to viruses, but overall, researchers have developed few medicines that inhibit viruses without killing infected host cells. Many viral diseases therefore remain incurable.

Antiviral drug development is complicated by the genetic variability of many viruses. Consider the common cold. Many different cold viruses exist, and their genomes mutate rapidly. As a result, a different virus strain is responsible every time you get the sniffles. Developing drugs that work against all of these variations has so far proved impossible.

Vaccination remains our most potent weapon against many viral diseases. A **vaccine** "teaches" the immune system to recognize one or more molecular components of a virus without actually exposing the person to the disease. Some vaccines confer immunity for years, whereas others must be repeated annually. The influenza vaccine is an example of the latter. Flu viruses mutate rapidly, so this year's vaccine is likely to be ineffective against next year's strains. ⓘ *vaccines,* p. 692

Thanks to successful global vaccination programs, smallpox has vanished from human populations, and polio is nearly defeated. Childhood vaccinations have greatly reduced the incidence of

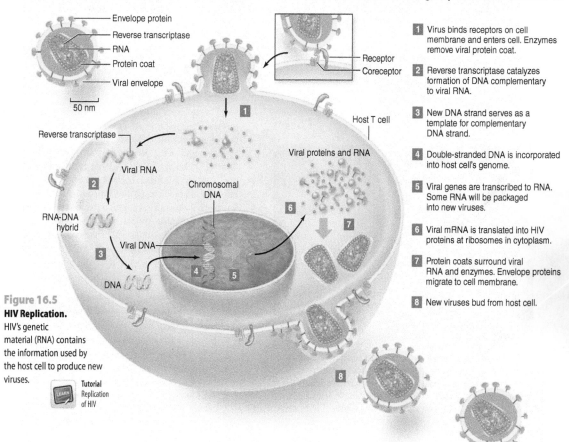

Envelope protein
Reverse transcriptase
RNA
Protein coat
Viral envelope

50 nm

Reverse transcriptase

Viral RNA

RNA-DNA hybrid

Viral DNA

DNA

Chromosomal DNA

Host T cell

Viral proteins and RNA

Receptor
Corecoptor

1 Virus binds receptors on cell membrane and enters cell. Enzymes remove viral protein coat.

2 Reverse transcriptase catalyzes formation of DNA complementary to viral RNA.

3 New DNA strand serves as a template for complementary DNA strand.

4 Double-stranded DNA is incorporated into host cell's genome.

5 Viral genes are transcribed to RNA. Some RNA will be packaged into new viruses.

6 Viral mRNA is translated into HIV proteins at ribosomes in cytoplasm.

7 Protein coats surround viral RNA and enzymes. Envelope proteins migrate to cell membrane.

8 New viruses bud from host cell.

Figure 16.5
HIV Replication.
HIV's genetic material (RNA) contains the information used by the host cell to produce new viruses.

Tutorial
Replication of HIV

Apply It **Now**

Anti-HIV Drugs

HIV spreads by contact with infected blood, semen, vaginal secretions, and breast milk. As the virus replicates, it kills T cells in the immune system. An infected person therefore becomes increasingly vulnerable to cancer and infectious diseases. Fortunately, decades of painstaking research on HIV at the molecular level has enabled biologists to develop medications that slow the replication of this deadly virus or may even prevent new infections. Here are some ways that these drugs work:

- **Keep viruses out of uninfected host cells.** Entry inhibitors block the receptors that HIV uses to recognize and enter a host cell. The drug enfuvirtide (Fuzeon) is an example.
- **Inhibit replication of viral genetic information.** Azidothymidine (AZT) and a few other drugs stop reverse transcriptase from making a DNA copy of HIV's RNA genome.
- **Inhibit viral DNA integration into host DNA.** Integrase inhibitors keep viral DNA from inserting into the host cell's chromosome.
- **Inhibit assembly of new viruses inside infected host cells.** Protease inhibitors prevent viral enzymes called proteases from cleaving the proteins that make up HIV's protein coat. The protein coat cannot form properly, so fewer mature viruses leave infected cells, and the rate of infection slows.

Researchers are also beginning to use gene therapy to treat HIV infections, genetically altering T cells to omit a coreceptor that HIV requires for entry. Without the coreceptor, HIV cannot bind (figure 16.B). An extension of this strategy is to delete the gene encoding the coreceptor from stem cells that produce immune cells, so the patient's own body can generate receptor-free T cells. Gene therapy, however, is not yet a mainstream treatment for HIV. ⓘ *gene therapy*, p. 230

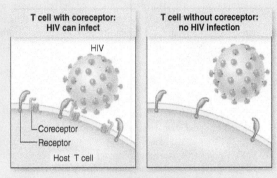

Figure 16.B   Role of Coreceptors in HIV Infection.

measles, mumps, and many other potentially serious illnesses. Unfortunately, researchers have been unable to develop vaccines against many deadly viruses, including HIV.

To produce viruses in a laboratory for vaccine manufacture or testing, scientists must inoculate host cells. The choice of host depends on the virus; bacteria, cultured animal cells, live animals, and live plants are all candidates. Fertilized chicken eggs, for example, provide the cells needed to produce the raw materials of the influenza vaccine (figure 16.6).

The antibiotic drugs that kill bacteria never work against viruses, which lack the structures targeted by antibiotics. Physicians sometimes prescribe the drugs anyway. This needless exposure to antibiotics selects for drug-resistance genes in harmless bacteria, which can later share those genes with disease-causing microbes. Drug-resistant bacteria are an enormous and growing public health problem. ⓘ *antibiotic resistance*, p. 237

Nevertheless, a viral infection can sometimes trigger bacterial growth. For example, patients sometimes develop sinus infections as a complication of influenza or the common cold. Physicians may prescribe antibiotics to treat these secondary bacterial infections, but the drugs will not affect the underlying virus.

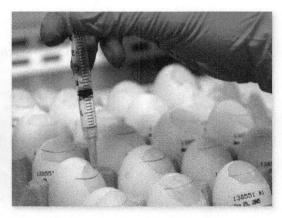

Figure 16.6   Viruses from Eggs. Influenza viruses replicate inside fertilized chicken eggs in a laboratory that produces the flu vaccine. Because the vaccine may contain egg residues, people with egg allergies should consult a physician before receiving a flu shot. (The yellow spots on the eggs are iodine, which helps maintain sterile conditions.)

16.4   MASTERING CONCEPTS

1. How can a person acquire and transmit a viral infection?
2. How do symptoms of a viral infection develop?
3. What is a latent animal virus?
4. How are some latent viral infections linked to cancer?
5. Describe how HIV replicates in host cells.
6. How are viral infections treated and prevented?

16.5 Viruses Cause Diseases in Plants

Like all organisms, plants can have viral infections. The first virus ever discovered was tobacco mosaic virus (see figure 16.2a), which affects not only tobacco but also tomatoes, peppers, and more than 120 other plant species.

To infect a plant cell, a virus must penetrate waxy outer leaf layers and thick cell walls. Most viral infections spread when plant-eating insects such as leafhoppers and aphids move virus-infested fluid from plant to plant on their mouthparts. ⓘ *plant cell wall*, p. 64

Once inside a plant, viruses multiply at the initial site of infection. The killed plant cells often appear as small dead spots on the leaves. Over time, the viruses spread from cell to cell through plasmodesmata (bridges of cytoplasm between plant cells). They can also move throughout a plant by entering the vascular tissues that distribute sap. Depending on the location and extent of the viral infection, symptoms may include blotchy, mottled leaves or abnormal growth. A few symptoms, such as the streaking of some flower petals, appear beautiful to us (figure 16.7).

Although plants do not have the same forms of immunity as do animals, they can fight off viral infections. For example, virus-infected cells may "commit suicide" before the infection has a chance to spread to neighboring cells. Alternatively, a plant cell may destroy the mRNA transcribed from viral genes. Since the viral mRNA is never translated into proteins, this defense prevents the assembly of new viruses.

Figure 16.7 Sick Plants. Cucumber mosaic virus causes a characteristic mottling (spotting) of squash leaves. A virus has also caused the streaking on the petals of these tulips.

16.5 MASTERING CONCEPTS

1. How do viruses enter plant cells and spread within a plant?
2. What are some symptoms of a viral infection in plants?

Burning Question

Can a person get cancer by having sex?

Cancer usually has nothing to do with sex, but there are exceptions. Each year, cervical cancer affects about 10,000 women in the United States and 510,000 women worldwide. Most cases are caused by a sexually transmitted virus.

The cancer-causing virus is called human papillomavirus, abbreviated HPV. About 100 strains of this virus exist, some causing harmless ailments such as warts on the soles of the feet. Thirty or so strains infect the genitals and are passed among male and female sexual partners. Usually the infection goes unnoticed. But some strains of HPV cause genital warts, and the virus can also cause cervical cancer in women.

What are the best ways to prevent cervical cancer? One important strategy is to have regular Pap tests, which detect abnormal, precancerous cells in the cervix. Another way to prevent cervical cancer is to reduce the chance of exposure to HPV. Abstaining from sex, limiting the number of sexual partners, and using a condom are all commonsense ways to help prevent the spread of HPV.

A vaccine can also help prevent cervical cancer by protecting against four strains of HPV. Two of these strains are associated with 70% of cervical cancer cases; the other two cause 90% of genital warts. Health professionals recommend vaccination at age 11 or 12. Vaccinating girls before they become sexually active makes sense because the vaccine does not work in people who have already been exposed to the virus. Since the vaccine was introduced, HPV infection among teenage girls has dropped by over 50%.

Experts also recommend vaccinating 11- to 12-year-old boys, partly to prevent the transmission of HPV to females and partly because males are also at risk of contracting HPV-associated cancers. The virus can spread through oral sex and is associated with cancers of the mouth and throat, especially in men.

Submit your burning question to
Marielle.Hoefnagels@mheducation.com

16.6 Viroids and Prions Are Other Noncellular Infectious Agents

The idea that something as simple as a virus can cause devastating illness may seem amazing. Yet some infectious agents are even simpler than viruses.

A. A Viroid Is an Infectious RNA Molecule

A **viroid** is a highly wound circle of RNA that lacks a protein coat; it is simply naked RNA that can infect a plant cell. The viroid coils tightly to form a double-stranded RNA. This configuration helps prevent degradation by host cell enzymes.

Although viroid RNA does not encode protein, it can nevertheless cause severe disease in many important crop plants, including tomatoes (figure 16.8). Apparently the viroid's RNA interferes with the plant's ability to produce one or more essential proteins.

B. A Prion Is an Infectious Protein

Another type of infectious agent is a **prion**, which stands for "<u>pr</u>oteinaceous <u>in</u>fectious particle." A prion protein (PrP for short) is a normal membrane protein that can exist in multiple three-dimensional shapes, at least one of which is abnormal and can cause disease (figure 16.9). Upon contact with an abnormal form of PrP, a normal prion protein switches to the abnormal PrP configuration. The change triggers another round of protein refolding, and so on. As a result of this chain reaction, masses of abnormal prion proteins accumulate inside cells. ⓘ *protein folding*, p. 32

Animation
Prions

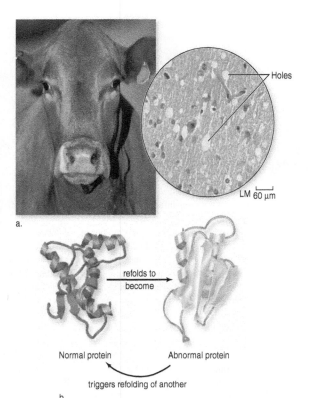

Holes

LM 60 µm

a.

refolds to become

Normal protein   Abnormal protein

triggers refolding of another

b.

Figure 16.9 Prion Disease. (a) The brain of a cow with bovine spongiform encephalopathy ("mad cow disease") is riddled with holes caused by prions. (b) A normal prion protein refolds into an abnormal shape, which can trigger refolding of more proteins in a chain reaction.

The misshapen prion proteins cause brain cells to die. The brain eventually becomes riddled with holes, like a sponge. Prion diseases are therefore called spongiform encephalopathies. "Mad cow disease" is one example. A cow may acquire this disease after ingesting infected cattle. Affected cattle grow fearful, then aggressive, and then lose weight and die.

Prions cause a few human diseases, all of them fatal (but rare). Kuru is associated with cannibalism. Creutzfeldt–Jakob disease (CJD) may occur spontaneously, be acquired in medical procedures using tainted materials, or be inherited as a gene that encodes the abnormal prion protein. Another heritable prion disease causes insomnia, dementia, and death.

Prions are extremely hardy; heat, radiation, and chemical treatments that destroy bacteria and viruses have no effect on prions. Luckily, commonsense precautions that keep brains and spinal cords out of food and medical products can prevent the transmission of prion diseases.

Figure 16.8 Viroid Disease. The plant on the left has a viroid-caused disease called "tomato bunchy top"; the one on the right is healthy.

GCCUG

Viroid
(circular RNA)

16.6   MASTERING CONCEPTS

1. How are viroids and prions different from viruses?
2. How do viroids and prions cause disease?
3. What is the best way to avoid prion diseases?

16.7 Scientific Detectives Follow HIV's Trail

Anyone who watches crime dramas on TV knows that detectives collect many types of evidence when trying to match a suspect to a crime. Do footprints found at the scene match the suspect's shoes? Do skin cells found under the victim's fingernails contain DNA matching the suspect's? Was the suspect in the victim's neighborhood at the time of the crime?

Epidemiologists use similar tactics when they test hypotheses about the evolution of viruses. For example, scientists have suggested that the ancestor of HIV is a virus called simian immunodeficiency virus (SIV). Many strains of SIV exist. They typically cause symptomless infections in monkeys and apes, although some can cause an AIDS-like disease in chimpanzees.

Researchers have tested hypotheses about the origin of HIV by asking five independent questions:

1. Do the genomes of HIV and SIV consist of the same type of genetic material and have the same order, number, and types of genes?

2. Do the viral genes (and their encoded proteins) share similar sequences?

3. Is SIV common enough in its natural host that it has a chance of spreading to other hosts, including humans?

4. Do SIV and HIV occur in the same geographic region?

5. Is there a plausible transmission pathway for SIV to spread from its original host to humans?

The two major strains of HIV, called HIV-1 and HIV-2, apparently arose independently. By the late 1980s and early 1990s, scientists had used the five criteria to identify SIVsm (a strain from sooty mangabey monkeys) as the source of HIV-2.

Although the origin of HIV-1 remained unknown, evidence pointed to a different source: SIVcpz (for chimpanzee). University of Alabama medical researcher Beatrice Hahn, along with a multinational team of scientists, wanted to learn more about HIV-1's evolutionary history. They started with frozen tissue collected in 1985 after the death of a chimpanzee named Marilyn, who tested positive for antibodies against HIV-1. Hahn and her colleagues used the polymerase chain reaction (PCR) to make copies of the viral DNA from Marilyn's tissue. When they analyzed the DNA, they found sequences that were similar to both HIV-1 and SIV. ⓘ *polymerase chain reaction*, p. 223

Marilyn's virus was only the fourth SIV strain ever found in chimpanzees. Two other SIV-infected chimps belonged to the same subspecies (the central chimpanzee) as Marilyn. The third was an eastern chimpanzee born in the Democratic Republic of Congo. These four SIV strains provided a critical clue to HIV's origin (figure 16.10). Amino acid sequences of a viral protein suggested that all three subgroups of HIV-1 (dubbed M, N, and O) were related to SIV from central chimpanzees.

The researchers thus used the epidemiological criteria to demonstrate the origin of HIV-1. Clearly, SIVcpz and HIV-1 share genetic similarities (criteria 1 and 2). Moreover, the habitat of central chimpanzees overlaps with the region of Africa where HIV-1 occurs (criterion 4), and humans who hunt chimps for meat provide a likely transmission route (criterion 5).

Only the third criterion remained questionable: If SIV is common in chimpanzees, why had scientists found it in only four animals out of more than 1500 tested? Hahn and her coauthors suggested that this low infection rate was a predictable consequence of studying chimps that were either wild-caught as infants or born in captivity. Compared with wild chimps, these captive animals would have fewer opportunities to acquire the virus. Indeed, a subsequent study revealed SIVcpz infection rates as high as 18% among wild chimpanzees in Tanzania.

Many questions remain about HIV-1's origin from SIV. How and when did the virus jump from chimpanzees to humans? Why do HIV-1 subgroups N and O remain rare, whereas subgroup M is causing the global AIDS epidemic? Can we use HIV-1 and HIV-2 to learn about the potential for other viruses to emerge as human pathogens? The scientific detectives continue to search for the answers.

Gao, Feng, Elizabeth Bailes, David L. Robertson, and nine coauthors, including Beatrice Hahn. 1999. Origin of HIV-1 in the chimpanzee *Pan troglodytes troglodytes*. *Nature*, vol. 397, pages 436–441.

16.7 MASTERING CONCEPTS

1. What hypothesis was Hahn's team investigating, and how did they test their hypothesis?

2. Explain how the relationships in figure 16.10 support the researchers' hypotheses.

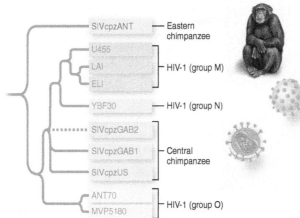

Figure 16.10 HIV-1 from SIV. Amino acid sequences of one viral protein reveal that the eastern chimpanzee's strain of SIV (blue) is distinct from all other SIVcpz strains (red) and from all known HIV-1 subgroups (green).

CHAPTER SUMMARY

16.1 Viruses Are Infectious Particles of Genetic Information and Protein

A. Viruses Are Smaller and Simpler Than Cells
- A **virus** is a nucleic acid (DNA or RNA) in a **capsid.** A membranous **envelope** surrounds some viruses.
- A virus must infect a living cell to reproduce.
- Table 16.1 lists some of the differences between cells and viruses.
- Many viruses, including some **bacteriophages,** have relatively complex structures.

B. A Virus's Host Range Consists of the Organisms It Infects
- The species that a virus infects constitute its **host range.** The **reservoir** of a virus is its natural habitat, often an animal in which it does not cause symptoms.

C. Are Viruses Alive?
- Viruses are intracellular parasites that most biologists do not consider to be alive.
- Many viral genomes mutate rapidly.
- Scientists classify viruses based on the type of genetic material, the shape of the capsid, the presence or absence of an envelope, the replication strategy, and the type of disease.

16.2 Viral Replication Occurs in Five Stages

- After a virus infects a cell, its host manufactures many copies of the viral proteins and nucleic acids, then assembles these components into new viruses.
- The five stages of viral replication within a host cell are attachment, penetration, synthesis, assembly, and release (figure 16.11).

16.3 Cell Death May Be Immediate or Delayed

A. Some Viruses Kill Cells Immediately
- In a **lytic infection,** new viruses are immediately manufactured, assembled, and released.

B. Viral DNA Can "Hide" in a Cell
- In a **lysogenic infection,** the virus's nucleic acid replicates along with that of a dividing cell without causing symptoms. The viral DNA may integrate as a **prophage** into the host chromosome.

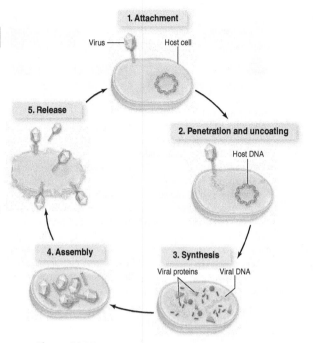

Figure 16.11 Viral Replication: A Summary.

16.4 Effects of a Viral Infection May Be Mild or Severe

A. Symptoms Result from Cell Death and the Immune Response
- The effects of a virus depend on the cell types it infects. Viruses cause disease by killing infected cells and by stimulating immune responses.

B. Some Animal Viruses Linger for Years
- HIV and some other viruses remain **latent,** or dormant, inside animal cells. Some latent viruses are associated with cancer.

C. Drugs and Vaccines Help Fight Viral Infections
- Antiviral drugs and **vaccines** combat some viral infections.
- Antibiotics, drugs that kill bacteria, are ineffective against viruses.

16.5 Viruses Cause Diseases in Plants

- Viruses infect plant cells, then spread via plasmodesmata.

16.6 Viroids and Prions Are Other Noncellular Infectious Agents

A. A Viroid Is an Infectious RNA Molecule
- **Viroids** are naked RNA molecules that infect plants.

B. A Prion Is an Infectious Protein
- A **prion** protein can take multiple shapes, at least one of which can cause diseases such as transmissible spongiform encephalopathies. Treatments that destroy other infectious agents have no effect on prions.

16.7 Investigating Life: Scientific Detectives Follow HIV's Trail

- Scientists have tested hypotheses about HIV's origin by collecting multiple types of information.
- The subgroups of HIV-1 evolved independently from simian immunodeficiency viruses (SIV) infecting chimpanzees.

TABLE 16.1   Cells and Viruses Compared

Feature	Cells	Viruses
Size	Typically 1–100 μm	Typically ~80 nm
Nucleus/membrane-bounded organelles	Eukaryotes only	No
Cytoplasm	Yes	No
Ribosomes	Yes	No
Enzymes	Yes	Some viruses
Cell membrane	Yes	No
Viral envelope	No	Some viruses
Protein coat (capsid)	No	Yes
Genetic material	DNA	DNA or RNA
Metabolism	Yes	No
Independent replication	Yes	No

MULTIPLE CHOICE QUESTIONS

1. Which of the following is NOT a feature associated with viruses?
   a. Cytoplasm   c. Protein coat
   b. Genetic information   d. Envelope

2. Which of the following is the largest?
   a. HIV   c. *E. coli* cell
   b. RNA molecule   d. human T cell

3. Which of the following characteristics of life does a virus have?
   a. Reproduction   c. Homeostasis
   b. Evolution   d. Growth

4. At which stage in viral replication does the genetic information enter the host cell?
   a. Penetration   c. Assembly
   b. Synthesis   d. Release

5. Which of the following consists of double-stranded RNA?
   a. Capsid   c. Viroid
   b. Prophage   d. Prion

6. Although some viruses are complete after the assembly stage, others do not complete replication until they acquire their _____ during the release stage.
   a. DNA   c. proteins
   b. RNA   d. envelope

7. What occurs during a lysogenic infection?
   a. Viral particles attach to, but do not penetrate, a host cell.
   b. Viral particles fill a host cell and cause it to burst.
   c. Viral genetic material replicates as a host cell divides.
   d. The viral prophage DNA is packaged into a capsid.

8. The severity of the symptoms associated with a viral infection is related to
   a. the response of the immune system.
   b. the type of genetic material in the virus.
   c. the number and types of cells that become infected.
   d. both a and c.

9. What is a prion?
   a. A highly wound circle of RNA
   b. A virus that has not yet acquired its envelope
   c. A protein that can alter the shape of a second protein
   d. The protein associated with a latent virus

Answers to these questions are in appendix A.

WRITE IT OUT

1. Describe the basic parts of a virus and how each contributes to viral replication.

2. Your biology lab instructor gives you a petri dish of agar covered with visible colonies. Your lab partner says the colonies are viruses, but you disagree. How do you know the colonies are bacteria?

3. Why is it inaccurate to refer to the "growth" of viruses?

4. Rhinoviruses replicate in the mucus-producing cells in a person's nose, throat, and lungs, causing the common cold. Papillomaviruses, which infect skin cells, cause growths called warts. HIV infects T cells and causes AIDS. How do these three types of viruses "know" which human cells to infect?

5. As described in this chapter's Burning Question box, human papillomavirus (HPV) infects cells of the skin and genitals, but it has never been shown to infect T cells. If a researcher put HPV and T cells

in the same petri dish, which step of HPV replication would fail? Explain your answer.

6. This chapter's Apply It Now box describes many treatments for HIV. Considering the high mutation rate of the HIV genome, why might HIV-positive patients take several anti-HIV drugs in combination?

7. Refer to figure 16.B, then explain why a mutation in a gene encoding a T cell coreceptor might be beneficial.

8. Chapter 7 compared chromosomes to cookbooks and genes to recipes. How could you incorporate viruses into this analogy?

9. Search the Internet for information about the injectable flu vaccine (a "flu shot"). Why is the flu shot administered annually when many other vaccines last for years? Is it possible for a flu shot to cause influenza?

10. Why do antibiotics kill bacteria but leave viruses unharmed?

11. Use the Internet to find three examples of viruses that infect humans but are not mentioned in the chapter. Describe the symptoms associated with each infection.

12. Gene therapy aims to replace faulty or disease-causing genes with healthy DNA sequences. How might you use a virus to deliver these new genes into a cell?

13. How is a biological virus similar to and different from a computer virus?

PULL IT TOGETHER

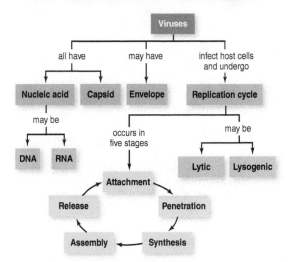

Figure 16.12 Pull It Together: Viruses.

Refer to figure 16.12 and the chapter content to answer the following questions.

1. What are the four types and configurations of nucleic acids in viruses?

2. How is a virus similar to and different from a bacterium, a viroid, and a prion?

3. Add *reservoir*, *latent*, and *vaccines* to the concept map.

CHAPTER

17

Bacteria and Archaea

SEM (false color) 5 μm

Slimy Teeth. The plaque that accumulates on teeth is a familiar example of a bacterial biofilm.

Enhance your study |BIOLOGY
of this chapter with practice quizzes,
animations and videos, answer keys,
and downloadable study tools.
www.mhhe.com/hoefnagels

"Mob Mentality" on a Microscopic Scale

BACTERIA ARE ONE-CELLED ORGANISMS, SO IT IS TEMPTING TO THINK OF THEM AS RUGGED INDIVIDU-ALISTS. Instead, however, they often build complex communities in which cells communicate, protect one another, and even form structures with specialized functions. These organized aggregations of bacterial cells are called biofilms.

A biofilm forms when bacteria settle and reproduce on a solid surface. Once the cells reach a critical density, they express genes that trigger the secretion of a sticky slime made of polysaccharides. As cells continue to divide, they pile up into mushroom-shaped structures that maximize the biofilm's surface area. Occasionally, cells released from the biofilm colonize new habitats, starting the process anew.

Microbiologists are still learning about the cues that trigger biofilm formation. For example, bacteria use signaling molecules to detect the density of cells around them. These "quorum-sensing" signals allow the cells in a biofilm to coordinate their activities, somewhat like a multicellular organism. Shortly after the biofilm forms, the bacteria turn off genes controlling the production of a flagellum; life in a biofilm does not require the ability to swim. Meanwhile, the cells produce new proteins that enable them to attach to a solid surface.

Video
Quorum Sensing

Interest in biofilms extends far beyond idle curiosity about bacterial life. These microbial mats degrade sewage in wastewater treatment plants, help mine copper ore, and coat the surfaces of plants' roots. Much of the attention that biofilms receive, however, is medical. Persistent biofilms can form in catheters, on teeth, and on the mucous membranes of lungs and sinuses. Bacteria in biofilms are much more resistant to immune defenses and antibiotic treatment than are individual cells.

As microbiologists learn more about biofilm formation, they may be able to develop new treatments to combat medically important bacteria. For example, it may be possible to disrupt biofilm formation by silencing quorum-sensing signals. Conversely, learning how to trigger biofilm formation in beneficial soil bacteria may enhance efforts to clean up toxic wastes.

The more scientists learn about prokaryotes—bacteria and archaea—the more we can appreciate the amazing capabilities of Earth's simplest organisms. This chapter offers a taste of the microbial world, beginning with a tour of prokaryotic cells. A sampling of their diversity comes next, and the chapter ends by explaining why microbes are essential to all other life. As you will see, microbes are much more than just "germs."

LEARNING OUTLINE

 17.1 Prokaryotes Are a Biological Success Story

 17.2 Prokaryote Classification Traditionally Relies on Cell Structure and Metabolism
   A. Microscopes Reveal Cell Structures
   B. Metabolic Pathways May Be Useful in Classification
   C. Molecular Data Reveal Evolutionary Relationships
   D. Horizontal Gene Transfer Complicates Classification

 17.3 Prokaryotes Include Two Domains with Enormous Diversity
   A. Domain Bacteria Includes Many Familiar Groups
   B. Many, But Not All, Archaea Are "Extremophiles"

 17.4 Bacteria and Archaea Are Important to Human Life
   A. Microbes Form Vital Links in Ecosystems
   B. Bacteria and Archaea Live In and On Us
   C. Humans Put Many Prokaryotes to Work

 17.5 Investigating Life: A Bacterial Genome Solves Two Mysteries

 LEARN HOW TO LEARN
Skipping Class?
Attending lectures is important, but you may need to skip class once in a while. How will you find out what you missed? If your instructor does not provide complete lecture notes, you may be able to copy them from a friend. Whenever you borrow someone else's notes, it's a good idea to compare them with the assigned reading to make sure the notes are complete and accurate. You might also want to check with the instructor if you have lingering questions about what you missed.

 17.1 Prokaryotes Are a Biological Success Story

The microscopic world of life may be invisible to the naked eye, but its importance is immense. Chapter 16 described viruses, tiny infectious particles that straddle the line between life and nonlife. The remaining chapters in this unit focus squarely on life, beginning with the prokaryotes.

A **prokaryote** is a single-celled organism that lacks a nucleus and membrane-bounded organelles. DNA sequences and other lines of evidence suggest the existence of two prokaryotic domains: **Bacteria** and **Archaea** (figure 17.1).

Microbiologists have probably discovered just a tiny fraction of prokaryotic life on Earth. Soil, water, and even the human body teem with microbes that have yet to be named and described. The total number of species in both domains may be anywhere between 100,000 and 10,000,000; no one knows.

Although we have much to learn of their diversity, it is clear that prokaryotic cells have had a huge influence on Earth's natural history. The earliest known fossils closely resemble today's bacteria, suggesting that the first cells were prokaryotic. Ancient photosynthetic microbes also contributed oxygen gas (O_2) to Earth's atmosphere, creating a protective ozone layer and paving the way for aerobic respiration. Along the road of evolution, bacteria probably gave rise to the chloroplasts and mitochondria of eukaryotic cells. ⓘ *aerobic respiration*, p. 106; *endosymbiosis*, p. 311

The reign of the prokaryotes continues today. Virtually no place on Earth is free of bacteria and archaea; their cells live within rocks and ice, high in the atmosphere, far below the ocean's surface, in thermal vents, nuclear reactors, hot springs, animal intestines, plant roots, and practically everywhere else. Many species prefer hot, cold, acidic, alkaline, or salty habitats that humans consider "extreme." This chapter's Burning Question, on page 353, describes some of the few places where microbes do not live.

Most of what we know about the biology of bacteria and archaea comes from studies in the laboratory. However, many prokaryotes thrive only if they receive just the right types of nutrients, and they may also require a specific combination of salt and water availability, oxygen concentration, light, pH, temperature, and so on. These complex requirements may be unique to each species. Consequently, microbiologists can only simulate the natural environment of relatively few species, which do not represent the total diversity of all prokaryotes. Microbial ecologists therefore extract DNA directly from the environment, without culturing the cells first. These studies have revealed much about microbes that we could never have learned from cultured cells alone.

Before embarking on a tour of prokaryote biology and ecology, it is worth noting that the term *prokaryote* has become somewhat controversial among microbiologists. One reason is that the word falsely implies a close evolutionary relationship between bacteria and archaea, despite strong evidence that archaea are actually more closely related to eukaryotes. A related reason is

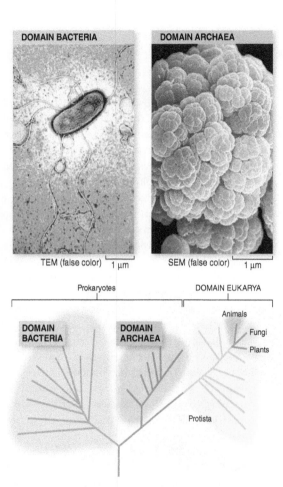

DOMAIN BACTERIA

DOMAIN ARCHAEA

TEM (false color) 1 μm   SEM (false color) 1 μm

Prokaryotes   DOMAIN EUKARYA

DOMAIN BACTERIA   DOMAIN ARCHAEA

Animals
Fungi
Plants

Protista

Figure 17.1 Diversity of Prokaryotic Life. Domains Bacteria and Archaea form two of the three main branches of life.

that prokaryotes do not form a single, complete clade; that is, they are a paraphyletic group. The tree in figure 17.1 shows that the prokaryotes exclude some of the descendants of the common ancestor that bacteria and archaea share. Nevertheless, many biologists continue to use the term as a handy shortcut for describing all cells that lack nuclei. ⓘ *paraphyletic groups*, p. 299

17.1 MASTERING CONCEPTS

1. What are two domains that contain prokaryotes?
2. List several ways that prokaryotes have influenced evolution.
3. In what habitats do bacteria and archaea live?
4. Why are most species of prokaryotes little understood?

17.2 Prokaryote Classification Traditionally Relies on Cell Structure and Metabolism

At about 1 to 10 μm long, a typical prokaryotic cell is 10 to 100 times smaller than most eukaryotic cells (see figure 3.2). Bacteria and archaea also lack the membranous organelles that characterize eukaryotic cells (see table 3.2). How do microbiologists classify the diversity of life within these two domains, given the tiny cell sizes and scarcity of distinctive internal structures?

The answer to that question has evolved over time. For hundreds of years, biologists classified microbes based on close scrutiny of their cells and metabolism. This section describes some of the most important features; figure 17.2 provides a partial list of the similarities and differences between bacteria and archaea.

A. Microscopes Reveal Cell Structures

Viewing cells with a microscope is an essential step in identifying bacteria and archaea. Light microscopes (and sometimes electron microscopes) reveal the internal and external features unique to each species. Figure 17.3 illustrates a typical bacterial cell; in reading through this section, remember that a given cell may have some or all of the structures pictured.

Internal Structures   Like the cells of other organisms, all bacteria and archaea are bounded by a cell membrane that encloses cytoplasm, DNA, and ribosomes. A prokaryotic cell's DNA typically consists of one circular chromosome. The **nucleoid** is the region where this DNA is located, along with some RNA and a few proteins. Unlike the nucleus of a eukaryotic cell, a membranous envelope does not surround the nucleoid.

The cells of many bacteria and archaea also contain one or more **plasmids,** circles of DNA apart from the chromosome. The genes on a plasmid may encode the proteins necessary to replicate and transfer the plasmid to another cell. Other genes may provide the ability to resist a drug or toxin, cause disease,

Similarities between Bacteria and Archaea

- Prokaryotic cells (no nucleus or other membrane-bounded organelles)
- Size ~1-10 μm
- Circular chromosome
- Predominantly unicellular
- Some can fix nitrogen or grow at temperatures above 80°C

Features Unique to Bacteria	**Features Unique to Archaea**
• Cell wall typically composed of peptidoglycan	• Cell wall composed of molecules other than peptidoglycan
• Membrane based on fatty acids	• Membrane based on nonfatty acid lipids
• Some use chlorophyll in photosynthesis	• Do not use chlorophyll
• Cannot generate methane	• Some generate methane
• Sensitive to streptomycin	• Insensitive to streptomycin
• Genes do not contain introns	• Genes may contain introns

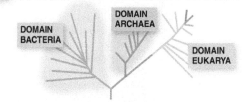

Figure 17.2   Bacteria and Archaea Compared.

or alter the cell's metabolism. Recombinant DNA technology uses plasmids to ferry genes from one kind of cell to another. ⓘ *transgenic organisms,* p. 219

The **ribosomes** are structures that use the information in RNA to assemble proteins, a process described in chapter 7. Bacterial, archaean, and eukaryotic ribosomes all make proteins in essentially the same way, but they are structurally different from one another. Some antibiotics, such as streptomycin, kill bacteria without harming eukaryotic host cells by exploiting this difference. This chapter's Apply It Now box describes more examples of how antibiotics work.

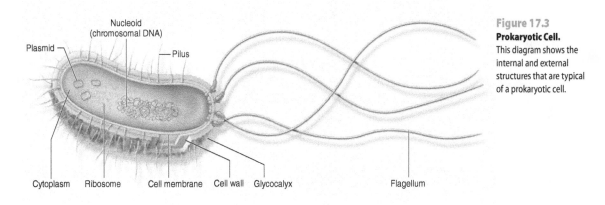

Figure 17.3
Prokaryotic Cell.
This diagram shows the internal and external structures that are typical of a prokaryotic cell.

Plasmid — Nucleoid (chromosomal DNA) — Pilus

Cytoplasm   Ribosome   Cell membrane   Cell wall   Glycocalyx   Flagellum

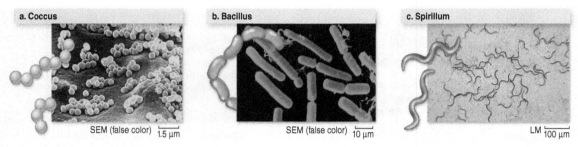

Figure 17.4 Cell Shapes. (a) Cocci are spherical. (b) A bacillus is rod-shaped. (c) A spirillum is spiral-shaped.

External Structures

External Structures   The **cell wall** is a rigid barrier that surrounds the cells of most bacteria and archaea. In most species of bacteria, the cell wall contains **peptidoglycan,** a complex polysaccharide that does not occur in the cell walls of archaea. The antibiotic penicillin inhibits the reproduction of bacteria (but not archaea) by interfering with the final steps in peptidoglycan synthesis.

The wall gives a cell its shape (figure 17.4). Three of the most common forms are **coccus** (spherical), **bacillus** (rod-shaped), and **spirillum** (spiral or corkscrew shaped). In addition, the arrangement of the cells in pairs, clusters (*staphylo-*), or chains (*strepto-*) is sometimes important in classification. The disease-causing bacterium *Staphylococcus,* for example, forms grapelike clusters of spherical cells.

The **Gram stain** reaction distinguishes between two types of cell walls (figure 17.5). After a multistep staining procedure, gram-positive cells appear purple, whereas gram-negative bacteria stain pink. Structural differences between the cell walls account for the distinctive colors (see figure 17.5b and c). The walls of gram-positive bacteria are made primarily of a thick layer of peptidoglycan. Gram-negative cells have much thinner cell walls.

Medical technicians often use Gram staining as a first step in identifying bacteria that cause infections. The distinction is important because gram-positive and gram-negative bacteria are susceptible to different antibiotic drugs.

Besides the thin inner layer of peptidoglycan, the cell walls of gram-negative bacteria have a protective outer membrane of lipid, polysaccharide, and protein. This outer membrane causes the toxic effects of many medically important gram-negative bacteria, such as *Salmonella.* The human immune system recognizes parts of the outer layer; the resulting fever and inflammation helps the body eliminate the bacteria (see chapter 33).

Many prokaryotic cells have distinctive structures outside the cell wall (figure 17.6). A **glycocalyx,** also sometimes called a capsule or slime layer, is a sticky layer composed of proteins or polysaccharides that may surround the cell wall. The glycocalyx has many functions, including attachment, resistance to drying, and protection from immune system cells. It also plays a role in the formation of biofilms, as described in the chapter-opening essay.

Some cells have **pili** (singular: pilus), which are short, hair-like projections made of protein (figure 17.6b). Attachment pili enable cells to adhere to objects. The bacterium that causes

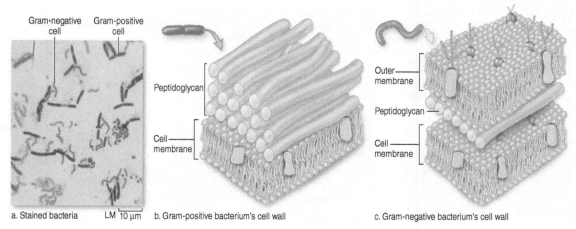

Figure 17.5 Gram Stain. The Gram stain procedure distinguishes bacteria on the basis of cell wall structure. (a) This stained smear contains both gram-positive and gram-negative bacteria. (b) Structure of a gram-positive cell wall. (c) Structure of a gram-negative cell wall.

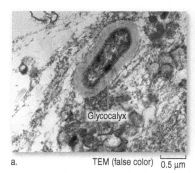
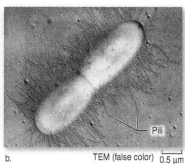
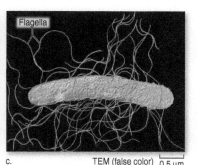

a.   TEM (false color) 0.5 µm   b.   TEM (false color) 0.5 µm   c.   TEM (false color) 0.5 µm

Figure 17.6 **External Structures of Prokaryotic Cells.** (a) A glycocalyx enables a cell to adhere to a surface. (b) Pili attach cells to objects, surfaces, and other cells. This is *E. coli.* (c) The numerous flagella on this bacterial cell enable it to move.

cholera, for example, uses pili to attach to a human's intestinal wall. Other projections, called sex pili, aid in the transfer of DNA from cell to cell, as described in section 17.2D.

Not all prokaryotes can move, but many can. In a response called **taxis,** cells move toward or away from an external stimulus such as food, a toxin, oxygen, or light. Cells that can move have a **flagellum,** which is a whiplike extension that rotates like a propeller. The bacterium in figure 17.6c has many flagella; other cells have one or a few. (Some eukaryotic cells also have flagella, but they are not homologous to those on bacterial or archaean cells.)

Endospores Two genera of gram-positive bacteria produce **endospores,** which are dormant, thick-walled structures that can survive harsh conditions (figure 17.7). The endospore wall surrounds DNA and a small amount of cytoplasm. An endospore can withstand boiling, drying, ultraviolet radiation, and disinfectants. Once environmental conditions improve, the endospore germinates and develops into a normal cell. Some researchers have reported reviving endospores preserved millions of years ago in amber.

One spore-forming soilborne bacterium is *Clostridium botulinum.* Food canning processes typically include a high-pressure heat sterilization treatment to destroy endospores of this species. If any endospores survive, they may germinate inside the can,

— Endospore

LM   2 µm

Figure 17.7 **Endospores.** *Clostridium botulinum* bacteria survive environmental extremes by forming thick-walled endospores.

producing cells that thrive in the absence of oxygen. The cells produce a toxin that causes botulism, a severe (and sometimes deadly) form of food poisoning. Green beans, corn, and other vegetables that are improperly home-canned are the most frequent sources of foodborne botulism.

Another spore-forming bacterium is *Bacillus anthracis.* This organism, ordinarily found in soil, can cause a deadly disease called anthrax when inhaled. Cultures of *B. anthracis* can be dried to induce the formation of endospores, then ground into a fine powder that remains infectious for decades. This property makes anthrax a potential biological weapon.

B. Metabolic Pathways May Be Useful in Classification

Over billions of years, bacteria and archaea have developed a tremendous diversity of chemical reactions that allow them to metabolize everything from organic matter to metal. One way to group microorganisms is to examine some of these key metabolic pathways.

The methods by which organisms acquire carbon and energy form one basis for classification. **Autotrophs,** for example, are "self-feeders"; they assemble their own organic molecules using carbon from inorganic sources such as carbon dioxide (CO_2). Plants and algae are familiar autotrophs. **Heterotrophs,** on the other hand, are "other-feeders," acquiring carbon by consuming organic molecules produced by other organisms. *Escherichia coli,* a notorious intestinal bacterium, is a heterotroph. The organism's energy source is also important. **Phototrophs** derive energy from the sun; **chemotrophs** oxidize inorganic or organic chemicals.

By combining these terms for carbon and energy sources, a biologist can describe how a microbe fits into the environment. Plants and cyanobacteria, for example, are photoautotrophs; they use sunlight (*photo-*) for energy and CO_2 (*auto-*) for carbon, as described in chapter 5. Many disease-causing bacteria are chemoheterotrophs because they use organic molecules from their hosts as sources of both carbon and energy.

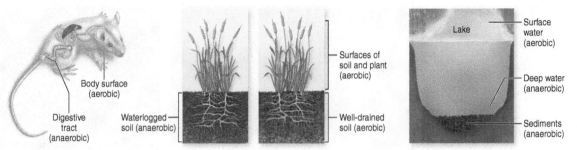

Figure 17.8 **Habitats with and Without Oxygen.** Microorganisms thrive in aerobic and anaerobic habitats. Aerobic habitats house obligate aerobes and facultative anaerobes; anaerobic habitats are home to obligate and facultative anaerobes.

In addition, oxygen requirements are often important in classification. **Obligate aerobes** require O_2 for generating ATP in cellular respiration (see chapter 6). For **obligate anaerobes,** O_2 is toxic, and they live in habitats that lack it. *Clostridium tetani,* the bacterium that causes tetanus, is one example. **Facultative anaerobes,** which include the intestinal microbes *E. coli* and *Salmonella,* can live either with or without O_2. Obligate and facultative anaerobes use fermentation or anaerobic respiration to generate ATP in the absence of O_2 (see section 6.8).

Figure 17.8 shows habitats with varying O_2 availability. O_2-rich areas include a mouse's skin, a plant's leaves, and the surface of a lake. Anaerobic habitats include the animal's digestive tract and the lake's sediments. Note that soil may contain abundant O_2 or be anaerobic, depending on whether it is waterlogged or well-drained.

 Apply It **Now**

Antibiotics and Other Germ Killers

When a person develops a bacterial infection, a physician may prescribe antibiotics. These drugs typically inhibit structures and functions present in bacteria but not in host cells. Some mechanisms of action include:

- **Inhibiting cell wall synthesis:** Penicillin is an antibiotic that interferes with cell wall formation. A bacterium that cannot make a rigid cell wall will burst and die. **Video** Dying Bacteria

- **Disrupting cell membranes:** All life depends on an intact membrane that regulates what enters and leaves a cell. Polymyxin antibiotics exploit differences between bacterial and eukaryotic cell membranes. (i) *membranes,* p. 54

- **Inhibiting protein synthesis:** No organism can survive if it cannot make proteins. The antibiotics streptomycin, chloramphenicol, and erythromycin bind to different parts of bacterial ribosomes, but all have the same effect—they kill bacteria without killing us. (i) *ribosomes,* p. 131

- **Inhibiting transcription:** Gene expression requires RNA synthesis. Rifamycin antibiotics prevent RNA synthesis in bacteria by binding to a bacterial form of RNA polymerase. (i) *transcription,* p. 128

- **Inhibiting metabolic enzymes:** Theoretically, antibiotics could block any bacterial metabolic pathway that does not occur in host cells. Sulfanilamide, for example, mimics the substrate of a bacterial enzyme that participates in an essential chain of chemical reactions. (i) *enzymes,* p. 78

Unfortunately, the misuse of antibiotics in medicine and agriculture has selected for antibiotic-resistant bacteria. How does this occur? Bacterial DNA accumulates mutations each time a cell divides; cells may

also acquire new genes, as described in section 17.2D. Therefore, new bacterial strains that are resistant to one or more classes of antibiotics occasionally emerge. Each time we use an antibiotic drug, we kill the susceptible strains and select for the resistant ones. The result is an ever-increasing incidence of antibiotic-resistant bacteria (see section 17.5).

Fortunately, ordinary people can help prevent antibiotic-resistant bacteria. Patients should not demand antibiotics for viral infections, such as the flu or the common cold. And if a physician does prescribe antibiotics, it is important to finish the entire prescription, even if you feel better. Otherwise, only the weakest bacteria will die, leaving the strongest to reproduce and spread.

C. Molecular Data Reveal Evolutionary Relationships

Traditionally, the classification of prokaryotes has relied on easy-to-observe characteristics such as cell shape. This method of organizing prokaryotes, however, groups together organisms that are only distantly related to one another.

Molecular data such as DNA sequences are harder to obtain and analyze, but they have triggered a revolution in microbial taxonomy and evolutionary biology. Once microbiologists began to analyze the DNA sequences encoding ribosomal RNA (rRNA), they realigned all organisms into three domains (see figure 17.1). The prokaryotes fell into two domains—Archaea and Bacteria—rather than one kingdom as previously thought. Moreover, studies of DNA extracted from soil, water, and other habitats have revealed many previously unknown species of microbes.

DNA sequence data have brought scientists closer to a classification system that reflects evolutionary relationships. Still, phylogenetic trees depicting their diversity remain too preliminary to include in this chapter.

D. Horizontal Gene Transfer Complicates Classification

Like all organisms, bacteria and archaea transmit DNA from generation to generation as they reproduce, a process sometimes called **vertical gene transfer.** In prokaryotes, reproduction occurs by binary fission, an asexual process that replicates DNA and distributes it and other cell parts into two daughter cells (see figure 8.7). Genetic diversity typically arises from mutations in a cell's DNA.

 Video Bacterial Cell Division

However, bacteria and archaea can also acquire new genetic material from **horizontal gene transfer:** a cell receives DNA from another cell that is not its ancestor. Horizontal gene transfer occurs in three ways (figure 17.9). First, a dying cell may release its genetic material as it bursts; **transformation** occurs when other cells absorb stray bits of its DNA. Second, viruses sometimes mistakenly package host cell DNA along with their own. In **transduction,** a virus transfers this combined DNA to a bacterial cell. Third, in **conjugation,** one cell receives DNA via direct contact with another cell. A **sex pilus** is the appendage through which DNA passes from donor to recipient.

Horizontal gene transfer has profound implications in fields as diverse as origin-of-life research, medicine, systematics, and biotechnology. Both transduction and conjugation, for example, move antibiotic-resistance genes among bacteria, a serious and growing public health problem. Yet at the same time, biologists take advantage of horizontal gene transfer when they create new types of genetically modified bacteria. ① *transgenic bacteria*, p. 219; *antibiotic resistance*, p. 237

17.2 | MASTERING CONCEPTS

1. What are the three most common cell shapes of microbes?
2. What are plasmids, and how are they important?
3. What does the Gram stain reveal about a cell?
4. What are the functions of a glycocalyx, pili, flagella, and endospores?
5. What terms do microbiologists use to describe carbon sources, energy sources, and oxygen requirements?
6. How are molecular data changing microbial taxonomy?
7. Create a Venn diagram depicting the characteristics of the three types of horizontal gene transfer.

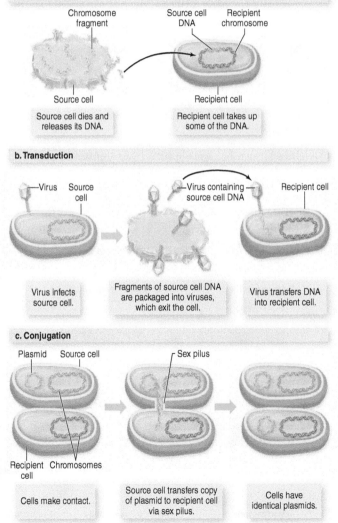

Figure 17.9 Horizontal Gene Transfer. Three forms of horizontal gene transfer include (a) transformation, (b) transduction, and (c) conjugation.

17.3 Prokaryotes Include Two Domains with Enormous Diversity

Tutorial
Prokaryote
Diversity

For many decades, the tendency to lump together all prokaryotic organisms hid much of the diversity in the microbial world. We now know of so many species of bacteria and archaea in so many habitats that it would take many books to describe them all—and many more species remain undiscovered. This section contains a small sampling of this extraordinary diversity.

A. Domain Bacteria Includes Many Familiar Groups

Scientists have identified 23 phyla within domain Bacteria, but the evolutionary relationships among them remain unclear. Table 17.1 lists a few of the main groups, and figure 17.10 illustrates two examples.

Phylum Proteobacteria is a group of gram-negative bacteria that exemplify the overall diversity within the domain. Some proteobacteria, including the purple sulfur bacteria, carry out photosynthesis. Others play important roles in nitrogen or sulfur cycling, whereas still others form a medically important group that includes enteric bacteria and vibrios. *Helicobacter,* the bacterium that causes ulcers in humans, is a proteobacterium, as are the intestinal bacteria *E. coli* and *Salmonella.* (*E. coli* is the subject of this chapter's Focus on Model Organisms.)

Cyanobacteria is a second phylum in domain Bacteria. Billions of years ago, these autotrophs were the first to produce O_2

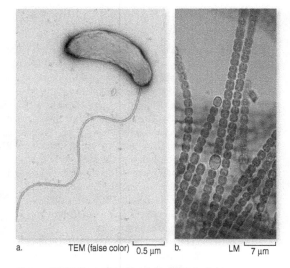

a.   TEM (false color) `0.5 µm`   b.   LM `7 µm`

Figure 17.10   Examples of Bacteria. (a) *Vibrio cholerae,* a proteobacterium. (b) Filaments of *Anabaena,* a cyanobacterium.

as a byproduct of photosynthesis. They also gave rise to the chloroplasts inside the cells of land plants and green algae. Cyanobacteria remain important in ecosystems, forming the base of aquatic food chains and participating in symbiotic relationships with fungi on land (see section 20.7). In nutrient-polluted water, however, populations of cyanobacteria can explode; the bacteria form unsightly mats and release toxic chemicals that can harm people and aquatic animals. ① *eutrophication,* p. 782

TABLE **17.1**   **Selected Phyla in Domain Bacteria**

Phylum	Features	Example(s)
Proteobacteria	Largest group of gram-negative bacteria	
Purple sulfur bacteria	Bacterial photosynthesis using H_2S (not H_2O) as electron donor	*Chromatium vinosum*
Enteric bacteria	Rod-shaped, facultative anaerobes in animal intestinal tracts	*Escherichia coli, Salmonella* species (cause gastrointestinal disease)
Vibrios	Comma-shaped, facultative anaerobes common in aquatic environments	*Vibrio cholerae* (causes cholera)
Cyanobacteria	Photosynthetic; some fix nitrogen; free-living or symbiotic with plants, fungi (in lichens), or protists	*Nostoc, Anabaena*
Spirochaetes	Spiral-shaped; some pathogens of animals	*Borrelia burgdorferi* (causes Lyme disease), *Treponema pallidum* (causes syphilis)
Firmicutes	Gram-positive bacteria with a low proportion of G+C in their DNA; aerobic or anaerobic; rods or cocci	*Bacillus anthracis* (causes anthrax), *Clostridium tetani* (causes tetanus), *Staphylococcus, Streptococcus*
Actinobacteria	Filamentous gram-positive bacteria with a high proportion of G+C in their DNA	*Streptomyces*
Chlamydiae	Grow only inside host cells; cell walls lack peptidoglycan	*Chlamydia*

Burning Question

Are there areas on Earth where no life exists?

Sand, bare rock, and polar ice may seem devoid of life, but they are not. Scientists using microscopes and molecular tools have discovered microbes living in the hottest, coldest, wettest, driest, saltiest, highest, most radioactive, and most pressurized places on the planet. Bacteria and archaea colonize every imaginable habitat, including places where no other organism can survive.

There are a few places, however, that humans keep artificially microbe-free for the sake of our own health. For example, people in many professions use autoclaves, radiation, and filters to sterilize everything from surgical tools, to medicines and bandages, to processed foods. Artificial sterilization eliminates microbes that could otherwise cause infections, food poisoning, or other illnesses.

Our own bodies are home to many, many microbes, both inside and out. Yet we manage to keep many of our internal fluids and tissues germ-free, including the sinuses, muscles, brain and spinal cord, ovaries and testes, blood, cerebrospinal fluid, urine in kidneys and the bladder, and semen before it enters the urethra. These areas are among the few places where microbes do not ordinarily live; if a bacterial infection does occur, the resulting illness can be deadly.

Submit your burning question to
Marielle.Hoefnagels@mheducation.com

SEM
(false color)   1 μm

Figure 17.11 Extremophiles. Archaea such as *Sulfolobus* thrive in boiling mud pools. This is Krafla caldera in Iceland.

A third phylum, Spirochaetes, contains some medically important bacteria. These spiral-shaped organisms include *Borrelia burgdorferi,* a bacterium that can cause Lyme disease when transmitted to humans in a tick's bite. *Treponema pallidum* causes the sexually transmitted disease syphilis.

Phylum Firmicutes contains gram-positive bacteria with a unique genetic signature: they have a low proportion of guanine and cytosine (G+C) in their DNA. Some of the firmicutes form endospores; examples include *Bacillus anthracis* (the cause of anthrax) and *Clostridium tetani* (the cause of tetanus). Others include *Staphylococcus* and *Streptococcus,* both of which can cause lethal infections throughout the body (see section 17.5).

The actinobacteria form another phylum of gram-positive bacteria. These filamentous, soil-dwelling microbes are also medically important: they are the source of infection-fighting antibiotics, including streptomycin.

Bacteria in phylum Chlamydiae are unusual in that they cannot generate ATP on their own, so they are obligate parasites—that is, they must live inside a host cell. When they infect cells lining the human genital tract, they cause a sexually transmitted disease called chlamydia. The cell walls of these bacteria lack peptidoglycan, so penicillin cannot kill them. Fortunately, a chlamydia infection can be treated with certain other antibiotics.

B. Many, But Not All, Archaea Are "Extremophiles"

Archaea are often collectively described as "extremophiles" because scientists originally found them in habitats that lacked

oxygen or that were extremely hot, acidic, or salty (figure 17.11). At first, the organisms were informally divided into groups based on habitat. The thermophiles, for example, live in habitats such as boiling hot springs, whereas the halophiles prefer salt concentrations of up to 30%, and the acidophiles tolerate pH as low as 1.0. As more archaea are discovered in moderate environments such as soil or the open ocean, however, formal taxonomic descriptions become more important.

Microbiologists now tentatively divide domain Archaea into three phyla. One phylum, Euryarchaeota, contains archaea that live in stagnant waters and the anaerobic intestinal tracts of many animals, generating large quantities of methane gas. The same phylum also includes halophilic archaea that use light energy to produce ATP in very salty habitats such as seawater, evaporating ponds, and salt flats.

A second phylum, Crenarchaeota, includes species that thrive in acidic hot springs or at hydrothermal vents on the ocean floor. The same phylum also contains a wide variety of soil and water microorganisms with moderate temperature requirements.

Other thermophiles are classified into a third phylum, Korarchaeota, known mostly from genes extracted from their habitats. They seem to be most closely related to the Crenarchaeota.

The importance of archaea in ecosystems is slowly becoming clearer as scientists decipher more about their roles in global carbon, nitrogen, and sulfur cycles. Many live in ocean waters and sediments, a hard-to-explore habitat in which the role of archaea is especially poorly understood. Their immense numbers, however, suggest that archaea are critical players in ocean ecology.

17.3 MASTERING CONCEPTS

1. In what ways are bacteria and archaea similar and different?
2. What are some examples of phyla within domain Bacteria?
3. What are the three phyla in domain Archaea?

17.4 Bacteria and Archaea Are Important to Human Life

Many people think of microbes as harmful "germs" that cause disease. Indeed, most of the familiar examples of bacteria listed in the previous section are pathogens. Although some bacteria do make people sick, most microbes do not harm us at all. This section describes some of the ways that bacteria and archaea affect our lives.

A. Microbes Form Vital Links in Ecosystems

Although it may seem hard to believe that one-celled organisms can be essential, the truth is that all other species would die without bacteria and archaea. For example, microbes play essential roles in the global carbon cycle. They decompose organic matter in soil and water, releasing CO_2. Other microorganisms absorb CO_2 in photosynthesis. And all kinds of microbes, both heterotrophs and autotrophs, are eaten by countless organisms in every imaginable habitat. Chapter 39 explains these community interactions in more detail. ⓘ *carbon cycle,* p. 780

Another essential process is **nitrogen fixation,** the chemical reactions in which prokaryotes convert atmospheric nitrogen gas (N_2) to ammonia (NH_3). The element nitrogen is a component of protein, DNA, and many other organic molecules. The only organisms that can use N_2 directly by fixing nitrogen are a few species of bacteria and archaea. Ultimately, if not for nitrogen fixers releasing NH_3 that plants and other organisms can absorb, most of Earth's nitrogen would be locked in the atmosphere. The nitrogen cycle—and therefore all life—would eventually cease without these crucial microbes. ⓘ *nitrogen cycle,* p. 781

Some nitrogen-fixing bacteria live in soil or water. Others, such as those in the genus *Rhizobium,* induce the formation of nodules in the roots of clover and other host plants in the legume family (figure 17.12). Inside the nodules, *Rhizobium* cells share the nitrogen that they fix with their hosts; in exchange, the bacteria receive nutrients and protection.

B. Bacteria and Archaea Live In and On Us

No matter how hard you scrub, it is impossible to escape the fact that you are a habitat for microorganisms. A menagerie of microbes lives on the skin and in the mouth, large intestine, urogenital tract, and upper respiratory tract (figure 17.13). These microscopic companions are beneficial because they crowd out disease-causing bacteria, "train" the immune system to ignore harmless molecules, and produce certain vitamins (among other benefits).

Most people never notice these invisible residents unless something disrupts their personal microbial community. Suppose, for example, that your cat scratches your leg and the wound becomes infected. If you take antibiotics to fight the infection, the drug will probably also kill off some of the normal microbes in your body. As they die, harmful ones can take their place. The resulting microbial imbalance in the intestines or genital tract causes unpleasant side effects such as diarrhea or a vaginal yeast infection. These problems subside in time as the normal microbes divide and restore their populations.

Although most bacteria in and on the human body are harmless, some cause disease. (So far, no archaea are linked to human illnesses.) To cause an infection, bacteria must first enter the body. Animal bites transmit some bacteria, as can sexual activity; section 35.4 describes sexually transmitted diseases in more

F🔍CUS on Model Organisms

Escherichia coli

Of all the model organisms profiled in this unit, *Escherichia coli,* commonly called *E. coli,* may be the best understood (figure 17.A). Dr. Theodor Escherich (1857 to 1911) discovered this normal resident of the human intestinal tract in 1885, and it quickly became a popular lab organism. Biologists have studied every aspect of this bacterium for over a century, and its contributions to biology are enormous. The following are a few highlights:

- **DNA is genetic material:** In 1950, Hershey and Chase used virus-infected *E. coli* cells to demonstrate that DNA, not protein, is the genetic material. ⓘ *Hershey and Chase,* p. 124
- **Genetic exchange:** In the 1940s and 1950s, biologists studying *E. coli* discovered conjugation and transduction (see section 17.2D). Both phenomena have important implications for bacterial evolution and transgenic technology.
- **DNA replication:** In the late 1950s, Matthew Meselson and Franklin Stahl used *E. coli* in their famous experiments that demonstrated how DNA copies itself. ⓘ *DNA replication,* p. 150

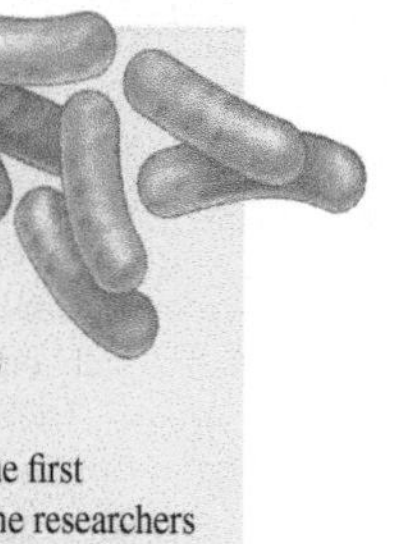

Figure 17.A *Escherichia coli.*

- **Gene regulation:** The 1961 description of the *lac* operon in *E. coli* revealed how cells can turn genes on or off, depending on environmental conditions such as the type of sugar present. ⓘ *operons,* p. 134
- **Transgenic technology:** In 1973, *E. coli* became the first organism to receive a gene from another species. The researchers used the newly discovered restriction enzyme *Eco*R1, derived from *E. coli,* to produce the recombinant plasmids. Since then, *E. coli* cells have received countless genes from many other species. ⓘ *transgenic organisms,* p. 219
- **Gene function:** The *E. coli* genome has been sequenced, and many scientists are working to describe the functions of hundreds of *E. coli* genes. Many genes in other organisms, including humans, will no doubt have similar DNA sequences and functions. Such studies of homologous genes yield new insights into disease and cell function.

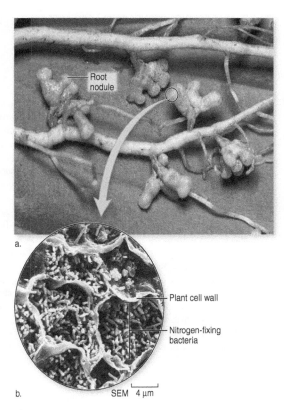

a.

b.   SEM 4 μm

Figure 17.12 **Nitrogen-Fixing Bacteria.** *Rhizobium* bacteria infect these sweet clover roots, producing root nodules where nitrogen fixation occurs. The inset shows a cross section of a root nodule, revealing bacteria inside the plant's cells.

Root nodule

Plant cell wall

Nitrogen-fixing bacteria

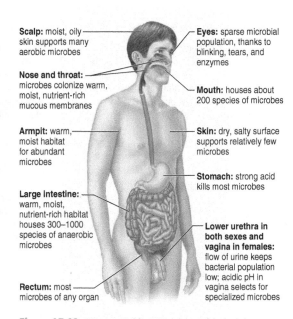

Scalp: moist, oily skin supports many aerobic microbes

Nose and throat: microbes colonize warm, moist, nutrient-rich mucous membranes

Armpit: warm, moist habitat for abundant microbes

Large intestine: warm, moist, nutrient-rich habitat houses 300–1000 species of anaerobic microbes

Rectum: most microbes of any organ

Eyes: sparse microbial population, thanks to blinking, tears, and enzymes

Mouth: houses about 200 species of microbes

Skin: dry, salty surface supports relatively few microbes

Stomach: strong acid kills most microbes

Lower urethra in both sexes and vagina in females: flow of urine keeps bacterial population low; acidic pH in vagina selects for specialized microbes

Figure 17.13 **A Human Habitat.** Many parts of the body house thriving populations of microorganisms. The blood, nervous system, urinary bladder, and some other areas normally remain sterile.

detail. A person can also inhale air containing respiratory droplets from a sick coworker or ingest bacteria in contaminated food or water. Bacteria can also enter the body through open wounds.

Once inside the host, pili or slime capsules attach the pathogens to host cells. As the invaders multiply, disease symptoms may develop. Some symptoms result from damage caused by the bacteria themselves. The cells may produce enzymes that break down host tissues, for example, or they may release toxins that harm the host's circulatory, digestive, or nervous system. These toxins may help the pathogens invade the host, acquire nutrients, escape the immune system, or spread to new hosts. ⓘ *enzymes*, p. 78

To illustrate bacterial toxins, consider *E. coli,* a normal inhabitant of animal intestines. Sometimes, cattle droppings containing *E. coli* contaminate water, milk, raw fruits and vegetables, hamburger, and other foods. Most strains of *E. coli* are harmless, but one particularly nasty variety multiplies inside the body and produces a toxin that can cause belly pain, bloody diarrhea, and, in some

Video
Battling
E. coli

cases, life-threatening kidney failure. Outbreaks of foodborne *E. coli* have led to widely publicized recalls of everything from raw spinach to ground beef to unpasteurized apple juice.

Raw eggs and other foods contaminated with animal feces also may contain *Salmonella,* a close relative of *E. coli. Salmonella, Staphylococcus aureus,* and *Bacillus cereus* are all examples of microbes that thrive in foods that have been improperly refrigerated or inadequately cooked. The toxins they produce in the food—not infection with the bacteria themselves—produce the vomiting and diarrhea associated with food poisoning.

Besides the effects of toxins, a bacterial infection may also trigger an immune reaction. As a result, the classic signs and symptoms of a bacterial infection develop: fever, swollen lymph nodes, pain, and nausea, among others (see chapter 33). Eventually, strong immune defenses usually defeat a bacterial infection.

But the arms race extends to the bacterial side as well. Natural selection favors bacteria that can evade the immune system by hiding inside host cells or forming protective biofilms (see the chapter-opening essay). Most pathogens also spread efficiently to new hosts. Bacteria exit the body in many ways: in respiratory droplets, feces, vaginal discharge, or semen, for example. Blood-feeding animals such as ticks and mosquitoes also transmit some pathogenic bacteria.

C. Humans Put Many Prokaryotes to Work

Humans have exploited the metabolic talents of microbes for centuries, long before we could see cells under a microscope (figure 17.14). For instance, many foods are the products of bacterial metabolism. Vinegar, sauerkraut, sourdough bread, pickles, olives, yogurt, and cheese are just a few examples; organic acids released in fermentation produce the tart flavors of these foods. ⓘ *fermentation*, p. 115

Microbes also have many industrial applications, many of which are related to the burgeoning field of biotechnology (see chapter 11). Vats of fermenting bacteria can produce enormous quantities of vitamin B_{12} and of useful chemicals such as ethanol and acetone. Transgenic bacteria mass-produce human proteins, including insulin and blood-clotting factors. In addition, heat-tolerant enzymes isolated from bacteria can degrade proteins and fats in hot water, boosting the cleaning power of detergents used in laundry machines and dishwashers.

Water and waste treatment also use bacteria and archaea. Sewage treatment plants in most communities, for example, rely on biofilms consisting of countless microbes that degrade organic wastes. And a technique called bioremediation uses microorganisms to metabolize and detoxify pollutants such as petroleum and mercury. Given the right conditions, microbes can consume huge quantities of organic wastes. For example, oil- and gas-munching bacteria consumed much of the oil spilled in the Gulf of Mexico after a disastrous well blowout in 2010.

17.4   MASTERING CONCEPTS

1. In what ways are bacteria and archaea essential to eukaryotic life?
2. How are the microbes that colonize your body beneficial?
3. What adaptations enable pathogenic bacteria to enter the body and cause disease?
4. What are some practical uses of bacteria and archaea?

INVESTIGATING LIFE

17.5 A Bacterial Genome Solves Two Mysteries

DNA has astonishing power as a tool for detecting evolutionary change. Genetic material from organisms that lived hundreds of thousands of years ago can provide clues about life in the distant past (see section 19.6). The same molecule can also teach us about events that occurred within the past 30 years.

Consider, for example, a bacterium called *Staphylococcus aureus*. Most people harbor this common gram-positive organism without becoming ill. If the bacteria breach the skin's defenses or enter the bloodstream, however, they can cause everything from painful boils to blood infection and death. Toxic shock syndrome, scalded skin syndrome, and damage to the heart's inner lining are a few of the potentially life-threatening consequences of a "staph" infection.

This variety of symptoms stems from *S. aureus*'s genetic diversity. Researcher James Musser and his colleagues at the National Institute of Allergy and Infectious Diseases wanted to learn more about the relationship between genetic variation, pathogenicity, and evolution in *S. aureus*. His team studied 37 strains representing the range of known genetic variability in *S. aureus* isolated in the United States, Europe, Canada, and Japan.

The design of Musser's study was simple. The researchers constructed special glass slides loaded with short DNA sequences from a reference strain of *S. aureus* with a known genome sequence. They washed the slides, called microarrays, with DNA extracted from each of the test strains. If a bacterium's nucleotide sequence matched a spot on the microarray, its DNA stuck there; if not, it simply washed away. The more matches, the more genetically similar each test strain was to the reference. Moreover, the researchers could use the microarray patterns to deduce how similar the strains were to one another.

a.

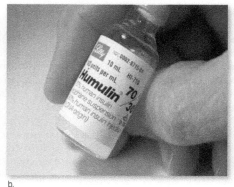
b.

c.

Figure 17.14 Bacteria at Work. (a) Bacteria of genus *Lactococcus* manufacture cheddar cheese from fermenting milk. (b) Transgenic bacteria produce many drugs, including human insulin. (c) Raw sewage is sprayed on a trickling filter at a municipal wastewater treatment plant. Bacterial biofilms on the filter degrade the organic matter in the sewage.

Musser and his team were especially interested in the origin of *S. aureus* strains that resist treatment with antibiotics. One such group is called methicillin-resistant *S. aureus*, abbreviated MRSA. These bacteria, which first appeared in the 1960s, earned the public's attention in the 1990s when they began causing frequent infections in hospital patients.

Scientists have offered two competing explanations for the origin of MRSA. One hypothesis is that MRSA evolved many times through horizontal transfer of the gene that confers antibiotic resistance. An alternative hypothesis is that the resistance gene arose by random mutation only once in a formerly susceptible cell. With replication and additional mutations, the descendants of that cell gave rise to multiple resistant strains.

The researchers tested both hypotheses by assembling their microarray data into an evolutionary tree. The study included 12 MRSA strains. If a single lineage (tree "branch") had contained all of the resistant strains, it would have supported the hypothesis that all MRSA originated from a single ancestor. Instead, the resistant strains were scattered throughout the tree diagram, supporting the multiple-origin hypothesis (figure 17.15).

A related, hotly debated question is the origin of the toxic shock syndrome epidemic of 1980 (figure 17.16). Most cases were linked with the use of high-absorbency tampons among previously healthy young women. When technicians cultured bacteria from the vaginas of the ill women, they found *S. aureus* 90% of the time.

Why the sudden epidemic in 1980? Epidemiologists have proposed two hypotheses. One possibility is that the increasing use of ultra-high-absorbency tampons at that time created a new type of environment; many strains of *S. aureus* may have independently exploited this change. Another explanation is that one cell mutated and became a successful "superpathogen."

The researchers' tree diagram again led to the answer (see figure 17.15). The 11 strains from toxic shock syndrome patients formed a cluster but were not identical, as would be expected if all were clones of the same pathogen. The team therefore concluded that multiple *S. aureus* strains caused the epidemic.

DNA evidence is most famous for its role in solving crimes, but it is equally valuable to the "detectives" who study infectious disease. Understanding how bacteria have evolved in the recent past gives scientists a head start in anticipating future epidemics.

Fitzgerald, J. Ross and four coauthors, including James M. Musser. July 17, 2001. Evolutionary genomics of *Staphylococcus aureus*: Insights into the origin of methicillin-resistant strains and the toxic shock syndrome epidemic. *Proceedings of the National Academy of Sciences*, vol. 98, pages 8821–8826.

17.5   MASTERING CONCEPTS

1. How did Musser's team use their data set to help answer two different questions?

2. Propose a change to figure 17.15 that would support the hypothesis that all strains associated with toxic shock syndrome arose from one "superpathogen."

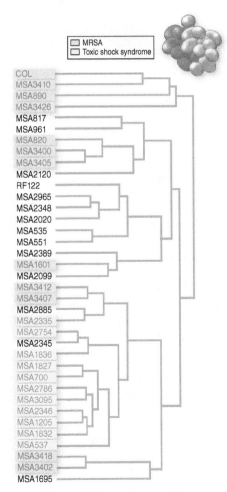

Figure 17.15 *Staphylococcus aureus* **Relationships.** This tree helped reveal the origins of MRSA and toxic shock syndrome.

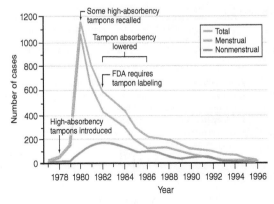

Figure 17.16 **Toxic Shock Syndrome Epidemic.** Ultra-high-absorbency tampons were linked to a spike in toxic shock syndrome cases in 1980.

CHAPTER SUMMARY

17.1 Prokaryotes Are a Biological Success Story

- **Prokaryotes** (domains **Bacteria** and **Archaea**) were the first organisms.
- Bacteria and archaea are very abundant and diverse, and they occupy a great variety of habitats.

17.2 Prokaryote Classification Traditionally Relies on Cell Structure and Metabolism

A. Microscopes Reveal Cell Structures

- Like other organisms, prokaryotic cells contain DNA and **ribosomes,** and they are surrounded by a cell membrane.
- The chromosome is located in an area called the **nucleoid. Plasmids** are circles of DNA apart from the chromosome.
- A **cell wall** surrounds most prokaryotic cells and confers the cell's shape: a spherical **coccus,** rod-shaped **bacillus,** or spiral-shaped **spirillum.**
- **Gram staining** reveals differences in cell wall architecture. Gram-positive bacteria have a thick **peptidoglycan** layer; gram-negative bacteria have an outer membrane surrounding the thinner peptidoglycan cell wall.
- A **glycocalyx** outside the cell wall provides attachment to surfaces or protection from host immune system cells.
- **Pili** are projections that allow cells to adhere to surfaces or transfer DNA to other cells.
- **Flagella** rotate to allow a motile cell to move toward or away from a stimulus, a process called **taxis.**
- Some bacteria survive harsh conditions by forming **endospores.**

B. Metabolic Pathways May Be Useful in Classification

- Bacteria and archaea are metabolically diverse. **Autotrophs** acquire carbon from inorganic sources, and **heterotrophs** obtain carbon from other organisms. A **phototroph** derives energy from the sun, and a **chemotroph** acquires energy from organic or inorganic chemicals.
- **Obligate aerobes** require oxygen, **facultative anaerobes** can live whether or not oxygen is present, and **obligate anaerobes** cannot function in the presence of oxygen.

C. Molecular Data Reveal Evolutionary Relationships

- Microbiologists are using molecular data to reconsider the traditional classification of bacteria and archaea.

D. Horizontal Gene Transfer Complicates Classification

- Binary fission (cell division) is a form of **vertical gene transfer,** in which DNA is transferred to the next generation.
- Prokaryotes can also acquire new DNA directly from the environment (**transformation**), a virus (**transduction**), or another cell via a **sex pilus** (**conjugation**). All three are routes of **horizontal gene transfer.**

17.3 Prokaryotes Include Two Domains with Enormous Diversity

A. Domain Bacteria Includes Many Familiar Groups

- Proteobacteria, cyanobacteria, spirochetes, firmicutes, actinobacteria, and chlamydias are a few examples of diversity within domain Bacteria.

B. Many, But Not All, Archaea Are "Extremophiles"

- Domain Archaea contains methanogens, halophiles, thermophiles, and many organisms that thrive in moderate conditions.

17.4 Bacteria and Archaea Are Important to Human Life

- Bacteria and archaea are nearly everywhere (figure 17.17).

A. Microbes Form Vital Links in Ecosystems

- All life depends on the bacteria and archaea that contribute gases to the atmosphere, recycle organic matter, and **fix nitrogen.**

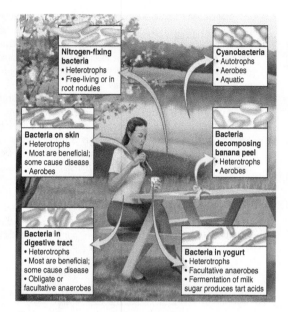

Figure 17.17 Microbes in a Selection of Habitats.

B. Bacteria and Archaea Live In and On Us

- Pathogenic bacteria adhere to host cells and colonize tissues. Disease symptoms often result from the immune system's reaction to the infection.
- Toxins produced by bacteria, plus the ability to spread to new hosts, also contribute to disease.

C. Humans Put Many Prokaryotes to Work

- Bacteria and archaea are used in the manufacture of many foods, drugs, and other chemicals, in sewage treatment, and in bioremediation.

17.5 Investigating Life: A Bacterial Genome Solves Two Mysteries

- Molecular studies revealed that *Staphylococcus aureus* strains resistant to multiple antibiotics arose independently several times, as did those that caused the toxic shock syndrome epidemic of 1980.

MULTIPLE CHOICE QUESTIONS

1. A prokaryotic cell is one that
   a. lacks DNA.
   b. has membrane-bounded organelles.
   c. lacks a nucleus.
   d. lacks a plasma membrane.

2. Which of these is a distinguishing characteristic between the domains Bacteria and Archaea?
   a. Their size
   b. The chemical composition of the cell wall and cell membrane
   c. Their ability to grow at high temperatures
   d. The shape of their mitochondria

3. What feature distinguishes gram-positive and gram-negative bacteria?
   a. A peptidoglycan cell wall in gram-positive bacteria
   b. A peptidoglycan cell wall in gram-negative bacteria
   c. A second lipid bilayer in gram-positive bacteria
   d. A second lipid bilayer in gram-negative bacteria

4. What type of organism may use inorganic chemicals for both energy and a carbon source?
   - a. A photoautotroph
   - b. A photoheterotroph
   - c. A chemoautotroph
   - d. A chemoheterotroph

5. Which form of prokaryote would be the most challenging to isolate and culture?
   - a. A facultative anaerobe
   - b. A phototroph
   - c. An obligate anaerobe
   - d. A chemotroph

6. Which of the following requires the participation of a virus?
   - a. Conjugation
   - b. Transformation
   - c. Transduction
   - d. Transfection

7. How do scientists induce prokaryotes to produce human proteins?
   - a. They insert human genes into bacterial genomes.
   - b. They cross bacterial strains until the proteins arise at random.
   - c. They inject bacteria into human muscles.
   - d. All of the above are correct.

8. Which of the following processes occurs ONLY in prokaryotes?
   - a. Nitrogen fixation
   - b. Photosynthesis
   - c. Asexual reproduction
   - d. All of the above are correct.

Answers to these questions are in appendix A.

WRITE IT OUT

1. Explain why the antibiotics penicillin and polymyxin are not effective against archaea. (Review the Apply It Now box on page 350.)

2. Why do some microbiologists disagree with classifying bacteria and archaea as "prokaryotes"?

3. Give five examples that illustrate how bacteria and archaea are important to other types of organisms.

4. If you were developing a new "broad-spectrum" antibiotic to kill a wide variety of bacteria, which cell structures and pathways would you target? Which of those targets also occur in eukaryotic cells, and why is that important? How would your strategy change if you were designing a new "narrow-spectrum" antibiotic active against only a few types of bacteria?

5. Describe your own metabolic classification. Are you a photoautotroph, photoheterotroph, chemoautotroph, or chemoheterotroph? Are you an obligate aerobe, an obligate anaerobe, or a facultative anaerobe? Are you a nitrogen fixer?

6. How do prokaryotes reproduce, and what are three ways they can acquire genes other than by vertical gene transfer?

7. Ernst Mayr defined a biological species as a population whose members can exchange genetic material during reproduction (see chapter 14). How does horizontal gene transfer complicate this definition of species?

8. Why did the discovery of archaea generate interest in searching for cells on other planets?

9. Why is it incorrect to say that bacteria produce toxins to harm their host?

10. How have humans harnessed the metabolic diversity of bacteria and archaea for industrial purposes?

11. Ecosystems rely on nitrogen-fixing bacteria, which convert atmospheric nitrogen (N_2) into ammonia (NH_3). Into what types of organic molecules do plants incorporate the nitrogen in ammonia?

12. Stomach ulcers, once thought to be entirely a product of spicy food or high stress, are now known to be caused by bacteria (*Helicobacter pylori*). How has ulcer treatment changed because of this new knowledge?

13. Probiotics are dietary supplements consisting of live bacteria that are normally found in the human digestive tract. Some people claim that consuming probiotics promotes digestive health. Design an experiment that would help you determine whether (a) the bacteria in a probiotic supplement survive the trip from the mouth, through the stomach and small intestine, and into the large intestine and (b) whether probiotics actually do promote digestive health.

14. Botox is a toxin produced by the bacterium *Clostridium botulinum*. When ingested with tainted food, Botox can kill by paralyzing muscles needed for breathing and heartbeat. Physicians inject small quantities of diluted Botox into facial muscles to paralyze them and reduce the appearance of wrinkles. Some people have expressed concern about a trend in which people come together for "Botox parties" at hair salons and other nonmedical settings. What are the risks of getting injections in such a setting?

15. If you worked for a school confronting an outbreak of *S. aureus*, how would you determine whether the strains were MRSA? What measures would you recommend to control the outbreak?

16. *Mycobacterium tuberculosis* causes most cases of tuberculosis. Recently, strains of this bacterium that are resistant to all known antibiotic drugs have become increasingly common. Explain how this change occurred; use the terms *mutation, DNA,* and *natural selection* in your answer.

PULL IT TOGETHER

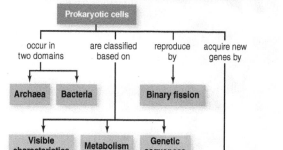

Figure 17.18 Pull It Together: Bacteria and Archaea.

Refer to figure 17.18 and the chapter content to answer the following questions.

1. Add *autotrophs, heterotrophs, phototrophs,* and *chemotrophs* to this concept map.

2. Where do obligate aerobes, obligate anaerobes, and facultative anaerobes fit on this map?

3. Where could you place humans on this concept map?

4. Describe each of the ways prokaryotes acquire new genes.

5. Create a new concept map that includes the internal and external parts of a prokaryotic cell.

6. What are the cell features and metabolic criteria by which biologists classify microbes?

18 Protists

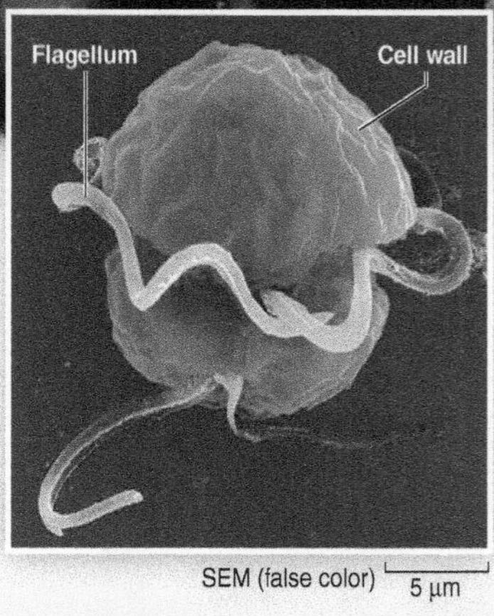

Pfiesteria Fish Lesions. Toxins produced by the protist *Pfiesteria* cause gaping sores on fish; the inset shows one *Pfiesteria* cell.

Flagellum   Cell wall

SEM (false color)   5 µm

connect plus+

Enhance your study |BIOLOGY
of this chapter with practice quizzes,
animations and videos, answer keys,
and downloadable study tools.
www.mhhe.com/hoefnagels

Science Lessons from a Killer Cell

OF THE MANY THOUSANDS OF SPECIES OF PROTISTS, THE VAST MAJORITY ARE HARMLESS TO ANIMALS. One exception, however, is *Pfiesteria*, which lives in water off the east coast of the United States. *Pfiesteria* belongs to a group of protists called dinoflagellates. Typically, *Pfiesteria* is nontoxic, feeding on algae and bacteria in coastal waters. But a few of the stages in its life cycle can produce extremely potent toxins that kill fish and accumulate in shellfish, making them poisonous to humans.

Pfiesteria produces at least two toxins. One is a powerful neurotoxin, and the other causes disintegration of the skin of a fish. Although the toxins break down rapidly, the infected fish often develop open sores. Many fish die. In humans, *Pfiesteria* toxins can produce rashes, open sores, fatigue, erratic heart-beat, breathing difficulty, personality changes, and extreme memory loss.

The on-again, off-again nature of the toxins has made them very difficult for scientists to study. Controversy erupted in 2002, when scientists reported that a species called *Pfiesteria shumwayae* did not produce toxins. In making their case, the research-ers used several experimental strategies, none of which yielded evidence of toxins.

Later in the same year, however, other researchers refuted these results, saying that the first group raised the *Pfiesteria* cells under conditions that suppressed toxin production (the cells must grow with live fish to produce toxins). This second group used the same form of *P. shumwayae* as the first group, but they also included two control forms: one known to make toxins and the other known to be nontoxic. The results indicated that, under some conditions, *P. shumwayae* did indeed produce toxins that harmed fish.

These conflicting studies illustrate two important features of science. First, the conditions under which scientists conduct experiments can greatly affect their conclusions. Second, com-munication is vital. When the first group published their results, they described their *Pfiesteria* forms and experimental tech-niques in detail. The second group used this information to iden-tify conditions known to suppress toxin production. The careful reporting of materials and methods enables scientists to evaluate one another's work.

This chapter's content illustrates a third feature of science: adaptability to new information. Protists were once considered a single kingdom, but we now know that the protists are much too diverse to fit into one neat category. This chapter presents a sam-pling of that diversity.

LEARNING OUTLINE

 18.1 Protists Lie at the Crossroads Between Simple and Complex Organisms
   A. What Is a Protist?
   B. Protists Are Important in Many Ways
   C. Protists Have a Lengthy Evolutionary History

 18.2 Many Protists Are Photosynthetic
   A. Euglenoids Are Heterotrophs and Autotrophs
   B. Dinoflagellates Are "Whirling Cells"
   C. Golden Algae, Diatoms, and Brown Algae Contain Yellowish Pigments
   D. Red Algae Can Live in Deep Water
   E. Green Algae Are the Closest Relatives of Land Plants

 18.3 Some Heterotrophic Protists Were Once Classified as Fungi
   A. Slime Molds Are Unicellular and Multicellular
   B. Water Molds Are Decomposers and Parasites

 18.4 Protozoa Are Diverse Heterotrophic Protists
   A. Several Flagellated Protozoa Cause Disease
   B. Amoeboid Protozoa Produce Pseudopodia
   C. Ciliates Are Common Protozoa with Complex Cells
   D. Apicomplexans Include Nonmotile Animal Parasites

 18.5 Protist Classification Is Changing Rapidly
 18.6 Investigating Life: Shining a Spotlight on Danger

 LEARN HOW TO LEARN
What's the Point of Rewriting Your Notes?

Your notes are your record of what happened in class, so why should you rewrite them after the lecture is over? One answer is that the abbreviations and shorthand that make perfect sense while you take notes will become increasingly mysterious as time goes by. Rewriting the information in complete sentences not only reinforces learning but also makes your notes much easier to study before an exam.

18.1 Protists Lie at the Crossroads Between Simple and Complex Organisms

Our tour of life's diversity began with viruses, infectious particles that lie on the border between the living and the nonliving. Chapter 17 then described the two domains of prokaryotes, the Bacteria and the Archaea. Early prokaryotes played pivotal roles in the evolution of life, inventing countless metabolic pathways and releasing oxygen into Earth's atmosphere.

About 2 billion years ago, the prokaryotes gave rise to a new, more complex cell type: the eukaryote. Unlike a prokaryote, a **eukaryotic cell** has a nucleus and other membrane-bounded organelles, such as mitochondria and chloroplasts. Figures 3.8 and 3.9 clearly show the compartmentalization and division of labor typical of eukaryotic cells, and section 3.2 offers a more complete description of the distinctions among the cell types. We now embark on a tour of the protists, the simplest eukaryotes.

A. What Is a Protist?

Until recently, biologists recognized four eukaryotic kingdoms: Protista, Plantae, Fungi, and Animalia. The plants, fungi, and

Tutorial
Protist Diversity

animals are distinguished based on their characteristics. Kingdom Protista, in contrast, was a paraphyletic group defined by *exclusion*. An organism was designated a **protist** if it was a eukaryote that did not fit the description of a plant, fungus, or animal. Kingdom Protista was, in effect, a convenient but artificial "none of the above" category (figure 18.1). The nearly 100,000 named species of protists therefore display great variety in size, nutrition, locomotion, and reproduction. (i) *paraphyletic groups,* p. 299

Biologists have traditionally grouped the protists based on the organisms they resemble: the plantlike algae, funguslike slime molds, and animal-like protozoa. Modern systematists, however, group organisms based on evolutionary relationships. DNA sequences provide the most objective measure of relatedness. Based on these new molecular data, the former Kingdom Protista has shattered into dozens of groups whose relationships to one another remain uncertain. (i) *systematics,* p. 294

Because the classification of protists is in transition and many of the new groupings are not universally accepted, this chapter uses the traditional approach to classification. Section 18.5, however, revisits modern trends in protist taxonomy.

B. Protists Are Important in Many Ways

The metabolic diversity among protists means they have an astonishingly wide variety of functions and roles in human life. In ecosystems, the autotrophic ("self-feeding") algae carry out photosynthesis, producing much of the O_2 in Earth's atmosphere and supporting food webs in oceans, lakes, rivers, and ponds. In addition, lichens are unique "dual organisms" consisting of algae living among the threads of fungi. Their activities help build soil from bare rock. (i) *food webs,* p. 775; *lichens,* p. 411

Medically important protists include parasites that infect plant and animal hosts (including humans), at a cost of billions of dollars, incalculable suffering, and millions of deaths annually. As you will see, insects transmit some of these organisms; others enter new hosts in contaminated food or water. Symptoms of infection by the latter group may include diarrhea, an adaptation that allows the parasite to move from an infected host to water.

Protists also have found their way into diverse industrial applications. Some algae, for example, help make chocolate smooth and creamy, whereas others help make paints reflective. Still other species have left distinctive fossils that point the way to petroleum reserves. Conversely, biologists may one day be able to reduce our reliance on petroleum by harnessing protist photosynthesis and reproduction in "bioreactors" that use sunlight and CO_2 to produce oil and other biofuels. (i) *biofuels,* p. 384

C. Protists Have a Lengthy Evolutionary History

Animation
Origin of Eukaryotes

Evolutionary biologists are especially interested in protists. One reason is that the cells of today's protists may retain clues to important milestones in eukaryote history. The endosymbiosis theory, for example, suggests that early eukaryotes originally

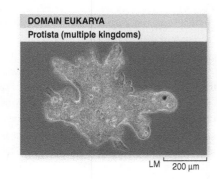

DOMAIN EUKARYA
Protista (multiple kingdoms)

LM ⊢ 200 µm

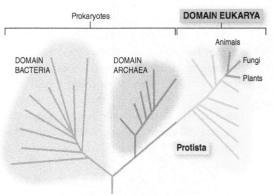

Prokaryotes

DOMAIN EUKARYA

DOMAIN BACTERIA

DOMAIN ARCHAEA

Animals
Fungi
Plants

Protista

Figure 18.1   Protists at the Crossroads. "Kingdom" Protista consists of many lineages, each of which may eventually be considered its own kingdom. Plants, fungi, and animals trace their ancestry to protists, living or extinct.

obtained mitochondria and chloroplasts by engulfing bacterial cells. Nearly all eukaryotes have mitochondria, so the aerobic bacteria that became these organelles were probably engulfed first. Biologists can learn more about the origin of mitochondria by studying protists whose mitochondrial genomes are very much like those of bacteria. ⓘ *endosymbiosis,* p. 311

Chloroplasts have an especially colorful evolutionary history (figure 18.2). Biologists studying chloroplast DNA, membrane structure, and photosynthetic pigments suggest that the chloroplasts of red algae, green algae, and land plants all arose from cyanobacteria engulfed by some ancient eukaryotic cell. The chloroplasts in these species are surrounded by two membranes. In other photosynthetic protists, three or more membranes surround each chloroplast. The evidence suggests that these organelles originated long ago when red algae or green algae were themselves engulfed by other cells—an event called secondary endosymbiosis. We are just beginning to unravel the events surrounding the origins of all the different types of chloroplasts.

Another important milestone in eukaryote history is the origin of multicellularity. Biologists do not know how unicellular eukaryotes adopted a multicellular lifestyle. We do know, however, that multicellularity arose independently in multiple lineages. After all, genetic evidence clearly suggests that plants, fungi, and animals arose from different lineages of unicellular protists. Biologists hope to gain insight into the steps that led to multicellularity by studying protists that form colonies in which individuals interact as they move and obtain food. ⓘ *multicellularity,* p. 312

A second reason that protists are important to studies of evolutionary biology is that these simple eukaryotes shed light on the evolutionary history of plants, fungi, and animals. Genetic and cellular similarities, for example, illustrate the strong evolutionary connection between green algae and plants. Likewise, DNA evidence suggests that heterotrophic protists called choanoflagellates are the closest existing relatives to sponges, the simplest animals (see figure 21.1). ⓘ *sponges,* p. 423

Clearly, depicting the diversity of the protists in just one chapter is a challenge. In exploring these organisms, remember that the examples in each section represent just a small sampling of some of the most intriguing members of this uniquely variable group.

18.1 MASTERING CONCEPTS

1. What features define the protists?
2. Describe examples of how protists are important.
3. Why are evolutionary biologists interested in protists?

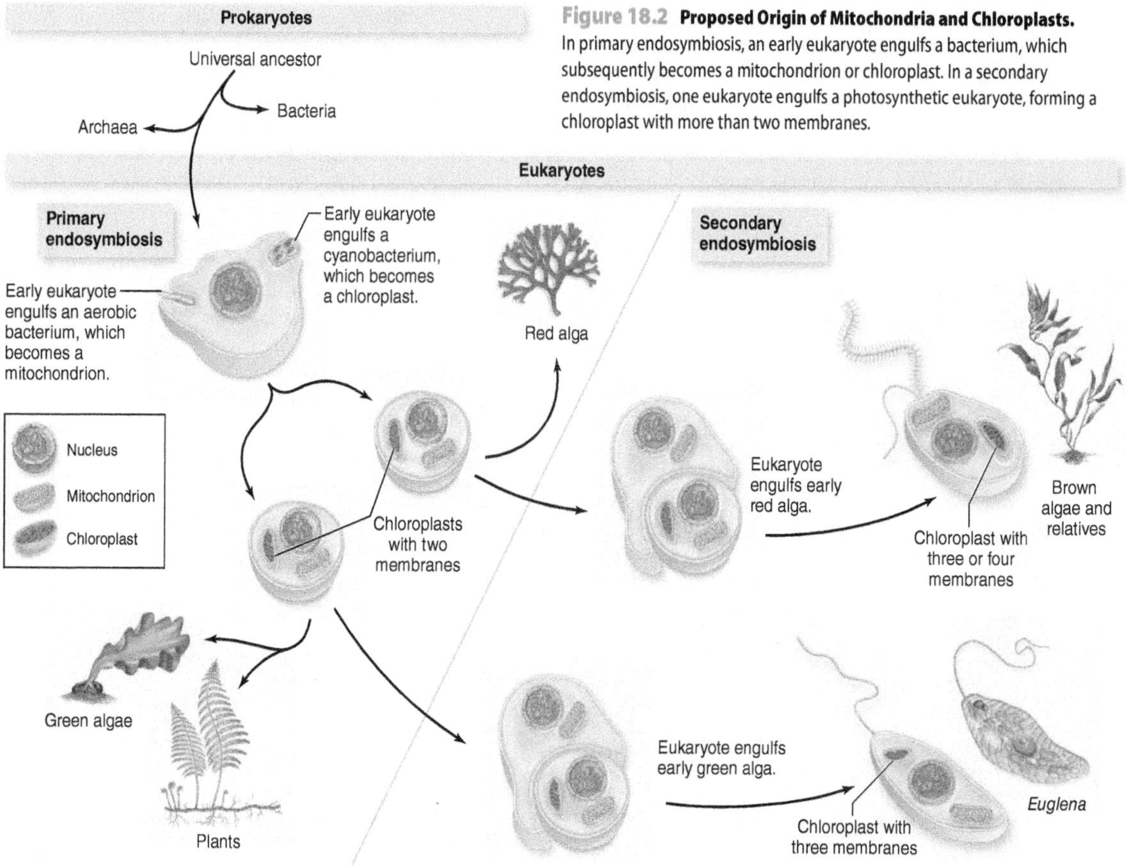

Figure 18.2 Proposed Origin of Mitochondria and Chloroplasts. In primary endosymbiosis, an early eukaryote engulfs a bacterium, which subsequently becomes a mitochondrion or chloroplast. In a secondary endosymbiosis, one eukaryote engulfs a photosynthetic eukaryote, forming a chloroplast with more than two membranes.

18.2 Many Protists Are Photosynthetic

Most people probably think of algae as pond scum, but **algae** is a general term that refers to any photosynthetic protist that lives in water. Although the cyanobacteria were traditionally called "blue-green algae," most biologists now reserve the term *algae* for eukaryotes.

The cells of algae contain chloroplasts that house a rainbow of yellow, gold, brown, red, and green photosynthetic pigments. These organelles use light energy and CO_2 to produce carbohydrates and other organic molecules that support freshwater and marine food webs. They also release O_2 as a waste product.

Algae may be single-celled, colonial, filamentous, or multicellular. Some of the more complex species produce differentiated tissues. Although the body forms may resemble those of plants, algae are considered protists because they lack the distinctive reproductive structures that define plants. This section describes the major types of algae.

A. Euglenoids Are Heterotrophs and Autotrophs

The **euglenoids** are unicellular protists with elongated cells (figure 18.3). Most have a long, whiplike flagellum used in locomotion and a short flagellum that does not extend from the cell. Supporting the cell membrane is a pellicle, a protective layer made of rigid or elastic protein strips. An eyespot helps the cell orient toward light.

Most euglenoids inhabit fresh water. About one third of the species are photosynthetic, and the rest feed on organic compounds suspended in the water. But these metabolic roles are not always fixed. Photosynthetic euglenoids such as *Euglena,* for example, may occasionally feed on organic matter. In darkness, their cells become entirely heterotrophic, although photosynthesis resumes once light returns.

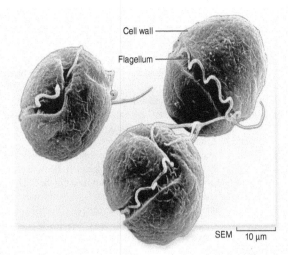

Figure 18.4 Dinoflagellates. Note the flagella and cellulose plates that make up the cell walls of these dinoflagellates.

B. Dinoflagellates Are "Whirling Cells"

The marine protists known as **dinoflagellates** are characterized by two flagella of different lengths (figure 18.4). One of the flagella propels the cell with a whirling motion (the Greek *dinein* means "to whirl"); the other mainly acts as a rudder. In addition, many dinoflagellates have cell walls of overlapping cellulose plates.

Dinoflagellates are a major component of the ocean's food webs. About half the species are photosynthetic. Several species live within the tissues of jellyfishes, corals, sea anemones, or giant clams, providing carbohydrates to their host animals. Many other species are predators or parasites. Some are bioluminescent, producing flashing lights in coastal waters (see section 18.6).

A red tide is a sudden population explosion, or "bloom," of dinoflagellates that turn the water red (figure 18.5). Some of these algae produce toxins, which can make red tides deadly (see this chapter's opening essay). The toxins may become concentrated in the tissues of clams, scallops, oysters, and mussels. A person who eats tainted shellfish might develop the numb mouth, lips, face, and limbs that are characteristic of paralytic shellfish poisoning.

A red tide is just one of several types of so-called harmful algal bloom, defined as an overgrowth of algae that release toxins or harm ecosystems in other ways. Usually these blooms occur in response to a boost in the nutrient content of the water, as described in this chapter's Burning Question.

 Video Good Poison

Figure 18.3 *Euglena.* The pond-dwelling *Euglena* has a flagellum and chloroplasts, but it can also ingest food particles.

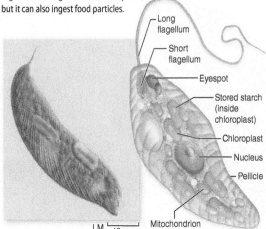

Figure 18.5 Harmful Algal Bloom. Huge populations of dinoflagellates cause red tides.

Why and how do algae form?

Algae are common aquatic organisms, but they are often inconspicuous. Sometimes, however, their populations grow so large that they seem to take over; ponds and poorly maintained swimming pools can turn bright green with algae (figure 18.A). This population explosion occurs when nutrients and sunlight are abundant.

Algal blooms are normal in some ecosystems, such as in many ponds. A bloom where water is normally clear, however, usually indicates that nutrients from sewage, fertilizer, or animal waste are polluting the waterway. The use of lawn fertilizers is a common cause of algal blooms in ponds in residential settings.

Algae may seem harmless, but algal blooms induced by nutrient pollution can devastate aquatic life. After the algae die, bacteria and other microbes decompose their bodies. Respiration by these decomposers depletes oxygen in the water, causing fishes and other aquatic species to suffocate. ⓘ *eutrophication*, p. 782

Submit your burning question to
Marielle.Hoefnagels@mheducation.com

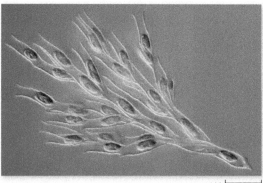

Figure 18.6 **Golden Algae.** *Dinobryon* is a colonial golden alga.

Like *Euglena*, golden algae can act as autotrophs or heterotrophs. In some aquatic ecosystems, photosynthesis by golden algae provides a significant source of food for zooplankton. When light or nutrient supplies dwindle, however, many golden algae can consume bacteria or other protists.

Some golden algae can be harmful. In nutrient-rich streams and lakes, blooms of golden algae can release toxins that kill fish (although humans are apparently unaffected).

Diatoms **Diatoms** are unicellular algae with two-part silica cell walls that confer a variety of ornate shapes (figure 18.7). These protists occupy just about every moist habitat on Earth, from oceans to streams to fish tanks to damp soil. Their populations are sensitive to water pH, salinity, and other environmental conditions. Biologists therefore periodically sample freshwater diatom populations as indicators of environmental quality.

Although diatoms occur nearly everywhere, most live in oceans. Their tiny photosynthetic cells can reach huge

Figure 18.7 **Diatoms.** The "glass houses" (silica cell walls) of these photosynthetic protists exhibit a dazzling variety of forms.

C. Golden Algae, Diatoms, and Brown Algae Contain Yellowish Pigments

Three groups of algae contain a yellowish photosynthetic pigment called fucoxanthin in addition to chlorophylls *a* and *c*. This accessory pigment gives these organisms a golden, olive green, or brown hue.

Golden Algae The **golden algae** are named for their color (figure 18.6). Their cells usually have two flagella. Most are unicellular, but filamentous and colonial forms also exist. *Dinobryon* is an example of a freshwater genus of golden algae; in these protists, individual vase-shaped cells stack end to end to produce branched or unbranched chains.

densities, removing CO_2 from the atmosphere and providing food for zooplankton. Over millions of years, the glassy shells of diatoms have accumulated thick deposits on the ocean floor. The abrasive shells mined from these deposits are used in swimming pool filters, polishes, toothpaste, and many other products. Diatoms also impart the distinct reflective quality of paints used in roadway signs and license plates.

Few microorganisms fossilize as well as diatoms, and biologists know of some 35,000 extinct species. In some undisturbed lake sediments, diatoms have left complete records of the evolution of entirely new species.

Brown Algae   The **brown algae** are the largest and most complex protists. Although they are multicellular, they resemble the golden algae in their pigments and their reproductive cells, each of which bears two flagella.

Brown algae live in marine habitats all over the world. The Sargasso Sea in the northern Atlantic Ocean, for example, is named after floating masses of brown algae called *Sargassum.* The kelps, which are the largest of the brown algae, produce enormous underwater forests that provide food and habitat for many animals (figure 18.8). Some kelps exceed 30 meters in length.

Humans consume several species of kelp. *Laminaria digitata,* for example, is an ingredient in many Asian dishes. Algin, a chemical extracted from the cell walls of brown algae, is used as an emulsifying, thickening, and stabilizing agent in products including ice cream, candies, chocolate, salad dressings, toothpaste, cosmetics, polishes, latex paint, and paper.

Figure 18.8   **A Giant Kelp.** A holdfast organ anchors a brown alga to a substrate, while the gas-filled bladders add buoyancy. The leaflike blades expand the surface area for photosynthesis.

Blade

Bladder

Holdfast

Figure 18.9   **A Red Alga.** The blades of this alga, called dulse, grow to 50 cm. People on the northern Atlantic coast consider it a healthy snack.

D. Red Algae Can Live in Deep Water

Most **red algae** are relatively large (figure 18.9), although some are microscopic. These marine organisms are somewhat similar to green algae in that they store carbohydrates as a modified form of starch, have cell walls containing cellulose, and produce chlorophyll *a.*

Red algae, however, can live in water exceeding 200 meters in depth, thanks to reddish and bluish photosynthetic pigments that absorb wavelengths of light that chlorophyll *a* cannot capture. All light becomes dimmer with increasing depth, but the wavelengths do not dissipate equally. The pigments in red algae can use some of the wavelengths that persist in deep water.

Figure It Out

Consult figure 5.4 to see the light absorption spectrum for chlorophyll *a.* Predict the most likely range of wavelengths absorbed by the photosynthetic pigments unique to red algae.

Answer: Between 500 and 650 nm

Humans use red algae in many ways. Agar, for example, is a polysaccharide in the cell walls of some species. This jellylike substance is used as a culture medium for microorganisms in petri dishes; agar is also sometimes used as a gel in canned meats and a thickener in ice cream and yogurt. Another useful product is carrageenan, a polysaccharide that emulsifies fats in chocolate bars and stabilizes paints, cosmetics, and creamy foods. A red alga called nori is used for wrapping sushi.

E. Green Algae Are the Closest Relatives of Land Plants

The **green algae** are the protists that share the most similarities with plants. They use chlorophyll *a* and *b* as photosynthetic pigments, use starch as a storage carbohydrate, and have cell walls containing cellulose. Like plants, many green algae also have life cycles that feature an **alternation of generations,** in which a multicellular haploid (gametophyte) phase is followed by a diploid (sporophyte) phase (figure 18.10).

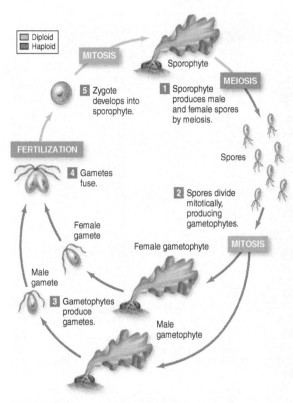

Figure 18.10 Life Cycle of a Green Alga. The sea lettuce *Ulva* has a life cycle that features an alternation of haploid and diploid generations.

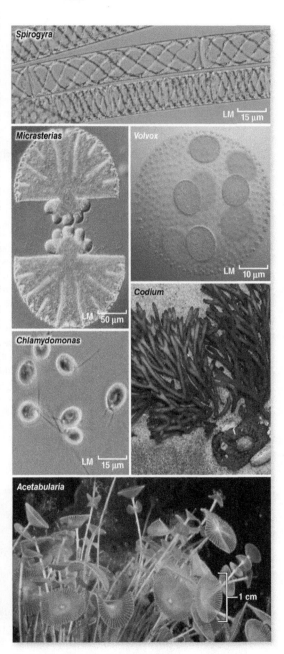

Figure 18.11 Gallery of Green Algae. Green algae have a variety of forms, from solitary microscopic cells to complex multicellular bodies.

The habitats and body forms of green algae are diverse (figure 18.11). Most live in fresh water or in moist habitats on land, although some live in symbiotic relationships with fungi, forming lichens. Green algae range in size from the smallest eukaryote *(Micromonas)*, only 1 μm in diameter, to sea lettuce *(Ulva)*, exceeding 1 meter in length. Green algae may be unicellular, filamentous, colonial, or multicellular. The multicellular species may have rootlike and stemlike structures, but they are far less specialized than plants. ⓘ *lichens*, p. 411

One well-studied green alga is *Chlamydomonas*, a unicellular organism that reproduces asexually and sexually. Scientists study these algae to learn about the evolution of sex, how an individual's sex is determined, and how cells of opposite sexes recognize each other. A classroom favorite is the colonial green alga, *Volvox*. Hundreds to thousands of *Volvox* cells form hollow balls; the cells move their flagella to move the sphere. New colonies remain within the parental ball of cells until they burst free.

Other green algae include the geometrically shaped desmids *(Micrasterias)*, mermaid's wineglass *(Acetabularia)*, the ribbon-like *Spirogyra*, and the tubular *Codium*. One species, *Chlorella*, is being considered as a food and oxygen source on prolonged space flights. An advantage of *Chlorella* over plants is that green algae can multiply very quickly, as evidenced by the rapid "greening" of a poorly maintained aquarium or swimming pool.

18.2 MASTERING CONCEPTS

1. What mode of nutrition do the algae use?
2. Describe several criteria for classifying the algae.
3. List and describe the characteristics of the major groups of algae.

18.3   Some Heterotrophic Protists Were Once Classified as Fungi

Slime molds and water molds are protists that resemble fungi in some ways: they are heterotrophic, and some produce filamentous feeding structures similar to those in fungi. They also commonly occur alongside fungi in many habitats. Nevertheless, DNA sequences clearly indicate that they are not closely related to fungi.

A. Slime Molds Are Unicellular and Multicellular

The slime molds are informally divided into two groups whose relationship to each other remains unclear. Both types live in damp habitats such as forest floors. In addition, each type of organism exists as single, amoeboid cells and as large masses that behave as one multicellular organism. The major difference between the two types is reflected in their names: plasmodial and cellular slime molds.

The feeding stage of a **plasmodial slime mold** consists of a plasmodium, which is a mass of thousands of diploid nuclei enclosed by a single cell membrane. This structure gives these organisms their other common name, the "acellular" slime molds. The plasmodium may be a conspicuous, slimy, bright yellow or orange mass up to 25 cm in diameter (figure 18.12). It migrates along the forest floor, engulfing bacteria and other microorganisms on leaves, debris, and rotting logs.

In times of drought or food shortages, the plasmodium halts and forms fruiting bodies, which produce thick-walled reproductive cells called spores. When favorable conditions return, the spores germinate and form haploid cells. Two of these cells may fuse, forming a diploid zygote nucleus that divides repeatedly by mitosis,

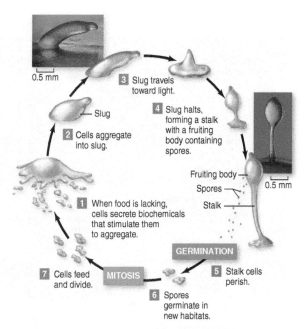

Figure 18.13   Life Cycle of a Cellular Slime Mold. (*1*) Starvation stimulates cells to (*2*) aggregate into a multicellular "slug," which (*3*) crawls to a new habitat and (*4*) forms a fruiting body that releases spores. (*5*) Stalk cells die, but (*6*) spores develop into (*7*) amoeboid cells that consume bacteria. Only asexual reproduction is shown; all cells shown are haploid.

forming a new multinucleate plasmodium. Scientists use plasmodial slime molds to study cell division and the movements of cytoplasm inside a cell.

In contrast to the plasmodial slime molds, individual cells of a **cellular slime mold** retain their membranes throughout the life cycle. The cells exist as haploid amoebae, engulfing bacteria and other microorganisms in fresh water, moist soil, and decaying vegetation.

When food becomes scarce, the amoebae secrete chemical attractants that stimulate the neighboring cells to aggregate into a sluglike structure (figure 18.13). The "slug" moves toward light, stops, and forms a stalk topped by a fruiting body that produces haploid spores. The cells of the stalk perish, but the spores survive; water, soil animals, or birds spread them to new habitats. The spores then germinate to form haploid amoebae, and the cycle begins anew. Sexual reproduction also occurs in some conditions. *Dictyostelium discoideum* is a cellular slime mold used in many scientific studies (see this chapter's Focus on Model Organisms).

B. Water Molds Are Decomposers and Parasites

The **water molds,** or oomycetes, are decomposers or parasites of plants and animals in moist environments (figure 18.14). The filaments of water molds secrete digestive enzymes into their surroundings and absorb the nutrients. In addition, like fungi called chytrids, water molds produce swimming spores that aid their dispersal in water and wet soil. Despite the similarities, however,

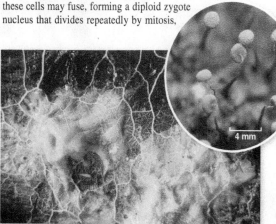

Figure 18.12   Plasmodial Slime Mold. Streaming masses of *Physarum* ooze across dead logs, leaf litter, and other organic matter. The inset shows the spore-producing structures of a slime mold.

a.   b.

Figure 18.14 Water Molds. (a) *Phytophthora infestans* is a water mold that causes late blight of potatoes and was responsible for the Irish potato famine in the mid-1840s. (b) *Saprolegnia* infects a dead insect.

water molds are unlike fungi in many ways. The filaments of water molds are diploid, for example, whereas most fungal filaments are haploid. Also, fungi have cell walls containing chitin, but water mold cell walls contain cellulose.

The best-known water molds are those that ruin crops, causing such diseases as downy mildew of grapes and lettuce. In the 1870s, downy mildew of grapes nearly destroyed the French wine industry. The water mold *Phytophthora infestans,* which means "plant destroyer," causes late blight of potato. This disease caused the devastating Irish potato famine from 1845 to 1847, during which more than a million people starved and millions more emigrated from Ireland. The Irish potato famine followed several rainy seasons, which fostered the rapid spread of the plant disease. A newly

discovered relative of *P. infestans,* called *Phytophthora ramorum,* causes a tree disease called sudden oak death. Another well-known water mold is *Saprolegnia,* a protist that forms cottony masses on fishes and other aquatic organisms that are weakened or dead.

18.3 MASTERING CONCEPTS

1. What mode of nutrition do the slime molds and water molds use?
2. Compare and contrast the plasmodial and cellular slime molds.
3. What has been the role of water molds in the environment and history?

F⊙CUS on Model Organisms

Cellular Slime Mold: *Dictyostelium discoideum*

Slime molds have such an unappealing name that it may seem hard to imagine why anyone would study them. But *Dictyostelium discoideum* is an unusual organism, one that straddles the boundary between the unicellular and the multicellular. As illustrated in figure 18.13, its life cycle includes individual amoeba-like cells, a multicellular migrating "slug," and a spore-producing structure.

Dictyostelium discoideum is useful as a model because, like other model organisms, it is easy to grow in the laboratory and has a short generation time. In addition, its cells are readily accessible to microscopy and genetic studies. As a result, *D. discoideum* (affectionately called "Dicty" by its researchers) remains a fascinating organism. Researchers have made several discoveries in this species:

- **Cell movement:** A "Dicty" cell eats by producing extensions that engulf and absorb food particles by phagocytosis. Scientists have discovered that this movement is possible because proteins such as actin and myosin move rapidly within the cell. These same proteins produce muscle movement in animals. ⓘ *muscle movement,* p. 598

- **Cytokinesis:** Researchers observing cell division in *D. discoideum* have discovered that the protein myosin is also

required for cytokinesis (the physical division of one cell into two). ⓘ *cytokinesis,* p. 156

- **Chemotaxis:** Starving Dicty cells move toward one another and form a multicellular "slug." This movement toward a chemical stimulus, called chemotaxis, requires membrane proteins that not only detect the signals from other Dicty cells but also transmit the information to the inside of the cell. Similar signal transduction systems occur in many organisms. ⓘ *cell membrane,* p. 54

- **Cell differentiation:** When individual Dicty cells come together, chemical signals presumably determine which cells will become stalk cells (and die) and which will become spore cells (and survive). Researchers have discovered a sterol-like compound that induces the differentiation of stalk cells. Such research may help answer questions about the origin of multicellularity. ⓘ *sterols,* p. 39

18.4 Protozoa Are Diverse Heterotrophic Protists

Finding a list of characteristics that unite the diverse **protozoa** is difficult. Most are unicellular, and the vast majority are heterotrophs, but several autotrophic species exist. They move by flagella, cilia, or pseudopodia. Some are free-living, and others are obligate parasites. Most are asexual, but sexual reproduction occurs in many species.

This chapter describes four groups of distantly related protozoa that are defined by locomotion and morphology. New molecular techniques are redefining the protozoa, but until the newer system of classification is better defined and more widely accepted, these four groups remain practical for general biology, education, and medicine.

A. Several Flagellated Protozoa Cause Disease

The **flagellated protozoa** are unicellular organisms with one or more flagella. Most are free-living in fresh water, the ocean, and soil. The euglenoids and dinoflagellates, groups already described with the algae, are flagellates. This section turns to a few of the heterotrophic species (figure 18.15).

One example of a flagellated protozoan is *Trichonympha*, a protist that lives in the intestines of termites. The cells of *Trichonympha*, in turn, harbor bacteria that digest cellulose. This bacterium-within-protist living organization enables termites to "digest" wood. Exposing termites to high oxygen or high temperature kills the symbionts. The insects soon die, with guts full of undigested wood.

Some parasitic flagellated protozoa cause disease in humans. For example, *Trichomonas vaginalis* resides in the urogenital tracts of both men and women. It is sexually transmitted and causes a form of vaginitis in females. *Giardia intestinalis* (also known as *Giardia lamblia*) causes "hiker's diarrhea," or giardiasis. People ingest the cysts of the organism in contaminated water. As *Giardia* cells divide in the small intestine, they impair the host's ability to absorb nutrients, resulting in diarrhea and cramping.

Another group of disease-causing flagellates are the **trypanosomes.** These whip-shaped parasites invade the bloodstream and, in some cases, the brain. Insects transmit trypanosomes to humans. Tsetse flies, for example, carry *Trypanosoma brucei*, the organism that causes African sleeping sickness. In South and Central America, kissing bugs transmit *Trypanosoma cruzi* to humans from rodents, armadillos, and dogs. The resulting illness, called Chagas disease, kills 45,000 people annually. The sand fly transmits a related parasite, *Leishmania*.

B. Amoeboid Protozoa Produce Pseudopodia

The **amoeboid protozoa** produce cytoplasmic extensions known as pseudopodia (Latin, meaning "false feet"), which are important in **Video** Amoeba Locomotion
locomotion and capturing food via phagocytosis. One familiar species is *Amoeba proteus*, a common freshwater microbe that engulfs bacteria, algae, and other protists in its pseudopodia (figure 18.16). The human digestive tract may be invaded by another species, *Entamoeba histolytica*, which can cause fever and severe diarrhea. ⓘ *phagocytosis*, p. 84

The **foraminiferans**, or forams, are an ancient group of mostly marine amoeboid protozoa. They have complex, brilliantly colored tests (shells) made primarily of calcium carbonate (figure 18.17a). Their populations are immense: about one-third of the ocean floor is made of the shells of the marine foram *Globigerina*. England's White Cliffs of Dover, among other limestone and chalk deposits, are made largely of the tests of forams and other marine organisms that have been lifted out of the water by geologic forces. Paleontologists studying extinct forams have learned which species correlate with oil and gas deposits. The shells are also useful in dating rock strata.

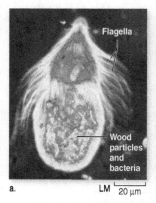
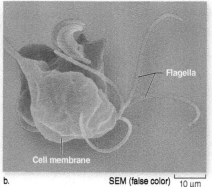
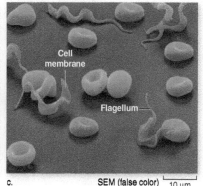

Figure 18.15 Flagellated Protozoa. (a) *Trichonympha* lives inside the intestines of termites. Note the fringe of flagella. (b) *Trichomonas vaginalis* causes the sexually transmitted disease trichomoniasis. These organisms have multiple flagella. (c) A blood smear from a patient with African sleeping sickness reveals *Trypanosoma brucei* (purple) among the blood cells (red). Each trypanosome features a single flagellum.

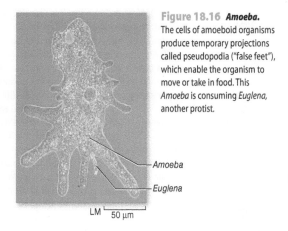

Figure 18.16 *Amoeba.* The cells of amoeboid organisms produce temporary projections called pseudopodia ("false feet"), which enable the organism to move or take in food. This *Amoeba* is consuming *Euglena*, another protist.

— Amoeba

— Euglena

LM ⌐ 50 μm

The **radiolarians** are among the oldest protozoa. They are planktonic organisms with intricate tests made of silica (figure 18.17b); pseudopodia extend through holes in the shells. "Radiolarian ooze" is sediment consisting of large numbers of their tests. On the ocean floor, radiolarian ooze can be as thick as 4000 meters.

C. Ciliates Are Common Protozoa with Complex Cells

The **ciliates** are complex, mostly unicellular protists that are characterized by abundant hairlike cilia (figure 18.18). The cilia have multiple functions. Waves of moving cilia propel the organism through the water. Cilia also sweep bacteria, algae, and other ciliates into the cell's oral groove. ⓘ *cilia*, p. 63

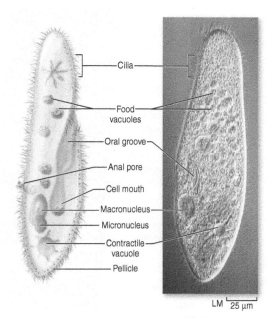

— Cilia

— Food vacuoles

— Oral groove

— Anal pore

— Cell mouth

— Macronucleus

— Micronucleus

— Contractile vacuole

— Pellicle

LM ⌐ 25 μm

Figure 18.18 **Anatomy of *Paramecium*.** Structures in *Paramecium* include a micronucleus and a macronucleus; an oral groove with a "mouth" into which cilia wave food; food vacuoles for storage; contractile vacuoles that maintain solute concentrations; and an anal pore, which releases wastes.

Ciliate cells have other distinctive features as well. A food vacuole surrounds and transports each captured meal inside the cell, and a permanent anal pore releases the wastes. In freshwater habitats, water may enter the cell by osmosis. An organelle called a

Video Contractile Vacuoles

Test LM 200 μm
(shell)

Pseudopodia

a.

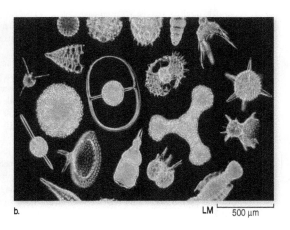

b.

LM ⌐ 500 μm

Figure 18.17 **Foraminiferans and Radiolarians.** (a) Foraminiferans form vast amounts of ocean sediment. The White Cliffs of Dover are composed of mostly foraminiferan tests. (b) These intricate silica shells are the remains of radiolarians.

contractile vacuole helps maintain water balance by pumping the excess fluid out of the cell. ⓘ *osmosis,* p. 81

In addition, many ciliates have two types of nuclei, a small micronucleus and a larger macronucleus. The DNA in the micronucleus is passed on during sexual reproduction, whereas the genes in the macronucleus have metabolic and developmental functions.

The habitats of ciliates are diverse. Most are free-living, motile cells such as *Paramecium* and its predator, *Didinium.* Several ciliate species, such as *Stentor,* are sessile or attached forms living on a variety of substrates. Nearly one third of ciliates are symbiotic, living in the bodies of crustaceans, mollusks, and vertebrates. Some inhabit the stomachs of cattle, where they house bacteria that break down the cellulose in grass. Others are parasites. *Ichthyophthirius multifilis,* for example, is familiar to many aquarium owners as the cause of a freshwater fish disease called "ich." Symptoms include white spots on the skin and gills.

D. Apicomplexans Include Nonmotile Animal Parasites

The **apicomplexans** are nonmotile, spore-forming, internal parasites of animals. The name *apicomplexa* comes from the apical complex, a cluster of microtubules and organelles at one end of the cell. This structure, visible only with an electron microscope, apparently helps the parasite attach to and invade host cells.

Apicomplexans include several organisms that cause illness. This chapter's Apply It Now box describes *Cryptosporidium,* a genus containing several species that cause waterborne disease. Another example is *Toxoplasma gondii,* a protist that infects cats and other mammals. A person who handles feces from infected cats can accidentally ingest *Toxoplasma* cysts. The resulting infection may remain symptomless or develop into an illness called toxoplasmosis, especially in people with weakened immune systems. In the most severe cases, the parasite can damage the brain and eyes. The infection can also pass to a fetus, which is why pregnant women should avoid cat litter boxes.

Another example of a human illness caused by an apicomplexan is malaria. Four species of *Plasmodium* cause mosquito-borne malaria. (*Plasmodium,* a genus of apicomplexans, is not to be confused with the plasmodium produced by some slime molds.) The life cycle is complex, involving many stages in multiple hosts and including both asexual and sexual reproduction (figure 18.19).

A cycle of malaria begins when an infected mosquito of any of 60 *Anopheles* species feeds on human blood. The insect's saliva transmits small haploid cells called sporozoites to the human host (figure 18.19, step 1). The sporozoites travel in the bloodstream (step 2) and enter the liver cells, where they multiply rapidly (step 3). Eventually the cells emerge as merozoites, which continue the infection within the human host. Some merozoites reproduce in red blood cells; every 48 to 72 hours, they

Apply It **Now**

Don't Drink That Water

The sign says, "Please shower before entering pool." What is the purpose of that request? Isn't showering a wasteful prelude to taking a refreshing plunge?

The truth is that the preswim shower is an important public health measure. Washing thoroughly with soap and hot water helps eliminate harmful microbes before they have a chance to contaminate the pool's water.

Cryptosporidium, or "crypto," is one example of a contagious microorganism that spreads easily in water. This apicomplexan protist lives in the intestinal tracts of infected humans, entering the body through the mouth and exiting in feces. It produces tough-walled cysts that can survive for days in the chlorinated water of public pools, water parks, splash pads, and other places where people gather to play in the water.

Even tiny amounts of feces, invisible to the unaided eye, can contaminate water with *Cryptosporidium* cysts, triggering an outbreak. Swimmers who accidentally swallow the tainted water typically become ill within a week, as cells released from the cysts invade the lining of the digestive tract. Symptoms include diarrhea, cramps, fever, vomiting, and dehydration.

Crypto outbreaks periodically occur in communities throughout the United States. One notable episode occurred in Milwaukee, Wisconsin, in 1993. A malfunctioning water treatment plant distributed contaminated water to hundreds of thousands of households, sickening about 25% of Milwaukee's population and killing 100 people.

LM 5 μm

Scattered small outbreaks also have occurred in pools and other recreational water venues, where the victims are often young children who ingest the water. Simple preventive measures include keeping children with diarrhea out of the water, washing hands thoroughly after using the toilet or changing diapers, and—as the sign says—showering before entering the pool.

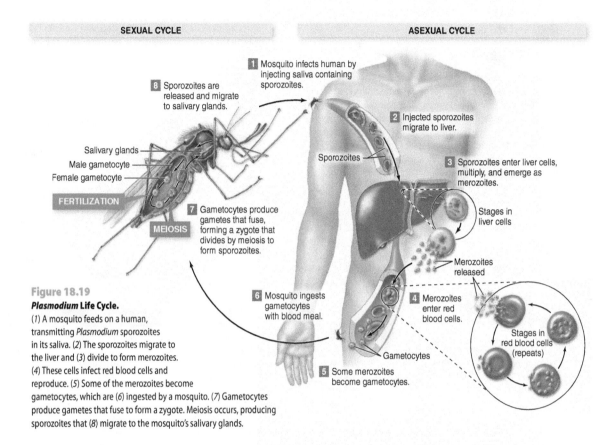

| SEXUAL CYCLE | ASEXUAL CYCLE |

8 Sporozoites are released and migrate to salivary glands.

1 Mosquito infects human by injecting saliva containing sporozoites.

2 Injected sporozoites migrate to liver.

Salivary glands
Male gametocyte
Female gametocyte

Sporozoites

3 Sporozoites enter liver cells, multiply, and emerge as merozoites.

FERTILIZATION

MEIOSIS

Stages in liver cells

7 Gametocytes produce gametes that fuse, forming a zygote that divides by meiosis to form sporozoites.

Merozoites released

6 Mosquito ingests gametocytes with blood meal.

4 Merozoites enter red blood cells.

Stages in red blood cells (repeats)

Gametocytes

5 Some merozoites become gametocytes.

Figure 18.19

***Plasmodium* Life Cycle.**

(*1*) A mosquito feeds on a human, transmitting *Plasmodium* sporozoites in its saliva. (*2*) The sporozoites migrate to the liver and (*3*) divide to form merozoites. (*4*) These cells infect red blood cells and reproduce. (*5*) Some of the merozoites become gametocytes, which are (*6*) ingested by a mosquito. (*7*) Gametocytes produce gametes that fuse to form a zygote. Meiosis occurs, producing sporozoites that (*8*) migrate to the mosquito's salivary glands.

burst out and infect other red blood cells (step 4). This release is often synchronized throughout the victim's body, causing the characteristic recurrent chills and fever of malaria.

Other merozoites become specialized as male and female sexual forms called gametocytes (step 5). When mosquitoes ingest the gametocytes from an infected person's blood (step 6), the cells unite in the insect's stomach (step 7). After several additional steps, sporozoites form. These move to the mosquito's salivary glands (step 8), ready to enter a new host when the insect seeks its next blood meal.

From 300 million to 500 million people a year suffer from malaria, with more than 90% of them in sub-Saharan Africa. Globally, 2 million to 3 million people die each year from this disease. Among very ill children, the death rate is 50%. Even survivors may retain dormant forms of the parasite, becoming ill again months or years after the initial infection.

Despite decades of research, malaria continues to be the world's most significant infectious disease. No effective vaccine has been developed, and nations troubled by poverty and civil unrest struggle to distribute drugs to prevent or treat malaria. Moreover, *Plasmodium* continues to develop resistance to drugs that were effective in the past. Malaria prevention efforts therefore focus on repelling and killing mosquitoes (even as the use of

insecticides has selected for resistance in mosquitoes). The careful use of antimalarial drugs, alone and in combination, helps prevent and treat malaria and reduces selection for resistant parasites.

Not everyone is equally susceptible to malaria. People with one copy of the recessive sickle cell allele are much less likely to contract malaria than are people with two dominant alleles. In areas of the world where malaria is endemic, human populations have a relatively high incidence of the sickle cell allele. In malaria-free areas, the sickle cell allele is much rarer. This pattern illustrates the selective force that malaria exerts on the human population. ⓘ *sickle cell trait*, p. 138; *balanced polymorphism*, p. 250

18.4 MASTERING CONCEPTS

1. What mode of nutrition do protozoa use?
2. What are the characteristics of each major group of protozoa?
3. List three diseases caused by flagellated protozoa.
4. Compare and contrast amoebae, foraminiferans, and radiolarians.
5. How do ciliates move and eat?
6. What are the distinguishing characteristics of apicomplexans?

18.5 Protist Classification Is Changing Rapidly

This chapter illustrates some of the difficulties in classifying the protists. For example, the euglenoids and dinoflagellates could easily fall into either of two groups: the algae (because they photosynthesize) or the flagellated protozoa (because they have flagella and may be heterotrophic). Likewise, the water molds are traditionally grouped with slime molds because they share a habitat with fungi, but water molds are actually closely related to brown algae. Clearly, the traditional scheme groups unrelated organisms.

New research based on genetic sequences is helping to assign each species into a lineage with its closest relatives. Nevertheless, biologists have not yet firmly established the number of taxonomic groups, their ranks, their names, or the evolutionary relationships among them.

One scheme organizes all eukaryotes into six "supergroups," which are summarized in table 18.1. A supergroup unites organisms that share a common evolutionary lineage, whether those organisms are microorganisms (i.e., most of the protists) or multicellular (i.e., the plants, fungi, and animals). Along these lines, note that the supergroup Archaeplastida unites the red algae, green algae, and land plants, all of which have chloroplasts derived from primary endosymbiosis. Likewise, supergroup Opisthokonta includes fungi, animals, and their common ancestor.

Note also that several of the supergroups listed in this table unite organisms once thought to be dissimilar. Consider, for example, supergroup Chromalveolata, which includes two other new groups: the alveolates and the stramenopiles. Alveolates are eukaryotes that have a series of flattened sacs, or alveoli, just beneath the cell membrane. The alveolates include dinoflagellates, ciliates, apicomplexans, foraminiferans, and radiolarians.

The stramenopiles are the water molds, diatoms, brown algae, and golden algae. The word *stramenopile* means "flagellum-hair" (*stramen* = straw or flagellum, and *pilos* = hair). At some point in their life cycles, stramenopiles produce cells with two flagella, one of which is covered with tubular hairs. In addition, the photosynthetic members of this group produce the yellowish accessory pigment fucoxanthin.

The placement of many—if not most—protists remains unresolved, and the evidence supporting most of the supergroups remains relatively weak. Nevertheless, no one has yet proposed a better system. Protistan classification will continue to evolve as research reveals new molecular sequences, but it will likely remain a work in progress for years to come.

18.5   MASTERING CONCEPTS

1. How have molecular sequences changed protist classification?
2. What features unite some of the major lineages of eukaryotes?

TABLE **18.1**   **Proposed Eukaryotic "Supergroups": A Summary**

Supergroup (pictured below)	Distinguishing Features	Examples
Archaeplastida (a)	Photosynthetic eukaryotes with chloroplasts derived from primary endosymbiosis.	Red algae, green algae, land plants
Opisthokonta (b)	Motile cells have one flagellum.	Choanoflagellates, animals, fungi
Chromalveolata (c)	Chloroplasts (if present) are derived from secondary endosymbiosis.	
Alveolates	Flattened sacs (alveoli) beneath cell membrane.	Dinoflagellates, apicomplexans, ciliates (including *Paramecium*)
Stramenopiles	Motile cells with two flagella, one of which has tubular hairs; fucoxanthin is an accessory pigment in photosynthetic forms.	Water molds, diatoms, brown algae, golden algae
Amoebozoa (d)	Amoeboid movement via pseudopodia; feed by phagocytosis; slime molds form spores.	*Amoeba*, many slime molds (including *Physarum* and *Dictyostelium*)
Excavata (e)	Unicellular flagellated protists; may lack mitochondria; photosynthetic or parasitic; chloroplasts (when present) are derived from secondary endosymbiosis.	*Trichomonas, Trichonympha, Giardia, Euglena,* trypanosomes
Rhizaria (f)	Amoeboid movement; many produce shells.	Radiolarians, foraminiferans

Red alga   Choanoflagellate   Paramecium   Brown alga   Amoeba   Giardia   Euglena   Foraminiferan

a.   b.   c.   d.   e.   f.

18.6 Shining a Spotlight on Danger

As waves break after sunset near La Jolla, California, blue-green light explodes from millions of algae (figure 18.20). It is a beautiful sight that is not limited to this southern California beach— bioluminescent protists are common throughout the world's oceans. But their glow, however awe-inspiring, did not evolve for the curious eyes of humans. Why has evolution selected some algae to release light when they are disturbed?

Bioluminescence, or the production of light by an organism, has been studied in dinoflagellates for several decades. In that time, many research groups have tested hypotheses about how and why these algae emit light when agitated. For example, some proposed that the light startles small herbivores called copepods, which graze on dinoflagellates at night. But that explanation does not explain why copepods might avoid the light, which is harmless. After all, natural selection should favor bold grazers that take a meal whether it is flashing or not. ⓘ *bioluminescence*, p. 77

Researchers Mark Abrahams and Linda Townsend of the Pacific Biological Station in Canada hoped to shed light on the evolution of protist bioluminescence. They hypothesized that emitting light is adaptive to dinoflagellates because it attracts the predators of the copepods (figure 18.21a). If so, then copepods grazing on bioluminescent dinoflagellates should face a higher risk of predation than do copepods given only non-bioluminescent dinoflagellates to eat.

Abrahams and Townsend collected a dinoflagellate species called *Gonyaulax polyedra*, which is native to the Pacific coast of North America. The researchers conducted their experiment in 20 large jars in the laboratory. Each jar contained 500 copepods and one stickleback fish, a copepod predator. Half of the jars received dinoflagellates that would bioluminesce when copepods approached. The other 10 jars served as controls—each contained dinoflagellates that would not emit light. The experimenters then darkened the room, allowing copepods to graze on dinoflagellates and sticklebacks to prey on copepods. After 3.5 hours, they counted the remaining copepods.

Figure 18.20 Blue Glow of Algae. A man and his son admire the neon blue light emitted by algae inhabiting coastal waters near La Jolla.

The results aligned with the predictions: stickleback fish eat more copepods when bioluminescent dinoflagellates are present (figure 18.21b). This outcome suggests that a protist can avoid being eaten by increasing the threat of predation on its grazers; the copepod benefits more from fleeing than from continuing to graze. Since light-emitting protists are less likely to be a copepod's dinner, natural selection maintains bioluminescence in dinoflagellates as well.

If you ever visit La Jolla, drop a tiny pebble in the water. You'll see sparkles of light from the protists you disturbed—a beacon to predators that a grazer may be nearby. And if you look closely, you might also see a fish looking for a copepod dinner.

Abrahams, Mark V. and Linda D. Townsend. 1993. Bioluminescence in dinoflagellates: a test of the burglar alarm hypothesis. *Ecology*, vol. 74, pages 258–260.

18.6 MASTERING CONCEPTS

1. Use the food chain in figure 18.21a to explain why bioluminescence is adaptive to dinoflagellates.
2. What selects for a copepod's light-avoidance response?

Figure 18.21 Dangerous Light. (a) A simplified experimental food chain. (b) Copepods sharing a jar with light-emitting dinoflagellates were more likely to be eaten by stickleback fish than were copepods in a jar with dinoflagellates that did not produce light.

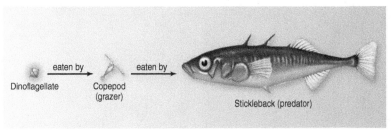

Dinoflagellate — eaten by → Copepod (grazer) — eaten by → Stickleback (predator)

a.

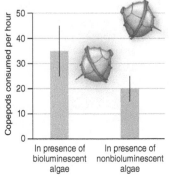

b.

CHAPTER SUMMARY

18.1 Protists Lie at the Crossroads Between Simple and Complex Organisms

A. What Is a Protist?
- **Protists** are **eukaryotes** that are not plants, fungi, or animals. The protists are diverse in ecology, motility, and other traits (table 18.2).
- Classification of protists is changing as molecular data are considered.

B. Protists Are Important in Many Ways
- Photosynthetic protists support food webs and release oxygen, whereas parasitic protists cause disease. Some protists have industrial uses.

C. Protists Have a Lengthy Evolutionary History
- Mitochondria and chloroplasts originated as free-living prokaryotes that were engulfed by early eukaryotes in a process called endosymbiosis. Subsequent secondary endosymbiosis events explain differences in chloroplasts among the photosynthetic protists.
- Some protists may provide clues to the origins of multicellularity and to the ancestors of the plant, fungi, and animal lineages.

18.2 Many Protists Are Photosynthetic

- The photosynthetic protists are known as **algae.**

A. Euglenoids Are Heterotrophs and Autotrophs
- **Euglenoids** are unicellular, elongated flagellates.

B. Dinoflagellates Are "Whirling Cells"
- The **dinoflagellates** have two different-sized flagella at right angles that generate a whirling movement. Dinoflagellates cause red tides.

C. Golden Algae, Diatoms, and Brown Algae Contain Yellowish Pigments
- The **golden algae** are photosynthetic but can consume other microorganisms when light or nutrient supplies decline.

- **Diatoms** are microscopic phytoplankton with intricate silica shells.
- **Brown algae** are large, multicellular seaweeds such as kelp.

D. Red Algae Can Live in Deep Water
- **Red algae** contain pigments that expand their photosynthetic range.

E. Green Algae Are the Closest Relatives of Land Plants
- **Green algae** store carbohydrates as starch and use the same pigments as plants. Many have **alternation of generations.** The green algae have diverse body forms, ranging from microscopic to multicellular.

18.3 Some Heterotrophic Protists Were Once Classified as Fungi

A. Slime Molds Are Unicellular and Multicellular
- **Plasmodial slime molds** form plasmodia, masses containing thousands of diploid nuclei. A plasmodium feeds by engulfing other cells.
- In **cellular slime molds,** individual cells retain their separate cell membranes throughout the life cycle.

B. Water Molds Are Decomposers and Parasites
- **Water molds** are filamentous heterotrophs that live in moist or wet environments. Some are pathogens and others are decomposers.

18.4 Protozoa Are Diverse Heterotrophic Protists

- Most **protozoa** are heterotrophs, and most have motile cells.

A. Several Flagellated Protozoa Cause Disease
- Several species of **flagellated protozoa,** such as *Giardia, Trichomonas,* the **trypanosomes,** and *Leishmania,* cause disease in humans.

B. Amoeboid Protozoa Produce Pseudopodia
- **Amoeboid protozoa** move by means of "false feet," or pseudopodia. This group includes amoebae, **foraminiferans,** and **radiolarians.**

C. Ciliates Are Common Protozoa with Complex Cells
- **Ciliates** have complex cells with cilia, vacuoles, and two types of nuclei.

TABLE **18.2** **The Protists: A Summary**

Group (pictured below)	Autotrophic (photosynthetic)?	Heterotrophic?	Parasitic?	Motile?	Supergroup
Euglenoids (a)	Some	Yes	Some	Yes	Excavata
Dinoflagellates (b)	Some	Some	Some	Yes	Chromalveolata
Golden algae (c)	Yes	Yes	No	Yes	Chromalveolata
Diatoms (d)	Yes	No	No	No	Chromalveolata
Brown algae (e)	Yes	No	No	Gametes only	Chromalveolata
Red algae (f)	Yes	No	No	No	Archaeplastida
Green algae (g)	Yes	No	No	Some gametes	Archaeplastida
Slime molds (h)	No	Yes	No	Yes	Amoebozoa, Excavata, and Rhizaria
Water molds (i)	No	Yes	Some	Spores only	Chromalveolata
Flagellated protozoa (j)	Some	Most	Many	Yes	Excavata
Amoeboid protozoa (k)	No	Yes	Some	Some	Rhizaria, Amoebozoa, and Chromalveolata
Ciliates (l)	No	Yes	Some	Some	Chromalveolata
Apicomplexans (m)	No	Yes	Yes	No	Chromalveolata

a. b. c. d. e. f. g. h. i. j. k. l. m.

D. Apicomplexans Include Nonmotile Animal Parasites

- **Apicomplexans** are obligate parasites characterized by an apical complex of organelles. These protists cause malaria and toxoplasmosis.

18.5 Protist Classification Is Changing Rapidly

- The traditional means of classifying protists is giving way to newer eukaryote "supergroups" that reflect shared ancestry.
- The relationships among most lineages of protists remain unclear.

18.6 Investigating Life: Shining a Spotlight on Danger

- Light produced by bioluminescent dinoflagellates may attract stickleback fish, which eat the copepods that would otherwise graze on the dinoflagellates.

MULTIPLE CHOICE QUESTIONS

1. Which of the following is NOT a characteristic of all protists?
   a. Unicellular
   b. Cells contain membrane-bounded organelles
   c. Cells contain a nucleus
   d. Eukaryotic

2. Suppose you are studying a protist under a microscope. If it is a known species of protist, then it could be
   a. a parasite.
   b. a decomposer.
   c. photosynthetic.
   d. All of the above are correct.

3. Some protist lineages arose from secondary endosymbiosis. How many membranes would surround the chloroplasts of these organisms?
   a. 0   c. 2
   b. 1   d. 3 or more

4. What property distinguishes an alga from a protozoan?
   a. The presence of a flagellum
   b. The ability to live in water
   c. The ability to use photosynthesis
   d. Both a and b are correct.

5. Why is the classification of protists based on DNA sequences considered useful?
   a. Because only protists have DNA
   b. Because genetic sequences have confirmed the traditional categories of protists
   c. Because DNA reveals evolutionary relationships, even among organisms that look different
   d. All of the above are correct.

Answers to these questions are in appendix A.

WRITE IT OUT

1. Explain why evolutionary biologists are interested in choanoflagellates, green algae, and organisms with mitochondria whose genomes resemble those of bacteria.

2. List some examples of protist diversity. How do different protist groups obtain energy? How do they move? Describe the differences in protist appearance.

3. Describe the relationship between nutrient pollution and harmful algal blooms. Why might harmful algal blooms be more frequent in summer? What steps could coastal communities take to prevent nutrient pollution?

4. Explain why the fossil record for diatoms is much more complete than that of other protists, such as amoebae and slime molds.

5. How is it adaptive for a red alga to have pigments other than chlorophyll?

6. Explain at least one line of evidence that green algae are the closest relatives of plants.

7. Natural selection favors stalk formation in cellular slime molds even though the cells of the stalk die. Explain this observation.

8. Why might overwatering your plants make them more susceptible to infection by some kinds of heterotrophic protists?

9. Give three examples of protists for which the classifications have recently changed. In each case, what was the justification for the old category, and what is the justification for the change?

10. Suppose someone hands you a microscope and a single-celled organism. Create a flowchart that you could use to identify the specimen.

PULL IT TOGETHER

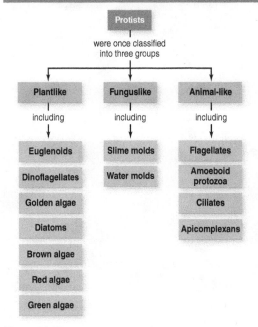

Figure 18.22 Pull It Together: Protists.

Refer to figure 18.22 and the chapter content to answer the following questions.

1. Name at least one unique characteristic of each protist group in figure 18.22.

2. Molecular data have changed protist classification. Use a red pen to circle the protist groups classified as stramenopiles; use a blue pen to circle the groups classified as alveolates.

3. Name examples of disease-causing organisms in each of the four groups of protozoa.

CHAPTER

19 Plants

Natural Biofuel. *Sphagnum*, the source of peat moss, grows in bogs. This man is cutting peat that will be used as fuel.

Enhance your study **|BIOLOGY**
of this chapter with practice quizzes,
animations and videos, answer keys,
and downloadable study tools.
www.mhhe.com/hoefnagels

Peat Moss, Pot Scrubbers, Drugs, and More: The Many Uses of Plants

MOST PEOPLE KNOW WHY PLANTS ARE ESSENTIAL TO ANIMAL LIFE: VEGETATION PROVIDES FOOD AND HABITAT, AND PHOTOSYNTHESIS PRODUCES OXYGEN GAS. Yet plants serve us in many unexpected ways as well. Here are some interesting examples from the four main plant lineages.

- **Peat moss:** Gardeners and houseplant lovers recognize peat moss as a major ingredient in potting mixes. Peat comes from partially decomposed sphagnum moss harvested from enormous bogs. The dried moss is unusually spongy, absorbing 20 times its weight in water. When mixed with soil, peat slowly releases water to plant roots. People also burn peat as cooking fuel or to generate electricity.

- **Horsetail:** *Equisetum,* or the horsetail, is a seedless plant related to ferns. Some horsetails are called "scouring rushes" because their stems and leaves contain abrasive silica particles. Native Americans used horsetails to polish bows and arrows, and early colonists and pioneers used them to scrub pots and pans. Some people believe that horsetails, taken as a dietary supplement, can strengthen fingernails and prevent osteoporosis.

- **Pacific yew:** *Taxus brevifolia,* the Pacific yew, is a conifer that contains the compound paclitaxel in its bark. Paclitaxel has anticancer properties, particularly for treating breast cancer. But Pacific yews are slow-growing trees, and harvesting them for their bark would mean their extinction. Fortunately, paclitaxel is now synthesized in the laboratory and marketed under the trade name Taxol.

- **Cotton:** You probably own many garments made of cotton, a cloth that comes from flowering plants in genus *Gossypium.* Cotton seeds develop in a dense web of cellulose fibers, which textile manufacturers spin into threads that make up T-shirts, blue jeans, underwear, towels, sheets, and many other cloth products. The seeds themselves also produce cooking oil. About three fourths of the U.S. cotton crop is genetically modified to produce its own insecticides (see section 10.10).

Peat moss, horsetail, the Pacific yew, and cotton are just four of the many plants that humans use, and they represent only a tiny percentage of the diverse kingdom Plantae. This chapter highlights some of the history and diversity of these essential organisms.

LEARNING OUTLINE

 19.1 Plants Have Changed the World
    A. Green Algae Are the Closest Relatives of Plants
    B. Plants Are Adapted to Life on Land

 19.2 Bryophytes Are the Simplest Plants
    A. Bryophytes Lack Vascular Tissue
    B. Bryophytes Have a Conspicuous Gametophyte

 19.3 Seedless Vascular Plants Have Xylem and Phloem But No Seeds
    A. Seedless Vascular Plants Include Ferns and Their Close Relatives
    B. Seedless Vascular Plants Have a Conspicuous Sporophyte and Swimming Sperm

 19.4 Gymnosperms Are "Naked Seed" Plants
    A. Gymnosperms Include Conifers and Three Related Groups
    B. Conifers Produce Pollen and Seeds in Cones

 19.5 Angiosperms Produce Seeds in Fruits
    A. Most Angiosperms Are Eudicots or Monocots
    B. Flowers and Fruits Are Unique to the Angiosperm Life Cycle
    C. Wind and Animals Often Participate in Angiosperm Reproduction

 19.6 Investigating Life: Genetic Messages from Ancient Ecosystems

 LEARN HOW TO LEARN
Take Notes on Your Reading

Many classes have reading assignments. Taking notes as you read should help you not only retain information but also identify what you don't understand. Before you take notes, skim through the assigned pages once; otherwise, you may have trouble distinguishing between main points and minor details. Then read it again. This time, pause after each section and write the most important ideas in your own words. What if you can't remember it or don't understand it well enough to summarize the passage? Read it again, and if that doesn't work, ask for help with whatever isn't clear.

19.1 Plants Have Changed the World

If you glance at your surroundings in almost any outdoor setting, the plants are the first things you see. Grasses, trees, shrubs, ferns, or mosses exist nearly everywhere, at least on land (table 19.1 and figure 19.1). Members of kingdom **Plantae** dominate habitats from moist bogs to parched deserts. They are so familiar that it is difficult to imagine a world without plants.

Video Plants and Ecosystems

Plants are autotrophs: they use sunlight as an energy source to assemble CO_2 and H_2O into sugars (chapter 5 describes the reactions of photosynthesis). The sugars, in turn, provide the energy and raw materials that maintain and build a plant's body. Moreover, the chemical reactions of photosynthesis release oxygen gas, O_2, as a waste product. Animals and other organisms that use aerobic respiration need this gas; in addition, O_2 in the atmosphere helps form the ozone layer that protects life from the sun's harmful ultraviolet radiation.

Figure 19.1   Plants Galore. Nearly every ecosystem on land is dominated by plants.

Today's plants transform the landscape, but their effect on the evolution of life is even more dramatic. Once plants settled the land some 450 million years ago, they set into motion a complex series of changes that would profoundly affect both the nonliving and the living worlds. The explosion of photosynthetic activity from plants altered the atmosphere, lowering CO_2 levels and raising O_2 content. Moreover, as plants gradually expanded from the water's edge to the world's driest habitats, they formed the bases of intricate food webs, providing diverse habitats for many types of animals, fungi, and microbes.

Of course, plants remain essential to life today. Herbivores consume living leaves, stems, roots, seeds, and fruits. Dead leaves accumulating on the soil surface feed countless soil microorganisms, insects, and worms. When washed into streams and rivers, this leaf litter supports a spectacular assortment of fishes and other aquatic animals.

From a human perspective, farms and forests provide the foods we eat, the paper we read, the lumber we use to build our homes, many of the clothes we wear, and some of the fuel we burn. (This chapter's Burning Question introduces biofuels derived from plants.) The list goes on and on. It is amazing to think that plants do so much with such modest raw materials: sunlight, water, minerals, and CO_2.

A. Green Algae Are the Closest Relatives of Plants

All plants, from mosses to maple trees, are multicellular organisms with eukaryotic cells. With the exception of a few parasitic species, plants are autotrophs. A careful reading of section 18.2, however, will reveal that brown, red, and some green algae are also multicellular eukaryotes that carry out photosynthesis. Which of the many lineages of algae, then, gave rise to plants?

The answer is that green algae apparently share the most recent common ancestor with plants. About 480 to 470 million years ago, or perhaps earlier, one group of green algae related to today's **charophytes** likely gave rise to plants (figure 19.2).

TABLE **19.1**   **Phyla of Plants**

Phylum	Examples	Number of Existing Species
Nonvascular plants		
Marchantiophyta	Liverworts	9000
Anthocerotophyta	Hornworts	100
Bryophyta	True mosses	15,000
Seedless vascular plants		
Lycopodiophyta	Club mosses, spike mosses	1200
Pteridophyta	Whisk ferns, true ferns, horsetails	11,500
Gymnosperms		
Cycadophyta	Cycads	130
Ginkgophyta	Ginkgo	1
Pinophyta	Pines, firs, and other conifers	630
Gnetophyta	Gnetophytes	80
Angiosperms		
Magnoliophyta	All flowering plants, including roses, grasses, fruit trees, and oaks	>260,000

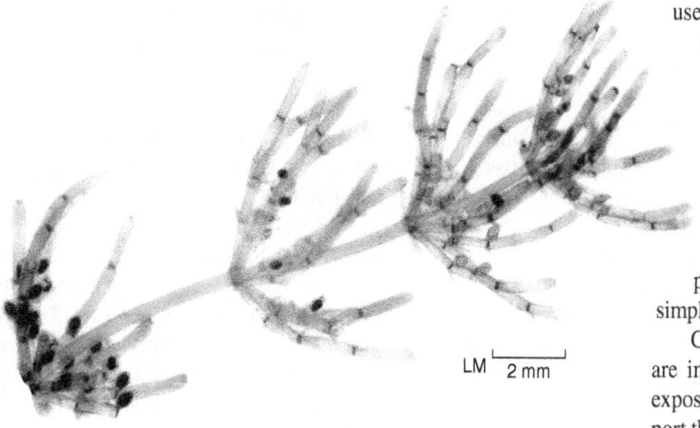

use starch as a nutrient reserve. Similar DNA sequences offer additional evidence of a close relationship. ⓘ *green algae,* p. 366; *polysaccharides,* p. 31

Nevertheless, the body forms of algae are quite different from those of plants, in part because water presents selective forces that are far different from those in the terrestrial landscape. Consider the aquatic habitat. Light, water, minerals, and dissolved gases surround the whole body of a submerged green alga, and the buoyancy of water provides physical support. In sexual reproduction, an alga simply releases swimming (flagellated) gametes into the water.

On land, the water and minerals essential for plant growth are in the soil, and only the aboveground part of the plant is exposed to light. Air not only provides much less physical support than does water, but it also dries out the plant's aerial tissues. Furthermore, the dispersal of gametes for sexual reproduction becomes more complicated on dry land.

These conditions have selected for unique adaptations in the body forms and reproductive strategies of plants. As described in the next section, biologists use some of these features to organize land plants into four main groups (figure 19.3): the bryophytes, seedless vascular plants, gymnosperms, and angiosperms.

Figure 19.2 Charophyte. This green alga, called *Chara,* may resemble the ancestors of land plants.

Evidence for this evolutionary connection includes chemical and structural similarities. For example, the chloroplasts of plants and green algae contain the same photosynthetic pigments. In addition, like green algae, plants have cellulose-rich cell walls and

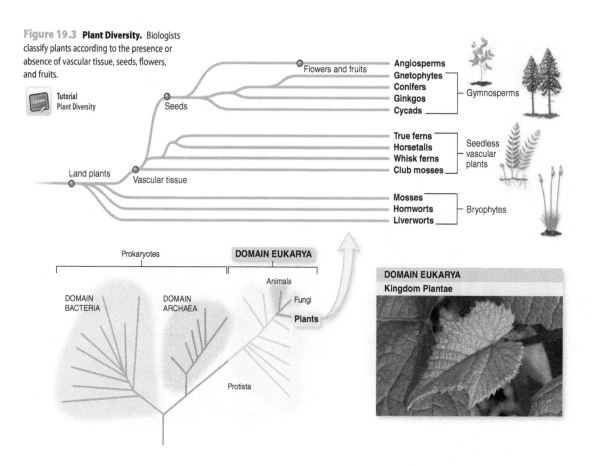

Figure 19.3 Plant Diversity. Biologists classify plants according to the presence or absence of vascular tissue, seeds, flowers, and fruits.

Tutorial
Plant Diversity

Flowers and fruits

Angiosperms
Gnetophytes
Conifers   — Gymnosperms
Ginkgos
Cycads

Seeds

True ferns
Horsetails   Seedless
Whisk ferns   vascular plants
Club mosses

Land plants

Vascular tissue

Mosses
Hornworts   — Bryophytes
Liverworts

Prokaryotes   DOMAIN EUKARYA

Animals

DOMAIN   DOMAIN   Fungi
BACTERIA   ARCHAEA
                               Plants

Protista

DOMAIN EUKARYA
Kingdom Plantae

B. Plants Are Adapted to Life on Land

Figure 19.4 illustrates many of the adaptations that enable plants to grow upright, retain moisture, survive, and reproduce on land. Refer to this figure often while reading the rest of this section.

Obtaining Resources
A suite of adaptations enables plants to acquire light, CO_2, water, and minerals. Most plants, for example, have aboveground stems that support multiple leaves. The extensive surface area of the leaves maximizes exposure to sunlight and CO_2. Below the ground surface, highly branched root systems not only absorb water and minerals but also anchor the plant in the soil.

A plant that dries out will not survive. After all, water is a critical ingredient in photosynthesis. Water also exerts turgor pressure on cell walls, enabling the plant to stay upright and grow. One water-conserving adaptation is the **cuticle**, a waxy coating that minimizes water loss from the aerial parts of a plant. Dry habitats such as deserts select for extra-thick cuticles; plants in moist habitats typically have thin cuticles. ⓘ *turgor pressure*, p. 82

The waxy cuticle is impermeable not only to water but also to gases such as CO_2 and O_2. Plants exchange these gases with the atmosphere through **stomata**, which are pores that can open and close. As gases diffuse through open stomata in leaves and stems, water also escapes from the plant's tissues. Plants close their stomata in dry weather, minimizing water loss. ⓘ *plant epidermis*, p. 468

Internal Transportation and Support
The division of labor in a plant poses a problem: roots need the food produced at the leaves, whereas leaves and stems need water and minerals from soil. In small plants called bryophytes, cell-to-cell diffusion meets these needs. Other plants have **vascular tissue**, a collection of tubes that transport sugar, water, and minerals throughout the plant.

Animation
Vascular
Tissue

The two types of vascular tissue are xylem and phloem. **Xylem** conducts water and dissolved minerals from the roots to the leaves. **Phloem** transports sugars produced in photosynthesis to the roots and other nongreen parts of the plant. This internal transportation system has supported the evolution of specialized roots, stems, and leaves, many of which have adaptations that enable plants to exploit extremely dry habitats.

In addition, xylem is rich in **lignin**, a complex polymer that strengthens cell walls. The additional support from lignin means that vascular plants can grow tall and form branches, important adaptations in the intense competition for sunlight.

Reproduction
Plants have a life cycle called **alternation of generations**, in which a multicellular diploid stage alternates with a multicellular haploid stage (figure 19.5). The **sporophyte** (diploid) generation develops from a zygote that forms when gametes come together at fertilization. In a mature sporophyte, some cells undergo meiosis and produce haploid spores, which divide mitotically to form the gametophyte. The haploid

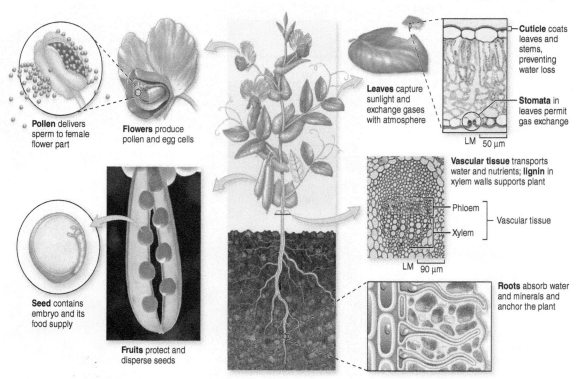

Pollen delivers sperm to female flower part

Flowers produce pollen and egg cells

Seed contains embryo and its food supply

Fruits protect and disperse seeds

Leaves capture sunlight and exchange gases with atmosphere

Cuticle coats leaves and stems, preventing water loss

Stomata in leaves permit gas exchange

LM   50 μm

Vascular tissue transports water and nutrients; **lignin** in xylem walls supports plant

Phloem
Xylem
Vascular tissue

LM   90 μm

Roots absorb water and minerals and anchor the plant

Figure 19.4 Plant Adaptations. Pea plants have many features that support life on land.

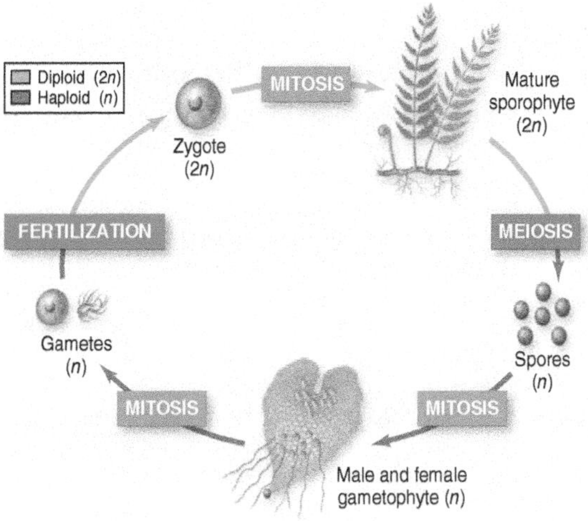

Diploid (2n)
Haploid (n)

Zygote (2n)

MITOSIS

Mature sporophyte (2n)

FERTILIZATION

MEIOSIS

Gametes (n)

Spores (n)

MITOSIS

MITOSIS

Male and female gametophyte (n)

Figure 19.5 Alternation of Generations.
Plants have multicellular haploid (gametophyte) and diploid (sporophyte) generations.

Tutorial
Alternation of Generations

gametophyte produces gametes by mitotic cell division; these sex cells fuse at fertilization, starting the cycle anew.

A prominent trend among land plants is a change in the relative sizes and independence of the gametophyte and sporophyte generations (figure 19.6). In a moss, for example, the gametophyte is the most prominent generation, and the sporophyte depends on it for nutrition. In more complex plants, the sporophyte is photosynthetic and much larger than the gametophyte.

Plant reproduction has other variations as well. The sperm cells of mosses and ferns swim in water to reach an egg, limiting the distance over which gametes can spread. Gymnosperms and angiosperms can reproduce over far greater distances, thanks to pollen. **Pollen** consists of the male gametophytes of seed plants; each pollen grain produces sperm. In **pollination,** wind or animals deliver pollen to female plant parts, eliminating the need for water in sexual reproduction.

Gymnosperms and angiosperms also share another reproductive adaptation: seeds. A **seed** is a dormant plant embryo packaged with a food supply; a tough outer coat keeps the seed's interior from drying out. The food supply sustains the young plant between the time the seed germinates and when the seedling begins photosynthesis.

The origin of pollen and seeds was a significant event in the evolution of plants. The spores of mosses and ferns—the seedless plants—take little energy to produce, but they are short-lived and tend to remain relatively close to the mother plant. The gymnosperms and angiosperms, in contrast, can disperse their gametes and seeds over long distances and in dry conditions. Moreover, seeds can remain dormant for years, germinating when conditions are favorable. Pollen and seeds therefore give gymnosperms and angiosperms a competitive edge in many habitats.

Two additional reproductive adaptations occur only in the angiosperms: flowers and fruits (see figure 19.4). **Flowers** are reproductive structures that produce pollen and egg cells. After fertilization, parts of the flower develop into a **fruit** that contains the seeds. Flowers and fruits help angiosperms protect and disperse both their pollen and their offspring. These adaptations are spectacularly successful; angiosperms far outnumber all other plants, both in numbers and species diversity.

Biologists classify plants based on the presence or absence of transport tissues, seeds, flowers, and fruits. The next four sections of this chapter describe the diversity of plants; unit 5 delves more deeply into the anatomy and physiology of angiosperms.

19.1 MASTERING CONCEPTS

1. What is the evidence that plants evolved from green algae?
2. Suppose a plant has a mutation that prevents it from closing its stomata. What would be the consequence?
3. How does vascular tissue adapt plants to land?
4. Describe the reproductive adaptations of plants.

	Bryophytes	Seedless Vascular Plants	Gymnosperms	Angiosperms
Gametophyte (haploid generation)			♂ ♀	♂ ♀
Size relative to sporophyte?	Varies	Small	Microscopic	Microscopic
Depends on sporophyte for nutrition?	No	No	Yes	Yes
Sporophyte (diploid generation)				
Size relative to gametophyte?	Varies	Large	Large	Large
Depends on gametophyte for nutrition?	Yes	No	No	No

Figure 19.6 Changes in the Generations. As plants became more complex, the gametophyte generation was reduced to just a few cells that depend on the sporophyte for nutrition.

19.2 Bryophytes Are the Simplest Plants

Angiosperms

Gymnosperms

Seedless vascular plants

Bryophytes

The earliest plants, which probably resembled modern bryophytes, emerged onto land during the Ordovician period some 450 million years ago. All **bryophytes** are seedless plants that lack vascular tissue, but evidence suggests that they do not form a single clade (a group that includes one common ancestor and all of its descendants). This section describes them together, however, because they share some important features. ⓘ *cladistics,* p. 296

A. Bryophytes Lack Vascular Tissue

Without vascular tissue and lignin, bryophytes lack the physical support to grow very large. Bryophytes are therefore small, compact plants. Their diminutive size means that each cell can absorb minerals and water directly from its surroundings. Materials move from cell to cell within the plant by diffusion and osmosis, not within specialized transport tissues.

Although bryophytes lack true leaves and roots, many have structures that are superficially similar to these organs. For example, photosynthesis occurs at flattened leaflike areas. In addition, hairlike extensions called rhizoids cover a bryophyte's lower surface, anchoring the plant to its substrate. Unlike true roots, rhizoids cannot tap distant sources of water. Many species are therefore restricted to moist, shady habitats that are unlikely to dry out.

a.   b.   c.

Figure 19.7 **A Gallery of Bryophytes.** (a) The leaflike gametophytes of this liverwort are low to the ground. The umbrella-shaped structures produce sperm or egg cells. (b) In the hornwort *Anthoceros,* the tapered hornlike structures are sporophytes, below which the flat gametophytes are visible. (c) Short sporophytes topped with dark capsules peek above the gametophytes of *Sphagnum* moss.

BurningQuestion

What are biofuels?

Petroleum and other fossil fuels consist of organisms buried millions of years ago; burning these fuels releases their ancient carbon into the atmosphere as CO_2. Biofuels are plant-based substitutes for fossil fuels. They have attracted attention recently, in part because they can help decrease reliance on foreign oil. The biofuel crops also carry out photosynthesis, temporarily removing CO_2 from the atmosphere and helping to reduce global climate change. ⓘ *global climate change,* p. 816

Two types of biofuels are biodiesel and ethanol. Currently, most biodiesel comes from oil extracted from crushed soybeans or canola seeds. To avoid driving up the price of these food crops, researchers are looking for economical, nonfood sources of biodiesel. Examples include everything from green algae to the seeds of a plant called the jatropha tree. This long-lived tree uses little water and tolerates poor soil, so it does not compete with food plants for rich farmland.

Ethanol, the other main biofuel, is a gasoline substitute. Corn kernels are the main source of ethanol in the United States. Starch extracted from the corn kernel is enzymatically digested to sugar, which is fermented into ethanol. Sugarcane, the main source of ethanol in

Brazil, is a more economical alternative in the tropics. Its tissues are high in sugar, not starch, so biofuel manufacturers can omit the costly enzymes from the ethanol production process. ⓘ *fermentation,* p. 115

Researchers are also searching for nonfood sources of sugar to use in ethanol production. The inedible stems of corn or of prairie grasses such as switchgrass would be ideal; bacterial and fungal enzymes easily break the cellulose in the plant cell walls into simple sugars. One problem, however, is that the stems also contain lignin, a complex molecule that interferes with cellulose extraction. So far, the heat and acid treatment needed to eliminate the lignin is too costly and inefficient to make cellulose-derived ethanol economical.

Burning biodiesel or ethanol returns the CO_2 absorbed in photosynthesis to the atmosphere, but it is important to realize that biofuels are not exactly "carbon-neutral." Most biofuel crops require fertilizers and pesticides, both of which come from fossil fuels—and cause additional environmental problems of their own.

Submit your burning question to
Marielle.Hoefnagels@mheducation.com

Biologists classify the 24,000 or so species of bryophytes into three phyla (figure 19.7):

- **Liverworts** (phylum Marchantiophyta) have flattened leaflike structures. The diverse liverworts may be the bryophytes most closely related to ancestral land plants.

- **Hornworts** (phylum Anthocerotophyta) are the smallest group of bryophytes, with only about 100 species. They are named for their sporophytes, which are shaped like tapered horns.

- **Mosses** (phylum Bryophyta) are the closest living relatives to the vascular plants. The gametophytes resemble short "stems" with many "leaves."

Nonvascular plants play important roles in ecosystems. For example, mosses can survive on bare rock or in a very thin layer of soil. As their tissues die, they contribute organic matter, helping build soil that larger plants subsequently colonize.

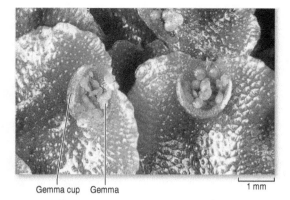

Gemma cup   Gemma   1 mm

Figure 19.8   Asexual Reproduction. The gametophytes of liverworts can produce fragments called gemmae. Raindrops splash the gemmae from the cups, and then each gemma develops into an identical new plant.

B. Bryophytes Have a Conspicuous Gametophyte

Bryophytes reproduce asexually and sexually. Asexual reproduction in liverworts occurs at gemmae, small pieces of tissue that detach and grow into new plants (figure 19.8). Mosses also produce gemmae.

The bryophyte sexual life cycle is illustrated in figure 19.9. The sporophyte is a stalk attached to the gametophyte. At the tip of the stalk, specialized cells inside a sporangium undergo meiosis and produce haploid spores. After the spores are released, they germinate, giving rise to new haploid gametophytes. Gametes form by mitosis in separate sperm- and egg-producing structures on the gametophyte. Sperm swim to the egg cell in a film of water that coats the plants. Sexual reproduction therefore requires water, another factor that limits these plants to moist areas. The sporophyte generation begins at fertilization, with the formation of the diploid zygote. This cell divides mitotically, producing the sporophyte's stalk.

Bryophytes produce large numbers of spores, which offer temporary protection against drying out. Thanks to their tough walls, bryophyte spores are preserved in the fossil record. In fact, the earliest evidence of plants on land is a fossilized spore resembling those of today's liverworts.

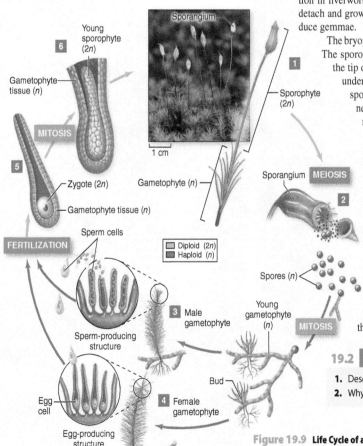

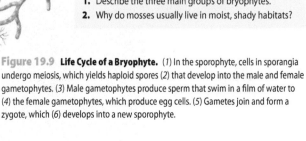

Figure 19.9   Life Cycle of a Bryophyte. (1) In the sporophyte, cells in sporangia undergo meiosis, which yields haploid spores (2) that develop into the male and female gametophytes. (3) Male gametophytes produce sperm that swim in a film of water to (4) the female gametophytes, which produce egg cells. (5) Gametes join and form a zygote, which (6) develops into a new sporophyte.

19.2   MASTERING CONCEPTS

1. Describe the three main groups of bryophytes.
2. Why do mosses usually live in moist, shady habitats?

19.3 Seedless Vascular Plants Have Xylem and Phloem But No Seeds

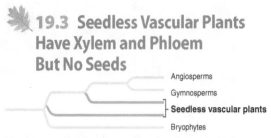

Angiosperms

Gymnosperms

Seedless vascular plants

Bryophytes

Most nonvascular plants are small and easily overlooked. Not so for the **seedless vascular plants,** the 12,000 species that have xylem and phloem but do not produce seeds. These plants have much larger representatives than their bryophyte counterparts.

A. Seedless Vascular Plants Include Ferns and Their Close Relatives

The earliest species of seedless vascular plants are extinct, but fossil evidence suggests that they originated in the middle of the Silurian period, about 425 million years ago. The club mosses (not to be confused with the true mosses, which are bryophytes), are descendants of these early vascular plants. The other seedless

vascular plants, including the ferns, first appeared about 50 million years later.

As described in section 19.1, vascular tissue enabled plants to grow much larger than nonvascular plants, both in height and in girth. This increase in size was adaptive because taller plants have the edge over their shorter neighbors in the competition for sunlight. Larger plants also triggered evolutionary changes in other organisms by providing new habitats and more diverse food sources for arthropods, vertebrates, and other land animals.

Unlike the bryophytes, the seedless vascular plants typically have true roots, stems, and leaves. In many species, the leaves and roots arise from underground stems called rhizomes. Rhizomes sometimes also store carbohydrates that provide energy for the growth of new leaves and roots.

The seedless vascular plants include four lineages grouped into two phyla (figure 19.10):

- **Club mosses** (phylum Lycopodiophyta) are small plants in genus *Lycopodium*. These plants have simple leaves that resemble scales or needles, and the name reflects their club-shaped reproductive structures. Their close relatives

Figure 19.10 A Gallery of Seedless Vascular Plants. (a) The club moss *Lycopodium* produces upright stems. (b) The spike moss, *Selaginella,* has scalelike foliage. (c) Yellowish spore-producing structures are visible on this whisk fern, *Psilotum.* (d) *Equisetum* is a horsetail. (e) This narrow beech fern has the fronds typical of a true fern.

are the spike mosses *(Selaginella).* Collectively, club mosses and spike mosses are sometimes called lycopods.

- **Whisk ferns** (phylum Pteridophyta) are simple plants that have rhizomes but not roots. Most species have no obvious leaves. Their name comes from the highly branched stems of *Psilotum,* which resemble whisk brooms.

- **Horsetails** (phylum Pteridophyta) grow along streams or at the borders of forests. The only living genus of horsetails, *Equisetum,* includes plants with branched rhizomes that give rise to green aerial stems bearing spores at their tips. Horsetails are also called scouring rushes because of the abrasive silica particles in their tissues (see the chapter-opening essay).

- **True ferns** (phylum Pteridophyta) make up the largest group of seedless vascular plants, with about 11,000 species. The fronds, or leaves, of ferns are their most obvious feature; some species are popular as ornamental plants. Ferns were especially widespread and abundant during the Carboniferous period, when their huge fronds dominated warm, moist forests. Their remains form most coal deposits. ⓘ *coal,* p. 319

Most seedless vascular plants live on land, where their roots and rhizomes help stabilize soil and prevent erosion. Some species of ferns and horsetails are especially adept at colonizing disturbed soils such as road cuts. But not all species are terrestrial. The tiny fern *Azolla* lives in water, where its leaves house cyanobacteria that fix nitrogen. In Asia, farmers cultivate *Azolla* within rice paddies to help add nitrogen to their crops. ⓘ *nitrogen fixation,* p. 486

B. Seedless Vascular Plants Have a Conspicuous Sporophyte and Swimming Sperm

Figure 19.11 illustrates the life cycle of a fern. The sporophyte produces haploid spores by meiosis in collections of sporangia on the underside of each frond. Once shed, the spores germinate and develop into tiny, heart-shaped gametophytes that produce gametes by mitotic cell division. The swimming sperm require a film of water to reach the egg cell. The gametes fuse, forming a zygote. This diploid cell divides mitotically and forms the sporophyte, which quickly dwarfs the gametophyte.

Many seedless vascular plants live in shady, moist habitats. Like bryophytes, these plants produce swimming sperm and therefore cannot reproduce sexually in the absence of water.

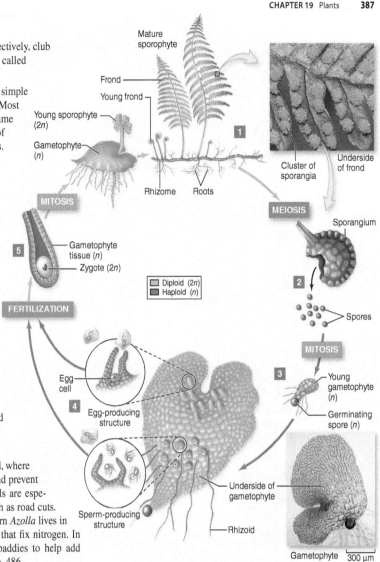

Figure 19.11 Life Cycle of a True Fern. (*1*) Sporangia on the sporophyte's fronds house cells that (*2*) produce spores by meiosis. (*3*) A haploid spore develops into a gametophyte, which (*4*) produces egg cells and sperm cells. Sperm swim in a film of water to reach eggs. (*5*) These gametes join and produce a zygote, which develops into the sporophyte.

Tutorial Fern Reproduction

19.3 MASTERING CONCEPTS

1. Describe the four groups of seedless vascular plants.
2. How do seedless vascular plants reproduce?
3. How are seedless vascular plants similar to and different from bryophytes?

19.4 Gymnosperms Are "Naked Seed" Plants

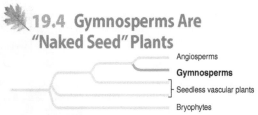

Angiosperms

Gymnosperms

Seedless vascular plants

Bryophytes

Bryophytes and seedless vascular plants dominated Earth's vegetation for more than 150 million years. But during the Permian period, about 300 million years ago, plants with pollen and seeds appeared. The new reproductive adaptations allowed these plants to outcompete the seedless plants in many habitats.

The first seed plants were gymnosperms. The term **gymnosperm** derives from the Greek words *gymnos,* meaning "naked," and *sperma,* meaning "seed." The seeds of these plants are "naked" because they are not enclosed in fruits.

A. Gymnosperms Include Conifers and Three Related Groups

Living gymnosperms are remarkably diverse in reproductive structures and leaf types. The sporophytes of most gymnosperms are woody trees or shrubs, although a few species are more vine-like. Leaf shapes range from tiny reduced scales to needles, flat blades, and large fernlike leaves. The 800 or so species of gymnosperms group into four phyla (figure 19.12):

- **Cycads** (phylum Cycadophyta) live primarily in tropical and subtropical regions. They have palmlike leaves, and they produce large cones. Cycads dominated Mesozoic era landscapes. Today, cycads are popular ornamental plants, but many species are near extinction in the wild because of slow growth, low reproductive rates, and shrinking habitats.

- The **ginkgo** (phylum Ginkgophyta), also called the maidenhair tree, has distinctive, fan-shaped leaves that have remained virtually unchanged for 80 million years. Only one species exists: *Ginkgo biloba.* It no longer grows wild in nature, but it is a popular cultivated tree. Ginkgos have male and female organs on separate plants; landscapes avoid planting female ginkgo trees because the fleshy seeds produce a foul odor.

- **Conifers** (phylum Pinophyta) such as pine trees are by far the most familiar gymnosperms. These plants often have needlelike or scalelike leaves, and they produce egg cells and pollen in cones. Conifers are commonly called "evergreens" because most retain their leaves all year, unlike deciduous trees. This term is somewhat misleading, however, because conifers do shed their needles. They just do it a few needles at a time, turning over their entire needle supply every few years.

- **Gnetophytes** (phylum Gnetophyta) include some odd plants. One example is *Welwitschia,* a desert plant with a single pair of large, strap-shaped leaves that persist throughout its life. The *Ephedra* in figure 19.12d is another example. Botanists struggle with the classification of gnetophytes. Some of the details of gnetophyte life history suggest a close relationship with flowering plants, but molecular evidence places these plants with the conifers.

a.   b.   c.   d.

Figure 19.12 A Gallery of Gymnosperms. (a) Cycads are ancient seed plants with cones that form within a crown of large leaves. A seed cone is shown here. (b) The leaves of *Ginkgo biloba* turn yellow in the fall. The lower photo shows the fleshy seed. (c) This pinyon pine is an example of a conifer. The seed cone has woody scales. (d) *Ephedra* is a gnetophyte with cones that resemble tiny flowers.

B. Conifers Produce Pollen and Seeds in Cones

Pine trees illustrate the gymnosperm life cycle (figure 19.13). The mature sporophyte produces **cones,** the organs that bear the reproductive structures. Female cones bear two sporangia, called **ovules,** on the upper surface of each scale. Through meiosis, each ovule produces four haploid structures called megaspores, only one of which develops into a female gametophyte. Over many months, the female gametophyte undergoes mitosis and gives rise to two to six egg cells. At the same time, male cones bear sporangia on thin, delicate scales. Through meiosis, these sporangia produce microspores, which eventually become wind-blown pollen grains (immature male gametophytes). Pollination occurs when pollen grains settle between the scales of female cones and adhere to drops of a sticky secretion.

The pollen grain germinates, giving rise to a pollen tube that grows through the ovule toward the egg cell. Two haploid sperm nuclei develop inside the pollen tube; one sperm nucleus fertilizes the haploid egg cell, and the other disintegrates. The resulting zygote is the first cell of the sporophyte. The whole process is so slow that fertilization occurs about 15 months after pollination.

Within the ovule, the haploid tissue of the female gametophyte nourishes the developing diploid embryo, which soon becomes dormant. Meanwhile, the ovule develops a tough, protective seed coat. Eventually, the seed is shed and dispersed by wind or animals. If conditions are favorable, the seed germinates, giving rise to a new tree that can begin the cycle again.

19.4 MASTERING CONCEPTS

1. What are the characteristics of gymnosperms?
2. What are the four groups of gymnosperms?
3. What is the role of cones in conifer reproduction?
4. What happens during and after pollination?

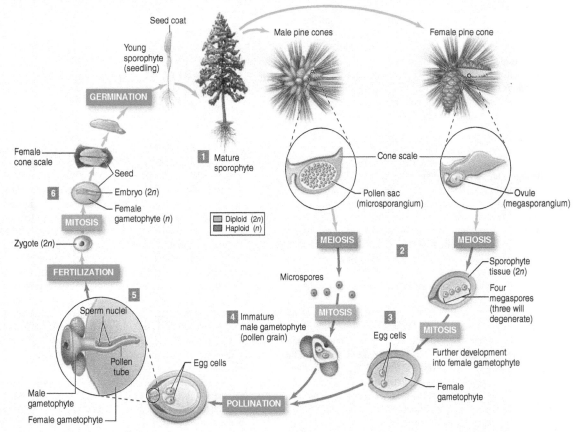

Figure 19.13 Life Cycle of a Pine. (*1*) The mature sporophyte produces male and female cones. (*2*) Cells in the male and female cone scales undergo meiosis, producing spores that develop into haploid gametophytes that consist of just a few cells each. (*3*) On the female cones, each scale has two ovules (only one is shown), each of which yields an egg-producing gametophyte. (*4*) The male cones produce pollen, the male gametophytes. (*5*) A pollen grain delivers a sperm nucleus to an egg cell via a pollen tube. The fertilized egg (zygote) will become the embryo. (*6*) The embryo is packaged inside a seed, which will eventually germinate and yield a pine seedling.

Tutorial Conifer Reproduction

19.5 Angiosperms Produce Seeds in Fruits

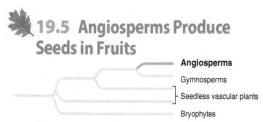

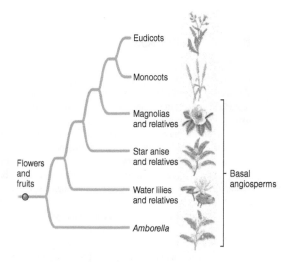

Figure 19.14 Angiosperm Phylogeny. This phylogenetic tree depicts the proposed evolutionary relationships among the eudicots, monocots, and basal angiosperms.

The bryophytes, seedless vascular plants, and gymnosperms make up less than 5% of all modern plant species. The other 95% are **angiosperms,** or flowering plants (phylum Magnoliophyta). Examples include apple trees, corn, roses, petunias, lilies, grasses, and many other familiar plants, including those we grow for our own food.

Flowers and fruits are reproductive structures that are unique to the angiosperms. The plant's flowers produce pollen and egg cells. After pollination and fertilization, flowers develop into fruits that enclose the plant's seeds. The name *angiosperm* is a tribute to this unique life cycle; the prefix *angio-* derives from the Greek word for "vessel." A fruit, then, is a "seed vessel."

Multiple lines of evidence place the origin of angiosperms in the Jurassic period, at least 144 million years ago. By 100 million years ago, all of today's major lineages of angiosperms were in place. Biologists have long puzzled about the sudden appearance and rapid diversification of the flowering plants. The adaptive radiation of the angiosperms coincided with the diversification of vertebrates and arthropods on land, but no one has established a definite cause-and-effect link. (i) *adaptive radiation,* p. 290

A. Most Angiosperms Are Eudicots or Monocots

Biologists are still working to sort out the evolutionary relationships among the angiosperms; figure 19.14 shows one hypothesis. The two largest clades are the eudicots and the monocots. The **eudicots** have two cotyledons (the first leaf structures to arise in the embryo), and their pollen grains feature three or more pores. About 175,000 species exist, representing about two thirds of all angiosperms. The diverse eudicots include roses, daisies, sunflowers, oaks, tomatoes, beans, and many others. *Arabidopsis thaliana,* the subject of this chapter's Focus on Model Organisms, is a eudicot.

Most of the other angiosperms are **monocots,** which are named for their single cotyledon; in addition, their pollen grains have just one pore. (Monocots and eudicots also differ by other characteristics, further described in chapter 22.) Examples of the 70,000 species of monocots are the orchids, lilies, grasses, bananas, and ginger. The grasses include not only lawn plants but also sugarcane and grains such as rice, wheat, barley, and corn (see this chapter's Apply It Now box).

Finally, about 3% or so of the flowering plants form a paraphyletic group informally called the basal angiosperms. These plants belong to lineages that diverged from ancestral plants before eudicots and monocots evolved (see figure 19.14). Examples of basal angiosperms are magnolias, nutmeg, avocados, black pepper, water lilies, and star anise. (i) *paraphyletic group,* p. 299

B. Flowers and Fruits Are Unique to the Angiosperm Life Cycle

The angiosperm life cycle is similar to that of gymnosperms in some ways (figure 19.15). For example, the sporophyte is the only conspicuous generation, and both types of plants produce pollen and seeds.

Yet the life cycles differ in important ways. Most obviously, the reproductive organs in angiosperms are flowers, not cones. Another difference is that an angiosperm's ovules develop into seeds inside the flower's ovary. The ovary develops into the fruit, which helps to protect and disperse the seeds. By comparison, a gymnosperm's seeds are never enclosed in a fruit; rather, they are produced "naked" on the female cone's scales (see figure 19.13).

One other unique feature of the angiosperm life cycle is double fertilization. Each pollen grain delivers two sperm nuclei to the ovule, which contains the female gametophyte. One of the sperm nuclei fertilizes an egg, yielding a diploid zygote that later develops into an embryo. The other sperm nucleus fertilizes a pair of nuclei in the gametophyte's central cell. This fertilization event produces a triploid nucleus that develops into the endosperm. The embryo and endosperm, together with a seed coat, make up the angiosperm seed; one or more seeds develop inside each fruit.

The endosperm's function is to supply nutrients to the embryo until the seed germinates and the seedling begins to produce its own food in photosynthesis. Endosperm tissue therefore often contains energy-rich starch or oils. For example, the endosperm of wheat and other grains is starchy; bakers grind these seeds into flour to make bread and other baked goods. Coconuts and castor seeds are two sources of useful oils derived from endosperm.

Chapter 24 considers angiosperm reproduction in more detail.

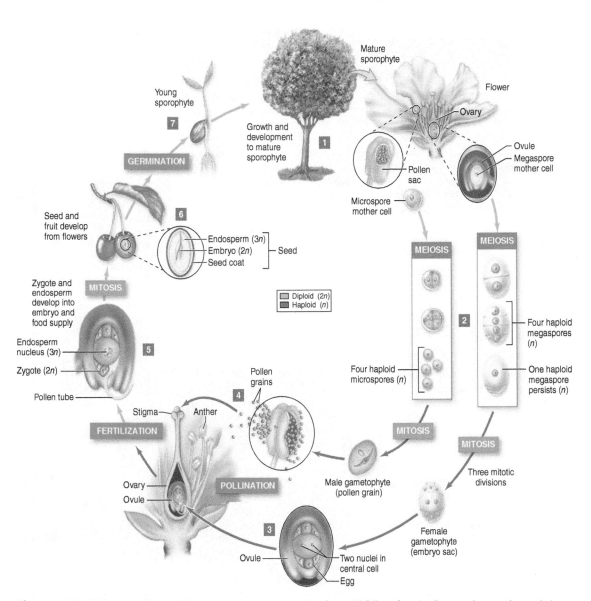

Figure 19.15 Life Cycle of an Angiosperm. (*1*) The mature sporophyte produces flowers. (*2*) Cells in a flower's pollen sac and ovary undergo meiosis, producing spores that develop into haploid male and female gametophytes. (*3*) Inside each ovule, the female gametophyte includes one egg cell and two nuclei in a central cell. (*4*) The pollen sac produces pollen, the male gametophytes. (*5*) A pollen grain delivers two sperm nuclei; one fertilizes the egg and the other fertilizes the nuclei in the central cell, forming a triploid cell that develops into the endosperm. (*6*) Each ovule develops into a seed; the fruit develops from the ovary wall. (*7*) Seed germination reveals the young sporophyte.

Tutorial
Angiosperm
Reproduction

Apply It **Now**

Corn, Corn, Everywhere

Even if you don't eat the kernels off the cob, you likely have much more corn in your diet than you imagine. Besides fresh corn, frozen corn, canned corn, corn meal, corn oil, and corn starch, these are some of the many unexpected fates of corn:

- baking powder and confectioners ("powdered") sugar, which often contain corn starch.

- corn syrup, a liquid sugar derived from corn starch, that sweetens soft drinks, ketchup, and many other foods.

- vanilla extract, which is often made with corn syrup.

- dextrin and maltodextrins are derived from corn starch; these polysaccharides thicken syrups and provide texture to low-fat foods (among many other uses).

- the sugars dextrose (glucose) and fructose.

- margarine, which often contains corn oil.

- the grain alcohol in bourbon whiskey. Ethanol from corn is also a biofuel (see this chapter's Burning Question).

- animal feed. Chickens, hogs, and cattle on commercial farms are fed corn, effectively converting the nutrients in corn to meat.

The corn plant has also played a major role in the history of biology. In the 1940s, Barbara McClintock discovered transposons, or "jumping genes," in Indian corn. She won the 1983 Nobel Prize for physiology or medicine for this work, which has led to new ways to mutate genes and, in turn, new insights into gene function. ① *transposons,* p. 140

C. Wind and Animals Often Participate in Angiosperm Reproduction

Pollination and seed dispersal are at the heart of angiosperm sexual reproduction. After all, sexual reproduction stops if pollen does not travel from one flower to another. And natural selection favors plants that scatter their offspring far and wide, a strategy that simultaneously reduces competition with the parent and promotes genetic diversity.

 Video Pollinators

Wind and animals are the two main transportation modes for pollen (figure 19.16). Wind pollination is relatively inefficient, since most pollen carried by the breeze does not reach a flower of the same species. Plants pollinated by wind produce abundant pollen in flowers that are typically plain and easily overlooked. Grasses, along with the maples and the cattails in figure 19.16a, are common examples of wind-pollinated plants.

Many angiosperms rely on animal "couriers" that unwittingly carry pollen from flower to flower. Because animals typically visit only a limited number of plant species, this strategy is much more efficient than is wind pollination. However, arthropods and vertebrates do not pollinate plants as an act of charity; they usually visit flowers in search of food. Animal pollination therefore has a different cost: The plants invest in large petals, bright colors, alluring scents, and sweet rewards such as nectar that attract animals. The chamomile and banana flowers in figure 19.16b illustrate some of these adaptations.

The relationship between angiosperms and their pollinators is sometimes so tight that one cannot reproduce or survive without the other. This situation can lead to **coevolution,** in which a genetic change in one species selects for subsequent change in another species. For example, an alteration in the shape or color of a flower can select for new adaptations in its pollinator (see

section 14.7). The reverse can also occur: a change in the curve of a hummingbird's beak, for example, can select for corresponding modifications in the flower that it pollinates.

a. Pollination by wind

b. Pollination by animals

Figure 19.16 A Gallery of Angiosperms. (a) Wind-pollinated plants include (*left*) red maple trees and (*right*) cattails. The brown cylinders on the cattail plant are elongated clusters of tiny brown flowers. (b) Animal-pollinated plants include (*left*) German chamomile and (*right*) banana trees. Bats pollinate banana flowers in the wild, but commercial varieties bear fruit without pollination.

F◯CUS on Model Organisms

Mouse-Ear Cress: *Arabidopsis thaliana*

The choice of a "star" model organism for plants is simple: *Arabidopsis thaliana* easily beats out all others (figure 19.A). This tiny angiosperm, a mustard relative, has become a staple of plant biology laboratories because of its small size, easy cultivation, and prolific reproduction. In addition, biologists can use a bacterium called *Agrobacterium tumefaciens* to carry new genes into *Arabidopsis* cells.

The amount of attention devoted to this plant may seem extravagant, considering its insignificance as a commercial plant. Because angiosperms are closely related to one another, however, discoveries in *Arabidopsis* will likely apply directly to economically important crop plants. For example, genetic and molecular studies of *Arabidopsis* can help researchers identify genes that enable plants to grow on poor soil. Understanding these genes may help plant scientists develop improved varieties of food crops such as rice, barley, wheat, and corn.

Moreover, many genes in *Arabidopsis* have counterparts in humans and other organisms, so research on this plant can have far-reaching applications. For example, scientists have discovered that *Arabidopsis* has at least 139 genes that correspond to human disease genes. Studies of *Arabidopsis* can therefore help us understand illnesses from colitis to Alzheimer disease to arthritis.

The following list includes a few of the important discoveries resulting from work on *Arabidopsis*:

- **Control of gene expression:** Each cell type in a multicellular organism turns on a different combination of genes. One way that cells regulate gene expression is to attach methyl groups to unneeded DNA; another is to produce small pieces of RNA that bind to genes that have already been transcribed. Researchers have studied both processes in *Arabidopsis*, in part because problems in gene expression cause some types of cancer in humans. ⓘ *regulation of gene expression*, p. 134
- **Genome duplication:** The *Arabidopsis* genome sequencing project was completed in 2000. Analysis of the DNA suggests that the entire genome has duplicated two or three times, fueling speculation that all plants are polyploids. This finding may help shed light on the evolutionary history of plants. ⓘ *polyploidy*, p. 177
- **Disease resistance:** Some plants construct a sort of "fire break" around the spot where a bacterium or fungus has entered. Small areas of surrounding plant tissue die, and this zone of dead cells prevents the invader from spreading throughout the plant. Study of this response in *Arabidopsis* has led to new insights into how genes regulate this form of programmed cell death; this research may one day help plant breeders improve disease resistance in other crops as well. ⓘ *apoptosis*, p. 162

- **Response to the environment:** A plant cannot avoid extremes of temperature, light availability, and salinity by moving to a better location. Instead, it must adjust its physiology. *Arabidopsis* has genes that control its response when the weather turns cold, a finding that could help crop plants survive freezing.
- **Hormones:** Ethylene is a gas that helps control fruit ripening and plant senescence (aging). Mutant *Arabidopsis* plants that do not respond to ethylene have helped researchers find ethylene receptor proteins. Researchers have also discovered that the ethylene response requires copper, which the plant transports using a protein similar to one that transports copper in humans. (When faulty in humans, this protein causes Menkes disease.) ⓘ *ethylene*, p. 508
- **Circadian rhythms:** Circadian processes occur in 24-hour cycles. In *Arabidopsis*, for example, proteins encoded by clock genes ensure that the expression of genes needed for photosynthesis peaks at around noon. The same genes are repressed at night. Pigments called phytochromes "reset" the clock each day. ⓘ *phytochrome*, p. 511
- **Flowering:** Angiosperms delay flowering until they reach reproductive maturity. How do they "know" when the time comes, and how do they build flower parts in the right places? *Arabidopsis* research has revealed genes that control the timing of flowering, the differentiation of cells that give rise to flowers, the development of individual flower parts, and the development of ovules inside the flower. For example, some genetic mutations induce flowers to develop into shoots; others promote early flowering.

Figure 19.A
Arabidopsis thaliana.

Like pollination, seed dispersal also usually involves wind or animals. Some fruits, such as those of dandelions and maples, have "parachutes" or "wings" that promote wind dispersal. Others, however, spread only with the help of animals. Some have burrs that cling to animal fur. Others are sweet and fleshy, attracting animals that eat the fruits and later spit out or discard the seeds in their feces. ⓘ *seed dispersal*, p. 505

Video
Fruit Eaters

19.5   MASTERING CONCEPTS

1. What are the two largest clades of angiosperms?
2. In what ways are the life cycles of angiosperms similar to and different from those of conifers?
3. What is the relationship between flowers and fruits?
4. How do animals participate in angiosperm reproduction?

INVESTIGATING LIFE

19.6 Genetic Messages from Ancient Ecosystems

Psychics claim to be able to communicate with the spirits of the dead. Although scientists do not assert the same spiritual connection, they can bring back the genetic remnants of species that lived and died long ago.

When an organism dies, its DNA usually degrades rapidly. But in some special cases, the genetic material remains intact indefinitely. Freezing is one way to preserve DNA. An ideal source of diverse ancient DNA is a landscape that once teemed with life but that has since become permanently frozen.

One such example is the land bridge, called Beringia, that once connected present-day northeastern Siberia to Alaska. Long ago, giant mammals such as mammoth, bear, bison, and large cats roamed the grassy Beringian landscape. But climates shift, and much of Beringia is now permanently frozen land in Siberia, Alaska, and the Yukon. Could DNA trapped in frozen soil reveal which plants supported the ancient Beringian ecosystem?

Danish researchers Eske Willerslev, Anders Hansen, and their colleagues drove metal cylinders deep into the Siberian permafrost and removed long, thin rods (called "cores") of ice, soil, and organic material (figure 19.17). The deepest holes yield the oldest deposits, because new sediments accumulate over old ones. Radiometric dating, pollen analysis, and other techniques helped them estimate the age of each layer of material in the cores. ⓘ *radiometric dating*, p. 266

Willerslev and colleagues tried to extract DNA from eight sediment samples ranging in age from modern to about 2 million years old. Wherever DNA was present, they searched for two sets of genes. One target was part of the gene encoding the protein rubisco, which is essential for photosynthesis (see chapter 5). This presence of this gene indicates plant material.

The other targets were fragments of genes found only in the mitochondria of vertebrate animals such as mammals.

Sediments from 300,000 to 400,000 years old contained plant DNA, including a tremendous diversity of mosses, herbs (grasses and other nonwoody plants), shrubs, and trees. On the other hand, the oldest mitochondrial DNA from vertebrates was only about 20,000 to 30,000 years old. Some came from grazers that still exist today, such as the horse, lemming, hare, musk ox, and reindeer, but the researchers also found genes from extinct mammoth and bison. The presence of genes from animals that vanished long ago suggests that the sediment DNA was authentic and not simply a modern contaminant.

These gene fragments can help scientists reconstruct ancient ecosystems. The chloroplast DNA, for example, reveals that herbs dominated the Beringian landscape 300,000 or so years ago but lost ground to shrubs over time (figure 19.18). The most dramatic decline of grasses occurred in the past 10,000 years, a time that coincided with the extinction of the mammoth and bison. Did one event cause the other? What role did increasing human populations play? These questions remain unanswered for now.

Willerslev's team hopes their work will inspire others to extract DNA from ancient sediments around the world. The resulting patchwork of gene fragments, pieced together, will reveal valuable information about the changes that shaped ancient ecosystems—without the help of a psychic.

Willerslev, E., A. J. Hansen, J. Binladen, et al. May 2, 2003. Diverse plant and animal genetic records from Holocene and Pleistocene sediments. *Science*, vol. 300, pages 791–795.

19.6 MASTERING CONCEPTS

1. Why do researchers collect DNA from permafrost?
2. What are some alternative hypotheses for why the researchers failed to recover any DNA from sediments that were more than 300,000 to 400,000 years old? How would you test your hypotheses?

Figure 19.17 Core Sample. Cores of frozen sediment taken from permafrost may contain ancient DNA.

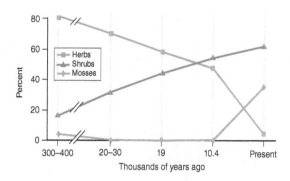

Figure 19.18 Changing Communities. Chloroplast DNA isolated from sediment samples shows that grasses and other herbs have become much less common, while shrubs have become more common, over the past 400,000 or so years.

CHAPTER SUMMARY

19.1 Plants Have Changed the World

- Members of kingdom **Plantae** provide food and habitat for other organisms, remove CO_2 from the atmosphere, and produce O_2. Humans rely on plants for food, lumber, clothing, paper, and many other resources.

A. Green Algae Are the Closest Relatives of Plants

- The ancestor of land plants may have resembled green algae called **charophytes**. Plants emerged onto land about 450 million years ago.
- Like many green algae, plants are multicellular, eukaryotic autotrophs that have cellulose cell walls and use starch as a carbohydrate reserve. Green algae and plants also use the same photosynthetic pigments. Unlike green algae, plants are adapted to conditions on land.

B. Plants Are Adapted to Life on Land

- Adaptations that enable plants to obtain and conserve resources include roots, leaves, a waterproof **cuticle,** and **stomata.**
- **Vascular tissue** is a transportation system inside many plants. **Xylem** transports water and minerals; **phloem** carries sugars. **Lignin** strengthens xylem cell walls, providing physical support.
- Figure 19.19 illustrates the **alternation of generations** in the plant life cycle. The diploid **sporophyte** produces haploid spores by meiosis; the haploid **gametophyte** produces haploid sperm and egg cells by mitosis. Fertilization restores the diploid number.
- In the simplest plants, the gametophyte generation is most prominent; in more complex plants, the sporophyte dominates (see figure 19.19).
- In gymnosperms and angiosperms, reproductive adaptations include **pollen** and **seeds. Pollination** delivers sperm to egg. The resulting

zygote develops into an embryo, which is packaged along with a food supply into a seed. Angiosperms also produce **flowers** and **fruits.**
- Plants are classified by the presence or absence of vascular tissue, seeds, flowers, and fruits.
- Figure 19.20 on page 396 summarizes plant diversity.

19.2 Bryophytes Are the Simplest Plants

A. Bryophytes Lack Vascular Tissue

- **Bryophytes** are small green plants lacking vascular tissue, leaves, roots, and stems.
- The three groups of bryophytes are **liverworts, hornworts,** and **mosses.**

B. Bryophytes Have a Conspicuous Gametophyte

- In bryophytes, the gametophyte stage is dominant. Many bryophytes reproduce asexually by fragmentation of the gametophyte. Sperm require water to swim to egg cells.

19.3 Seedless Vascular Plants Have Xylem and Phloem But No Seeds

A. Seedless Vascular Plants Include Ferns and Their Close Relatives

- **Seedless vascular plants** have vascular tissue but lack seeds. This group includes **club mosses, whisk ferns, horsetails,** and **true ferns.**

B. Seedless Vascular Plants Have a Conspicuous Sporophyte and Swimming Sperm

- The diploid sporophyte generation is the most obvious stage of a fern life cycle, but the haploid gametophyte forms a tiny separate plant.
- In the sexual life cycle of ferns, collections of sporangia appear on the undersides of fronds. Meiosis occurs in the sporangia and yields haploid spores, which germinate in soil and develop into gametophytes. The gametophytes produce egg cells and swimming sperm.

19.4 Gymnosperms Are "Naked Seed" Plants

A. Gymnosperms Include Conifers and Three Related Groups

- **Gymnosperms** are vascular plants with seeds that are not enclosed in fruits. The four groups of gymnosperms are **cycads, ginkgos, conifers,** and **gnetophytes.**

B. Conifers Produce Pollen and Seeds in Cones

- In pines (a type of conifer), **cones** house the reproductive structures. Male cones release pollen, and female cones produce egg cells inside **ovules.** Pollen germination yields a pollen tube through which a sperm nucleus travels to the egg cell. After fertilization, the resulting embryo remains dormant in a seed until germination.
- In conifers, the sperm do not require water to swim to the egg cell. Instead, most gymnosperms rely on wind to spread pollen.

19.5 Angiosperms Produce Seeds in Fruits

A. Most Angiosperms Are Eudicots or Monocots

- **Angiosperms** are vascular plants that produce flowers and fruits. The two largest clades of angiosperms are **eudicots** and **monocots.**

B. Flowers and Fruits Are Unique to the Angiosperm Life Cycle

- Flowers produce pollen and egg cells. After pollination, the flower parts develop into the fruit, which protects the seeds.

C. Wind and Animals Often Participate in Angiosperm Reproduction

- Most angiosperms are wind- or animal-pollinated. Corresponding adaptations in animals and plants illustrate **coevolution.**
- Angiosperm fruits aid in seed dispersal, usually by wind or animals.

19.6 Investigating Life: Genetic Messages from Ancient Ecosystems

- Researchers have extracted DNA from plants and animals buried long ago in frozen sediments. The DNA evidence reveals changes in the landscape over hundreds of thousands of years.

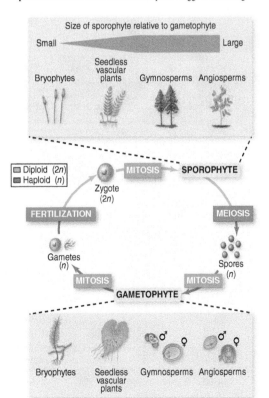

Figure 19.19 Alternation of Generations: A Summary.

Figure 19.20 Plant Diversity: A Summary.

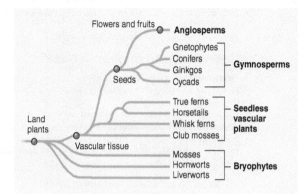

■ **Angiosperms (flowering plants)**
- >260,000 species
- Monocots, eudicots, basal angiosperms
- Independent sporophyte
- Pollen and egg cells develop in flowers
- Usually pollinated by wind or animals
- Seeds develop inside fruits

■ **Pines and other gymnosperms**
- ~830 species
- Cycads, ginkgos, conifers, gnetophytes
- Independent sporophyte
- Pollen and seeds usually develop on cone scales
- Usually wind-pollinated

■ **Ferns and other seedless vascular plants**
- ~12,000 species
- Club mosses, whisk ferns, horsetails, true ferns
- Independent sporophyte

■ **Mosses and other bryophytes (nonvascular plants)**
- ~24,000 species
- Liverworts, hornworts, mosses
- Sporophyte depends on gametophyte for nutrition

Group	Swimming Sperm	Vascular Tissue	Pollen	Seeds	Flowers	Fruits
Bryophytes	Yes	No	No	No	No	No
Seedless vascular plants	Yes	Yes	No	No	No	No
Gymnosperms	No	Yes	Yes	Yes	No	No
Angiosperms	No	Yes	Yes	Yes	Yes	Yes

MULTIPLE CHOICE QUESTIONS

1. Which of the following is NOT a similarity between land plants and green algae?
   a. Photosynthesis
   b. Starch as a storage form of energy
   c. Cellulose cell walls
   d. The presence of a cuticle and stomata

2. In the alternation of generations in plants, the gametophyte is _____ and produces gametes by _____.
   a. haploid; mitosis
   b. diploid; mitosis
   c. haploid; meiosis
   d. diploid; meiosis

3. What conditions did plants face when they moved to land?
   a. Air provides less physical support than water.
   b. Drying out became more likely.
   c. They were adapted to gamete dispersal in water.
   d. All of the above are correct.

4. Which of the following is present in all land plants?
   a. Wind-blown sperm
   b. A seed coat that prevents embryos from drying out
   c. Vessels that transport water and nutrients throughout the plant
   d. None of the above are present in all land plants.

5. How does the presence of vascular tissue (xylem and phloem) affect a plant?
   a. It reduces the plant's dependence on a moist environment.
   b. It allows specialization of roots, leaves, and stems.
   c. It allows for the growth of larger plants.
   d. All of the above are correct.

6. Which of the following terms is most inclusive?
   a. Monocot
   b. Seed plant
   c. Gymnosperm
   d. Angiosperm

7. Which type of plant produces seeds enclosed in fruits?
   a. Bryophyte
   b. Gymnosperm
   c. Angiosperm
   d. True fern

8. Reproduction in a pine tree is associated with
   a. male and female cones.
   b. windblown pollen.
   c. the formation of pollen tubes.
   d. All of the above are correct.

9. What is a key adaptation that is unique to the angiosperms?
   a. Dominant gametophyte generation
   b. Pollen grains that use pollen tubes to fertilize egg cells
   c. Flowers as reproductive structures
   d. Both a and b are correct.

10. What plant group is correctly matched with an adaptation of its members?
    a. Cycads: Vascular tissue
    b. Liverworts: True leaves
    c. Whisk ferns: Seeds
    d. Conifers: Fruit

Answers to these questions are in appendix A.

WRITE IT OUT

1. What characteristics do all land plants have in common?

2. Analyze the alternation of generations common to all plants. If you isolated all of the gametes that one gametophyte produced and analyzed the DNA, would you see variation among the gametes?

3. How are terrestrial habitats different from aquatic habitats? List the adaptations that enable plants to obtain resources, transport materials, and reproduce; explain how each adaptation contributes to a plant's reproductive success on land.

4. List the characteristics that distinguish the four major groups of plants, then provide an example of a plant within each group.

5. Give at least two explanations for the observation that bryophytes are much smaller than most vascular plants. How can increased height be adaptive? In what circumstances is small size adaptive?

6. A fern plant can produce as many as 50 million spores a year. How are these spores similar to and different from seeds? In a fern population that is neither shrinking nor growing, approximately what proportion of these spores is likely to survive long enough to reproduce? What factors might determine whether an individual spore successfully produces a new fern plant?

7. How do the adaptations of gymnosperms and angiosperms enable them to live in drier habitats than bryophytes and seedless vascular plants?

8. Describe how the petals, ovary, and ovule of flowers participate in reproduction. What happens to each part after fertilization?

9. Draw a bar graph showing the number of species in each group of plants. Is there a correlation between the age of the plant group and the group's diversity?

10. The immature fruit of the opium poppy produces many chemicals that affect animal nervous systems. In what way might these chemicals benefit the plant?

11. Scientists have studied plant populations that have colonized areas with low rates of herbivory compared to the plant's previous habitat. After many generations in the new habitat, the plants produce fewer defense chemicals and grow larger than plants in the ancestral population. How does natural selection explain these observations? (Hint: Producing defense chemicals uses energy.)

12. In a sentence or two, either support or refute the following statement: The pollen grains of angiosperms are homologous to the spores of bryophytes.

13. Some angiosperm species have exclusive relationships with just one species of pollinator. How would this relationship benefit the plant? What are the risks to the plant?

14. Compare and contrast the life cycles of the four groups of plants. How does each group represent a variation on the common theme of alternation of generations?

15. A slight change in a plant species' flower structure might favor a different pollinator. How might such a change in flower structure lead to a new plant species? How does coevolution between flowering plants and animal pollinators help explain the huge diversity of angiosperms?

16. Suppose you and a friend are hiking and you see an unfamiliar plant. What observations would you make in trying to determine which type of plant it is?

17. People often move plants from one part of the world to another. Sometimes, an introduced plant species can become invasive, taking over native plant populations. The U.S. Department of Agriculture manages the National Invasive Species Information Center, whose website maintains a list of invasive plants. Which plant species are considered invasive in your home state? Why are those species harmful? Should invasive plants be eradicated? How?

18. Human activities and natural phenomena can drive plant species to extinction. The U.S. Department of Agriculture Natural Resources Conservation Service maintains lists of threatened and endangered plant species. What are some examples of threatened or endangered species in your area? What are the most important threats to those species? What are the potential consequences of a plant species extinction? What steps should we take to save threatened and endangered plants?

19. What are the pros and cons of pursuing biofuels as alternatives to fossil fuels? In your opinion, do the pros outweigh the cons, or vice versa? Justify your answer.

PULL IT TOGETHER

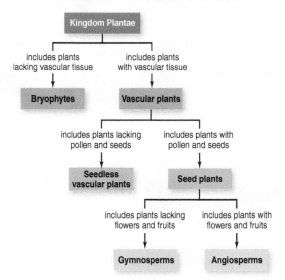

Figure 19.21 Pull It Together: Plants.

Refer to figure 19.21 and the chapter content to answer the following questions.

1. Describe an adaptation that arose in each group of vascular plants.

2. Circle each plant group that produces spores.

3. How do bryophytes and seedless vascular plants reproduce if they lack pollen and seeds?

4. What is the relationship between pollen and seeds?

20 Fungi

Mushrooms in the Morning. Parasol mushrooms sometimes seem to come from nowhere, appearing overnight after a rain. But what you see is not the whole organism; most of the fungus remains underground.

Enhance your study |BIOLOGY
of this chapter with practice quizzes,
animations and videos, answer keys,
and downloadable study tools.
www.mhhe.com/hoefnagels

The Mushroom Mystique

FOR MANY PEOPLE, THE WORD *FUNGI* CONJURES IMAGES OF MUSHROOMS, ALONG WITH EMOTIONS THAT RANGE FROM DELIGHT TO REVULSION. Enthusiasts know that mushrooms can be delectable, yet fairy tales associate toadstools with dank, lonely forests teeming with witches and evil spirits.

Mushroom imagery is common in everyday language. A phrase such as "mushrooming private enterprise in China," for example, evokes the amazing growth rates of fungi. When warm weather follows a rain, mushrooms seem to pop up overnight on lawns and around trees. This extraordinarily rapid growth adds to their mystique.

How can mushrooms appear so suddenly? Like an apple on a tree, a mushroom is a reproductive structure attached to a much larger organism. Most of the fungal body, however, is underground. Fungi produce filaments that feed by penetrating their food, absorbing nutrients as they go. Sometimes two threads unite, and the combined organism prepares to reproduce. When the temperature and moisture are just right, the cells of tiny "premushrooms" absorb water, expanding rapidly. Mushrooms erupt out of the ground and shed reproductive cells called spores. Afterward, the mushrooms wilt, vanishing as quickly as they appeared.

Picking and eating wild mushrooms can be extremely dangerous. One of the deadliest mushrooms is the death angel (*Amanita virosa*). The poisons can be deceptive. Initial symptoms of nausea and diarrhea are followed by a lag of a day or two, during which the mushroom's toxins quietly destroy the liver, kidney, and other organs. By the time symptoms return, the damage is irreversible, and an emergency organ transplant is the only hope for survival. Unfortunately, there is no simple way to tell poisonous species from safe ones.

Commercial mushroom growers cultivate many edible fungi. The familiar white "button mushroom" grows on a compost of horse manure and straw. Shiitakes live on hardwood logs or compressed sawdust; oyster mushrooms prefer wheat or rice straw. Hobbyists can purchase kits to grow these species at home.

Mushrooms represent only a small subset of kingdom Fungi. Diverse fungi spoil food and cause Dutch elm disease, chestnut blight, athlete's foot, diaper rash, ringworm, and yeast infections. On the other hand, they are essential decomposers in ecosystems, and they help humans manufacture cheese, bread, alcoholic beverages, soy sauce, antibiotics, dyes, and many other useful substances. Moreover, research on yeasts and other simple fungi has helped biologists learn about genetics and basic cell processes. This chapter opens the door to this fascinating group.

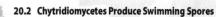

LEARNING OUTLINE

 20.1 Fungi Are Essential Decomposers
- A. Fungi Are Eukaryotic Heterotrophs That Digest Food Externally
- B. Fungal Classification Is Traditionally Based on Reproductive Structures

20.2 Chytridiomycetes Produce Swimming Spores

20.3 Zygomycetes Are Fast Growing and Prolific

20.4 Glomeromycetes Colonize Living Plant Roots

20.5 Ascomycetes Are the Sac Fungi

20.6 Basidiomycetes Are the Familiar Club Fungi

 20.7 Fungi Interact with Other Organisms
- A. Endophytes Live in Aerial Plant Parts
- B. Mycorrhizal Fungi Live on or in Roots
- C. Some Ants Cultivate Fungi
- D. Lichens Are Distinctive Dual Organisms

20.8 Investigating Life: The Battle for Position in Cacao Tree Leaves

 LEARN HOW TO LEARN

Use All Your Resources

Textbooks come with online quizzes, animations, and other resources that can help you learn biology. After you have studied the material in a chapter, test yourself by taking an online quiz. Jot down the questions for which you are unsure of the answers, and remember to go back to study those topics again. Also, check for animations that take you through complex processes one step at a time. Sometimes, the motion of an animation can help you understand what's happening more easily than studying a static image.

20.1 Fungi Are Essential Decomposers

The members of kingdom **Fungi** live nearly everywhere—in soil, in and on plants and animals, in water, even in animal dung (figure 20.1). Microscopic fungi infect the cells of protists, while massive fungi extend enormous distances. For example, a single underground fungus extends over nearly 9 million square meters in an Oregon forest. Mycologists (biologists who study

fungi) have identified more than 80,000 species of fungi, but 1.5 million or so are thought to exist (table 20.1).

Many people know that fungi can cause disease and turn foods moldy, so these organisms have a rather unsavory reputation. The chapter-opening essay described why this reputation is undeserved. Fungi benefit humans directly in many ways: some are edible, others aid in food and beverage production, and still others are useful in biological research. In addition, fungi are vitally important in ecosystems. Many fungi secrete digestive enzymes that break down dead plants and animals, releasing inorganic nutrients and recycling them to plants. These decomposers are, in a sense, the garbage processors of the planet. Other fungi help plants absorb minerals or fight disease.

A. Fungi Are Eukaryotic Heterotrophs That Digest Food Externally

The evolutionary history of fungi remains unclear. The hypothetical common ancestor of all fungi is an aquatic, single-celled, flagellated protist resembling contemporary fungi called chytrids. The identity of the closest living relative to the fungi, however, remains controversial.

Biologists do know, however, that fungi are more closely related to animals than to plants. This finding may surprise those who notice the superficial similarities between plants and fungi. Unlike plants, however, fungi cannot carry out photosynthesis. Moreover, fungi share many chemical and metabolic features with animals.

Fungi have a unique combination of characteristics:

- The cells of fungi are eukaryotic, as are the cells of protists, plants, and animals.

- Fungi are heterotrophs, as are animals, but these two groups acquire food in different ways. Animals ingest their food and digest it internally; fungi secrete enzymes that break down organic matter outside their bodies. The fungus then absorbs the nutrients.

- Fungal cell walls are composed primarily of the modified carbohydrate chitin. This tough, flexible molecule also forms the exoskeletons of some animals. ① *carbohydrates*, p. 31

a.   SEM (false color) |⎯⎯| 5 μm   b.

LM 150 μm

c.   d.

e.

Figure 20.1 A Gallery of Fungi. (a) These microscopic yeast cells are reproducing by budding. (b) Powdery mildew fungi live on leaf surfaces and produce microscopic reproductive structures (inset). (c) This moth was killed by a parasitic fungus, which has produced eerie yellow spikes. (d) A cluster of "honey mushrooms" erupts from this decaying tree. (e) A man harvests mushrooms from a commercial crop.

TABLE **20.1**   **Phyla of Fungi**

Phylum	Examples	Number of Existing Species
Chytridiomycota	Parasite of frog skin	1000
Zygomycota	Black bread mold	1000
Glomeromycota	Arbuscular mycorrhizal fungi	200
Ascomycota	Morels, truffles	More than 50,000
Basidiomycota	Mushrooms, puffballs	30,000

BurningQuestion

Why does food get moldy?

Fungal spores are everywhere. They germinate and grow into colonies on any surface that provides enough food, oxygen, and moisture. Fresh bread, cheese, fruits, and vegetables are all perfect for fungal growth. Often, a fruit such as the tomato at right remains mold-free until its protective skin is punctured, but fungi quickly take over once they gain access to the moist interior.

Perhaps this would be a better question: Why *don't* some foods get moldy? Humans have devised many ways to preserve food. Refrigeration dramatically slows the rate of fungal growth. Salt and sugar, in sufficiently high concentrations, also retard mold growth by limiting the fungus's ability to take up

water by osmosis. Dried foods are preserved in the same way. Cooking and pickling prevent spoilage by damaging microbial enzymes. ⓘ *osmosis*, p. 81

One additional method is to add chemical preservatives to foods. Organic acids such as sodium benzoate are common food additives that inhibit mold growth by disrupting fungal cell membranes. Many processed foods are so laden with preservatives that their shelf lives extend for years, a remarkable accomplishment in a world full of hungry microbes. ⓘ *junk foods*, p. 37; *membranes*, p. 54

Submit your burning question to
Marielle.Hoefnagels@mheducation.com

- The storage carbohydrate of fungi is glycogen, the same as for animals (see figure 2.17).

- Most fungi are multicellular, but **yeasts** are unicellular (see figure 20.1a). The distinction between yeasts and multicellular fungi, however, is not absolute; some species can switch between uni- and multicellular phases.

- Fungi have unique reproductive cycles. Some fungi remain haploid throughout most of the life cycle. Others have a **dikaryotic** stage, which forms when cells of two different individuals unite but the nuclei from the two parents remain separate (figure 20.2). Only fungi have dikaryotic cells. The two nuclei eventually fuse, producing the diploid zygote; in most fungi, the zygote is the only diploid cell. The zygote immediately undergoes meiosis and yields haploid nuclei, which then divide mitotically as the organism grows. (Chapters 8 and 9 describe mitosis and meiosis in detail.)

The body of a fungus is much more extensive than just a mushroom or the visible fuzz on a moldy piece of food (figure 20.3). Instead, fungi usually consist of an enormous number of microscopic, threadlike filaments called **hyphae** (singular: hypha). These filaments branch rapidly within a food source, growing and absorbing nutrients at their tips. A **mycelium** is a mass of aggregated hyphae that may form visible strands in soil or decaying wood.

While the feeding hyphae remain hidden in the food, the reproductive structures emerge at the surface. Most fungi produce abundant **spores,** which are microscopic reproductive cells (see this chapter's Burning Question). Spores that land on a

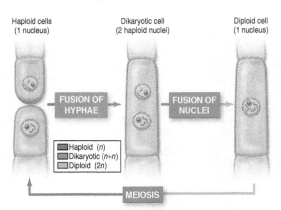

Figure 20.2 Haploid, Dikaryotic, or Diploid? In most fungi, haploid or dikaryotic cells are abundant; typically the only diploid cell is the zygote.

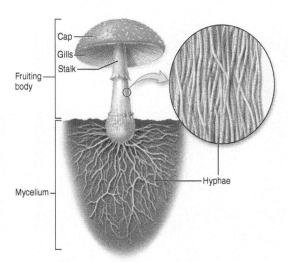

Figure 20.3 The Fungal Body. A mushroom arises from hyphae penetrating the fungus's food source. The mushroom itself is composed of hyphae that are tightly aligned to form a solid structure.

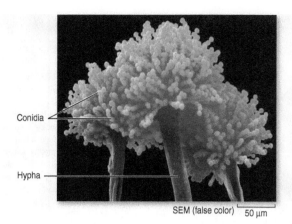

Figure 20.4 **Conidia.** This fungus, a common mold, is producing abundant asexual spores.

suitable habitat can germinate and give rise to feeding hyphae, starting a new colony.

Spores can be asexually or sexually produced. **Conidia** are asexual spores (figure 20.4); the greenish or black powder on moldy food consists entirely of conidia. The production of sexual spores can be considerably more complex. In most fungal species, hyphae aggregate to form a **fruiting body,** a specialized sexual spore-producing organ such as a mushroom, puffball, or truffle. In the mushroom illustrated in figure 20.3, for example, the stalk supports a cap with numerous gills, each of which produces many spores.

B. Fungal Classification Is Traditionally Based on Reproductive Structures

Mycologists classify fungi into five phyla based on the presence and types of sexual structures (figure 20.5). The chytridiomycetes, or chytrids, produce gametes and asexual spores with flagella. Zygomycetes produce thick-walled sexual zygospores. Glomeromycetes do not reproduce sexually at all; instead, they have large, distinctive asexual spores. Ascomycetes produce sexual spores in characteristic sacs, and basidiomycetes release sexual spores from club-shaped structures.

Biologists are still studying the evolutionary relationships among the chytrids, zygomycetes, and glomeromycetes. The ascomycetes and basidiomycetes, however, are clearly sister groups, as figure 20.5 indicates. These are the most complex fungi. Their fruiting bodies, which include morels, truffles, mushrooms, and puffballs, are usually visible with the unaided eye.

20.1   MASTERING CONCEPTS

1. In what ways are fungi important in ecosystems?
2. What characteristics define the fungi?
3. What evidence suggests that fungi are more closely related to animals than to plants?
4. Describe the major structures of a fungus.

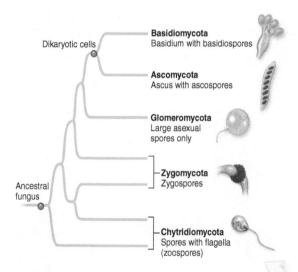

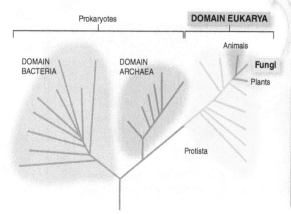

Figure 20.5 **Fungal Diversity.** The fungal kingdom contains five phyla, distinguished mainly on the basis of spore type.

Tutorial
Diversity
of Fungi

20.2 Chytridiomycetes Produce Swimming Spores

Basidiomycetes
Ascomycetes
Glomeromycetes
Zygomycetes
Chytridiomycetes

The 1000 or so species of **chytridiomycetes** (phylum Chytridio-mycota) may provide a glimpse of what the earliest fungi were like. Their body forms vary from single cells to slender hyphae. Chytrids are the only fungi to produce swimming cells, typically with a single flagellum. Some of these motile cells act as gametes; others are asexually produced, in which case they are termed **zoospores** (figure 20.6). Most chytrid life cycles are poorly understood.

These microscopic fungi are powerful decomposers, secreting enzymes that degrade cellulose, chitin, and kera-tin. One ecosystem where resident chytrids are particularly valuable is a ruminant's digestive tract. There, anaerobic chytrids start digesting the cellulose in a cow's grassy meal, paving the way for bacteria to continue the process.

Chytrids also contribute to the ongoing worldwide decline in amphibian populations. The culprit is a chytrid that causes a lethal disease called cutaneous chytridiomycosis in frogs (figure 20.7). The fungus feeds on keratin in the frog's skin and coats the host's legs and undersides, impairing the frog's ability to breathe through its skin. The fungus spreads to new hosts by releasing zoospores into the water. ⓘ *amphibians*, p. 446

The chytrids and zygomycetes are sometimes called the basal fungi because of their simple structures and position close to the base of the fungal family tree. Each group was once considered to be monophyletic, but molecular data have argued against that

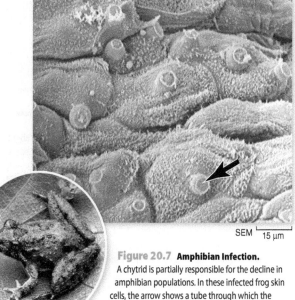

SEM | 15 µm

Figure 20.7 Amphibian Infection.
A chytrid is partially responsible for the decline in amphibian populations. In these infected frog skin cells, the arrow shows a tube through which the chytrid's zoospores leave the host. The inset shows a cricket frog, a species that is often infected with the chytrid.

hypothesis. Instead, each phylum apparently contains representa-tives from multiple lineages, and many fungi once considered to be chytrids have since been reclassified as zygomycetes.

20.2 | MASTERING CONCEPTS

1. How do flagellated cells adapt chytrids to moist environments?
2. What do chytrids eat?

Gamete-producing structures

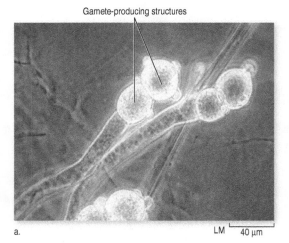

a. | LM | 40 µm

Nucleus Flagellum

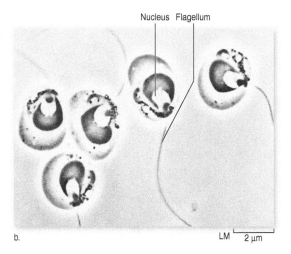

b. | LM | 2 µm

Figure 20.6 Chytrids. (a) Hyphae and spore sacs of the chytrid *Allomyces*. Flagellated gametes will emerge from the rounded sacs at the tips of the hyphae. (b) Zoospores from the chytrid *Blastocladiella*.

20.3 Zygomycetes Are Fast Growing and Prolific

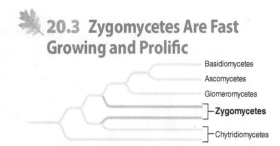

Basidiomycetes
Ascomycetes
Glomeromycetes
Zygomycetes
Chytridiomycetes

The **zygomycetes** (phylum Zygomycota) account for only about 1% of identified fungi, but the 1000 or so species include some familiar organisms. The black mold, *Rhizopus stolonifer*, which grows on bread, fruits, and vegetables, is a zygomycete. In addition to forming black fuzz on refrigerated leftovers, zygomycetes occur on decaying plant and animal matter in soil. Some are parasites of insects, and others must pass through the digestive system of an herbivore to complete their life cycles.

The zygomycetes are known for their spectacular growth rates, but they take their name from their mode of sexual reproduction: the prefix *zygo-* is derived from a Greek word that implies a pairing, or the joining of two parts. As illustrated in figure 20.8, this "pairing" occurs when two hyphae fuse. Then their haploid nuclei merge into a new structure, a diploid

zygospore protected within a distinctive spiny, dark wall (the zygosporangium). After the merger, the hyphae appear as two vacated areas that hug the zygosporangium.

The diploid zygospore nucleus undergoes meiosis, and a haploid hypha emerges. The hypha immediately produces a spore sac, which breaks open and releases numerous haploid spores; as the products of meiosis, they are genetically variable. Each spore then gives rise to a hypha that grows into a haploid mycelium.

Zygomycetes typically produce few zygospores but many conidia. These asexual spores are the products of mitosis, so the spores produced by each hypha are genetically identical. The abundant haploid conidia spread easily to new habitats; figure 20.9 shows two of the more unusual dispersal mechanisms. Spore germination produces a hypha, which quickly grows and branches as it digests its food. Within days, the new mycelium sprouts its own spore sacs, and the cycle begins anew.

20.3 MASTERING CONCEPTS

1. Where do zygomycetes occur?
2. How do zygomycetes reproduce asexually and sexually?
3. How does the zygospore fit into the zygomycete life cycle?

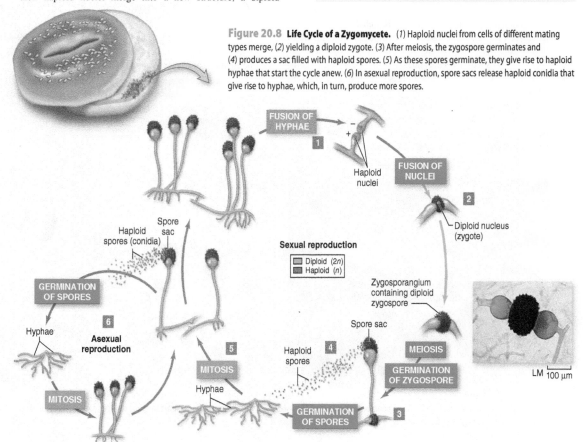

Figure 20.8 Life Cycle of a Zygomycete. (*1*) Haploid nuclei from cells of different mating types merge, (*2*) yielding a diploid zygote. (*3*) After meiosis, the zygospore germinates and (*4*) produces a sac filled with haploid spores. (*5*) As these spores germinate, they give rise to haploid hyphae that start the cycle anew. (*6*) In asexual reproduction, spore sacs release haploid conidia that give rise to hyphae, which, in turn, produce more spores.

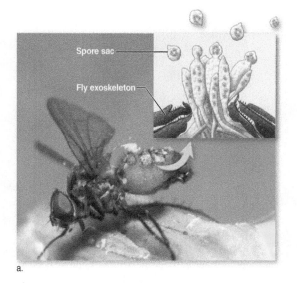

Spore sac

Fly exoskeleton

a.

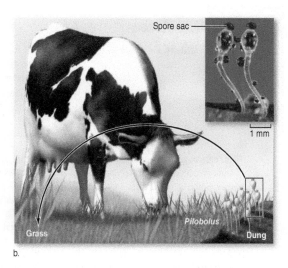

Spore sac

1 mm

Grass

Pilobolus

Dung

b.

Figure 20.9 Zygomycete Spore Dispersal. (a) Spores of *Entomophthora muscae* produce hyphae that penetrate a fly's exoskeleton. Within days, the fly is dead. The fungus emerges, producing a shower of spores *(inset)* that infect additional flies. (b) On the dung of an herbivore, *Pilobolus* grows a stalk topped with a black sac containing thousands of spores *(inset)*. The spore sac is explosively launched from the stalk. Spores that land on the grass are eaten by cattle, which pass the intact spores in their dung.

Video
Pilobolus
Hitchhikers

20.4 Glomeromycetes Colonize Living Plant Roots

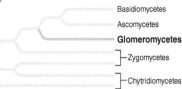

Basidiomycetes

Ascomycetes

Glomeromycetes

Zygomycetes

Chytridiomycetes

The **glomeromycetes** (phylum Glomeromycota) form the smallest group of fungi, with only about 200 known species. Their place in kingdom Fungi is still uncertain. These organisms were once classified as zygomycetes, but molecular evidence suggests they form their own clade.

Glomeromycetes have some unusual features. First, they live only in association with living plant roots; they cannot grow in laboratory petri dishes. Their partnership with plants is called a **mycorrhiza** (literally, "fungus-root"). In a mycorrhiza, fungal hyphae colonize plant roots in a way that benefits both partners. The hyphae absorb water and minerals from the soil and share these resources with the plant; in return, the fungus gains carbohydrates that the plant produces in photosynthesis.

Glomeromycetes form a type of mycorrhiza in which the exchange of materials occurs at structures called arbuscules. The fungus produces the highly branched arbuscules inside the root cells (figure 20.10). Ascomycetes and basidiomycetes form a different type of mycorrhiza; section 20.7 describes these partnerships in more detail.

A second notable feature of the glomeromycetes is their unusually large asexual spores (see figure 20.10); some of the

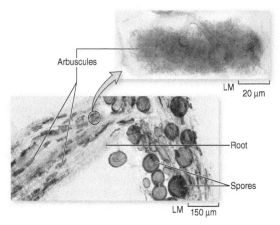

Arbuscules

LM   20 μm

Root

Spores

LM   150 μm

Figure 20.10 Mycorrhizal Root. The arbuscules and large spores of a glomeromycete fill this root. A stain colors the fungal structures blue, making them easily visible with the microscope.

largest are visible with the unaided eye. At the same time, the glomeromycetes are not known to produce sexual spores. Because biologists classify most fungi based on their sexual structures, the absence of a sexual life cycle is partly responsible for the difficulty in placing these fungi in the phylogenetic tree.

20.4   MASTERING CONCEPTS

1. What are the distinctive features of glomeromycetes?
2. Describe arbuscular mycorrhizae.

20.5 Ascomycetes Are the Sac Fungi

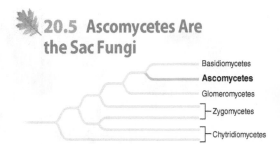

Basidiomycetes

Ascomycetes

Glomeromycetes

Zygomycetes

Chytridiomycetes

With more than 50,000 species, the **ascomycetes** (phylum Ascomycota) make up the largest group of fungi. Their lifestyles vary widely. Some colonize living insects, others decompose organic matter, and still others form partnerships with photosynthetic organisms (see section 20.7). A few are carnivores (figure 20.11).

Some ascomycetes are pests. They cause most fungal diseases of plants, including Dutch elm disease and chestnut blight. A few species cause skin infections such as athlete's foot and other human diseases. Many of the common molds that ravage flood-damaged homes are ascomycetes (figure 20.12).

Nevertheless, ascomycetes also benefit humans. Truffles and morels are prized for their delicious flavors (figure 20.13). The common mold *Penicillium* is famous for secreting penicillin, the first antibiotic discovered. *Penicillium* species also lend their sharp flavors to Roquefort cheese. Fermentation by yeasts such as *Saccharomyces* is essential for baking bread, brewing beer, and making wine. Humans also exploit fermentation by a filamentous ascomycete to produce soy sauce, sake, and rice vinegar. Cyclosporine, a drug that suppresses the immune systems of organ transplant recipients, comes from an ascomycete. The red bread mold, *Neurospora crassa,* has contributed to biological research (see the Focus on Model Organisms box). ⓘ *fermentation,* p. 115

Ascomycetes can produce enormous numbers of asexual and sexual spores (figure 20.14). In sexual reproduction, the hyphae of compatible mating types fuse, but the individual nuclei from the two parents do not immediately merge. The resulting cell is dikaryotic; when the cell divides, the two nuclei undergo mitosis separately.

Figure 20.12 **Mold Everywhere.** This home was flooded during a hurricane. Shortly after the water receded, ascomycetes began to grow in the damp walls. The uppermost colonies indicate how high the water rose.

The fruiting body consists of tightly woven hyphae, often in a cuplike or bottlelike shape, that form a fertile layer of dikaryotic cells. Eventually, the two nuclei in each dikaryotic cell fuse, forming a diploid zygote. The zygote immediately undergoes meiosis and produces four haploid nuclei, each of which usually divides once by mitosis. The result is eight haploid **ascospores,** so named because they form in a saclike **ascus** (plural: asci). After dispersal by wind, water, or animals, ascospore germination yields a new haploid individual.

20.5 | MASTERING CONCEPTS

1. List examples of ascomycetes that are important to humans.
2. Describe asexual and sexual reproduction in an ascomycete.
3. How do dikaryotic cells fit into the ascomycete life cycle?
4. How does an ascus come to contain eight ascospores?

Figure 20.11 **A Carnivorous Fungus.** Threadlike loops of the fungus *Drechslerella anchonia* constrict around a nematode worm. The fungus will thread its hyphae into its prey, releasing digestive enzymes and eating it from within.

SEM   15 μm

a.   b.

Figure 20.13 **Edible Ascomycetes.** (a) Truffles are familiar ascomycetes; they produce asci on internal folds of tissue. (b) Each "pit" in a morel's cap produces thousands of asci. This morel is about 10 cm tall.

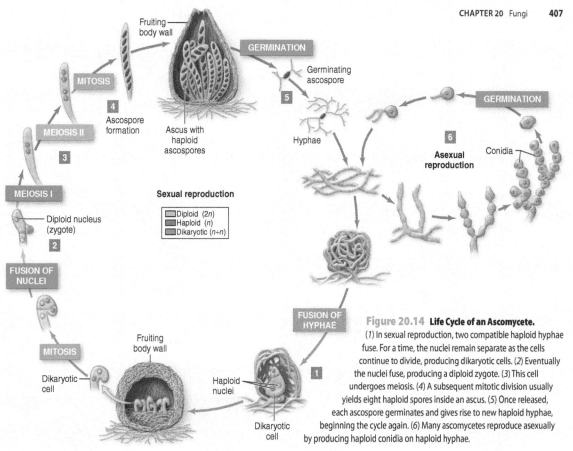

Fruiting body wall

GERMINATION

Germinating ascospore

MITOSIS

4

Ascospore formation

MEIOSIS II

3

Ascus with haploid ascospores

Hyphae

5

6

GERMINATION

MEIOSIS I

Diploid nucleus (zygote)

2

Asexual reproduction

Conidia

Sexual reproduction

☐ Diploid (2n)
☐ Haploid (n)
☐ Dikaryotic (n+n)

FUSION OF NUCLEI

MITOSIS

Fruiting body wall

Dikaryotic cell

Haploid nuclei

Dikaryotic cell

FUSION OF HYPHAE

1

Figure 20.14 Life Cycle of an Ascomycete.
(1) In sexual reproduction, two compatible haploid hyphae fuse. For a time, the nuclei remain separate as the cells continue to divide, producing dikaryotic cells. (2) Eventually the nuclei fuse, producing a diploid zygote. (3) This cell undergoes meiosis. (4) A subsequent mitotic division usually yields eight haploid spores inside an ascus. (5) Once released, each ascospore germinates and gives rise to new haploid hyphae, beginning the cycle again. (6) Many ascomycetes reproduce asexually by producing haploid conidia on haploid hyphae.

F🔍CUS on Model Organisms

Red Bread Mold: *Neurospora crassa*

Why would biologists study *Neurospora crassa* (figure 20.A), a filamentous ascomycete commonly known as red bread mold? First, *N. crassa* can tell us about other ecologically, industrially, and medically important fungi. Second, *N. crassa* has the traits that all model organisms share: it is small and easy to grow, and it has a rapid reproductive cycle. Third, this fungus has special advantages for tracing inheritance patterns. Because its hyphae are haploid, *N. crassa* expresses every recessive or mutated allele in its DNA (in diploid organisms, dominant alleles can mask the presence of their recessive counterparts).

A full accounting of *Neurospora*'s contributions to basic biology could literally fill a book. The following list, however, details some ways this fungus has enhanced our understanding of life:

- **Crossing over:** In the 1920s and 1930s, *Neurospora* provided the first clear evidence of crossing over, which occurs during prophase I of meiosis. *Neurospora*'s narrow, tube-shaped asci are especially well suited to such studies because they retain the products of meiosis in the original order in which the cells divided (see figure 20.14). ⓘ *crossing over*, p. 174

- **One-gene/one-enzyme hypothesis:** In the 1940s, George Beadle, Edward Tatum, and their colleagues isolated *Neurospora* mutants

Figure 20.A *Neurospora crassa*.
This photo shows the asci from a single squashed fruiting body. Note that each ascus contains exactly eight spores.

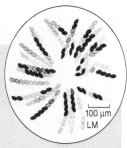

100 μm
LM

with unusual nutritional requirements. Their observation that each mutant had a single enzyme deficiency provided convincing evidence for the idea that one gene encodes each protein in a cell, a topic described in detail in chapter 7.

- **Circadian rhythms:** *Neurospora* cultures produce conidia at roughly 24-hour intervals, a phenomenon called a circadian rhythm (*circa*, "about"; *dies*, "day"). Mutants that produce conidia constantly or not at all have yielded insights into regulation of the so-called clock-controlled genes.

- **Gene regulation:** Some genes in a cell are "silent" at any given time. *Neurospora* has helped reveal some of the ways cells regulate gene expression. For example, cells can "tag" DNA with chemical groups that prevent transcription, or they may destroy RNA after transcription. ⓘ *regulation of gene expression*, p. 134

Apply It **Now**

Fungi and Human Health

Although most fungi are harmless (or even beneficial), some can threaten human health by causing mild to fatal infections, allergic reactions, or poisonings.

Infection: Fungi that degrade the protein keratin can infect our skin, hair, and nails, causing ringworm, athlete's foot, and other irritating diseases. Some fungi, such as *Candida albicans,* normally inhabit the mucous membranes of the mouth, intestines, or vagina. In a yeast infection, populations of these fungi grow out of control. Yeast infections commonly occur when the body's normal microbial community is disrupted or when the immune system is weakened.

Other fungi enter body tissues via wounds or the lungs. People who inhale dust containing spores of a fungus called *Coccidioides immitis* may develop a potentially fatal disease called valley fever. Similarly, *Histoplasma capsulatum* inhabits bird droppings; inhaling the spores may result in a pneumonia-like infection called histoplasmosis.

Allergic reactions: People in many parts of the United States receive "mold spore counts" along with their weather reports, and residents with mold allergies avoid going outside when the counts are high. Common allergenic fungi include species of *Alternaria* and *Aspergillus,* both of which produce abundant asexual spores. They can produce enormous spore masses in mold-infested buildings. ⓘ *allergies,* p. 694

Toxicity: Some people report symptoms such as headaches and memory loss after living or working in moldy buildings. *Stachybotrys atra,* the toxic "black mold," is a commonly cited culprit, but proof that fungal toxins cause these symptoms is lacking.

Poisonous mushrooms such as those described in the chapter-opening essay are the most famous toxic fungi, but others produce potent chemicals as well. *Claviceps purpurea* is an ascomycete that causes a plant disease called ergot (figure 20.B). People who eat bread made from ergot-contaminated grain can develop convulsions, gangrene, and psychotic delusions. Some of the women in Salem, Massachusetts, who were executed as witches in the late 1690s may have been suffering from ergotism, although their uncontrollable movements were attributed to demons. The drug lysergic acid diethylamide (LSD) comes from lysergic acid, a chemical found in ergots.

Another toxin-producing fungus is the ascomycete *Aspergillus flavus.* Hyphae of *A. flavus* feed on nuts, grains, or other stored crops and release aflatoxin, a potent cancer-causing compound that can also be deadly at high doses. Acute toxicity is rare in humans, but in 2006, dozens of dogs died of liver failure after eating aflatoxin-tainted pet food.

Ergot

Figure 20.B Ergot. These black ergots are masses of hyphae.

20.6 Basidiomycetes Are the Familiar Club Fungi

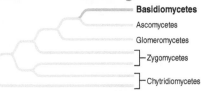

Basidiomycetes
Ascomycetes
Glomeromycetes
Zygomycetes
Chytridiomycetes

The 30,000 or so species of **basidiomycetes** (phylum Basidiomycota) include familiar representatives such as mushrooms, puffballs, stinkhorns, bracket fungi, and bird's nest fungi (figure 20.15). These organisms spread their spores in many ways. Wind carries the spores of puffballs and mushrooms; the putrid odor of the stinkhorn's slimy spore mass attracts flies, which carry the spores on their feet; raindrops splash the spore-laden "eggs" out of a bird's nest fungus.

Basidiomycetes play many roles in human life. Some mushrooms are edible, some are deadly, and others are hallucinogenic (see this chapter's Apply It Now box). Basidiomycetes called smuts and rusts are plant pathogens, causing serious diseases of cereal crops such as corn and wheat. In forests, wood-decaying fungi return carbon locked in trees to Earth's

a.   2.5 cm   b.

c.   1 cm   d.   0.5 cm

Figure 20.15 A Gallery of Basidiomycetes. The club fungi, or basidiomycetes, include (a) puffballs, (b) stinkhorns, (c) turkey tail bracket fungi, and (d) bird's nest fungi.

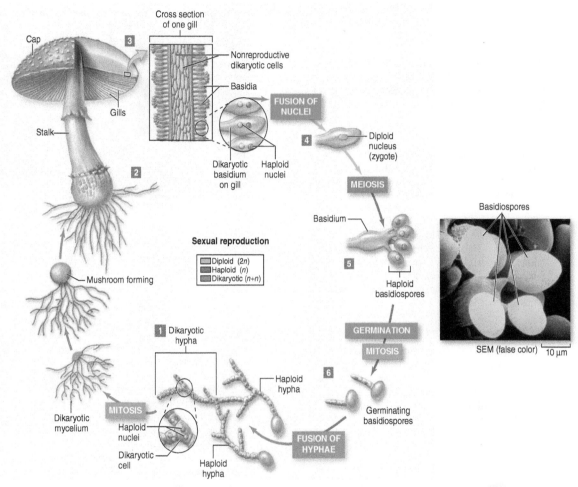

Cross section
of one gill

Cap

3

Nonreproductive
dikaryotic cells

Basidia

Gills

Stalk

FUSION OF
NUCLEI

4

Diploid
nucleus
(zygote)

Dikaryotic
basidium
on gill

Haploid
nuclei

2

MEIOSIS

Basidium

Basidiospores

Sexual reproduction

☐ Diploid (2n)
☐ Haploid (n)
☐ Dikaryotic (n+n)

5

Haploid
basidiospores

Mushroom forming

GERMINATION

MITOSIS

SEM (false color)   10 μm

6

1 Dikaryotic
hypha

Haploid
hypha

Germinating
basidiospores

MITOSIS

Dikaryotic
mycelium

Haploid
nuclei

Dikaryotic
cell

Haploid
hypha

FUSION OF
HYPHAE

Figure 20.16 Life Cycle of a Basidiomycete. (*1*) Hyphae of compatible mating types unite and form a dikaryotic mycelium with two nuclei per cell. (*2*) The dikaryotic fungus grows and forms a mushroom. (*3*) Basidia form on gills on the underside of the mushroom cap. (*4*) The two nuclei in the basidium fuse, creating a diploid zygote that undergoes meiosis. (*5*) The resulting haploid nuclei migrate into four basidiospores, which the mature mushroom sheds. (*6*) The spores germinate, and new haploid hyphae grow.

Tutorial
Basidiomycete
Reproduction

atmosphere. Unfortunately, their talent for degrading the cellulose and lignin in fallen logs also makes them serious pests in another context: they cause dry rot in wooden wall studs and other building materials.

Basidiomycetes can reproduce asexually via conidia, but the sexual portion of the life cycle is usually the most prominent. As figure 20.16 shows, the fusion of two haploid hyphae creates a dikaryotic mycelium. This mycelium typically grows unseen within its food source. When environmental conditions are favorable, however, one or more mushrooms emerge. Lining each mushroom's gills are numerous dikaryotic, club-shaped cells called **basidia** (singular: basidium). Inside each basidium, the haploid nuclei fuse, giving rise to a diploid zygote. The zygote immediately undergoes meiosis, yielding four haploid nuclei.

Each nucleus migrates into a **basidiospore,** which germinates after dispersal. The cycle begins anew.

Sometimes, a circle of mushrooms emerges from the ground all at once. The growth pattern of the underground mycelium explains this phenomenon. Hyphae extend outward in all directions from a colony's center. Mushrooms poke up at the margins of the mycelium, creating the "fairy rings" of folklore.

20.6 MASTERING CONCEPTS

1. What are some familiar basidiomycetes?
2. How are basidiomycetes different from ascomycetes?
3. Describe the sexual life cycle of basidiomycetes.
4. How does a "fairy ring" form?

20.7 Fungi Interact with Other Organisms

Fungi are decomposers and parasites, but they also form symbiotic relationships with living organisms in which both partners benefit (a situation called a mutualism). Here we profile a few interesting examples. ⓘ *mutualism, p. 769*

A. Endophytes Live in Aerial Plant Parts

Endophytes are fungi that live between the cells of a plant's leaves and stems without triggering disease symptoms (*endo-* means inside, and *-phyte* means plant). Every known plant, from mosses to angiosperms, harbors endophytes (figure 20.17). The ubiquity of endophytes has led some researchers to comment that "all plants are part fungi."

Some of these internal fungi neither help nor harm the plant. Others secrete substances that help defend the plants against herbivores. In grasses such as fescue, for example, endophytes can produce toxins that sicken grazing animals. Section 20.8 describes research showing that endophytes can also defend plants against other fungi.

B. Mycorrhizal Fungi Live On or In Roots

Mycorrhizae are associations between fungi and living roots that were introduced in section 20.4. About 80% of all land plants, including grasses, shrubs, and trees, form mycorrhizae. Some plants, such as orchids, cannot live without their fungal associates. Other plant species depend less on the fungi, especially in nutrient-rich soils.

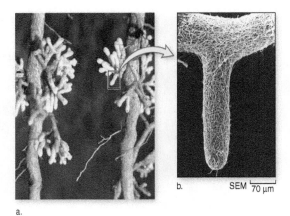

b.   SEM ⌐70 μm

a.

Figure 20.18 Ectomycorrhizae. (a) The creamy white root tips of this buckthorn tree are colonized by an ectomycorrhizal fungus. (b) The hyphae of a mycorrhizal fungus wrap around a host's root tip.

Glomeromycetes form the most common types of mycorrhizae. The fungi pierce the host plant's root cells and produce highly branched arbuscules through which the partners exchange materials (see figure 20.10). Hyphae also extend into the soil, absorbing water and minerals. Basidiomycetes and ascomycetes form a different type of mycorrhiza. In ectomycorrhizae, the fungal hyphae wrap around root tips and reach into the surrounding soil (figure 20.18). The filaments may extend into the root, but they never penetrate individual cells.

Many edible fungi depend on their ectomycorrhizal relationships with live tree roots; these mushrooms are difficult to cultivate commercially. The popularity and high price of these wild delicacies have lured many mushroom pickers into the woods. Scientists are debating whether the wild mushroom trade will harm populations of fungi—and the trees that rely on them—in the long term.

C. Some Ants Cultivate Fungi

The leaf-cutter ants of Central and South America and the southern United States cultivate a basidiomycete in special underground chambers. Into each chamber, the ants transport a paste made from saliva and the disks that they cut from green leaves (figure 20.19). The fungi grow on the paste. Adult and larval ants eat the hyphae so quickly that mushrooms never get a chance to form.

The ants and their fungal gardens constitute a mutualistic partnership; both the ants and the fungi have a steady food supply. Both benefit. But how do the ants keep out competitors or pathogens? Biologists once thought that the ants simply ate all interlopers, but then they discovered a third partner: Bacteria coating parts of the ants' exoskeletons. These microbes secrete a potent toxin, which kills an ascomycete that attacks the cultivated fungus.

Leaf tissue   Hyphae of endophyte

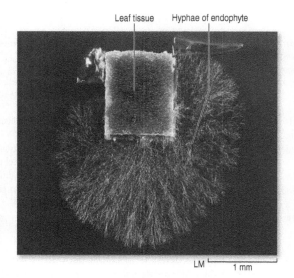

LM ⌐ 1 mm

Figure 20.17 Endophytes. Hyphae of an endophytic fungus grow out of a tiny piece of leaf tissue.

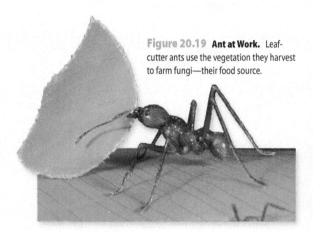

Figure 20.19 **Ant at Work.** Leaf-cutter ants use the vegetation they harvest to farm fungi—their food source.

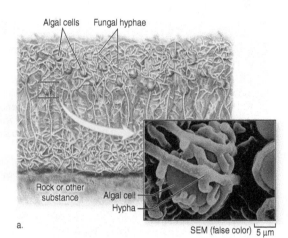

Algal cells   Fungal hyphae

Rock or other substance   Algal cell   Hypha

a.   SEM (false color) 5 μm

D. Lichens Are Distinctive Dual Organisms

A **lichen** forms when a fungus, either an ascomycete or a basidiomycete, harbors green algae or cyanobacteria among its hyphae (figure 20.20). The photosynthetic partner contributes carbohydrates; the fungus absorbs water and essential minerals.

Lichens are sometimes called "dual organisms" because the two species—the fungus and its autotrophic partner—appear to be one individual when viewed with the unaided eye. The body forms can vary widely. Many lichens are colorful, flattened crusts, but others form upright structures that resemble mosses or miniature shrubs. Still others are long, scraggly growths that dangle from tree branches.

Lichens are important ecologically because they secrete acids that break down rock, a first step in the soil-building process. Many also harbor nitrogen-fixing cyanobacteria, which make usable nitrogen available to plants. In addition, some animals, including caribou, eat lichens. ⓘ *nitrogen fixation*, p. 486

Just about any stable surface, from tree bark to boulders to soil, can support lichens. They live everywhere from the driest deserts to the wettest tropical rain forests to the frozen Arctic. Lichens survive dehydration by suspending their metabolism, only to revive when moisture returns. One type of habitat, however, is hostile to lichens: polluted areas. Lichens absorb toxins but cannot excrete them. Toxin buildup hampers photosynthesis, and the lichen dies. Disappearance of native lichens is a sign that pollution is disturbing the environment; scientists therefore use lichens to monitor air quality.

b.

20.7 | MASTERING CONCEPTS

1. What are endophytes?
2. Which types of fungi form arbuscular mycorrhizae and ectomycorrhizae?
3. How do ants, plants, fungi, and bacteria interact in leaf-cutter ant colonies?
4. How do fungi and autotrophs interact in a lichen?
5. How do scientists use lichens to monitor pollution?

c.   SEM (false color) 2 mm   d.

Figure 20.20 **Anatomy of a Lichen.** (a) Cross section of a lichen encrusting a rock; the fungal hyphae wrap tightly around their photosynthetic "partner" cells. (b) The lichens living on this rock look like single organisms when viewed at a large scale. (c) The tiny stalked cups of this trumpet lichen are fruiting bodies. (d) Gray tube lichens and greenish beard lichens colonize a tree branch.

INVESTIGATING LIFE

20.8 The Battle for Position in Cacao Tree Leaves

Chocolate has many friends; its delectable taste and healthful antioxidants make it a favorite food. But chocolate also has its detractors, beyond low-fat diet enthusiasts. Most of its enemies are microbial pathogens of the cacao tree (*Theobroma cacao;* figure 20.21), the source of cocoa. Protists and fungi frequently attack the tree's foliage, branches, and seed pods.

All organisms, including plants, defend themselves against disease. Waxy coverings on leaves and stems prevent the entry of many pathogens, and plant cells produce an array of noxious chemicals that deter microbes that manage to enter. Besides these innate protections, some plants also enlist endophytes in the war against predators and pathogens.

The cacao tree acquires its resident fungi from the environment. A brand-new leaf is endophyte-free, but fungal spores soon arrive in wind or rain and germinate on the young foliage. The hyphae penetrate the waxy leaf cuticle and set up shop within the plant's tissues, absorbing water and nutrients that leak out of the leaf veins. Oddly, the endophytes do not trigger the plant's defenses. This raises an interesting question: What does the tree gain from allowing plant-eating fungi to live inside its tissues?

University of Arizona biologist A. Elizabeth Arnold, along with a research team at the Smithsonian Tropical Research Institute in Panama, wondered whether the endophytes help protect cacao trees from disease. The researchers needed endophyte-free plants to test their hypothesis, so they planted seeds from cacao plants in a greenhouse and protected them from fungal spores that might blow in from outside. Once the trees were 100 days old, the team ensured that the plants were endophyte-free.

Figure 20.21   The Cacao Tree. The pods of *Theobroma cacao* are the source of chocolate.

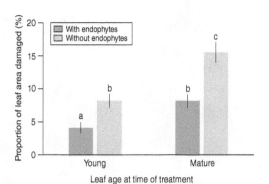

Figure 20.22   Helpful Partners. Endophytic fungi protected young and mature cacao leaves from damage by the pathogen *Phytophthora.* (Letters on bars indicate statistical significance; see appendix B.)

Next, they sprayed spores from several species of endophyte fungi on some of the leaves, so each tree had some treated leaves and some that remained free of the fungi. Once the fungi were thriving in the sprayed leaves, the researchers were ready to test their hypothesis. They inoculated both endophyte-treated and control leaves with spores of a protist called *Phytophthora,* which causes black pod disease of cacao.

Fifteen days later, Arnold and her team counted the number of dead leaves on each tree and measured the *Phytophthora*-damaged area on surviving leaves. These combined measures showed that plant parts without endophytes lost twice as much leaf area as those with the resident fungi (figure 20.22).

No one is sure what the endophytes gain from the relationship, other than the nutrients they absorb from inside the leaf. One hypothesis is that their biggest gain comes after their home leaf ages, dies, and falls to the ground. Perhaps the endophytes colonize a living leaf to get "first dibs" on the dead tissue.

Win–win relationships, such as the one between the cacao tree and its resident fungi, are common in life. Scientists are trying to develop some of these cooperative organisms into biological control agents that might prevent disease in cacao plants without the use of harmful chemicals. Our endophyte allies are already living quietly in the stems and leaves of our crop plants. Perhaps one day farmers will enlist these friendly fungi in a more aggressive fight to preserve our chocolate fix.

Arnold, A. Elizabeth, Luis Carlos Mejia, Damond Kyllo, et al. December 23, 2003. Fungal endophytes limit pathogen damage in a tropical tree. *Proceedings of the National Academy of Sciences,* U.S.A., vol. 100, pages 15649–15654.

20.8   MASTERING CONCEPTS

1. According to figure 20.22, were young leaves with endophytes significantly less damaged than those without endophytes? Explain how you know.

2. How would you design an experiment to determine whether one species of endophyte or some combination of multiple species protects leaves against pathogens?

CHAPTER SUMMARY

20.1 Fungi Are Essential Decomposers

- Fungi are widespread and profoundly affect ecosystems by feeding on living and dead organic material.

A. Fungi Are Eukaryotic Heterotrophs That Digest Food Externally

- Fungi are more closely related to animals than to plants.
- Fungal characteristics include heterotrophy, chitin cell walls, and glycogen. Fungi have both asexual and sexual reproduction, and some have unique **dikaryotic** cells with two genetically different nuclei.
- A fungal body includes a **mycelium** built of threads called **hyphae,** which may form a **fruiting body.** Some fungi occur both as filamentous hyphae and as unicellular **yeasts.**
- Fungi reproduce using asexual and sexual **spores** (figure 20.23). **Conidia** are asexually produced spores.

B. Fungal Classification Is Traditionally Based on Reproductive Structures

- The five main groups of fungi are chytridiomycetes, zygomycetes, glomeromycetes, ascomycetes, and basidiomycetes.
- Molecular evidence indicates that ascomycetes and basidiomycetes are sister groups.
- Figure 20.24 on page 414 summarizes the diversity of the fungi.

20.2 Chytridiomycetes Produce Swimming Spores

- **Chytridiomycetes** are microscopic fungi that produce flagellated cells; if the cells are asexually produced, they are termed **zoospores.**
- Chytrids decompose major biological carbohydrates such as cellulose, chitin, and keratin.

20.3 Zygomycetes Are Fast Growing and Prolific

- **Zygomycetes** reproduce rapidly via asexually produced, haploid, thin-walled spores.
- Sexual reproduction occurs when hyphae of different mating types fuse their nuclei into a **zygospore.** The zygospore undergoes meiosis, then generates a spore sac. Spore germination yields haploid hyphae, continuing the cycle.

20.4 Glomeromycetes Colonize Living Plant Roots

- **Glomeromycetes** form **mycorrhizae,** which are mutually beneficial associations between fungi and roots. Mycorrhizal plants have extra surface area for absorbing nutrients, and the fungus acquires carbohydrates from its plant host.
- Glomeromycetes have no known sexual stage.

20.5 Ascomycetes Are the Sac Fungi

- **Ascomycetes** include important plant pathogens, but they also have many uses in industry.
- Hyphae are haploid for most of the life cycle. Asexual reproduction typically occurs via conidia.
- In sexual reproduction, haploid hyphae join, producing a brief dikaryotic stage. After the nuclei fuse, meiosis yields haploid **ascospores** in a saclike **ascus.**

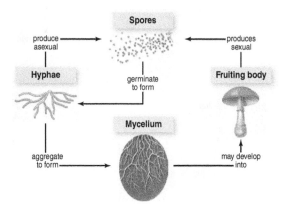

Figure 20.23 Fungal Reproduction: A Summary.

20.6 Basidiomycetes Are the Familiar Club Fungi

- **Basidiomycetes** include mushrooms and other familiar fungi. Wood decay fungi are important in ecosystems but also rot building materials. Some are plant pathogens.
- Basidiomycetes are dikaryotic for most of the life cycle. Asexual reproduction occurs by budding, by fragmentation, or with asexual spores.
- Sexual reproduction occurs when haploid nuclei in **basidia** along the gills of mushrooms fuse. The resulting zygote then undergoes meiosis, producing haploid **basidiospores.** Shortly after spore germination, hyphae fuse, regenerating the dikaryotic state.

20.7 Fungi Interact with Other Organisms

A. Endophytes Live in Aerial Plant Parts

- **Endophytes** are fungi that colonize plant leaves and stems without triggering disease symptoms.

B. Mycorrhizal Fungi Live on or in Roots

- Glomeromycetes form arbuscular mycorrhizae, whereas ascomycetes and basidiomycetes form ectomycorrhizae.

C. Some Ants Cultivate Fungi

- Leaf-cutter ants cultivate basidiomycetes on a nutritious paste made from leaf disks, and bacteria on the ants kill a parasitic ascomycete.

D. Lichens Are Distinctive Dual Organisms

- A **lichen** is a compound organism that consists of a fungus in intimate association with a cyanobacterium or a green alga.
- Lichens are useful air pollution indicators.

20.8 Investigating Life: The Battle for Position in Cacao Tree Leaves

- Experimental evidence indicates that endophytes protect cacao tree leaves from *Phytophthora* pathogens.

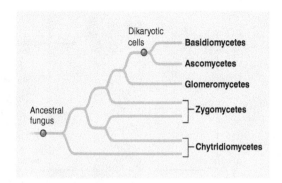

Basidiomycota
- ~30,000 species
- Basidiospores on basidia
- Mushrooms, stinkhorns, puffballs
- Ectomycorrhizae, some lichens

Ascomycetes
- ~50,000 species
- Ascospores inside ascus
- Asexual reproduction common
- Ectomycorrhizae, most lichens
- Many plant pathogens, truffles, morels, most yeasts, *Penicillium*

Glomeromycetes
- ~200 species
- No sexual spores; large asexual spores
- Most are obligate mutualists with land plants
- Arbuscular mycorrhizae

Chytridiomycetes
- ~1,000 species; paraphyletic group
- Spores have single flagellum
- Mostly aquatic
- Decomposers and parasites on many organisms, including amphibians

Zygomycetes
- ~1,000 species; paraphyletic group
- Zygospores
- Black bread mold
- Asexual reproduction more common than sexual reproduction
- Decomposers and parasites

Phylum	Flagellated Cells	Spore Types	Dikaryotic Cells	Complex Fruiting Body
Chytridiomycota	Yes	Zoospores	No	Absent
Zygomycota	No	Zygospores; conidia	No	Absent
Glomeromycota	No	Large asexual spores only	No	Absent
Ascomycota	No	Ascospores in ascus; conidia	Yes	Present
Basidiomycota	No	Basidiospores on basidium; conidia	Yes	Present

Figure 20.24 Fungal Diversity: A Summary.

MULTIPLE CHOICE QUESTIONS

1. The ancestral fungus shown in the evolutionary tree illustrated in figure 20.24 was probably most similar to what type of organism?
   a. A bacterium   c. An animal
   b. A plant   d. A chytrid

2. Fungi get nutrients through their
   a. fruiting body.   c. spores.
   b. hyphae.   d. All of the above are correct.

3. Fungi are traditionally classified based on their
   a. habitat.   c. spore type.
   b. dikaryotic cells.   d. method of acquiring energy.

4. Which phylum of fungi is not known to have a sexual stage in its life cycle?
   a. Chytridiomycetes   c. Basidiomycetes
   b. Glomeromycetes   d. Zygomycetes

5. Why is the zygospore diploid?
   a. Because it forms through meiosis
   b. Because it forms when two haploid nuclei fuse
   c. Because it forms by mitosis of the compatible mating types
   d. Because it forms from a multicellular stage in the life cycle

6. A dikaryotic cell is produced when
   a. two haploid cells fuse but the two nuclei remain separate.
   b. two diploid nuclei fuse.
   c. mitosis occurs without cytokinesis.
   d. meiosis occurs once and cytokinesis occurs twice.

7. The fruiting body of a basidiomycete is often a mushroom, which
   a. makes up most of the volume of the fungus.
   b. produces haploid spores.
   c. is composed mostly of dikaryotic cells.
   d. Both b and c are correct.

8. The feeding hyphae of a basidiomycete are mostly
   a. haploid.   c. dikaryotic.
   b. diploid.   d. All of the above are correct.

9. What is a lichen?
   a. A type of photosynthetic fungus
   b. A combination of a fungus and an alga or cyanobacterium
   c. A combination of two phyla of fungi
   d. A combination of a fungus and a root

10. How does a mycorrhizal fungus differ from a free-living basidiomycete?
   a. It gains its nutrients from a living plant.
   b. It has no sexual stage in its life cycle.
   c. It is not edible.
   d. All of the above are correct.

Answers to these questions are in appendix A.

WRITE IT OUT

1. Give examples of fungi that are important economically, ecologically, and as food for humans.

2. Fungi and animals are both heterotrophs. What does this mean? How do fungi and animals differ in how they obtain food?

3. Suppose you are digging in forest soil and find a stringy, whitish structure. If you had access to a microscope, what features would you look for to determine whether the object is a plant root or a fungus?

4. Create a Venn diagram including the characteristics of fungi, animals, and plants.

5. What characteristics distinguish each phylum of fungi?

6. Many fungi produce chemicals that inhibit bacterial growth. Why might the genes encoding these chemicals be adaptive to fungi?

7. Review figure 19.5, which shows the alternation of generations in plants. Compare and contrast the life cycles of zygomycetes, ascomycetes, and basidiomycetes with the basic plant life cycle.

8. Sketch each of the following structures: mycelium; ascus with ascospores; zoospore; zygospore; basidium with basidiospores.

9. Create a table with three columns. Write the following terms in the first column: mycelium, zygospore, basidium, conidium, and hyphae. Define the terms in the second column, and classify the terms as diploid, dikaryotic, or haploid in the third column.

10. How are hyphae similar to plant roots? How are these structures different?

11. Describe the difference between sexual and asexual reproduction in zygomycetes. Why might asexual reproduction be more common than sexual reproduction?

12. Other than shared DNA sequences, what characteristics place ascomycetes and basidiomycetes together as sister groups?

13. Each ascus within an ascomycete fruiting body contains eight cells. Are these cells haploid, diploid, or dikaryotic? Is every cell within an ascus genetically unique? What is the fate of each cell?

14. An ascomycete causes chestnut blight, a disease that has killed most of the chestnut trees in the United States. If you were a plant breeder trying to bring back the chestnut, how would you use artificial selection to create disease-resistant varieties of the tree?

15. Compare and contrast endophytes, mycorrhizae, and lichens.

16. Use the Internet to find examples of chytrids, zygomycetes, ascomycetes, and basidiomycetes that cause diseases in plants or animals. How does each fungus infect a host and spread to new hosts? What can humans do to fight each disease? What are the costs and benefits of doing so?

17. Some endophytes produce compounds that fight bacteria, making them potential new sources of antibiotics. Describe an experimental method that would allow you to screen endophytes for antibacterial activity.

18. Describe how experiments might show that
    a. chytrids are killing amphibians.
    b. fungi benefit more from a lichen relationship than do algae.
    c. bacteria help leaf-cutting ants cultivate one fungus while killing another.
    d. overharvesting of mycorrhizal basidiomycetes harms forest health.
    e. mold on a building's walls can cause illness in the building's occupants.

19. Genome sequencing projects are complete or in progress for many fungi other than *Neurospora crassa*. Search the Internet for a list of these fungi, choose one, and describe some discoveries that have come from research on the species you chose.

20. Why might it be challenging to produce drugs that treat fungal infections without harming human cells?

21. White nose syndrome is an illness that weakens and kills bats roosting in caves. Affected animals have a white fungus around their muzzle and on their wings, but no one knows if the fungus causes the illness or simply infects bats that are weakened by some other disease. White nose syndrome was discovered in 2006 and has since spread to several states in the eastern and midwestern United States. Search the Internet for the latest information about white nose syndrome, then propose a testable hypothesis to explain how the fungus might have entered bat populations. What information would you need to determine whether the fungus actually causes the disease? How can people help prevent the spread of the fungus from cave to cave? If the disease continues to spread, how might the widespread death of bats affect ecosystems?

22. Create a graph showing the number of species in each group of fungi. Which group is least diverse? Based on the habitats and reproductive structures of these fungi, propose an explanation for their relatively low diversity.

PULL IT TOGETHER

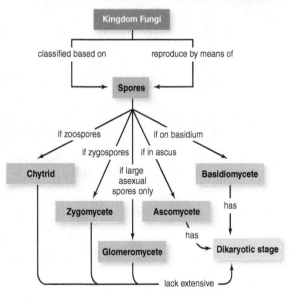

Figure 20.25 **Pull It Together: Fungi.**

Refer to figure 20.25 and the chapter content to answer the following questions.

1. Add at least one characteristic of each group of fungi to the concept map.

2. Why are fungi important to other species?

3. Add *hyphae* and *mycelium* to the concept map.

CHAPTER

21 Animals

Trilobite. A hand holds a trilobite fossil found in the Burgess Shale in Yoho National Park, British Columbia, Canada. Trilobites were animals that originated more than 500 million years ago (MYA). They lived in the oceans until they became extinct about 250 MYA.

Enhance your study |BIOLOGY
of this chapter with practice quizzes,
animations and videos, answer keys,
and downloadable study tools.
www.mhhe.com/hoefnagels

An Explosion of Animal Fossils

THE CAMBRIAN EXPLOSION FASCINATES BIOLOGISTS. After all, the major phyla of animals appeared during an eventful 25-million-year interval of the Cambrian period, which lasted from 543 to 490 million years ago (MYA). Some of the best Cambrian fossils are preserved in exquisite detail at the Burgess Shale, a site in the Canadian Rockies. These remains, representing animals from sponges to worms to arthropods to early chordates, provide a fascinating window into the past.

Burgess Shale fossils, and others from the Cambrian period, suggest that animal diversification was explosive. But what caused the rapid changes in animal body plans that occurred during the Cambrian? Multiple lines of evidence suggest that environmental, developmental, and ecological factors all spurred animal diversification.

Among the most important environmental factors was the amount of dissolved oxygen in the oceans. Chemical analyses of ancient ocean sediments suggest that the oxygen level in the deep ocean started rising about 570 MYA. Biologists speculate that higher oxygen levels fueled higher metabolic rates which, in turn, supported larger bodies.

The genes that control animal development also help explain rapid diversification. DNA sampled from living animals has revealed that the genes guiding the development of complex animal bodies originated millions of years before the Cambrian period (see section 21.17). When a favorable environment arose, these genes began to diversify, leading to new animal forms.

Once complex animal forms began arising, positive feedback sustained the pace of change as new animal activities altered the physical and chemical environment. For example, a sponge feeds by filtering organic particles from the water column. When the sponge dies, that carbon is transferred to the ocean sediment, providing food for bottom-dwelling animals. Likewise, burrowing animals create tunnels that increase the oxygen levels in ocean sediments. Changes such as these likely made the oceans a more favorable habitat for other animal groups, which then manipulated the environment in additional ways and selected for still other new types of animals.

Explanations of the Cambrian explosion continue to evolve as scientists find new data. We will return to animal origins in section 21.17. But first, this chapter will explore the evolutionary relationships among the nine major animal phyla, all of which trace their origins to the Cambrian.

LEARNING OUTLINE

21.1 Animals Live Nearly Everywhere

21.2 Sponges Are Simple Animals That Lack Differentiated Tissues

21.3 Cnidarians Are Radially Symmetrical, Aquatic Animals

21.4 Flatworms Have Bilateral Symmetry and Incomplete Digestive Tracts

21.5 Mollusks Are Soft, Unsegmented Animals

21.6 Annelids Are Segmented Worms

21.7 Nematodes Are Unsegmented, Cylindrical Worms

21.8 Arthropods Have Exoskeletons and Jointed Appendages

21.9 Echinoderm Adults Have Five-Part, Radial Symmetry

21.10 Most Chordates Are Vertebrates

21.11 Tunicates and Lancelets Are Invertebrate Chordates

21.12 Hagfishes and Lampreys Are Craniates Lacking Jaws

21.13 Fishes Are Aquatic Vertebrates with Jaws, Gills, and Fins

21.14 Amphibians Lead a Double Life on Land and in Water

21.15 Reptiles Were the First Vertebrates to Thrive on Dry Land

21.16 Mammals Are Warm, Furry Milk-Drinkers

21.17 Investigating Life: Sponges Fill Holes in Animal Evolution

LEARN HOW TO LEARN

Think While You Search the Internet

Some assignments may require you to use the Internet. But the Internet is full of misinformation, so you must evaluate every site you visit. Collaborative sites such as Wikipedia are unreliable because anyone can change any article. For other sites, ask the following questions: Are you looking at someone's personal page? Is there an educational, governmental, nonprofit, or commercial sponsor? Is the author reputable? Does the page contain opinions or facts? Are facts backed up with documentation? Answering these questions will help ensure that the sites you use are credible.

21.1 Animals Live Nearly Everywhere

Think of any animal. There's a good chance that the example that popped into your head was a mammal such as a dog, cat, horse, or cow. Although it makes sense that we think first of our most familiar companions, the 5800 species of mammals represent only a tiny subset of organisms in kingdom **Animalia.**

Biologists have described about 1,300,000 animal species, distributed among 37 phyla. This chapter considers nine of the largest phyla in detail (table 21.1); the Burning Question box on page 433 briefly describes three others. The vast majority of animals are **invertebrates** (animals without backbones). The phylum Arthropoda, for example, includes more than one million species of invertebrates such as insects, crustaceans, and spiders. Only about 57,000 known species are **vertebrates** (animals with backbones) such as mammals and birds.

The diversity of animals is astonishing. Animals live in us, on us, and around us. They are extremely diverse in size, habitat, body form, and intelligence. Whales are immense; roundworms can be microscopic. Bighorn sheep scale mountaintops; crabs scuttle on the deep ocean floor. Earthworms are squishy; clams surround themselves in heavy armor. Sponges are witless; humans, chimps, and dolphins are clever. This chapter explores some of this amazing variety; unit 6 explores animal anatomy and physiology in more detail.

TABLE 21.1   Nine Phyla of Animals

Phylum	Examples	Number of Existing Species
Porifera	Sponges	5000
Cnidaria	Hydras, jellyfishes, corals, sea anemones	11,000
Platyhelminthes (flatworms)	*Planaria*, tapeworms, flukes	25,000
Mollusca	Bivalves, chitons, snails, slugs, squids, octopuses	112,000
Annelida	Earthworms, leeches, polychaetes	15,000
Nematoda (roundworms)	Pinworms, hookworms, *C. elegans*	80,000
Arthropoda	Horseshoe crabs, spiders, scorpions, crustaceans, insects	More than 1,000,000
Echinodermata	Sea stars, sea urchins, sand dollars	7000
Chordata	Tunicates, lancelets, fishes, amphibians, reptiles, mammals	60,000

A. The First Animals Likely Evolved from Protists

The animal you thought of a moment ago probably lives on land, since terrestrial animals are the ones we see most often. Nevertheless, only 10 of the 37 known phyla include species that live on land, and no phylum contains only terrestrial animals. All of today's animals clearly have their origins in aquatic ancestors.

The first animals, which arose about 570 million years ago (MYA), may have been related to aquatic protists called choanoflagellates (figure 21.1), organisms that strongly resemble collar cells in sponges. Although no one knows exactly what the first animal looked like, the Ediacaran organisms that thrived during the Precambrian left some of the oldest animal fossils ever found (see figure 15.12). Animal life diversified spectacularly during the Cambrian period, which ended about 490 MYA. Most of today's phyla of animals, including sponges, jellyfishes, arthropods, mollusks, and many types of worms, originated in the Cambrian seas. Their fossils are exceptionally abundant in an area of British Columbia called the Burgess Shale (see the chapter-opening photo). ⓘ *Cambrian explosion*, p. 314

Aquatic animals were already diverse by the time plants and fungi colonized the land about 475 MYA. Arthropods, vertebrates, and other animals soon followed, diversifying as they adapted to new food sources and habitats.

As you read through this chapter, keep in mind the importance of habitat as a selective force shaping animal adaptations. Animal life started in the oceans, which provides buoyancy and generally stays within a certain range of temperature, salt concentration, oxygen concentration, and other environmental variables. Fresh water also provides buoyancy but contains less salt, may vary more in temperature, and may disappear seasonally or in the case of a drought. Terrestrial habitats nearly always have abundant oxygen, but air does not provide physical support like water does, and animals are at risk of drying out. While you study, note how each set of challenges selects for unique combinations of adaptations contributing to support, locomotion, reproduction, digestion, circulation, gas exchange, and waste disposal.

Figure 21.1 Animal Ancestor? An immediate animal ancestor may have resembled an aquatic protist (a choanoflagellate). Whatever the ancestor was, it eventually gave rise to all modern animals.

Solitary   Colonial

B. Animals Share Several Characteristics

Animals are diverse, but their shared evolutionary history means that all animal phyla have some features in common. First, they are multicellular organisms with eukaryotic cells lacking cell walls. (i) *animal cell*, p. 52

Second, all animals are heterotrophs, obtaining both carbon and energy from organic compounds produced by other organisms. Most animals ingest their food, break it down in a digestive tract, absorb the nutrients, and eject the indigestible wastes.

Third, animal development is unlike that of any other type of organism. After fertilization, the diploid zygote (the first cell of the new organism) divides rapidly. The early animal embryo begins as a solid ball of cells that quickly hollows out to form a **blastula,** a sphere of cells surrounding a fluid-filled cavity. (Embryonic stem cells, the source of so much controversy, come from embryos at this stage of development.) No other organisms go through a blastula stage of development. (i) *stem cells*, p. 226

Fourth, animal cells secrete and bind to a nonliving substance called the extracellular matrix. This complex mixture of proteins and other substances enables some cells to move, others to assemble into sheets, and yet others to embed in supportive surroundings, such as bone or shell. (Section 21.17 explains how key genes encoding extracellular matrix proteins have helped shed light on the Cambrian explosion.) (i) *extracellular matrix*, p. 522

C. Biologists Classify Animals Based on Shared Ancestry

Figure 21.2 compiles the nine animal phyla described in this chapter into a phylogenetic tree. As you will see, the members of each phylum share similarities because they evolved from a common ancestor with those features. Moreover, the phyla are themselves grouped based on shared features of their morphology, physiology, embryonic development, and DNA. As you read this section, refer back to the tree to recall the positions of the branching points.

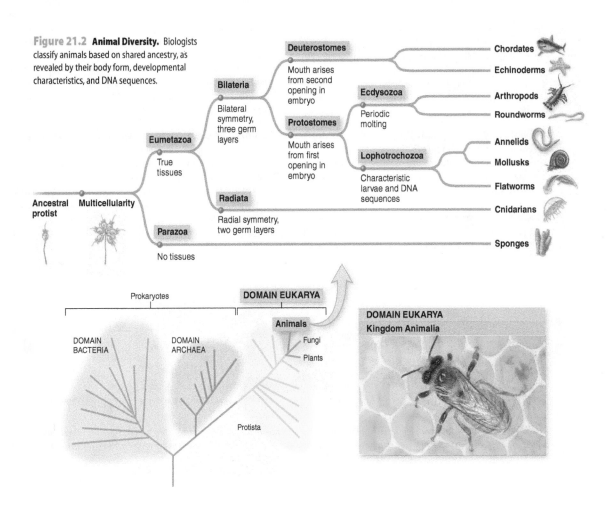

Figure 21.2 Animal Diversity. Biologists classify animals based on shared ancestry, as revealed by their body form, developmental characteristics, and DNA sequences.

Figure 21.3 Types of Symmetry. (a) Many sponges are asymmetrical. (b) A hydra has radial symmetry. (c) A crayfish has bilateral symmetry. Animals with bilateral symmetry have a front (anterior) and rear (posterior) end, and a dorsal (back or top) and ventral (bottom or belly) side.

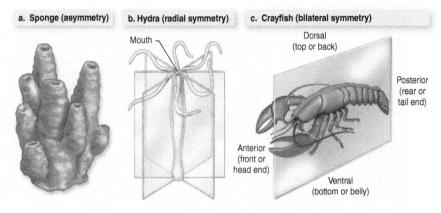

a. Sponge (asymmetry) b. Hydra (radial symmetry) c. Crayfish (bilateral symmetry)

Mouth

Dorsal (top or back)

Posterior (rear or tail end)

Anterior (front or head end)

Ventral (bottom or belly)

Cell and Tissue Organization

The first major branching point separates animals based on whether their bodies contain true tissues. The simplest animals, the **parazoans** (sponges), have several specialized cell types, but the cells do not interact to provide specific functions as they would in a true tissue. The other clade contains **eumetazoans,** animals with tissues. In most eumetazoans, multiple tissue types interact to form organs such as a heart, brain, or kidney. The organs, in turn, interact in systems that circulate and distribute blood, dispose of wastes, and carry out other functions. These interactions boost efficiency, which explains in part why eumetazoans are typically more active than sponges.

Body Symmetry and Cephalization

Body symmetry is another major criterion used in animal classification (figure 21.3). Many sponges are asymmetrical; that is, they lack symmetry. Other sponges, hydras, jellyfishes, adult sea stars, and their close relatives have **radial symmetry,** with parts arranged around a central axis.

Most animals, however, have **bilateral symmetry,** in which only one plane divides the animal into mirror images. Bilaterally symmetrical animals such as crayfish and humans have head (anterior) and tail (posterior) ends, and they typically move through their environment head first. Bilateral symmetry is correlated with **cephalization,** the tendency to concentrate sensory organs and a brain at an animal's head. Compared with radial symmetry, in which simple sensory cells are distributed across the body surface, bilateral symmetry is typically accompanied by more complex sense organs and a greater ability to evaluate and respond to environmental stimuli.

Bilateral symmetry is also associated with an elongated body form, often with paired appendages and organs on either side of the body. Among other benefits, these structures opened new options for animal locomotion.

Embryonic Development: Two or Three Germ Layers

Early embryos give other clues to evolutionary relationships (figure 21.4). In eumetazoans, the blastula folds in on itself to generate the **gastrula,** which is composed of two or three tissue layers called primary germ layers. The gastrulas of jellyfishes and their relatives have two germ layers: **ectoderm** to the outside, and **endoderm** to the inside. All other eumetazoans have a third germ layer, **mesoderm,** that forms between the ectoderm and endoderm.

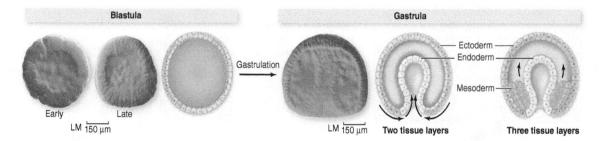

Blastula

Gastrula

Gastrulation

Early Late LM 150 μm

LM 150 μm Two tissue layers

Ectoderm
Endoderm
Mesoderm

Three tissue layers

Figure 21.4 Two or Three Primary Germ Layers. A fluid-filled ball of cells called a blastula folds in on itself and forms the gastrula. (The second blastula photo shows cells beginning to migrate inward, signaling the start of gastrula formation.) Animals with two primary germ layers have an outer ectoderm and an inner endoderm layer. In other animals, mesoderm forms between the ectoderm and endoderm.

These germ layers give rise to all of the body's tissues and organs. Ectoderm develops into the skin and nervous system, whereas endoderm becomes the digestive tract and the organs derived from it. Mesoderm gives rise to the muscles, the circulatory system, and many other specialized structures. Muscles, in turn, not only enhance locomotion but also power the movement of food through the digestive tract, boosting the speed and efficiency with which animals extract nutrients from food. Overall, animals with three germ layers have much greater variety in body forms and functions than do animals with two germ layers.

Embryonic Development: Protostomes and Deuterostomes

After an embryo has folded into a gastrula (see figure 21.4), the inner cell layer fuses with the opposite side of the embryo, forming a tube with two openings. This cylinder of endoderm will develop into the animal's digestive tract, with one opening becoming the mouth and the other becoming the anus.

But which end is which? The answer determines whether the animal belongs to the protostome or deuterostome clade (see figure 21.2). In most **protostomes,** the first indentation develops into the mouth, and the anus develops from the second opening. (*Protostome* literally means "mouth first"). In **deuterostomes,** such as echinoderms and chordates, the first indentation becomes the anus, and the mouth develops from the second opening. (*Deuterostome* means "mouth second.") We now know that some animals classified as protostomes do not conform to the "mouth first" pattern. Nevertheless, DNA sequences support their close relationship to other animals in the protostome clade.

As you can see from figure 21.2, protostomes are further divided into two main groups: ecdysozoans and lophotrochozoans. These groups are largely defined by their DNA sequences rather than by a combination of easily observable characteristics. Ecdysozoans, however, do share a visible feature (molting).

D. Biologists Also Consider Additional Characteristics

We have now seen the main features that unite each of the major clades of animals. Other adaptations, however, have also been important milestones in animal evolution. This section describes some other characteristics that you will encounter as you learn about the animal phyla in this chapter.

Body Cavity (Coelom)

A bilaterally symmetrical animal may or may not have a coelom (figure 21.5). The **coelom** (pronounced SEA-loam) is a fluid-filled body cavity that forms completely within the mesoderm. Animals that have a coelom include earthworms, snails, insects, sea stars, and chordates. In contrast, roundworms have a body cavity called a **pseudocoelom** ("false coelom") that is lined partly with mesoderm and partly with endoderm. Flatworms lack a coelom, although evidence suggests their ancestors may have had body cavities.

The coelom's chief advantage is flexibility. As internal organs such as the heart, lungs, liver, and intestines develop, they push into the coelom. The fluid of the coelom cushions the organs, protects them, and enables them to shift as the animal bends and moves.

In many animals, the coelom or pseudocoelom serves as a hydrostatic skeleton that provides support and movement. In a **hydrostatic skeleton,** muscles push against a constrained fluid. The earthworm, for example, burrows through soil by alternately contracting and relaxing muscles surrounding its coelom. Note that jellyfishes, flatworms, and other invertebrates also have hydrostatic skeletons, even though they lack a coelom or pseudocoelom. Instead, their muscles push against fluid in the digestive tract or between the body cells.

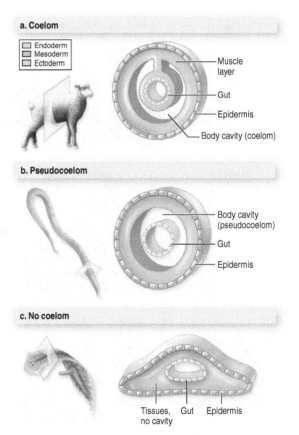

Figure 21.5 Body Cavities. (a) Like many other animals, a sheep has a coelom. (b) A roundworm has a pseudocoelom. (c) A flatworm lacks a coelom. Note that these drawings are abstractions. In the sheep, for example, the internal organs grow into the coelom, greatly distorting the cavity's shape.

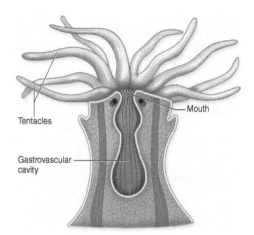

Figure 21.6 Incomplete Digestive Tract. An animal with a gastrovascular cavity, such as this sea anemone, takes in food and ejects wastes through the same opening (its mouth).

Digestive Tract   A sponge lacks a digestive tract; instead, the animal has pores through which water enters and leaves the body. In other animals, the digestive tract may be incomplete or complete. Cnidarians and flatworms have an **incomplete digestive tract,** in which the mouth both takes in food and ejects wastes (figure 21.6). In these animals, digestion occurs in the **gastrovascular cavity,** which secretes digestive enzymes and distributes nutrients to all parts of the animal's body.

In animals with a **complete digestive tract,** food passes in one direction from mouth to anus. A complete digestive tract allows the animal to process its food stepwise in specialized compartments. For example, cells near the mouth can secrete digestive enzymes into the tract, while "downstream" cells can absorb nutrients and those near the anus can help eject wastes. These specialized regions increase the efficiency with which nutrients are extracted from food. As a result, more nutrients are available for hunting, defense, and reproduction.

Segmentation   Segmentation is the division of an animal body into repeated parts (figure 21.7). In centipedes, millipedes, and earthworms, the segments are clearly visible. Insects and vertebrate animals also have segmented bodies, although the subdivisions may be less obvious. Segmentation adds to the body's flexibility, and it enormously increases the potential for the development of specialized body

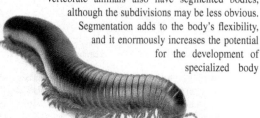

Figure 21.7 Segmentation. This millipede illustrates segmentation—the division of the body into repeated parts.

parts. Activating different combinations of genes in each segment can create regions with unique functions. Antennae can form on an insect's head, for example, while wings or legs sprout from other segments.

Reproduction and Development   Most animals reproduce sexually, and the development of the resulting embryo follows either of two paths (figure 21.8). Animals that undergo **direct development** have no larval stage; at hatching or birth, they already resemble adults. A newborn elephant or newly hatched cricket, for example, looks like a smaller version of the adult.

In contrast, an animal with **indirect development** may spend part of its life as a **larva,** which is an immature stage that does not resemble the adult. The larvae eventually undergo **metamorphosis,** in which their bodies change greatly as they mature into adults. Larvae often live in different habitats and eat different foods from the adults, an adaptation that may help reduce competition between the generations. Insects (such as butterflies) and amphibians (such as frogs) are the most familiar examples of animals that undergo indirect development.

21.1   MASTERING CONCEPTS

1. What characteristics do all animals share?
2. When and in what habitat did animals likely originate, and when did today's major groups of animals arise?
3. What evidence do biologists use to construct the animal phylogenetic tree?
4. What are the events of early embryonic development in an animal?
5. Which animals have tissues, and which have organs?
6. What is the difference between radial and bilateral symmetry?
7. Distinguish between a coelom and a pseudocoelom.
8. What are the two main types of digestive tracts?
9. What advantages does segmentation confer?
10. How does direct development differ from indirect development?

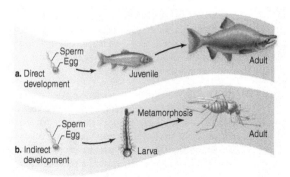

Figure 21.8 Animal Development. (a) The young of animals that undergo direct development resemble the adult. (b) In indirect development, metamorphosis transforms a larva into a very different-looking adult.

21.2 Sponges Are Simple Animals That Lack Differentiated Tissues

The **sponges** belong to phylum Porifera, which means "pore-bearers"—an apt description of these simple animals (figure 21.9). Sponges have all of the animal-defining features described in section 21.1B, including multicellularity. But unlike in other animals, a sponge's cells do not interact to form tissues. Their structural simplicity means that sponges bear little resemblance to the rest of the animal kingdom.

All sponges are aquatic. Most are marine, although some live in fresh water. In addition, sponges are generally considered sessile, meaning they remain anchored to their substrate. Together, their watery habitat and sessile lifestyle have selected for a unique combination of features.

A sponge's body is either radially symmetrical or asymmetrical. It is also hollow, and its body wall is riddled with pores. These specialized channels allow water to pass through the body wall, into a main chamber, and out a hole at the top. This arrangement enables sponges to acquire food and oxygen, dispose of wastes, and reproduce.

To understand how sponges carry out these functions without moving, look at the body wall in figure 21.9. Several types of cells are embedded in a jellylike matrix (the mesohyl). Lining the inner surface of the body wall is a layer of "collar cells," which strongly resemble choanoflagellates. (These protists, which are close relatives of animals, are illustrated in figure 21.1.) As the flagella on the collar cells wave, water moves into the sponge through the pores. This water current carries not only oxygen but also microscopic particles of organic matter—the sponge's food. Collar cells trap and partially digest the food particles and pass them to another cell type, the amoebocyte. These cells complete digestion and distribute the food to other cells.

Amoebocytes also secrete protein fibers and spicules, which are sharp slivers of silica or calcium carbonate (see figure 21.9). The spicules, along with an arsenal of toxic chemicals, help these sessile animals deter predators.

The porous body wall also participates in reproduction. Sponges are hermaphrodites, which means the same individual makes both sperm and egg cells. Cells in the body wall produce these gametes. The sperm are released into the water, but the animal retains its eggs. Meanwhile, sperm from nearby sponges enter its body through the pores. After fertilization, the zygote develops into a blastula, which is released and drifts briefly before settling into a new habitat. Some sponges also reproduce asexually by budding or fragmentation.

Because sponges are aquatic, few people encounter them in their natural habitat. However, some people use natural sponges in bathing. Also, the chemicals that protect sponges from predators may yield useful anticancer and antimicrobial drugs.

Key features

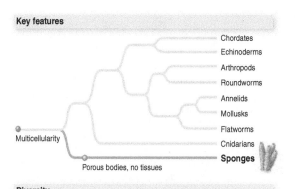

Diversity

Anatomy

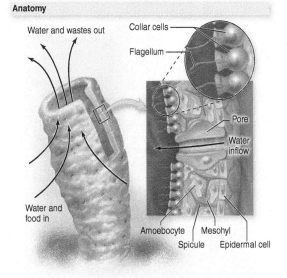

Figure 21.9 **Sponges (Phylum Porifera).**

21.2 MASTERING CONCEPTS

1. How is a sponge's body different from that of other animals?
2. How does a sponge's body structure suit its aquatic habitat and sessile lifestyle?
3. Explain how the arrangement of cells in a sponge is adaptive to its feeding strategy.
4. How do sponges reproduce sexually and asexually?

21.3 Cnidarians Are Radially Symmetrical, Aquatic Animals

Phylum Cnidaria (pronounced nigh-DARE-ee-ah) includes several familiar aquatic animals, including jellyfishes, hydras, corals, and sea anemones (figure 21.10). These animals are commonly called **cnidarians.** Most cnidarians are marine, although some (such as hydra) live in fresh water.

The cnidarians share several similarities, the most obvious being radial symmetry. One end of the body has an opening, the mouth, which is surrounded by a ring of tentacles. (The mouth is clearly visible on the sea anemones in figure 21.10.) In a sessile cnidarian, called a **polyp,** a stalk holds the tentacles upward into the water. Hydras, corals, and sea anemones are examples of polyps. In a **medusa,** on the other hand, tentacles dangle downward from a free-swimming bell. A jellyfish illustrates the medusa body form.

The cross sections in figure 21.10 reveal another characteristic unique to the cnidarians. The body wall is composed of just two thin layers: an outer epidermis (derived from ectoderm) and an inner layer lining the dead-end gastrovascular cavity (derived from endoderm). Between these two layers is a jellylike, noncellular substance called mesoglea. The mesoglea acts as a hydrostatic skeleton that maintains the body's shape in water.

Although a cnidarian's tissues do not form organs such as a brain or muscles, these animals can nevertheless make coordinated movements as they swim or capture prey. In the epidermis, groups of linked neurons called nerve nets coordinate the contraction of specialized cells. In this way, for example, a jellyfish can force water out of its bell to propel itself through water.

One additional feature unique to the cnidarians is the stinging cells embedded in the epidermis (see the inset in figure 21.10). These cells, called **cnidocytes,** contain tiny harpoons that can sting the animal's prey or a predator. (The name of phylum Cnidaria comes from the Greek word for "nettle," a stinging plant.) Anyone who has accidentally stepped on a jellyfish on the beach knows that the sting may cause skin irritation or cramps; a few species have toxins that can be lethal on contact.

Cnidarians use their stinging tentacles to grab and paralyze passing prey, which can range from tiny water fleas to small fish. Once the animal has captured its prey, cells in the tentacles contract to stuff the meal directly into the animal's gastrovascular cavity. Cells lining this digestive tract secrete enzymes that digest the food. After absorbing the nutrients, the animal ejects indigestible matter through the mouth.

Thanks to its digestive tract, cnidarians can handle much larger prey than can the filter-feeding sponges. The resulting boost in feeding efficiency means cnidarians can acquire much more energy for movement and reproduction.

The simple cnidarian body also is adapted to gas exchange in water. The thin body wall has a high surface area, and all body parts are in contact with the water. This arrangement means that each cell can use simple diffusion to acquire O_2 from the environment and to dispose of CO_2 and other metabolic wastes.

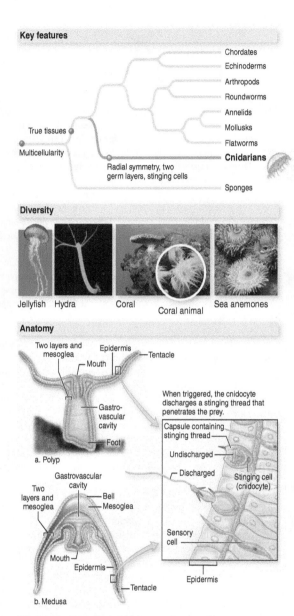

Figure 21.10   Cnidarians (Phylum Cnidaria).

Cnidarians can be very prolific breeders, and reproduction may be sexual and asexual (figure 21.11). In the moon jelly *Aurelia,* for example, male and female medusae release gametes into the water, where fertilization occurs. The resulting larvae attach to a surface and develop into the polyp form. The polyp then buds asexually, generating a colony of additional polyps and, eventually, medusae. In some areas, huge swarms of jellyfish are

Video Coral Reproduction

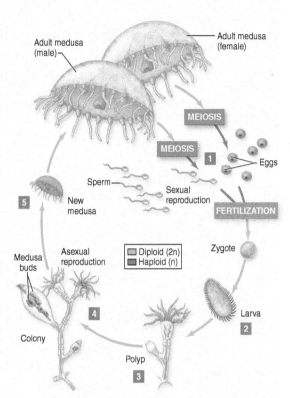

Figure 21.11 **Cnidarian Reproduction.** The life cycle of *Aurelia* includes an alternation of generations between medusa and polyp stages. (*1*) Medusae release sperm and egg cells. After fertilization, (*2*) a larva develops, attaches to a surface, and becomes (*3*) a polyp, which reproduces asexually to form (*4*) a colony. (*5*) New medusae form by budding off the polyp colony.

becoming increasingly common, presenting a nuisance for tourist destinations and fisheries.

Among the cnidarians in figure 21.10, the coral animals are unusual in that they secrete calcium carbonate exoskeletons. Over many generations, the exoskeletons secreted by countless coral animals have built magnificent coral reefs. These complex underwater structures house many commercially important species of fishes and other animals, and they protect coastlines from erosion. ⓘ *coral reefs*, p. 802

21.3 MASTERING CONCEPTS

1. Using the evolutionary trees in this chapter, compare cnidarians to sponges and to the clade containing flatworms, mollusks, and annelids. What features are similar among these groups? What features are different?
2. Compare and contrast a polyp and a medusa.
3. How do cnidarians feed, move, and reproduce?
4. In what ways are cnidarians important?

21.4 Flatworms Have Bilateral Symmetry and Incomplete Digestive Tracts

Phylum Platyhelminthes includes the **flatworms.** (*Platy* means "flat"; *helminth* means "worm"). Some of these animals are surprisingly beautiful, whereas others look downright scary (figure 21.12). The three main classes of flatworms are the **free-living flatworms** (such as a marine flatworm and a freshwater planarian) and the parasitic **flukes** and **tapeworms.**

The phylogenetic tree in figure 21.12 shows that flatworms and the other six phyla to be described in this chapter all form a clade characterized by bilateral symmetry and three germ layers. As explained in section 21.1C, animals in these seven phyla therefore have the potential to develop more complex bodies and more varied responses to the environment than do the sponges and cnidarians.

Flatworms, annelids, and mollusks occupy the protostome ("mouth first") branch of the evolutionary tree (see section 21.1C). Within the protostome clade, the most obvious feature that defines the flatworms is the flattened body shape that gives this phylum its name. A related, but less conspicuous, feature is the absence of a coelom. In many other animals, the fluid-filled coelom helps circulate oxygen throughout the body. Thanks to

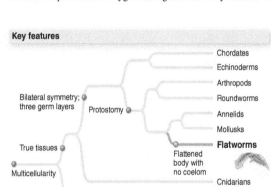

Key features

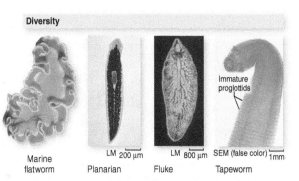

Diversity

Figure 21.12 **Flatworms (Phylum Platyhelminthes).**

the flatworm's shape, however, each of the animal's cells is near enough to the body surface to exchange gases directly with its environment. In fact, the flat body enables even the largest of flatworms to meet its metabolic needs without a specialized circulatory or respiratory system.

All flatworms share these characteristics, but each lineage within this phylum also has unique traits. Figure 21.13, for example, shows some adaptations of free-living flatworms. These animals usually are predators or scavengers in aquatic food webs. The mouth opens into a muscular, tubelike pharynx located at the midpoint of the body (figure 21.13a). The pharynx takes food into the incomplete digestive tract. The highly branched gut ensures that every body cell is near enough to the digestive tract to acquire nutrients by simple diffusion. Undigested food is ejected from the body through the pharynx and mouth.

The flatworm nervous system can sense environmental stimuli and coordinate the animal's movements. The planarian in figure 21.13b, for example, has a ladderlike arrangement of nerve cords running the length of its body, with a simple brain and sensory structures concentrated at the head end. Ear-shaped structures detect touch and chemicals. Eyespots detect light intensity, helping the animals find shelter by avoiding bright light. The worm can then creep or swim toward food or shelter, either by gliding on cilia along a film of mucus or by contracting its muscles in a rolling motion. Loosely packed cells surrounded by fluid inside the body act as a hydrostatic skeleton. ⓘ *invertebrate eyes*, p. 565

Many flatworms reproduce asexually. For example, a free-living flatworm may simply split into two pieces, with each half regenerating the missing parts. Sexual reproduction is also common. These animals are hermaphrodites, simultaneously producing both sperm and egg cells. In a mating pair, each animal fertilizes the eggs of its partner.

The two other flatworm groups, the flukes and the tapeworms, are adapted to a parasitic lifestyle. For example, a tough outer layer protects against the host's digestive enzymes and immune system. In addition, investing energy into some organs—such as eyes—is not adaptive for an internal parasite; certain organ systems are therefore often reduced or absent. Flukes and tapeworms also have multiple hosts and produce huge numbers of offspring, maximizing the chance that at least a few will encounter a suitable host.

Figure 21.14 illustrates the life cycle of the blood fluke. Larval worms enter the human body through the skin and mature in blood vessels surrounding the intestines or urinary bladder. As they develop, the parasites feed on blood and other host tissues. Adult flukes mate, and the fertilized eggs migrate into the host's bladder or gut. From there, they leave the host's body in urine or feces and hatch into larvae upon reaching water. These larvae infect their intermediate host, a snail, where the flukes continue to mature. The resulting larvae—now at a different developmental stage—emerge from the snail and infect a new human host.

Tapeworms have a different set of adaptations. A tapeworm lacks a mouth and digestive system. Instead, hooks or suckers on its head attach to the host's intestine, and the worm absorbs the host's already-digested food through its body wall. Most of the tapeworm body consists of repeated organs called proglottids, which contain fertilized eggs; proglottids break off from the worm and leave the host in feces. When an intermediate host such as a pig swallows proglottids in contaminated water, the eggs hatch. The larvae can migrate to the host's muscles, which may be consumed by a human host; this is how people acquire tapeworm infections by eating undercooked fish, beef, or pork.

21.4   MASTERING CONCEPTS

1. Using the evolutionary trees in this chapter, compare the defining features of flatworms to those of cnidarians, other protostomes, and deuterostomes. What features are similar among these groups? What features are different?
2. How does the body shape of a flatworm enhance gas exchange with the environment?
3. List and describe the three classes of flatworms.

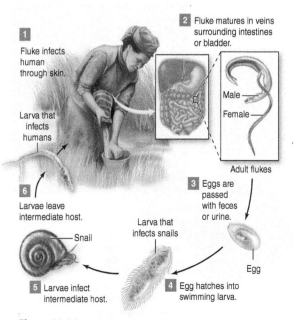

1. Fluke infects human through skin.
2. Fluke matures in veins surrounding intestines or bladder.
   - Male
   - Female
   - Adult flukes
3. Eggs are passed with feces or urine.
   - Egg
4. Egg hatches into swimming larva.
   - Larva that infects snails
5. Larvae infect intermediate host.
   - Snail
6. Larvae leave intermediate host.
   - Larva that infects humans

Figure 21.14 Life Cycle of a Blood Fluke.

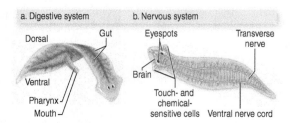

a. Digestive system
- Dorsal
- Gut
- Ventral
- Pharynx
- Mouth

b. Nervous system
- Eyespots
- Transverse nerve
- Brain
- Touch- and chemical-sensitive cells
- Ventral nerve cord

Figure 21.13 Flatworm Anatomy. (a) The pharynx is a muscular tube that opens into the incomplete digestive tract. (b) A brain and ladderlike nerve cords make up the nervous system.

21.5 Mollusks Are Soft, Unsegmented Animals

Mollusks form the second-largest phylum (after arthropods), and they include many familiar animals on land, in fresh water, and in the ocean (figure 21.15). The word *mollusk* comes from the Latin word for "soft," reflecting the fleshy bodies in this phylum.

The four largest classes of mollusks are the chitons, bivalves, gastropods, and cephalopods. **Chitons** are marine animals with eight flat shells that overlap like shingles. **Bivalves,** such as oysters, clams, scallops, and mussels, have two-part, hinged shells. **Gastropods** ("stomach-foot") are snails, slugs, sea slugs (nudibranchs), and limpets. Their name comes from the broad, flat foot on which they crawl. The **cephalopods** include marine animals such as octopuses, squids, and nautiluses. *Cephalopod* means "head-foot," a reference to the arms connected to the head of the animal. Cephalopods include the largest known invertebrate—the colossal squid, which may be up to 14 meters long.

Other than the fact that their soft bodies are unsegmented, the mollusks do not look much alike. Yet they share several features that reveal their close evolutionary relationship. One is the **mantle,** a fold of tissue that secretes a calcium carbonate shell in most species. The hard shells of chitons, bivalves, and snails protect against many predators, but they are heavy and limit the exposed surface area available for gas exchange. In the cephalopods, the shell is internal or absent.

The mantle is folded into a space called the mantle cavity that is exposed to the environment. The mantle cavity plays an important role in both gas exchange and excretion. In terrestrial snails and slugs, the lung is derived from the mantle cavity. In aquatic mollusks, a tubelike siphon pulls water into the mantle cavity, which houses the gills that exchange O_2 and CO_2 with the environment. Meanwhile, an excretory organ empties wastes into the mantle cavity to be flushed away.

In some mollusks, the mantle cavity participates in locomotion and filter feeding. Cephalopods, for example, are the speediest invertebrates; they move by "jet propulsion" as they shoot water out of the mantle cavity's siphon. Clams use their two siphons in a completely different way. One siphon draws water into the mantle cavity; the clam absorbs oxygen and food particles, and the water leaves the body through the other siphon.

Another characteristic common to all mollusks is a muscular **foot,** which typically provides locomotion. All mollusks have a **Video** Robo-Snails
hydrostatic skeleton; the animal moves when muscles act on the constrained fluid of the coelom. The speed and type of locomotion, however, vary among the mollusks. On land, snails and slugs glide on a trail of mucus. Bivalves use the muscular foot to burrow into sediments. In cephalopods, the foot is modified into multiple arms or tentacles that participate in locomotion but also grasp prey. **Video** Clam Locomotion

Besides the mantle and foot, the third major region of a mollusk's body is the **visceral mass,** which contains the digestive, circulatory, excretory, and reproductive organs. Consider, for

Key features

Chordates
Echinoderms
Arthropods
Roundworms
Annelids
Mollusks — Mantle, muscular foot, visceral mass
Flatworms
Cnidarians
Sponges

Bilateral symmetry; three germ layers
Protostomy
True tissues
Multicellularity

Diversity

Chiton
Scallop (bivalve)
Snail (gastropod)
Slug (gastropod)
Octopus (cephalopod)
Squid (cephalopod)

Anatomy

Visceral mass

Shell
Mantle
Gill
Mantle cavity
Anus
Foot
Excretory system
Coelom
Heart
Reproductive organ
Digestive tract
Nerve collar
Radula
Mouth

Figure 21.15 Mollusks (Phylum Mollusca).

example, the digestive system. The mollusks, along with the remaining animals we will encounter in this chapter, have a complete digestive tract (you can trace the one-way digestive tract from mouth to anus in figure 21.15). Note that cnidarians and flatworms have a digestive tract with just one opening, the mouth. As described in section 21.1D, the main advantage of a two-opening digestive tract is improved nutrient extraction from food.

The mouth cavity of many mollusks contains a **radula,** a tonguelike strap with teeth made of chitin (a tough polysaccharide). Chitons, snails, and slugs use the radula to scrape algae off rocks or tear vegetation apart. But other mollusks use different feeding strategies. For example, cephalopods capture fast-moving prey, and bivalves are filter feeders.

Natural selection has also modified the molluskan nervous system in many ways. The tentacles on a snail's head, for example, contain sensory cells that detect odors and eyespots that detect light. The nervous system in these animals is relatively simple. An octopus's nervous system is much more complex, with a large brain, highly developed eyes, and an excellent sense of touch. These organs work together to coordinate the animal's camouflage, reproducing the color and texture of its surroundings. Moreover, in lab studies, octopuses have displayed remarkable problem-solving abilities.

With all the variation we have seen so far, it is not surprising that mollusks have multiple reproductive strategies. Many bivalves shed gametes into the water, where external fertilization occurs. Gastropods and cephalopods, on the other hand, mate and fertilize eggs internally. In many marine mollusks, a ciliated, pear-shaped larva settles to the bottom of the sea and develops into an adult. In cephalopods and snails, however, the hatchlings resemble adults. The development of snails is especially unusual. The body twists inside its shell as it develops, so that in the adult animal, the anus empties digestive wastes near the head.

Mollusks have diverse effects on human life, health, and environmental quality. We harvest pearls from oysters, many people collect the shells of bivalves, and we eat clams, mussels, oysters, snails, squids, and octopuses. Bivalves can become poisonous, however, if they accumulate pollutants or toxins produced by protists called dinoflagellates. On land, snails are garden pests; in water, some snails host parasitic worms (see figure 21.14), and the venom of a cone snail can kill a human. Invasive zebra mussels have disrupted the ecology of the Great Lakes. ⓘ *dinoflagellates*, p. 364; *invasive species*, p. 818

21.5   MASTERING CONCEPTS

1. Refer to the evolutionary trees in sections 21.4, 21.5, and 21.6. What features are present in mollusks but absent from the flatworms and annelids? What defining characteristics do all three groups share?

2. What are the four largest classes of mollusks, and where do they live?

3. How do mollusks feed, move, reproduce, and protect themselves?

4. In what ways might having a shell be a disadvantage?

21.6 Annelids Are Segmented Worms

Earthworms and other segmented worms are **annelids.** Unlike their close relatives, the flatworms and the mollusks, annelids have bodies divided into repeated segments (figure 21.16). The name of the phylum, Annelida, derives from the Latin word *annulus* ("little ring") and is a reference to the segments that divide the body into repeated compartments.

Earthworms and **leeches** are by far the most familiar types of annelids. These segmented worms, which are closely related to each other, have a distinctive feature in common: a saddlelike thickening near the head end (this region is especially obvious in an earthworm). This structure secretes a protective "cocoon" for the fertilized eggs when the animal reproduces.

Virtual Lab
Earthworm
Dissection

Although earthworms and leeches are closely related, they live in very different habitats, which have selected for unique adaptations in each group. Earthworms ingest soil, digest the organic matter, and eliminate the indigestible particles as castings. Each segment of an earthworm's body sports a few bristles that provide traction as the animal burrows through soil.

Most leeches, on the other hand, live in fresh water. The leech body consists of segments lacking bristles. These animals consume the blood of vertebrates (including humans) or eat small organisms such as arthropods, snails, or other annelids. Each end of the flattened, darkly pigmented leech has a sucker with which it attaches itself to a surface or to its prey.

The other major group of annelids, the **polychaetes,** contains the marine segmented worms. Most polychaetes have pairs of fleshy, paddlelike appendages that they use in locomotion. The name *polychaete* comes from the many bristles (*chaetae*) embedded in each of these appendages.

Annelids lack a specialized respiratory system. Instead, earthworms and leeches exchange gases by diffusion across the body wall. (Some polychaetes have feathery gills.) Gas exchange can occur only across a moist surface. Leeches and polychaetes, which live in water, are always wet, but earthworms are vulnerable. They rapidly dry out and die if removed from moist soil.

The segmented worms do, however, have other organ systems. The unbranched digestive tract extends along the length of the animal, as do two main blood vessels. Multiple aortic arches pump blood from one vessel to the other. Within each segment, small channels connect the main vessels, completing the loop.

The nervous system includes a simple "brain," a mass of nerve cells at the head end of the animal. These cells connect to a ventral nerve cord that runs along the entire body. Lateral nerves branch into each segment. Together, the nerves stimulate contraction of the circular and longitudinal muscles in the body wall. These muscles push against the coelom as the worm crawls, burrows, or swims to find food or avoid predators.

Some organs are repeated in each segment. For example, each segment contains a pair of excretory organs. These structures draw in fluid from the coelom, return some ions and other

Key features

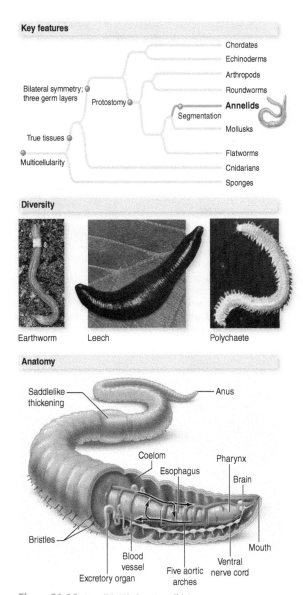

Chordates
Echinoderms
Arthropods
Roundworms
Annelids
Mollusks
Flatworms
Cnidarians
Sponges

Bilateral symmetry;
three germ layers

Protostomy

Segmentation

True tissues

Multicellularity

Diversity

Earthworm   Leech   Polychaete

Anatomy

Saddlelike thickening

Anus

Coelom

Pharynx

Esophagus

Brain

Bristles

Blood vessel

Mouth

Excretory organ

Five aortic arches

Ventral nerve cord

Figure 21.16 Annelids (Phylum Annelida).

substances to the blood, and discharge the waste-laden fluid outside the body through a pore.

Leeches and earthworms are hermaphrodites, which means that each individual has the reproductive organs of both sexes. Two individuals copulate, each discharging sperm for the other's eggs. After fertilization, the animal secretes fluid that forms a protective "cocoon" into which it lays its eggs. The baby worms hatch a couple of weeks later.

Humans benefit from annelids in many ways. Earthworms aerate and fertilize soil, and worm farms raise many types of

Apply It **Now**

Start Your Own Worm Farm

You may have heard of cow manure being used as a fertilizer, but what about worm castings? These pinhead-sized droppings are rich in the water-soluble nutrients that plants need. You can buy plant fertilizers made of worm castings, but if you produce food scraps in your kitchen, you can easily build a small-scale worm farm of your own.

To start the farm, acquire two stackable plastic tubs, one nesting inside the another. Drill holes in the bottom of the upper tub, which will contain the worms. The lower tub will collect the waste fluids that drain through the holes; like the castings, this liquid is an excellent fertilizer.

Purchase live worms locally or online. Common garden earthworms are not a good choice; they prefer to burrow deep into soil and are therefore poorly suited for life in a shallow container. Instead, red wigglers (*Eisenia fetida*) work best because they eat a lot and reproduce rapidly. But they are introduced from Europe and (like any nonnative species) may damage local ecosystems, so they should not be released from the worm farm.

Create bedding by shredding black and white newsprint or computer paper. Toss in a couple of handfuls of garden soil and some crushed, cooked egg shells. After you moisten the mixture, add your worms and some food. Worms can eat vegetable scraps, most fruits, stale bread, leftover pasta, coffee grounds, tea leaves, paper, and cardboard. Avoid meat and dairy products, which will produce unpleasant odors. In addition, onions and garlic repel worms, and citrus fruits cause the bins to become too acidic. Keep your farm in a dark, quiet location at room temperature.

When the bedding and food have decayed, it is time to harvest the castings. Drill holes into a third tub and prepare a fresh bedding mixture. Place the new bin on top of the one containing the worms. If the bottom of the tub is resting lightly on the old bedding, the worms will crawl through the holes into the new tub. After about two weeks, the lower tub will contain nothing but castings, which you can add to your plants.

worms for sale as fishing bait or as soil conditioners (see this section's Apply It Now box). In medicine, a blood-thinning chemical from leeches can stimulate circulation in surgically reattached digits and ears, and physicians sometimes apply leeches to remove excess fluids that accumulate after damage to the nervous system.

21.6 MASTERING CONCEPTS

1. What defining feature arose in the annelid lineage that distinguishes annelids from mollusks? Explain why natural selection might have favored this characteristic.

2. Compare the digestive tract of an earthworm and a flatworm. How is each worm's digestive system adaptive?

3. What features distinguish the two classes of annelids, and where do members of each group live?

4. How do annelids feed, exchange gases, and move?

5. In what ways are annelids important?

21.7 Nematodes Are Unsegmented, Cylindrical Worms

Most **roundworms** (phylum Nematoda) are barely visible to the unaided eye, but they are extremely abundant in every known habitat—on land, in fresh water, and in oceans from the tropics to the poles. A small scoop of mud can yield millions of tiny nematodes, representing hundreds of species. Overall, biologists have described more than 80,000 nematode species, and hundreds of thousands (or even millions) more species may remain undescribed. Most roundworms are microscopic, but the giant intestinal roundworm *(Ascaris)* can reach 40 cm long.

The nematodes are just one of three groups of worms in the protostome clade. Recall that flatworms are flat and unsegmented, and they lack a coelom; earthworms (annelids) are cylindrical

FOCUS on Model Organisms

Caenorhabditis elegans and *Drosophila melanogaster*

Two invertebrates, a roundworm and an arthropod, share the spotlight in this box. Both have the characteristics common to all model organisms: small size, easy cultivation in the lab, and rapid life cycles. Each has provided crucial insights into life's workings.

The nematode: *Caenorhabditis elegans*

This roundworm, a soil inhabitant, is arguably the best understood of all animals. This was the first animal to have its genome sequenced (in 1998), revealing about 18,000 genes. A small sampling of the contributions derived from research on *C. elegans* includes the following:

- **Animal development:** An adult *C. elegans* consists of only about 1000 cells. Because the worm is transparent, biologists can watch each organ form, cell by cell, as the animal develops from a zygote into an adult. Eventually, researchers hope to understand every gene's contribution to the development of this worm.
- **Apoptosis:** Programmed cell death, or apoptosis, is the planned "suicide" of cells as a normal part of development. Researchers already know which cells die at each stage. Learning about genes that promote apoptosis may help researchers to better understand cancer, a family of diseases in which cell division is unregulated. ⓘ *cancer*, p. 156; *apoptosis*, p. 162
- **Muscle function:** The first *C. elegans* gene to be cloned, *unc-54*, revealed the amino acid sequence of one part of myosin, a protein required for muscle contraction. ⓘ *myosin*, p. 599
- **Drug development:** Nematodes provide a good forum for preliminary testing of new pharmaceutical drugs. For example, researchers might identify a *C. elegans* mutant lacking a functional insulin gene, then test new diabetes drugs for the ability to replace the function of the missing gene. ⓘ *diabetes*, p. 585
- **Aging:** Worms with mutations in some genes have life spans that are twice as long as normal. Insights on aging in *C. elegans* may eventually help increase the human life span.
- **Origin of sex:** *C. elegans* is a hermaphrodite, so the same individuals produce both sperm and eggs. They can also reproduce asexually. Section 9.9 describes how hermaphroditic nematodes have helped biologists understand the evolution of sexual reproduction.

The fruit fly: *Drosophila melanogaster*

Drosophila melanogaster is only about 3 mm long, but like *C. elegans*, it is a giant in the biology lab. The flies are easy to rear in plugged jars containing rotting fruit or a mix of water, yeast, sugar, cornmeal, and agar. The fruit fly's genome sequence was completed in 1999; many of its 13,600 genes have counterparts in humans. But these relatively recent findings belie *Drosophila*'s century-long history as a model organism. This list includes some of the most important research areas:

- **Heredity:** In the early 1900s, Thomas Hunt Morgan and his colleagues used *Drosophila* to show that chromosomes carry the information of heredity. Studies on mutant flies with different-colored eyes led to the discovery of sex-linked traits. Morgan's group also demonstrated that genes located on the same chromosome are often inherited together. In the process, they discovered crossing over. ⓘ *crossing over*, p. 174; *linked genes*, p. 196; *sex linkage*, p. 201
- **Human disease:** The similarity of some *Drosophila* genes to those in the human genome has led to important insights into muscular dystrophy, cancer, and many other diseases. For example, researchers have studied the fly version of the human *p53* gene, which induces damaged cells to commit suicide (apoptosis). When that gene is faulty, the cell may continue to divide uncontrollably. The result: cancer.
- **Animal development:** Homeotic genes are "master switch" genes that regulate the overall development of the body, including segmentation and wing placement. Researchers discovered these genes in mutant flies with dramatic abnormalities, such as legs growing in place of antennae on the fly's head (see figure 7.20). Later, researchers discovered comparable genes in many organisms, including mice, leading to new insights into mammalian development. ⓘ *the mouse as model organism*, p. 452
- **Circadian rhythms:** The expression of some genes in bacteria, plants, fungi, and animals cycles throughout a 24-hour day. How do the rhythmically expressed genes "know" what time it is? In *Drosophila*, clock genes called *period* and *timeless* encode proteins that turn off their own expression, much like a thermostat turns off a heater when the temperature is too high. This "master clock" controls the animal's other daily cycles of hormone secretion and behavior.

and segmented, and they have a coelom. Nematodes, in contrast, have cylindrical, unsegmented bodies that have a pseudocoelom (figure 21.17). The name of the phylum reflects this long, thin shape; the Greek word *nema* means "thread."

A nematode's pseudocoelom has multiple functions. For example, fluid in the pseudocoelom distributes nutrients, O_2, and CO_2 throughout the body; these animals lack specialized circulatory or respiratory organs. Specialized cells maintain salt balance and remove nitrogenous wastes from the pseudocoelom. The waste fluid is eliminated through an excretory pore. A second function of the pseudocoelom is to act as a hydrostatic skeleton. Nematodes are limited to back-and-forth, thrashing motions because only longitudinal (lengthwise) muscles act on the pseudocoelom. As a result, a nematode can neither crawl nor lift its body above its substrate.

Although nematodes may superficially resemble other worms, the evolutionary tree in figure 21.17 shows that arthropods are actually their closest relatives. Molting provides one clue to this shared evolutionary heritage. That is, both nematodes and arthropods shed and replace their tough external covering (called a cuticle) several times during development.

The nematode nervous system includes a simple brain at the head end and two nerve cords running the length of the body. Although the thick cuticle is a barrier to many sensory stimuli, bristles and other structures on the body surface enable the worms to detect touch and chemicals. For example, soil-dwelling nematodes may remain dormant until they detect distinctive molecules secreted by a suitable food source.

Free-living nematodes live in soil or the sediments of freshwater or marine ecosystems. Many of them have the remarkable ability to survive extreme heat, cold, or drying by entering a state of suspended animation; life resumes when favorable conditions return. The worms eat bacteria, protists, fungi, plants, insect larvae, or decomposing organic matter, playing essential roles in nutrient cycling. (Biologists also use the free-living nematode *Caenorhabditis elegans* in scientific research; see the Focus on Model Organisms box on page 430.)

Nematodes can also parasitize plants. The worms use their spearlike mouthparts to pierce the cells of roots or shoots. They then suck out the contents, reducing the yields of important crops such as cotton and soybeans. Nematodes also spread harmful viruses on their mouthparts as they move from plant to plant.

But the most familiar nematodes infect humans and other animals. Examples include intestinal parasites such as pinworms, hookworms, and *Ascaris*. Other parasitic roundworms, including *Trichinella*, live in the muscle tissue of humans and pigs and are transmitted by eating undercooked pork. Still other nematodes cause elephantiasis or African river blindness; in both cases, insects transmit the worms. Moreover, heartworms are nematodes that infect the hearts, lungs, and blood vessels of dogs and cats.

Like the flukes and tapeworms described in section 21.4, roundworms that infect animals have several adaptations to the parasitic lifestyle. For example, the worm may attach to host tissues with hooks or suckers, then suck blood or consume digested food in the host's intestines. The thick cuticle protects against the host's digestive enzymes and immune defenses. The worms may even secrete chemicals that suppress the host's immune system.

Parasitic worms also produce huge numbers of fertilized eggs that subsequently leave the host's body, often in feces. The tough eggs can survive drying and exposure to damaging chemicals, making them very hard to kill. The eggs hatch into larvae that infect new hosts by ingestion or through the skin.

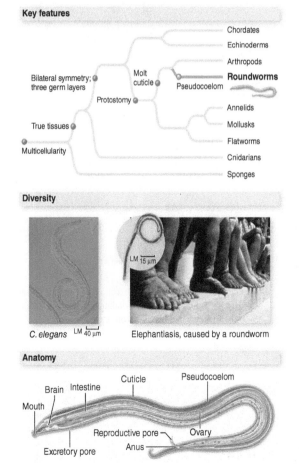

Key features

- Chordates
- Echinoderms
- Arthropods
- **Roundworms**
- Annelids
- Mollusks
- Flatworms
- Cnidarians
- Sponges

Bilateral symmetry; three germ layers

Molt cuticle

Pseudocoelom

Protostomy

True tissues

Multicellularity

Diversity

LM 15 µm

C. elegans   LM 40 µm   Elephantiasis, caused by a roundworm

Anatomy

Brain Intestine Cuticle Pseudocoelom

Mouth

Reproductive pore Ovary

Excretory pore Anus

Figure 21.17 Nematodes (Phylum Nematoda).

21.7 MASTERING CONCEPTS

1. Refer to the evolutionary trees in this chapter. What key features do nematodes share with other protostomes? With arthropods? What feature is unique to nematodes?
2. What are some examples of roundworms?
3. Compare and contrast the roundworm body structure with those of a flatworm and an annelid.
4. How do nematodes feed, excrete metabolic wastes, move, and reproduce?
5. In what ways are roundworms important?

21.8 Arthropods Have Exoskeletons and Jointed Appendages

If diversity and sheer numbers are the measure of biological success, then phylum Arthropoda certainly is the most successful group of animals. They thrive on land, in air, in the oceans, and in fresh water. More than one million species of **arthropods** have been recorded already, and biologists speculate that this number could double.

Arthropods intersect with human society in about every way imaginable. Mosquitoes, flies, fleas, and ticks transmit infectious diseases as they consume human blood. Bees and scorpions sting, termites chew wood in our homes, and many insects destroy crops. Yet entire industries rely on arthropods—consider beeswax, honey, silk, and delicacies such as shrimp, crabs, and lobsters. Insects pollinate many plants, and spiders eat crop pests. On a much smaller scale, dust mites eat flakes of skin that we shed as we move about our homes, while follicle mites inhabit our pores (see the Apply It Now box in this section).

A. Arthropods Have Complex Organ Systems

Arthropods are the fifth (and final) group of protostomes described in this chapter (figure 21.18). These animals share a branch of the evolutionary tree with nematodes; evidence for this close relationship includes the observation that both types of animals periodically molt as they grow (see section 21.7).

Arthropoda means "jointed foot," a reference to the most distinctive feature of this phylum: their jointed appendages. These appendages include not only the feet and legs with which arthropods crawl on solid surfaces, but also antennae, copulatory organs, ornaments, weapons, and mouthparts. The many modifications to their mouthparts mean that arthropods eat almost everything imaginable, including dead organic matter, plant parts, and other animals.

Video
Dung Beetles

In addition, all arthropods have a versatile, lightweight **exoskeleton** made mostly of chitin, protein, and (sometimes) calcium salts. The tough exoskeleton protects the animal, keeps it from drying out on land, gives the animal's body its shape, and enables it to move. Thin, flexible areas create the moveable joints between body segments and within appendages. Internal muscles span the joints between body segments and within appendages. Contracting these muscles generates precise, forceful movements as the animal crawls, jumps, swims, or flies. This arrangement enables ants to carry items that are much heavier than their own bodies; likewise, thanks to the exoskeleton and associated muscles, grasshoppers and fleas can jump great distances.

An exoskeleton has a drawback, though—to grow, an animal must molt and secrete a bigger one, leaving the animal vulnerable while its new exoskeleton is still soft. However, the exoskeleton is not the only arthropod defense. Many arthropods bite, sting, pinch, make noises, or emit foul odors or toxins

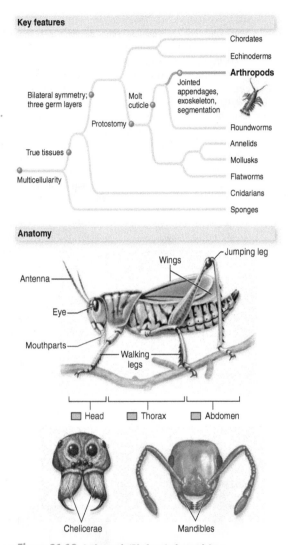

Key features

Chordates
Echinoderms
Arthropods — Jointed appendages, exoskeleton, segmentation
Roundworms
Annelids
Mollusks
Flatworms
Cnidarians
Sponges

Bilateral symmetry; three germ layers — Molt cuticle — Protostomy
True tissues
Multicellularity

Anatomy

Antenna
Eye
Mouthparts
Wings
Jumping leg
Walking legs

Head   Thorax   Abdomen

Chelicerae   Mandibles

Figure 21.18   Arthropods (Phylum Arthropoda).

that deter predators. Some have excellent camouflage that enables them to blend into their surroundings. Others have defensive behaviors; they may jump, run, roll into a ball, dig into soil, or fly away when threatened. Some moths display wings with dramatic eyespots that startle or confuse predators.

Besides the distinctive exoskeleton and jointed appendages, arthropod bodies are divided into segments. As we saw in section 21.6, annelids are segmented as well, but this trait arose independently in the two groups. Unlike in a leech or earthworm, an arthropod's segments usually do not all function alike. Instead, in many arthropods, the segments group into three major body regions: the head, thorax, and abdomen. Within each body region, segments develop highly specialized functions including feeding, walking, or even flying.

Many arthropods are active, fast, and sensitive to their environment. Consider, for example, the speed with which a fly can avoid a swatter. Arthropod eyes, bristles, antennae, and other sensory structures can detect light, sound, touch, vibrations, air currents, and chemical signals. All of these clues help arthropods find food, identify mates, and escape predation. ⓘ *firefly bioluminescence*, p. 77

Arthropods have open circulatory systems, meaning that the blood is not confined to vessels (see figure 30.1). Instead, a tubelike heart propels the blood, which circulates freely in the space surrounding most of the animal's organs (figure 21.19). An open circulatory system is generally associated with slow-moving animals such as snails and clams. Yet some arthropods are among the most active animals known. How can this be?

Part of the answer relates to the arthropod respiratory system. In most land arthropods, the body wall is perforated with holes (spiracles) that open into a series of branching tubes called tracheae, transporting O_2 and CO_2 directly to and from tissues (see figure 31.2). Aquatic arthropods have efficient gills, and spiders and scorpions have stacked folds of tissue called book lungs that have a large surface area for gas exchange.

Most arthropods have separate sexes. In aquatic arthropods, both external and internal fertilization occur. But on land, gametes released in external fertilization would dry out; natural selection therefore has selected for internal fertilization in terrestrial

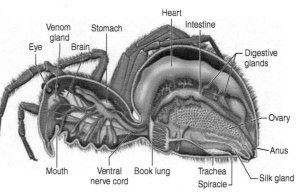

Figure 21.19 Arthropod Organs. The internal anatomy of a spider reveals complex organ systems.

arthropods. The male commonly produces a waterproof packet of sperm. The female takes the sperm packet into her body, often after a courtship ritual that may involve cannibalism (see section 35.7). In most species, the female then lays the fertilized eggs, although mites and scorpions bear live young. Ants and bees tend their young, but in most other arthropods, parental care is minimal.

BurningQuestion

Are there really only nine kinds of animals?

The nine phyla described in this chapter represent a diverse cross-section of the 37 known animal phyla. But it would be a mistake to conclude that these nine groups contain the only important or interesting animals. Here are three additional invertebrate phyla, each representing microscopic animals with unusual features (figure 21.A):

Phylum Placozoa ("flat animals"): This phylum contains just one named species, *Trichoplax adhaerens*. An adult consists of a few thousand cells that are differentiated into just four cell types. The transparent, asymmetrical body resembles a microscopic sandwich, with an upper surface, a lower surface, and a connecting layer in between. Cilia enable the animal to glide or flow along a solid surface, like a slime mold. Biologists first discovered placozoans living in aquaria, and the phylogenetic position of these strange animals has been debated ever since. *Trichoplax* has the smallest genome of any animal, and its body plan is even simpler than that of a sponge. Yet genetic sequences suggest the placozoans are eumetazoans. ⓘ *slime molds*, p. 368

Phylum Rotifera ("wheel bearer"): Like placozoans, the rotifers have tiny, transparent, unsegmented bodies. But the 2000 or so species of rotifers are considerably more complex, with bilateral symmetry and a complete digestive tract. These animals are named for the wheel-like tufts of cilia that sweep particles of decomposing organic matter into the mouth. Tiny hard "jaws" then grind the food. Rotifers inhabit fresh water and moist soil, and they can survive drying for years by suspending their metabolism. As with the placozoans, the phylogenetic position of rotifers remains controversial. The cuticle and pseudocoe-

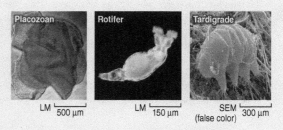

LM 500 μm   LM 150 μm   SEM 300 μm (false color)

Figure 21.A A Placozoan, a Rotifer, and a Tardigrade.

lom suggest a close relationship to nematodes, but molecular data place rotifers in a clade with annelids, mollusks, and flatworms.

Phylum Tardigrada ("slow walker"): These charismatic little animals are commonly called "water bears," owing to their aquatic habitat and overall shape. Their segmented bodies have eight legs, each ending in a claw. Covering the body is a cuticle of chitin, and the animal molts as it grows. These features place the tardigrades in a clade with arthropods and nematodes. More than 1000 species have been collected from habitats all over the world, from the poles to the tropics. Like rotifers, tardigrades can enter suspended animation, a state in which they can survive extreme cold or heat, desiccation, the vacuum of space, high pressure, or radiation doses that would kill a human.

Submit your burning question to
Marielle.Hoefnagels@mheducation.com

Figure 21.20 Trilobites. These extinct marine arthropods have three distinct regions along the length of the body: a long central lobe plus flanking right and left lobes.

B. Arthropods Are the Most Diverse Animals

Phylum Arthropoda is divided into five subphyla. One contains the 17,000 species of extinct **trilobites** (figure 21.20). Biologists infer the evolutionary relationships among the other four subphyla partly from mouthpart shape (see figure 21.18). Spiders, scorpions, and other **chelicerates** have grasping, clawlike mouthparts called chelicerae. The three subphyla of **mandibulates** have chewing, jawlike mouthparts termed mandibles.

Chelicerates: Spiders and Their Relatives Most chelicerates have two major body regions: an abdomen and a fused head and thorax (figure 21.21). They also have four or more pairs of walking legs, but they lack antennae.

The two most familiar groups of chelicerates are horseshoe crabs and arachnids. **Horseshoe crabs** are primitive-looking animals whose name refers to the hard, horseshoe-shaped exoskeleton, which covers a wide abdomen and a long tailpiece. The four species of horseshoe crabs are not true crabs, which are

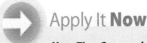

Apply It **Now**

Your Tiny Companions

Video Lyme Disease

Even when you think you are alone, you aren't; your body may host a diverse assortment of arthropods. Head lice and body lice are biting insects that cause skin irritation. Ticks latch onto the skin and suck your blood, sometimes transmitting the bacteria that cause Lyme disease. The tiny larvae of chigger mites produce saliva that digests small areas of skin tissue, causing intense itching.

Lice, ticks, and chiggers are hard to ignore, but you may never notice one inconspicuous companion: the follicle mite, *Demodex* (figure 21.B). This arachnid, which is less than half a millimeter long, lives in hair follicles and nearby oil glands, where it eats skin secretions and dead skin cells. *Demodex* mites are by no means rare. Nearly everyone has them, and each follicle may house up to 25 of the tiny animals. (If you would like to see your own follicle mites, carefully remove an eyebrow hair or eyelash and examine it with a compound microscope.) Luckily, the infestation is typically symptomless, although occasionally the mites may cause a rash.

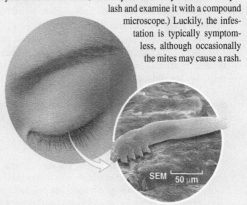

SEM 50 µm

Figure 21.B Follicle Mites. Tiny *Demodex* mites live in skin pores and hair follicles.

Horseshoe crab

Tick

Spider

Scorpion

b.   c.   d.

Figure 21.21 Chelicerate Arthropods. Chelicerates include (a) horseshoe crabs, (b) ticks, (c) spiders, and (d) scorpions.

crustaceans. Humans have found an unusual way to exploit the horseshoe crab's blood, which contains a unique immune system compound that binds to bacteria. Technicians routinely use this compound to test medical supplies for bacterial contamination.

The more than 100,000 species of **arachnids** are eight-legged arthropods, including mites and ticks; spiders; harvestmen ("daddy longlegs"); and scorpions. Spiders make "silk" and use it to produce webs, tunnels, egg cases, and spiderling nurseries. Some spiderlings use silk driftlines to float to a new habitat.

Mandibulates: Millipedes and Centipedes
About 13,000 species of **millipedes** and **centipedes** make up a group of terrestrial arthropods called myriapods (figure 21.22a). In these animals, the head features mandibles and one pair of antennae. The rest of the body is divided into repeating subunits, each with one pair (centipedes) or two pairs (millipedes) of appendages. Millipedes eat decaying plants and are generally harmless to humans, but centipedes are predators, and their venomous bite can be painful.

Mandibulates: Crustaceans
The **crustaceans** form a group of about 52,000 species, including crabs, shrimp, and lobsters. Smaller aquatic crustaceans include brine shrimp, water fleas (*Daphnia*), copepods, barnacles, and krill. Isopods, commonly known as pill bugs or "roly-polies," are the only terrestrial crustaceans; all other crustaceans live in water. Their bodies are extremely variable, but all have two pairs of antennae.

Mandibulates: Insects
Scientists know of well over one million species of **insects**, with many more awaiting formal description. All of these animals have mandibles; one pair of antennae; a body divided into a head, thorax, and abdomen; six legs; and (usually) two pairs of wings.

The ancestors of today's insects colonized land shortly after plants, about 475 MYA, and they diversified rapidly in one of life's great adaptive radiations. Why did this group diversify into so many species? Biologists point to several possible explanations. For example, mutations in homeotic genes can modify the body segments of insects into seemingly unlimited variations; some biologists compare the insect body plan to the versatility of a Swiss army knife. ① *homeotic genes,* p. 140

Wings may also partly account for insect success. Although flight later evolved independently in birds and in bats, insects were the first animals to fly. They use their wings to disperse to new habitats, escape predators, court mates, and find food that other animals cannot reach. Many of today's flowering plants evolved in conjunction with flying insects, trading nectar for rapid, efficient pollination services. ① *pollination,* p. 501

Insect reproductive strategies may also play a role. Insects have high reproductive rates, and their eggs can survive in dry habitats. In some insect species, such as crickets, the offspring change only gradually from molt to molt. Most insect life cycles, however, include a metamorphosis, in which a larva (such as a caterpillar or maggot) undergoes a transformation into an adult (such as a butterfly or housefly). As described in section 21.1D, indirect development helps reduce competition for food between adults and their young.

Whatever the explanation, the variety of insect species alive today almost defies description (see figure 21.22c). Familiar examples include silverfish, mayflies, dragonflies, roaches, crickets, grasshoppers, lice, cicadas, aphids, beetles, ants, wasps, bees, butterflies, moths, fleas, and flies. (The fruit fly, *Drosophila melanogaster,* is profiled in the Focus on Model Organisms box on page 430.) Insects range in size from wingless soil-dwellers less than 1 mm long to fist-sized beetles, foot-long walking sticks, and flying insects with foot-wide wingspans. Some extinct dragonflies

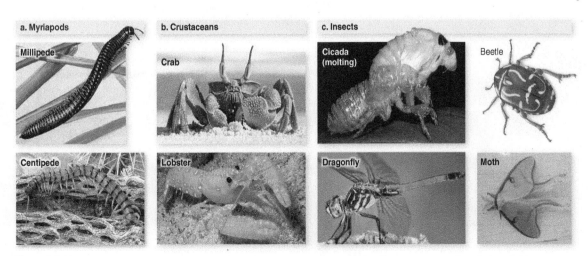

Figure 21.22 Mandibulate Arthropods. (a) Myriapods include millipedes, which have two pairs of legs per segment, and centipedes, which have one pair per segment. (b) Crustaceans include crabs and lobsters. (c) Insects include cicadas, dragonflies, beetles, and moths.

were even larger—one had a wingspan of about 75 cm! Most of these species are terrestrial, but some insects live or reproduce in fresh water. The ocean, high altitudes, and extremely cold habitats are about the only places that are nearly devoid of insects.

21.8 MASTERING CONCEPTS

1. Using the evolutionary tree in figure 21.18, list the key features that distinguish arthropods from nematodes. What characteristic do these phyla share?
2. What are the main body regions of an arthropod?
3. How do arthropods use their jointed appendages?
4. Describe how arthropods feed, respire, sense their environment, move, reproduce, and defend themselves.
5. What are the advantages and disadvantages of an exoskeleton?
6. In what ways are arthropods important?
7. How are chelicerates different from mandibulates?
8. Give an example of an animal in each subphylum of arthropods. Describe one characteristic unique to each group.

21.9 Echinoderm Adults Have Five-Part, Radial Symmetry

The **echinoderms** (phylum Echinodermata) are some of the most colorful and distinctive sea animals (figure 21.23). This phylum includes sea urchins, sea stars, sea cucumbers, and sand dollars. Many of these animals are familiar to people who visit tide pools and beaches.

It is hard to imagine animals less similar to ourselves than sea stars, yet chordates and echinoderms share a branch on the evolutionary tree. What is the evidence for this close relationship? Early development patterns provide part of the answer: Echinoderms and chordates are both deuterostomes. That is, during the gastrula stage of development, the first indention becomes the anus (see figure 21.4). Molecular evidence, such as ribosomal RNA sequences, confirms the close relationship between echinoderms and chordates.

The evolutionary tree in figure 21.23 also holds another surprise. Even though echinoderms belong to the large clade containing animals with bilateral symmetry, adult sea stars and other echinoderms have radially symmetrical bodies divided into five parts. This body form is most obvious in the sea stars and brittle stars, which usually have five arms. Although other echinoderms lack arms, close inspection reveals the five-part symmetry. Radial symmetry is typically associated with a sessile lifestyle, as we saw in the sponges and cnidarians. However, most of today's echinoderms are motile. Biologists continue to debate how and why radial symmetry evolved in this group.

Regardless of the answer, a close look at a developing sea star reveals that echinoderms are related to the other bilateral animals. Echinoderms usually reproduce sexually, with male and female gametes from separate individuals combining in the sea. The resulting larvae start out with bilateral symmetry (see figure 21.23), but a radical metamorphosis soon occurs. Through a complex series of events, the left side of a larva develops into the underside of the young animal, while the

Video
Sea Urchin
Reproduction

Key features

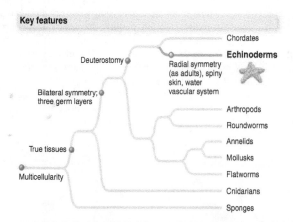

- Chordates
- **Echinoderms**
- Deuterostomy
- Radial symmetry (as adults), spiny skin, water vascular system
- Bilateral symmetry; three germ layers
- Arthropods
- Roundworms
- Annelids
- True tissues
- Mollusks
- Flatworms
- Multicellularity
- Cnidarians
- Sponges

Figure 21.23 Echinoderms (Phylum Echinodermata).

Diversity

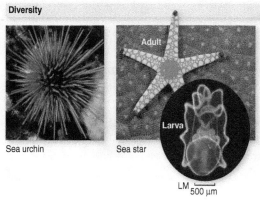
Adult
Larva
LM 500 μm

Sea urchin   Sea star

Sand dollars

Sea cucumber

right side becomes the upper surface. Once the transformation is complete, the animal's body betrays few clues to its bilateral beginnings.

Echinoderms have other unique characteristics as well. For example, the name *echinoderm* literally means "spiny skin," a feature clearly visible in the sea urchins. The spines are connected to the animal's internal skeletal plates (in sea urchins and sand dollars, these plates fuse into a protective shell). The spines have multiple functions. Defense is the most obvious one, but some sea urchins can use their spines to "walk" along the sea floor, and some echinoderms have spines modified for feeding or deflecting waves.

Besides spines, echinoderm skin also offers other defenses. Small pincers embedded in the skin may deter predators. The epidermis may also contain glands that secrete toxins, along with pigments that provide camouflage or warn predators to stay away.

Another feature unique to the echinoderms is the **water vascular system,** a series of fluid-filled canals that end in hundreds of hollow tube feet (figure 21.24). Coordinated muscle contractions extend and retract each foot, which can bend from side to side or create a suction-cup effect when applied to a hard surface. The wavelike pumping of water in and out of the tube feet allows echinoderms to glide slowly while maintaining a firm grip on the substrate, a clear advantage in a wave-pounded environment.

Tube feet have many other functions besides locomotion. For example, sensory cells in tube feet can detect light and chemicals. Moreover, tube feet can also help echinoderms acquire food. Consider a sea star, which is a predator that eats mussels and other bivalves. The sea star attaches its tube feet to a mussel's shell and steadily pulls until the prey's muscles tire and the shell opens. Part of the sea star's stomach comes out through its mouth and enters the mussel's shell, secreting digestive enzymes into the mussel. When the stomach retracts, it carries with it the partially digested food. Digestive glands along the sea star's arms secrete additional digestive enzymes and absorb nutrients. Undigested food is ejected through the anus on the dorsal surface.

Echinoderms lack complex circulatory, respiratory, and excretory systems, but the versatile water vascular system fulfills many of the same functions. The animal's internal canals can exchange water with the ocean via a specialized pore. As a result, the thin-walled tube feet can function like gills, exchanging gases between ocean water and the internal fluid. Some metabolic wastes can also diffuse out of the tube feet and into the ocean.

The bodies of echinoderms are unusual in other ways, too. They have a unique, collagen-rich tissue that can rapidly interchange between soft and hard, allowing the animal to squeeze into tight spaces or, alternatively, stiffen to aid in feeding or to defend against predation. They can also regenerate arms lost to predators; in some species, even a small part of an arm can grow into an entire new animal!

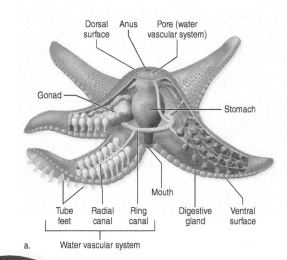

a. Water vascular system

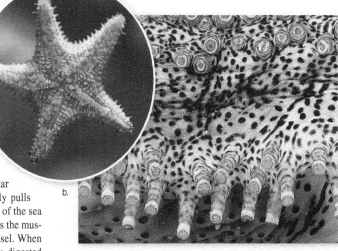

b.

c.

Figure 21.24 Sea Star Anatomy. (a) A sea star's internal anatomy includes a complete digestive tract, reproductive organs, and a unique water vascular system. (b) The ventral surface of a sea star reveals the mouth and tube feet. (c) A close-up view of a sea cucumber's tube feet.

21.9 MASTERING CONCEPTS

1. Review figure 21.23. List the features that determine the echinoderms' position on the evolutionary tree.
2. What is a water vascular system and why is it adaptive?
3. What are some examples of echinoderms?
4. How do echinoderms eat, respire, excrete metabolic wastes, sense their environment, move, reproduce, and defend themselves?

21.10 Most Chordates Are Vertebrates

Many people find phylum Chordata to be the most interesting of all, at least in part because it contains humans and many of the animals that we eat, keep as pets, and enjoy observing in zoos and in the wild. The **chordates** are a diverse group of at least 60,000 species (table 21.2). From the tiniest tadpole to fearsome sharks and lumbering elephants, chordates are dazzling in their variety of forms.

No one knows what the common ancestor of chordates was, but it was certainly an aquatic invertebrate, and it apparently arose along with most other animal phyla during the Cambrian explosion. Despite their invertebrate heritage, however, the most familiar chordates are the vertebrates—fishes, amphibians, nonavian reptiles, birds, and mammals. All of these animals have an internal skeleton (endoskeleton) that includes a protective, flexible, segmented backbone.

A. Four Key Features Distinguish Chordates

The common ancestor of the chordate clade had several key features; this chapter will concentrate on four of the most important ones. Every chordate has inherited these features and expresses each one at some point during its life (figure 21.25):

1. **Notochord:** The notochord is a flexible rod that extends along the length of a chordate's back. In most vertebrates, the notochord does not persist into adulthood but rather is replaced by the backbone that surrounds the spinal cord.
2. **Dorsal, hollow nerve cord:** The dorsal, hollow nerve cord is parallel to the notochord. In many chordates, the nerve cord develops into the spinal cord and enlarges at the anterior end, forming a brain. ⓘ *central nervous system,* p. 548
3. **Pharyngeal slits (or pouches):** In most chordate embryos, slits or pouches form in the pharynx, the muscular tube that begins at the back of the mouth. These structures have multiple functions. Invertebrate chordates feed by straining food particles out of water that passes through the slits. In vertebrates, the pouches develop into gills, the middle ear cavity, or other structures.
4. **Postanal tail:** A muscular tail extends past the anus in all chordate embryos. In humans, chimpanzees, and gorillas, the body normally absorbs most of the tail before birth; only the tailbone remains as a vestige. (Rarely, a human baby is born with a tail, which is removed in minor surgery.) In fishes, salamanders, lizards, cats, and many other species, adults retain the tail.

TABLE **21.2**   **Major Taxonomic Groups in Phylum Chordata**

Group	Examples	Number of Existing Species
Tunicates (subphylum Urochordata)	Sea squirt	3000
Lancelets (subphylum Cephalochordata)	Amphioxus	30
Hagfishes and lampreys (superclass Agnatha)	Slime hag, sea lamprey	70 (hagfishes) 38 (lampreys)
Cartilaginous and bony fishes (superclass Osteichthyes)	Shark, salmon, lungfish, coelacanth	30,000
Amphibians (class Amphibia)	Frog, salamander, caecilian	6000
Reptiles (class Reptilia and class Aves)	Turtle, lizard, snake, tuatara, crocodile, chicken, ostrich	8000 (nonavian reptiles) 9000 to 10,000 (birds)
Mammals (class Mammalia)	Platypus, kangaroo, dog, whale, human	5800

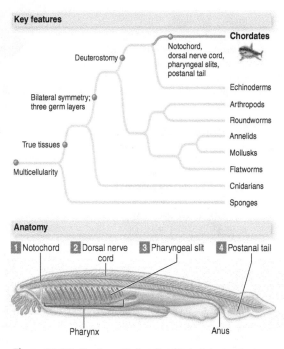

Figure 21.25 Chordates (Phylum Chordata). A simple animal called a lancelet illustrates four characteristics present in all chordates.

B. Many Features Reveal Evolutionary Relationships Among Chordates

Figure 21.26 depicts the evolutionary relationships within phylum Chordata. If you have previously studied the chordates, you may be surprised at the absence of a separate branch for birds in the phylogenetic tree. At one time, the nonavian reptiles such as snakes, lizards, turtles, and crocodiles were considered to form a separate clade from the birds. We now know, from molecular, fossil, and anatomical evidence, that birds are a type of reptile. Figure 21.26 reflects this new understanding.

This section explains the features that determine the branches on the chordate evolutionary tree, and the rest of this chapter considers each chordate group separately.

Cranium In most chordates, a bony or cartilage-rich **cranium** surrounds and protects the brain (figure 21.27). Hagfishes and vertebrates form two clades of **craniates,** animals that have a cranium.

Vertebrae Vertebrates are chordates that have a vertebral column, or backbone, composed of cartilage or bone (see figure 21.27). **Vertebrae** protect the spinal cord and provide attachment points for muscles, giving the animal a greater range of movement.

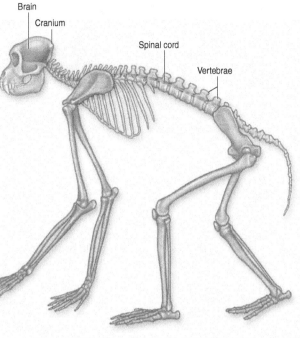

Figure 21.27 Skull and Backbone. A cranium and vertebrae are two characteristics that are common to most chordates.

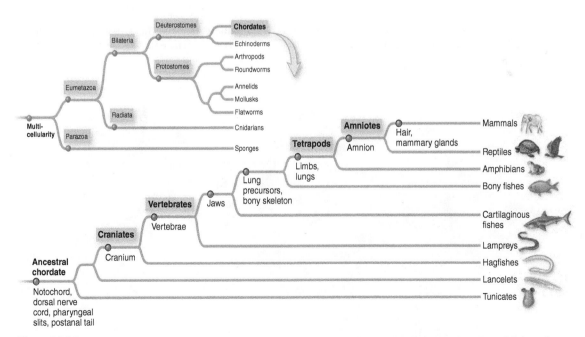

Figure 21.26 Chordate Diversity. Chordates include several groups of animals, including the invertebrate tunicates and lancelets and the better-known fishes, amphibians, reptiles (including birds), and mammals.

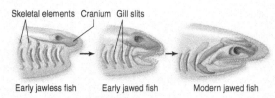

Skeletal elements Cranium Gill slits

Early jawless fish   Early jawed fish   Modern jawed fish

Figure 21.28 Possible Origin of Jaws. Jaws may have developed from skeletal elements that supported gill slits near the mouth of the fish. The two elements closest to the mouth of the jawless fish were lost in animals with jaws.

Jaws   Jaws are the bones that frame the entrance to the mouth. The development of hinged jaws from gill supports, shown in **Video** Versatile Jaws
figure 21.28, has greatly expanded the ways that vertebrate animals can feed. In many vertebrate species, teeth or a beak are attached to the jaw. These features enhance the ability of the animal to grasp prey or gather small food items.

Lungs   Most fishes have gills that absorb O_2 from water and release CO_2. In contrast, most air-breathing vertebrates have internal saclike **lungs** as the organs of respiration. Lungs are homologous to the swim bladders of bony fishes. Both structures apparently arose from simple outgrowths of the esophagus. These sacs, which allowed fishes to gulp air in shallow water, developed into air-breathing lungs in the ancestors of terrestrial vertebrates. (Section 31.1 shows gills and lungs in more detail.)

Limbs   **Tetrapods** are vertebrates with two pairs of limbs that enable the animals to walk on land (*tetrapod* means "four

legs"). Amphibians, reptiles (including birds), and mammals are all tetrapods. Some animals classified as tetrapods, however, have fewer than four limbs. Snakes, for example, lack limbs entirely. The limbs of whales, dolphins, and sea lions are either modified into flippers or too small to project from the body. Anatomical and molecular evidence, however, clearly links all of these animals to tetrapod ancestors (see figure 13.11 and section 13.7).

Amnion   The eggs of fishes and amphibians must remain moist, or the embryos inside will die. In contrast, reptiles (including birds) and mammals form a clade of **amniotes** that can breed in arid environments, in part because of the evolution of the **amniotic egg** (figure 21.29). Its leathery or hard outer layer surrounds a yolk that nourishes the developing embryo and enables it to survive outside of water. Also inside the egg are several membranes (the amnion, chorion, and allantois) that cushion the embryo, provide for gas exchange, and store metabolic wastes. These membranes are homologous to the protective structures that surround a developing fetus in the uterus of a female mammal.

Body Coverings   Fish scales are bony, and amphibians have naked, unscaly skin. In the three groups of amniotes, the body coverings all are composed of the same protein—keratin (figure 21.30). Nonavian reptiles such as snakes and crocodiles have dry, tough scales all over their bodies. Birds have similar scales on their legs; feathers cover the rest of the body. Mammals have hair (often called fur, depending on the animal).

Thermoregulation   The regulation of body temperature is an additional characteristic that is important in animal biology.

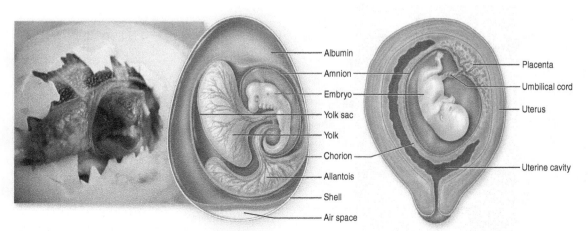

Albumin
Amnion
Embryo
Yolk sac
Yolk
Chorion
Allantois
Shell
Air space

Placenta
Umbilical cord
Uterus

Uterine cavity

Figure 21.29 The Amnion. The amnion is a sac that encloses the developing embryo of a reptile or mammal. In an amniotic egg, the embryo is encased in a hard, protective shell, and it is supported internally by three membranes—the amnion, allantois, and chorion. Placental mammals also enclose embryos in an amnion.

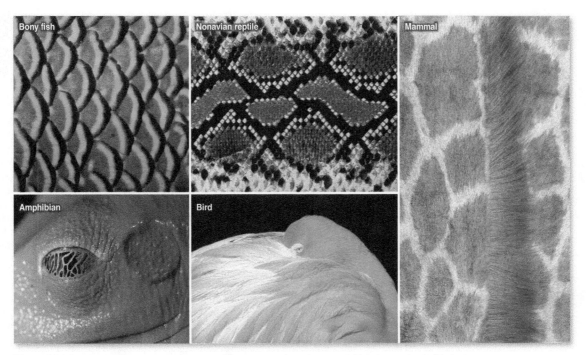

Figure 21.30 Body Coverings. Vertebrate body coverings include (clockwise from upper left) the bony scales of a fish; the dry, keratin-rich scales of a snake (a reptile); the fur of a mammal; the feathers of a bird; and the naked, unscaly skin of an amphibian.

Thermoregulation strategies vary widely, but in general, biologists often classify animals as ectotherms or endotherms. The body temperature of an **ectotherm** tends to fluctuate with the environment; these animals lack internal mechanisms that keep their temperature within a narrow range. Invertebrates, fishes, most amphibians, and most nonavian reptiles are ectotherms. Many behaviors, such as basking in the sun or burrowing into the ground during the hottest part of the day, help an ectotherm adjust its temperature.

Endotherms maintain their body temperature mostly by using heat generated from their own metabolism. Birds and mammals are endotherms, as are some nonavian reptiles and a few other types of animals. Endothermy requires an enormous amount of energy, which explains why birds and mammals must eat so much more food than ectotherms of the same size. Section 33.6 explores the origin of fur and feathers, which help endothermic animals conserve body heat.

Heart Chambers   The structure of the heart marks another set of evolutionary milestones in vertebrates (see figure 30.2). Fishes have a two-chambered heart, with one atrium and one ventricle. In amphibians and most nonavian reptiles, the heart has two atria and one ventricle. Four chambers (two atria and two ventricles) make up the hearts of crocodiles, birds, and mammals. The more heart chambers, the better the separation of

oxygen-rich blood from oxygen-poor blood, and the greater the efficiency with which blood delivers oxygen—a necessity in an energy-hungry endothermic animal. ⓘ *vertebrate circulatory systems*, p. 610

In the first half of this chapter, the emphasis was on large-scale developmental patterns, which highlight the dramatic evolutionary transitions between the simplest animals and the most complex. The rest of this chapter takes a slightly different approach. Chordates share a similar embryonic body plan and have complex organ systems. So we focus here on how unique selective forces in each group's habitat have shaped its anatomy and physiology.

21.10   MASTERING CONCEPTS

1. What are four key defining characteristics of chordates?
2. Which chordates are craniates, and which of those are also vertebrates?
3. How did the origin of jaws, lungs, limbs, and the amnion affect the course of vertebrate evolution?
4. How do the body coverings of fishes, amphibians, nonavian reptiles, birds, and mammals differ?
5. Differentiate between an ectotherm and an endotherm.
6. How does the number of heart chambers affect the efficiency of oxygen delivery to body tissues?

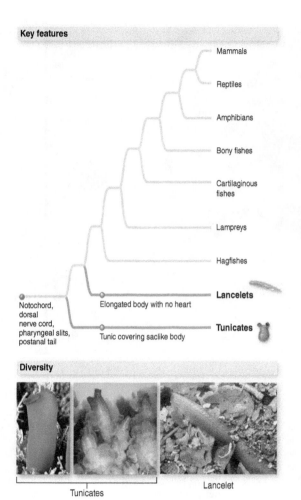

Key features

Mammals

Reptiles

Amphibians

Bony fishes

Cartilaginous fishes

Lampreys

Hagfishes

Lancelets

Elongated body with no heart

Notochord,
dorsal
nerve cord,
pharyngeal slits,
postanal tail

Tunicates

Tunic covering saclike body

Diversity

Tunicates

Lancelet

Anatomy

Exit siphon   Intake siphon

Water and wastes out

Water and food in

Anus

Genital duct

Intestine

Stomach

Tunic

Pharynx

Pharyngeal slits

Gonads (ovary and testis)

Heart

Water and food in

Mouth with tentacles

Pharynx

Pharyngeal slits

Gut

Water and wastes out

Anus

Figure 21.31 Tunicates and Lancelets.

21.11 Tunicates and Lancelets Are Invertebrate Chordates

Tunicates and lancelets form two subphyla of invertebrate chordates; their bodies have neither a cranium nor vertebrae (figure 21.31). These animals would probably attract little attention if not for one fact: They are the modern organisms that most resemble the ancestral chordates. Biologists continue to debate which group is more closely related to vertebrates.

The 3000 species of **tunicates** take their name from the tunic, a protective, flexible body covering that the epidermis secretes. The best studied tunicates, the ascidians, are marine animals that resemble a bag with two siphons. Cilia pull water in through one siphon. As the water moves across slits in the pharynx, oxygen diffuses into nearby blood vessels, and carbon dioxide diffuses out. Mucus covering the slits traps suspended food particles, and the water exits through the other siphon. These animals are also called sea squirts because they can forcibly eject water from their siphons if disturbed.

The free-swimming tunicate larva resembles a tadpole, and it has all four chordate characteristics. Once it settles headfirst onto a solid surface, however, the tail and notochord disappear, and the nerve cord shrinks to nearly nothing. The adults, which are usually sessile, retain only the pharyngeal slits. Neither adult nor larva is segmented.

Some invasive tunicate species are a major nuisance in coastal areas. Huge colonies of rapidly reproducing sea squirts coat dock pilings and boats, and they smother shellfish that are economically and environmentally important.

Lancelets (also called amphioxus) resemble small, eyeless fishes with translucent bodies. They live in shallow seas, with their tails buried in sediment and their mouths extending into the water. Cilia and mucus secreted onto the pharyngeal slits trap and move food particles into the digestive tract. The water passes out of the pharynx through the slits, leaving the body through a separate pore. Blood distributes nutrients to body cells, but gas exchange occurs directly across the skin. To reproduce, males and females release gametes into the water at the same time. The larvae, like the adults, resemble tiny fish.

Biologists have identified some 30 species of lancelets. These animals clearly display all four major chordate characteristics, as well as inklings of the organ systems that appear in the vertebrates.

Like vertebrates, lancelets have segmented blocks of muscles. Furthermore, the lancelet nervous system consists of a nerve cord with a slight swelling at the head end, plus sensory receptors on the body. The simple lancelet brain appears to share some of the same divisions as the more elaborate vertebrate brain. However, these animals lack the sophisticated sensory organs, complex brains, and mobility of vertebrates.

21.11 MASTERING CONCEPTS

1. Compare and contrast the features of tunicates and lancelets.
2. How do tunicates use their siphons in feeding and gas exchange?
3. What is the relationship among tunicates, lancelets, and the vertebrate chordates?

Figure 21.32 Hagfishes and Lampreys.

Key features

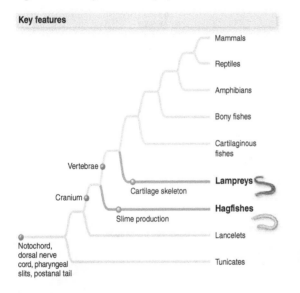

- Mammals
- Reptiles
- Amphibians
- Bony fishes
- Cartilaginous fishes
- Vertebrae ●
- **Lampreys**
- Cartilage skeleton
- Cranium ●
- **Hagfishes**
- Slime production
- Lancelets
- ● Notochord, dorsal nerve cord, pharyngeal slits, postanal tail
- Tunicates

21.12 Hagfishes and Lampreys Are Craniates Lacking Jaws

Animation Jawless Fishes

Hagfishes and lampreys are two groups of chordates that share several similarities (figure 21.32): They have long, slender bodies with gills and specialized sense organs clustered near the head end, and their mouths lack jaws. Scientists are still debating the relationship between hagfishes and lampreys; in this section we discuss them together as jawless, fishlike animals.

The common ancestor of the craniates may have resembled a **hagfish.** In a hagfish, cartilage makes up the cranium and supports the tail. But because vertebrae do not surround the nerve cord, hagfishes are not vertebrates.

The 70 or so species of hagfishes live in cold ocean waters, eating marine invertebrates such as shrimp and worms or using their raspy tongues to scavenge the soft tissues of dead or near-dead animals. Their eyes are poorly developed, but touch- and chemical-sensitive tentacles near the mouth help locate food.

These animals have some unusual abilities. They can slide their flexible bodies in and out of knots to pull on food, escape predation, or clean themselves. Hagfishes are also called "slime hags," in recognition of the glands that release copious amounts of a sticky white slime when the animal is disturbed.

Lampreys are the simplest organisms to have cartilage around the nerve cord, so they are vertebrates. About 38 species exist in salty or fresh waters around the world. They spend most of their lives as larvae, straining food from the water column. The adults eat small invertebrates, although some species use their suckers to consume the blood of fish. Over the past century, sea lampreys have ventured beyond their natural Lake Ontario range into the other Great Lakes, where they have been largely responsible for the decline in populations of lake trout and whitefish. ⓘ *invasive species*, p. 818

21.12 MASTERING CONCEPTS

1. How do hagfishes and lampreys differ from true fishes?
2. How do hagfishes eat and defend themselves?
3. Compare and contrast hagfishes and lampreys.

Diversity

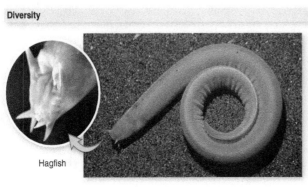

Hagfish

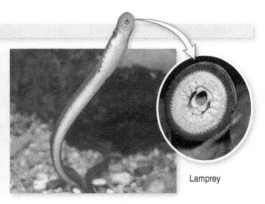

Lamprey

21.13 Fishes Are Aquatic Vertebrates with Jaws, Gills, and Fins

Fishes are the most diverse and abundant of the vertebrates, with more than 30,000 known species that vary greatly in size, shape, and color (figure 21.33). They occupy nearly all types of water, from fresh to salty, from clear to murky, and from frigid to warm, although they cannot tolerate hot springs.

Fishes play important roles in their aquatic habitats. They graze on algae, scavenge dead organic matter, or prey on other animals, eating everything from mosquito larvae and other small invertebrates to one another. Tuna and many other fish species are also an important source of dietary protein for people (and their pets) on every continent. Angling for trout, bass, salmon, and other fishes remains a popular sport. Fishes also inspire a wide range of emotions, from an intense fear of sharks to the peace and tranquility that come from watching tropical fish in a home aquarium.

Fishes originated some 500 MYA from an unknown ancestor with jaws, gills, and paired fins. Millions of years later, they diversified into two main clades: the cartilaginous fishes and the bony fishes.

A. Cartilaginous Fishes Include Sharks, Skates, and Rays

The **cartilaginous fishes,** the most ancient clade of fishes, include about 800 species of sharks, skates, and rays. As the name implies, their skeletons are made of cartilage.

Sharks are the most notorious of the cartilaginous fishes. Although some sharks feed on plankton, the carnivorous species are famous for their ability to detect blood in the water. Their sense organs also include a **lateral line,** which extends along both sides of the fish. The lateral line is a series of canals that detect vibration in nearby water, helping the animal to find prey and escape predation.

Many people believe that a shark will die if it stops swimming. In fact, this is true only for some species of sharks and other cartilaginous fishes, which must swim to maintain a constant flow of water through the mouth and over the gills. Other cartilaginous fishes, however, can pump water over their gills while at rest.

B. Bony Fishes Include Two Main Lineages

The **bony fishes** form a clade that includes 96% of existing fish species. They have skeletons of bony tissue reinforced with mineral deposits of calcium phosphate (figure 21.34). Like sharks,

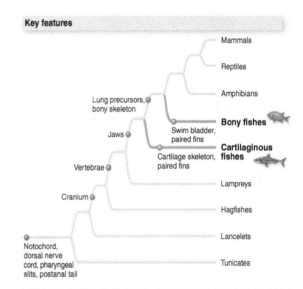

Key features

Mammals
Reptiles
Amphibians
Lung precursors, bony skeleton
Bony fishes
Jaws
Swim bladder, paired fins
Cartilaginous fishes
Cartilage skeleton, paired fins
Vertebrae
Lampreys
Cranium
Hagfishes
Lancelets
Notochord, dorsal nerve cord, pharyngeal slits, postanal tail
Tunicates

Diversity

Figure 21.33 The Fishes.

Stingray (cartilaginous fish)

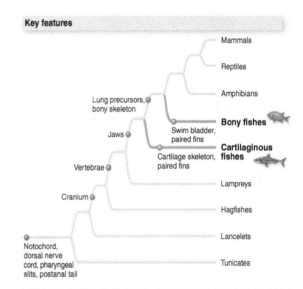

Shark (cartilaginous fish)

Ray-finned fish (bony fish)

Lungfish (bony fish)

Coelacanth (bony fish)

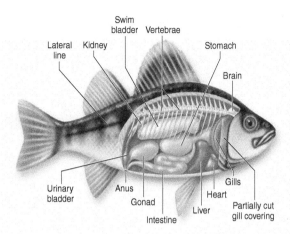

Figure 21.34 Anatomy of a Bony Fish. This illustration shows some of a fish's adaptations to life in water, including fins, a swim bladder, and gills.

bony fishes have a lateral line system. Unlike cartilaginous fishes, however, the bony fishes have a hinged gill covering that can direct water over the gills, eliminating the need for constant swimming. The swim bladder is also unique to the bony fishes. By expanding or contracting the volume of its swim bladder, a bony fish can adjust its buoyancy.

Bony fishes are divided into two classes, the ray-finned and lobe-finned fishes.

Ray-Finned Fishes   The **ray-finned fishes** include nearly all bony fishes: eels, minnows, catfish, trout, tuna, salmon, and many others. Their name comes from their fan-shaped fins, which consist of slender, bony spines (the "rays") supporting thin, flexible webs of skin.

The extraordinary diversity and abundance of the ray-finned fishes are testament to their superb adaptations to a watery world. In particular, the ray-finned fishes are notable for the wide-ranging modifications of their jaws. Thanks to a large number of movable bones in the skull, fish jaws are extremely versatile. While some fish consume algae or small animals from the water column, others have specialized jaws reflecting limited diets, such as the scales, fins, eggs, or eyes of other fish.

Lobe-Finned Fishes   The 10 or so existing species of **lobe-finned fishes** are the bony fishes most closely related to the tetrapods, based on the anatomical structure of their fleshy paired fins consisting of bone and muscle. This group includes the lungfishes and the coelacanths. **Lungfishes** have lungs that are homologous to those of tetrapods. During droughts, a lungfish burrows into the mud beneath stagnant water, gulping air and temporarily slowing its metabolism. **Coelacanths** are called "living fossils"; they originated during the Devonian and remain the oldest existing lineage of vertebrates with jaws.

Animation
Lobe-Finned Fish

C. Fishes Changed the Course of Vertebrate Evolution

Several features arose in fishes that would have profound effects on vertebrate evolution. A segmented backbone, with its multiple muscle attachment points, expanded the range of motion. Jaws opened new feeding opportunities, which in turn selected for a more complex brain that could develop a hunting strategy or plan an escape route.

Two of the adaptations that enabled vertebrates to thrive on land originated in fishes: lungs and limbs. Lungs developed in a few species of fishes, and the air-breathing descendants of these animals eventually colonized the land. No fish has true limbs, but some fishes have pectoral fins with stronger bones and more flesh than the delicate, swimming fins of other fishes. These robust fins may have enabled tetrapod ancestors to move along the sediments of their shallow water homes. Whatever their original selective advantage, pectoral and pelvic fins eventually evolved into the limbs that define tetrapods (figure 21.35).

21.13   MASTERING CONCEPTS

1. What features do all fishes share?
2. What are the major types of cartilaginous and bony fishes?
3. Describe the major vertebrate adaptations that arose in fishes. Which of these features are also adaptive on land?

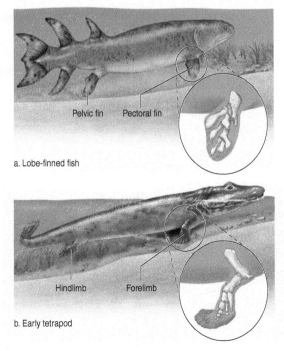

a. Lobe-finned fish

b. Early tetrapod

Figure 21.35 Fins to Limbs. Adaptations to the pectoral and pelvic fins in some fish lineages led to the four limbs characteristic of the tetrapods.

21.14 Amphibians Lead a Double Life on Land and in Water

The word **amphibian** is Greek for "double-life," referring to the ability of these tetrapod vertebrates to live in fresh water and on land (figure 21.36). Amphibians are important in ecosystems, controlling both algae and populations of insects that transmit human disease. The chorus of mating calls from frogs, ranging from squeaks to grunts and croaks, adds ambience to springtime evenings in many areas. Scientists are also studying toxins in amphibian skin as possible painkilling drugs.

Many biologists are concerned about dramatic declines in amphibian populations worldwide. The destruction of wetlands and forests devastates amphibians' breeding areas, and infection with a chytrid fungus has killed many of them outright (see section 20.2). Collecting animals for the pet trade also takes a toll, as described in this section's Apply It Now box.

In addition, amphibians have porous skin that makes them especially vulnerable to pollution. They are therefore useful as indicators of environmental quality.

A. Amphibians Were the First Tetrapods

It is easy to envision how gulping lungfishes might have fore-shadowed the lungs of amphibians or how the fleshy fins of lobe-finned fishes might have become legs. New fossil finds continue to fill in the pieces of the fish–amphibian transition, which occurred about 375 MYA (see figure 15.15 and section 13.7). ⓘ *Paleozoic life*, p. 314

Life on land offered amphibian ancestors space, protection, food, and plentiful oxygen, compared with the crowded aquatic habitat. But the land also presented new challenges. The animals faced wider swings in temperature, and delicate gills collapsed without the buoyancy of water. The new habitat therefore selected for new adaptations (figure 21.37). Lungs improved, and circula-tory systems (including a three-chambered heart) grew more complex and powerful. The skeleton became denser and better able to withstand the force of gravity. Natural selection also favored acute hearing and sight, with tear glands and eyelids keeping eyes moist.

Yet amphibians retain a strong link to the water. Amphibian eggs, which lack protective shells and membranes, will die if they dry out. Also, the larvae respire through external gills, which require water. Although adults typically have lungs, these simple organs are not very efficient. The thin skin provides an additional gas exchange surface and must therefore remain moist.

An amphibian's skin may also help the animal avoid preda-tion. Whereas some are camouflaged, others display vibrant col-ors that warn of toxins secreted from glands in the skin. The poison dart frogs of Central and South America are famous for their toxins, which they acquire by eating ants and other prey. (Captive frogs fed diets lacking these toxins therefore eventually become nonpoisonous, although their bright colors remain.)

Key features

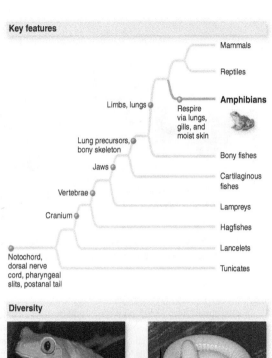

Diversity

Frog

Caecilian

Salamander

Figure 21.36 The Amphibians.

B. Amphibians Include Three Main Lineages

The amphibians are grouped into three orders: frogs; salaman-ders and newts; and caecilians.

Frogs   Most amphibian species are **frogs,** a group that includes both the smooth-skinned "true frogs" and the warty-skinned toads. Adults have large mouths, and they are "neckless"; that is, their heads are fused to their trunks. Their bodies lack tails and scales.

Apply It **Now**

Wild-Caught Pets

Wild animals make fascinating and unique pets, but owning one is not usually a good idea. This box summarizes four arguments against owning animals caught in the wild.

- **Population pressures:** Many vertebrate species are already endangered by habitat loss and pollution. Collecting for the pet trade only adds to the threat of extinction. For example, huge numbers of North American box turtles are captured each year. These animals have low reproductive rates, so it is difficult for the wild populations to recover. The problem is not limited to turtles; the pet trade puts pressure on many animal species, from coral reef fishes to parrots to primates (figure 21.C). Trapping these animals threatens not only their populations but also the ecosystems where they normally live. To make matters worse, many wild-caught animals die in transit.

- **Threats to native species:** Virtually every animal in the pet industry is an introduced species, including birds, ferrets, gerbils, sugar gliders, snakes, lizards, amphibians, fishes, and invertebrates. If an exotic pet escapes or if its owner releases it, the animal may prey on, compete with, or spread disease to native

organisms. Domesticated Asian goldfish, for example, are a nuisance species in the Pacific Northwest.

- **Physical dangers:** Large animals such as crocodiles and large cats represent a physical threat to their owners, becoming more dangerous as they grow.

- **Disease:** Wild-caught animals can carry disease.

Figure 21.C **Slow Loris for Sale in Vietnam.**

In 2003, monkeypox spread among people who kept prairie dogs as pets. The prairie dogs caught the disease from African rodents imported into the United States. Wild birds can also carry diseases that can infect native birds, poultry, and people. Likewise, hamsters, turtles, and iguanas can carry *Salmonella*.

In most species, the female frog lays her eggs directly in the water as a male clasps her back and releases sperm. The fertilized eggs **Video** Frog Reproduction
hatch into legless, aquatic tadpoles. Most tadpoles feed on algae. As they mature, tadpoles typically undergo a dramatic change in body form—a metamorphosis. They develop legs and lungs, lose the tail, and acquire carnivorous tastes.

A frog's toxic skin is a potent defense, but frogs also have behavioral adaptations that help them escape predation. For example, frogs can use their powerful legs to jump away. They can also play dead or inflate their mouths so that a predator cannot swallow them.

Salamanders and Newts   **Salamanders** and newts have tails and four legs, so they resemble lizards. Unlike lizards, however, their skin lacks scales, their digits lack claws, and they always live near water. In most salamanders, the male deposits a sperm packet near the female; she takes the packet into her body and subsequently lays the fertilized eggs in water, moist soil, or another damp location. Free-swimming larvae with a finlike tail hatch from the eggs. Both adults and young are carnivores, eating arthropods, worms, snails, fish, and other salamanders. In some groups of salamanders, the adults have larval features. The North American mudpuppy, for example, swims on pond bottoms and retains external gills.

Caecilians   The **caecilians** are unusual amphibians in that their bodies lack limbs; as a result, they resemble giant earthworms. Most species burrow under the soil in tropical forests, but a few inhabit shallow freshwater ponds. In reproduction, they use internal fertilization; a male uses a sex organ to deliver sperm inside a female's body. Caecilians are carnivores, eating insects and worms.

Fat body
Spleen
Stomach
Vertebrae
Brain
Esophagus
Trachea
Gonad
Kidney
Urinary bladder
Cloaca
Large intestine
Small intestine
Lung
Heart
Liver
Gall bladder
Pancreas

Figure 21.37 Anatomy of a Frog. Although amphibians have adaptations to life on land, their small lungs, thin skin, and reproductive requirements tie them to moist or wet habitats.

 Virtual Lab Frog Dissection

21.14   MASTERING CONCEPTS

1. What features do all amphibians share?
2. What role does water play in amphibian gas exchange and reproduction?
3. What features distinguish the three orders of amphibians?

21.15 Reptiles Were the First Vertebrates to Thrive on Dry Land

The changeability of scientific knowledge is evident in any modern discussion of **reptiles** and **birds.** The word *reptile* traditionally referred only to snakes, lizards, crocodiles, and other amniotes with dry, scaly skin. Birds had feathery body coverings and were considered a separate lineage. But that point of view has changed. We now know that birds form one of several clades of reptiles (figure 21.38). As a consequence, modern use of the term *reptile* includes both the nonavian reptiles and the birds.

Reptiles evolved from amphibians during the Carboniferous period, between 363 and 290 MYA. They dominated animal life during the Mesozoic era, until their decline beginning 65 MYA. Although many reptile species survived to the present day, many others are known only from fossils. The extinct groups include the terrestrial dinosaurs, the marine ichthyosaurs and plesiosaurs, and the flying pterosaurs. Of these, the dinosaurs especially capture the imagination (see the Burning Question in this section). ⓘ *Mesozoic life,* p. 317

Unlike their amphibian ancestors, most reptiles have a suite of adaptations that enable them to live and reproduce on dry land (figure 21.39). Tough, keratin-rich scales reduce water loss from the skin, and the kidneys excrete only small amounts of water. Internal fertilization means that reptiles do not require moist habitats to reproduce. After fertilization, most reptiles lay shelled, amniotic eggs that are adapted to dry conditions (see figure 21.29). Finally, reptiles also have greater lung capacity and enhanced circulation compared with their aquatic ancestors.

A. Nonavian Reptiles Include Four Main Groups

The 8000 or so species of nonavian reptiles include turtles and tortoises; lizards and snakes; tuataras; and crocodilians (figure 21.40). Like fishes and amphibians, the nonavian reptiles are typically ectothermic.

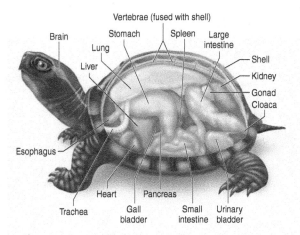

Figure 21.39   Anatomy of a Tortoise. The skin, lungs, heart, and reproductive system of a tortoise adapt this animal to life on land.

Burning Question

What characteristics distinguished dinosaurs from other reptiles?

Dinosaurs were terrestrial reptiles that lived during the Mesozoic era, between 245 and 65 MYA. They ranged in stature from chicken-sized to truly gargantuan—the largest could have peeked into the sixth story of a modern-day building.

Biologists divide the hundreds of dinosaur species into two main lineages. One clade includes the beaked plant-eaters such as *Stegosaurus* and *Triceratops.* The other contains long-necked herbivores and theropods, the only carnivorous dinosaurs; *Tyrannosaurus rex* belonged to this group, as did the ancestors of modern birds.

Many people mistakenly believe that all reptiles (or even mammals) that lived during the Mesozoic era were dinosaurs. In reality, lizards, snakes, crocodiles, and other terrestrial reptiles lived alongside the dinosaurs. The Mesozoic also saw marine reptiles such as plesiosaurs and flying reptiles such as pterodactyls, but they were not dinosaurs either; all dinosaurs were terrestrial. Nor did all dinosaurs live at the same time. As some species appeared, others went extinct throughout the Mesozoic.

Despite movie plots suggesting the contrary, humans and dinosaurs never coexisted. The last of the dinosaurs were gone by the time our own mammalian lineage—the primates—was just getting started. Tens of millions of years later, humans finally roamed the Earth and found the fossils that prove that these huge reptiles once existed.

Submit your burning question to
Marielle.Hoefnagels@mheducation.com

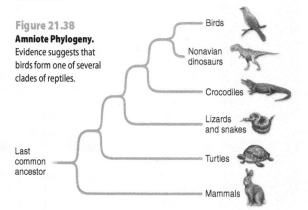

Figure 21.38

Amniote Phylogeny. Evidence suggests that birds form one of several clades of reptiles.

Birds

Nonavian dinosaurs

Crocodiles

Lizards and snakes

Turtles

Mammals

Last common ancestor

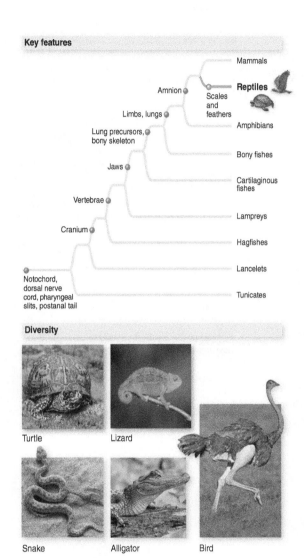

Key features

Mammals

Reptiles

Amnion

Scales and feathers

Limbs, lungs

Amphibians

Lung precursors, bony skeleton

Bony fishes

Jaws

Cartilaginous fishes

Vertebrae

Lampreys

Cranium

Hagfishes

Lancelets

Notochord, dorsal nerve cord, pharyngeal slits, postanal tail

Tunicates

Diversity

Turtle   Lizard

Snake   Alligator   Bird

Figure 21.40 The Reptiles.

Movies depict snakes, alligators, and crocodiles as terrifying killers, but most reptiles are inconspicuous animals that cannot harm people. Yet they are an important link in ecosystems, controlling populations of rodents and insects while providing food for owls and other predatory birds. In addition, some people keep snakes, lizards, or turtles as pets. In some parts of the world, reptiles have an even greater economic effect; the skins of farm-raised snakes and crocodiles are the raw material for boots, belts, and wallets, and some restaurants serve alligator meat.

Turtles and Tortoises With a reputation for being "slow and steady," **turtles** and tortoises may not seem to have a recipe for success. Yet they have persisted in marine, freshwater, and terrestrial habitats since the Triassic period. Nowadays, habitat destruction threatens many land turtles, as does the pet trade.

The turtle's trademark feature is its shell, made of bony plates and a covering derived from the animal's epidermis. The shell's plates are fused to the animal's vertebrae and ribs, so it forms an integral part of the skeleton.

The largest member of this group is the giant leatherback sea turtle. These migratory animals are endangered worldwide because they are hunted for food, become trapped in fishing nets, swallow garbage, and ingest toxic chemicals. The destruction of nesting areas also takes its toll.

Lizards and Snakes Almost 95% of nonavian reptile species are **snakes** or **lizards.** Snakes probably evolved from burrowing lizards, so these animals share many similarities. The most obvious difference, however, is that lizards usually have legs and snakes do not. Also, snakes never have external ear openings or moveable eyelids, and most lizards lack the distinctive forked tongue that characterizes snakes.

Several adaptations help lizards and snakes feed and avoid becoming food. An iguana might detach its tail as it escapes a predator; a basilisk lizard can scamper across water. Camouflage and the ability to hold perfectly still enable snakes to surprise their prey, then subdue it by injecting venom or wrapping coils around the victim and squeezing the life out of it. Unique jaw adaptations then enable a snake to open its jaw so far that it can swallow prey much larger than its own body (see the opening figure for chapter 6).

 Video Basilisk Lizard

Video Snake Eating

Tuataras **Tuataras** are reptiles that closely resemble lizards. The order containing tuataras once contained many species, all but two of which are now extinct. A captive breeding program may help restore populations of these endangered animals, which are native only to a few islands near New Zealand.

Crocodilians The **crocodilians** (crocodiles, alligators, and their relatives) are carnivores that live in or near water. Their horizontally held heads have eyes on top and nostrils at the end of the elongated snout. Heavy scales cover their bodies; four legs project from the sides. Unlike most other nonavian reptiles, they have a four-chambered heart.

These reptiles look somewhat primitive, and indeed they are ancient animals. They arose some 230 MYA, about the same time that the first dinosaurs roamed the land. Yet they have acute senses and complex behaviors, comparable to those of birds. For example, crocodilians lay eggs in nests, which the adults guard. The adults also care for the hatchlings, which stay with their mothers while they are young and call to the adults when they are in danger. Adults mark their territories by smacking their heads or jaws on the water surface. Like many birds and mammals, they even have dominance hierarchies.

B. Birds Are Warm, Feathered Reptiles

The behavioral similarities between crocodilians and birds are unsurprising in light of evolutionary history. Birds, dinosaurs, and crocodilians all belonged to a reptilian group called archosaurs, of which only the birds and crocodilians survive today.

Chickens and crocodiles look quite different, so what evidence suggests that birds really are reptiles? As described in chapters 12 and 13, *Archaeopteryx* and fossils of feathered reptiles provide important clues to the evolutionary history of birds, as do the skeletal similarities between birds and nonavian reptiles. The bird's amniotic egg, with its hard calcium-rich shell, is another clue, as are the keratin-rich scales on a bird's legs and the four-chambered heart of birds and crocodilians.

Of course, the 9000 or so species of birds have unique features that set them apart from other reptiles. Most birds can fly, thanks to anatomical adaptations including wings and a tapered body with a streamlined profile (figure 21.41). Their lightweight bones are hollow, with internal struts that add support. The powerful four-chambered heart and unique lungs supply the oxygen that supports the high metabolic demands of flight muscles (see figures 30.2 and 31.5).

Birds are the only modern animals that have **feathers,** keratin-rich epidermal structures that provide insulation and enable birds to fly. Feathers are also important in mating behavior, as anyone who has watched a peacock show off his plumage can attest. In fact, evidence of glossy, iridescent feathers in the fossils of winged dinosaurs suggests that the first feathers may have been adaptive not in flight but in sexual signaling.

Unlike other reptiles, birds are endothermic. Paleontologists debate whether dinosaurs, the ancestors of birds, were endotherms or ectotherms. Many dinosaur features argue for endothermy, but some evidence suggests otherwise (see section 33.6).

Today, birds are a part of everyday human life. People eat hundreds of millions of chickens and turkeys every year, along with countless chicken eggs. We keep caged birds as pets, and we use feathers in everything from hats to blankets. Songbirds enrich the lives of many birdwatchers, and hunters pursue wild turkeys, doves, and ducks. Birds are important in ecosystems as well. Some pollinate plants and disperse fruits and seeds, whereas others eat rodents, insects, and other vermin. But birds can also be pests. Starlings and pigeons are a nuisance in cities, fouling buildings and sidewalks with their droppings and speeding the rusting of bridges. Moreover, ducks and other domesticated birds transmit bird flu and other diseases to humans.

21.15   MASTERING CONCEPTS

1. What features do all reptiles share?
2. How do scales and amniotic eggs adapt reptiles to land?
3. Describe each of the major groups of nonavian reptiles.
4. What characteristics place the birds within other reptiles?
5. What are the functions of feathers?
6. What adaptations enable birds to fly?

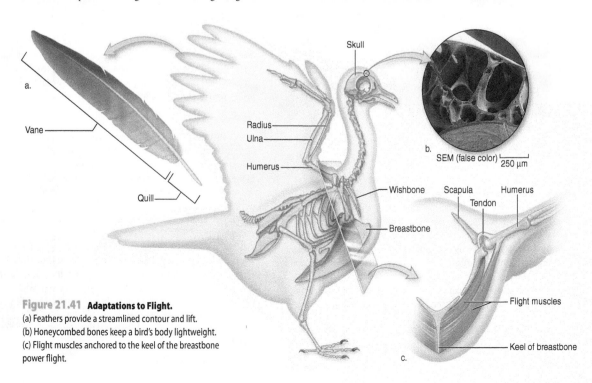

Figure 21.41   Adaptations to Flight.
(a) Feathers provide a streamlined contour and lift.
(b) Honeycombed bones keep a bird's body lightweight.
(c) Flight muscles anchored to the keel of the breastbone power flight.

a.
Vane
Quill

Skull
Radius
Ulna
Humerus
Wishbone
Breastbone

b.
SEM (false color)   250 µm

Scapula
Tendon
Humerus
Flight muscles
Keel of breastbone
c.

🍁 21.16 Mammals Are Warm, Furry Milk-Drinkers

Mammals are by far the most familiar vertebrates, not only because we *are* them but also because we surround ourselves with them. We keep dogs, cats, rabbits, gerbils, hamsters, and ferrets as pets. Farmers raise many types of mammals for their meat or milk, including cows, pigs, and goats. Lambs and adult sheep provide meat and wool, and leather from cows makes up everything from upholstery to shoes. Horses, oxen, mules, and dogs are important work animals. Many people enjoy hunting deer for food and sport, and trappers kill mink, fox, beaver, and other mammals for their fur.

Mammals also play important roles in eco- **Video** Fishing Bat
systems. Coyotes, wolves, and foxes keep pop-
ulations of herbivorous deer, rodents, rabbits, and other mammals in check. Some bats eat countless insects, and others pollinate plants. On the other hand, pests such as rats, mice, and skunks thrive alongside human populations. Some transmit diseases, including hantavirus and rabies.

A. Mammals Share a Common Ancestor with Reptiles

The 5800 or so species of mammals trace their ancestry to the late Triassic period (about 200 MYA). DNA similarities and the existence of egg-laying mammals suggest that mammals and reptiles share a common ancestor (figure 21.42). Fossil evidence, particularly details of skull structure, also provides clues to their origin.

Some time after mammals and reptiles diverged, the traits that are unique to the mammalian clade arose. For example, the most common ancestor of the mammals had **mammary glands,** structures that secrete milk in the female. (The word *mammal* derives from the Latin *mammae* for "breast.") Infant mammals are nourished by their mother's milk. In addition, the skin is keratin-rich and waterproof, and it produces hair—another distinctive mammalian feature. Hair is composed of keratin and helps conserve body heat. (Even whales and dolphins have hair at birth, but they lose it as they mature into their streamlined shapes.) Depending on the species, mammals may also produce other structures out of keratin, including horns, hooves, claws, and nails.

Because mammary glands and hair do not leave fossils, ancient mammals are distinguished from reptilian fossils in other ways. A mammal has three middle ear bones compared with the reptilian one or two, and the lower jaw consists of one bone, compared with the reptile's several. Mammalian teeth are distinctive, too, with four types: molars, premolars, canines, and incisors. Reptile teeth are much more uniform in size and shape.

Mammals also share a few other features. First, like birds, mammals have a four-chambered heart, which evolved independently in the two groups. Second, the outer layer of the mammalian brain is very well developed, enabling mammals to learn, remember, plan, and purposefully respond to stimuli. Third, only mammals have a dome-shaped muscular diaphragm, which draws air into the lungs.

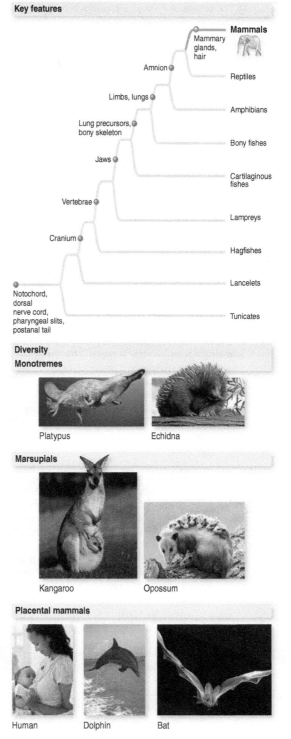

Figure 21.42 **The Mammals.**

B. Mammals Lay Eggs or Bear Live Young

Most mammals were small until after the mass extinction that occurred 65 MYA. The loss of so many reptiles paved the way for the rapid diversification of many larger species of mammals. At the same time, flowering plants became increasingly prominent, providing new types of food and habitats for mammals. ⓘ *adaptive radiation*, p. 290; *Cenozoic life*, p. 318

Biologists divide mammals into two subclasses, one containing egg-laying monotremes and the other containing live-bearing mammals. The latter is subdivided into two clades, the marsupials and the placental mammals (see figure 21.42).

The **monotremes** are mammals that lay eggs, such as the duck-billed platypus and the echidna. The name *monotreme* comes from the distinctive anatomy of these animals: the urinary, digestive, and reproductive tracts share a single ("mono") opening to the outside of the body. Reptiles have a similar anatomy. The amniotic eggs in this group reveal another link to reptiles.

When a helpless young monotreme hatches, it crawls along its mother's fur until it reaches milk-secreting pores in the skin. After a few months of suckling, the offspring leaves the safety of its mother's burrow and begins hunting its own food.

Marsupials, such as kangaroos and opossums, give birth to tiny, immature young about 4 to 5 weeks after conception. In many marsupials, the babies crawl from the mother's vagina to a **marsupium,** or pouch, where they suckle milk and continue developing. Some species, however, have poorly developed pouches, and the young drink from exposed nipples.

The **placental mammals,** also called eutherians, are the most diverse of the three groups. In these species, the young develop inside the female's uterus, where a **placenta** connects the maternal and fetal circulatory systems (see figure 21.29). The placenta nourishes and removes wastes from the developing offspring. (This section's Focus on Model Organisms describes the mouse, a placental mammal.)

Placental mammals diversified and displaced most marsupials early in the Cenozoic era, about 65 MYA. Australian marsupials, however, continued to diversify long after marsupials on other continents had gone extinct; section 13.3 describes how continental drift explains this biogeographical pattern.

The two largest groups of placental mammals are rodents and bats, but the clade also includes carnivores (dogs and cats), hoofed mammals, elephants, and many other familiar animals. Some groups reinvaded the water, including manatees, otters, seals, beavers, hippos, whales, and dolphins. Humans are placental mammals as well. We belong to an order, Primates, that arose some 60 MYA. Section 15.4 describes the evolution of primates.

21.16   MASTERING CONCEPTS

1. Which characteristics define a mammal?
2. What evidence suggests that mammals share a common ancestor with reptiles?
3. How do monotremes, marsupials, and placental mammals differ in how they reproduce?

FOCUS on Model Organisms

The Mouse: *Mus musculus*

The history of the mouse, *Mus musculus*, as the stereotypical lab animal dates back to the early 1900s. Researchers discovered that the mouse's small size made it an excellent research animal. Also, mice are famous for their prolific breeding. They reach sexual maturity at the age of about 4 weeks, are sexually receptive every few days, and give birth to litters of 1 to 10 pups after a gestation of only about 3 weeks. Over a life span of 1.5 to 3 years, a single pair of mice can produce hundreds of offspring.

Researchers have benefited from biotechnology in their studies of mice. Transgenic mice have been available since the 1980s (see chapter 7). These mice are modified in countless ways, including altered susceptibility to human diseases. Another biotechnology, cloning, was applied to mice in 1998, making possible the production of genetically identical animals ideal for testing new disease treatments. ⓘ *cloning*, p. 227

The mouse genome sequence was completed in 2002, revealing about 30,000 genes divided among 20 chromosomes. Not surprisingly, more than 99% of mouse genes have counterparts in the human genome. This genetic similarity has made possible some of the following ways in which *Mus musculus* has contributed to biological research:

- **Immune function:** In the 1930s, the discovery that mice reject transplants from all but their very close relatives led to the discovery of the major histocompatibility complex (MHC). Since that time, biologists have discovered an array of genes related to immune function (see chapter 34).

- **Human disease:** Mice have been used to study human disease since the 1930s, when researchers discovered that mice could contract yellow fever. Vaccines were subsequently tested in mice. The availability of transgenic mice has opened new possibilities for research on the cause and treatment of human disease, including muscular dystrophy, Alzheimer disease, obesity, Parkinson disease, cancer, and HIV/AIDS. ⓘ *cancer*, p. 156; *HIV*, p. 337

- **X chromosome inactivation:** In the 1960s, biologist Mary Lyon proposed that in female mammals, one of the two X chromosomes is inactivated early in embryonic development. This phenomenon, which is now often illustrated using calico cats, was first proved in mice with mottled coats. ⓘ *X inactivation*, p. 203

- **Stem cells:** These undifferentiated cells, which can be derived from embryos or adults, can specialize into many other cell types. Mouse stem cell research has shown great promise in treating spinal cord injuries and many other ailments. ⓘ *stem cells*, p. 226

INVESTIGATING LIFE

21.17 Sponges Fill Holes in Animal Evolution

For billions of years, animal life was absent from Earth. About 530 MYA, however, animals representing almost all of today's phyla appeared in the fossil record within a period spanning about 25 million years (see the chapter opening essay). This era of rapid animal diversification is often called the "Cambrian explosion." Explaining how evolution shaped the diversity of animal body plans during the Cambrian is an intriguing question for many scientists. Did mutations accumulate unusually quickly during this period, speeding up evolution? Does the fossil record tell the whole story?

The simplest animals, the sponges, could offer some insight into the events of the Cambrian. Evidence suggests that eumetazoans (animals with true tissues) evolved from a spongelike ancestor, and yet sponges remained simple while other animal groups diversified. One hypothesis to explain these observations is that sponges lack some of the critical genes that guide the development of complex animal bodies. If this hypothesis is correct, then how did developmental genes arise in other animal groups so quickly during the Cambrian?

A research group led by Nicole King at the University of California, Berkeley, hoped to use sponges to "soak up" new information about animal diversification. The group isolated genetic material from marine sponges called *Oscarella carmela* and searched for genes known to guide body plan development in eumetazoans. They were especially interested in genes encoding proteins on cell surfaces and in the extracellular matrix; these proteins should play important roles in the development of complex animals, whose cells interact in tissues. The researchers then used gene databases to compare each developmental gene found in *O. carmela* with developmental genes of related groups.

The comparisons revealed that diverse animal groups contain many of the 68 developmental genes found in *O. carmela* sponges (figure 21.43). Most of these genes are absent in more distantly related groups of protists and fungi. The data suggest that the genes encoding complex animal body plans probably arose sometime between the first parazoan and the last common ancestor of *O. carmela* and eumetazoans. Therefore, animal diversification occurred for millions of years before the Cambrian, hidden within the genes of simple sponges.

This finding makes the rapid diversification of eumetazoans during the Cambrian less surprising. The genetic toolbox was already in place. An environmental change, such as a rising concentration of oxygen in the water, may have opened new niches for animals to inhabit. With developmental genes and a permissive environment, natural selection could have shaped diverse animal phyla in a relatively short period.

On the other hand, another question arises from these results: If sponges contain the same developmental genes as eumetazoans, why did sponge body plans not diversify as well? The researchers speculate that natural selection changed the expression patterns of developmental genes in some lineages during the Cambrian, leading to new and diverse animal body plans. ① *regulation of gene expression*, p. 134; *homeotic genes*, p. 140

Since fossils cannot reveal how DNA changed in the earliest ancestors of animals, the puzzling appearance of new animal groups during the Cambrian explosion may simply represent the most visible step in a largely hidden evolutionary process. This study clearly illustrates why scientists analyze several lines of evidence before making decisive conclusions. As scientists continue to challenge one another's findings, future studies will surely lead to additional revisions to the history of animal phyla.

Nichols, Scott A., William Dirks, John S. Pearse, and Nicole King. August 15, 2006. Early evolution of animal cell signaling and adhesion genes. *Proceedings of the National Academy of Science*, vol. 103, pages 12451–12456.

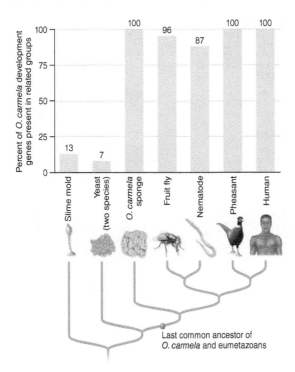

Figure 21.43 Developmental Genes Across Taxa. Diverse animal groups share many of the developmental genes found in sponges, whereas protists and fungi do not.

21.17 MASTERING CONCEPTS

1. How did the researchers use the DNA of living sponges to make conclusions about events occurring hundreds of millions of years ago?

2. If the researchers had analyzed the developmental genes of *Arabidopsis* plants, would you have expected the percent similarity to sponge developmental genes to be low or high? Explain your answer.

CHAPTER SUMMARY

21.1 Animals Live Nearly Everywhere

- Of the 1,300,000 or so species in kingdom **Animalia,** most are **invertebrates;** only one phylum contains **vertebrates,** which have a segmented backbone of cartilage or bone.
- Figure 21.44 summarizes the characteristics of the nine major animal phyla.

Figure 21.44 Animal Diversity: A Summary.

A. The First Animals Likely Evolved from Protists

- The immediate ancestor of animals probably resembled a protist called a choanoflagellate.
- The earliest fossil evidence of animals is from about 570 MYA. The first animals lived in water, and existing animal diversity strongly reflects this aquatic heritage.

B. Animals Share Several Characteristics

- Animals are multicellular, eukaryotic heterotrophs whose cells secrete extracellular matrix but do not have cell walls. Most digest their food internally.
- The **blastula** is a stage in embryonic development that is unique to animals (figure 21.45).

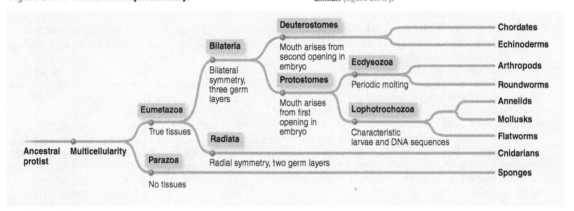

■ **Chordates**
- ~60,000 species
- Notochord, dorsal hollow nerve cord, pharyngeal slits, postanal tail
- Fishes, amphibians, reptiles (including birds), mammals

■ **Echinoderms**
- ~7000 species
- Five-part symmetry
- Water vascular system
- Sea stars, sea urchins, sand dollars

■ **Arthropods**
- >1,000,000 species
- Jointed appendages; exoskeleton
- Trilobites, spiders and other arachnids, crustaceans, insects, millipedes, centipedes

■ **Roundworms**
- ~80,000 species
- Unsegmented, cylindrical worms
- Free-living or parasitic
- Pinworms, hookworms, heartworms

■ **Annelids**
- ~15,000 species
- Segmented worms
- Earthworms, polychaetes, leeches

■ **Mollusks**
- ~112,000 species
- Mantle secretes shell
- Chitons, bivalves, cephalopods, gastropods

■ **Flatworms**
- ~25,000 species
- Flat bodies
- Free-living or parasitic
- Marine flatworms, planarians, flukes, tapeworms

■ **Cnidarians**
- ~11,000 species
- Medusa or polyp forms
- Stinging cells
- Hydra, jellyfish, coral

■ **Sponges**
- ~5000 species
- Porous bodies
- Filter feeders

Phylum	Level of Organization	Symmetry	Cephalization	Coelom	Digestive Tract	Segmentation
Porifera (sponges)	Cellular	Asymmetrical or radial	No	No	Absent	No
Cnidaria	Tissue	Radial	No	No	Incomplete	No
Platyhelminthes (flatworms)	Organ system	Bilateral	Yes	No	Incomplete (when present)	No
Mollusca	Organ system	Bilateral	Yes (usually)	Yes	Complete	No
Annelida	Organ system	Bilateral	Yes	Yes	Complete	Yes
Nematoda (roundworms)	Organ system	Bilateral	Yes	Pseudocoelom	Complete	No
Arthropoda	Organ system	Bilateral	Yes	Yes	Complete	Yes
Echinodermata	Organ system	Bilateral larvae; radial adults	No	Yes	Complete	No
Chordata	Organ system	Bilateral	Yes	Yes	Complete	Yes (usually)

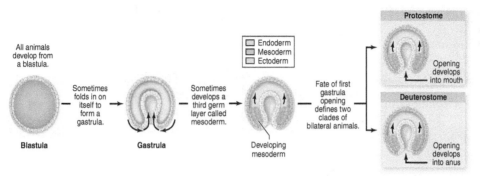

Figure 21.45
**Animal Development:
A Summary.**

C. Biologists Classify Animals Based on Shared Ancestry

- Animal bodies exhibit varying levels of organization. **Parazoans** are animals without tissues; **eumetazoans** have tissues that are typically arranged into organs and organ systems.
- In most phyla, body symmetry is **radial** or **bilateral. Cephalization** is correlated with bilateral symmetry.
- An animal zygote divides mitotically to form a blastula and then usually a **gastrula.** In some animals, the gastrula has two tissue layers (**ectoderm** and **endoderm**). In others, a third layer (**mesoderm**) forms between the other two.
- Bilaterally symmetrical animals are **protostomes** if the gastrula's first indentation forms into the mouth. In **deuterostomes,** the first indentation develops into the anus.

D. Biologists Also Consider Additional Characteristics

- Some types of animals have a body cavity (**coelom** or **pseudocoelom**) that can act as a **hydrostatic skeleton.**
- Digestive tracts are **incomplete** or **complete;** a **gastrovascular cavity** is an incomplete digestive tract.
- **Segmentation** improves flexibility and increases the potential for specialized body parts.
- Most animals reproduce sexually. The resulting embryo may undergo **direct development** or **indirect development,** in which **metamorphosis** transforms a **larva** into an adult.

21.2 Sponges Are Simple Animals That Lack Differentiated Tissues

- **Sponges** are aquatic, sessile animals that are either asymmetrical or radially symmetrical.
- The body wall is porous, allowing water to pass through the animal.
- Sponges lack tissues, but they have specialized cell types. Collar cells create a water current and filter food particles out of the water. Amoebocytes complete digestion and secrete the skeleton.
- Sponges may bud asexually and reproduce sexually. After fertilization, the offspring develops into a blastula but not a gastrula.

21.3 Cnidarians Are Radially Symmetrical, Aquatic Animals

- **Cnidarians** are mostly marine animals. Examples include corals, hydras, and jellyfishes.
- The cnidarian body form is radially symmetrical and may be a sessile **polyp** or a swimming **medusa.**
- The body wall consists of jellylike material constrained between two tissue layers. Cnidarians move by contracting muscle cells that act on this hydrostatic skeleton.
- Cnidarians capture prey with tentacles and stinging **cnidocytes.** They digest food in a gastrovascular cavity.
- Reproduction is sexual or asexual.

21.4 Flatworms Have Bilateral Symmetry and Incomplete Digestive Tracts

- **Flatworms** are unsegmented protostomes that lack a coelom. This phylum includes **free-living flatworms** such as planarians. **Flukes** and **tapeworms** are parasitic.
- The flat body shape allows individual cells to exchange gases with their environment.
- Free-living flatworms and flukes have an incomplete digestive tract; tapeworms absorb the host's food directly through the body wall. Flukes and tapeworms have many additional adaptations to the parasitic lifestyle.

21.5 Mollusks Are Soft, Unsegmented Animals

- **Mollusks** are unsegmented protostomes with a complete digestive tract. The main groups of mollusks are **chitons, bivalves, gastropods,** and **cephalopods.**
- The mollusk body includes a **mantle,** a muscular **foot,** and a **visceral mass.**
- The mantle secretes a shell in most mollusks. Natural selection has shaped the mantle and foot into many variations.
- Mollusks are filter feeders, herbivores, or predators. Many have a tonguelike **radula.**
- Cephalopods have complex sensory and nervous systems.
- Sexes are usually separate in the mollusks; fertilization may be internal or external.

21.6 Annelids Are Segmented Worms

- **Annelids** are segmented protostomes. The group includes **earthworms, leeches,** and **polychaetes.**
- These animals lack a specialized respiratory system, but they have a complete digestive tract and a closed circulatory system.
- Excretory structures, blood vessels, nerves, and muscles are repeated in each segment. The coelom acts as a hydrostatic skeleton.
- Leeches and earthworms are hermaphrodites that lay eggs in a protective "cocoon."

21.7 Nematodes Are Unsegmented, Cylindrical Worms

- **Roundworms** are unsegmented worms with a pseudocoelom. They molt periodically, a feature they share with arthropods.
- The pseudocoelom aids in circulation and acts as a hydrostatic skeleton.
- Nematodes include parasitic and free-living species in soil and aquatic sediments.

21.8 Arthropods Have Exoskeletons and Jointed Appendages

- **Arthropods** are segmented animals with jointed appendages and a chitin-rich **exoskeleton.** Like nematodes, arthropods molt periodically as they grow.

A. Arthropods Have Complex Organ Systems

- Arthropods include over a million species that live on land and on water. Depending on the habitat, natural selection has sculpted a great variety of defenses, feeding and reproductive strategies, respiratory systems, and nervous systems.

B. Arthropods Are the Most Diverse Animals

- The extinct **trilobites** were arthropods, as are the **chelicerates** (**horseshoe crabs** and **arachnids**). **Mandibulate** arthropods include **centipedes** and **millipedes; crustaceans;** and **insects.**
- Insects are by far the most diverse arthropods. Segmented bodies, flight, and metamorphosis all may account for today's enormous number of insect species.

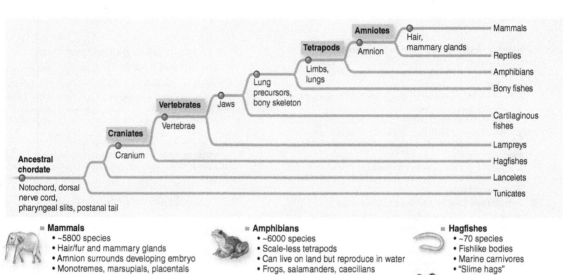

Mammals
- ~5800 species
- Hair/fur and mammary glands
- Amnion surrounds developing embryo
- Monotremes, marsupials, placentals

Birds
- ~10,000 species
- Feathers and hollow bones
- Amniotic eggs

Nonavian reptiles
- ~8000 species
- Dry, scaly skin; amniotic eggs
- Turtles, lizards, snakes, tuataras, crocodilians

Amphibians
- ~6000 species
- Scale-less tetrapods
- Can live on land but reproduce in water
- Frogs, salamanders, caecilians

Fishes
- ~30,000 species
- Scale-covered bodies with gills and fins
- Cartilaginous fishes (sharks and rays) and bony fishes

Lampreys
- 38 species
- Fishlike bodies; jawless
- Consume invertebrates or parasitize fish

Hagfishes
- ~70 species
- Fishlike bodies
- Marine carnivores
- "Slime hags"

Tunicates and lancelets
- ~3000 species (tunicates)
- ~30 species (lancelets)
- Invertebrate filter feeders
- Sea squirts and amphioxus

Subphylum/ Class	Cranium	Vertebrae	Jaws	Skeleton	Lungs	Limbs	Amnion	Body Temperature Regulation	Number of Heart Chambers
Tunicates and lancelets	No	No	No	Absent	No	No	No	Ectotherm	–
Hagfishes	Yes	No	No	Cartilage	No	No	No	Ectotherm	–
Lampreys	Yes	Yes	No	Cartilage	No	No	No	Ectotherm	–
Fishes	Yes	Yes	Yes	Cartilage or bone	No (usually)	No	No	Ectotherm	2
Amphibians	Yes	Yes	Yes	Bone	Yes	Yes	No	Ectotherm	3
Nonavian reptiles	Yes	Yes	Yes	Bone	Yes	Yes	Yes	Ectotherm	3 (4 in crocodilians)
Birds	Yes	Yes	Yes	Bone	Yes	Yes	Yes	Endotherm	4
Mammals	Yes	Yes	Yes	Bone	Yes	Yes	Yes	Endotherm	4

Figure 21.46 Chordate Diversity: A Summary.

21.9 Echinoderm Adults Have Five-Part, Radial Symmetry

- **Echinoderms** are spiny-skinned marine animals. They are deuterostomes, as are the chordates.
- Adult echinoderms have radial symmetry. The bilaterally symmetrical larvae look very different from the adults.
- The **water vascular system** enables echinoderms to move, sense their environment, acquire food, exchange gases, and get rid of metabolic wastes.
- Most echinoderms reproduce sexually. The bilaterally symmetrical larvae look very different from the adults.

21.10 Most Chordates Are Vertebrates

A. Four Key Features Distinguish Chordates

- **Chordates** share many characteristics, including a **notochord,** a **dorsal hollow nerve cord, pharyngeal slits** or pouches in the pharynx, and a **postanal tail.** Figure 21.46 summarizes diversity within the chordates.

B. Many Features Reveal Evolutionary Relationships Among Chordates

- The **craniates** (hagfishes and vertebrates) have a bony or cartilage-rich **cranium** protecting the brain. Tunicates and lancelets lack a cranium.
- Other features that distinguish chordates from one another include **vertebrae, jaws, lungs,** and the presence of limbs in **tetrapods.**
- Reptiles and mammals are **amniotes;** in these animals, the **amniotic egg** or amnion protects the developing embryo. Each group of chordates also has a characteristic type of body covering.
- **Ectotherms** lack internal temperature-control mechanisms, whereas **endotherms** use heat from metabolism to maintain body temperature. Endotherms require much more energy than do ectotherms.
- Fishes have two heart chambers, amphibians and most nonavian reptiles have three, and birds and mammals have four.
- Figure 21.47 summarizes vertebrate adaptations.

Key Vertebrate Adaptations		
Adaptation	**Adaptive significance**	**Animals with adaptation**
Vertebrae 	Expand range of motion	Lampreys, fishes, amphibians, reptiles, mammals
Jaws 	Increase feeding versatility	Fishes, amphibians, reptiles, mammals
Lungs 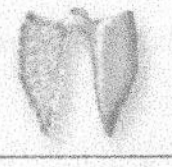	Enable animal to breathe air	Bony fishes (a few species), amphibians, reptiles, mammals
Limbs 	Allow for locomotion on land	Amphibians, reptiles, mammals
Amnion 	Enables reproduction away from water	Reptiles, mammals

Figure 21.47 **Vertebrate Adaptations: A Summary.**

21.11 Tunicates and Lancelets Are Invertebrate Chordates

- **Tunicates** obtain food and oxygen with a siphon system. A tunicate larva has all four chordate characteristics, but adults retain only the pharyngeal slits.
- **Lancelets** resemble eyeless fishes; adults have all four chordate characteristics.

21.12 Hagfishes and Lampreys Are Craniates Lacking Jaws

- **Hagfishes** have a cranium of cartilage, but they are not vertebrates. They secrete slime and lack jaws.
- **Lampreys** are vertebrates that resemble fishes, but they are jawless.

21.13 Fishes Are Aquatic Vertebrates with Jaws, Gills, and Fins

- **Fishes** are abundant and diverse vertebrates.

A. Cartilaginous Fishes Include Sharks, Skates, and Rays

- The **cartilaginous fishes** are the most ancient lineage of fishes. They include sharks, skates, and rays, all of which have a skeleton of cartilage.
- Sharks detect vibrations from prey with a **lateral line** system.

B. Bony Fishes Include Two Main Lineages

- The **bony fishes** account for 96% of existing fish species. Bony fishes have lateral line systems and swim bladders, which enable them to control their buoyancy.
- The two groups of bony fishes are **ray-finned fishes** and **lobe-finned fishes,** which are further subdivided into **lungfishes** and **coelacanths.**

C. Fishes Changed the Course of Vertebrate Evolution

- Adaptations in fishes that allowed vertebrates to move onto land include lungs and fleshy, paired fins that were later modified as limbs.

21.14 Amphibians Lead a Double Life on Land and in Water

A. Amphibians Were the First Tetrapods

- **Amphibians** breed in water and must keep their skin moist to breathe. Adaptations to life on land include a sturdy skeleton, lungs, limbs, and a three-chambered heart.

B. Amphibians Include Three Main Lineages

- Amphibians include **frogs; salamanders** and newts; and **caecilians.**

21.15 Reptiles Were the First Vertebrates to Thrive on Dry Land

- **Reptiles** (including **birds**) have efficient excretory, respiratory, and circulatory systems. Internal fertilization and amniotic eggs permit reproduction on dry land.

A. Nonavian Reptiles Include Four Main Groups

- Nonavian reptiles include **turtles** and tortoises; **lizards** and **snakes; tuataras;** and **crocodilians.**

B. Birds Are Warm, Feathered Reptiles

- Birds retain scales and egg-laying from reptilian ancestors. Like crocodilians, birds have a four-chambered heart.
- Honeycombed bones, streamlined bodies, and **feathers** are adaptations that enable flight.
- Like mammals but unlike the other reptiles, birds are endothermic.

21.16 Mammals Are Warm, Furry Milk-Drinkers

A. Mammals Share a Common Ancestor with Reptiles

- **Mammals** have fur, secrete milk from **mammary glands,** and have distinctive teeth and highly developed brains. The four-chambered mammalian heart evolved independently from that of crocodilians and birds.

B. Mammals Lay Eggs or Bear Live Young

- **Monotremes** are mammals that hatch from an egg. The young of **marsupial** mammals are born after a short pregnancy and often develop inside the mother's **marsupium. Placental mammals** have longer pregnancies; the young are nourished by the **placenta** in the mother's uterus.

21.17 Investigating Life: Sponges Fill Holes in Animal Evolution

- Researchers have discovered that key genes required for the development of complex animals were already present in sponges, the simplest animals. These genes may have set the stage for the Cambrian explosion.

MULTIPLE CHOICE QUESTIONS

1. Following gastrulation, the cells that have folded inward develop into
   a. endoderm.
   c. ectoderm.
   b. mesoderm.
   d. All of these are correct.

2. Which of the following groups includes all of the others?
   a. Protostomes
   c. Eumetazoans
   b. Echinoderms
   d. Ecdysozoans

3. What is a key characteristic of all arthropods?
   a. Six legs
   c. Hydrostatic skeleton
   b. Pseudocoelom
   d. Exoskeleton

4. How is the body structure of an annelid different from that of an arthropod?
   a. Annelids lack jointed appendages.
   b. Annelids have a complete digestive tract.
   c. Annelids have cephalization.
   d. Annelids have bilateral symmetry.

5. Which of the following applies to a squid?
   a. Cephalization
   c. Complete digestive tract
   b. True coelom
   d. All of these are correct.

6. Which animal phylum contains the most known species?
   a. Chordata
   c. Arthropoda
   b. Nematoda
   d. Cnidaria

7. Echinoderms have _____ symmetry as embryos and _____ symmetry as adults.
   a. radial; radial
   c. bilateral; radial
   b. radial; bilateral
   d. bilateral; bilateral

8. Which of the following has pharyngeal slits at some point in its life?
   a. A snake
   c. A lobster
   b. A sea star
   d. All of these are correct.

9. What is a notochord?
   a. The spine of a chordate animal
   b. One segment in a chordate's backbone
   c. A type of germ layer
   d. A fibrous rod that runs down the back of a chordate

10. Since a tunicate is considered to be a chordate, it must have a(n)
    a. cranium.
    c. amniotic egg.
    b. notochord.
    d. lung.

11. Lobe-finned fishes are important because they
    a. were the first vertebrates.
    c. are closely related to tetrapods.
    b. were the earliest animals.
    d. lack jaws.

12. To which of the following is a salamander most closely related?
    a. A snail
    c. A shark
    b. A beetle
    d. A catfish

13. How do reptiles and mammals differ from amphibians?
    a. Only reptiles and mammals are amniotes.
    b. Only reptiles and mammals are tetrapods.
    c. Only reptiles and mammals have lungs.
    d. All of the above are correct.

14. What feature(s) do birds and crocodilians share?
    a. Four-chambered hearts
    c. Scales
    b. Egg laying
    d. All of the above are correct.

15. Since a whale is a mammal, it must
    a. have scales.
    c. produce milk.
    b. have gills.
    d. All of the above are correct.

Answers to these questions are in appendix A.

WRITE IT OUT

1. Compare the nine major animal phyla in the order in which the chapter presents them, listing the new features for each group.

2. Suppose you watch a video showing the development of an unknown animal. What clues can the developmental pattern give you about how this organism is classified? Creating a flow chart might be useful.

3. List the criteria used to distinguish: (a) animals from other organisms; (b) vertebrates from invertebrates; (c) protostomes from deuterostomes; (d) ectotherms from endotherms.

4. Distinguish between (a) radial and bilateral symmetry; (b) blastula and gastrula; (c) direct and indirect development; (d) complete and incomplete digestive tract; (e) coelom and pseudocoelom.

5. Analyze the evolutionary tree in figure 21.2, and then write an argument supporting or refuting this statement: Annelids are more closely related to flatworms than to roundworms.

6. Insects are the most diverse group of animals. How do biologists explain the tremendous success of insects?

7. Segmented animals occur in multiple phyla. How might segmentation benefit an animal? If segmentation is adaptive, why do unsegmented animals still exist?

8. Make a chart showing the characteristics of each subphylum of arthropods. Suppose you could examine a fossilized arthropod; use your chart to describe how you would assign the fossil to a subphylum.

9. What is the evidence for the surprisingly close relationship between echinoderms and chordates?

10. Create lists of animal phyla that (a) are cephalized, (b) have an incomplete digestive tract, (c) have segmented bodies, and (d) have a coelom.

11. What are four distinguishing characteristics of chordates?

12. How do tunicates and lancelets differ from fishes and tetrapods?

13. Draw from memory a phylogenetic tree that traces the evolutionary history of vertebrates. Include the features that mark each branching point in your tree.

14. List the evidence that biologists use to classify earthworms, caecilians, and snakes in different clades despite the superficial similarities between these animals.

15. List five adaptations that enable (a) fishes to live in water; (b) amphibians to live on land; (c) snakes to live in the desert; (d) birds to fly.

16. The chapter-opening essay and section 21.17 describe the origin of animal phyla. Summarize the events that led to the divergence of many diverse animal groups around 550 MYA.

17. How are a fish's and a bird's skeletons similar in structure and function?

18. Fishes are adapted to life in water, and tetrapods to life on land. Cite two criteria for assessing which group has been more successful.

19. Summarize the evidence for the idea that birds are reptiles. How does the changing placement of birds in the vertebrate family tree illustrate the scientific process? Why does this type of research matter?

20. If you found a fossil and were not sure whether it was from a reptile or a mammal, how might you tell the difference?

21. Tunicates and lancelets did not leave fossil evidence because their bodies lack hard parts. The hair and mammary glands that distinguish mammals are not hard either, yet mammals have a rich fossil record. Explain this difference.

22. If the success of an animal group is determined by the number of species it contains, how successful are mammals compared to other chordate classes? How successful are mammals compared to insects?

23. How are fishes, amphibians, nonavian reptiles, birds, and mammals important to humans? How are they important in ecosystems?

24. Give three examples of interactions between animals classified in different phyla.

25. Explain how a sessile or slow-moving lifestyle, such as that of sponges, sea cucumbers, and tunicates, might select for bright colors and an arsenal of toxic chemicals.

26. Search the Internet to answer this question: Other than *Caenorhabditis elegans*, *Drosophila melanogaster*, and *Mus musculus*, what are some examples of invertebrate or vertebrate animals that have contributed to scientists' knowledge of general biology and animal biology? What other genomes of animals have scientists sequenced, and what are some resulting discoveries?

27. Invasive animal species are disrupting ecosystems around the world. Search the Internet for a list of invasive animal species. Which phyla are represented in the list? What harm do invasive species do? How important is it to try to eradicate invasive species?

PULL IT TOGETHER

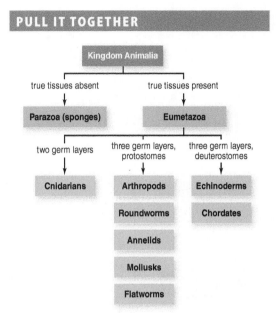

Figure 21.48 Pull It Together: Animals.

Refer to figure 21.48 and the chapter content to answer the following questions.

1. Write connecting phrases to separate arthropods and roundworms from annelids, mollusks, and flatworms.

2. Write connecting phrases to separate echinoderms from chordates.

3. Draw a concept map that summarizes the chordates, including both invertebrates and vertebrates.

Appendix A | *Answers to Multiple Choice Questions*

Answers to *Mastering Concepts, Write it Out,* and *Pull It Together* questions by chapter can be found under the heading "Answer Keys" on the companion website at **www.mhhe.com/hoefnagels.**

Chapter 1
1. d 2. d 3. c 4. a 5. d 6. b 7. b 8. b 9. c 10. d

Chapter 2
1. a 2. c 3. c 4. b 5. a 6. a

Chapter 3
1. c 2. d 3. d 4. a 5. b 6. c 7. d

Chapter 4
1. b 2. c 3. a 4. a 5. d 6. d 7. b

Chapter 5
1. c 2. b 3. a 4. c 5. a 6. d 7. b 8. d

Chapter 6
1. b 2. d 3. b 4. a 5. c 6. a 7. a 8. c

Chapter 7
1. c 2. a 3. c 4. a 5. c 6. d 7. a 8. d 9. b 10. d

Chapter 8
1. d 2. c 3. a 4. c 5. a

Chapter 9
1. c 2. a 3. a 4. c 5. c 6. a 7. b

Chapter 10
1. c 2. b 3. a 4. c 5. b 6. b 7. b 8. d 9. c 10. c

Chapter 11
1. c 2. a 3. c 4. c 5. a 6. d 7. b

Chapter 12
1. c 2. b 3. b 4. d 5. a 6. b 7. c 8. a 9. b

Chapter 13
1. d 2. b 3. a 4. c 5. a 6. a 7. c

Chapter 14
1. c 2. d 3. b 4. b 5. c

Chapter 15
1. d 2. d 3. a 4. b 5. d 6. d 7. c 8. c 9. d 10. a

Chapter 16
1. a 2. d 3. b 4. a 5. c 6. d 7. c 8. d 9. c

Chapter 17
1. c 2. b 3. d 4. c 5. c 6. c 7. a 8. a

Chapter 18
1. a 2. d 3. d 4. c 5. c

Chapter 19
1. d 2. a 3. d 4. d 5. d 6. b 7. c 8. d 9. c 10. a

Chapter 20
1. d 2. b 3. c 4. b 5. b 6. a 7. d 8. c 9. b 10. a

Chapter 21
1. a 2. c 3. d 4. a 5. d 6. c 7. c 8. a 9. d 10. b 11. c 12. d 13. a 14. d 15. c

Chapter 22
1. c 2. a 3. b 4. d 5. a 6. c 7. d 8. b 9. d 10. a

Chapter 23
1. b 2. b 3. d 4. d 5. b

Chapter 24
1. b 2. c 3. b 4. a 5. c

Chapter 25
1. d 2. c 3. d 4. a 5. d 6. b 7. c 8. b 9. d

Chapter 26
1. a 2. a 3. a 4. a 5. d 6. c 7. c

Chapter 27
1. d 2. d 3. d 4. c 5. a

Chapter 28
1. d 2. a 3. c 4. d 5. b 6. a 7. c

Chapter 29
1. b 2. d 3. d 4. d 5. a

Chapter 30
1. b 2. d 3. c 4. a 5. a 6. c 7. d 8. c 9. d

Chapter 31
1. d 2. b 3. c 4. b 5. c 6. a 7. c 8. b

Chapter 32
1. c 2. d 3. d 4. c 5. d 6. d

Chapter 33
1. d 2. a 3. b 4. d 5. a 6. a 7. d

Chapter 34
1. b 2. b 3. a 4. a 5. a 6. b 7. b 8. c 9. c 10. b

Chapter 35
1. b 2. c 3. a 4. c 5. b 6. d 7. d 8. c 9. a 10. d

Chapter 36
1. c 2. d 3. a 4. c 5. b 6. d 7. c

Chapter 37
1. b 2. a 3. d 4. b 5. c

Chapter 38
1. a 2. c 3. c 4. c 5. d 6. b 7. a 8. b 9. d 10. b

Chapter 39
1. d 2. a 3. d 4. a 5. b 6. c 7. b

Chapter 40
1. a 2. b 3. b 4. d 5. b 6. c 7. c 8. d 9. c 10. d

Appendix B | *A Brief Guide to Statistical Significance*

Experiments often yield numerical data, such as the height of a plant or the incidence of illness in vaccinated children (see, for example, figure 1.12). But how are we to know whether an observed difference between two samples is "real"? For example, if we do find that 100 vaccinated children become sick slightly less often than 100 unvaccinated ones, how can we make sure that this outcome does not simply reflect random variation between samples of 100 children?

A statistical analysis can help. The dictionary definition of *statistics* is "the science that deals with the collection, analysis, and interpretation of numerical data, often using probability theory." Note that the analysis is grounded in probability theory, a branch of mathematics that deals with random events. A statistical test is therefore a mathematical tool that assesses variation, with the goal of determining whether any observed differences between treatments can be explained by the variation that random events produce.

Researchers use many types of statistical tests, depending on the type of data collected and the design of the experiment. A

description of these tests is beyond the scope of this appendix. For now, it is enough to understand that in each statistical test, the researcher computes a value (the "test statistic") that takes into account the sample size and the variability in the data. The researcher then determines the likelihood that the observed test statistic could be explained by chance alone.

An imaginary experiment will help you understand the role of variability in accepting or rejecting a hypothesis. Suppose that you have two friends, Pat and Kris, both of whom play softball. Pat claims to be able to hit a ball farther than Kris, but Kris disagrees. You therefore set up a test of the null hypothesis, which is that Pat and Kris can hit the ball equally far. You ask both of your friends to hit the ball one time, and Pat's ball does go farther. But Kris wants to re-do the test. This time, Kris's ball goes farther. Evidently, two hits apiece is not sufficient for you to settle the matter.

You therefore decide to improve the experiment (figure B.1). This time, each player gets to hit 10 balls, and you use a tape measure to determine how far each ball traveled from home plate. Figure B.2 shows two possible outcomes of the contest. In each

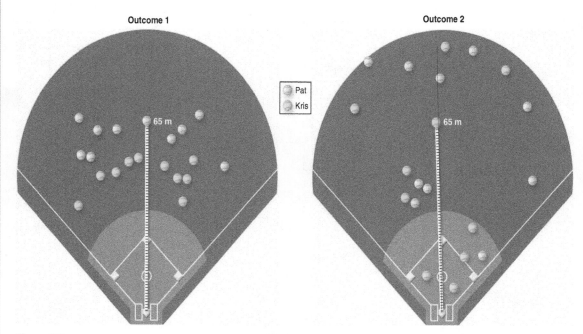

Figure B.1   Hitting Competition. These illustrations show two possible outcomes in a hitting contest between Pat and Kris. Note that the batting distances in Outcome 1 were much less variable than they were in Outcome 2.

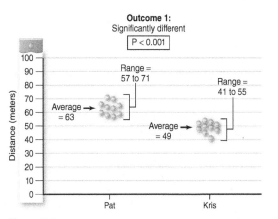

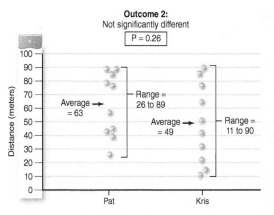

Figure B.2 Statistical Significance. In Outcome 1, the difference between Pat and Kris is considered highly significant at P<0.001; in Outcome 2, however, the variability in hitting distances means that the difference between the two batters is not statistically significant.

scenario, Pat's average distance is 63 meters, compared with 49 meters for Kris. Pat therefore appears to be the better hitter.

But look more closely at the data. In Outcome 1, the hitting distances are much less variable than they are in Outcome 2. How does this variability influence our conclusions about Pat and Kris?

The answer lies in statistical tests. The goal of each statistical test is to calculate the probability that an observed outcome would arise *if the null hypothesis were true.* This probability is called the P value. The lower the P value, the greater the chance that the difference between two treatments is "real."

Generally, biologists accept a P value of 0.05 or smaller as being statistically significant. In other words, a difference between two treatments is statistically significant when the probability that we would observe that result by chance alone is 5% or less. Moreover, a P value of 0.01 or smaller is considered highly significant. Note that the meaning of the word *significant* is different from its use in everyday language. Ordinarily, "significant" means "important." Not so in statistics, where "significant" simply means "likely to be true," and "highly significant" means "very likely to be true."

Returning to our experiment, the null hypothesis is that Pat and Kris are equally good hitters. The amount of variability in

Outcome 1 was small, and the calculated value of our test statistic suggests that we can reject this null hypothesis with a P value of <0.001. In other words, there is a 99.999% chance that Pat really is a better hitter than Kris and that our results are not simply due to chance (see figure B.2). In Outcome 2, however, the hitting distances were much more variable, and the calculated P value is 0.26. We therefore cannot reject the null hypothesis with confidence. After all, given these data, the chance that Pat really is the better batter is only 74%. In science, a 26% chance of incorrectly rejecting the null hypothesis is unacceptably high.

Scientists often include information about statistical analyses along with their data (figure B.3). The most common technique is to graph the average for each treatment and then add error bars that reflect the amount of variability in the data. The longer the error bar, the greater the amount of variability and the less confident we are in the accuracy of our result.

An error bar usually indicates either the standard error or the 95% confidence interval; you may wish to consult a statistics reference to learn more about each. Because these two measures have slightly different meanings, researchers should always note the type of error bar depicted on a graph.

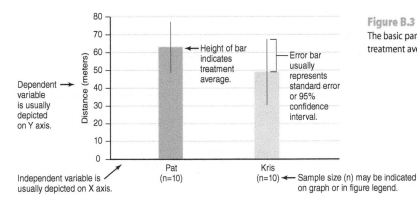

Figure B.3 Representing Statistics on a Graph.
The basic parts of a bar graph include the axes, treatment averages, and error bars.

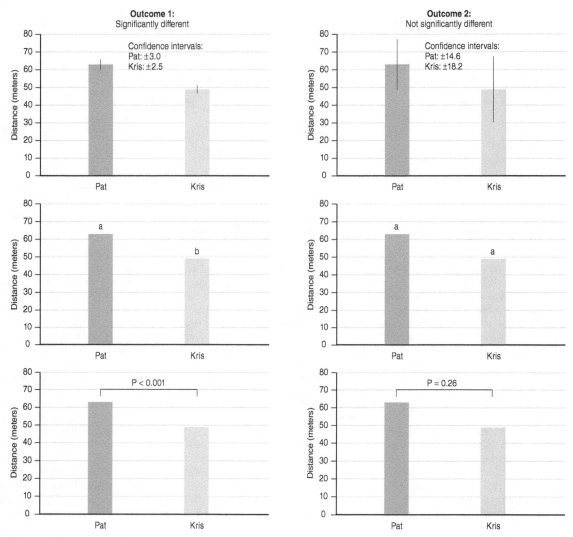

Figure B.4 Three Ways to Represent Statistics. Error bars, letters, and P values are all ways to indicate whether the difference between two treatments is statistically significant.

Figure B.4 shows three common ways to indicate whether an observed difference is statistically significant. Examine the error bars on the top pair of graphs in figure B.4. These bars indicate the 95% confidence intervals that were calculated for the two possible outcomes in our hitting competition. Because the data in Outcome 1 are much less variable than for Outcome 2, the error bars for Outcome 1 are smaller than for Outcome 2. The overlapping error bars for Outcome 2 indicate that the difference between Pat and Kris is not statistically significant.

Figure B.4 also shows that researchers sometimes use other methods to illustrate which data points are significantly different from one another. The middle pair of graphs in figure B.4 shows one approach. In Outcome 1 of our batting experiment, Pat was a significantly better hitter than Kris, so the bars depicting their averages are topped with different letters (*a* and *b*). In Outcome 2, however, Pat and Kris were not significantly different, so their bars have the same letter, *a*. A third possibility is to simply report the P values between pairs of treatments; the last pair of graphs in figure B.4 illustrates this strategy.

Appendix C | *Units of Measurement*

Metric Prefixes

Symbol	Prefix	Increase or Decrease	
G	giga	One billion	1,000,000,000
M	mega	One million	1,000,000
k	kilo	One thousand	1,000
h	hecto	One hundred	100
da	deka (or deca)	Ten	10
d	deci	One-tenth	0.1
c	centi	One-hundredth	0.01
m	milli	One-thousandth	0.001
μ	micro	One-millionth	0.000001
n	nano	One-billionth	0.000000001

Metric Units and Conversions

	Metric Unit	Metric to English Conversion	English to Metric Conversion
Length	1 meter (m)	1 km = 0.62 mile 1 m = 1.09 yards = 39.37 inches 1 cm = 0.394 inch 1 mm = 0.039 inch	1 mile = 1.609 km 1 yard = 0.914 m 1 foot = 0.305 m = 30.5 cm 1 inch = 2.54 cm
Mass	1 gram (g) 1 metric ton (t) = 1,000,000 g = 1,000 kg	1 t = 1.102 tons (U.S.) 1 kg = 2.205 pounds 1 g = 0.0353 ounce	1 ton (U.S.) = 0.907 t 1 pound = 0.4536 kg 1 ounce = 28.35 g
Volume (liquids)	1 liter (l)	1 l = 1.06 quarts 1 ml = 0.034 fluid ounce	1 gallon = 3.79 l 1 quart = 0.95 l 1 pint = 0.47 l 1 fluid ounce = 29.57 ml
Temperature	Degrees Celsius (°C)	°C = (°F − 32)/1.8	°F = (°C × 1.8) + 32
Energy and Power	1 joule (J)	1 J = 0.239 calorie 1 kJ = 0.239 kilocalorie ("food calorie")	1 calorie = 4.186 J 1 kilocalorie ("food calorie") = 4186 J
Time	1 second (sec)		

Appendix D | *Periodic Table of the Elements*

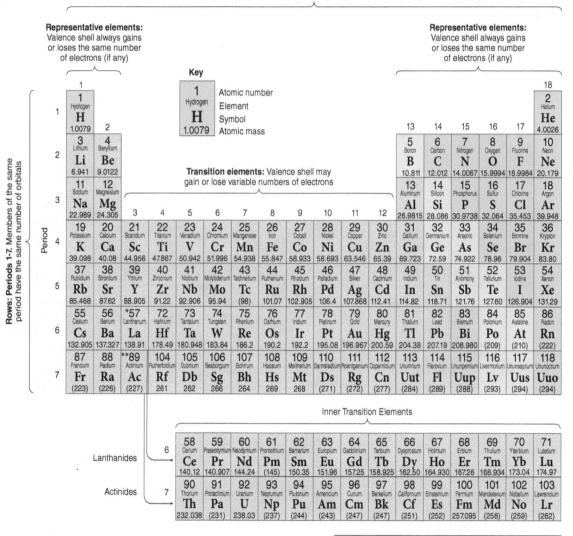

Columns: Groups 1-18. Members of the same group have the same number of valence electrons

Representative elements:
Valence shell always gains
or loses the same number
of electrons (if any)

Representative elements:
Valence shell always gains
or loses the same number
of electrons (if any)

Key

1
Hydrogen
H
1.0079

Atomic number
Element
Symbol
Atomic mass

Transition elements: Valence shell may
gain or lose variable numbers of electrons

Rows: Periods 1-7. Members of the same period have the same number of orbitals

Period

1	Hydrogen **H** 1.0079	2												13	14	15	16	17	18 2 Helium **He** 4.0026
2	3 Lithium **Li** 6.941	4 Beryllium **Be** 9.0122												5 Boron **B** 10.811	6 Carbon **C** 12.012	7 Nitrogen **N** 14.0067	8 Oxygen **O** 15.9994	9 Fluorine **F** 18.9984	10 Neon **Ne** 20.179
3	11 Sodium **Na** 22.989	12 Magnesium **Mg** 24.305	3	4	5	6	7	8	9	10	11	12		13 Aluminum **Al** 26.9815	14 Silicon **Si** 28.086	15 Phosphorus **P** 30.9738	16 Sulfur **S** 32.064	17 Chlorine **Cl** 35.453	18 Argon **Ar** 39.948
4	19 Potassium **K** 39.098	20 Calcium **Ca** 40.08	21 Scandium **Sc** 44.956	22 Titanium **Ti** 47.867	23 Vanadium **V** 50.942	24 Chromium **Cr** 51.996	25 Manganese **Mn** 54.938	26 Iron **Fe** 55.847	27 Cobalt **Co** 58.933	28 Nickel **Ni** 58.693	29 Copper **Cu** 63.546	30 Zinc **Zn** 65.39		31 Gallium **Ga** 69.723	32 Germanium **Ge** 72.59	33 Arsenic **As** 74.922	34 Selenium **Se** 78.96	35 Bromine **Br** 79.904	36 Krypton **Kr** 83.80
5	37 Rubidium **Rb** 85.468	38 Strontium **Sr** 87.62	39 Yttrium **Y** 88.905	40 Zirconium **Zr** 91.22	41 Niobium **Nb** 92.906	42 Molybdenum **Mo** 95.94	43 Technetium **Tc** (98)	44 Ruthenium **Ru** 101.07	45 Rhodium **Rh** 102.905	46 Palladium **Pd** 106.4	47 Silver **Ag** 107.868	48 Cadmium **Cd** 112.41		49 Indium **In** 114.82	50 Tin **Sn** 118.71	51 Antimony **Sb** 121.76	52 Tellurium **Te** 127.60	53 Iodine **I** 126.904	54 Xenon **Xe** 131.29
6	55 Cesium **Cs** 132.905	56 Barium **Ba** 137.327	*57 Lanthanum **La** 138.91	72 Hafnium **Hf** 178.49	73 Tantalum **Ta** 180.948	74 Tungsten **W** 183.84	75 Rhenium **Re** 186.2	76 Osmium **Os** 190.2	77 Iridium **Ir** 192.2	78 Platinum **Pt** 195.08	79 Gold **Au** 196.967	80 Mercury **Hg** 200.59		81 Thallium **Tl** 204.38	82 Lead **Pb** 207.19	83 Bismuth **Bi** 208.980	84 Polonium **Po** (209)	85 Astatine **At** (210)	86 Radon **Rn** (222)
7	87 Francium **Fr** (223)	88 Radium **Ra** (226)	**89 Actinium **Ac** (227)	104 Rutherfordium **Rf** 261	105 Dubnium **Db** 262	106 Seaborgium **Sg** 266	107 Bohrium **Bh** 264	108 Hassium **Hs** 269	109 Meitnerium **Mt** 268	110 Darmstadtium **Ds** (271)	111 Roentgenium **Rg** (272)	112 Copernicium **Cn** (277)		113 Ununtrium **Uut** (284)	114 Flerovium **Fl** (289)	115 Ununpentium **Uup** (288)	116 Livermorium **Lv** (293)	117 Ununseptium **Uus** (294)	118 Ununoctium **Uuo** (294)

Inner Transition Elements

Lanthanides 6

58 Cerium **Ce** 140.12	59 Praseodymium **Pr** 140.907	60 Neodymium **Nd** 144.24	61 Promethium **Pm** (145)	62 Samarium **Sm** 150.35	63 Europium **Eu** 151.96	64 Gadolinium **Gd** 157.25	65 Terbium **Tb** 158.925	66 Dysprosium **Dy** 162.50	67 Holmium **Ho** 164.930	68 Erbium **Er** 167.26	69 Thulium **Tm** 168.934	70 Ytterbium **Yb** 173.04	71 Lutetium **Lu** 174.97

Actinides 7

90 Thorium **Th** 232.038	91 Protactinium **Pa** (231)	92 Uranium **U** 238.03	93 Neptunium **Np** (237)	94 Plutonium **Pu** (244)	95 Americium **Am** (243)	96 Curium **Cm** (247)	97 Berkelium **Bk** (247)	98 Californium **Cf** (251)	99 Einsteinium **Es** (252)	100 Fermium **Fm** 257.095	101 Mendelevium **Md** (258)	102 Nobelium **No** (259)	103 Lawrencium **Lr** (262)

☐ **Metals:** Lose electrons in redox reactions
☐ **Nonmetals:** Gain electrons in redox reactions (except for group 18)
☐ **Semi-metals (metalloids):** Intermediate properties

Appendix E | *Amino Acid Structures*

Nonpolar

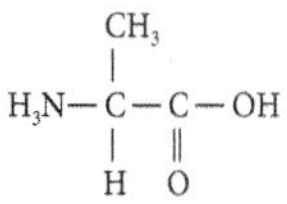

Alanine
(Ala; A)

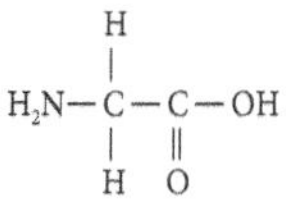

Glycine
(Gly; G)

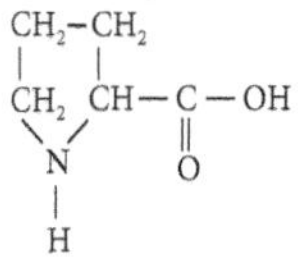

Proline
(Pro; P)

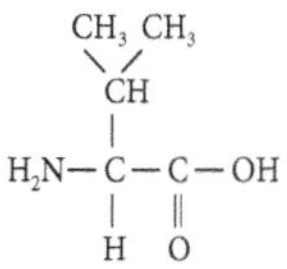

Valine
(Val; V)

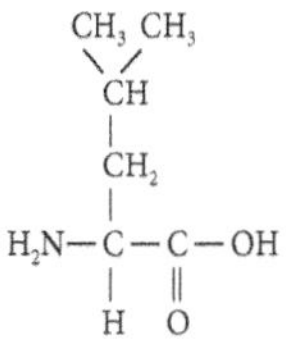

Leucine
(Leu; L)

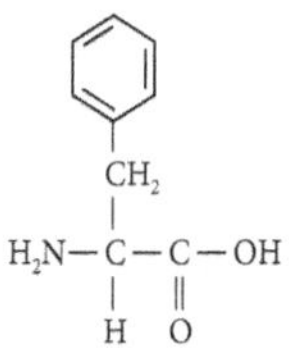

Phenylalanine
(Phe; F)

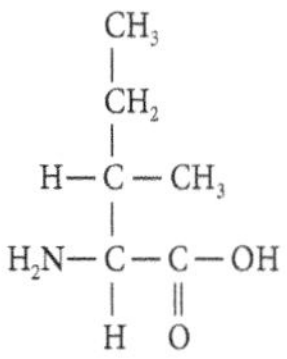

Isoleucine
(Ile; I)

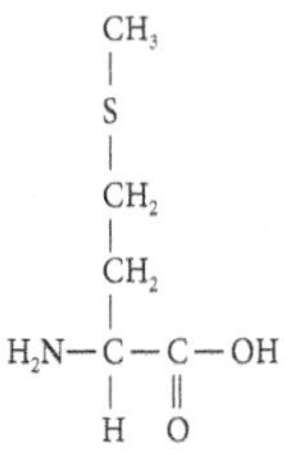

Methionine
(Met; M)

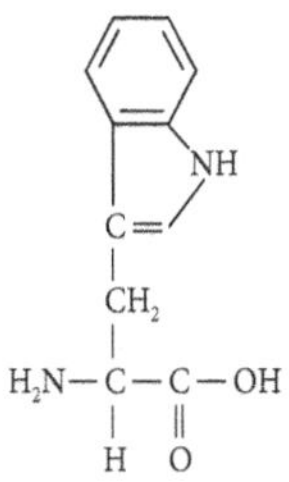

Tryptophan
(Trp; W)

Polar

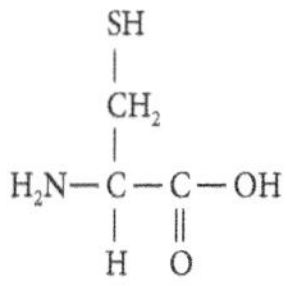

Cysteine
(Cys; C)

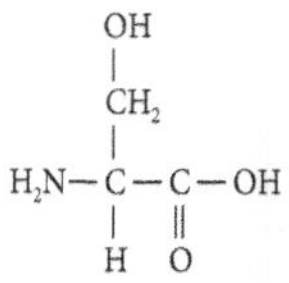

Serine
(Ser; S)

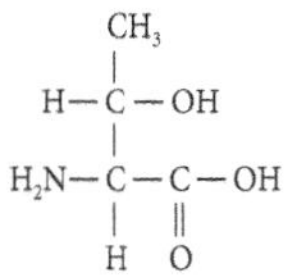

Threonine
(Thr; T)

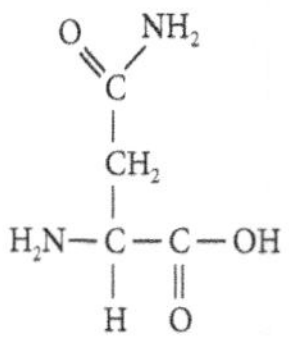

Asparagine
(Asn; N)

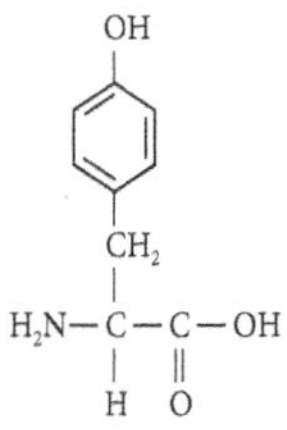

Tyrosine
(Tyr; Y)

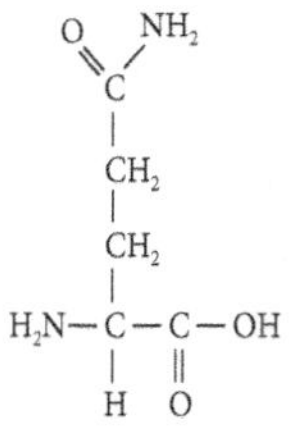

Glutamine
(Gln; Q)

Electrically charged / basic

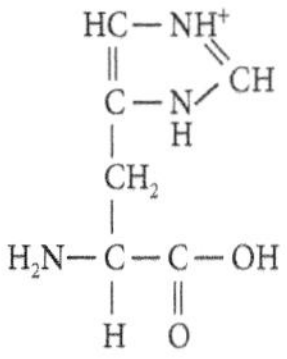

Histidine
(His; H)

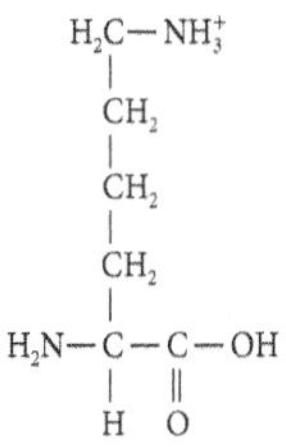

Lysine
(Lys; K)

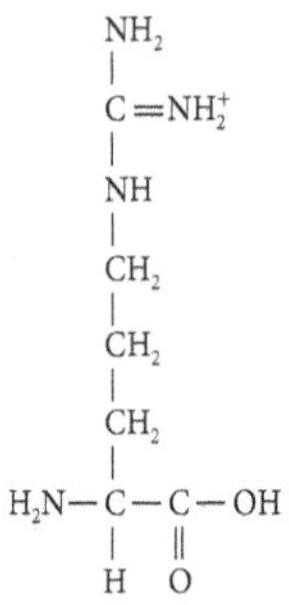

Arginine
(Arg; R)

Electrically charged / acidic

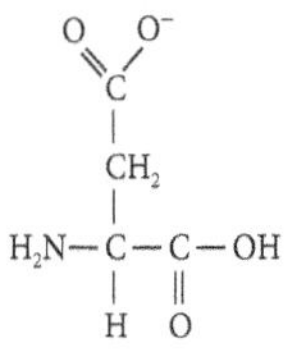

Aspartic
acid (Asp; D)

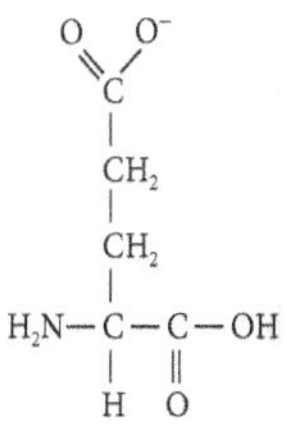

Glutamic
acid (Glu; E)

Note: Amino acids are arranged according to each R group's chemical properties.

Glossary

A

abiotic: nonliving

abscisic acid: plant hormone that inhibits seed germination and plant growth

abscission zone: specialized layer of cells from which leaf petiole detaches from plant

absolute dating: determining the age of a fossil in years

absorption: the process of taking in and incorporating nutrients or energy

accessory pigment: photosynthetic pigment other than chlorophyll *a* that extends the range of light wavelengths useful in photosynthesis

acetyl CoA: molecule that enters the Krebs cycle in cellular respiration; product of partial oxidation of pyruvate

acid: a molecule that releases hydrogen ions into a solution

acid deposition: low pH precipitation or particles that form when air pollutants react with water in the upper atmosphere

acrosome: protrusion covering the head of a sperm cell, containing enzymes that enable the sperm to penetrate layers around the oocyte

actin: protein that forms thin filaments in muscle cells; also part of cytoskeleton

action potential: all-or-none electrochemical change across the cell membrane of a neuron; the basis of a nerve impulse

activation energy: energy required for a chemical reaction to begin

active immunity: immunity generated by an organism's production of antibodies

active site: the part of an enzyme to which substrates bind

active transport: movement of a substance across a membrane against its concentration gradient, using a carrier protein and energy from ATP

adaptation: inherited trait that permits an organism to survive and reproduce

adaptive immunity: defense system in vertebrates that recognizes and remembers specific antigens

adaptive radiation: divergence of multiple new species from a single ancestral type in a relatively short time

adenosine triphosphate (ATP): a molecule whose high-energy phosphate bonds power many biological processes

adhesion: the tendency of water to hydrogen bond to other compounds

adipose tissue: type of connective tissue consisting of fat cells embedded in a minimal matrix

adrenal cortex: outer portion of an adrenal gland; secretes mineralocorticoids, glucocorticoids, and small amounts of sex hormones

adrenal gland: one of two endocrine glands atop the kidneys

adrenal medulla: inner portion of an adrenal gland; secretes epinephrine and norepinephrine

adrenocorticotropic hormone (ACTH): hormone produced in the anterior pituitary

adult stem cell: cell that can give rise to a limited subset of cells in the body

adventitious root: roots arising from stem or leaf

aerobic respiration: complete oxidation of glucose to CO_2 in the presence of O_2, producing ATP

age structure: distribution of age classes in a population

agglutination: clumping together of cells

alcoholic fermentation: metabolic pathway in which NADH from glycolysis reduces acetaldehyde, producing ethanol and CO_2

aldosterone: mineralocorticoid hormone produced in the adrenal cortex

alga: aquatic, photosynthetic protist

alimentary canal: two-opening digestive tract; also called gastrointestinal (GI) tract

alkaline: having a pH greater than 7

allantois: extraembryonic membrane that forms as an outpouching of the yolk sac

allele: one of two or more alternative forms of a gene

allele frequency: number of copies of one allele, divided by the number of alleles in a population

allergen: antigen that triggers an allergic reaction

allergy: exaggerated immune response to a harmless substance

allopatric speciation: formation of new species after a physical barrier separates a population into groups that cannot interbreed

alternation of generations: the sexual life cycle of plants and many green algae, which alternates between a diploid sporophyte stage and a haploid gametophyte stage

altruism: behavior that lowers an animal's fitness for the good of others

alveolus (pl. alveoli): microscopic air sac in the mammalian lungs, where gas exchange occurs; sac beneath cell membrane in alveolate protist

amino acid: an organic molecule consisting of a central carbon atom bonded to a hydrogen atom, an amino group, a carboxyl group, and an R group

amino group: a nitrogen atom single-bonded to two hydrogen atoms

ammonia: nitrogenous waste (NH_3) generated by breakdown of amino acids

amnion: extraembryonic membrane that contains amniotic fluid

amniote: vertebrate in which protective membranes surround the embryo (amnion, chorion, and allantois); reptiles and mammals

amniotic egg: reptile or monotreme egg containing fluid and nutrients within membranes that protect the embryo

amoeboid protozoan: unicellular protist that produces pseudopodia

amphibian: tetrapod vertebrate that can live on land, but requires water to reproduce

amygdala: forebrain structure involved in emotions

anaerobic respiration: cellular respiration using an electron acceptor other than O_2

analogous: similar in function but not in structure because of convergent evolution, not common ancestry

anaphase: stage of mitosis in which the spindle pulls sister chromatids toward opposite poles of the cell

anaphase I: anaphase of meiosis I, when spindle fibers pull homologous chromosomes toward opposite poles of the cell

anaphase II: anaphase of meiosis II, when centromeres split and spindle fibers pull sister chromatids toward opposite poles of the cell

anaphylactic shock: rapid, widespread, severe allergic reaction

anatomy: the study of an organism's structure

ancestral character: characteristic already present in the ancestor of a group being studied

anchoring (or adhering) junction: connection between two adjacent animal cells that anchors intermediate filaments in a single spot on the cell membrane

angiogenesis: the production of new blood vessels

angiosperm: a seed plant that produces flowers and fruits; includes monocots and eudicots

Animalia: kingdom containing multicellular eukaryotes that are heterotrophs by ingestion

annelid: segmented worm; phylum Annelida

anorexia nervosa: eating disorder characterized by refusal to maintain normal body weight

antenna pigment: photosynthetic pigment that passes photon energy to the reaction center of a photosystem

anterior pituitary: the front part of the pituitary gland

anther: pollen-producing structure at tip of stamen

antibody: protein that binds to an antigen

anticodon: a three-base portion of a tRNA molecule; the anticodon is complementary to one codon

antidiuretic hormone (ADH): hormone released from the posterior pituitary; also called vasopressin

antigen: molecule that elicits an immune reaction by B and T cells

anus: exit from a complete digestive tract

aorta: the largest artery leaving the heart

apical dominance: intact terminal bud of a plant suppresses growth of lateral buds

apical meristem: meristem at tip of root or shoot

apicomplexan: non-motile protist with cell containing an apical complex; obligate animal parasite

apoptosis: programmed cell death that is a normal part of development

appendicular skeleton: the limb bones and the bones that support them in the vertebrate skeleton

arachnid: type of chelicerate arthropod; spiders, ticks, mites, and scorpions

Archaea: one of two domains of prokaryotes

arteriole: small artery

artery: vessel that carries blood away from the heart

arthropod: segmented animal with an exoskeleton and jointed appendages; phylum Arthropoda

artificial selection: selective breeding strategy in which a human allows only organisms with desired traits to reproduce

ascomycete: fungus that produces sexual spores in a sac called an ascus

ascospore: haploid sexual spore produced in an ascus

ascus (pl. asci): in ascomycetes, a saclike structure in which ascospores are produced

asexual reproduction: form of reproduction in which offspring arise from only one parent

associative learning: type of learning in which an animal connects two stimuli or a stimulus and a behavior

atom: a particle of matter; composed of protons, neutrons, and electrons

atomic number: the number of protons in an atom's nucleus

atomic weight: the average mass of all isotopes of an element

ATP: adenosine triphosphate; a molecule whose high-energy phosphate bonds power many biological processes

ATP synthase: enzyme complex that admits protons through a membrane, where they trigger phosphorylation of ADP to ATP

atrioventricular (AV) node: specialized cardiac muscle cells that delay the heartbeat, giving the ventricles time to fill

atrioventricular (AV) valve: flap of heart tissue that prevents the flow of blood from a ventricle to an atrium

atrium: heart chamber that receives blood

auditory canal: ear canal; funnels sounds from the outer ear to the eardrum

auditory nerve: nerve fibers that connect the cochlea and vestibular apparatus to the brain

autoimmune disorder: immune reaction to the body's own cells

autonomic nervous system: in the peripheral nervous system, motor pathways that lead to smooth muscle, cardiac muscle, and glands

autosomal dominant: inheritance pattern of a dominant allele on an autosome

autosomal recessive: inheritance pattern of a recessive allele on an autosome

autosome: a nonsex chromosome

autotroph: organism that produces organic molecules by acquiring carbon from inorganic sources; primary producer

auxin: plant hormone that promotes cell elongation in stems and fruits

axial skeleton: the central axis of a vertebrate skeleton; consists of the bones of the head, vertebral column, and rib cage

axillary bud: undeveloped shoot in the angle between stem and petiole

axon (nerve fiber): extension of a neuron that transmits messages away from the cell body and toward another cell

B

B cell: type of lymphocyte that produces antibodies

bacillus (pl. bacilli): rod-shaped prokaryote

background extinction rate: steady, gradual loss of species through natural competition or loss of genetic diversity

Bacteria: one of two domains of prokaryotes

bacteriophage (phage): a virus that infects bacteria

balanced polymorphism: condition in which multiple alleles persist indefinitely in a population

bark: tissues outside the vascular cambium

base: a molecule that either releases hydroxide ions into a solution or removes hydrogen ions from it

basidiomycete: fungus that produces sexual spores on a basidium

basidiospore: haploid sexual spore produced on a basidium

basidium (pl. basidia): in basidiomycetes, a club-shaped structure that produces basidiospores

basilar membrane: the lower wall of the cochlear canal; vibrates in response to sound

basophil: type of white blood cell that triggers inflammation and allergy

behavioral ecology: study of the survival value and the evolution of behavioral patterns

benign tumor: mass of abnormal cells that does not have the potential to spread

benthic zone: sediment at the bottom of an ocean or lake

bilateral symmetry: body form in which only one plane divides the animal into mirror image halves

bile: digestive biochemical that emulsifies fats

binary fission: type of asexual reproduction in which a prokaryotic cell divides into two identical cells

biodiversity: the variety of life on Earth

biogeochemical cycle: geological and biological processes that recycle elements vital to life

biogeography: the study of the distribution patterns of species across the planet

biological species: a population, or group of populations, whose members can interbreed and produce fertile offspring

biomagnification: increasing concentrations of a chemical in higher trophic levels

biome: one of the world's several major types of ecosystems, characterized by a distinctive climate and group of species

biosphere: part of Earth where life can exist

biotic: living

bird: tetrapod vertebrate with feathers, wings, and an amniotic egg

birth defect: abnormality that causes death or disability in a newborn

birth rate: the number of new individuals produced per 1000 individuals per unit time

bivalve: type of mollusk

blade: flattened part of a leaf

blastocyst: preembryonic stage consisting of a fluid-filled ball of cells

blastula: stage of early animal embryonic development; a sphere of cells surrounding a fluid-filled cavity

blood: type of connective tissue consisting of cells and platelets suspended in a liquid matrix

blood clot: plug of solidified blood

blood-brain barrier: close-knit cells that form capillaries in the brain, limiting the substances that can enter

blood pressure: force that blood exerts against artery walls

bone: type of connective tissue consisting of osteocytes and other cells embedded in a mineralized matrix; also, in the vertebrate skeleton, an organ consisting of bone tissue, cartilage, and other tissues

bony fish: jawed fish with a skeleton made of bone; ray-finned fishes and lobe-finned fishes

bottleneck: sudden reduction in the size of a population

brain: a distinct concentration of nervous tissue, often encased within a skull, at the anterior end of an animal

brainstem: continuation of the spinal cord into the vertebrate hindbrain

breast: milk-producing organ in female mammals

bronchiole: small branched airway that connects bronchi to alveoli

bronchus (pl. bronchi): one of two large tubes that branch from the trachea

brown alga: multicellular photosynthetic aquatic protist with swimming spores and brownish accessory pigments

bryophyte: plant that lacks vascular tissue; includes liverworts, hornworts, and mosses

buffer: weak acid/base pair that resists changes in pH

bulbourethral gland: small gland near the male urethra that secretes mucus

bulimia: eating disorder in which a person eats large quantities and then intentionally vomits or uses laxatives shortly afterward

bulk element: an element that an organism requires in large amounts

bulk feeder: animal that ingests large pieces of food

bundle-sheath cell: thick-walled plant cell surrounding veins; site of Calvin cycle in C_4 plants

C

C_3 pathway: the Calvin cycle

C_4 pathway: a carbon fixation pathway in which CO_2 combines with a three-carbon molecule to form a four-carbon compound

caecilian: type of amphibian

calcitonin: thyroid hormone that decreases blood calcium levels

Calorie: one kilocalorie

calorie: the energy required to raise the temperature of 1 gram of water by 1°C under standard conditions

Calvin cycle: in photosynthesis, metabolic pathway in which CO_2 is fixed and incorporated into a three-carbon carbohydrate

CAM pathway: carbon fixation that occurs at night; CO_2 is later released for use in the Calvin cycle during the day

cancer: class of diseases characterized by uncontrolled division of cells that invade or spread to other tissues

capillary: tiny vessel that connects an arteriole with a venule

capillary bed: network of capillaries

capsid: protein coat of a virus

carbohydrate: compound containing carbon, hydrogen, and oxygen in a ratio 1:2:1

carbon fixation: the initial incorporation of carbon from CO_2 into an organic compound

carbon reactions: the reactions of photosynthesis that use ATP and NADPH to synthesize carbohydrates from carbon dioxide

carboxyl group: a carbon atom double-bonded to an oxygen and single-bonded to a hydroxyl group

cardiac cycle: sequence of contraction and relaxation that makes up the heartbeat

cardiac muscle: involuntary muscle tissue composed of branched, striated, single-nucleated contractile cells

cardiac output: the volume of blood that the heart pumps each minute

cardiovascular system: circulatory system

carnivore: animal that eats animals

carpel: leaflike structure enclosing an angiosperm's ovule

carrying capacity: maximum number of individuals that an ecosystem can support indefinitely

cartilage: type of connective tissue consisting of cells surrounded by a rubbery collagen matrix

cartilaginous fish: jawed fish with a skeleton made of cartilage; sharks, skates, and rays

Casparian strip: waxy barrier in root endodermis

catastrophism: the idea that brief upheavals such as floods, volcanic eruptions, and earthquakes are responsible for most geological formations

cecum: the entrance to the large intestine

cell: smallest unit of life that can function independently

cell body: enlarged portion of a neuron that contains most of the organelles

cell cycle: sequence of events that occur in an actively dividing cell

cell membrane: the boundary of a cell, consisting of proteins embedded in a phospholipid bilayer

cell plate: in plants, the materials that begin to form the wall that divides two cells

cell theory: the ideas that all living matter consists of cells, cells are the structural and functional units of life, and all cells come from preexisting cells

cell wall: a rigid boundary surrounding cells of many prokaryotes, protists, plants, and fungi

cell-mediated immunity: branch of adaptive immune system in which defensive cells kill invaders by direct cell-cell contact

cellular slime mold: protist in which feeding stage consists of individual cells that come together as a multicellular "slug" when food runs out

centipede: type of mandibulate arthropod

central nervous system (CNS): brain and the spinal cord

centromere: small section of a chromosome where sister chromatids attach to each other

centrosome: part of the cell that organizes microtubules

cephalization: development of sensory structures and a brain at the head end of an animal

cephalopod: type of mollusk

cerebellum: area of the hindbrain that coordinates subconscious muscular responses

cerebral cortex: outer layer of the cerebrum

cerebrospinal fluid: fluid that bathes and cushions the central nervous system

cerebrum: region of the forebrain that controls intelligence, learning, perception, and emotion

cervix: lower, narrow part of the uterus

chaparral: Mediterranean shrubland

charophyte: type of green algae thought to be most closely related to terrestrial plants

chelicerate: arthropod with clawlike mouthparts (chelicerae); horseshoe crabs and arachnids

chemical bond: attractive force that holds atoms together

chemical reaction: interaction in which bonds break and new bonds form

chemiosmotic phosphorylation: reactions that produce ATP using ATP synthase and the potential energy of a proton gradient

chemoreceptor: sensory receptor that responds to chemicals

chemotroph: organism that derives energy by oxidizing inorganic or organic chemicals

chiton: type of mollusk

chlorophyll *a*: green pigment that plants, algae, and cyanobacteria use to harness the energy in sunlight

chloroplast: organelle housing the reactions of photosynthesis in eukaryotes

chordate: animal that at some time during its development has a notochord, hollow nerve cord, pharyngeal slits or pouches, and a postanal tail; phylum Chordata

chorion: outermost extraembryonic membrane

chorionic villus: fingerlike projection extending from the chorion to the uterine lining

choroid: middle layer of the eyeball, between the sclera and the retina

chromatid: one of two identical DNA molecules that make up a replicated chromosome

chromatin: collective term for all of the DNA and its associated proteins in the nucleus of a eukaryotic cell

chromosome: a continuous molecule of DNA wrapped around protein in the nucleus of a eukaryotic cell; also, the genetic material of a prokaryotic cell

chyme: semifluid mass of food and gastric juice that moves from the stomach to the small intestine

chytridiomycete (chytrid): microscopic fungus that produces motile zoospores

ciliate: protist with cilia-covered cell surface

cilium (pl. cilia): one of many short, movable protein projections extending from a cell

circadian rhythm: physiological cycle that repeats daily

circulatory system: organ system that distributes blood (or a comparable fluid) throughout the body

clade: monophyletic group of organisms consisting of a common ancestor and all of its descendants

cladistics: phylogenetic system that defines groups by distinguishing between ancestral and derived characters

cladogram: treelike diagram built using shared derived characteristics

classical conditioning: type of associative learning in which an animal pairs two stimuli

cleavage: period of rapid cell division following fertilization

cleavage furrow: in animals, the initial indentation between two daughter cells in mitosis

climax community: community that persists indefinitely if left undisturbed

clitoris: small, highly sensitive female sexual organ

clonal deletion: elimination of lymphocytes with receptors for self antigens

clonal selection: rapid division of a stimulated B cell, generating memory B cells and plasma cells that are clones of the original B cell

cloning vector: a self-replicating structure that carries DNA from cell to cell

closed circulatory system: circulatory system in which blood remains confined to vessels

club moss: a type of seedless vascular plant

cnidarian: animal with radial symmetry, two germ layers, a jellylike interior, and cnidocytes; phylum Cnidaria

cnidocyte: cell in cnidarians that can fire a toxic barb for predation or defense

coccus (pl. cocci): spherical prokaryote

cochlea: spiral-shaped part of the inner ear, where vibrations are translated into nerve impulses

codominance: mode of inheritance in which two alleles are fully expressed in the heterozygote

codon: a triplet of mRNA bases that specifies a particular amino acid

coelacanth: type of lobe-finned fish

coelom: fluid-filled animal body cavity that forms completely within mesoderm

coevolution: genetic change in one species selects for subsequent change in another species

cofactor: inorganic or organic substance required for activity of an enzyme

cohesion: the attraction of water molecules to one another

cohesion-tension theory: theory that explains how water moves under tension in xylem

collecting duct: tubule in the kidney into which nephrons drain urine

collenchyma: elongated living plant cells with thick, elastic cell walls

commensalism: type of symbiosis in which one member benefits without affecting the other member

community: group of interacting populations that inhabit the same region

compact bone: solid, hard bone tissue consisting of tightly packed concentric rings of bone cells in a mineralized matrix

companion cell: parenchyma cells adjacent to sieve tube elements

competition: struggle between organisms for the same limited resource

competitive exclusion principle: the idea that two or more species cannot indefinitely occupy the same niche

competitive inhibition: change in an enzyme's activity occurring when an inhibitor binds to the active site, competing with the enzyme's normal substrate

complement: group of proteins that help destroy pathogens

complementary: in DNA and RNA, the precise pairing of purines (A and G) to pyrimidines (C, T, and U)

complete digestive tract: digestive tract through which food passes in one direction from mouth to anus

compound: a molecule including different elements

compound leaf: leaf that is divided into leaflets

concentration gradient: difference in solute concentrations between two adjacent regions

cone: a pollen- or ovule-bearing structure in many gymnosperms

cone cell: photoreceptor cell in the retina that detects colors

conidium: asexually produced fungal cell

conifer: a type of gymnosperm

conjugation: a form of horizontal gene transfer in which one cell receives DNA via direct contact with another cell

connective tissue: animal tissue consisting of widely spaced cells in a distinctive extracellular matrix

conservation biology: study of the preservation of biodiversity

constant region: amino acid sequence that is the same for all antibodies

consumer (heterotroph): organism that uses organic sources of energy and carbon

contact inhibition: property of most noncancerous eukaryotic cells; inhibits cell division when cells contact one another

contraception: use of devices or practices that prevent pregnancy

control: untreated group used as a basis for comparison with a treated group in an experiment

convergent evolution: the evolution of similar adaptations in organisms that do not share the same evolutionary lineage

coral reef: underwater deposit of calcium carbonate formed by colonies of coral animals

cork cambium: lateral meristem that produces cork cells and parenchyma in woody plant

cornea: in the eye, a modified portion of the sclera that forms a transparent curved window that admits light

coronary artery: artery that provides blood to the heart muscle

corpus luteum: gland formed from a ruptured ovarian follicle that has recently released an oocyte

cortex: ground tissue between epidermis and vascular tissue in roots and stems

cotyledon: seed leaf in angiosperms

countercurrent exchange: arrangement in which two adjacent currents flow in opposite directions and exchange materials or heat

coupled reactions: two simultaneous chemical reactions, one of which provides the energy that drives the other

covalent bond: type of chemical bond in which two atoms share electrons

craniate: animal with a cranium

cranium: part of the skull that encloses the brain

creatine phosphate: molecule stored in muscle fibers that can donate its high-energy phosphate to ADP, regenerating ATP

crista (pl. cristae): fold of the inner mitochondrial membrane along which many of the reactions of cellular respiration occur

crocodilian: type of reptile

cross bridge: contact between a myosin molecule's head and an actin molecule in a myofibril

crossing over: exchange of genetic material between homologous chromosomes during prophase I of meiosis

crustacean: type of mandibulate arthropod

culture: the knowledge, beliefs, and behaviors that humans transmit from generation to generation

cuticle: waterproof layer covering the aerial epidermis of a plant

cycad: a type of gymnosperm

cytokine: messenger protein synthesized in immune cells that influences the activity of other immune cells

cytokinesis: distribution of cytoplasm into daughter cells in cell division

cytokinin: plant hormone that stimulates cell division

cytoplasm: the watery mixture that occupies much of a cell's volume. In eukaryotic cells, it consists of all materials, including organelles, between the nuclear envelope and the cell membrane

cytoskeleton: framework of protein rods and tubules in eukaryotic cells

cytotoxic T cell: lymphocyte that kills invading cells by binding them and releasing chemicals

D

day-neutral plant: plant that does not rely on photoperiod to stimulate flowering

death rate: the number of deaths per 1000 individuals per unit time

decomposer: organism that consumes wastes and dead organic matter, returning inorganic nutrients to the ecosystem

deforestation: removal of tree cover from a previously forested area

dehydration synthesis: formation of a covalent bond between two molecules by loss of water

deletion: loss of one or more genes from a chromosome

demographic transition: phase of economic development during which birth and death rates shift from high to low

denaturation: modification of a protein's shape so that its function is destroyed

dendrite: thin neuron branch that receives neural messages and transmits information to the cell body

denitrification: conversion of nitrites and nitrates to N_2

dense connective tissue: type of connective tissue with fibroblasts and dense collagen tracts

density-dependent factor: population-limiting condition whose effects increase when populations are large

density-independent factor: population-limiting condition that acts irrespective of population size

dependent variable: response that may be under the influence of an independent variable

deposit feeder: type of substrate feeder that strains partially decayed organic matter from sediment

derived character: characteristic not found in the ancestor of a group being studied

dermal tissue: tissue covering a plant's surface

dermis: layer of connective tissue that lies beneath the epidermis in vertebrate skin

descent with modification: Darwin's term for evolution, describing gradual change from an ancestral type of organism

desert: type of terrestrial biome; very low precipitation

determinate growth: growth that halts at maturity

detritivore: animal that eats decomposing organic matter

detritus: feces and dead organic matter

deuterostome: clade of bilaterally symmetrical animals in which the first opening in the gastrula develops into the anus

diabetes: disease resulting from an inability to produce or use insulin

diastolic pressure: lower number in a blood pressure reading; reflects relaxation of the ventricles

diatom: photosynthetic aquatic protist with two-part silica wall

differentiation: process by which cells acquire specialized functions

diffusion: movement of a substance from a region where it is highly concentrated to an area where it is less concentrated

digestion: the physical and chemical breakdown of food

digestive system: organ system that dismantles food, absorbs nutrient molecules, and eliminates indigestible wastes

dihybrid cross: mating between two individuals that are heterozygous for two genes

dikaryotic: containing two genetically distinct haploid nuclei

dinoflagellate: unicellular aquatic protist with two flagella of unequal length; many have cellulose plates

diploid cell: cell containing two full sets of chromosomes, one from each parent; also called $2n$

direct development: gradual development of a juvenile animal into an adult, without an intervening larval stage

directional selection: form of natural selection in which one extreme phenotype is fittest, and the environment selects against the others

disaccharide: a simple sugar that consists of two bonded monosaccharides

disruptive selection: form of natural selection in which the two extreme phenotypes are fittest

distal convoluted tubule: region of the renal tubule that connects the nephron loop to the collecting duct

distraction display: behavior that distracts a predator away from a nest or young

DNA (deoxyribonucleic acid): genetic material consisting of a double helix of nucleotides

DNA microarray: collection of short DNA fragments of known sequence placed in defined spots on a small square of glass

DNA polymerase: enzyme that adds new DNA nucleotides and corrects mismatched base pairs in DNA replication

DNA profiling: biotechnology tool that uses DNA to detect genetic differences between individuals

DNA probe: labeled, single-stranded fragment of DNA used to reveal the presence of a complementary DNA sequence

DNA technology: practical application of knowledge about DNA

domain: broadest (most inclusive) taxonomic category

dominance hierarchy: social order with dominant and submissive members

dominant allele: allele that is expressed whenever it is present

dormancy: state of decreased metabolism

dorsal, hollow nerve cord: tubular nerve cord that forms dorsal to the notochord; one of the four characteristics of chordates

double fertilization: in angiosperms, process by which one sperm nucleus fertilizes the egg and another fertilizes the two haploid nuclei in the embryo sac's central cell

duplication: chromosomal abnormality that produces multiple copies of part of a chromosome

E

ear: sense organ of hearing and equilibrium

eardrum: structure that transmits sound from air to the middle ear

earthworm: type of annelid

echinoderm: unsegmented deuterostome with a five-part body plan, radial symmetry in adults, and a spiny outer covering; phylum Echinodermata

ecological footprint: measure of the land area needed to support one or more humans

ecology: study of relationships among organisms and the environment

ecosystem: a community and its nonliving environment

ectoderm: outermost germ layer in an animal embryo

ectotherm: animal that lacks an internal mechanism that keeps its temperature within a narrow range; invertebrates, fishes, amphibians, and nonavian reptiles

effector: any structure that responds to a stimulus

ejaculation: discharge of semen through the penis

ejaculatory duct: tube that deposits sperm into the urethra

electromagnetic spectrum: range of naturally occurring radiation

electron: a negatively charged particle that orbits the atom's nucleus

electron transport chain: membrane-bound molecular complex that shuttles electrons to slowly extract their energy

electronegativity: an atom's tendency to attract electrons

electrophoresis: technique used to sort DNA fragments by size

element: a pure substance consisting of atoms containing a characteristic number of protons

elimination: the expulsion of waste from the body

embryo sac: mature female gametophyte in angiosperms

embryonic disc: in the preembryo, a flattened, two-layered mass of cells that develops into the embryo

embryonic stage: stage of human development lasting from the end of the second week until the end of the eighth week of gestation

embryonic stem cell: stem cell that can give rise to all types of cells in the body

emergent property: quality that results from interactions of a system's components

emigration: movement of individuals out of a population

endangered species: species facing a high risk of extinction in the near future

endergonic reaction: a chemical reaction that requires a net input of energy

endocrine gland: concentration of hormone-producing cells in an animal

endocrine system: organ system consisting of glands and cells that secrete hormones

endocytosis: form of transport in which the cell membrane engulfs extracellular material

endoderm: innermost germ layer in an animal embryo

endodermis: the innermost cell layer of root cortex

endomembrane system: eukaryotic organelles that exchange materials in transport vesicles

endometrium: inner uterine lining

endophyte: fungus that colonizes a plant without triggering disease symptoms

endoplasmic reticulum: interconnected membranous tubules and sacs in a eukaryotic cell

endorphin: pain-killing protein produced in the anterior pituitary

endoskeleton: skeleton on the inside of an animal

endosperm: triploid tissue that stores food for the embryo in an angiosperm seed

endospore: dormant, thick-walled structure that enables some bacteria to survive harsh conditions

endosymbiont theory: the idea that mitochondria and chloroplasts originated as free-living bacteria engulfed by other prokaryotic cells

endothelium: layer of epithelial tissue that lines blood vessels and the heart

endotherm: animal that maintains its body temperature by using heat generated from its own metabolism; birds and mammals

energy: the ability to do work

energy shell: group of electron orbitals that share the same energy level

enhancer: DNA sequence that helps regulate gene expression and lies outside the promoter

entropy: randomness or disorder

envelope: the membrane layer surrounding the protein coat of some viruses

environmental resistance: combination of factors that limit population growth

enzyme: an organic molecule that catalyzes a chemical reaction without being consumed

eosinophil: type of white blood cell that attacks multicellular parasites

epidermis: in animals, the outermost layer of skin; in plants, cells covering the leaves, stems, and roots

epididymis: tube that receives and stores sperm from one testis

epiglottis: cartilage that covers the glottis, routing food to the digestive tract during swallowing

epinephrine (adrenaline): hormone secreted by the adrenal medulla; also can act as a neurotransmitter

epistasis: one gene masks another gene's expression

epithelial tissue (epithelium): animal tissue consisting of tightly packed cells that form linings, coverings, and glands

equilibrium (K-selected) life history: reproductive strategy characterized by long-lived, late-maturing individuals that produce few offspring, with each receiving heavy parental investment

erosion: wearing away of soil by water and wind

esophagus: muscular tube that leads from the pharynx to the stomach

essential nutrient: substance vital for an organism's metabolism, growth, and reproduction

estrogen: steroid hormone produced in ovaries of female vertebrates

estuary: area where fresh water in a river meets salty water of an ocean

ethylene: volatile plant hormone that ripens fruit

eudicot: one of the two main clades of angiosperms

euglenoid: unicellular flagellated protist with elongated cell

Eukarya: domain containing eukaryotes

eukaryote: organism composed of one or more cells containing a nucleus and other membrane-bounded organelles

eumetazoan: animal with true tissues

eusociality: social organization reflecting extensive division of labor in reproduction

eutrophic: nutrient-rich

eutrophication: addition of nutrients to a body of water

evaporation: the conversion of a liquid to a vapor (gas)

evolution: descent with modification; change in allele frequencies in a population over time

excretion: elimination of metabolic wastes

exergonic reaction: an energy-releasing chemical reaction

exhalation: movement of air out of the lungs

exocytosis: form of transport in which vesicles containing cell secretions fuse with the cell membrane

exon: portion of an mRNA that is translated after introns are removed

exoskeleton: skeleton on the outside of an animal

expanding repeat mutation: type of mutation in which the number of copies of a three- or four-nucleotide sequence increases over several generations

experiment: a test of a hypothesis under controlled conditions

exponential growth: population growth pattern in which the number of new individuals is proportional to the size of the population

external fertilization: release of gametes by males and females into the same environment

extinction: disappearance of a species

extracellular matrix: nonliving substances that surround animal cells; includes ground substance and fibers

eye: organ that detects light and produces the sense of sight

F

F_1 (first filial) generation: the offspring of the P generation in a genetic cross

F_2 (second filial) generation: the offspring of the F_1 generation in a genetic cross

facilitated diffusion: form of passive transport in which a substance moves down its concentration gradient with the aid of a transport protein

facultative anaerobe: organism that can live with or without O_2

fast-twitch fiber: large muscle cell that produces twitches of short duration

fatty acid: long-chain hydrocarbon terminating with a carboxyl group

feather: in birds, an epidermal outgrowth composed of keratin

feces: solid waste that leaves the digestive tract

fermentation: metabolic pathway in the cytoplasm in which NADH from glycolysis reduces pyruvate

fertilization: the union of two gametes

fetal stage: stage of human development lasting from the beginning of the ninth week of gestation through birth

fever: rise in the body's temperature

fiber: elongated sclerenchyma cell

fibrous root system: branching root system arising from stem

filtration: removal of water and solutes from the blood, as occurs at the glomerulus

first law of thermodynamics: energy cannot be created or destroyed, just converted from one form to another

fish: vertebrate animal with fins and external gills

fitness: an organism's contribution to the next generation's gene pool

fixed action pattern: type of innate behavior; stereotyped sequence of events that is performed to completion once initiated

flagellated protozoan: unicellular heterotrophic protist with one or more flagella

flagellum (pl. flagella): a long whiplike appendage a cell uses for motility

flatworm: unsegmented worm lacking a coelom; phylum Platyhelminthes

flower: the reproductive structure in angiosperms that produces pollen and eggs

fluid feeder: animal that drinks its food

fluid mosaic: two-dimensional structure of movable phospholipids and proteins that form biological membranes

fluke: type of parasitic flatworm

follicle cell: nourishing cell surrounding an oocyte

follicle-stimulating hormone (FSH): reproductive hormone produced in the anterior pituitary

food chain: series of organisms that successively eat each other

food web: network of interconnecting food chains

foot: ventral muscular structure that provides movement in mollusks

foraging: animal behavior related to finding and collecting food

foraminiferan: amoeboid protozoan with a calcium carbonate shell

forebrain: front part of the vertebrate brain

fossil: any evidence of an organism from more than 10,000 years ago

founder effect: genetic drift that occurs when a small, nonrepresentative group of individuals leaves their ancestral population and begins a new settlement

frameshift mutation: type of mutation in which nucleotides are added or deleted by any number other than a multiple of three, altering the reading frame

free-living flatworm: planarian or marine flatworm

frog: type of amphibian

fruit: seed-containing structure in angiosperms

fruiting body: multicellular spore-bearing organ of a fungus

Fungi: kingdom containing mostly multicellular eukaryotes that are heterotrophs by external digestion

G

G_0 phase: resting phase of the cell cycle in which the cell continues to function but does not divide

G_1 phase: gap stage of interphase in which the cell grows and carries out its basic functions

G_2 phase: gap stage of interphase in which the cell synthesizes and stores membrane components and spindle proteins

gallbladder: organ that stores bile from the liver and releases it into the small intestine

gamete: a sex cell; sperm or egg cell

gametophyte: haploid, gamete-producing stage of the plant life cycle

ganglion: cluster of neuron cell bodies

ganglion cell: interneuron in the retina that generates action potentials

gap junction: connection between two adjacent animal cells that allows cytoplasm to flow between them

gastric juice: mixture of water, mucus, salts, hydrochloric acid, and enzymes produced at the stomach lining

gastrointestinal (GI) tract: two-opening digestive tract; also called alimentary canal

gastropod: type of mollusk

gastrovascular cavity: digestive chamber with a single opening

gastrula: stage of early animal embryonic development during which three tissue layers form

gene: sequence of DNA that codes for a specific protein or RNA molecule

gene flow: the movement of alleles between populations

gene pool: all of the genes and their alleles in a population

gene therapy: treatment that supplements a faulty gene in a cell with a functioning version of the gene

genetic code: correspondence between specific nucleotide sequences and amino acids

genetic drift: change in allele frequencies that occurs purely by chance

genome: all the genetic material in an organism

genotype: an individual's combination of alleles for a particular gene

genotype frequency: number of individuals of one genotype, divided by the number of individuals in the population

genus: taxonomic category that groups closely related species

geologic time scale: a division of Earth's history into eons, eras, periods, and epochs defined by major geological or biological events

germ cell: cell that gives rise to gametes in an animal

germination: resumption of growth after seed dormancy is broken

gibberellin: plant hormone that promotes shoot elongation

gill: highly folded respiratory surface containing blood vessels that exchange gases in water

ginkgo: a type of gymnosperm

gland: organ that secretes substances into the bloodstream or into a duct

global climate change: long-term changes in Earth's weather patterns

glomeromycete: fungus lacking sexual spores that form mycorrhizae

glomerular (Bowman's) capsule: cup-shaped end of a nephron; surrounds the glomerulus

glomerulus: ball of capillaries containing blood to be filtered at a nephron

glottis: slitlike opening between the vocal cords

glucagon: pancreatic hormone that raises blood sugar level by stimulating liver cells to break down glycogen into glucose

glucocorticoid: hormone secreted by the adrenal cortex

glycerol: a three-carbon alcohol that forms the backbone of triglycerides and phospholipids

glycocalyx: sticky layer composed of proteins and/or polysaccharides that surrounds some prokaryotic cell walls; slime layer or capsule

glycolysis: a metabolic pathway occurring in the cytoplasm of all cells; one molecule of glucose splits into two molecules of pyruvate

gnetophyte: a type of gymnosperm

golden alga: photosynthetic aquatic protist with two flagella and carotenoid accessory pigments

Golgi apparatus: a system of flat, stacked, membrane-bounded sacs that packages cell products for export

gonad: gland that manufactures hormones and gametes in animals; ovary or testis

gonadotropin-releasing hormone (GnRH): reproductive hormone produced in the hypothalamus

graded potential: a local flow of electrical current in a neuron; the flow weakens with distance from the source of the stimulus

gradualism: theory that proposes that evolutionary change occurs gradually, in a series of small steps

Gram stain: technique for classifying bacteria into two main groups based on cell wall structure

granum (pl. grana): a stack of flattened thylakoid discs in a chloroplast

gravitropism: directional growth response to gravity

gray matter: nervous tissue in the central nervous system; consists mostly of neuron cell bodies, dendrites, and synapses

green alga: photosynthetic protist that has pigments, starch, and cell walls similar to those of land plants

greenhouse effect: increase in surface temperature caused by carbon dioxide and other atmospheric gases

ground tissue: plant tissue that makes up most of the primary plant body; composed mostly of parenchyma

growth factor: a protein that signals a cell to divide

growth hormone (GH): hormone produced in the anterior pituitary

guard cells: pair of cells flanking a stoma

gustation: the sense of taste

gymnosperm: a plant with seeds that are not enclosed in a fruit; includes conifers, *Ginkgo*, gnetophytes, and cycads

H

habitat: physical place where an organism normally lives

habituation: type of learning in which an animal learns not to respond to irrelevant stimuli

hagfish: jawless animal with a cranium but not vertebrae

hair cell: mechanoreceptor that initiates sound transduction in the cochlea

half-life: the time it takes for half the atoms in a sample of a radioactive substance to decay

haploid cell: cell containing one set of chromosomes; also called *n*

Hardy–Weinberg equilibrium: situation in which allele frequencies do not change from one generation to the next

heart: muscular organ that pumps blood (or a comparable fluid) throughout the body

heartwood: dark-colored, nonfunctioning secondary xylem in woody plant

helper T cell: lymphocyte that coordinates activities of other immune system cells

hemisphere: one of two halves of the cerebrum

hemoglobin: pigment that carries oxygen in red blood cells

herbaceous plant: plant with green, soft stem at maturity

herbivore: animal that eats plants

heterotroph: organism that obtains carbon and energy by eating another organism; consumer

heterozygote advantage: condition in which a heterozygote has greater fitness than homozygotes, maintaining balanced polymorphism in a population

heterozygous: possessing two different alleles for a particular gene

hindbrain: lower, posterior portion of the vertebrate brain

hippocampus: forebrain structure involved in memory formation

histamine: biochemical that dilates blood vessels and increases their permeability; involved in inflammation and allergies

homeostasis: the ability of an organism to maintain a stable internal environment despite changes in the external environment

homeotic: describes any gene that, when mutated, leads to organisms with structures in the wrong places

hominid: any of the "great apes" (orangutans, gorillas, chimpanzees, and humans)

hominin: extinct or modern human

hominine: gorilla, chimpanzee, or human

hominoid: any lesser or great ape, including humans

homologous: similar in structure or position because of common ancestry

homologous pair: two chromosomes that look alike and have the same sequence of genes

homozygous: possessing two identical alleles for a particular gene

horizontal gene transfer: transfer of genetic information from one cell to another cell that is not its descendant

hormone: biochemical synthesized in small quantities in one place and transported to another

hornwort: a type of bryophyte

horseshoe crab: type of chelicerate arthropod

horsetail: a type of seedless vascular plant

host range: the kinds of organisms or cells that a virus can infect

human chorionic gonadotropin (hCG): hormone secreted by an embryo; prevents menstruation

human immunodeficiency virus (HIV): virus that causes acquired immune deficiency syndrome (AIDS)

humoral immunity: branch of adaptive immune system in which B cells secrete antibodies in response to a foreign antigen

humus: chemically complex jellylike organic substance in soil

hybrid: producing a mix of offspring for one or more traits; heterozygous

hydrogen bond: weak chemical bond between opposite partial charges on two molecules or within one large molecule

hydrolysis: splitting a molecule by adding water

hydrophilic: attracted to water

hydrophobic: repelled by water

hydrostatic skeleton: skeleton consisting of constrained fluid in a closed body compartment

hypertonic: describes a solution in which the solute concentration is greater than on the other side of a semipermeable membrane

hypha (pl. hyphae): a fungal filament; the basic structural unit of a multicellular fungus

hypoglycemia: low blood sugar caused by excess insulin or insufficient carbohydrate intake

hypothalamus: small forebrain structure beneath the thalamus that controls homeostasis and links the nervous and endocrine systems

hypothesis: a testable, tentative explanation based on prior knowledge

hypotonic: describes a solution in which the solute concentration is less than on the other side of a semipermeable membrane

I

immigration: movement of individuals into a population

immune system: organ system consisting of cells that defend the body against infections, cancer, and foreign substances

immunodeficiency: condition in which the immune system lacks one or more components

impact theory: idea that mass extinctions were caused by impacts of extraterrestrial origin

implantation: embedding of the blastocyst into the uterine lining

imprinting: type of learning that occurs during a sensitive period early in life and occurs without obvious reinforcement

inclusive fitness: the sum of an individual's direct and indirect fitness

incomplete digestive tract: digestive tract with one opening that takes in food and ejects wastes

incomplete dominance: mode of inheritance in which a heterozygote's phenotype is intermediate between the phenotypes of the two homozygotes

independent variable: hypothesized influence on a dependent variable

indeterminate growth: growth that persists indefinitely

indirect development: development of a juvenile animal into an adult while passing through intervening larval stages

inflammation: immediate, localized reaction to an injury or any pathogen that breaches the body's barriers

ingestion: the act of taking food into the digestive tract

inhalation: movement of air into the lungs

inheritance of acquired characteristics: the idea that an organism can inherit the traits that its parent acquired during its lifetime

innate: describing an instinctive behavior that develops independently of experience

innate defense: cell or substance that provides generalized protection against all infectious agents

inner cell mass: cells in the blastocyst that develop into the embryo

insect: type of mandibulate arthropod

insulin: pancreatic hormone that lowers blood sugar level by stimulating body cells to take up glucose from the blood

integumentary system: organ system consisting of skin and its outgrowths

intercalary meristem: meristem between the nodes of a mature stem

interferon: type of cytokine released by a virus-infected cell

interleukin: type of cytokine involved in communication between white blood cells

intermediate filament: component of the cytoskeleton; intermediate in size between a microtubule and a microfilament

intermembrane compartment: the space between a mitochondrion's two membranes

internal fertilization: use of a copulatory organ to deposit sperm inside a female's body

interneuron: neuron that connects one neuron to another in the central nervous system

internode: stem areas between the points of leaf attachment

interphase: stage preceding mitosis or meiosis, when the cell carries out its functions, replicates its DNA, and grows

intersexual selection: choice of mates by one sex from among competing members of the opposite sex

interstitial cell: testosterone-secreting endocrine cell in a testis

interstitial fluid: liquid that bathes cells in a vertebrate's body

intertidal zone: region along a coastline between the high and low tide marks

intrasexual selection: competition between members of the same sex for access to the opposite sex

intron: portion of an mRNA molecule that is removed before translation

invasive species: introduced species that establishes a breeding population in a new location and spreads widely from the original point of introduction

inversion: abnormality in which a portion of a chromosome flips and reinserts itself

invertebrate: animal without a backbone

ion: an atom or group of atoms that has lost or gained electrons, giving it an electrical charge

ionic bond: attraction between oppositely charged ions

iris: colored part of the eye; regulates the size of the pupil

isotonic: condition in which a solute concentration is the same on both sides of a semipermeable membrane

isotope: any of the forms of an element, each having a different number of neutrons in the nucleus

J

jaws: bones that frame the entrance to the mouth

joint: area where two bones meet

J-shaped curve: plot of exponential growth over time

K

karyotype: a size-ordered chart of the chromosomes in a cell

keystone species: species whose effect on community structure is disproportionate to its biomass

kidney: excretory organ in the vertebrate urinary system

kilocalorie (kcal): one thousand calories; one food Calorie.

kin selection: the sacrifice of one individual's fitness for the sake of the genes it shares with related animals

kinetic energy: energy being used to do work; energy of motion

kinetochore: protein that attaches a chromosome to the spindle in cell division

kingdom: taxonomic category below domain

Krebs cycle: stage in cellular respiration that completely oxidizes the products of glycolysis

L

lac **operon:** in *E. coli*, three lactose-degrading genes plus the promoter and operator that control their transcription

lactic acid fermentation: metabolic pathway in which NADH from glycolysis reduces pyruvate, producing lactic acid

lamprey: type of jawless fish

lancelet: type of invertebrate chordate

large intestine: part of the digestive tract that connects the small intestine to the anus

larva: immature stage of animal development; does not resemble the adult of the species

larynx: boxlike structure in front of the pharynx

latent: describes an infection in which viral genetic material in a host cell is not expressed

lateral line: network of canals that extends along the sides of fishes and houses receptor organs that detect vibrations

lateral meristem: meristem whose daughter cells thicken a root or stem

law of independent assortment: Mendel's law stating that during gamete formation, the segregation of the alleles for one gene does not influence the segregation of the alleles for another gene

law of segregation: Mendel's law stating that the two alleles of each gene are packaged into separate gametes

leaf: flattened organ that carries out photosynthesis

learning: alteration of an animal's behavior to reflect experience

leech: type of annelid

lens: structure in the eye that bends incoming light

leukemia: cancer in which bone marrow overproduces white blood cells

lichen: association of a fungus and a green alga or cyanobacterium

life history: the events of an organism's life, especially those that are related to reproduction

life table: chart that shows the probability of surviving to any given age

ligament: band of fibrous connective tissue that connects bone to bone across a joint

ligase: enzyme that catalyzes formation of covalent bonds in the DNA sugar-phosphate backbone

light reactions: photosynthetic reactions that harvest light energy and store it in molecules of ATP or NADPH

lignin: tough, complex molecule that strengthens the walls of some plant cells

limbic system: collection of forebrain structures involved in emotion and memory

limnetic zone: layer of open water in a lake or pond where light penetrates

linkage group: group of genes that tend to be inherited together because they are on the same chromosome

linkage map: diagram of gene order and spacing on a chromosome, based on crossover frequencies

linked genes: genes on the same chromosome

lipid: hydrophobic organic molecule consisting mostly of carbon and hydrogen

littoral zone: shallow region along the shore of a lake or pond where rooted plants occur

liver: organ that produces bile, detoxifies blood, stores glycogen and fat-soluble vitamins, synthesizes blood proteins, and monitors blood glucose level

liverwort: a type of bryophyte

lizard: type of reptile

lobe-finned fish: type of bony fish; coelacanths and lungfishes

locus: physical location of a gene on a chromosome

logistic growth: the leveling-off of a population in response to environmental resistance

long-day plant: plant that flowers when light periods are longer than a critical length

long-term memory: memory that can last from hours to a lifetime

loose connective tissue: type of connective tissue with widely spaced fibroblasts and a loose network of fibers

lung: saclike structure where gas exchange occurs in air-breathing vertebrates

lungfish: type of lobe-finned fish

luteinizing hormone (LH): reproductive hormone produced in the anterior pituitary

lymph: fluid in lymph vessels

lymph capillary: dead-end vessel that collects lymph

lymph node: lymphatic structure located along lymph capillary; contains white blood cells and fights infection

lymphatic system: organ system consisting of lymphoid organs and lymph vessels that recover excess tissue fluid and aid in immunity

lymphocyte: type of white blood cell; T cell, or B cell, or natural killer cell

lysogenic infection: type of viral infection in which the genetic material of a virus is replicated along with the host cell's chromosome

lysosome: organelle in a eukaryotic cell that buds from the Golgi apparatus and enzymatically dismantles molecules, bacteria, and worn-out cell parts

lytic infection: type of viral infection in which a virus enters a cell, replicates, and causes the host cell to burst (lyse) as it releases the new viruses

M

macroevolution: large-scale evolutionary change

macronutrient: nutrient required in large amounts

macrophage: type of phagocyte

major histocompatibility complex (MHC): cluster of genes that encode "self" proteins on cell surfaces

malignant tumor: mass of abnormal cells that has the potential to invade adjacent tissues and spread throughout the body

mammal: amniote with hair and mammary glands

mammary gland: milk-producing gland in mammals

mandibulate: arthropod with jawlike mouthparts (mandibles); crustaceans, insects, centipedes, and millipedes

mantle: dorsal fold of tissue that secretes a shell in most mollusks

marrow cavity: space in a bone shaft that contains marrow

marsupial: mammal that bears live young after a short gestation

marsupium: pouch in which the immature young of many marsupial mammals nurse and develop

mass extinction: the disappearance of many species over relatively short expanses of time

mass number: the total number of protons and neutrons in an atom's nucleus

mast cell: immune system cell that triggers inflammation and allergy

matrix: the inner compartment of a mitochondrion

matter: substance that takes up space and is made of atoms

mechanoreceptor: sensory receptor sensitive to physical deflection

Mediterranean shrubland: type of terrestrial biome; rainy winters and dry summers (also called chaparral)

medulla oblongata: part of the brainstem nearest the spinal cord

medusa: free-swimming form of a cnidarian

megaspore: in seed plants, spore that gives rise to female gametophyte

meiosis: division of genetic material that halves the chromosome number and yields genetically variable gametes

melatonin: hormone produced in the pineal gland

memory cell: lymphocyte produced in an initial infection; launches a rapid immune response upon subsequent exposure to an antigen

meninges: membranes that cover and protect the central nervous system

menstrual cycle: hormonal cycle that prepares the uterus for pregnancy

meristem: localized region of active cell division in a plant

mesoderm: embryonic germ layer between ectoderm and endoderm in an animal embryo

mesophyll: photosynthetic ground tissue in leaves

messenger RNA (mRNA): a molecule of RNA that encodes a protein

metabolism: the biochemical reactions of a cell

metamorphosis: developmental process in which an animal changes drastically in body form between the juvenile and the adult

metaphase: stage of mitosis in which chromosomes are aligned down the center of a cell

metaphase I: metaphase of meiosis I, when homologous chromosome pairs align down the center of a cell

metaphase II: metaphase of meiosis II, when replicated chromosomes align down the center of a cell

microevolution: relatively short-term changes in allele frequencies within a population or species

microfilament: component of the cytoskeleton; made of the protein actin

micronutrient: nutrient required in small amounts

microspore: in seed plants, spore that gives rise to male gametophyte

microtubule: component of the cytoskeleton; made of subunits of tubulin protein

microvillus (pl. microvilli): extension of the plasma membrane of epithelial cells of a villus

midbrain: part of the brain between the forebrain and hindbrain

millipede: type of mandibulate arthropod

mineral: essential element other than C, H, O, or N

mineralocorticoid: hormone secreted by the adrenal cortex

mitochondrion: organelle that houses the reactions of cellular respiration in eukaryotes

mitosis: division of genetic material that yields two genetically identical cells

modern evolutionary synthesis: the idea that genetic mutations create the variation upon which natural selection acts

molecular clock: application of the rate at which DNA mutates to estimate when two types of organisms diverged from a shared ancestor

molecule: two or more atoms joined by chemical bonds

mollusk: unsegmented animal with a soft body, mantle, muscular foot, and visceral mass; phylum Mollusca

monocot: one of the two main clades of angiosperms

monocyte: type of white blood cell that gives rise to macrophages

monogamy: mating system in which males and females have one sexual partner

monohybrid cross: mating between two individuals that are heterozygous for the same gene

monomer: a single unit of a polymeric molecule

monophyletic: describes a group of organisms consisting of a common ancestor and all of its descendants

monosaccharide: a sugar that is one five- or six-carbon unit

monotreme: egg-laying mammal

morula: preembryonic stage consisting of a solid ball of cells

moss: a type of bryophyte

motor neuron: neuron that transmits a message from the central nervous system toward a muscle or gland

motor unit: a motor neuron and all the muscle fibers it contacts

muscle: organ that powers movements in animals by contracting; consists of muscle tissue and other tissue types

muscle fiber: muscle cell

muscle tissue: animal tissue consisting of contractile cells that provide motion

muscular system: organ system consisting of skeletal muscles whose contractions form the basis of movement and posture

mutagen: any external agent that causes a mutation

mutant: a genotype, phenotype, or allele that is not the most common in a population or that has been altered from the "typical" (wild-type) condition

mutation: a change in a DNA sequence

mutualism: type of symbiosis that improves the fitness of both partners

mycelium: assemblage of hyphae that forms an individual fungus

mycorrhiza: mutually beneficial association of a fungus and the roots of a plant

myelin sheath: fatty material that insulates some nerve fibers in vertebrates, speeding nerve impulse transmission

myocardium: thick, muscular middle layer of the heart wall

myofibril: cylindrical subunit of a muscle fiber, consisting of parallel protein filaments

myosin: protein that forms thick filaments in muscle cells

N

NADH: coenzyme that carries electrons in glycolysis and respiration

NADPH: coenzyme that carries electrons in photosynthesis

natural killer cell: type of lymphocyte that participates in innate defenses

natural selection: differential reproduction of organisms based on inherited traits

negative feedback: metabolic pathway in which a reaction's product inhibits the enzyme that catalyzes the reaction; also, a mechanism for maintaining homeostasis in which a change in a condition triggers action that reverses the change

nephron: functional unit of the kidney

nephron loop: hairpin-shaped region of the renal tubule that connects the proximal and distal convoluted tubules

neritic zone: region of an ocean from the coast to the edge of the continental shelf

nerve: bundle of nerve fibers (axons) bound together in a sheath of connective tissue

nerve ladder: nervous system consisting of two nerve cords connected by transverse nerves

nerve net: diffuse network of neurons

nervous system: organ system that specializes in rapid communication

nervous tissue: tissue type whose cells (neurons and neuroglia) form a communication network

net primary production: energy available to consumers in a food chain, after cellular respiration and heat loss by producers

neural tube: embryonic precursor of the central nervous system

neuroglia: one of two cell types in nervous tissue

neuron: one of two cell types in nervous tissue

neurotransmitter: chemical passed from a neuron to receptors on another neuron or on a muscle or gland cell

neutral: neither acidic nor basic. Also, not electrically charged

neutron: a particle in an atom's nucleus that is electrically neutral

neutrophil: type of white blood cell that functions as a phagocyte

niche: all resources a species uses for survival, growth, and reproduction

nitrification: conversion of ammonia to nitrites and nitrates

nitrogen fixation: conversion of N_2 to NH_4^+, a form plants can use

nitrogenous base: a nitrogen-containing compound that forms part of a nucleotide

node: point at which leaves attach to a stem

node of Ranvier: short region of exposed axon between two sections of myelin sheath

nodule: root growth housing nitrogen-fixing bacteria

noncompetitive inhibition: change in an enzyme's shape occurring when an inhibitor binds to a site other than the active site

nondisjunction: failure of chromosomes to separate at anaphase I or anaphase II of meiosis

nonpolar covalent bond: a covalent bond in which atoms share electrons equally

norepinephrine (noradrenaline): hormone secreted by the adrenal medulla; also can act as a neurotransmitter

nose: organ that forms the entrance to the nasal cavity inside the head; functions in breathing and olfaction

notochord: flexible rod that forms the framework of the vertebral column and induces formation of the neural tube; one of the four characteristics of chordates

nuclear envelope: the two membranes bounding a cell's nucleus

nuclear pore: a hole in the nuclear envelope

nucleic acid: a long polymer of nucleotides; DNA or RNA

nucleoid: the part of a prokaryotic cell where the DNA is located

nucleolus: a structure within the nucleus where components of ribosomes are assembled

nucleosome: the basic unit of chromatin; consists of DNA wrapped around eight histone proteins

nucleotide: building block of a nucleic acid, consisting of a phosphate group, a nitrogenous base, and a five-carbon sugar

nucleus: central part of an atom; also, the membrane-bounded sac that contains DNA in a eukaryotic cell

nutrient: any substance that an organism uses for metabolism, growth, maintenance, and repair of its tissues

O

obesity: unhealthy amount of body fat; body mass index greater than 30

obligate aerobe: organism that requires O_2 for generating ATP

obligate anaerobe: organism that must live in the absence of O_2

observational learning: type of learning in which an animal imitates the behavior of others

oceanic zone: open sea beyond the continental shelf

olfaction: the sense of smell

oligodendrocyte: type of neuroglia that forms a myelin sheath around some axons in the central nervous system

oligosaccharide: intermediate-length carbohydrate consisting of 3 to 100 monosaccharides

oligotrophic: describes water containing few nutrients

omnivore: animal that eats many types of food, including plants and animals

oncogene: gene that normally stimulates cell division but when overexpressed leads to cancer

oogenesis: the production of egg cells

oogonium: diploid germ cell that divides mitotically to yield two primary oocytes

open circulatory system: circulatory system in which blood circulates freely through the body cavity

operant conditioning: type of associative learning in which an animal connects a behavior with its consequences

operator: in an operon, the DNA sequence between the promoter and the protein-encoding regions

operon: group of related bacterial genes plus a promoter and operator that control the transcription of the entire group at once.

opportunistic pathogen: infectious agent that cannot cause disease in a healthy individual

opportunistic (r-selected) life history: reproductive strategy characterized by short-lived, early-maturing individuals that have many offspring, with each receiving little parental investment

optic nerve: nerve fibers that connect the retina to the brain

optimal foraging theory: theory that predicts an animal should maximize energy collection per unit time

orbital: volume of space where a particular electron is likely to be

organ: two or more tissues that interact and function as an integrated unit

organ system: two or more physically or functionally linked organs

organelle: compartment of a eukaryotic cell that performs a specialized function

organic molecule: compound containing both carbon and hydrogen

organism: a single living individual

orgasm: pleasurable sensation, accompanied by involuntary muscle contractions, associated with sexual activity

osmoregulation: control of an animal's ion concentration

osmosis: simple diffusion of water through a semipermeable membrane

osteocyte: mature bone cell surrounded by matrix

osteoporosis: condition in which bones become less dense

ostracoderm: extinct jawless fish

outgroup: basis for comparison in a cladistics analysis

oval window: membrane between the middle ear and the inner ear

ovarian cycle: hormonal cycle that controls the timing of oocyte maturation in the ovaries

ovary: in angiosperms, base of carpel plus their enclosed ovules; in animals, the female gonad

overexploitation: harvesting a species faster than it can reproduce

ovulation: release of an oocyte from an ovarian follicle

ovule: egg-bearing structure that develops into a seed in gymnosperms and angiosperms

oxidation: the loss of one or more electrons by a participant in a chemical reaction

oxidation-reduction (redox) reaction: chemical reaction in which one reactant is oxidized and another is reduced

oxygen debt: after vigorous exercise, a period in which the body requires extra oxygen to restore ATP and creatine phosphate to muscle and to recharge oxygen-carrying proteins

oxytocin: hormone released from the posterior pituitary

ozone layer: atmospheric zone rich in ozone gas (O_3), which absorbs the sun's ultraviolet radiation

P

P (parental) generation: the first, true-breeding generation in a genetic cross

pacemaker: specialized cardiac cells that set the tempo of the heartbeat

pain receptor: sensory receptor that detects mechanical damage, temperature extremes, or chemicals released from damaged cells

paleontology: the study of fossil remains or other clues to past life

pancreas: gland between the spleen and the small intestine; produces hormones, digestive enzymes, and bicarbonate

pancreatic islet (islet of Langerhans): cluster of cells in the pancreas that secretes insulin and glucagon

parapatric speciation: formation of new species when part of a population enters a habitat bordering the parent species' range, and the two groups become reproductively isolated

paraphyletic: describes a group of organisms that contains a common ancestor and some, but not all, of its descendants

parasitism: type of symbiosis in which one member increases its fitness at the expense of a living host

parasympathetic nervous system: part of the autonomic nervous system; dominates during relaxed times and opposes the sympathetic nervous system

parathyroid gland: one of four small groups of cells behind the thyroid gland

parathyroid hormone (PTH): hormone produced in the parathyroid gland

parazoan: animal without true tissues; a sponge

parenchyma: unspecialized plant cells making up majority of ground tissue

parental chromatid: chromatid containing genetic information from only one parent

parsimonious: in cladistics, describes the evolutionary tree that requires the fewest steps to construct from a set of observations

particulate: small piece of matter suspended in air

passive immunity: immunity generated when an organism receives antibodies from another organism

passive transport: movement of a solute across a membrane without the direct expenditure of energy

pathogen: disease-causing agent

pattern formation: developmental process that establishes the body's overall shape and structure

pectoral girdle: bones that connect the forelimbs to the axial skeleton

pedigree: chart showing family relationships and phenotypes

peer review: evaluation of scientific results by experts before publication in a journal

pelagic zone: all water above the ocean floor

pelvic girdle: bones that connect the hind limbs to the axial skeleton

penis: male organ of copulation and urination

pepsin: enzyme that begins the digestion of proteins in the stomach

peptide bond: a covalent bond between adjacent amino acids; results from dehydration synthesis

peptide hormone: water-soluble, amino acid–based hormone that cannot freely diffuse through a cell membrane

peptidoglycan: material in bacterial cell wall

per capita rate of increase (r): difference between the birth rate and the death rate in a population

perception: the brain's interpretation of a sensation

pericardium: connective tissue sac that encloses the heart

pericycle: outermost layer of root vascular cylinder; produces branch roots

periderm: dermal tissue covering woody plant part

periodic table: chart that lists elements according to their properties

peripheral nervous system: neurons that transmit information to and from the central nervous system

peristalsis: waves of muscle contraction that propel food along the digestive tract

peritubular capillaries: blood vessels that surround a nephron

permafrost: permanently frozen ground in tundra

peroxisome: membrane-bounded sac that houses enzymes that break down fatty acids and dispose of toxic chemicals

persistent organic pollutant: carbon-based chemical pollutants that remain in ecosystems for long periods

petal: flower part interior to sepals

petiole: stalk that supports a leaf blade

pH scale: a measurement of how acidic or basic a solution is

phagocyte: cell that engulfs and digests foreign material and cell debris

phagocytosis: form of endocytosis in which the cell engulfs a large particle

pharyngeal slit (or pouch): opening in the pharynx of a chordate embryo; one of the four characteristics of chordates

pharynx: tube just behind the oral and nasal cavities; the throat

phenotype: observable characteristic of an organism

pheromone: volatile chemical an organism releases that elicits a response in another member of the species

phloem: vascular tissue that transports sugars and other dissolved organic substances in plants

phloem sap: solution of water, minerals, sucrose, and other biochemicals in phloem

phospholipid: molecule consisting of two hydrophobic fatty acids and a hydrophilic phosphate group

phospholipid bilayer: double layer of phospholipids that forms in water; forms the majority of a cell's membranes

phosphorylation: the addition of a phosphate to a molecule

photic zone: region in a water body where light is sufficient for photosynthesis

photon: a packet of light or other electromagnetic radiation

photoperiod: day length

photoreceptor: molecule or cell that detects quality and quantity of light

photorespiration: a metabolic pathway in which rubisco reacts with O_2 instead of CO_2, counteracting photosynthesis

photosynthesis: biochemical reactions that enable organisms to harness sunlight energy to manufacture organic molecules

photosystem: cluster of pigment molecules and proteins in a chloroplast's thylakoid membrane

phototroph: organism that derives energy from sunlight

phototropism: directional growth response to unidirectional light

phylogenetics: field of study that attempts to explain the evolutionary relationships among species

phylogeny: graphical depiction of evolutionary relationships among species

physiology: the study of the functions of organisms and their parts

phytochrome: a type of photoreceptor in plants

phytoplankton: microscopic photosynthetic organisms that drift in water

pilus: short projection made of protein on a prokaryotic cell

pineal gland: small gland in the brain that secretes melatonin

pioneer species: the first species to colonize an area devoid of life

pith: ground tissue inside a ring of vascular bundles in roots and stems

pituitary gland: pea-sized endocrine gland attached to the hypothalamus

placebo: inert substance used as an experimental control

placenta: structure that connects the developing fetus to the maternal circulation in placental mammals

placental mammal: mammal in which the developing fetus is nourished by a placenta

placoderm: extinct armored fishes with jaws

Plantae: kingdom consisting of multicellular, eukaryotic autotrophs

plasma: watery, protein-rich fluid that forms the matrix of blood

plasma cell: B cell that secretes large quantities of one antibody

plasmid: small circle of double-stranded DNA separate from a cell's chromosome

plasmodesma (pl. plasmodesmata): connection between plant cells that allows cytoplasm to flow between them

plasmodial slime mold: protist in which the feeding stage consists of a plasmodium containing multiple nuclei

plate tectonics: theory that Earth's surface consists of several plates that move in response to forces acting deep within the planet

platelet: cell fragment that orchestrates clotting in blood

pleiotropy: multiple phenotypic effects of one genotype

polar body: small cell produced in female meiosis

polar covalent bond: a covalent bond in which electrons are attracted more to one atom's nucleus than to the other

pollen: immature male gametophyte in seed plants (gymnosperms and angiosperms)

pollen sac: pollen-producing cavity in anther

pollination: transfer of pollen to female reproductive part

pollution: physical, chemical, or biological change in the environment that harms organisms

polychaete: type of annelid

polygamy: mating system in which males or females have multiple sexual partners

polygenic: caused by more than one gene

polymer: a long molecule composed of similar subunits (monomers)

polymerase chain reaction (PCR): biotechnology tool that rapidly produces millions of copies of a DNA sequence of interest

polyp: sessile form of a cnidarian

polypeptide: a long polymer of amino acids

polyphyletic: describes a group of organisms that excludes the most recent common ancestor of all members of the group

polyploid cell: cell with extra chromosome sets

polysaccharide: carbohydrate consisting of hundreds of monosaccharides

pons: oval mass in the brainstem where white matter connects the forebrain to the medulla and cerebellum

population: interbreeding members of the same species occupying the same region

population density: number of individuals of a species per unit area or volume of habitat

population distribution: pattern in which individuals are scattered throughout a habitat

population dynamics: study of the factors that influence changes in a population's size

portal system: arrangement of blood vessels in which a capillary bed drains into a vein that drains into another capillary bed

positive feedback: a process that reinforces an existing condition

postanal tail: muscular tail that extends past the anus; one of the four characteristics of chordates

posterior pituitary: the back part of the pituitary gland

postsynaptic cell: neuron, muscle cell, or gland cell that receives a message at a synapse

postzygotic reproductive isolation: separation of species due to selection against hybrid offspring

potential energy: stored energy available to do work

prebiotic simulation: experiment that attempts to recreate the conditions on early Earth that gave rise to the first cell

predator: animal that kills and eats other animals

preembryonic stage: first two weeks of human development

preimplantation genetic diagnosis (PGD): use of DNA probes to detect genetic illness in an embryo before implanting it into a uterus

pressure flow theory: theory that explains how phloem sap moves from source to sink

presynaptic cell: neuron that releases neurotransmitters into a synaptic cleft

prey: animal that a predator eats

prezygotic reproductive isolation: separation of species due to factors that prevent the formation of a zygote

primary growth: growth from apical meristems

primary immune response: immune system's response to its first encounter with a foreign antigen

primary oocyte: in oogenesis, a diploid cell that undergoes the first meiotic division and yields a haploid polar body and a haploid secondary oocyte

primary producer: species forming the base of a food web; autotroph

primary spermatocyte: a diploid cell that undergoes the first meiotic division and yields two haploid secondary spermatocytes

primary structure: the amino acid sequence of a protein

primary succession: appearance of organisms in an area previously devoid of life

primate: mammal with opposable thumbs, eyes in front of the skull, a relatively large brain, and flat nails instead of claws; includes prosimians, simians, and hominoids

primitive streak: furrow that appears along the back of the embryonic disc in the third week of human development

principle of superposition: the idea that lower rock layers are older than those above them

prion: infectious protein particle

producer (autotroph): organism that uses inorganic sources of energy and carbon

product: the result of a chemical reaction

product rule: the chance of two independent events occurring equals the product of the individual chances of each event

profundal zone: deep region of a lake or ocean where light does not penetrate

progenote: collection of nucleic acid, protein, and lipids that was the forerunner to cells

progesterone: steroid hormone produced in ovaries of female vertebrates

prokaryote: a cell that lacks a nucleus and other membrane-bounded organelles; bacteria and archaea

prolactin: hormone produced in the anterior pituitary

prometaphase: stage of mitosis just before metaphase, when the nuclear membrane breaks up and spindle fibers attach to kinetochores

promoter: a control sequence at the start of a gene; attracts RNA polymerase and (in eukaryotes) transcription factors

prophage: DNA of a lysogenic bacteriophage that is inserted into a host cell's chromosome

prophase: stage of mitosis when chromosomes condense and the mitotic spindle begins to form

prophase I: prophase of meiosis I, when chromosomes condense and become visible, and crossing over occurs

prophase II: prophase of meiosis II, when chromosomes condense and become visible

proprioceptor: sensory receptor that detects the position of body parts

prosimian: type of primate; a lemur, aye-aye, loris, tarsier, or bush baby

prostate gland: male structure that produces a milky, alkaline fluid that activates sperm

protein: a polymer consisting of amino acids and folded into its functional three-dimensional shape

protista: eukaryotic organism that is not a plant, fungus, or animal

proton: a particle in an atom's nucleus carrying a positive charge

protostome: clade of bilaterally symmetrical animals in which the first opening in the gastrula develops into the mouth

protozoan: unicellular protist that is heterotrophic and (usually) motile

proximal convoluted tubule: region of the renal tubule between the glomerular capsule and the nephron loop

proximate: describing the mechanistic causes of behavior

pseudocoelom: fluid-filled animal body cavity lined by endoderm and mesoderm

pseudogene: a DNA sequence that is very similar to that of a gene; a pseudogene is transcribed but its mRNA is not translated

pulmonary artery: artery that leads from the right ventricle to the lungs

pulmonary circulation: blood circulation between the heart and lungs

pulmonary vein: vein that leads from the lungs to the left atrium

punctuated equilibrium: theory that life's history has been characterized by bursts of rapid evolution interrupting long periods of little change

Punnett square: diagram that uses the genotypes of the parents to reveal the possible results of a genetic cross

pupil: opening in the iris that admits light into the eye

pyramid of energy: diagram depicting energy stored at each trophic level at a given time

pyruvate: the three-carbon product of glycolysis

Q

quaternary structure: the shape arising from interactions between multiple polypeptide subunits of the same protein

R

R group: an amino acid side chain

radial symmetry: body form in which any plane passing through the body from the mouth to the opposite end divides the body into mirror images

radioactive isotope: atom that emits particles or rays as its nucleus disintegrates

radiolarian: amoeboid protozoan with a silica shell

radiometric dating: a type of absolute dating that uses known rates of radioactive decay to date fossils

radula: a chitinous, tonguelike strap in many mollusks

rain shadow: downwind side of a mountain, with a drier climate than the upwind side

ray: parenchyma cells extending from center of woody stem or root

ray-finned fish: type of bony fish

reabsorption: renal tubule's return of useful substances to the blood

reactant: a starting material in a chemical reaction

reaction center: a molecule of chlorophyll *a* (and associated proteins) that participates in the light reactions of photosynthesis

receptacle: attachment point for flower parts

receptor potential: localized change in membrane potential (a graded potential) in a sensory receptor

recessive allele: allele whose expression is masked if a dominant allele is present

reciprocal altruism: altruistic act performed in anticipation of payback in the future

recombinant chromatid: chromatid containing genetic information from both parents as a result of crossing over

recombinant DNA: genetic material spliced together from multiple sources

red alga: multicellular, photosynthetic, marine protist with red or blue accessory pigments

red bone marrow: marrow that gives rise to blood cells and platelets

red blood cell: disc-shaped blood cell that contains hemoglobin

reduction: the gain of one or more electrons by a participant in a chemical reaction

reflex: type of innate behavior; an instantaneous, automatic response to a stimulus

reflex arc: neural pathway that links a sensory receptor and an effector

relative dating: placing a fossil into a sequence of events without assigning it a specific age

renal tubule: portion of a nephron that adjusts the composition of filtrate

repressor: in an operon, a protein that binds to the operator and prevents transcription

reproductive system: organ system that produces and transports gametes and may nurture developing offspring

reptile: tetrapod vertebrate with an amniote egg and a dry scaly body covering

reservoir: an organism that acts as a source of the virus to infect other species

resource partitioning: use of the same resource in different ways or at different times by multiple species

respiratory cycle: one inhalation followed by one exhalation

respiratory surface: part of an animal's body that exchanges gases with the environment

respiratory system: organ system that acquires oxygen gas and releases carbon dioxide

resting potential: electrical potential inside a neuron not conducting a nerve impulse

restriction enzyme: enzyme that cuts double-stranded DNA at a specific base sequence

retina: sheet of photoreceptors that forms the innermost layer of the eye

reverse transcriptase: enzyme that uses RNA as a template to construct a DNA molecule

rhodopsin: pigment that transduces light into an electrochemical signal in photoreceptors

ribosomal RNA (rRNA): a molecule of RNA that, along with proteins, forms a ribosome

ribosome: a structure built of RNA and protein where mRNA anchors during protein synthesis

ribulose bisphosphate (RuBP): the five-carbon molecule that reacts with CO_2 in the Calvin cycle

RNA (ribonucleic acid): nucleic acid typically consisting of a single strand of nucleotides

RNA polymerase: enzyme that uses a DNA template to produce a molecule of RNA

RNA world: the idea that the first independently replicating life form was RNA

rod cell: photoreceptor in the retina that provides black-and-white vision

root: belowground part of most plants

root cap: cells that protect root apical meristem from abrasion

root hair: epidermal outgrowth that increases root surface area

rough endoplasmic reticulum: ribosome-studded portion of the ER where secreted proteins are synthesized

roundworm: unsegmented worm with a pseudocoelom; phylum Nematoda

rubisco: enzyme that adds CO_2 to ribulose bisphosphate in the carbon reactions of photosynthesis

ruminant: herbivore with a four-chambered organ specialized for grass digestion

S

S phase: the synthesis phase of interphase, when DNA replicates

S-shaped curve: plot of logistic growth over time

salamander: type of amphibian

sample size: number of subjects in each experimental group

sapwood: light-colored, functioning secondary xylem in woody plant

sarcomere: one of many repeated units in a myofibril of a muscle cell

saturated fatty acid: a fatty acid with single bonds between all carbon atoms

savanna: type of terrestrial biome; grassland with scattered trees

Schwann cell: type of neuroglia that forms a myelin sheath around some axons in the peripheral nervous system

scientific method: a systematic approach to understanding the natural world based on evidence and testable hypotheses

sclera: the outermost layer of the eye; the white of the eye

sclereid: relatively short sclerenchyma cell

sclerenchyma: rigid plant cells that support mature plant parts

scrotum: the sac containing the testes

search image: improvement in a predator's ability to detect inconspicuous prey

second law of thermodynamics: every reaction loses some energy to the surroundings as heat; entropy always increases

second messenger: molecule that translates a stimulus at the cell's exterior into an effect inside the cell

secondary growth: increase in girth from cell division in lateral meristem

secondary immune response: immune system's response to subsequent encounters with a foreign antigen

secondary oocyte: haploid cell that undergoes the second meiotic division and yields a polar body and a haploid egg cell

secondary sex characteristic: trait that distinguishes the sexes but does not participate directly in reproduction

secondary spermatocyte: haploid cell that undergoes the second meiotic division and yields two haploid spermatids

secondary structure: a "substructure" within a protein, resulting from hydrogen bonds between parts of the peptide backbone

secondary succession: change in a community's species composition following a disturbance

secretion: addition of substances to the fluid in a renal tubule

seed: in gymnosperms and angiosperms, a plant embryo packaged with a food supply inside a tough outer coat

seed coat: protective outer layer of seed

seedless vascular plant: plant with vascular tissue but not seeds; includes true ferns, club mosses, whisk ferns, and horsetails

segmentation: division of an animal body into repeated subunits

selfish herd: group in which each animal tries to move as close to the center as possible

semen: fluid that carries sperm cells out of the body

semicircular canal: one of three perpendicular fluid-filled structures in the inner ear; provides information on the position of the head

semilunar valve: flap of heart tissue that prevents the flow of blood from an artery to a ventricle

seminal vesicle: structure that contributes fluid, fructose, and prostaglandins to semen

seminiferous tubule: tubule within a testis where sperm form and mature

senescence: aging

sensation: information that reaches the central nervous system about a stimulus

sensor: in homeostatic responses, a structure that monitors changes in a parameter

sensory adaptation: lessening of sensation with prolonged exposure to a stimulus

sensory neuron: neuron that transmits information from a stimulated body part to the central nervous system

sensory receptor: cell that detects stimulus information

sepal: part of the outermost whorl of a flower

Sertoli cell: cell that supports developing sperm cells within a seminiferous tubule

severe combined immunodeficiency (SCID): inherited immune system disorder in which neither T nor B cells function

sex chromosome: a chromosome that carries genes that determine sex

sex pilus: a bridge of cytoplasm that transfers DNA from one cell to another in conjugation

sex-linked: describes genes or traits on the X or Y chromosome

sexual dimorphism: difference in appearance between males and females

sexual reproduction: the combination of genetic material from two individuals to create a third individual

sexual selection: type of natural selection resulting from variation in the ability to obtain mates

sexually transmitted disease: illness that spreads during sexual contact

shoot: aboveground part of a plant

short-day plant: plant that flowers when light periods are shorter than a critical length

short tandem repeat (STR): short DNA sequences that vary in length among individuals in a population

short-term memory: memory only available for a few moments

sieve plate: porous area at end of sieve tube element

sieve tube element: conducting cell that makes up sieve tube in phloem

signal transduction: conversion of an external signal into a response inside a cell

simian: type of primate; a monkey

simple diffusion: form of passive transport in which a substance moves down its concentration gradient without the use of a transport protein

simple leaf: leaf with undivided blade

sink: plant part that does not photosynthesize

sinoatrial (SA) node: specialized cardiac muscle cells that set the pace of the heartbeat; the pacemaker

skeletal muscle: voluntary muscle tissue consisting of long, unbranched, striated cells with multiple nuclei; also, an organ composed of bundles of skeletal muscle cells and other tissue types that generates voluntary movements between pairs of bones

skeletal system: organ system consisting of bones and ligaments that support body structures and attach to muscles

skeleton: structure that supports an animal's body

skin: the outer surface of the body

sliding filament model: sliding of actin and myosin past each other to shorten a muscle cell

slow-twitch fiber: small muscle fiber that produces twitches of long duration

small intestine: part of the digestive tract that connects the stomach with the large intestine; site of most chemical digestion and absorption

smog: type of air pollution that forms a visible haze in the lower atmosphere

smooth endoplasmic reticulum: portion of the ER that produces lipids and detoxifies poisons

smooth muscle: involuntary muscle tissue consisting of nonstriated, spindle-shaped cells

snake: type of reptile

sodium-potassium pump: protein that uses energy from ATP to transport Na^+ out of cells and K^+ into cells

social behavior: interaction between members of the same species

sociobiology: study of social behavior in the context of an animal's fitness

soil: rock and mineral particles mixed with organic matter, air, and water

solute: a chemical that dissolves in a solvent, forming a solution

solution: a mixture of a solute dissolved in a solvent

solvent: a chemical in which other substances dissolve, forming a solution

somatic cell: body cell that does not give rise to gametes

somatic cell nuclear transfer: technique used to clone a mammal from an adult cell

somatic nervous system: in the peripheral nervous system, motor pathways carrying signals to skeletal (voluntary) muscles

source: plant part that produces or releases sugar

speciation: formation of new species

species: a distinct type of organism

species evenness: measure of biodiversity; considers the relative abundance of the species in a community

species richness: measure of biodiversity; number of species in a community

spermatid: haploid cell produced after meiosis II in spermatogenesis

spermatogenesis: the production of sperm

spermatogonium: diploid germ cell that divides mitotically to yield a stem cell and a primary spermatocyte

spermatozoon (pl. spermatozoa): mature sperm cell

sphincter: muscular ring that contracts to close an opening

spinal cord: tube of nervous tissue that extends through the vertebral column

spindle: a structure of microtubules that aligns and separates chromosomes in mitosis or meiosis

spirillum (pl. spirilla): spiral-shaped prokaryote

spleen: abdominal organ that produces and stores lymphocytes and destroys worn-out red blood cells

sponge: simple, asymmetrical animal lacking true tissues and gastrulation; phylum Porifera

spongy bone: bone tissue with large spaces between a web of bony struts

spore: reproductive cell of a plant or fungus

sporophyte: diploid, spore-producing stage of the plant life cycle

stabilizing selection: form of natural selection in which extreme phenotypes are less fit than the optimal intermediate phenotype

stamen: male flower part interior to petals

standardized variable: any factor held constant for all subjects in an experiment

statistically significant: unlikely to be attributed to chance

statolith: starch-containing plastid in root cap cell that functions as a gravity detector

stem: part of a plant that supports leaves

stem cell: undifferentiated cell that divides to give rise to additional stem cells and cells that specialize

steroid hormone: a lipid-soluble hormone that can freely diffuse through a cell membrane and bind to receptor inside the cell

sterol: lipid consisting of four interconnected carbon rings

stigma: in angiosperms, pollen-receiving tip of style

stoma (pl. stomata): pore in a plant's epidermis through which gases are exchanged with the atmosphere

stomach: J-shaped compartment in the digestive tract that receives food from the esophagus

stroma: the fluid inner region of the chloroplast

style: in angiosperms, the stalklike upper part of a carpel

substrate feeder: animal that lives in its food and eats it from the inside

substrate-level phosphorylation: ATP formation occurring when an enzyme transfers a phosphate group from a high-energy donor molecule to ADP

succession: change in the species composition of a community over time

survivorship curve: graph of the proportion of individuals that survive to a particular age

suspension feeder: animal that eats by straining particles out of water

symbiosis: a close and often lifelong ecological relationship in which one species typically lives in or on another

sympathetic nervous system: part of the autonomic nervous system; mobilizes the body to respond quickly to environmental stimuli and opposes the parasympathetic nervous system

sympatric speciation: formation of a new species within the boundaries of a parent species

synapse: junction at which a neuron communicates with another cell

synapsid: vertebrate with a single opening behind each eye orbit; mammals and their immediate ancestors

synaptic cleft: space into which neurotransmitters are released between two cells at a synapse

synaptic integration: a neuron's overall response to incoming excitatory and inhibitory neural messages

synaptic terminal: enlarged tip of an axon; contains synaptic vesicles

synovial joint: joint between two freely movable bones connected by a fluid-filled capsule of fibrous connective tissue

systematics: field of study that includes taxonomy and phylogenetics

systemic circulation: blood circulation between the heart and the rest of the body, except the lungs

systolic pressure: upper number in a blood pressure reading; reflects contraction of the ventricles

T

T cell: type of lymphocyte that coordinates adaptive immune response and destroys infected cells

taiga: type of terrestrial biome; the northern coniferous forest (also called boreal forest)

tapeworm: type of parasitic flatworm

taproot: large central root that persists throughout the life of the plant

target cell: cell that expresses receptors for a particular hormone

taste bud: cluster of cells that detect chemicals in food

taxis: directed movement toward or away from a stimulus

taxon: a group of organisms at any rank in the taxonomic hierarchy

taxonomy: the science of describing, naming, and classifying organisms

tectorial membrane: membrane in contact with hair cells of the cochlea

telomerase: enzyme that extends telomeres, enabling cells to divide continuously

telomere: non-coding DNA at the tip of a eukaryotic chromosome

telophase: stage of mitosis in which chromosomes arrive at opposite poles and nuclear envelopes form

telophase I: telophase of meiosis I, when homologs arrive at opposite poles

telophase II: telophase of meiosis II, when chromosomes arrive at opposite poles and nuclear envelopes form

temperate coniferous forest: type of terrestrial biome; coniferous trees dominate

temperate deciduous forest: type of terrestrial biome; deciduous trees dominate

temperate grassland: type of terrestrial biome; grazing, fire, and drought restrict tree growth

template strand: the strand in a DNA double helix that is transcribed

tendon: band of fibrous connective tissue that attaches a muscle to a bone

teratogen: substance that causes birth defects

terminator: sequence in DNA that signals where the gene's coding region ends

territory: a space that an animal defends against intruders

tertiary structure: the overall shape of a polypeptide, resulting mostly from interactions between amino acid R groups and water

testcross: a mating of an individual of unknown genotype to a homozygous recessive individual to reveal the unknown genotype

testis: male gonad

testosterone: steroid hormone produced in the testes of male vertebrates

tetanus: maximal muscle contraction caused by continual stimulation

tetrapod: vertebrate with four limbs

thalamus: forebrain structure that relays sensory input to the cerebrum

theory: well-supported scientific explanation

thermoreceptor: sensory receptor that responds to temperature

thermoregulation: control of an animal's body temperature

thick filament: in muscle cells, filament composed of myosin

thigmotropism: directional growth response to touch

thin filament: in muscle cells, filament composed of actin

threshold potential: potential to which a neuron's membrane must be depolarized to trigger an action potential

thylakoid: disclike structure that makes up the inner membrane of a chloroplast

thylakoid space: the inner compartment of the thylakoid

thymus: lymphoid organ in the upper chest where T cells learn to distinguish foreign antigens from self antigens

thyroid gland: gland in the neck that secretes two thyroid hormones (thyroxine and triiodothyronine) and calcitonin

thyroxine: one of two thyroid hormones that increases the rate of cellular metabolism

tidal volume: volume of air inhaled or exhaled during a normal breath

tight junction: connection between two adjacent animal cells that prevents fluid from flowing past the cells

tissue: group of cells that interact and provide a specific function

tongue: muscular structure on the floor of the mouth

tooth: mineral-hardened structure embedded in the jaw

topsoil: uppermost soil layer

trace element: an element that an organism requires in small amounts

trachea (pl. tracheae): in vertebrates, the respiratory tube just beneath the larynx; the "windpipe." In invertebrates, a branched tubule that brings air in close contact with cells, facilitating gas exchange

tracheid: long, narrow conducting cell in xylem

transcription: production of RNA using DNA as a template

transcription factor: in a eukaryotic cell, a protein that binds a gene's promoter and regulates transcription

transduction: transfer of DNA from one cell to another via a virus; also, conversion of energy from one form to another

transfer RNA (tRNA): a molecule of RNA that binds an amino acid at one site and an mRNA codon at its anticodon site

transformation: type of horizontal gene transfer in which an organism takes up naked DNA without cell-to-cell contact

trans fat: unsaturated fat with straight fatty acid tails

transgenic: containing DNA from multiple species

translation: assembly of an amino acid chain according to the sequence of nucleotides in mRNA

translocation: exchange of genetic material between nonhomologous chromosomes

transpiration: evaporation of water from a leaf

transposable element (transposon): DNA sequence that can move within a genome

triglyceride: lipid consisting of one glycerol bonded to three fatty acids

triiodothyronine: one of two thyroid hormones that increases the rate of cellular metabolism

trilobite: extinct type of arthropod

trophic level: an organism's position along a food chain

tropical rain forest: type of terrestrial biome; year-round high temperatures and precipitation

tropism: orientation toward or away from a stimulus

true breeding: always producing offspring identical to the parent for one or more traits; homozygous

true fern: a type of seedless vascular plant

trypanosome: flagellated protist that causes human diseases transmitted by biting flies

tuatara: type of reptile

tumor: abnormal mass of tissue resulting from cells dividing out of control

tumor suppressor gene: gene that normally prevents cell division but when inactivated or suppressed causes cancer

tundra: type of terrestrial biome; low temperature and short growing season

tunicate: type of invertebrate chordate

turgor pressure: the force of water pressing against the cell wall

turtle: type of reptile

twitch: contraction and relaxation of a muscle cell following a single stimulation

U

ultimate: describing the evolutionary origin or adaptive advantage of an animal's behavior

ultraviolet (UV) radiation: portion of the electromagnetic spectrum with wavelengths shorter than 400 nm

umbilical cord: ropelike structure that connects an embryo or fetus with the placenta

uniformitarianism: the idea that modern geological processes of erosion and sedimentation have also occurred in the past, producing changes in Earth over time

unsaturated fatty acid: a fatty acid with at least one double bond between carbon atoms

upwelling: upward movement of cold, nutrient-rich lower layers of a body of water

urea: nitrogenous waste derived from ammonia

ureter: muscular tube that transports urine from the kidney to the bladder

urethra: tube that transports urine (and semen in males) out of the body

uric acid: nitrogenous waste derived from ammonia

urinary bladder: muscular sac where urine collects

urinary system: organ system that filters blood and helps maintain concentrations of body fluids

urine: liquid waste produced by kidneys

uterine tube: tube that conducts an oocyte from an ovary to the uterus

uterus: muscular, saclike organ where embryo and fetus develop

V

vaccine: substance that initiates a primary immune response so that when an infectious agent is encountered, the secondary immune response can rapidly deactivate it

vacuole: membrane-bounded storage sac in a cell, especially the large central vacuole in a plant cell

vagina: conduit from the uterus to the outside of the body

valence shell: outermost occupied energy shell of an atom

variable: any changeable element in an experiment

variable region: amino acid sequence that is different for every antibody

vas deferens: tube that transports sperm from an epididymis to an ejaculatory duct

vascular bundle: collection of xylem, phloem, parenchyma, and sclerenchyma in plants

vascular cambium: lateral meristem that produces secondary xylem and phloem

vascular tissue: conducting tissue for water, minerals, and organic substances in plants

vasoconstriction: decrease in the diameter of a blood vessel

vasodilation: increase in the diameter of a blood vessel

vegetative plant parts: nonreproductive parts (roots, stems, and leaves)

vein: vascular bundle inside leaf; also, a vessel that returns blood to the heart

ventral nerve cord: nerve cord that runs along the ventral side of an animal

ventricle: heart chamber that pumps blood out of the heart

venule: small vein

vertebra: one unit of the vertebral column composed of bone or cartilage that supports and protects the spinal cord

vertebral column: bone or cartilage that supports and protects the spinal cord

vertebrate: animal with a backbone

vertical gene transfer: passage of DNA from one generation to the next; cell division

vesicle: a membrane-bounded sac that transports materials in a cell

vessel element: short, wide conducting cell in xylem

vestibular apparatus: structure in the inner ear that provides information on the position of the head and changes in velocity

vestigial: having no apparent function in one organism, but homologous to a functional structure in another species

villus (pl. villi): tiny projection on the inner lining of the small intestine

viroid: infectious RNA molecule

virus: infectious agent that consists of genetic information enclosed in a protein coat

visceral mass: part of a mollusk that contains the digestive and reproductive systems

vital capacity: maximal volume of air that can be forced out of the lungs during one breath

vocal cord: elastic tissue band that covers the larynx and vibrates as air passes, producing sound

vulnerable species: species facing a high risk of extinction in the distant future

vulva: external female genitalia

W

water mold: filamentous, heterotrophic protist; also called an oomycete

water vascular system: system of canals in echinoderms; provides locomotion and osmotic balance

wavelength: the distance a photon moves during a complete vibration

wax: lipid consisting of fatty acids connected to alcohol or other molecules

wetland: ecosystem in which soil is saturated with water

whisk fern: a type of seedless vascular plant

white blood cell: one of five types of blood cells that help fight infection

white matter: nervous tissue in the central nervous system; consists of myelinated axons

wild-type: the most common phenotype, genotype, or allele

wood: secondary xylem

woody plant: plant with stems and roots made of wood and bark

X

X inactivation: turning off all but one X chromosome in each cell of a mammal (usually female) early in development

X-linked: describes traits controlled by genes on the X chromosome

xylem: vascular tissue that transports water and dissolved minerals in plants

xylem sap: solution of water and dissolved minerals in xylem

Y

yeast: unicellular fungus

yellow bone marrow: fatty marrow that replaces red bone marrow as bones age

Y-linked: describes traits controlled by genes on the Y chromosome

yolk sac: extraembryonic membrane that forms beneath the embryonic disc and manufactures blood cells

Z

zoospore: flagellated spore produced by chytrids

zygomycete: fungus that produces zygospores

zygospore: diploid resting spore produced by fusion of haploid cells in zygomycetes

zygote: the fused egg and sperm that develops into a diploid individual

Credits

PHOTO CREDITS

Front Matter and Design Elements:

Inside end sheet (upper left): ©Pixtal/AGE Fotostock; (lower left): ©Hill Street Studios/Blend Images LLC; (upper right): ©JGI/Getty Images RF; (lower right): ©image100 Ltd; Icons (Learn How to Learn, Animation, Virtual Lab, Video, 3-D Animation, Activity, Tutorial, Focus on Model Organisms, Apply It Now): Elise Lansdon; Leaf: ©image broker/Alamy RF; Burning Question fire: ©Don Farrall/Getty Images RF; Author photo: Courtesy of Robert H. Taylor/University of Oklahoma.

Chapter 1

Opener: ©Pete Oxford/Minden Pictures; 1.1: ©SMC Images/The Image Bank/Getty Images; 1.2(population): ©Gregory G. Dimijian, M.D./Science Source; 1.2(community): ©Daryl Balfour/Gallo Images/Getty Images; 1.2(ecosystem): ©Manoj Shah/The Image Bank/Getty Images; 1.2(biosphere): ©Corbis RF; 1.5a: ©Design Pics/Kristy-Anne Glubish RF; 1.5b: ©John Rowley/Getty Images RF; 1.6a: ©Dorling Kindersley/Getty Images; 1.6b: ©Jadranko Markoc/flickr/Getty Images RF; 1.7: ©Mark Webster Wwwphoteccouk/Getty Images RF; 1.8.a(bottom): ©Dennis Kunkel Microscopy, Inc.; 1.8.a(top): ©Dr. Ken Greer/Visuals Unlimited; 1.9(bacteria): ©Kwangshin Kim/Science Source; 1.9(archaea): ©Ralph Robinson/Visuals Unlimited; 1.9(protista): ©Melba Photo Agency/PunchStock RF; 1.9(animalia): Courtesy of The National Human Genome Research Institute; 1.9(fungi): ©Corbis RF; 1.9(plantae): ©Photo by Keith Weller/USDA; 1.10: ©Patrick Landmann/Science Source; 1.11a: U.S. Fish & Wildlife Service/J&K Hollingsworth; 1.11b: ©Corbis RF; 1.13: ©Kjell Sandved/Alamy; p. 13(bottom): ©Getty Images/Photodisc RF; p. 14: ©Photodisc/Getty Images RF; p. 15(top left): ©Richard Milner; p. 15(bottom): ©Hulton Archive/Getty Images; 1.14: ©Mitsuhiko Imamori/Minden Pictures.

Chapter 2

Opener: ©Brand X Pictures/PunchStock RF; 2.6: ©Corbis RF; 2.9: ©McGraw-Hill Education/Jacques Cornell photographer; 2.10: ©Herman Eisenbeiss/Science Source; 2.11: ©Getty Images/flickr RF; 2.17c(top): ©Dr. Dennis Kunkel; 2.17c(middle): ©Gary Gaugler/Visuals Unlimited; 2.17c(bottom): ©Marshall Sklar/Science Source; 2.21(both): ©Ingram Publishing RF; p. 35: ©Masterfile RF; 2.24(left): ©D. Hurst/Alamy RF; 2.24(right): ©McGraw-Hill Education/Jacques Cornell photographer; p. 37: ©Comstock/Jupiter Images RF; p. 38(top): ©Ingram Publishing/Alamy RF; 2.25:

©BananaStock/PunchStock RF; 2.27: ©Peter Arnold/Digital Vision/Getty Images RF; p. 39(bottom), 2.A-B: ©McGraw-Hill Education/Jill Braaten photographer; 2.28(all): ©Tsutomu Tsuchida, PhD; 2.29: T. Tsuchida, et al. "Symbiotic bacterium modifies aphid body color," *Science*, Vol. 330, no. 6007, November 19, 2010, pp. 1102-1104. ©2010 AAAS. All rights reserved. Used with permission.

Chapter 3

Opener: ©The Columbian, Janet L. Mathews/AP Images; 3.1: ©Kathy Talaro/Visuals Unlimited; p. 46(right): ©Image Source/Getty Images RF; p. 47: ©McGraw-Hill Education/Don Rubbelke, photographer; 3.3a: ©Comstock/Alamy RF; 3.3a(inset): ©Michael Abbey/Visuals Unlimited; 3.3b: ©Inga Spence/Visuals Unlimited; 3.3b(inset): ©Dr. Dennis Kunkel/Visuals Unlimited; 3.3c: ©Inga Spence/Visuals Unlimited; 3.3c(inset): ©Microworks Color/Phototake; 3.3d: ©Inga Spence/Visuals Unlimited; 3.3d(inset): ©Steve Gschmeissner/Science Source; 3.5b: ©Wim van Egmond/Visuals Unlimited; 3.A: ©Dr. Philippa Uwins, Whister Research Pty/Science Source; 3.6b: ©Dr. Martin Oeggerli/Visuals Unlimited; 3.6c: ©David McCarthy/Science Source; 3.6d: ©Dennis Kunkel Microscopy, Inc./Visuals Unlimited; 3.7: ©Dr. Terry Beveridge/Visuals Unlimited; 3.8: ©Dr. Gopal Murti/Visuals Unlimited; 3.9: ©Dr. George Chapman/Visuals Unlimited; 3.13: ©Tim Flach/The Image Bank/Getty Images; 3.14: ©Dr. David M. Phillips/Science Source; 3.16: ©Prof. J. L. Kemeny/ISM/Phototake; 3.17, 3.19: ©Biophoto Associates/Science Source; 3.20: ©Dr. Donald Fawcett/Visuals Unlimited; 3.21: ©Bill Longcore/Science Source; 3.22: ©Biophoto Associates/Science Source; 3.23a: ©Corbis RF; 3.23b: ©Francois Paquet-Durand/Science Source; 3.23c: ©Ed Reschke/Peter Arnold/Getty Images; 3.23d: ©Kevin & Betty Collins/Visuals Unlimited; 3.24: ©Dennis Kunkel Microscopy, Inc./Visuals Unlimited; 3.25(left): ©Tomasz Szul/Visuals Unlimited/Corbis; 3.25(middle): ©Albert Tousson/Phototake; 3.25(right): ©Jennifer Waters/Science Source; 3.26a(top): ©Dr. David M. Phillips/Visuals Unlimited; 3.26a(bottom): ©Dennis Kunkel Microscopy, Inc./Phototake; 3.26b: ©D.W. Fawcett/Science Source; 3.26c: ©Dr. Tony Brain/Science Source; 3.28a-b: ©Biophoto Associates/Science Source; 3.29: ©Science VU/D. Balkwill-D. Maratea/Visuals Unlimited.

Chapter 4

Opener: ©Tyler Stableford/The Image Bank/Getty Images; 4.3(both): ©Ryan McVay/Riser/Getty Images; 4.4(top): ©Blair Seitz/Science Source;

4.4(bottom): ©Image Source/Corbis RF; 4.A: ©Darwin Dale/Science Source; 4.17(all): ©Dr. David M. Phillips/Visuals Unlimited; 4.18(both): ©Nigel Cattlin/Science Source; p. 83: ©Corbis RF; 4.20: ©Biology Media/Science Source.

Chapter 5

Opener: ©Andrew J. Martinez/Science Source; 5.1, 5.5(mesophyll): Electron micrograph by Wm. P. Wergin, courtesy of Eldon H. Newcomb, University of Wisconsin-Madison; 5.5(leaves): ©Steve Raymer/National Geographic Stock; p. 95: ©Corbis RF; 5.A: ©image100/Corbis RF; 5.11(left): ©Tony Sweet/Digital Vision/Getty Images RF; 5.11(middle): ©Joeseph Sohm-Visions of America/Getty Images RF; 5.11(right): ©Digital Vision/Getty Images RF; 5.12: Mary E. Rumpho, et al. "Solar-Powered Sea Slugs. Mollusc/Algal Chloroplast Symbiosis," *Plant Physiology*, Vol. 123, May 2000, pp. 29-38. © 2000 American Society of Plant Physiologists. All rights reserved. Used with permission.; 5.13: From Rumpho, Mary E. et al, "Horizontal gene transfer of the algal nuclear gene psbO to the photosynthetic sea slug Elysia chlorotica," *PNAS* vol. 105, no. 46, November 18, 2008, pp: 17867-17871, used by permission ©2013 National Academy of Sciences, U.S.A.

Chapter 6

Opener: ©Gunter Ziesler/Photoshot; 6.1: ©Thomas Deerinck, NCMIR/Science Source; 6.3(leaves): ©Steve Raymer/National Geographic Stock; 6.3(Mesophyll): Electron micrograph by Wm. P. Wergin, courtesy of Eldon H. Newcomb, University of Wisconsin-Madison; p. 112: ©Corbis RF; 6.9: ©Digital Vision/Getty Images RF; p. 114: ©Photodisc/Getty Images RF; 6.11(beer): ©Adam Woolfitt/Corbis; 6.11(yogurt): ©Scimat/Science Source; 6.13(both): ©Marc Gibernau, CNRS, Toulouse, France.

Chapter 7

Opener: ©Dr. Gopal Murti/Science Source; 7.1: ©Universal Pictures/Courtesy Everett Collection; 7.1(inset): ©Natural Visions/Alamy; 7.3: ©Oliver Meckes/MPI - Tubingen/Science Source; 7.4a-b: ©Science Source; 7.4c: ©Bettmann/Corbis; 7.13b: ©Tom Pantages/Phototake; 7.14: © Center for Molecular Biology of RNA, UC-Santa Cruz; p. 131(bottom): ©Jacana/Science Source; 7.16b: ©Kiseleva and Donald Fawcett/Visuals Unlimited; p. 137: ©Getty Images RF; 7.20a: ©Andrew Syred/Science Source; 7.20b: ©Science VU/Dr. F. R. Turner/Visuals Unlimited; 7.21a: ©Micro Discovery/Corbis; 7.21b: ©Dr. Gopal Murti/Science Source; 7.23a:

Index

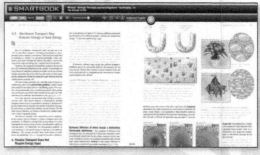

How can I make the most of my class time?

Reports

If you use LearnSmart, Smartbook, or Connect assignments before class, students will have a good grasp on the core terminology and concepts when they walk in. You can quickly identify where they do need help with real-time reports based on their LearnSmart, Smartbook, and Connect results. Reports such as **Most Challenging Objectives** give you an instant outline for your upcoming class.

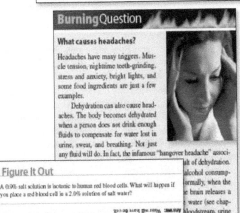

Active Learning

Wondering what to do with all the class time if students come already prepared? Engage them with active learning exercises based on the numerous chapter features. You'll find application questions to discuss and solve in the **Figure It Out** and **Mastering Concepts** highlights. **Burning Questions** are posed that engage students with real-life scenarios and give them an opportunity to send questions directly to the author. Learn more ideas for using the chapter features as active learning exercises on pages viii-x of the preface.

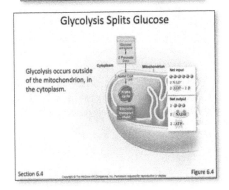

Presentation Tools

Maximize the effectiveness of your time with your students with powerful presentation tools. Start with customizable PowerPoint® lectures that focus on chapter concepts. Gauge student comprehension and increase engagement with conceptual clicker questions. Add 3-D animations, videos, and additional images from McGraw-Hill's collection to help tell your story your way.

How can I assess what my students are learning?

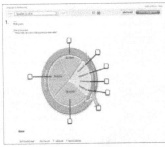

McGraw-Hill Connect®

If you're trying a new way of teaching, you should try a new way of assessment. Determine how well your methods are working and help your students learn more with the Connect question bank. Create homework and quizzes that can be used for grading, practice, and assessment at the same time. The Connect question bank has thousands of questions at every Bloom's level. Assign numerous small assessments for the students to complete; they get practice and you get data.

Learn How to Learn 🍎 STUDY TIPS

Unit 1 Science, Chemistry, and Cells

Chapter 1 Real Learning Takes Time

You got good at basketball, running, dancing, art, music, or video games by putting in lots of practice. Likewise, you will need to commit time to your biology course if you hope to do well. To get started, look for the "Learn How to Learn" tip in each chapter of this textbook. Each hint is designed to help you use your study time productively.

Chapter 2 Organize Your Time, and Don't Try to Cram

Get a calendar, and study the syllabus for every class you are taking. Write each due date in your calendar. Include homework assignments, quizzes, and exams, and add new dates as you learn them. Then, block out time before each due date to work on each task. Success comes much more easily if you take a steady pace instead of waiting until the last minute.

Chapter 3 Interpreting Images from Microscopes

Any photo taken through a microscope should include information that can help you interpret what you see. First, read the caption and labels so you know what you are looking at—usually an organ, a tissue, or an individual cell. Then study the scale bar and estimate the size of the image. Finally, check whether a light microscope (LM), scanning electron microscope (SEM), or transmission electron microscope (TEM) was used to create the image. Note that stains and false colors are often added to emphasize the most important features.

Chapter 4 Focus on Understanding, Not Memorizing

When you are learning the language of biology, be sure to concentrate on how each new term fits with the others. Are you studying multiple components of a complex system? Different steps in a process? The levels of a hierarchy? As you study, always make sure you can see how each part relates to the whole.

Chapter 5 See What's Coming

Check out the Learning Outline at the beginning of each chapter. Each heading is a complete sentence that summarizes the most important idea of the section. Read through these statements before you start each chapter. That way, you can keep the "big picture" in mind while you study. You can also flip to the end of the chapter before you start to read; the chapter summary and Pull It Together concept map can also provide a preview of what's to come.

Chapter 6 Don't Skip the Figures

As you read the narrative in the text, pay attention to the figures as well; they are there to help you learn. Some figures summarize the narrative, making it easier for you see the "big picture." Other illustrations show the parts of a structure or the steps in a process; still others summarize a technique or help you classify information. Also, remember that students use illustrations in different ways. Once you encounter a figure's callout, you may prefer to stop reading to absorb the entire figure, or you may switch back and forth between the narrative and the figure's parts. Being attentive to your preferences will help you to be more systematic as you study.

Unit 2 Biotechnology, Genetics, and Inheritance

Chapter 7 Pause at the Checkpoints

As you read, get out a piece of paper and see if you can answer the Figure It Out and Mastering Concepts questions. If not, you may want to study a bit more before you move on. Each section builds on the material that came before, and mastering one chunk at a time will make it much easier to learn whatever comes next.

Chapter 8—Explain It, Right or Wrong

As you work through the multiple choice questions at the end of each chapter, make sure you can explain why each correct choice is right. You can also test your understanding by taking the time to explain why each of the other choices is wrong.

Chapter 9 Write It Out—Really!

Get out a pen and a piece of scratch paper, and answer the open-ended Write It Out questions at the end of each chapter. This tip applies even if the exams in your class are multiple choice. Putting pen to paper (as opposed to just saying the answer in your head) forces you to organize your thoughts and helps you discover the difference between what you know and what you only THINK you know.

Chapter 10 Be a Good Problem Solver

This chapter is about the principles of inheritance, and you will find many sample problems within its pages; in addition, "Activity" icons indicate interactive problems available online. Need help? The "How to Solve a Genetics Problem" guide at the end of this chapter shows a systematic, step-by-step approach to answering the most common types of questions. Keep using the guide until you feel comfortable solving any problem type.

Chapter 11 Vary Your Study Plan for Healthy Learning

Your study sessions may become stale if you do the same things over and over. After all, it is difficult to focus after watching countless animations or listening to hours of podcasts. Instead, try switching between strategies that are passive (watching and listening) and those that are active (drawing and writing). You might watch a video on Punnett squares and then try to draw one yourself. Or you could listen to a podcast about cloning and then write a paragraph describing the process in your own words. Keeping variety in your study plan will help you stay engaged.

Unit 3 The Evolution of Life

Chapter 12 Practice Your Recall

Here's an old-fashioned study tip that still works. When you finish reading a passage, close the book and write what you remember— in your own words. In this chapter, for example, you will learn about several forces of evolutionary change. After you read about them, can you list and describe them without peeking at your book? Try it and find out!

Chapter 13 Make a Chart

One way to organize all of the information in a chapter is to make a summary chart or matrix. The chart's contents will depend on the chapter. For this chapter, for example, you might write the following headings along the top of a piece of paper: "Type of Evidence," "Definition," "How It Works," "What It Tells Us," and "Example." Then you would list the lines of evidence for evolution along the left edge of the chart. Start filling in your chart, using the book at first to find the information you need. Later, you should be able to recreate your chart from memory.

Chapter 14 Don't Neglect the Boxes

You may be tempted to skip the chapter–opening essays and boxed readings because they're not "required." Read them anyway. The contents should help you remember and visualize the material you are trying to learn. And who knows? You may even find them interesting.

Chapter 15 Write Your Own Test Questions

Have you ever tried putting yourself in your instructor's place by writing your own multiple-choice test questions? It's a great way to pull the pieces of a chapter together. The easiest questions to write are based on definitions and vocabulary, but those will not always be the most useful. Try to think of questions that integrate multiple ideas or that apply the concepts in a chapter. Write 10 questions, and then let a

Unit 4 The Diversity of Life

Chapter 16 Take the Best Possible Notes

Some students take notes only on what they consider "important" during a lecture. Others write down words but not diagrams, or they write what's on the board but not what the instructor is saying. All of these strategies risk losing vital information and connections between ideas that could help in later learning. Instead, write down as much as you can during lecture, including sketches of the diagrams and notes on what the instructor is telling you about the main ideas. It will be much easier to study later if you have a complete picture of what happened in every class

Chapter 17 Skipping Class?

Attending lectures is important, but you may need to skip class once in a while. How will you find out what you missed? If your instructor does not provide complete lecture notes, you may be able to copy them from a friend. Whenever you borrow someone else's notes, it's a good idea to compare them with the assigned reading to make sure they are complete and accurate. You might also want to check with the instructor if you have lingering questions about what you missed.

Chapter 18 What's the Point of Rewriting Your Notes?

Your notes are your record of what happened in class, so why should you rewrite them after lecture is over? One answer is that the abbreviations and shorthand that make perfect sense while you take notes will become increasingly mysterious as time goes by. Rewriting the information in complete sentences not only reinforces learning but also makes your notes much easier to study before an exam.

Chapter 19 Take Notes on Your Reading

Many classes have reading assignments. Taking notes as you read should help you not only retain information but also identify what you don't understand. Before you take notes, skim through the assigned pages once; otherwise, you may have trouble distinguishing between main points and minor details. Then read it again. This time, pause after each section and write the most important ideas in your own words. What if you can't remember it or don't understand it well enough to summarize the passage? Read it again, and if that doesn't work, ask for help with whatever isn't clear.

Chapter 20 Use All Your Resources

Textbooks come with online quizzes, animations, and other resources that can help you learn biology. After you have studied the material in a chapter, test yourself by taking an online quiz. Jot down the questions for which you are unsure of the answers, and remember to go back to study those topics again. Also, check for animations that take you through complex processes one step at a time. Sometimes, the motion of an animation can help you understand what's happening more easily than studying a static image.

Chapter 21 Think While You Search the Internet

Some assignments may require you to use the Internet. But the Internet is full of misinformation, so you must evaluate every site you visit. Collaborative sites such as Wikipedia are unreliable because anyone can change any article. For other sites, ask the following questions: Are you looking at someone's personal page? Is there an educational, governmental, nonprofit, or commercial sponsor? Is the author reputable? Does the page contain opinions or facts? Are facts backed up with documentation? Answering these questions will help ensure that the sites you use are credible.

Unit 5 Plant Life

Chapter 22 Bite-Sized Pieces

Many students think they need to read a whole chapter in one sitting. Instead, try working through one topic at a time. Read just one section of the chapter, compare it to your class notes, and test yourself on what you have learned. Think of each chapter as a meal: you eat a sandwich one bite at a time, so why not tackle biology the same way?

Chapter 23 A Quick Once-Over

Unless your instructor requires you to read your textbook in detail before class, try a quick preview. Read the chapter outline to identify the main ideas, then look at the figures and the key terms in the narrative. Previewing a chapter should help you follow the lecture, because you will already know the main ideas. In addition, note-taking will be easier if you recognize new vocabulary words from your quick once-over. Return to your book for an in-depth reading after class to help nail down the details.

Chapter 24 Know Yourself

Setting aside time to study is one important ingredient for academic success; another is paying attention to your work habits throughout the day and night. Are you most alert in the morning, afternoon, or evening? Block off time to study during periods when you are at your best. Your study time will be much more productive if you are not fighting to stay awake.

Unit 6 Animal Life

Chapter 25 Flashcard Excellence

While making flashcards, you may be tempted to focus on definitions. For example, after reading this chapter, you might make a flashcard with "simple squamous" on one side and "single layer of flattened cells" on the other. This description is correct, but it won't help you understand the bigger picture. Instead, your flashcards should include realistic questions that cover both the big picture and the small details. Try making flashcards that pose a question, such as "What are the four tissue types in an animal?" or "How do cells, tissues, organs, and organ systems relate to one another?" Write the full answer on the other side, then practice writing the answers on scratch paper until you are sure you know them all.

Chapter 26 How to Use a Study Guide

Some professors hand out study guides to help students prepare for exams. Used wisely, a study guide can be a valuable tool. One good way to use a study guide is AFTER you have studied the material, when you can go through the guide and make sure you haven't overlooked any important topics. Alternatively, you can cross off topics as you encounter them while you study. No matter which technique you choose, don't just memorize isolated facts. Instead, try to understand how the items on the study guide relate to one another. If you're unclear on the relationships, be sure to ask your instructor.

Chapter 27 Don't Throw That Exam Away!

Whether or not you were satisfied with your last exam, take the time to learn from your mistakes. Mark the questions that you missed and the ones that you got right but were unsure about. Then figure out what went wrong for each question. For example, did you neglect to study the information, thinking it wouldn't be on the test? Did you memorize a term's definition without understanding how it fits with other material? Did you misread the question? After you have finished your analysis, look for patterns and think about what you could have done differently. Then revise your study plan so that you can avoid making the same mistakes in the future.

Chapter 28 Use Those Office Hours

Most instructors maintain office hours. Do not be afraid to use this valuable resource! Besides getting help with course materials, office hours give you an opportunity to know your professors personally. After all, at some point you may need a letter of recommendation; a letter from a professor who knows you well can carry a lot of weight. If you do decide to visit during office hours, be prepared with specific questions. And if you request a separate appointment, it is polite to confirm that you intend to come at the time you have arranged.

Chapter 29 Make Appointments with Yourself

If you prefer to study alone but often find yourself putting off your solo study sessions, try making recurring "appointments" with yourself. That is, use your calendar to block off time that you dedicate to studying each day. You can reread chapters after class, quiz yourself on course materials, make concept maps, or work on homework assignments. Keep those appointments throughout the semester, so you never get behind.

Chapter 30 Studying in Groups

Study groups can offer a great way to learn from other students, but they can also dissolve into social events that accomplish little real work. Of course, your choice of study partners makes a huge difference; try to pick people who are at least as serious as you are about learning. To stay focused, plan activities that are well suited for groups. For example, you can agree on a list of vocabulary words and take turns adding them to a group concept map. You can also write exam questions for your study partners to answer, or you can simply explain the material to each other in your own words. Focus on what you need to learn, and your study sessions should be productive

Chapter 31 How to Use a Tutor

Your school may provide tutoring sessions for your class, or perhaps you have hired a private tutor. How can you make the most of this resource? First, meet regularly with your tutor for an hour or two each week; don't wait until just before an exam. Second, if possible, tell your tutor what you want to work on before each session, so he or she can prepare. Third, bring your textbook, class notes, and questions to your tutoring session. Fourth, be realistic. Your tutor can discuss difficult concepts and help you practice with the material, but don't expect him or her to simply give you the answers to your homework.

Chapter 32 Avoid Distractions

Despite your best intentions, constant distractions may take you away from your studies. Friends, music, TV, phone calls, text messages, video games, and the Internet all offer attractive diversions. How can you stay focused? One answer is to find your own place to study where no one can find you. Turn your phone off for a few hours; the world will get along without you while you study. And if you must use your computer, create a separate user account with settings that prevent you from visiting favorite websites during study time.

Chapter 33 Pay Attention in Class

It happens to everyone occasionally: your mind begins to wander while you are sitting in class, so you doodle or doze off. Before you know it, class is over, and you got nothing out of it. How can you keep from wasting your class time this way? One strategy is to get plenty of sleep and eat well, so your mind stays active instead of drifting off. Another is to prepare for class in advance, since getting lost can be an excuse for drifting off. When you get to class, sit near the front, listen carefully, and take good notes. Finally, a friendly reminder can't hurt; make a small PAY ATTENTION sign to put on your desk, where you can always see it.

Chapter 34 Find a Good Listener

For many complex topics, you may struggle to know how well you really understand what is going on. One tip is to try explaining what you think you know to somebody else. Choose a subject that takes a few minutes to explain. As you describe the topic in your own words, your partner should ask follow-up questions and note where your explanation is vague. Those insights should help draw your attention to important details that you overlooked.

Chapter 35 Don't Waste Old Exams

If you are lucky, your instructor may make old exams available to your class. If so, it is usually a bad idea to simply look up and memorize the answer to each question. Instead, use the old exam as a chance to test yourself before it really counts. Put away your notes and textbook, and set up a mock exam. Answer each question without "cheating," then check how many you got right. Use the questions you got wrong—or that you guessed right—as a guide to what you should study more.

Unit 7 The Ecology of Life

Chapter 36 What's Your Learning Style?

Students differ in how they prefer to receive information: some love to hear lectures, others like reading, and still others thrive on hands-on activities in lab. You may find it helpful to use an online learning styles inventory to discover more about your own preferences. At the very least, the advice on the website may alert you to study techniques that you have not tried before.

Chapter 37 Expand on What You're Learning

Many students make the mistake of memorizing information without really thinking about what they are learning. This strategy not only makes schoolwork boring but also limits your ability to answer questions. Instead of repeating someone else's words as you study, try elaborating on what you have learned. Here are some ideas: Explain how the topic relates to other course material or to your own life; draw a picture of important processes; discuss the topic with someone else; explain it to yourself out loud or in writing; or think of additional examples or analogies.

Chapter 38 Perform Your Best on Exams

Last-minute cramming for exams may be a classic college ritual, but it is not usually the best strategy. If you try to memorize everything right before an exam, you may become overwhelmed and find yourself distracted by worries that you'll never learn it all. Instead, work on learning the material as the course goes along. Then, on the night before the exam, get plenty of rest, and don't forget to eat on exam day. If you are too tired or too hungry to think, you won't be able to give the exam your best shot.

Chapter 39 Use Your Campus Resources

Many first-time college students struggle to keep up with assignments outside of class. Time management can be part of the problem, but poor reading and writing skills may also share the blame. Most campuses offer free resources that can help. For example, look for seminars and workshops aimed at improving reading comprehension. Writing centers are also common; the staff should include consultants trained to help you be a more proficient writer.

Chapter 40 Make Your Own Review Sheet

If you are facing a big exam, how can you make sense of everything you have learned? One way is to make your own review sheet. The best strategy will depend on what your instructor expects you to know, but here are a few ideas to try: Make lists; draw concept maps that link ideas within and between chapters; draw diagrams that illustrate important processes; and write mini-essays that explain the main points in each chapter's learning outline.

Student Quick Tips

Use this Student Quick Tips guide for a quick and easy start with McGraw-Hill Connect. You'll get valuable tips on registering, doing assignments, and accessing resources, as well as information about the support center hours.

How to Access Connect using the Code Inside of your McGraw-Hill Create™ PRINT textbook.

NOTE: *If you are using an eBook, please see the next set of instructions below.*

Getting Started

TIP: You will need a 20 digit unique code which comes with the purchase of your McGraw-Hill Create™ print textbook. This code is **located on the inside back cover** of your printed textbook.

Registration and Sign In

1. Find the ISBN of your Create textbook. This can be found on Connect instructions page which is the last printed page of your book (begins with 978…)
2. Visit www.mcgrawhillcreate.com/shop
3. Search for the 13 digit ISBN found in step 1 (978XXXXXXXXXX).
4. The book should match your course (i.e. school, instructor, course name/number) and should say "Free With Access Code." Enter your unique 20 digit code found on the inside back cover of your textbook.
5. Register as a new user or sign-in if you already have a McGraw-Hill account

TIP: Remember this username and password as you will need it when you get to Connect

6. Open a new browser and go to the unique URL provided by your instructor
(example: http://www.mcgrawhillconnect.com/class/instructorname_section_name)

> Sample of Connect Web Address
> http://www.mcgrawhillconnect.com/class/instructorname_section_name

7. Click the Register Now button and sign in using the same email address and password you created on the McGraw-Hill Bookstore (Step 5).

How to Access Connect Using the Code Inside of your McGraw-Hill Create™ eBOOK.

If you are viewing this page in your purchased Create ebook, then you only have a few more steps to complete your registration.

1. Open a new browser and go to the unique URL provided by your instructor
(example: http://www.mcgrawhillconnect.com/class/instructorname_section_name)

> Sample of Connect Web Address
> http://www.mcgrawhillconnect.com/class/instructorname_section_name

2. Click the Register Now button and sign in using the same email address and password you created on the McGraw-Hill Bookstore when you purchased/accessed your eBook.

Trouble Logging In?

- Ensure you are using the same email address you used during registration
- If you have forgotten your password, click on the "Forgot Password?" link at your Instructor's Connect Course Web Address
- When logged into Connect, you can update your account information (e.g. email address, password, and security question/answer) by clicking on the "*My Account*" link located at the top-right corner

Home (Assignments)

TIP: If you are unable to begin an assignment, verify the following:

- The assignment is available (start and due dates)
- That you have not exceeded the maximum number of attempts
- That you have not achieved a score of 100%
- If your assignment contains questions that require manual grading, you will not be able to begin your next attempt until your instructor has graded those questions

TIP: Based on the assignment policy settings established by your Instructor, you may encounter the following limitations when working on your assignment(s):

- Ability to Print Assignment
- Timed assignments – once you begin a "*timed assignment*," the timer will not stop by design

TIP: "*Save & Exit*" vs. "*Submit*" button

- If you are unable to complete your assignment in one sitting, utilize the "*Save & Exit*" button to save your work and complete it at a later time
- Once you have completed your assignment, utilize the "*Submit*" button in order for your assignment to be graded

Library

TIP: The *Library* section of your Connect account provides shortcuts to various resources.

- If you purchased ConnectPlus, you will see an *eBook* link, which can also be accessed from the section information widget of the *Home* tab

- *Recorded Lectures* can be accessed if your instructor is using *Tegrity Campus* to capture lectures. You may also access recorded lectures when taking an assignment by clicking on the projector icon in the navigation bar

- Many McGraw-Hill textbooks offer additional resources such as narrated slides and additional problems, which are accessible through the *Student Resources* link

Reports

TIP: Once you submit your assignment, you can view your available results in the *Reports* tab.

- If you see a dash (-) as your score, your instructor has either delayed or restricted your ability to see the assignment feedback

- Your instructor has the ability to limit the amount of information (e.g. questions, answers, scores) you can view for each submitted assignment

Need More Help?

CONTACT US ONLINE

Visit us at:

www.mcgrawhillconnect.com/support

Browse our support materials including tutorial videos and our searchable Connect knowledge base. If you cannot find an answer to your question, click on "Contact Us" button to send us an email.

GIVE US A CALL

Call us at:

1-800-331-5094

Our live support is available:

Mon-Thurs:	8 am – 11pm CT
Friday:	8 am – 6 pm CT
Sunday:	6 pm – 11 pm CT

Online Supplements

ConnectPlus Biology with LearnSmart Online Access for Biology: Concepts and Investigations, Third Edition

McGraw-Hill ConnectPlus® provides an online eBook and immediate feedback on online assignments, quizzes, and practice tests, providing a learning experience that is personalized for YOU. Study more efficiently and engage with your learning process – Connect with future success!

HOW TO REGISTER

Using a <u>Print Book</u>?
To register and activate your ConnectPlus account, simply follow these easy steps:
1. **Go to the ConnectPlus course web address provided by your instructor or visit the Connect link set up on your instructor's course within your campus learning management system.**
2. **Click on the link to register.**
3. **When prompted, enter the ConnectPlus code found on the inside back cover of your book and click Submit. Complete the brief registration form that follows to begin using Connect.**

Using an <u>eBook</u>?
To register and activate your ConnectPlus account, simply follow these easy steps:
1. **Upon purchase of your eBook, you will be granted automatic access to ConnectPlus.**
2. **Go to the ConnectPlus course web address provided by your instructor or visit the Connect link set up on your instructor's course within your campus learning management system.**
3. **Sign in using the same email address and password you used to register on the eBookstore. Complete your registration and begin using Connect.**

*Note: Access Code is for one use only. If you did not purchase this book new, the access code included in this book is no longer valid.

Need help? Visit mhhe.com/support